PEARSON ALWAYS LEARNING

Jane B. Reece • Lisa A. Urry • Michael L. Cain
• Steven A. Wasserman • Peter V. Minorsky • Robert B. Jackson

Campbell
Biology

Volume Two
BSC 2011

Custom Edition for Florida State College at
Jacksonville – South Campus

Taken from:
Campbell Biology, Ninth Edition
by Jane B. Reece, Lisa A. Urry, Michael L. Cain, Steven A. Wasserman,
Peter V. Minorsky, and Robert B. Jackson

Cover Art: Courtesy of Photodisc/Getty Images.

Taken from:

Campbell Biology, Ninth Edition
by Jane B. Reece, Lisa A. Urry, Michael L. Cain, Steven A. Wasserman, Peter V. Minorsky, and Robert B. Jackson

Published by Benjamin Cummings
San Francisco, California 94111

This special edition published in cooperation with Pearson Learning Solutions.

Pearson Learning Solutions, 501 Boylston Street, Suite 900, Boston, MA 02116
A Pearson Education Company
www.pearsoned.com

Printed in the United States of America

1 2 3 4 5 6 7 8 9 10 V0CR 17 16 15 14 13 12

000200010271292858

SE

PEARSON

ISBN 10: 1-256-65237-7
ISBN 13: 978-1-256-65237-3

Brief Contents

About the Authors

The Ninth Edition author team's contributions reflect their biological expertise as researchers and teaching sensibilities gained from years of experience as instructors at diverse institutions. The team's highly collaborative style continues to be evident in the cohesiveness and consistency of the Ninth Edition.

Jane B. Reece

The head of the Ninth Edition author team, Jane Reece was Neil Campbell's longtime collaborator. She has participated in every edition of *BIOLOGY*. Earlier, Jane taught biology at Middlesex County College and Queensborough Community College. She holds an A.B. in Biology from Harvard University, an M.S. in Microbiology from Rutgers University, and a Ph.D. in Bacteriology from the University of California, Berkeley. Jane's research as a doctoral student and postdoctoral fellow focused on genetic recombination in bacteria. Besides her work on CAMPBELL *BIOLOGY*, she has been a coauthor of *Biology: Concepts & Connections*, *Essential Biology*, and *The World of the Cell*.

Lisa A. Urry

Lisa Urry (Chapter 1 and Units 1–3) is a professor and developmental biologist and recent Chair of the Biology Department at Mills College. After graduating from Tufts University with a double major in Biology and French, Lisa completed her Ph.D. in molecular and developmental biology at Massachusetts Institute of Technology (MIT). She has published a number of research papers, most of them focused on gene expression during embryonic and larval development in sea urchins. Lisa is also deeply committed to promoting opportunities for women in science education and research.

Michael L. Cain

Michael Cain (Units 4 and 5) is an ecologist and evolutionary biologist who is now writing full-time. Michael earned a joint degree in Biology and Math at Bowdoin College, an M.Sc. from Brown University, and a Ph.D. in Ecology and Evolutionary Biology from Cornell University. As a faculty member at New Mexico State University and Rose-Hulman Institute of Technology, he taught a wide range of courses, including introductory biology, ecology, evolution, botany, and conservation biology. Michael is the author of dozens of scientific papers on topics that include foraging behavior in insects and plants, long-distance seed dispersal, and speciation in crickets. In addition to his work on CAMPBELL *BIOLOGY*, Michael is also the lead author of an ecology textbook.

Steven A. Wasserman

Steve Wasserman (Unit 7) is a professor at the University of California, San Diego (UCSD). He earned his A.B. in Biology from Harvard University and his Ph.D. in Biological Sciences from MIT. Through his research on regulatory pathway mechanisms in the fruit fly *Drosophila*, Steve has contributed to the fields of developmental biology, reproduction, and immunity. As a faculty member at the University of Texas Southwestern Medical Center and UCSD, he has taught genetics, development, and physiology to undergraduate, graduate, and medical students. He has also served as the research mentor for more than a dozen doctoral students and more than 50 aspiring scientists at the undergraduate and high school levels. Steve has been the recipient of distinguished scholar awards from both the Markey Charitable Trust and the David and Lucille Packard Foundation. In 2007, he received UCSD's Distinguished Teaching Award for undergraduate teaching.

Peter V. Minorsky

Peter Minorsky (Unit 6) is a professor at Mercy College in New York, where he teaches evolution, ecology, botany, and introductory biology. He received his B.A. in Biology from Vassar College and his Ph.D. in Plant Physiology from Cornell University. He is also the science writer for the journal *Plant Physiology*. After a postdoctoral fellowship at the University of Wisconsin at Madison, Peter taught at Kenyon College, Union College, Western Connecticut State University, and Vassar College. He is an electrophysiologist who studies responses of plants to stress. Peter received the 2008 Award for Teaching Excellence at Mercy College.

Robert B. Jackson

Rob Jackson (Unit 8) is a professor of biology and Nicholas Chair of Environmental Sciences at Duke University. Rob holds a B.S. in Chemical Engineering from Rice University, as well as M.S. degrees in Ecology and Statistics and a Ph.D. in Ecology from Utah State University. Rob directed Duke's Program in Ecology for many years and just finished a term as the Vice President of Science for the Ecological Society of America. Rob has received numerous awards, including a Presidential Early Career Award in Science and Engineering from the National Science Foundation. He also enjoys popular writing, having published a trade book about the environment, *The Earth Remains Forever*, and two books of poetry for children, *Animal Mischief* and *Weekend Mischief*.

Neil A. Campbell

Neil Campbell combined the investigative nature of a research scientist with the soul of an experienced and caring teacher. He earned his M.A. in Zoology from UCLA and his Ph.D. in Plant Biology from the University of California, Riverside, where he received the Distinguished Alumnus Award in 2001. Neil published numerous research articles on desert and coastal plants and how the sensitive plant (*Mimosa*) and other legumes move their leaves. His 30 years of teaching in diverse environments included general biology courses at Cornell University, Pomona College, and San Bernardino Valley College, where he received the college's first Outstanding Professor Award in 1986. Neil was a visiting scholar in the Department of Botany and Plant Sciences at the University of California, Riverside. In addition to his authorship of this book, he coauthored *Biology: Concepts & Connections* and *Essential Biology* with Jane Reece. For the Ninth Edition of this book, we honor Neil's contributions to biology education by adopting the title *CAMPBELL BIOLOGY*.

Preface

Biology is an enormous subject, one that can seem overwhelming to students and scientists alike. Moreover, discoveries are being made at an unprecedented pace—from new kinds of small RNA molecules to the Neanderthal genome, from new biofuels to communities of organisms thriving beneath vast glaciers, from emerging infectious diseases to cancer vaccines. As a result, a general biology course faces a daunting challenge: to keep students from suffocating under an avalanche of information. *CAMPBELL BIOLOGY* addresses this challenge by providing a strong foundation for understanding both current knowledge and new developments in the context of underlying biological concepts.

Key Concepts and Unifying Themes

In each chapter of this textbook, a framework of three to six carefully chosen **Key Concepts** provide context for supporting details, helping students distinguish the "forest" from the "trees." The numbered Key Concepts are presented at the beginning of the chapter and then serve as headings for each chapter section. *Concept Check Questions* at the end of each section provide a hierarchical framework for self-assessment that builds students' confidence and then challenges them to push the limits of their understanding with several types of critical thinking questions. The *Summary of Key Concepts* at the end of the chapter refocuses students on the main points. *CAMPBELL BIOLOGY* also helps students organize and make sense of what they learn on a grander scale by emphasizing **evolution and other unifying themes** that pervade biology. These themes are introduced in Chapter 1 and integrated throughout the book.

New to This Edition: An Emphasis on Making Connections

In addition to Key Concepts and themes, we've created new features for the Ninth Edition that help students see the big picture by *making connections*. These include the following:

New Make Connections Questions: Making connections across chapters

New **Make Connections Questions** help students see how different areas of biology tie together, helping them overcome the tendency to compartmentalize information. Each question challenges students to move beyond memorization and gain a deeper understanding of biological principles by asking them to relate chapter content to material they learned earlier in the course. For example, we ask students to connect

- DNA replication (Chapter 16, see p. 319) to the cell cycle (Chapter 12);
- Soil formation (Chapter 37, see p. 789) to the properties of water (Chapter 3); and
- Aquatic biomes (Chapter 52, see p. 1163) to osmoregulation (Chapter 44).

At least three Make Connections Questions appear in each chapter. In addition, online *Make Connections Tutorials* in MasteringBiology® (see p. xi) connect content from two different chapters using figures from the book.

Expanded Evolution Coverage: Making connections to evolution in every chapter

Evolution is the core theme of biology, and in this edition it is more evident than ever. At least one **Evolution section in every chapter** focuses on evolutionary aspects of the chapter material, highlighted by a new Evolution banner. See, for example, the new discussions of enzyme evolution (p. 157), coevolution of flowers and pollinators (p. 806), and evolution of hormone function in animals (pp. 988–989).

New Impact Figures: Making connections between scientific advances and the real world

Our new **Impact Figures** motivate students by highlighting the dramatic impact of recent discoveries in biology. These figures feature high-interest topics such as induced pluripotent stem cells and regenerative medicine (Chapter 20, p. 417), the discovery of *Tiktaalik* (Chapter 34, p. 710), and the use of forensic ecology to track elephant poaching (Chapter 56, p. 1243). The *Why It Matters* section of each figure explains the relevance of the research to students' lives, global problems, or the field of biology itself. Each Impact Figure ends with a suggestion for *Further Reading* and a *What If?* or *Make Connections Question* to develop critical thinking skills.

New Visual Organizers and 3-D Art: Making connections visually

The new **Visual Organizer** format highlights the main parts of a figure, helping students see the key categories at a glance. See, for instance, Figure 17.24 on types of small-scale mutations (p. 345) or Figure 27.3, Gram staining (p. 557). Throughout the book, selected figures have been rendered in a more **3-D art style** while keeping an appropriate balance between realism and teaching effectiveness. Figure 52.3, Exploring Global Climate Patterns (p. 1146), is one example.

Restructured Chapter Reviews: Making connections at a higher level

In the chapter summaries, each concept section now concludes with a new **Summary of Key Concepts Question** that is tied to a major learning goal. Also, this edition increases student awareness of different levels of thinking by organizing the end-of-chapter questions into three levels based on **Bloom's taxonomy**, which classifies types of thinking that are important in learning. Our levels are (1) Knowledge/Comprehension, (2) Application/Analysis, and (3) Synthesis/Evaluation. (These same levels are used in the Campbell Test Bank.) The range of question types helps students develop critical thinking skills and prepare for the kinds of questions they'll encounter on exams. New **Write About a Theme Questions** give students practice writing short, coherent essays that connect the chapter's content to one of the book's themes. (A suggested grading rubric can be found on p. xv, and sample answers are provided for instructors in the MasteringBiology Instructor Resources area.) A new **MasteringBiology preview section** at the end of each chapter lists *Assignments*—tutorials, activities, and questions that instructors can assign. This section also directs students to the *eText* and *Study Area* for online self study.

New Content: Making connections to advances in science

As in each new edition, the Ninth Edition incorporates **new scientific content** and **organizational improvements**. These are summarized on pp. viii–ix, following this Preface.

MasteringBiology®: Making connections outside of class

MasteringBiology, the most widely used online assessment and tutorial program for biology, provides an extensive library of homework assignments that are graded automatically. In addition to BioFlix® Tutorials, other Tutorials, Activities, Reading Quiz Questions in every chapter, and 4,500 Test Bank Questions, MasteringBiology for the Ninth Edition features an **improved user interface** and the following **new Tutorials and Questions**: *Make Connections Tutorials, Student Misconceptions Questions* for every chapter, *Data Analysis Tutorials, Experimental Inquiry Tutorials, Video Tutor Sessions*, and *MasteringBiology: Virtual Biology Labs*. For more information, see pp. xvi–xix and www.masteringbiology.com.

Our Hallmark Features

Besides our Key Concepts and unifying themes, several other features have contributed to the success of CAMPBELL *BIOLOGY*. Because text and illustrations are equally important for learning biology, **integration of figures and text** has been a hallmark of this book since its inception. Our popular *Exploring Figures* on selected topics epitomize this approach: Each is a learning unit of core content that brings together related illustrations and text. Another example is our *Guided Tour Figures*, which use descriptions in blue type to walk students through complex figures like an instructor would, pointing out key structures, functions, and steps of processes.

To encourage **active learning**, recent editions have incorporated new types of questions: *What If? Questions, Figure Legend Questions*, and *Draw It Questions* that ask students to sketch a structure, annotate a figure, or graph data. In the Ninth Edition, these questions are augmented by the new *Make Connections Questions*. Online, the highly interactive *MasteringBiology tutorials* are sophisticated active-learning tools.

Finally, CAMPBELL *BIOLOGY* features **scientific inquiry**, an essential component of any biology course. Complementing stories of scientific discovery in the text narrative and the unit-opening interviews, *Inquiry Figures* help students understand "how we know what we know" and provide a model of how to think like a scientist. Each one begins with a research question and then describes how researchers designed an experiment, interpreted their results, and drew conclusions. The source article is referenced, and a What If? Question asks students to consider an alternative scenario. Selected Inquiry Figures invite students to read and analyze the original research article in the supplement *Inquiry in Action: Interpreting Scientific Papers* (see p. xxi). At the end of each chapter, *Scientific Inquiry Questions* give students additional opportunities to practice critical thinking by developing hypotheses, designing experiments, and analyzing real research data. Beyond the book, activities involving scientific inquiry are featured in MasteringBiology and other supplements, both print and electronic (see pp. xviii–xxi).

Our Partnership with Instructors

A core value underlying all our work as authors is our belief in the importance of our partnership with instructors. Our primary way of serving instructors, of course, is providing a textbook, supplements, and media resources that serve their students well. In addition, Benjamin Cummings makes available a rich variety of instructor resources, in both print and electronic form (see p. xx). In our continuing efforts to improve the book and its supplements, we benefit tremendously from instructor feedback, not only in formal reviews from hundreds of scientists, but also via informal communication, often by e-mail.

The real test of any textbook is how well it helps instructors teach and students learn. We welcome comments from the students and instructors who use CAMPBELL *BIOLOGY*. Please address your suggestions to any of us:

Jane Reece at janereece@cal.berkeley.edu
Lisa Urry (Chapter 1 and Units 1–3) at lurry@mills.edu
Michael Cain (Units 4 and 5) at mcain@bowdoin.edu
Peter Minorsky (Unit 6) at pminorsky@mercy.edu
Steve Wasserman (Unit 7) at stevenw@ucsd.edu
Rob Jackson (Unit 8) at jackson@duke.edu

New Content

This section provides just a few highlights of new content and organizational improvements in *CAMPBELL BIOLOGY*, Ninth Edition.

CHAPTER 1 Introduction: Themes in the Study of Life

We have added a separate new theme on energy flow while retaining a theme on environmental interactions. Concept 1.3, on the scientific method, has been reframed to more accurately reflect the scientific process, with a focus on observations and hypotheses. A new Concept 1.4 discusses the value of technology to society while emphasizing the cooperative nature of science and the value of diversity among scientists.

UNIT ONE The Chemistry of Life

For this edition, the basic chemistry is enlivened by new content connecting it to evolution, ecology, and other areas of biology. Examples of new material include omega-3 fatty acids, the isomeric forms of methamphetamine, arsenic contamination of groundwater, and the basis of mad cow disease. The burgeoning importance of nucleic acids throughout biology has prompted us to expand our coverage of DNA and RNA structures in this first unit. In fact, a general aim for the first two units is to infuse the chapters with more detail about nucleic acids, genes, and related topics. Another enhancement, in this and the next two units, is the inclusion of more computer models of important proteins in contexts where they support students' understanding of molecular function.

UNIT TWO The Cell

For Chapter 6, we developed an Exploring Figure on microscopy, which includes new types of microscopy, and we added micrographs of various cell types to the Exploring Figure on eukaryotic cells. We also expanded our description of chromosome composition, with the goal of preempting some common student misconceptions about chromosomes and DNA. New connections to evolution include an introduction to the endosymbiont theory in Chapter 6 and some interesting evolutionary adaptations of cell membranes in Chapter 7. We've added a new section to Chapter 8 on the evolution of enzymes with new functions, which not only strengthens enzyme coverage but also provides an early introduction to the concept that mutations contribute to molecular evolution. In Chapter 9, we simplified the glycolysis figure and emphasized pyruvate oxidation as a separate step to help students focus on the main ideas. In keeping with our increased focus on global issues in the Ninth Edition, Chapter 10 has an Impact Figure on biofuels and a discussion of the possible effect of climate change on the distribution of C_3 and C_4 plants. In Chapter 11, we have added an Impact Figure to highlight the importance and medical relevance of G protein-coupled receptors.

UNIT THREE Genetics

In Chapters 13–17, we have added material to stimulate student interest—for example, a new Impact Figure on genetic testing for disease-associated mutations. As done throughout the Ninth Edition, we ask students to make connections between chapters so that they avoid the trap of compartmentalizing the information in each chapter. For instance, Chapter 15 discusses the Philadelphia chromosome associated with chronic myelogenous leukemia and asks students to connect this information to what they learned about signaling in the cell cycle in Chapter 12. Also, we encourage students to connect what they learn about DNA replication and chromosome structure in Chapter 16 to the material on chromosome behavior during the cell cycle in Chapter 12. Chapter 16 has a new figure showing a current 3-D model of the DNA replication complex, with the lagging strand looping back through it.

Chapters 18–21 are extensively updated, with the changes dominated by new genomic sequence data and discoveries about the regulation of gene expression. (The introduction to genes, genomes, and gene expression in Units One and Two should help prepare students for these revisions.) Chapter 18 includes a new section on nuclear architecture, which describes the organization of chromatin in the nucleus in relation to gene expression. The roles of various types of RNA molecules in regulation also receive special attention. In the section on cancer, we describe how technical advances can contribute to personalized cancer treatments based on the molecular characteristics of an individual's tumor. Chapter 19 discusses the 2009 H1N1 flu pandemic. Chapter 20 includes advances in techniques for DNA sequencing and for obtaining induced pluripotent stem (iPS) cells. Finally, the heavily revised Chapter 21 describes what has been learned from the sequencing of many genomes, including those of a number of human individuals.

UNIT FOUR Mechanisms of Evolution

For this edition, we have continued to bolster our presentation of the vast evidence for evolution by adding new examples and figures that illustrate key conceptual points throughout the unit. For example, Chapter 22 now presents research data on adaptive evolution in soapberry bugs, fossil findings that shed light on the origins of cetaceans, and an Impact Figure on the rise of methicillin-resistant *Staphylococcus aureus*. Chapter 23 examines gene flow and adaptation in songbird populations. Chapter 24 incorporates several new examples of speciation research, including reproductive isolation in mosquitofish, speciation in shrimp, and hybridization of bear species. Other changes strengthen the storyline of the unit, ensuring that the chapters flow smoothly and build to a clear overall picture of what evolution is and how it works. For instance, new connections between Chapters 24 and 25 illustrate how differences in speciation and extinction rates shape the broad patterns in the history of life. We've also added earlier and more discussion of "tree thinking," the interpretation and application of phylogenetic trees, beginning in Chapter 22.

UNIT FIVE The Evolutionary History of Biological Diversity

One of our goals for the diversity unit was to expand the coverage of the scientific evidence underlying the evolutionary story told in the chapters. So, for example, Chapter 27 now presents new findings on the evolutionary origin of bacterial flagella. In keeping with our increased emphasis on big-picture "tree thinking," we've added an "evogram" on tetrapod evolution in Chapter 34. (An evogram is a diagram illustrating the multiple lines of evidence that support the hypothesis shown in an evolutionary tree.) In addition, to help engage students, we've included new applications and woven more ecological information into our discussions of groups of organisms. Examples include new material on global growth of photosynthetic protists (Chapter 28), endangered molluscs (Chapter 33), and the impact of a pathogenic chytrid fungus on amphibian population declines (Chapters 31 and 34).

UNIT SIX Plant Form and Function

Plant biology is in a transitional phase; some professors prefer strong coverage of classical botany while others seek more in-depth coverage of the molecular biology of plants. In developing the Ninth Edition, we have continued to balance the old and the new to provide students with a basic understanding of plant anatomy and function while highlighting dynamic areas of plant research and the many important connections between plants and other organisms. One major revision goal was to provide more explicit discussion of the evolutionary aspects of plant biology, such as the coevolution of flowering plants and pollinators (Chapter 38). Updates include new findings in plant development in Concept 35.5 and new material on the dynamism of plant architecture as it relates to resource acquisition in Chapter 36.

UNIT SEVEN Animal Form and Function

In revising this unit, we strove to introduce physiological systems through a comparative approach that underscores how adaptations are linked to shared physiological challenges. In particular, we have highlighted the interrelationship of the endocrine and nervous systems at multiple points in the unit, helping students appreciate how these two forms of communication link tissues, organs, and individuals. Other revisions aim to keep students focused on fundamental concepts amid the details of complex systems. For example, many figures have been reconceived to emphasize key information, including new figures comparing single and double circulation (Chapter 42) and examining the function of antigen receptors (Chapter 43), as well as new Exploring Figures on the vertebrate kidney (Chapter 44) and the structure and function of the human eye (Chapter 50). Chapter 43 has been significantly revised to support students' conceptual understanding of basic immunological responses and the key cellular players. Throughout the unit, new state-of-the-art images and material on current and compelling topics—such as circadian rhythms (Chapter 40), novel strains of influenza (Chapter 43), the effects of climate change on animal reproductive cycles (Chapter 46), and advances in understanding brain plasticity and function (Chapter 49)—will help engage students and encourage them to make connections beyond the text.

UNIT EIGHT Ecology

Our revision was informed by the fact that biologists are increasingly asked to apply their knowledge to help solve global problems, such as climate change, that already are profoundly affecting life on Earth. As part of our increased emphasis on global ecology in this edition, we have made significant changes to Unit Eight's organization and content. The organizational changes begin with the introductory chapter of the unit (Chapter 52), which includes a new Key Concept 52.1: "Earth's climate varies by latitude and season and is changing rapidly." Introducing the global nature of climate and its effects on life at the beginning of the chapter provides a logical foundation for the rest of the material. New content in Chapters 53 and 54 highlights factors that limit population growth, the ecological importance of disease, positive interactions among organisms, and biodiversity. Chapter 55 now explores restoration ecology together with ecosystem ecology because successful restoration efforts depend on understanding ecosystem structure and function. Finally, the new title of the unit's capstone, Chapter 56, reflects its emphasis on the combined importance of conservation and our changing Earth: "Conservation Biology and Global Change." Several new Impact Figures in the unit show students how ecologists apply biological knowledge and ecological theory at all scales to understand and solve problems in the world around them.

To the Student: How to Use This Book

Focus on the Key Concepts.

Each chapter is organized around a framework of 3 to 6 **Key Concepts** that will help you stay focused on the big picture and give you a context for the supporting details.

52

An Introduction to Ecology and the Biosphere

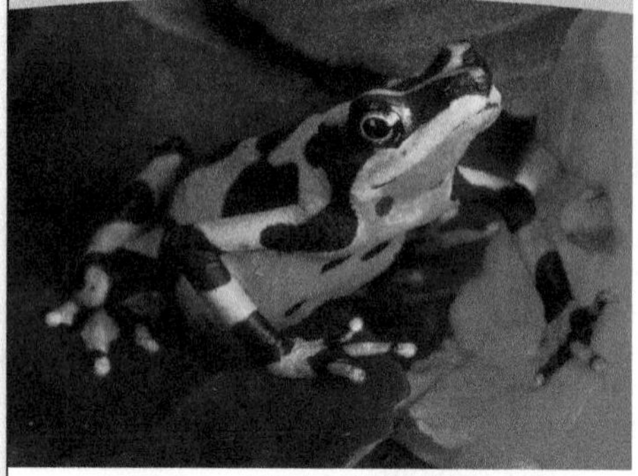

▲ Figure 52.1 **What threatens this amphibian's survival?**

Before you begin reading the chapter, get oriented by reading the **list of Key Concepts,** which introduces the big ideas covered in the chapter.

KEY CONCEPTS

52.1 Earth's climate varies by latitude and season and is changing rapidly
52.2 The structure and distribution of terrestrial biomes are controlled by climate and disturbance
52.3 Aquatic biomes are diverse and dynamic systems that cover most of Earth
52.4 Interactions between organisms and the environment limit the distribution of species

Each **Key Concept** serves as the heading for a major section of the chapter.

OVERVIEW

Discovering Ecology

When University of Delaware undergraduate Justin Yeager spent his summer abroad in Costa Rica, all he wanted was to see the tropical rain forest and to practice his Spanish. Instead, he rediscovered the variable harlequin toad (*Atelopus varius*), a species thought to be extinct in the mountain slopes of Costa Rica and Panama where it once lived (Figure 52.1). During the 1980s and 1990s, roughly two-thirds of the 82 known species of harlequin toads vanished. Scientists think that a disease-causing chytrid fungus, *Batrachochytrium dendrobatidis* (see Figure 31.26), contributed to many of these extinctions. Why was the fungus suddenly thriving in the rain forest? Cloudier days and warmer nights associated with global warming appear to have created an environment ideal for its success. As of 2009, the species that Yeager found was surviving as a single known population of fewer than 100 individuals.

What environmental factors limit the geographic distribution of harlequin toads? How do variations in their food supply or interactions with other species, such as pathogens, affect the size of their population? Questions like these are the subject of **ecology** (from the Greek *oikos*, home, and *logos*, study), the scientific study of the interactions between organisms and the environment. Ecological interactions occur at a hierarchy of scales that ecologists study, from single organisms to the globe (Figure 52.2).

Ecology's roots are in our basic human interest in observing other organisms. Naturalists, including Aristotle and Darwin, have long studied the living world and systematically recorded their observations. However, modern ecology involves more than observation. It is a rigorous experimental science that requires a breadth of biological knowledge. Ecologists generate hypotheses, manipulate environmental variables, and observe the outcome. In this unit, you will encounter many examples of ecological experiments, whose complex challenges have made ecologists innovators in experimental design and statistical inference.

In addition to providing a conceptual framework for understanding the field of ecology, Figure 52.2 provides the organizational framework for our final unit. In this chapter, we first describe Earth's climate and the importance of climate and other physical factors in determining the location of major life zones on land and in the oceans. We then examine how ecologists determine what controls the distribution and abundance of individual species. The next three chapters investigate population, community, and ecosystem ecology in detail, including approaches for restoring degraded ecosystems. The final chapter explores conservation biology and global ecology as we consider how ecologists apply biological knowledge to predict the global consequences of human activities and to conserve Earth's biodiversity.

CONCEPT 52.1

Earth's climate varies by latitude and season and is changing rapidly

The most significant influence on the distribution of organisms on land and in the oceans is **climate**, the long-term, prevailing weather conditions in a given area. Four physical

After reading a concept section, check your understanding using the **Concept Check Questions** at the end of the section. Work through these questions on your own or in a study group—they're good practice for the kinds of questions you might be asked on an exam.

What If? Questions ask you to apply what you've learned. New **Make Connections Questions** ask you to relate content in the chapter to a concept you learned earlier in the course.

If you can answer these questions (see Appendix A to check your work), you're ready to move on.

CONCEPT CHECK 52.1

1. Explain how the sun's unequal heating of Earth's surface leads to the development of deserts around 30° north and south of the equator.
2. What are some of the differences in microclimate between an unplanted agricultural field and a nearby stream corridor with trees?
3. **WHAT IF?** Changes in Earth's climate at the end of the last ice age happened gradually, taking centuries to thousands of years. If the current global warming happens very quickly, as predicted, how may this rapid climate change affect the ability of long-lived trees to evolve, compared with annual plants, which have much shorter generation times?
4. **MAKE CONNECTIONS** In Concept 10.4 (pp. 199–201), you learned about the important differences between C_3 and C_4 plants. Focusing just on the effects of temperature, would you expect the global distribution of C_4 plants to expand or contract as Earth becomes warmer? Why?

For suggested answers, see Appendix A.

Make connections across biology.

By relating the content of a chapter to material you learned earlier in the course, new **Make Connections Questions** help you develop a deeper understanding of biological principles.

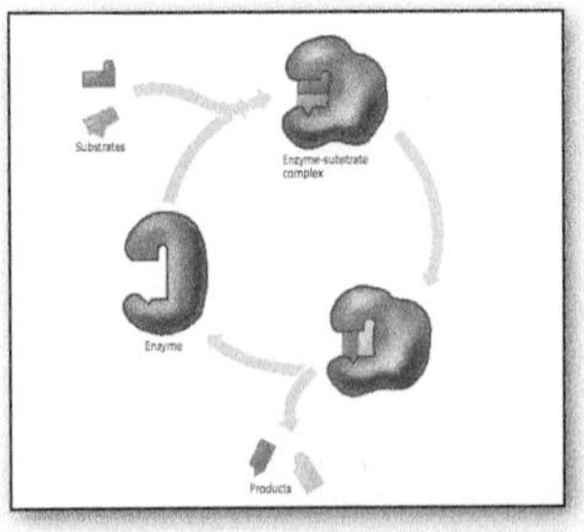

CONCEPT CHECK 41.1

2. **MAKE CONNECTIONS** Review the discussion of enzymes in metabolic reactions in Concept 8.4 (pp. 152–156). Then explain why vitamins are required in very small amounts in the diet.

Enzymes (Chapter 8) ⟷ **Animal nutrition** (Chapter 41)

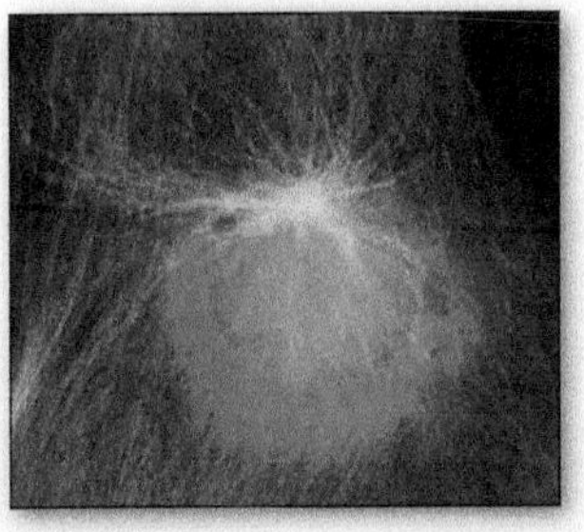

CONCEPT CHECK 16.2

3. **MAKE CONNECTIONS** What is the relationship between DNA replication and the S phase of the cell cycle? See Figure 12.6, page 231.

Cell cycle (Chapter 12) ⟷ **DNA replication** (Chapter 16)

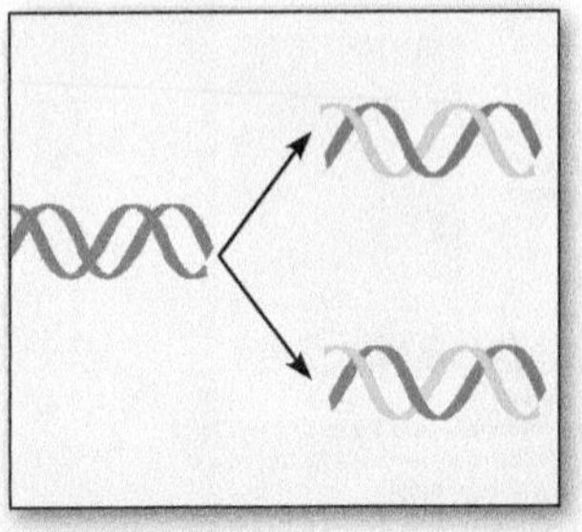

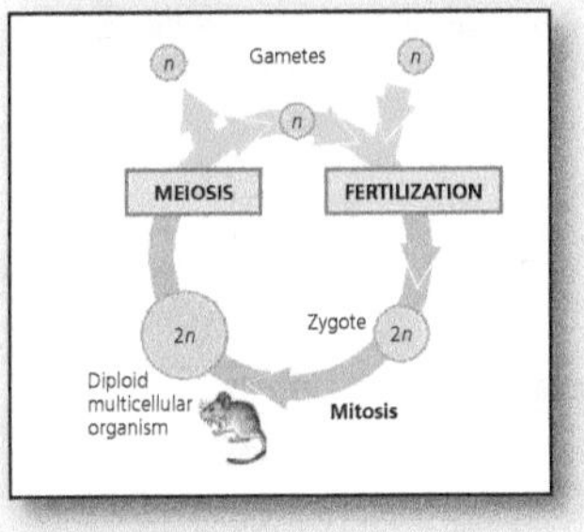

CONCEPT CHECK 31.2

1. **MAKE CONNECTIONS** Compare Figure 31.5 with Figure 13.6 (p. 252). In terms of haploidy versus diploidy, how do the life cycles of fungi and animals differ?

Meiosis (Chapter 13) ⟷ **Fungi** (Chapter 31)

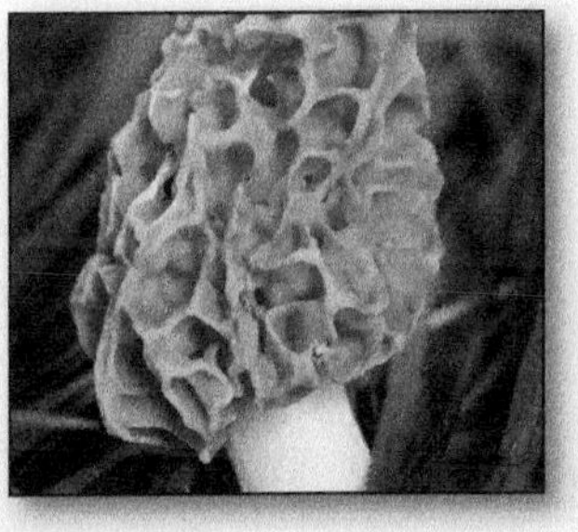

MasteringBIOLOGY®
www.masteringbiology.com

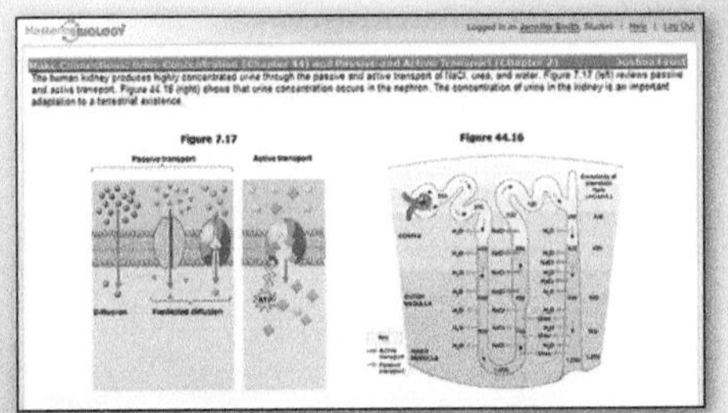

New **Make Connections Tutorials** help you connect biological concepts across chapters in an interactive way.

Make connections to **evolution**, the fundamental theme of biology.

Look for new **Evolution banners** highlighting sections in each chapter that focus on evolutionary aspects of the topic.

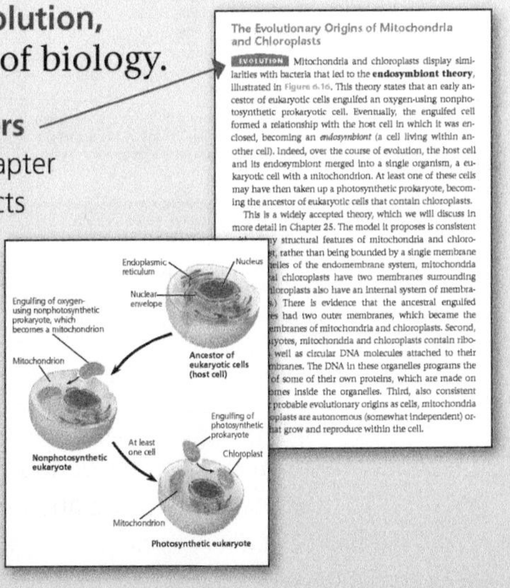

Practice thinking like a scientist.

New **Impact Figures** demonstrate the dramatic impact of recent discoveries in biology and show that biology is constantly changing as new discoveries add to our understanding. ▶

▼ Figure 56.9
IMPACT

Forensic Ecology and Elephant Poaching

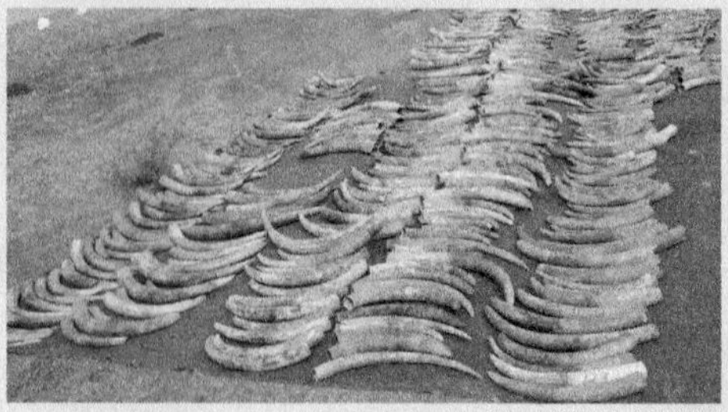

This array of severed tusks is part of an illegal shipment of 6,000 kg of ivory intercepted on its way from Africa to Singapore in 2002. Investigators wondered whether the elephants slaughtered for the ivory—perhaps as many as 6,500—were killed in the area where the shipment originated, primarily Zambia, or instead were killed across Africa, indicating a broader smuggling ring. Samuel Wasser, of the University of Washington, and colleagues amplified specific segments of DNA from the tusks using the polymerase chain reaction (PCR). These segments included stretches of DNA containing short tandem repeats (STRs; see Concept 20.4, pp. 420–421), the number of which varies among different elephant populations. The researchers then compared alleles at seven or more loci with a reference DNA database they had generated for elephants of known geographic origin. Their results showed conclusively that the elephants came from a narrow east-west band centered on Zambia rather than from across Africa.

Why It Matters explains the relevance of the research. ▶

WHY IT MATTERS The DNA analyses suggested that poaching rates were 30 times higher in Zambia than previously estimated. This news led to improved antipoaching efforts by the Zambian government. Techniques like those used in this study are being employed by conservation biologists to track the harvesting of many endangered species, including whales, sharks, and orchids.

Further Reading directs you to articles to explore. ▶

FURTHER READING S. K. Wasser et al., Forensic tools battle ivory poachers, *Scientific American* 399:68–76 (2009); S. K. Wasser et al., Using DNA to track the origin of the largest ivory seizure since the 1989 trade ban, *Proceedings of the National Academy of Sciences USA* 104:4228–4233 (2007).

A **Make Connections** or **What If? Question** encourages critical thinking. ▶

MAKE CONNECTIONS Figure 26.6 (p. 539) describes another example in which conservation biologists used DNA analyses to compare harvested samples with a reference DNA database. How are these examples similar, and how are they different? What limitations might there be to using such forensic methods in other suspected cases of poaching?

Inquiry Figures reveal "how we know what we know" by highlighting how researchers designed an experiment, interpreted their results, and drew conclusions.
▼

▼ Figure 37.14 **INQUIRY**

Does the invasive weed garlic mustard disrupt mutualistic associations between native tree seedlings and arbuscular mycorrhizal fungi?

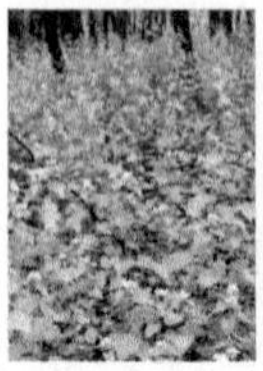

EXPERIMENT Kristina Stinson, of Harvard University, and colleagues investigated the effect of invasive garlic mustard on the growth of native tree seedlings and associated mycorrhizal fungi. In one experiment, they grew seedlings of three North American trees—sugar maple, red maple, and white ash—in four different soils. Two of the soil samples were collected from a location where garlic mustard was growing, and one of these samples was sterilized. The other two soil samples were collected from a location devoid of garlic mustard, and one was then sterilized. After four months of growth, the researchers harvested the shoots and roots and determined the dried biomass. The roots were also analyzed for percent colonization by arbuscular mycorrhizal fungi.

RESULTS Native tree seedlings grew more slowly and were less able to form mycorrhizal associations when grown either in sterilized soil or in unsterilized soil collected from a location that had been invaded by garlic mustard.

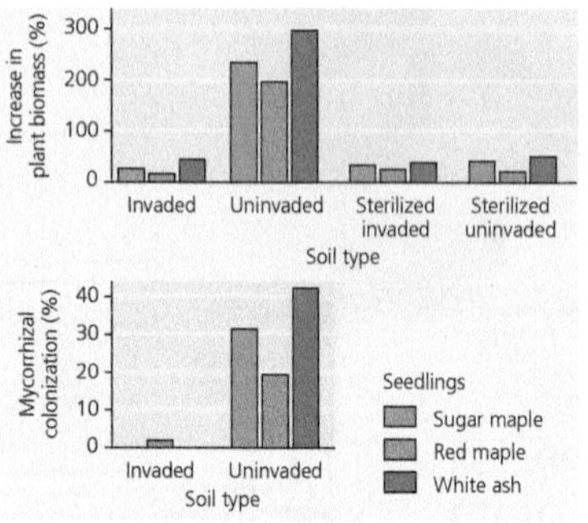

CONCLUSION The data support the hypothesis that garlic mustard suppresses growth of native trees by affecting the soil in a way that disrupts mutualistic associations between the trees and arbuscular mycorrhizal fungi.

SOURCE K. A. Stinson et al., Invasive plant suppresses the growth of native tree seedlings by disrupting belowground mutualisms, *PLoS Biol* (*Public Library of Science: Biology*) 4(5): e140 (2006).

INQUIRY IN ACTION Read and analyze the original paper in *Inquiry in Action: Interpreting Scientific Papers*.

WHAT IF? What effect would applying inorganic phosphate to soil invaded by garlic mustard have on the plant's ability to outcompete native species?

◀ Some **Inquiry Figures** invite you to read and analyze the original research paper in its complete form. You can find the journal article, along with a worksheet guiding you through it, in the separate book ***Inquiry in Action: Interpreting Scientific Papers.***

▲
After exploring the featured experiment, test your analytical skills by answering the **What If? Question**. Suggested answers are provided in Appendix A to help you gauge your understanding.

MasteringBIOLOGY
www.masteringbiology.com

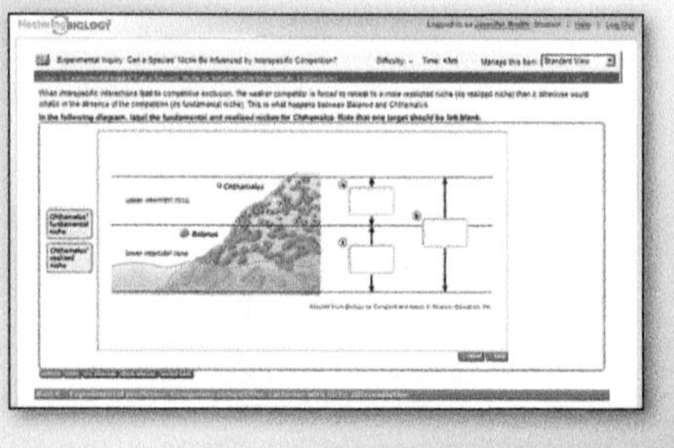

New **Experimental Inquiry Tutorials** give you practice analyzing experimental design and data and drawing conclusions.

Study the figures as you read the text.

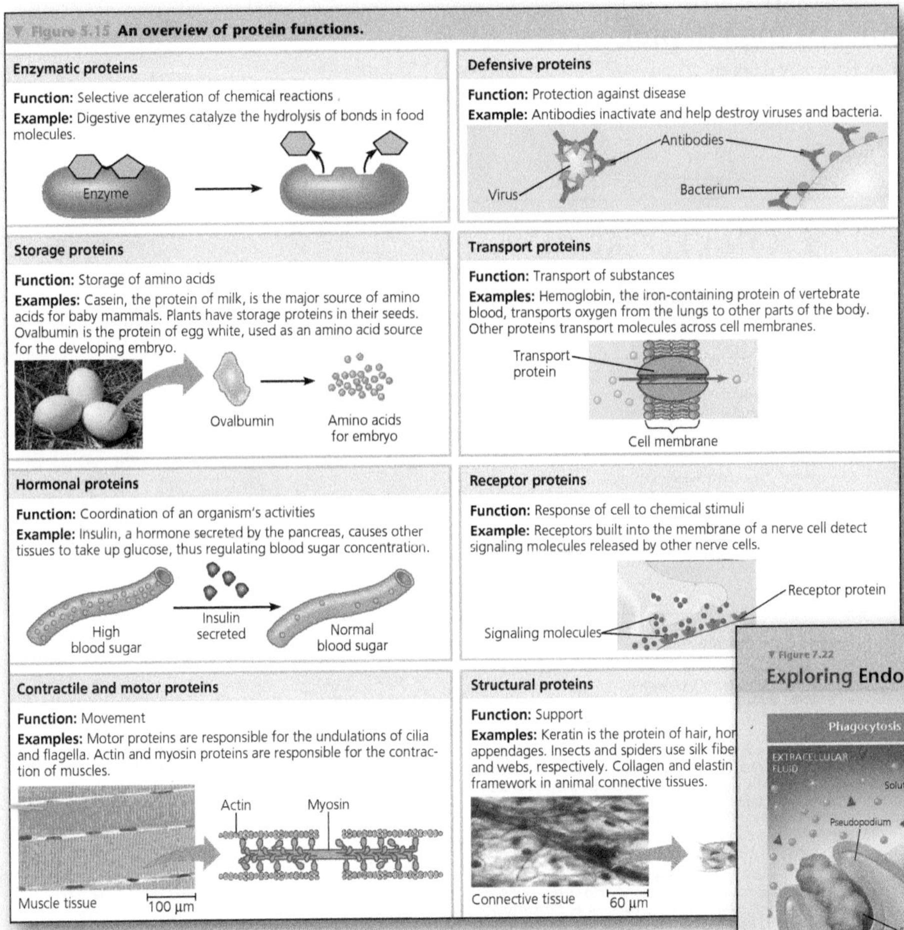

▼ Figure 5.15 **An overview of protein functions.**

Enzymatic proteins

Function: Selective acceleration of chemical reactions

Example: Digestive enzymes catalyze the hydrolysis of bonds in food molecules.

Defensive proteins

Function: Protection against disease

Example: Antibodies inactivate and help destroy viruses and bacteria.

Storage proteins

Function: Storage of amino acids

Examples: Casein, the protein of milk, is the major source of amino acids for baby mammals. Plants have storage proteins in their seeds. Ovalbumin is the protein of egg white, used as an amino acid source for the developing embryo.

Transport proteins

Function: Transport of substances

Examples: Hemoglobin, the iron-containing protein of vertebrate blood, transports oxygen from the lungs to other parts of the body. Other proteins transport molecules across cell membranes.

Hormonal proteins

Function: Coordination of an organism's activities

Example: Insulin, a hormone secreted by the pancreas, causes other tissues to take up glucose, thus regulating blood sugar concentration.

Receptor proteins

Function: Response of cell to chemical stimuli

Example: Receptors built into the membrane of a nerve cell detect signaling molecules released by other nerve cells.

Contractile and motor proteins

Function: Movement

Examples: Motor proteins are responsible for the undulations of cilia and flagella. Actin and myosin proteins are responsible for the contraction of muscles.

Structural proteins

Function: Support

Examples: Keratin is the protein of hair, hor appendages. Insects and spiders use silk fibe and webs, respectively. Collagen and elastin framework in animal connective tissues.

◀ New **Visual Organizers** help you to see important categories at a glance.

By integrating text and visuals, **Exploring Figures** help you learn more efficiently. ▼

In selected illustrations, **a three-dimensional art style** helps you visualize biological structures. ▶

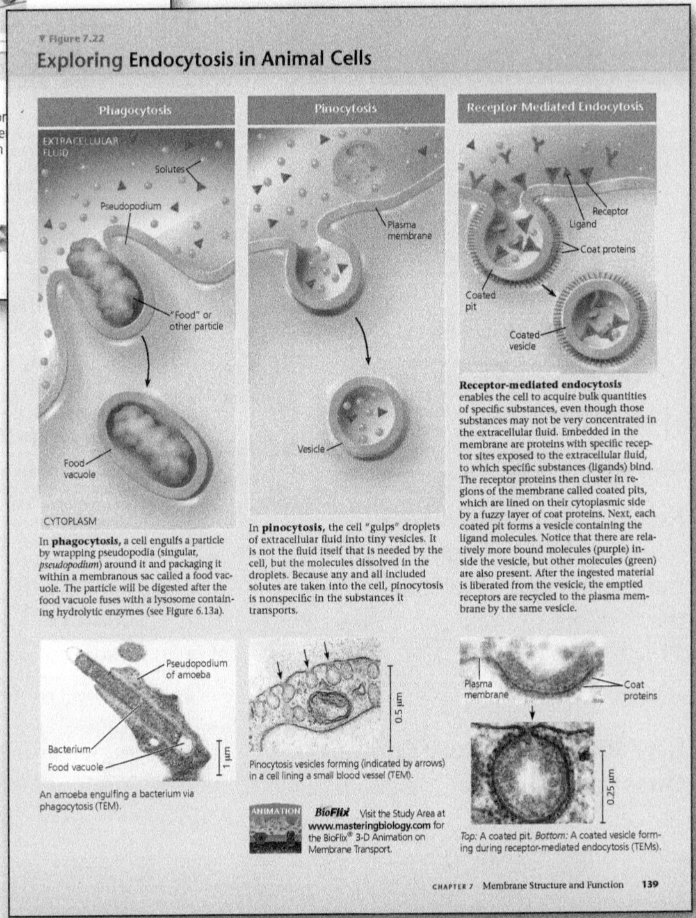

▼ Figure 7.22

Exploring Endocytosis in Animal Cells

In **phagocytosis,** a cell engulfs a particle by wrapping pseudopodia (singular, *pseudopodium*) around it and packaging it within a membranous sac called a food vacuole. The particle will be digested after the food vacuole fuses with a lysosome containing hydrolytic enzymes (see Figure 6.13a).

In **pinocytosis,** the cell "gulps" droplets of extracellular fluid into tiny vesicles. It is not the fluid itself that is needed by the cell, but the molecules dissolved in the droplets. Because any and all included solutes are taken into the cell, pinocytosis is nonspecific in the substances it transports.

Receptor-mediated endocytosis enables the cell to acquire bulk quantities of specific substances, even though those substances may not be very concentrated in the extracellular fluid. Embedded in the membrane are proteins with specific receptor sites exposed to the extracellular fluid, to which specific substances (ligands) bind. The receptor proteins then cluster in regions of the membrane called coated pits, which are lined on their cytoplasmic side by a fuzzy layer of coat proteins. Next, each coated pit forms a vesicle containing the ligand molecules. Notice that there are relatively more bound molecules (purple) inside the vesicle, but other molecules (green) are also present. After the ingested material is liberated from the vesicle, the emptied receptors are recycled to the plasma membrane by the same vesicle.

An amoeba engulfing a bacterium via phagocytosis (TEM).

Pinocytosis vesicles forming (indicated by arrows) in a cell lining a small blood vessel (TEM).

Top: A coated pit. *Bottom:* A coated vesicle forming during receptor-mediated endocytosis (TEMs).

ANIMATION **BioFlix** Visit the Study Area at **www.masteringbiology.com** for the BioFlix® 3-D Animation on Membrane Transport.

CHAPTER 7 Membrane Structure and Function 139

MasteringBIOLOGY www.masteringbiology.com

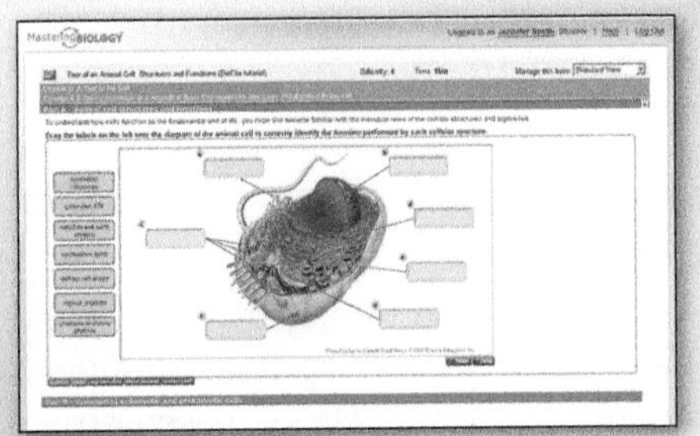

Many **Tutorials** and **Activities** integrate art from the textbook, providing a unified learning experience.

▲ **BioFlix®** icons direct you to high-impact 3-D animations in the Study Area at www.masteringbiology.com.

Review what you've learned.

Chapter Reviews help you efficiently master the chapter content by focusing on the main points of the chapter and offering opportunities to practice for exams.

Summary Figures present key information in a visual way.

23

The Evolution of Populations

▲ Figure 23.1 **Is this finch evolving?**

EVOLUTION

KEY CONCEPTS

23.1 Genetic variation makes evolution possible
23.2 The Hardy-Weinberg equation can be used to test whether a population is evolving
23.3 Natural selection, genetic drift, and gene flow can alter allele frequencies in a population
23.4 Natural selection is the only mechanism that consistently causes adaptive evolution

OVERVIEW

The Smallest Unit of Evolution

One common misconception about evolution is that individual organisms evolve. It is true that natural selection acts on individuals: Each organism's traits affect its survival and reproductive success compared with other individuals. But the evolutionary impact of natural selection is only apparent in the changes in a *population* of organisms over time.

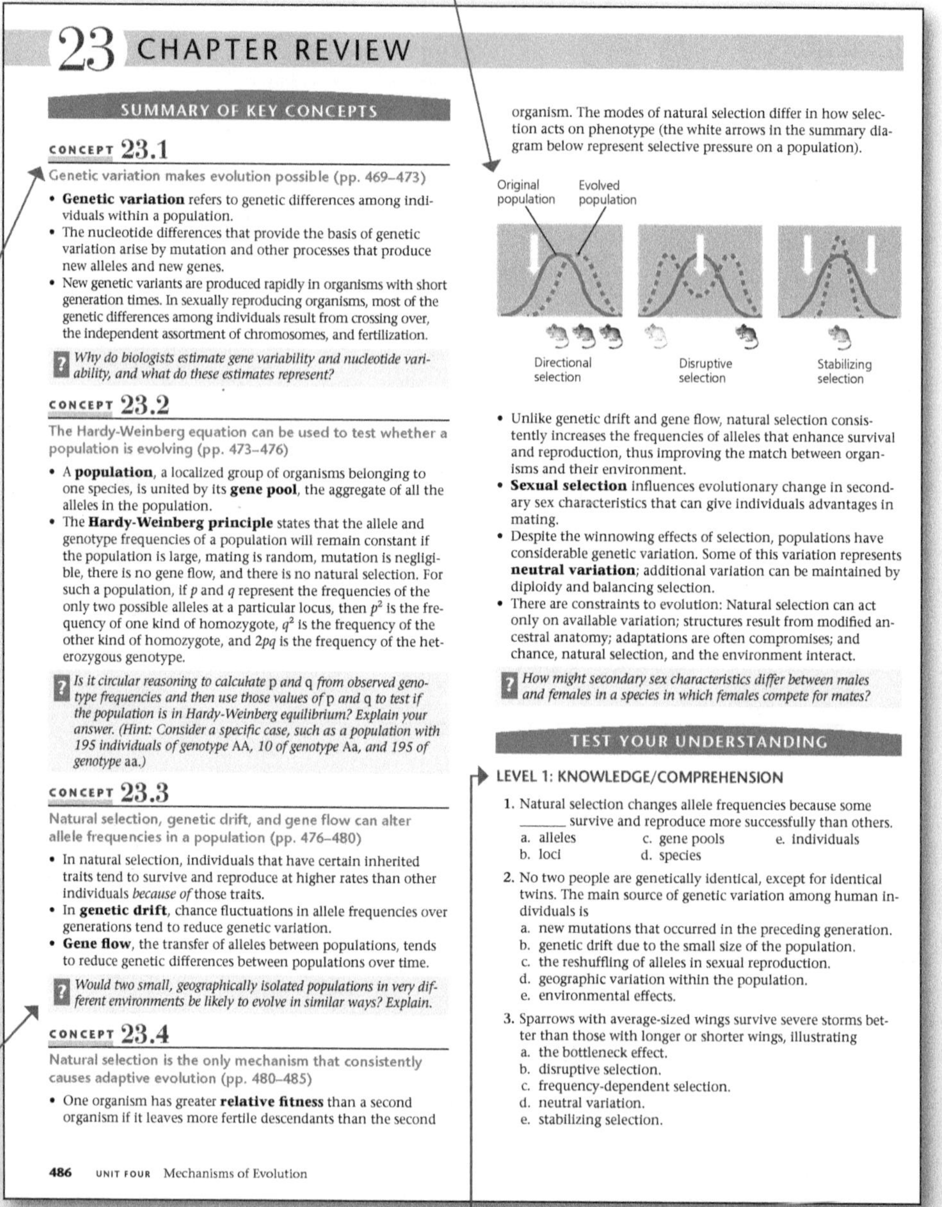
23 CHAPTER REVIEW

SUMMARY OF KEY CONCEPTS

CONCEPT 23.1

Genetic variation makes evolution possible (pp. 469–473)

- **Genetic variation** refers to genetic differences among individuals within a population.
- The nucleotide differences that provide the basis of genetic variation arise by mutation and other processes that produce new alleles and new genes.
- New genetic variants are produced rapidly in organisms with short generation times. In sexually reproducing organisms, most of the genetic differences among individuals result from crossing over, the independent assortment of chromosomes, and fertilization.

? *Why do biologists estimate gene variability and nucleotide variability, and what do these estimates represent?*

CONCEPT 23.2

The Hardy-Weinberg equation can be used to test whether a population is evolving (pp. 473–476)

- A **population**, a localized group of organisms belonging to one species, is united by its **gene pool**, the aggregate of all the alleles in the population.
- The **Hardy-Weinberg principle** states that the allele and genotype frequencies of a population will remain constant if the population is large, mating is random, mutation is negligible, there is no gene flow, and there is no natural selection. For such a population, if p and q represent the frequencies of the only two possible alleles at a particular locus, then p^2 is the frequency of one kind of homozygote, q^2 is the frequency of the other kind of homozygote, and $2pq$ is the frequency of the heterozygous genotype.

? *Is it circular reasoning to calculate* p *and* q *from observed genotype frequencies and then use those values of* p *and* q *to test if the population is in Hardy-Weinberg equilibrium? Explain your answer. (Hint: Consider a specific case, such as a population with 195 individuals of genotype* AA*, 10 of genotype* Aa*, and 195 of genotype* aa*.)*

CONCEPT 23.3

Natural selection, genetic drift, and gene flow can alter allele frequencies in a population (pp. 476–480)

- In natural selection, individuals that have certain inherited traits tend to survive and reproduce at higher rates than other individuals *because of* those traits.
- In **genetic drift**, chance fluctuations in allele frequencies over generations tend to reduce genetic variation.
- **Gene flow**, the transfer of alleles between populations, tends to reduce genetic differences between populations over time.

? *Would two small, geographically isolated populations in very different environments be likely to evolve in similar ways? Explain.*

CONCEPT 23.4

Natural selection is the only mechanism that consistently causes adaptive evolution (pp. 480–485)

- One organism has greater **relative fitness** than a second organism if it leaves more fertile descendants than the second organism. The modes of natural selection differ in how selection acts on phenotype (the white arrows in the summary diagram below represent selective pressure on a population).

- Unlike genetic drift and gene flow, natural selection consistently increases the frequencies of alleles that enhance survival and reproduction, thus improving the match between organisms and their environment.
- **Sexual selection** influences evolutionary change in secondary sex characteristics that can give individuals advantages in mating.
- Despite the winnowing effects of selection, populations have considerable genetic variation. Some of this variation represents **neutral variation**; additional variation can be maintained by diploidy and balancing selection.
- There are constraints to evolution: Natural selection can act only on available variation; structures result from modified ancestral anatomy; adaptations are often compromises; and chance, natural selection, and the environment interact.

? *How might secondary sex characteristics differ between males and females in a species in which females compete for mates?*

TEST YOUR UNDERSTANDING

LEVEL 1: KNOWLEDGE/COMPREHENSION

1. Natural selection changes allele frequencies because some ______ survive and reproduce more successfully than others.
   a. alleles
   b. loci
   c. gene pools
   d. species
   e. individuals
2. No two people are genetically identical, except for identical twins. The main source of genetic variation among human individuals is
   a. new mutations that occurred in the preceding generation.
   b. genetic drift due to the small size of the population.
   c. the reshuffling of alleles in sexual reproduction.
   d. geographic variation within the population.
   e. environmental effects.
3. Sparrows with average-sized wings survive severe storms better than those with longer or shorter wings, illustrating
   a. the bottleneck effect.
   b. disruptive selection.
   c. frequency-dependent selection.
   d. neutral variation.
   e. stabilizing selection.

486 UNIT FOUR Mechanisms of Evolution

Key Concepts, which were introduced in the beginning of the chapter and developed in the text, are summarized in the Chapter Review.

New **Summary of Key Concepts Questions** appear at the end of each concept summary. Check your answers using Appendix A.

To help you prepare for the various kinds of questions that may appear on a test, the end-of-chapter questions are now organized into three levels based on Bloom's Taxonomy:

Level 1: Knowledge/Comprehension
Level 2: Application/Analysis
Level 3: Synthesis/Evaluation

Evolution Connection Questions in the Chapter Review ask you to think critically about how an aspect of the chapter relates to evolution. ▶

Scientific Inquiry ▶ **Questions** at the end of each chapter give you opportunities to practice scientific thinking by developing hypotheses, designing experiments, and analyzing real research data.

Draw It Exercises in each chapter ask you to put pencil to paper and draw a structure, annotate a figure, or graph experimental data.

LEVEL 2: APPLICATION/ANALYSIS

4. If the nucleotide variability of a locus equals 0%, what is the gene variability and number of alleles at that locus?
   a. gene variability = 0%; number of alleles = 0
   b. gene variability = 0%; number of alleles = 1
   c. gene variability = 0%; number of alleles = 2
   d. gene variability > 0%; number of alleles = 2
   e. Without more information, gene variability and number of alleles cannot be determined.

5. There are 40 individuals in population 1, all with genotype *A1A1*, and there are 25 individuals in population 2, all with genotype *A2A2*. Assume that these populations are located far from each other and that their environmental conditions are very similar. Based on the information given here, the observed genetic variation is most likely an example of
   a. genetic drift.
   b. gene flow.
   c. disruptive selection.
   d. discrete variation.
   e. directional selection.

6. A fruit fly population has a gene with two alleles, *A1* and *A2*. Tests show that 70% of the gametes produced in the population contain the *A1* allele. If the population is in Hardy-Weinberg equilibrium, what proportion of the flies carry both *A1* and *A2*?
   a. 0.7 b. 0.49 c. 0.21 d. 0.42 e. 0.09

LEVEL 3: SYNTHESIS/EVALUATION

7. **EVOLUTION CONNECTION**
   How is the process of evolution revealed by the imperfections of living organisms?

8. **SCIENTIFIC INQUIRY**
   DRAW IT Richard Koehn, of the State University of New York, Stony Brook, and Thomas Hilbish, of the University of South Carolina, studied genetic variation in the marine mussel *Mytilus edulis* around Long Island, New York. They measured the frequency of a particular allele (lap^{94}) for an enzyme involved in regulating the mussel's internal saltwater balance. The researchers presented their data as a series of pie charts linked to sampling sites within Long Island Sound, where the salinity is highly variable, and along the coast of the open ocean, where salinity is constant:

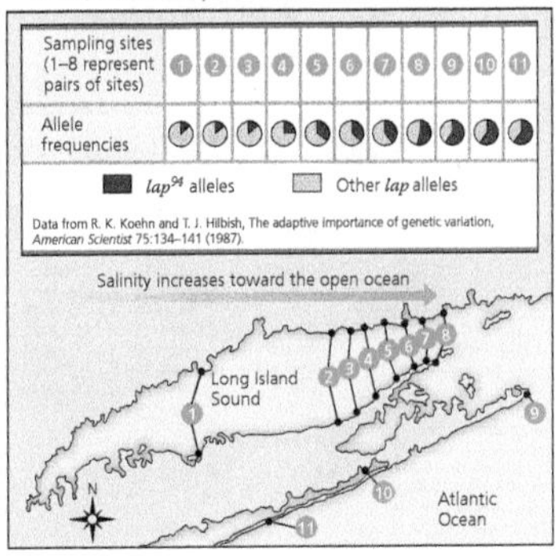

(Question 8, continued)
Create a data table for the 11 sampling sites by estimating the frequency of lap^{94} from the pie charts. (*Hint*: Think of each pie chart as a clock face to help you estimate the proportion of the shaded area.) Then graph the frequencies for sites 1–8 to show how the frequency of this allele changes with increasing salinity in Long Island Sound (from southwest to northeast). How do the data from sites 9–11 compare with the data from the sites within the Sound?

Construct a hypothesis that explains the patterns you observe in the data and that accounts for the following observations: (1) the lap^{94} allele helps mussels maintain osmotic balance in water with a high salt concentration but is costly to use in less salty water; and (2) mussels produce larvae that can disperse long distances before they settle on rocks and grow into adults.

9. **WRITE ABOUT A THEME**
   Emergent Properties Heterozygotes at the sickle-cell locus produce both normal and abnormal (sickle-cell) hemoglobin (see Concept 14.4). When hemoglobin molecules are packed into a heterozygote's red blood cells, some cells receive relatively large quantities of abnormal hemoglobin, making these cells prone to sickling. In a short essay (approximately 100–150 words), explain how these molecular and cellular events lead to emergent properties at the individual and population levels of biological organization.

For selected answers, see Appendix A.

MasteringBIOLOGY www.masteringbiology.com

1. MasteringBiology® Assignments
Make Connections Tutorial Hardy-Weinberg Principle (Chapter 23) and Inheritance of Alleles (Chapter 14)
Experimental Inquiry Tutorial Did Natural Selection of Ground Finches Occur When the Environment Changed?
BioFlix **Tutorial** Mechanisms of Evolution
Tutorial Hardy-Weinberg Principle
Activities Genetic Variation from Sexual Recombination • The Hardy-Weinberg Principle • Causes of Evolutionary Change • Three Modes of Natural Selection
Questions Student Misconceptions • Reading Quiz • Multiple Choice • End-of-Chapter

2. eText
Read your book online, search, take notes, highlight text, and more.

3. The Study Area
Practice Tests • Cumulative Test • *BioFlix* 3-D Animations • MP3 Tutor Sessions • Videos • Activities • Investigations • Lab Media • Audio Glossary • Word Study Tools • Art

CHAPTER 23 The Evolution of Populations 487

◀ New **Write About a Theme Questions** give you practice writing a short essay that connects the chapter's content to one of the bookwide themes introduced in Chapter 1.

◀ Each chapter now ends with a preview of the **MasteringBiology®** resources that can help you succeed in the course.

Suggested Grading Rubric for "Write About a Theme" Short-Answer Essays

	Understanding of Theme and Relationship to Topic	Use of Supporting Examples or Details	Appropriate Use of Terminology	Quality of Writing
4	Evidence of full and complete understanding	Examples well chosen, details accurate and applied to theme	Accurate scientific terminology enhances the essay	Excellent organization, sentence structure, and grammar
3	Evidence of good understanding	Examples or details are generally well applied to theme	Terminology is correctly used	Good sentence flow, sentence structure, and grammar
2	Evidence of a basic understanding	Supporting examples and details are adequate	Terminology used is not totally accurate or appropriate	Some organizational and grammatical problems
1	Evidence of limited understanding	Examples and details are minimal	Appropriate terminology is not present	Poorly organized. Grammatical and spelling errors detract from essay
0	Essay shows no understanding of theme	Examples lacking or incorrect	Terminology lacking or incorrect	Essay is very poorly written

◀ This **Writing Rubric** explains criteria on which your writing may be graded. The rubric and tips for writing good short-answer essays can be found in the Study Area at www.masteringbiology.com.

To the Student: How to Effectively

MasteringBIOLOGY®
www.masteringbiology.com

The Mastering system empowers you to take charge of your learning—at your convenience, 24/7.

Use the Study Area on your own or in a study group.

BioFlix

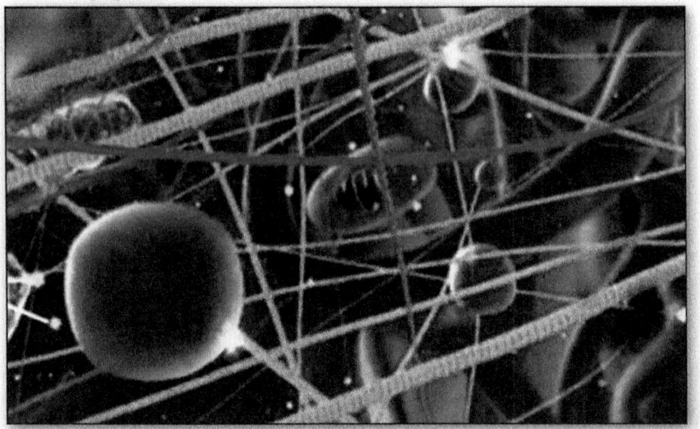

▲ **BioFlix® 3-D animations** explore the most difficult biology topics, reinforced with tutorials, quizzes, and more.

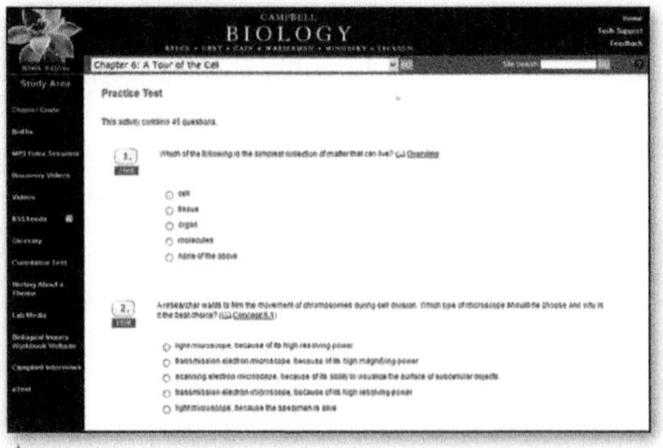

▲ **Practice Tests** help you assess your understanding of each chapter, providing feedback for right and wrong answers.

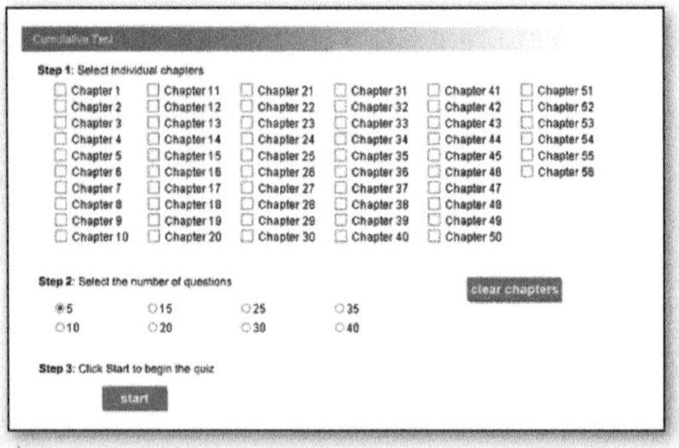

▲ The **Cumulative Test** allows you to build a practice test with questions from multiple chapters.

Access your book online.

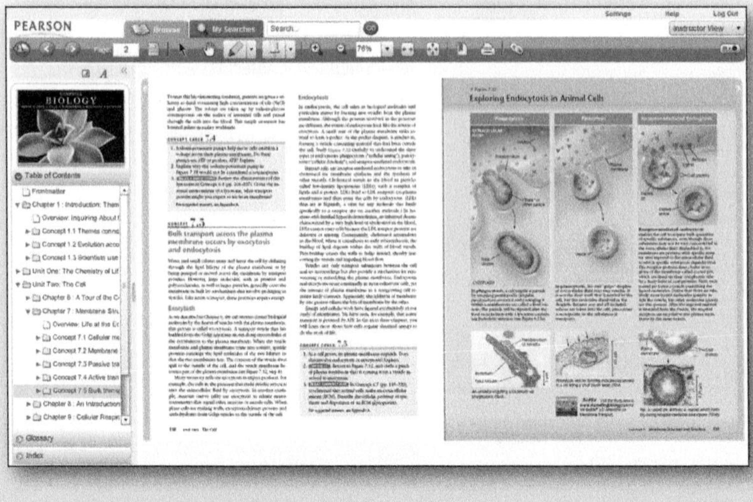

◀ The **Pearson eText** gives you access to the text whenever and wherever you can access the Internet. The eText includes powerful interactive and customization functions:

- write notes
- highlight text
- bookmark pages
- zoom
- click hyperlinked words to view definitions
- search
- link to media activities and quizzes

Your professor can also write notes for the class and highlight important material using a new tool that works like an electronic pen on a whiteboard.

Get personalized coaching & feedback.

Your instructor may assign self-paced **MasteringBiology® tutorials** that provide individualized coaching with specific hints and feedback on the toughest topics in the course.

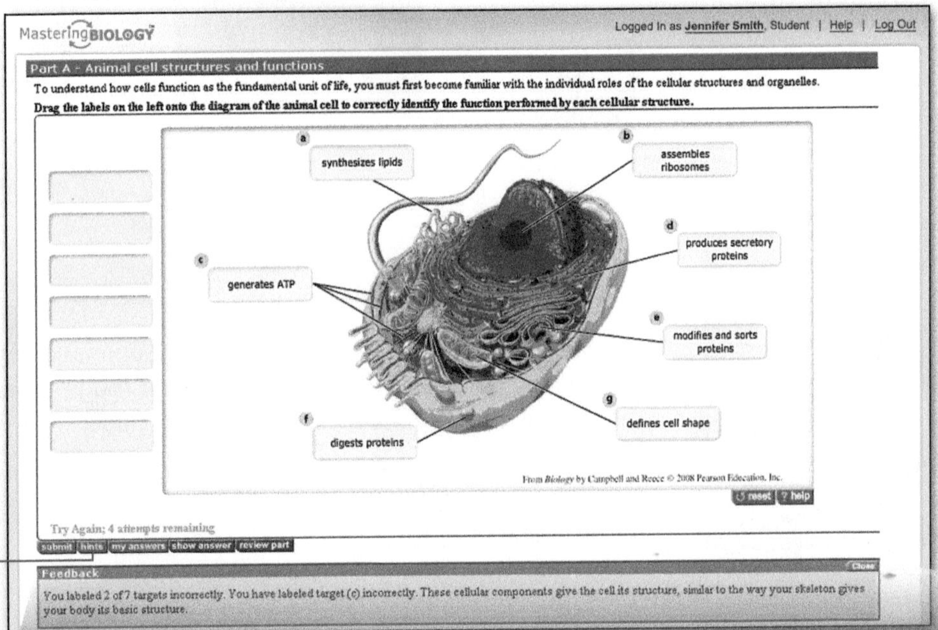

1 If you get stuck...

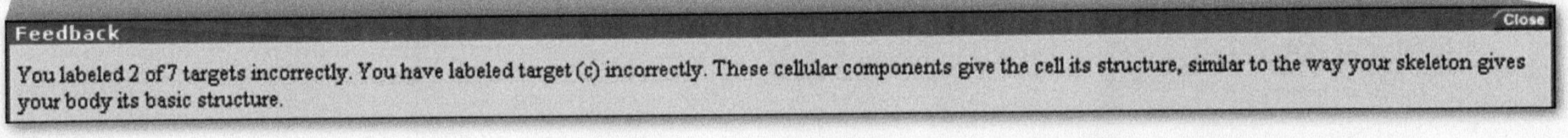

2 Specific wrong-answer **feedback** appears in the purple feedback box.

3 You are offered **hints** to coach you to the correct response.

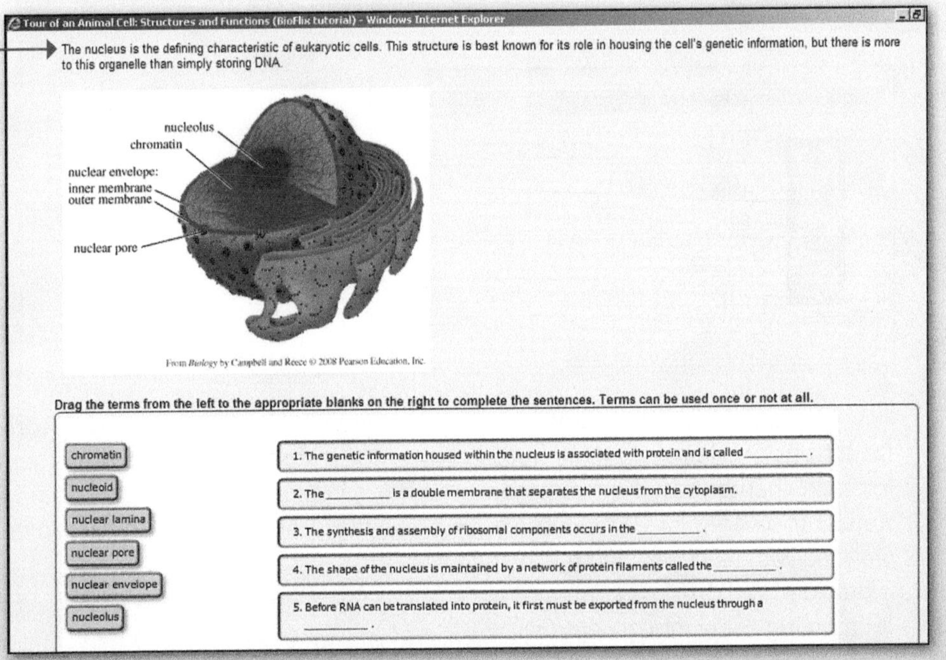

To the Instructor: New Content in

MasteringBIOLOGY®
www.masteringbiology.com

MasteringBiology is the most effective and widely used online science tutorial, homework, and assessment system available.

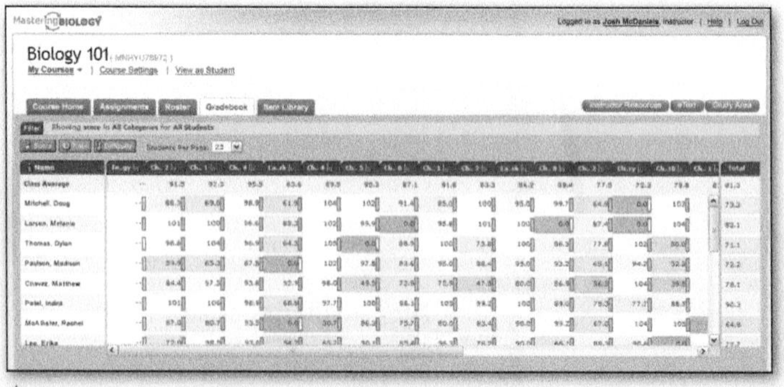

The MasteringBiology **gradebook** provides you with quick results and easy-to-interpret insights into student performance. Every assignment is **automatically graded** and shades of red highlight vulnerable students and challenging assignments.

BioFlix

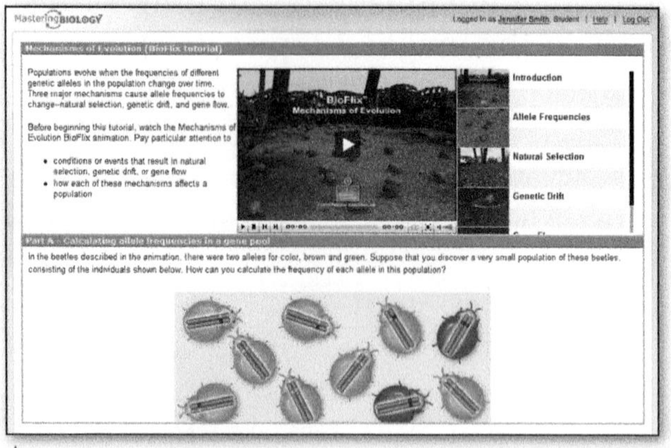

BioFlix® Tutorials use 3-D, movie-quality animations and coaching exercises to help students master tough topics outside of class. Tutorials and animations include:

- A Tour of the Animal Cell
- A Tour of the Plant Cell
- Membrane Transport
- Cellular Respiration
- Photosynthesis
- Mitosis
- Meiosis
- DNA Replication
- Protein Synthesis
- Mechanisms of Evolution
- Water Transport in Plants
- Homeostasis: Regulating Blood Sugar
- Gas Exchange
- How Neurons Work
- How Synapses Work
- Muscle Contraction
- Population Ecology
- The Carbon Cycle

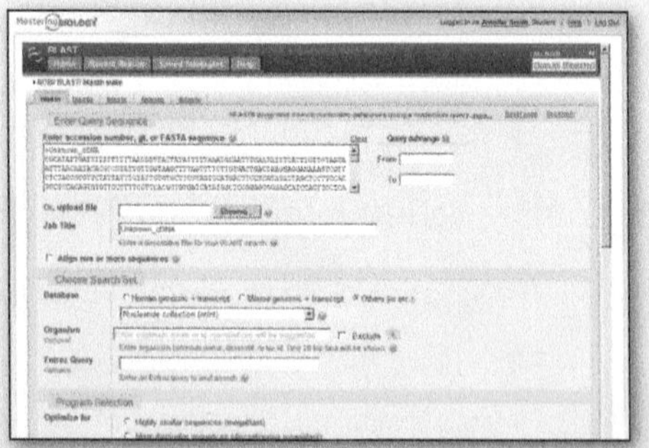

New **Data Analysis Tutorials** allow students to analyze real data from online databases.

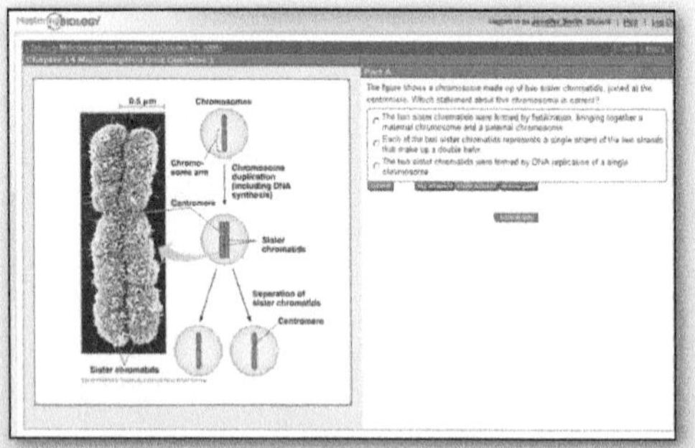

New **Student Misconceptions Questions** provide assignable quizzes for each chapter based on common student misconceptions. Students are provided with feedback, and the instructor is provided with in-class strategies for overcoming these misconceptions.

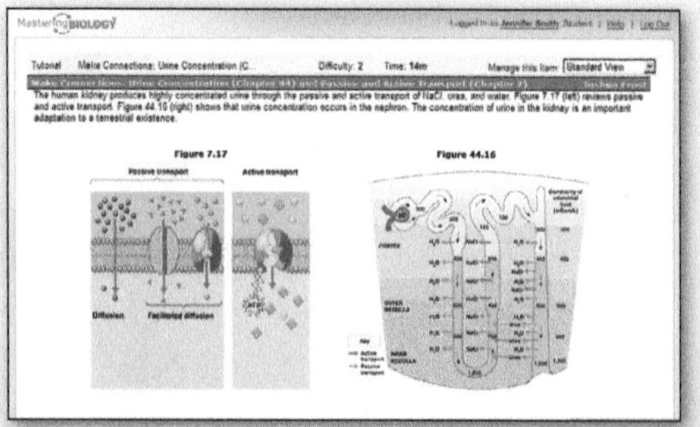

New **Make Connections Tutorials** help students connect what they are learning in one chapter with material they learned in an earlier chapter.

MasteringBiology®

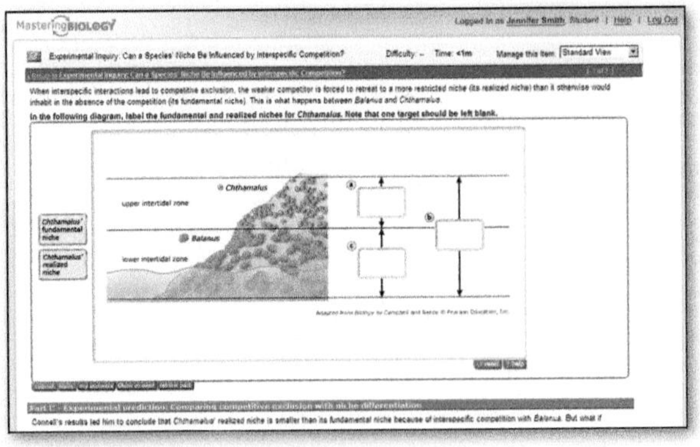

◀ New **Experimental Inquiry Tutorials,** based on some of biology's most influential experiments, give students practice analyzing experimental design and data, and help students understand how to reach conclusions based on collected data. Topics include:

- What Can You Learn About the Process of Science from Investigating a Cricket's Chirp?
- Which Wavelengths of Light Drive Photosynthesis?
- What Is the Inheritance Pattern of Sex-Linked Traits?
- Does DNA Replication Follow the Conservative, Semiconservative, or Dispersive Model?
- Did Natural Selection of Ground Finches Occur When the Environment Changed?
- What Effect Does Auxin Have on Coleoptile Growth?
- What Role Do Genes Play in Appetite Regulation?
- How Do Calcium Ions Help to Prevent Polyspermy During Egg Fertilization?
- Can a Species' Niche Be Influenced by Interspecific Competition?
- What Factors Influence the Loss of Nutrients from a Forest Ecosystem?

◀ The New **Video Tutor Sessions** walk students through tough topics with clearly explained visuals and demonstrations. Topics include:

- Mitosis and Meiosis
- Sex-Linked Pedigrees
- DNA Structure
- DNA Profiling Techniques
- Biodiversity
- Phylogenetic Trees

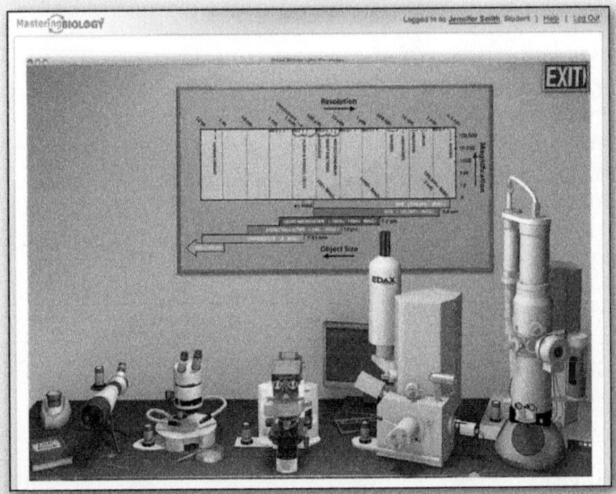

◀ The new **MasteringBiology: Virtual Biology Labs** online environment promotes critical thinking skills using virtual experiments and explorations that may be difficult to perform in a wet lab environment due to time, cost, or safety concerns.

- MasteringBiology: Virtual Biology Labs offer unique learning experiences in microscopy, molecular biology, genetics, ecology, and systematics.
- Choose from 20–30 automatically graded, "pre-set" lab activities that are ready to assign to students, or create your own from scratch.
- Each "pre-set" lab provides an assignable lab report with questions that are automatically graded and recorded in the MasteringBiology gradebook.
- Student subscriptions are available standalone or packaged with the *Campbell Biology* textbook.

Supplements

For Instructors

Instructor Resource DVD

978-0-321-67786-0 • 0-321-67786-2

Assets for each chapter include:

- All figures, photos, and tables in JPEG and PowerPoint®
- Prepared PowerPoint Presentations for each chapter, with lecture notes, editable figures from the text, and links to animations and videos
- Clicker Questions in PowerPoint
- 250+ Instructor Animations, including 3-D BioFlix®
- Discovery Channel™ Videos
- Test Bank questions in TestGen® software and Microsoft® Word

BioFlix® animations invigorate classroom lectures with 3-minute "movie quality" 3-D graphics (see list on p. xviii).

▼

Customizable PowerPoints provide a jumpstart for each lecture.

▼

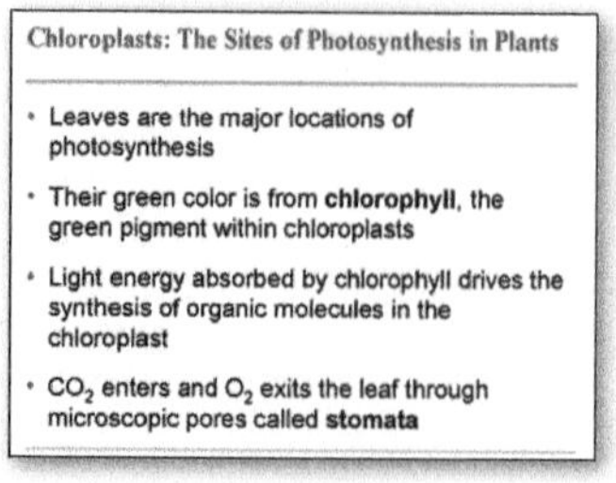

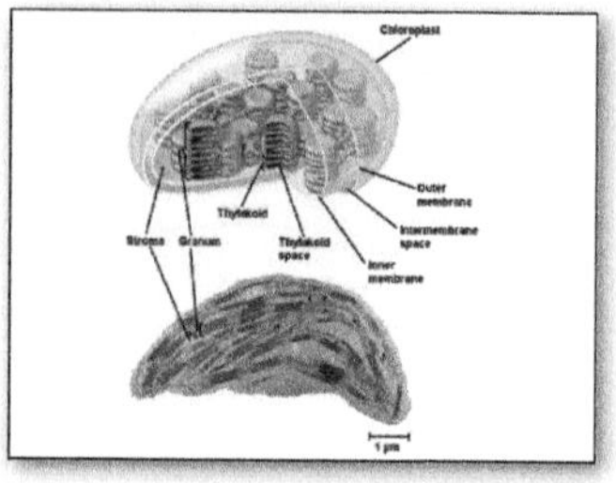

Clicker Questions can be used to stimulate effective classroom discussions (for use with or without clickers).

▼

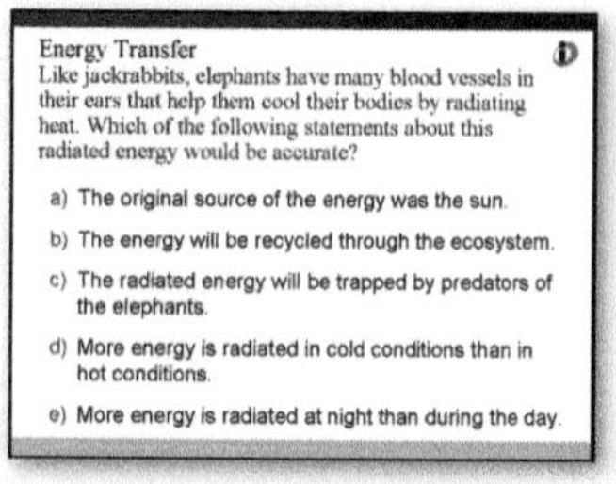

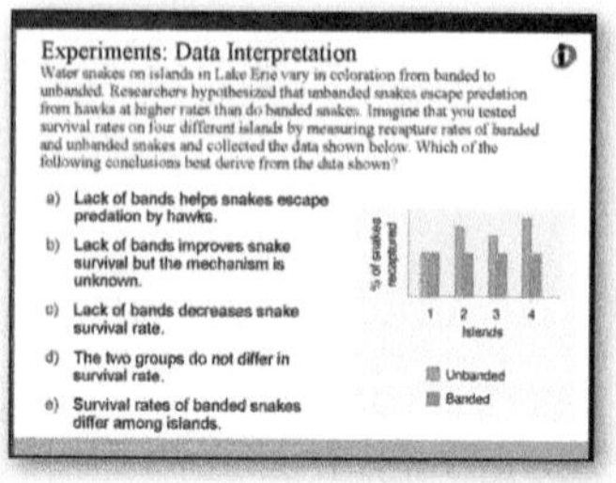

All of the art and photos from the book are provided with customizable labels. More than 1,600 photos from the text and other sources are included.

▼

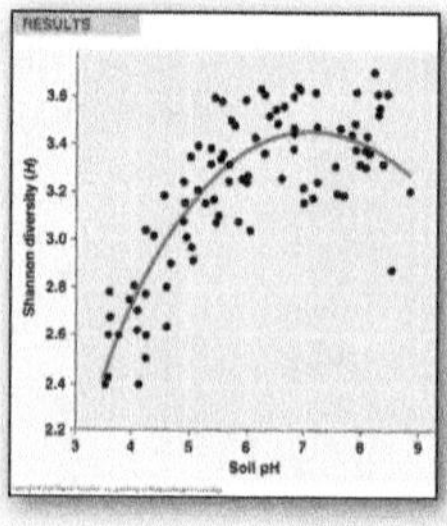

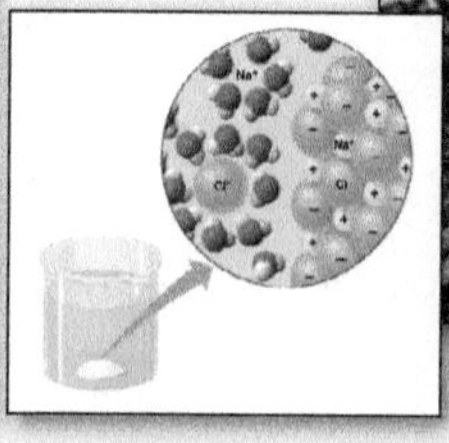

Printed Test Bank

by Louise Paquin, *McDaniel College*, Michael Dini, *Texas Tech University*, John Lepri, *University of North Carolina, Greensboro*, Jung Choi, *Georgia Institute of Technology*, John Zarnetske, *Hoosick Falls Central School*, and Ronald Balsamo, *Villanova University*

978-0-321-69729-5 • 0-321-69729-4

For the Ninth Edition, the Test Bank authors have increased the number of high-level application and synthesis questions.

Transparency Acetates

978-0-321-69708-0 • 0-321-69708-1

Course Management Systems

Test Bank questions, quizzes, and selected content from the Study Area of MasteringBiology are available in these popular course management systems:

CourseCompass™ (www.pearsonhighered.com)

Blackboard (www.pearsonhighered.com)

Instructor Resources Area in MasteringBiology

This area includes:

- PowerPoint® Lectures
- Clicker Questions
- JPEG Images
- Animations
- Videos
- Lecture Outlines
- Learning Objectives
- Strategies for Overcoming Common Student Misconceptions
- Instructor Guides for Supplements
- Write About a Theme: Tips for Grading Short-Answer Essays
- Suggested Answers for Essay Questions
- Test Bank Files
- Lab Media

For Students

***Study Guide,* Ninth Edition**
by Martha R. Taylor, *Cornell University*
978-0-321-62992-0 • 0-321-62992-2

This popular study guide helps students extract key ideas from the textbook and organize their knowledge of biology. Exercises include concept maps, chapter summaries, word roots, chapter tests, and a variety of interactive questions in various formats.

Inquiry in Action: Interpreting Scientific Papers,* Second Edition
by Ruth Buskirk, *University of Texas at Austin*, and Christopher M. Gillen, *Kenyon College*
978-0-321-68336-6 • 0-321-68336-6

Selected Inquiry Figures in the Ninth Edition direct students to read and analyze the complete original research paper. In this supplement, those articles are reprinted and accompanied by questions that help students analyze the article. The Inquiry Figures from the book are reprinted in the supplement.

Practicing Biology: A Student Workbook,* Fourth Edition
by Jean Heitz and Cynthia Giffen, *University of Wisconsin, Madison*
978-0-321-68328-1 • 0-321-68328-5

This workbook offers a variety of activities to suit different learning styles. Activities such as modeling and mapping allow students to visualize and understand biological processes. Other activities focus on basic skills, such as reading and drawing graphs.

Biological Inquiry: A Workbook of Investigative Cases,* Third Edition
by Margaret Waterman, *Southeast Missouri State University,* and Ethel Stanley, *BioQUEST Curriculum Consortium and Beloit College*
978-0-321-68320-5 • 0-321-68320-X

This workbook offers ten investigative cases. A student website is in the Study Area at **www.masteringbiology.com.**

***Study Card,* Ninth Edition**
978-0-321-68322-9 • 0-321-68322-6

This quick-reference card provides an overview of the entire field of biology and helps students see the connections between topics.

***Spanish Glossary,* Ninth Edition**
by Laura P. Zanello, *University of California, Riverside*
978-0-321-68321-2 • 0-321-68321-8

This resource provides definitions in Spanish for all the glossary terms.

Into the Jungle: Great Adventures in the Search for Evolution
by Sean B. Carroll, *University of Wisconsin, Madison*
978-0-321-55671-4 • 0-321-55671-2

These nine short tales vividly depict key discoveries in evolutionary biology and the excitement of the scientific process. Online resources available at www.aw-bc.com/carroll.

Get Ready for Biology
978-0-321-50057-1 • 0-321-50057-1

This engaging workbook helps students brush up on important math and study skills and get up to speed on biological terminology and the basics of chemistry and cell biology.

***A Short Guide to Writing About Biology,* Seventh Edition**
by Jan A. Pechenik, *Tufts University*
978-0-321-66838-7 • 0-321-66838-3

This best-selling writing guide teaches students to think as biologists and to express ideas clearly and concisely through their writing.

***An Introduction to Chemistry for Biology Students,* Ninth Edition**
by George I. Sackheim, *University of Illinois, Chicago*
978-0- 8053-9571-6 • 0-8053-9571-7

This text/workbook helps students review and master all the basic facts, concepts, and terminology of chemistry that they need for their life science course.

***The Chemistry of Life CD-ROM, Biology Version,* Second Edition**
by Robert M. Thornton, *University of California, Davis*
978-0-8053-3063-2 • 0-8053-3063-1

This CD-ROM uses animations, interactive simulations, and quizzes with feedback to help students learn or review the chemistry needed to succeed in introductory biology.

For Lab

***Investigating Biology Laboratory Manual,* Seventh Edition**
by Judith G. Morgan, *Emory University,* and M. Eloise Brown Carter, *Oxford College of Emory University*
978-0-321-66821-9 • 0-321-66821-9

The Seventh Edition emphasizes connections to recurring themes in biology, including structure and function, unity and diversity, and the overarching theme of evolution.

***Annotated Instructor Edition for Investigating Biology Laboratory Manual,* Seventh Edition**
by Judith G. Morgan, *Emory University,* and M. Eloise Brown Carter, *Oxford College of Emory University*
978-0-321-67668-9 • 0-321-67668-8

***Preparation Guide for Investigating Biology Laboratory Manual,* Seventh Edition**
by Judith G. Morgan, *Emory University*, and M. Eloise Brown Carter, *Oxford College of Emory University*
978-0-321-67669-6 • 0-321-67669-6

Symbiosis: The Benjamin Cummings Custom Laboratory Program for the Biological Sciences

www.pearsoncustom.com/database/symbiosis/bc.html

MasteringBiology®: Virtual Biology Labs

www.masteringbiology.com
This online environment promotes critical thinking skills using virtual experiments and explorations that may be difficult to perform in a wet lab environment due to time, cost, or safety concerns. Designed to supplement or substitute for existing wet labs, this product offers students unique learning experiences and critical thinking exercises in the areas of microscopy, molecular biology, genetics, ecology, and systematics.

* **An Instructor Guide is available for download in the Instructor Resources Area at www.masteringbiology.com.**

Featured Figures

Impact Figures

Exploring Figures

Inquiry Figures

* The Inquiry Figure, original research paper, and a worksheet to guide you through the paper are provided in *Inquiry in Action: Interpreting Scientific Papers*, Second Edition.
† See the related Experimental Inquiry Tutorial in MasteringBiology® (www.masteringbiology.com).

Research Method Figures

Interviews

Acknowledgments

The authors wish to express their gratitude to the global community of instructors, researchers, students, and publishing professionals who have contributed to this edition.

As authors of this text, we are mindful of the daunting challenge of keeping up to date in all areas of our rapidly expanding subject. We are grateful to the many scientists who helped shape this edition by discussing their research fields with us, answering specific questions in their areas of expertise, and sharing their ideas about biology education. We are especially grateful to the following, listed alphabetically: John Archibald, John Armour, Kristian Axelsen, Scott Bowling, Barbara Bowman, Andy Cameron, Scott Carroll, Amy Cheng-Vollmer, Michele Clamp, David DeRosier, Doug DeSimone, Binh An Diep, David Ehrhardt, Robert Fowler, Peter Fraser, Matt Friedman, Tom Gingeras, Anita Gondor, Ken Halanych, Jeff Hardin, Catherine Hurlbut, Adam Johnson, Dale Kaiser, Patrick Keeling, Emir Khatipov, Chris Killian, Andrew Knoll, Nikos Kyrpides, Teri Liegler, Zhe-Xi Luo, Kent MacDonald, Nick Matzke, Melissa Michael, Nadia Naffakh, Rolf Ohlsson, Aharon Oren, Tom Owens, Kevin Padian, Nathalie Pardigon, Bruce Pavlik, Kevin J. Peterson, Michael Pollock, Rebekah Rasooly, Andrew Roger, Ole Seehausen, Alastair Simpson, Betty Smocovitis, Frank Solomon, Pam Soltis, Hans Thewissen, Mark Uhen, Vance Vredenburg, Elisabeth Wade, Phil Zamore, and Christine Zardecki. In addition, a total of 168 biologists, listed on pages xxvi–xxvii, provided detailed reviews of chapters for this edition, helping us ensure the book's scientific accuracy and improve its pedagogical effectiveness. And finally, we thank Marty Taylor, author of all nine editions of the *Student Study Guide*, for her many contributions to the accuracy, clarity, and consistency of the book.

Thanks also to the other professors and students, from all over the world, who offered suggestions directly to the authors. We alone bear the responsibility for any errors that remain in the text, but the dedication of our consultants, reviewers, and other correspondents makes us confident in the accuracy and effectiveness of this edition.

Interviews with prominent scientists have been a hallmark of *CAMPBELL BIOLOGY* since its inception, and conducting these interviews was again one of the great pleasures of revising the book. To open the eight units of this edition, we are proud to include interviews with Susan Solomon, Bonnie Bassler, Joan Steitz, Geerat Vermeij, Ford Doolittle, Luis Herrera-Estrella, Toto Olivera, and Camille Parmesan.

The value of *CAMPBELL BIOLOGY* as a learning tool is greatly enhanced by the supplementary materials that have been created for instructors and students. We recognize that the dedicated authors of these materials are essentially writing mini (and not so mini) books. We much appreciate the hard work and creativity of all the authors listed, with their creations, on pages xx–xxi. In addition, we are grateful to Joan Sharp (*Lecture Outlines*, *Learning Objectives*, and *Student Misconceptions*) and Erin Barley and Kathleen Fitzpatrick (*PowerPoint® Lectures*).

The electronic media for this text are invaluable teaching and learning aids. We thank the hardworking and creative authors of the new material for this edition: Tom Owens, Joan Sharp, and Jennifer Yeh (*MasteringBiology®*); Richard Cowlishaw, Tod Duncan, and Stephanie Pandolfi (*Study Area Practice Tests*); and Eric Simon (*VideoTutors*). And we thank Brian White for his work. Also, we are grateful to the many other people—biology instructors, editors, artists, production experts, and narrators—who are listed in the credits for these and other elements of the electronic media that accompany the book. And we thank the reviewers and class testers of BioFlix® and MasteringBiology.

CAMPBELL BIOLOGY, Ninth Edition, results from an unusually strong synergy between a team of scientists and a team of publishing professionals. Our editorial team at Benjamin Cummings again demonstrated unmatched talents, commitment, and pedagogical insights. Our new Acquisitions Editor, Josh Frost, brought publishing savvy, intelligence, and a much appreciated level head to leading the whole team. The clarity and effectiveness of every page owe much to our extraordinary Supervising Editors Pat Burner and Beth Winickoff, who headed the top-notch development team: Developmental Editors John Burner, Matt Lee, and Mary Catherine Hager; and Developmental Artists Hilair Chism, Carla Simmons, Andrew Recher, and Jay McElroy. Our unsurpassed Senior Editorial Manager Ginnie Simione Jutson, Executive Director of Development Deborah Gale, Assistant Editor Logan Triglia, and Editor-in-Chief Beth Wilbur were indispensable in moving the project in the right direction. We also want to thank Robin Heyden for organizing the annual Biology Leadership Conferences and keeping us in touch with the world of AP Biology.

You would not have this beautiful book in your hands today if not for the work of the book production team: Executive Managing Editor Erin Gregg; Managing Editor Michael Early; Senior Production Project Manager Shannon Tozier; Senior Photo Editor Donna Kalal; Photo Researcher Maureen Spuhler; Copy Editor Janet Greenblatt; Art Editor Laura Murray; Proofreaders Joanna Dinsmore and Pete Shanks; Permissions Editors Sue Ewing and Beth Keister; Senior Project Editor Emily Bush, S4Carlisle; Composition Manager Holly Paige, S4Carlisle; Art Production Manager Kristina Seymour, Precision Graphics; Design Director Mark Ong; Designer Gary Hespenheide; and Manufacturing Buyer Michael Penne. We also thank those who worked on the book's supplements: Susan Berge, Nina Lewallen Hufford, Brady Golden, Jane Brundage, James Bruce, and John Hammett. And for creating the wonderful package of electronic media that accompanies the book, we are grateful to Tania Mlawer, Director of Editorial Content for MasteringBiology, and Jonathan Ballard, Deb Greco, Sarah Jensen, Mary Catherine Hager, Alice Fugate, Juliana Tringali, Josh Gentry, Steve Wright, Kristen Sutton, Katie Foley, Karen Sheh, and David Kokorowski, as well as Director of Media Development Lauren Fogel and Director of Media Strategy Stacy Treco.

For their important roles in marketing the book, we thank Christy Lawrence, Lauren Harp, Scott Dustan, Lillian Carr, Jane Campbell, Jessica Perry, Nora Massuda, and Jessica Tree.

We are grateful to Linda Davis, President of Pearson Math and Science, who has shared our commitment to excellence and provided strong support for five editions now. Moreover, we thank Paul Corey, President of Pearson Benjamin Cummings, and Editorial Director Frank Ruggirello for their enthusiasm, encouragement, and support.

The Pearson sales team, which represents *CAMPBELL BIOLOGY* on campus, is an essential link to the users of the text. They tell us what you like and don't like about the book, communicate the features of the book, and provide prompt service. We thank them for their hard work and professionalism. For representing our book to our international audience, we thank our sales and marketing partners throughout the world. They are all strong allies in biology education.

Finally, we wish to thank our families and friends for their encouragement and patience throughout this long project. Our special thanks to Paul, Dan, Maria, Armelle, and Sean (J.B.R.); Lily, Ross, Lily-too, and Alex (L.A.U.); Debra and Hannah (M.L.C.); Harry, Elga, Aaron, Sophie, Noah, and Gabriele (S.A.W.); Natalie (P.V.M.); and Sally, Robert, David, and Will (R.B.J.). And, as always, thanks to Rochelle, Allison, Jason, and McKay.

Jane Reece, Lisa Urry, Michael Cain,
Steve Wasserman, Peter Minorsky, and Rob Jackson

Reviewers

Ninth Edition Reviewers

Ann Aguanno, *Marymount Manhattan College*
Marc Albrecht, *University of Nebraska*
John Alcock, *Arizona State University*
Eric Alcorn, *Acadia University*
Terry Austin, *Temple College*
Brian Bagatto, *University of Akron*
Virginia Baker, *Chipola College*
Bonnie Baxter, *Westminster College*
Marilee Benore, *University of Michigan, Dearborn*
Catherine Black, *Idaho State University*
William Blaker, *Furman University*
Edward Blumenthal, *Marquette University*
David Bos, *Purdue University*
Scott Bowling, *Auburn University*
Beth Burch, *Huntington University*
Ragan Callaway, *The University of Montana*
Kenneth M. Cameron, *University of Wisconsin, Madison*
Patrick Canary, *Northland Pioneer College*
Cheryl Keller Capone, *Pennsylvania State University*
Karen I. Champ, *Central Florida Community College*
David Champlin, *University of Southern Maine*
Brad Chandler, *Palo Alto College*
Wei-Jen Chang, *Hamilton College*
Jung Choi, *Georgia Institute of Technology*
Steve Christensen, *Brigham Young University, Idaho*
James T. Colbert, *Iowa State University*
William Cushwa, *Clark College*
Shannon Datwyler, *California State University, Sacramento*
Eugene Delay, *University of Vermont*
Daniel DerVartanian, *University of Georgia*
Janet De Souza-Hart, *Massachusetts College of Pharmacy & Health Sciences*
Kathryn A. Durham, *Lorain Community College*
Curt Elderkin, *College of New Jersey*
Mary Ellard-Ivey, *Pacific Lutheran University*
George Ellmore, *Tufts University*
Robert C. Evans, *Rutgers University, Camden*
Sam Fan, *Bradley University*
Paul Farnsworth, *University of New Mexico*
Myriam Alhadeff Feldman, *Cascadia Community College*
Teresa Fischer, *Indian River Community College*
David Fitch, *New York University*
T. Fleming, *Bradley University*
Robert Fowler, *San Jose State University*
Robert Franklin, *College of Charleston*
Art Fredeen, *University of Northern British Columbia*
Matt Friedman, *University of Chicago*
Cynthia M. Galloway, *Texas A&M University, Kingsville*
Simon Gilroy, *University of Wisconsin, Madison*
Jim Goetze, *Laredo Community College*
Lynda Goff, *University of California, Santa Cruz*
Roy Golsteyn, *University of Lethbridge*
Barbara E. Goodman, *University of South Dakota*
David Grise, *Texas A&M University, Corpus Christi*
Devney Hamilton, *Stanford University (student)*
Matthew B. Hamilton, *Georgetown University*
Jeanne M. Harris, *University of Vermont*
Stephanie Harvey, *Georgia Southwestern State University*
Bernard Hauser, *University of Florida*
Andreas Hejnol, *Sars International Centre for Marine Molecular Biology*
Jason Hodin, *Stanford University*
Sara Huang, *Los Angeles Valley College*
Catherine Hurlbut, *Florida State College, Jacksonville*
Diane Husic, *Moravian College*
Thomas Jacobs, *University of Illinois*
Mark Jaffe, *Nova Southeastern University*
Douglas Jensen, *Converse College*
Lance Johnson, *Midland Lutheran College*
Cheryl Jorcyk, *Boise State University*
Caroline Kane, *University of California, Berkeley*
Jennifer Katcher, *Pima Community College*
Eric G. Keeling, *Cary Institute of Ecosystem Studies*
Chris Kennedy, *Simon Fraser University*
Hillar Klandorf, *West Virginia University*
Mark Knauss, *Georgia Highlands College*
Roger Koeppe, *University of Arkansas*
Peter Kourtev, *Central Michigan University*
Eliot Krause, *Seton Hall University*
Steven Kristoff, *Ivy Tech Community College*
William Kroll, *Loyola University*
Rukmani Kuppuswami, *Laredo Community College*
Lee Kurtz, *Georgia Gwinnett College*
Michael P. Labare, *United States Military Academy, West Point*
Ellen Lamb, *University of North Carolina, Greensboro*
William Lamberts, *College of St Benedict and St John's University*
Tali D. Lee, *University of Wisconsin, Eau Claire*
Hugh Lefcort, *Gonzaga University*
Alcinda Lewis, *University of Colorado, Boulder*
Graeme Lindbeck, *Valenica Community College*
Hannah Lui, *University of California, Irvine*
Cindy Malone, *California State University, Northridge*
Julia Marrs, *Barnard College (student)*
Kathleen Marrs, *Indiana University-Purdue University, Indianapolis*
Mike Mayfield, *Ball State University*
Kamau Mbuthia, *Bowling Green State University*
Tanya McGhee, *Craven Community College*
Darcy Medica, *Pennsylvania State University*
Susan Meiers, *Western Illinois University*
Alex Mills, *University of Windsor*
Eli Minkoff, *Bates College*
Subhash Minocha, *University of New Hampshire*
Ivona Mladenovic, *Simon Fraser University*
Courtney Murren, *College of Charleston*
Kimberlyn Nelson, *Pennsylvania State University*
Jacalyn Newman, *University of Pittsburgh*
Kathleen Nolta, *University of Michigan*
Aharon Oren, *The Hebrew University*
Henry R. Owen, *Eastern Illinois University*
Stephanie Pandolfi, *Michigan State University*
Nathalie Pardigon, *Institut Pasteur*
Cindy Paszkowski, *University of Alberta*
Andrew Pease, *Stevenson University*
Nancy Pelaez, *Purdue University*
Irene Perry, *University of Texas of the Permian Basin*
Roger Persell, *Hunter College*
Mark Pilgrim, *College of Coastal Georgia*
Vera M. Piper, *Shenadoah University*
Crima Pogge, *City College of San Francisco*
Michael Pollock, *Mount Royal University*
Roberta Pollock, *Occidental College*
Therese M. Poole, *Georgia State University*
Angela R. Porta, *Kean University*
Robert Powell, *Avila University*
Elena Pravosudova, *University of Nevada, Reno*
Terrell Pritts, *University of Arkansas, Little Rock*
Monica Ranes-Goldberg, *University of California, Berkeley*
Robert S. Rawding, *Gannon University*
Sarah Richart, *Azusa Pacific University*
Kenneth Robinson, *Purdue University*
Heather Roffey, *Marianopolis College*
Patricia Rugaber, *College of Coastal Georgia*
Scott Russell, *University of Oklahoma*
Louis Santiago, *University of California, Riverside*
Tom Sawicki, *Spartanburg Community College*
Thomas W. Schoener, *University of California, Davis*
Patricia Schulte, *University of British Colombia*
Brenda Schumpert, *Valencia Community College*
David Schwartz, *Houston Community College*
Brent Selinger, *University of Lethbridge*
Alison M. Shakarian, *Salve Regina University*
Robin L. Sherman, *Nova Southeastern University*
Sedonia Sipes, *Southern Illinois University, Carbondale*
Joel Stafstrom, *Northern Illinois University*
Alam Stam, *Capital University*
Judy Stone, *Colby College*
Cynthia Surmacz, *Bloomsburg University*
David Tam, *University of North Texas*
Yves Tan, *Cabrillo College*
Emily Taylor, *California Polytechnic State University*
Franklyn Tan Te, *Miami Dade College*
Kent Thomas, *Wichita State University*

Saba Valadkhan, *Center for RNA Molecular Biology*
Sarah VanVickle-Chavez, *Washington University, St. Louis*
William Velhagen, *New York University*
Janice Voltzow, *University of Scranton*
Margaret Voss, *Penn State Erie*
Charles Wade, *C.S. Mott Community College*
Claire Walczak, *Indiana University*
Jerry Waldvogel, *Clemson University*
Robert Lee Wallace, *Ripon College*
Fred Wasserman, *Boston University*
John Weishampel, *University of Central Florida*
Susan Whittemore, *Keene State College*
Janet Wolkenstein, *Hudson Valley Community College*
Grace Wyngaard, *James Madison University*
Paul Yancey, *Whitman College*
Anne D. Yoder, *Duke University*
Nina Zanetti, *Siena College*
Sam Zeveloff, *Weber State University*
Theresa Zucchero, *Methodist University*

Reviewers of Previous Editions

Kenneth Able *(State University of New York, Albany)*
Thomas Adams *(Michigan State University)*
Martin Adamson *(University of British Columbia)*
Dominique Adriaens *(Ghent University)*
Shylaja Akkaraju *(Bronx Community College of CUNY)*
John Alcock *(Arizona State University)*
George R. Aliaga *(Tarrant County College)*
Richard Almon *(State University of New York, Buffalo)*
Bonnie Amos *(Angelo State University)*
Katherine Anderson *(University of California, Berkeley)*
Richard J. Andren *(Montgomery County Community College)*
Estry Ang *(University of Pittsburgh, Greensburg)*
Jeff Appling *(Clemson University)*
J. David Archibald *(San Diego State University)*
David Armstrong *(University of Colorado, Boulder)*
Howard J. Arnott *(University of Texas, Arlington)*
Mary Ashley *(University of Illinois, Chicago)*
Angela S. Aspbury *(Texas State University)*
Robert Atherton *(University of Wyoming)*
Karl Aufderheide *(Texas A&M University)*
Leigh Auleb *(San Francisco State University)*
P. Stephen Baenziger *(University of Nebraska)*
Ellen Baker *(Santa Monica College)*
Katherine Baker *(Millersville University)*
William Barklow *(Framingham State College)*
Susan Barman *(Michigan State University)*
Steven Barnhart *(Santa Rosa Junior College)*
Andrew Barton *(University of Maine Farmington)*
Rebecca A. Bartow *(Western Kentucky University)*
Ron Basmajian *(Merced College)*
David Bass *(University of Central Oklahoma)*
Bonnie Baxter *(Hobart & William Smith Colleges)*
Tim Beagley *(Salt Lake Community College)*
Margaret E. Beard *(College of the Holy Cross)*
Tom Beatty *(University of British Columbia)*
Chris Beck *(Emory University)*
Wayne Becker *(University of Wisconsin, Madison)*
Patricia Bedinger *(Colorado State University)*
Jane Beiswenger *(University of Wyoming)*
Anne Bekoff *(University of Colorado, Boulder)*
Marc Bekoff *(University of Colorado, Boulder)*
Tania Beliz *(College of San Mateo)*
Adrianne Bendich *(Hoffman-La Roche, Inc.)*
Barbara Bentley *(State University of New York, Stony Brook)*
Darwin Berg *(University of California, San Diego)*
Werner Bergen *(Michigan State University)*
Gerald Bergstrom *(University of Wisconsin, Milwaukee)*
Anna W. Berkovitz *(Purdue University)*
Dorothy Berner *(Temple University)*
Annalisa Berta *(San Diego State University)*
Paulette Bierzychudek *(Pomona College)*
Charles Biggers *(Memphis State University)*
Kenneth Birnbaum *(New York University)*
Michael W. Black *(California Polytechnic State University, San Luis Obispo)*
Robert Blanchard *(University of New Hampshire)*
Andrew R. Blaustein *(Oregon State University)*
Judy Bluemer *(Morton College)*
Edward Blumenthal *(Marquette University)*
Robert Blystone *(Trinity University)*
Robert Boley *(University of Texas, Arlington)*
Jason E. Bond *(East Carolina University)*
Eric Bonde *(University of Colorado, Boulder)*
Cornelius Bondzi *(Hampton University)*
Richard Boohar *(University of Nebraska, Omaha)*
Carey L. Booth *(Reed College)*
Allan Bornstein *(Southeast Missouri State University)*
Oliver Bossdorf *(State University of New York, Stony Book)*
James L. Botsford *(New Mexico State University)*
Lisa Boucher *(University of Nebraska, Omaha)*
J. Michael Bowes *(Humboldt State University)*
Richard Bowker *(Alma College)*
Robert Bowker *(Glendale Community College, Arizona)*
Barbara Bowman *(Mills College)*
Barry Bowman *(University of California, Santa Cruz)*
Deric Bownds *(University of Wisconsin, Madison)*
Robert Boyd *(Auburn University)*
Sunny Boyd *(University of Notre Dame)*
Jerry Brand *(University of Texas, Austin)*
Edward Braun *(Iowa State University)*
Theodore A. Bremner *(Howard University)*
James Brenneman *(University of Evansville)*
Charles H. Brenner *(Berkeley, California)*
Lawrence Brewer *(University of Kentucky)*
Donald P. Briskin *(University of Illinois, Urbana)*
Paul Broady *(University of Canterbury)*
Chad Brommer *(Emory University)*
Judith L. Bronstein *(University of Arizona)*
Danny Brower *(University of Arizona)*
Carole Browne *(Wake Forest University)*
Mark Browning *(Purdue University)*
David Bruck *(San Jose State University)*
Robb T. Brumfield *(Louisiana State University)*
Herbert Bruneau *(Oklahoma State University)*
Gary Brusca *(Humboldt State University)*
Richard C. Brusca *(University of Arizona, Arizona-Sonora Desert Museum)*
Alan H. Brush *(University of Connecticut, Storrs)*
Howard Buhse *(University of Illinois, Chicago)*
Arthur Buikema *(Virginia Tech)*
Al Burchsted *(College of Staten Island)*
Meg Burke *(University of North Dakota)*
Edwin Burling *(De Anza College)*
William Busa *(Johns Hopkins University)*
Jorge Busciglio *(University of California, Irvine)*
John Bushnell *(University of Colorado)*
Linda Butler *(University of Texas, Austin)*
David Byres *(Florida Community College, Jacksonville)*
Guy A. Caldwell *(University of Alabama)*
Jane Caldwell *(West Virginia University)*
Kim A. Caldwell *(University of Alabama)*
R. Andrew Cameron *(California Institute of Technology)*
Alison Campbell *(University of Waikato)*
Iain Campbell *(University of Pittsburgh)*
W. Zacheus Cande *(University of California, Berkeley)*
Robert E. Cannon *(University of North Carolina, Greensboro)*
Deborah Canington *(University of California, Davis)*
Frank Cantelmo *(St. John's University)*
John Capeheart *(University of Houston, Downtown)*
Gregory Capelli *(College of William and Mary)*
Richard Cardullo *(University of California, Riverside)*
Nina Caris *(Texas A&M University)*
Jeffrey Carmichael *(University of North Dakota)*
Robert Carroll *(East Carolina University)*
Laura L. Carruth *(Georgia State University)*
J. Aaron Cassill *(University of Texas, San Antonio)*
David Champlin *(University of Southern Maine)*
Bruce Chase *(University of Nebraska, Omaha)*
P. Bryant Chase *(Florida State University)*
Doug Cheeseman *(De Anza College)*
Shepley Chen *(University of Illinois, Chicago)*
Giovina Chinchar *(Tougaloo College)*
Joseph P. Chinnici *(Virginia Commonwealth University)*
Jung H. Choi *(Georgia Institute of Technology)*
Geoffrey Church *(Fairfield University)*
Henry Claman *(University of Colorado Health Science Center)*
Anne Clark *(Binghamton University)*
Greg Clark *(University of Texas)*
Patricia J. Clark *(Indiana University-Purdue University, Indianapolis)*
Ross C. Clark *(Eastern Kentucky University)*
Lynwood Clemens *(Michigan State University)*
Janice J. Clymer *(San Diego Mesa College)*
William P. Coffman *(University of Pittsburgh)*
Austin Randy Cohen *(California State University, Northridge)*
J. John Cohen *(University of Colorado Health Science Center)*
Jim Colbert *(Iowa State University)*
Jan Colpaert *(Hasselt University)*

Robert Colvin *(Ohio University)*
Jay Comeaux *(McNeese State University)*
David Cone *(Saint Mary's University)*
Elizabeth Connor *(University of Massachusetts)*
Joanne Conover *(University of Connecticut)*
Gregory Copenhaver *(University of North Carolina, Chapel Hill)*
John Corliss *(University of Maryland)*
James T. Costa *(Western Carolina University)*
Stuart J. Coward *(University of Georgia)*
Charles Creutz *(University of Toledo)*
Bruce Criley *(Illinois Wesleyan University)*
Norma Criley *(Illinois Wesleyan University)*
Joe W. Crim *(University of Georgia)*
Greg Crowther *(University of Washington)*
Karen Curto *(University of Pittsburgh)*
Anne Cusic *(University of Alabama, Birmingham)*
Richard Cyr *(Pennsylvania State University)*
Marymegan Daly *(The Ohio State University)*
W. Marshall Darley *(University of Georgia)*
Cynthia Dassler *(The Ohio State University)*
Marianne Dauwalder *(University of Texas, Austin)*
Larry Davenport *(Samford University)*
Bonnie J. Davis *(San Francisco State University)*
Jerry Davis *(University of Wisconsin, La Crosse)*
Michael A. Davis *(Central Connecticut State University)*
Thomas Davis *(University of New Hampshire)*
John Dearn *(University of Canberra)*
Maria E. de Bellard *(California State University, Northridge)*
Teresa DeGolier *(Bethel College)*
James Dekloe *(University of California, Santa Cruz)*
Patricia A. DeLeon *(University of Delaware)*
Veronique Delesalle *(Gettysburg College)*
T. Delevoryas *(University of Texas, Austin)*
Roger Del Moral *(University of Washington)*
Charles F. Delwiche *(University of Maryland)*
Diane C. DeNagel *(Northwestern University)*
William L. Dentler *(University of Kansas)*
Daniel Dervartanian *(University of Georgia)*
Jean DeSaix *(University of North Carolina, Chapel Hill)*
Biao Ding *(Ohio State University)*
Michael Dini *(Texas Tech University)*
Andrew Dobson *(Princeton University)*
Stanley Dodson *(University of Wisconsin, Madison)*
Mark Drapeau *(University of California, Irvine)*
John Drees *(Temple University School of Medicine)*
Charles Drewes *(Iowa State University)*
Marvin Druger *(Syracuse University)*
Gary Dudley *(University of Georgia)*
Susan Dunford *(University of Cincinnati)*
Betsey Dyer *(Wheaton College)*
Robert Eaton *(University of Colorado)*
Robert S. Edgar *(University of California, Santa Cruz)*
Douglas J. Eernisse *(California State University, Fullerton)*
Betty J. Eidemiller *(Lamar University)*
Brad Elder *(Doane College)*
William D. Eldred *(Boston University)*
Michelle Elekonich *(University of Nevada, Las Vegas)*
Mary Ellard-Ivey *(Pacific Lutheran University)*
Norman Ellstrand *(University of California, Riverside)*
Johnny El-Rady *(University of South Florida)*
Dennis Emery *(Iowa State University)*
John Endler *(University of California, Santa Barbara)*
Margaret T. Erskine *(Lansing Community College)*
Gerald Esch *(Wake Forest University)*
Frederick B. Essig *(University of South Florida)*
Mary Eubanks *(Duke University)*
David Evans *(University of Florida)*
Robert C. Evans *(Rutgers University, Camden)*
Sharon Eversman *(Montana State University)*
Olukemi Fadayomi *(Ferris State University)*
Lincoln Fairchild *(Ohio State University)*
Peter Fajer *(Florida State University)*
Bruce Fall *(University of Minnesota)*
Lynn Fancher *(College of DuPage)*
Ellen H. Fanning *(Vanderbilt University)*
Paul Farnsworth *(University of Texas, San Antonio)*
Larry Farrell *(Idaho State University)*
Jerry F. Feldman *(University of California, Santa Cruz)*
Lewis Feldman *(University of California, Berkeley)*
Eugene Fenster *(Longview Community College)*
Russell Fernald *(University of Oregon)*
Rebecca Ferrell *(Metropolitan State College of Denver)*
Kim Finer *(Kent State University)*
Milton Fingerman *(Tulane University)*
Barbara Finney *(Regis College)*
Frank Fish *(West Chester University)*
David Fisher *(University of Hawaii, Manoa)*
Jonathan S. Fisher *(St. Louis University)*
Steven Fisher *(University of California, Santa Barbara)*
Kirk Fitzhugh *(Natural History Museum of Los Angeles County)*
Lloyd Fitzpatrick *(University of North Texas)*
William Fixsen *(Harvard University)*
Abraham Flexer *(Manuscript Consultant, Boulder, Colorado)*
Kerry Foresman *(University of Montana)*
Norma Fowler *(University of Texas, Austin)*
Robert G. Fowler *(San Jose State University)*
David Fox *(University of Tennessee, Knoxville)*
Carl Frankel *(Pennsylvania State University, Hazleton)*
James Franzen *(University of Pittsburgh)*
Bill Freedman *(Dalhousie University)*
Otto Friesen *(University of Virginia)*
Frank Frisch *(Chapman University)*
Virginia Fry *(Monterey Peninsula College)*
Bernard Frye *(University of Texas, Arlington)*
Jed Fuhrman *(University of Southern California)*
Alice Fulton *(University of Iowa)*
Chandler Fulton *(Brandeis University)*
Sara Fultz *(Stanford University)*
Berdell Funke *(North Dakota State University)*
Anne Funkhouser *(University of the Pacific)*
Zofia E. Gagnon *(Marist College)*
Michael Gaines *(University of Miami)*
Arthur W. Galston *(Yale University)*
Stephen Gammie *(University of Wisconsin, Madison)*
Carl Gans *(University of Michigan)*
John Gapter *(University of Northern Colorado)*
Andrea Gargas *(University of Wisconsin, Madison)*
Lauren Garner *(California Polytechnic State University, San Luis Obispo)*
Reginald Garrett *(University of Virginia)*
Patricia Gensel *(University of North Carolina)*
Chris George *(California Polytechnic State University, San Luis Obispo)*
Robert George *(University of Wyoming)*
J. Whitfield Gibbons *(University of Georgia)*
J. Phil Gibson *(Agnes Scott College)*
Frank Gilliam *(Marshall University)*
Simon Gilroy *(Pennsylvania State University)*
Alan D. Gishlick *(Gustavus Adolphus College)*
Todd Gleeson *(University of Colorado)*
Jessica Gleffe *(University of California, Irvine)*
John Glendinning *(Barnard College)*
David Glenn-Lewin *(Wichita State University)*
William Glider *(University of Nebraska)*
Tricia Glidewell *(Marist School)*
Elizabeth A. Godrick *(Boston University)*
Lynda Goff *(University of California, Santa Cruz)*
Elliott Goldstein *(Arizona State University)*
Paul Goldstein *(University of Texas, El Paso)*
Sandra Gollnick *(State University of New York, Buffalo)*
Anne Good *(University of California, Berkeley)*
Judith Goodenough *(University of Massachusetts, Amherst)*
Wayne Goodey *(University of British Columbia)*
Robert Goodman *(University of Wisconsin, Madison)*
Ester Goudsmit *(Oakland University)*
Linda Graham *(University of Wisconsin, Madison)*
Robert Grammer *(Belmont University)*
Joseph Graves *(Arizona State University)*
Phyllis Griffard *(University of Houston, Downtown)*
A. J. F. Griffiths *(University of British Columbia)*
William Grimes *(University of Arizona)*
Mark Gromko *(Bowling Green State University)*
Serine Gropper *(Auburn University)*
Katherine L. Gross *(Ohio State University)*
Gary Gussin *(University of Iowa)*
Mark Guyer *(National Human Genome Research Institute)*
Ruth Levy Guyer *(Bethesda, Maryland)*
R. Wayne Habermehl *(Montgomery County Community College)*
Mac Hadley *(University of Arizona)*
Joel Hagen *(Radford University)*
Jack P. Hailman *(University of Wisconsin)*
Leah Haimo *(University of California, Riverside)*
Ken Halanych *(Auburn University)*
Jody Hall *(Brown University)*
Douglas Hallett, *(Northern Arizona University)*
Rebecca Halyard *(Clayton State College)*
E. William Hamilton *(Washington and Lee University)*
Sam Hammer *(Boston University)*
Penny Hanchey-Bauer *(Colorado State University)*
William F. Hanna *(Massasoit Community College)*

Laszlo Hanzely *(Northern Illinois University)*
Jeff Hardin *(University of Wisconsin, Madison)*
Lisa Harper *(University of California, Berkeley)*
Richard Harrison *(Cornell University)*
Carla Hass *(Pennsylvania State University)*
Chris Haufler *(University of Kansas)*
Bernard A. Hauser *(University of Florida)*
Chris Haynes *(Shelton State Community College)*
Evan B. Hazard *(Bemidji State University, Emeritus)*
H. D. Heath *(California State University, East Bay)*
George Hechtel *(State University of New York, Stony Brook)*
S. Blair Hedges *(Pennsylvania State University)*
Brian Hedlund *(University of Nevada, Las Vegas)*
David Heins *(Tulane University)*
Jean Heitz *(University of Wisconsin, Madison)*
John D. Helmann *(Cornell University)*
Colin Henderson *(University of Montana)*
Susan Hengeveld *(Indiana University)*
Michelle Henricks *(University of California, Los Angeles)*
Caroll Henry *(Chicago State University)*
Frank Heppner *(University of Rhode Island)*
Albert Herrera *(University of Southern California)*
Scott Herrick *(Missouri Western State College)*
Ira Herskowitz *(University of California, San Francisco)*
Paul E. Hertz *(Barnard College)*
David Hibbett *(Clark University)*
R. James Hickey *(Miami University)*
William Hillenius *(College of Charleston)*
Kenneth Hillers *(California Polytechnic State University, San Luis Obispo)*
Ralph Hinegardner *(University of California, Santa Cruz)*
William Hines *(Foothill College)*
Robert Hinrichsen *(Indiana University of Pennsylvania)*
Helmut Hirsch *(State University of New York, Albany)*
Tuan-hua David Ho *(Washington University)*
Carl Hoagstrom *(Ohio Northern University)*
James Hoffman *(University of Vermont)*
A. Scott Holaday *(Texas Tech University)*
N. Michele Holbrook *(Harvard University)*
James Holland *(Indiana State University, Bloomington)*
Charles Holliday *(Lafayette College)*
Lubbock Karl Holte *(Idaho State University)*
Alan R. Holyoak *(Brigham Young University, Idaho)*
Laura Hoopes *(Occidental College)*
Nancy Hopkins *(Massachusetts Institute of Technology)*
Sandra Horikami *(Daytona Beach Community College)*
Kathy Hornberger *(Widener University)*
Pius F. Horner *(San Bernardino Valley College)*
Becky Houck *(University of Portland)*
Margaret Houk *(Ripon College)*
Daniel J. Howard *(New Mexico State University)*
Ronald R. Hoy *(Cornell University)*
Cristin Hulslander *(University of Oregon)*
Donald Humphrey *(Emory University School of Medicine)*
Robert J. Huskey *(University of Virginia)*
Steven Hutcheson *(University of Maryland, College Park)*
Sandra Hsu *(Skyline College)*
Linda L. Hyde *(Gordon College)*
Bradley Hyman *(University of California, Riverside)*
Mark Iked *(San Bernardino Valley College)*
Jeffrey Ihara *(Mira Costa College)*
Cheryl Ingram-Smith *(Clemson University)*
Alice Jacklet *(State University of New York, Albany)*
John Jackson *(North Hennepin Community College)*
John C. Jahoda *(Bridgewater State College)*
Dan Johnson *(East Tennessee State University)*
Lee Johnson *(The Ohio State University)*
Randall Johnson *(University of California, San Diego)*
Stephen Johnson *(William Penn University)*
Wayne Johnson *(Ohio State University)*
Kenneth C. Jones *(California State University, Northridge)*
Russell Jones *(University of California, Berkeley)*
Chad Jordan *(North Carolina State University)*
Alan Journet *(Southeast Missouri State University)*
Walter Judd *(University of Florida)*
Thomas W. Jurik *(Iowa State University)*
Caroline M. Kane *(University of California, Berkeley)*
Thomas C. Kane *(University of Cincinnati)*
Tamos Kapros *(University of Missouri)*
E. L. Karlstrom *(University of Puget Sound)*
Jennifer Katcher *(Pima Community College)*
Laura A. Katz *(Smith College)*
Maureen Kearney *(Field Museum of Natural History)*
Patrick Keeling *(University of British Columbia)*
Elizabeth A. Kellogg *(University of Missouri, St. Louis)*
Norm Kenkel *(University of Manitoba)*
Chris Kennedy *(Simon Fraser University)*
George Khoury *(National Cancer Institute)*
Rebecca T. Kimball *(University of Florida)*
Mark Kirk *(University of Missouri, Columbia)*
Robert Kitchin *(University of Wyoming)*
Attila O. Klein *(Brandeis University)*
Daniel Klionsky *(University of Michigan)*
Jennifer Knight *(University of Colorado)*
Ned Knight *(Linfield College)*
David Kohl *(University of California, Santa Barbara)*
Greg Kopf *(University of Pennsylvania School of Medicine)*
Thomas Koppenheffer *(Trinity University)*
Margareta Krabbe *(Uppsala University)*
Anselm Kratochwil *(Universität Osnabrück)*
Deborah M. Kristan *(California State University, San Marcos)*
William Kroll *(Loyola University, Chicago)*
Janis Kuby *(San Francisco State University)*
Justin P. Kumar *(Indiana University)*
David Kurijaka *(Ohio University)*
Marc-André Lachance *(University of Western Ontario)*
J. A. Lackey *(State University of New York, Oswego)*
Elaine Lai *(Brandeis University)*
Mohamed Lakrim *(Kingsborough Community College)*
Lynn Lamoreux *(Texas A&M University)*
William L'Amoreaux *(College of Staten Island)*
Carmine A. Lanciani *(University of Florida)*
Kenneth Lang *(Humboldt State University)*
Dominic Lannutti *(El Paso Community College)*
Allan Larson *(Washington University)*
John Latto *(University of California, Santa Barbara)*
Diane K. Lavett *(State University of New York, Cortland, and Emory University)*
Charles Leavell *(Fullerton College)*
C. S. Lee *(University of Texas)*
Daewoo Lee *(Ohio University)*
Robert Leonard *(University of California, Riverside)*
Michael R. Leonardo *(Coe College)*
John Lepri *(University of North Carolina, Greensboro)*
Donald Levin *(University of Texas, Austin)*
Mike Levine *(University of California, Berkeley)*
Joseph Levine *(Boston College)*
Bill Lewis *(Shoreline Community College)*
John Lewis *(Loma Linda University)*
Lorraine Lica *(California State University, East Bay)*
Harvey Liftin *(Broward Community College)*
Harvey Lillywhite *(University of Florida, Gainesville)*
Graeme Lindbeck *(Valencia Community College)*
Clark Lindgren *(Grinnell College)*
Diana Lipscomb *(George Washington University)*
Christopher Little *(The University of Texas, Pan American)*
Kevin D. Livingstone *(Trinity University)*
Andrea Lloyd *(Middlebury College)*
Sam Loker *(University of New Mexico)*
Christopher A. Loretz *(State University of New York, Buffalo)*
Jane Lubchenco *(Oregon State University)*
Douglas B. Luckie *(Michigan State University)*
Margaret A. Lynch *(Tufts University)*
Steven Lynch *(Louisiana State University, Shreveport)*
Richard Machemer Jr. *(St. John Fisher College)*
Elizabeth Machunis-Masuoka *(University of Virginia)*
James MacMahon *(Utah State University)*
Christine R. Maher *(University of Southern Maine)*
Linda Maier *(University of Alabama, Huntsville)*
Jose Maldonado *(El Paso Community College)*
Richard Malkin *(University of California, Berkeley)*
Charles Mallery *(University of Miami)*
Keith Malmos *(Valencia Community College, East Campus)*
Cindy Malone *(California State University, Northridge)*
Carol Mapes *(Kutztown University of Pennsylvania)*
William Margolin *(University of Texas Medical School)*
Lynn Margulis *(Boston University)*
Kathleen A. Marrs *(Indiana University-Purdue University, Indianapolis)*
Edith Marsh *(Angelo State University)*
Diane L. Marshall *(University of New Mexico)*
Linda Martin Morris *(University of Washington)*
Karl Mattox *(Miami University of Ohio)*
Joyce Maxwell *(California State University, Northridge)*
Jeffrey D. May *(Marshall University)*
Lee McClenaghan *(San Diego State University)*
Richard McCracken *(Purdue University)*
Andrew McCubbin *(Washington State University)*
Kerry McDonald *(University of Missouri, Columbia)*
Jacqueline McLaughlin *(Pennsylvania State University, Lehigh Valley)*
Neal McReynolds *(Texas A&M International)*

Lisa Marie Meffert *(Rice University)*
Michael Meighan *(University of California, Berkeley)*
Scott Meissner *(Cornell University)*
Paul Melchior *(North Hennepin Community College)*
Phillip Meneely *(Haverford College)*
John Merrill *(Michigan State University)*
Brian Metscher *(University of California, Irvine)*
Ralph Meyer *(University of Cincinnati)*
James Mickle *(North Carolina State University)*
Roger Milkman *(University of Iowa)*
Helen Miller *(Oklahoma State University)*
John Miller *(University of California, Berkeley)*
Kenneth R. Miller *(Brown University)*
John E. Minnich *(University of Wisconsin, Milwaukee)*
Michael J. Misamore *(Texas Christian University)*
Kenneth Mitchell *(Tulane University School of Medicine)*
Alan Molumby *(University of Illinois, Chicago)*
Nicholas Money *(Miami University)*
Russell Monson *(University of Colorado, Boulder)*
Joseph P. Montoya *(Georgia Institute of Technology)*
Frank Moore *(Oregon State University)*
Janice Moore *(Colorado State University)*
Randy Moore *(Wright State University)*
William Moore *(Wayne State University)*
Carl Moos *(Veterans Administration Hospital, Albany, New York)*
Michael Mote *(Temple University)*
Alex Motten *(Duke University)*
Jeanette Mowery *(Madison Area Technical College)*
Deborah Mowshowitz *(Columbia University)*
Rita Moyes *(Texas A&M College Station)*
Darrel L. Murray *(University of Illinois, Chicago)*
John Mutchmor *(Iowa State University)*
Elliot Myerowitz *(California Institute of Technology)*
Gavin Naylor *(Iowa State University)*
John Neess *(University of Wisconsin, Madison)*
Tom Neils *(Grand Rapids Community College)*
Raymond Neubauer *(University of Texas, Austin)*
Todd Newbury *(University of California, Santa Cruz)*
James Newcomb *(New England College)*
Harvey Nichols *(University of Colorado, Boulder)*
Deborah Nickerson *(University of South Florida)*
Bette Nicotri *(University of Washington)*
Caroline Niederman *(Tomball College)*
Maria Nieto *(California State University, East Bay)*
Anders Nilsson *(University of Umeå)*
Greg Nishiyama *(College of the Canyons)*
Charles R. Noback *(College of Physicians and Surgeons, Columbia University)*
Jane Noble-Harvey *(Delaware University)*
Mary C. Nolan *(Irvine Valley College)*
Peter Nonacs *(University of California, Los Angeles)*
Mohamed A. F. Noor *(Duke University)*
Shawn Nordell *(St. Louis University)*
Richard S. Norman *(University of Michigan, Dearborn, Emeritus)*
David O. Norris *(University of Colorado, Boulder)*
Steven Norris *(California State University, Channel Islands)*
Gretchen North *(Occidental College)*
Cynthia Norton *(University of Maine, Augusta)*
Steve Norton *(East Carolina University)*
Steve Nowicki *(Duke University)*
Bette H. Nybakken *(Hartnell College)*
Brian O'Conner *(University of Massachusetts, Amherst)*
Gerard O'Donovan *(University of North Texas)*
Eugene Odum *(University of Georgia)*
Mark P. Oemke *(Alma College)*
Linda Ogren *(University of California, Santa Cruz)*
Patricia O'Hern *(Emory University)*
Nathan O. Okia *(Auburn University, Montgomery)*
Jeanette Oliver *(St. Louis Community College, Florissant Valley)*
Gary P. Olivetti *(University of Vermont)*
John Olsen *(Rhodes College)*
Laura J. Olsen *(University of Michigan)*
Sharman O'Neill *(University of California, Davis)*
Wan Ooi *(Houston Community College)*
John Oross *(University of California, Riverside)*
Gay Ostarello *(Diablo Valley College)*
Catherine Ortega *(Fort Lewis College)*
Charissa Osborne *(Butler University)*
Thomas G. Owens *(Cornell University)*
Penny Padgett *(University of North Carolina, Chapel Hill)*
Kevin Padian *(University of California, Berkeley)*
Dianna Padilla *(State University of New York, Stony Brook)*
Anthony T. Paganini *(Michigan State University)*
Barry Palevitz *(University of Georgia)*
Michael A. Palladino *(Monmouth University)*
Daniel Papaj *(University of Arizona)*
Peter Pappas *(County College of Morris)*
Bulah Parker *(North Carolina State University)*
Stanton Parmeter *(Chemeketa Community College)*
Robert Patterson *(San Francisco State University)*
Ronald Patterson *(Michigan State University)*
Crellin Pauling *(San Francisco State University)*
Kay Pauling *(Foothill Community College)*
Daniel Pavuk *(Bowling Green State University)*
Debra Pearce *(Northern Kentucky University)*
Patricia Pearson *(Western Kentucky University)*
Shelley Penrod *(North Harris College)*
Imara Y. Perera *(North Carolina State University)*
Beverly Perry *(Houston Community College)*
David Pfennig *(University of North Carolina, Chapel Hill)*
David S. Pilliod *(California Polytechnic State University, San Luis Obispo)*
J. Chris Pires *(University of Missouri, Columbia)*
Bob Pittman *(Michigan State University)*
James Platt *(University of Denver)*
Martin Poenie *(University of Texas, Austin)*
Scott Poethig *(University of Pennsylvania)*
Jeffrey Pommerville *(Texas A&M University)*
Angela R. Porta *(Kean University)*
Warren Porter *(University of Wisconsin)*
Daniel Potter *(University of California, Davis)*
Donald Potts *(University of California, Santa Cruz)*
Andy Pratt *(University of Canterbury)*
David Pratt *(University of California, Davis)*
Halina Presley *(University of Illinois, Chicago)*
Mary V. Price *(University of California, Riverside)*
Mitch Price *(Pennsylvania State University)*
Rong Sun Pu *(Kean University)*
Rebecca Pyles *(East Tennessee State University)*
Scott Quackenbush *(Florida International University)*
Ralph Quatrano *(Oregon State University)*
Peter Quinby *(University of Pittsburgh)*
Val Raghavan *(Ohio State University)*
Deanna Raineri *(University of Illinois, Champaign-Urbana)*
Talitha Rajah *(Indiana University Southeast)*
Charles Ralph *(Colorado State University)*
Thomas Rand *(Saint Mary's University)*
Robert H. Reavis *(Glendale Community College)*
Kurt Redborg *(Coe College)*
Ahnya Redman *(Pennsylvania State University)*
Brian Reeder *(Morehead State University)*
Bruce Reid *(Kean University)*
David Reid *(Blackburn College)*
C. Gary Reiness *(Lewis & Clark College)*
Charles Remington *(Yale University)*
Erin Rempala *(San Diego Mesa College)*
David Reznick *(University of California, Riverside)*
Douglas Rhoads *(University of Arkansas)*
Fred Rhoades *(Western Washington State University)*
Eric Ribbens *(Western Illinois University)*
Christina Richards *(New York University)*
Christopher Riegle *(Irvine Valley College)*
Loren Rieseberg *(University of British Columbia)*
Bruce B. Riley *(Texas A&M University)*
Donna Ritch *(Pennsylvania State University)*
Carol Rivin *(Oregon State University East)*
Laurel Roberts *(University of Pittsburgh)*
Thomas Rodella *(Merced College)*
Rodney Rogers *(Drake University)*
William Roosenburg *(Ohio University)*
Mike Rosenzweig *(Virginia Polytechnic Institute and State University)*
Wayne Rosing *(Middle Tennessee State University)*
Thomas Rost *(University of California, Davis)*
Stephen I. Rothstein *(University of California, Santa Barbara)*
John Ruben *(Oregon State University)*
Albert Ruesink *(Indiana University)*
Neil Sabine *(Indiana University)*
Tyson Sacco *(Cornell University)*
Rowan F. Sage *(University of Toronto)*
Tammy Lynn Sage *(University of Toronto)*
Don Sakaguchi *(Iowa State University)*
Walter Sakai *(Santa Monica College)*
Mark F. Sanders *(University of California, Davis)*
Ted Sargent *(University of Massachusetts, Amherst)*
K. Sathasivan *(University of Texas, Austin)*
Gary Saunders *(University of New Brunswick)*
Thomas R. Sawicki *(Spartanburg Community College)*
Inder Saxena *(University of Texas, Austin)*
Carl Schaefer *(University of Connecticut)*
Maynard H. Schaus *(Virginia Wesleyan College)*

Renate Scheibe *(University of Osnabrück)*
David Schimpf *(University of Minnesota, Duluth)*
William H. Schlesinger *(Duke University)*
Mark Schlissel *(University of California, Berkeley)*
Christopher J. Schneider *(Boston University)*
Thomas W. Schoener *(University of California, Davis)*
Robert Schorr *(Colorado State University)*
Patricia M. Schulte *(University of British Columbia)*
Karen S. Schumaker *(University of Arizona)*
David J. Schwartz *(Houston Community College)*
Christa Schwintzer *(University of Maine)*
Erik P. Scully *(Towson State University)*
Robert W. Seagull *(Hofstra University)*
Edna Seaman *(Northeastern University)*
Duane Sears *(University of California, Santa Barbara)*
Orono Shukdeb Sen *(Bethune-Cookman College)*
Wendy Sera *(Seton Hill University)*
Timothy E. Shannon *(Francis Marion University)*
Joan Sharp *(Simon Fraser University)*
Victoria C. Sharpe *(Blinn College)*
Elaine Shea *(Loyola College, Maryland)*
Stephen Sheckler *(Virginia Polytechnic Institute and State University)*
Richard Sherwin *(University of Pittsburgh)*
Lisa Shimeld *(Crafton Hills College)*
James Shinkle *(Trinity University)*
Barbara Shipes *(Hampton University)*
Richard M. Showman *(University of South Carolina)*
Peter Shugarman *(University of Southern California)*
Alice Shuttey *(DeKalb Community College)*
James Sidie *(Ursinus College)*
Daniel Simberloff *(Florida State University)*
Rebecca Simmons *(University of North Dakota)*
Anne Simon *(University of Maryland, College Park)*
Robert Simons *(University of California, Los Angeles)*
Alastair Simpson *(Dalhousie University)*
Susan Singer *(Carleton College)*
Roger Sloboda *(Dartmouth University)*
John Smarrelli *(Le Moyne College)*
Andrew T. Smith *(Arizona State University)*
Kelly Smith *(University of North Florida)*
Nancy Smith-Huerta *(Miami Ohio University)*
John Smol *(Queen's University)*
Andrew J. Snope *(Essex Community College)*
Julio G. Soto *(San Jose State University)*
Mitchell Sogin *(Woods Hole Marine Biological Laboratory)*
Susan Sovonick-Dunford *(University of Cincinnati)*
Frederick W. Spiegel *(University of Arkansas)*
John Stachowicz *(University of California, Davis)*
Amanda Starnes *(Emory University)*
Karen Steudel *(University of Wisconsin)*
Barbara Stewart *(Swarthmore College)*
Gail A. Stewart *(Camden County College)*
Cecil Still *(Rutgers University, New Brunswick)*
Margery Stinson *(Southwestern College)*
James Stockand *(University of Texas Health Science Center, San Antonio)*
John Stolz *(California Institute of Technology)*
Richard D. Storey *(Colorado College)*
Stephen Strand *(University of California, Los Angeles)*
Eric Strauss *(University of Massachusetts, Boston)*
Antony Stretton *(University of Wisconsin, Madison)*
Russell Stullken *(Augusta College)*
Mark Sturtevant *(University of Michigan, Flint)*
John Sullivan *(Southern Oregon State University)*
Gerald Summers *(University of Missouri)*
Judith Sumner *(Assumption College)*
Marshall D. Sundberg *(Emporia State University)*
Lucinda Swatzell *(Southeast Missouri State University)*
Daryl Sweeney *(University of Illinois, Champaign-Urbana)*
Samuel S. Sweet *(University of California, Santa Barbara)*
Janice Swenson *(University of North Florida)*
Michael A. Sypes *(Pennsylvania State University)*
Lincoln Taiz *(University of California, Santa Cruz)*
Samuel Tarsitano *(Southwest Texas State University)*
David Tauck *(Santa Clara University)*
Emily Taylor *(California Polytechnic State University, San Luis Obispo)*
James Taylor *(University of New Hampshire)*
John W. Taylor *(University of California, Berkeley)*
Martha R. Taylor *(Cornell University)*
Thomas Terry *(University of Connecticut)*
Roger Thibault *(Bowling Green State University)*
William Thomas *(Colby-Sawyer College)*
Cyril Thong *(Simon Fraser University)*
John Thornton *(Oklahoma State University)*
Robert Thornton *(University of California, Davis)*
William Thwaites *(Tillamook Bay Community College)*
Stephen Timme *(Pittsburg State University)*
Eric Toolson *(University of New Mexico)*
Leslie Towill *(Arizona State University)*
James Traniello *(Boston University)*
Paul Q. Trombley *(Florida State University)*
Nancy J. Trun *(Duquesne University)*
Constantine Tsoukas *(San Diego State University)*
Marsha Turell *(Houston Community College)*
Robert Tuveson *(University of Illinois, Urbana)*
Maura G. Tyrrell *(Stonehill College)*
Catherine Uekert *(Northern Arizona University)*
Claudia Uhde-Stone *(California State University, East Bay)*
Gordon Uno *(University of Oklahoma)*
Lisa A. Urry *(Mills College)*
Saba Valadkhan *(Case Western Reserve University School of Medicine)*
James W. Valentine *(University of California, Santa Barbara)*
Joseph Vanable *(Purdue University)*
Theodore Van Bruggen *(University of South Dakota)*
Kathryn VandenBosch *(Texas A&M University)*
Gerald Van Dyke *(North Carolina State University)*
Brandi Van Roo *(Framingham State College)*
Moira Van Staaden *(Bowling Green State University)*
Steven D. Verhey *(Central Washington University)*
Kathleen Verville *(Washington College)*
Sara Via *(University of Maryland)*
Frank Visco *(Orange Coast College)*
Laurie Vitt *(University of California, Los Angeles)*
Neal Voelz *(St. Cloud State University)*
Thomas J. Volk *(University of Wisconsin, La Crosse)*
Leif Asbjørn Vøllestad *(University of Oslo)*
Susan D. Waaland *(University of Washington)*
William Wade *(Dartmouth Medical College)*
D. Alexander Wait *(Southwest Missouri State University)*
John Waggoner *(Loyola Marymount University)*
Jyoti Wagle *(Houston Community College)*
Edward Wagner *(University of California, Irvine)*
Dan Walker *(San Jose State University)*
Robert L. Wallace *(Ripon College)*
Jeffrey Walters *(North Carolina State University)*
Linda Walters *(University of Central Florida)*
Nickolas M. Waser *(University of California, Riverside)*
Margaret Waterman *(University of Pittsburgh)*
Charles Webber *(Loyola University of Chicago)*
Peter Webster *(University of Massachusetts, Amherst)*
Terry Webster *(University of Connecticut, Storrs)*
Beth Wee *(Tulane University)*
Andrea Weeks *(George Mason University)*
Peter Wejksnora *(University of Wisconsin, Milwaukee)*
Kentwood Wells *(University of Connecticut)*
David J. Westenberg, *(University of Missouri, Rolla)*
Richard Wetts *(University of California, Irvine)*
Matt White *(Ohio University)*
Ernest H. Williams *(Hamilton College)*
Kathy Williams *(San Diego State University)*
Stephen Williams *(Glendale Community College)*
Elizabeth Willott *(University of Arizona)*
Christopher Wills *(University of California, San Diego)*
Paul Wilson *(California State University, Northridge)*
Fred Wilt *(University of California, Berkeley)*
Peter Wimberger *(University of Puget Sound)*
Robert Winning *(Eastern Michigan University)*
E. William Wischusen *(Louisiana State University)*
Susan Whittemore *(Keene State College)*
Clarence Wolfe *(Northern Virginia Community College)*
Vickie L. Wolfe *(Marshall University)*
Robert T. Woodland *(University of Massachusetts Medical School)*
Joseph Woodring *(Louisiana State University)*
Denise Woodward *(Pennsylvania State University)*
Patrick Woolley *(East Central College)*
Sarah E. Wyatt *(Ohio University)*
Ramin Yadegari *(University of Arizona)*
Paul Yancey *(Whitman College)*
Philip Yant *(University of Michigan)*
Linda Yasui *(Northern Illinois University)*
Hideo Yonenaka *(San Francisco State University)*
Gina M. Zainelli *(Loyola University, Chicago)*
Edward Zalisko *(Blackburn College)*
Zai Ming Zhao *(University of Texas, Austin)*
John Zimmerman *(Kansas State University)*
Miriam Zolan *(Indiana University)*
Uko Zylstra *(Calvin College)*

Detailed Contents

23

The Evolution of Populations

▲ **Figure 23.1 Is this finch evolving?**

EVOLUTION

KEY CONCEPTS

- **23.1** Genetic variation makes evolution possible
- **23.2** The Hardy-Weinberg equation can be used to test whether a population is evolving
- **23.3** Natural selection, genetic drift, and gene flow can alter allele frequencies in a population
- **23.4** Natural selection is the only mechanism that consistently causes adaptive evolution

OVERVIEW

The Smallest Unit of Evolution

One common misconception about evolution is that individual organisms evolve. It is true that natural selection acts on individuals: Each organism's traits affect its survival and reproductive success compared with other individuals. But the evolutionary impact of natural selection is only apparent in the changes in a *population* of organisms over time.

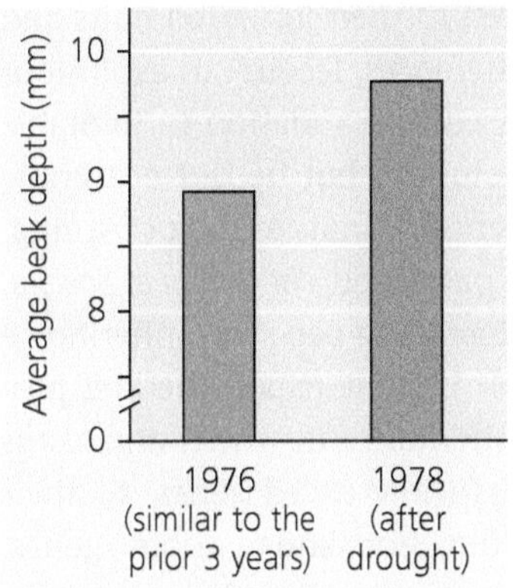

◀ **Figure 23.2 Evidence of selection by food source.** The data represent adult beak depth measurements of medium ground finches hatched in the generations before and after the 1977 drought. Beak sizes remained large until 1983, when changing conditions no longer favored large-beaked birds.

MB See the related Experimental Inquiry Tutorial in MasteringBiology.

Consider the medium ground finch (*Geospiza fortis*), a seed-eating bird that inhabits the Galápagos Islands (Figure 23.1). In 1977, the *G. fortis* population on the island of Daphne Major was decimated by a long period of drought: Of some 1,200 birds, only 180 survived. Researchers Peter and Rosemary Grant observed that during the drought, small, soft seeds were in short supply. The finches mostly fed on large, hard seeds that were more plentiful. Birds with larger, deeper beaks were better able to crack and eat these larger seeds, and they survived at a higher rate than finches with smaller beaks. Since beak depth is an inherited trait in these birds, the average beak depth in the next generation of *G. fortis* was greater than it had been in the pre-drought population (Figure 23.2). The finch population had evolved by natural selection. However, the *individual* finches did not evolve. Each bird had a beak of a particular size, which did not grow larger during the drought. Rather, the proportion of large beaks in the population increased from generation to generation: The population evolved, not its individual members.

Focusing on evolutionary change in populations, we can define evolution on its smallest scale, called **microevolution**, as change in allele frequencies in a population over generations. As we will see in this chapter, natural selection is not the only cause of microevolution. In fact, there are three main mechanisms that can cause allele frequency change: natural selection, genetic drift (chance events that alter allele frequencies), and gene flow (the transfer of alleles between populations). Each of these mechanisms has distinctive effects on the genetic composition of populations. However, only natural selection consistently improves the match between organisms and their environment (adaptation). Before we examine natural selection and adaptation more closely, let's revisit a prerequisite for these processes in a population: genetic variation.

CONCEPT 23.1

Genetic variation makes evolution possible

In *The Origin of Species*, Darwin provided abundant evidence that life on Earth has evolved over time, and he proposed natural selection as the primary mechanism for that change. He observed that individuals differed in their inherited traits and that selection acted on such differences, leading to evolutionary change. Thus, Darwin realized that variation in heritable traits was a prerequisite for evolution, but he did not know precisely how organisms pass heritable traits to their offspring.

Just a few years after Darwin published *The Origin of Species*, Gregor Mendel wrote a groundbreaking paper on inheritance in pea plants (see Chapter 14). In that paper, Mendel proposed a particulate model of inheritance in which organisms transmit discrete heritable units (now called genes) to their offspring. Although Darwin did not know about genes, Mendel's paper set the stage for understanding the genetic differences on which evolution is based. Here we'll examine such genetic differences and how they are produced.

Genetic Variation

You probably have no trouble recognizing your friends in a crowd. Each person is unique, exhibiting differences in their facial features, height, and voice. Indeed, individual variation occurs in all species. In addition to the differences that we can see or hear, individuals vary extensively at the molecular level. For example, you cannot identify a person's blood group (A, B, AB, or O) from his or her appearance, but this and many other molecular traits vary among individuals.

Individual variations often reflect **genetic variation**, differences among individuals in the composition of their genes or other DNA segments. As you read in earlier chapters, however, some phenotypic variation is not heritable (see Figure 23.3 for a striking example in a caterpillar of the southwestern United States). Phenotype is the product of an inherited genotype and many environmental influences. In a human example, bodybuilders alter their phenotypes dramatically but do not pass their huge muscles on to the next generation. In general, only the genetically determined part of phenotypic variation can have evolutionary consequences. As such, genetic variation provides the raw material for evolutionary change: Without genetic variation, evolution cannot occur.

Variation Within a Population

Characters that vary within a population may be discrete or quantitative. *Discrete characters*, such as the purple or white flower colors of Mendel's pea plants (see Figure 14.3), can be classified on an either-or basis (each plant has flowers that are either purple or white). Many discrete characters are determined by a single gene locus with different alleles that produce distinct phenotypes. However, most heritable variation involves *quantitative characters*, which vary along a continuum within a population. Heritable quantitative variation usually results from the influence of two or more genes on a single phenotypic character.

For both discrete and quantitative characters, biologists often need to describe how much genetic variation there is in a particular population. We can measure genetic variation at the whole-gene level (*gene variability*) and at the molecular level of DNA (*nucleotide variability*). Gene variability can be quantified as the **average heterozygosity**, the average percentage of loci that are heterozygous. (Recall that a heterozygous individual has two different alleles for a given locus, whereas a homozygous individual has two identical alleles for that locus.) As an example, on average the fruit fly *Drosophila melanogaster* is heterozygous for about 1,920 of its 13,700 loci (14%) and homozygous for all the rest. We can therefore say that a *D. melanogaster* population has an average heterozygosity of 14%. Analyses of this and many other species show that this level of genetic variation provides ample raw material for natural selection to operate, resulting in evolutionary change.

When determining gene variability, how do scientists identify heterozygous loci? One method is to survey the protein products of genes using gel electrophoresis (see Figure 20.9). However, this approach cannot detect silent mutations that

▲ **Figure 23.3 Nonheritable variation.** These caterpillars of the moth *Nemoria arizonaria* owe their different appearances to chemicals in their diets, not to differences in their genotypes. Caterpillars raised on a diet of oak flowers resembled the flowers **(a)**, whereas their siblings raised on oak leaves resembled oak twigs **(b)**.

alter the DNA sequence of a gene but not the amino acid sequence of the protein (see Figure 17.24). To include such silent mutations in their estimates of average heterozygosity, researchers must use other approaches, such as PCR-based methods and restriction fragment analyses (see Chapter 20).

To measure nucleotide variability, biologists compare the DNA sequences of two individuals in a population and then average the data from many such comparisons. The genome of *D. melanogaster* has about 180 million nucleotides, and the sequences of any two fruit flies differ on average by approximately 1.8 million (1%) of their nucleotides. Thus, the nucleotide variability of *D. melanogaster* populations is about 1%.

As in this example, gene variability tends to exceed nucleotide variability. Why is this true? Remember that a gene can consist of thousands of nucleotides. A difference at only one of these nucleotides can be sufficient to make two alleles of that gene different, increasing gene variability.

Variation Between Populations

In addition to variation observed within a population, species also exhibit **geographic variation**, differences in the genetic composition of separate populations. Figure 23.4 illustrates geographic variation in populations of house mice (*Mus musculus*) separated by mountains on the Atlantic island of Madeira. Inadvertently introduced by Portuguese settlers in the 15th century, several populations of mice have evolved in isolation from one another. Researchers have observed differences in the karyotypes (chromosome sets) of these isolated populations. In certain populations, some of the chromosomes have become fused. However, the patterns of fused chromosomes differ from one population to another. Because these chromosome-level changes leave genes intact, their phenotypic effects on the mice seem to be neutral. Thus, the variation between these populations appears to have resulted from chance events (drift) rather than natural selection.

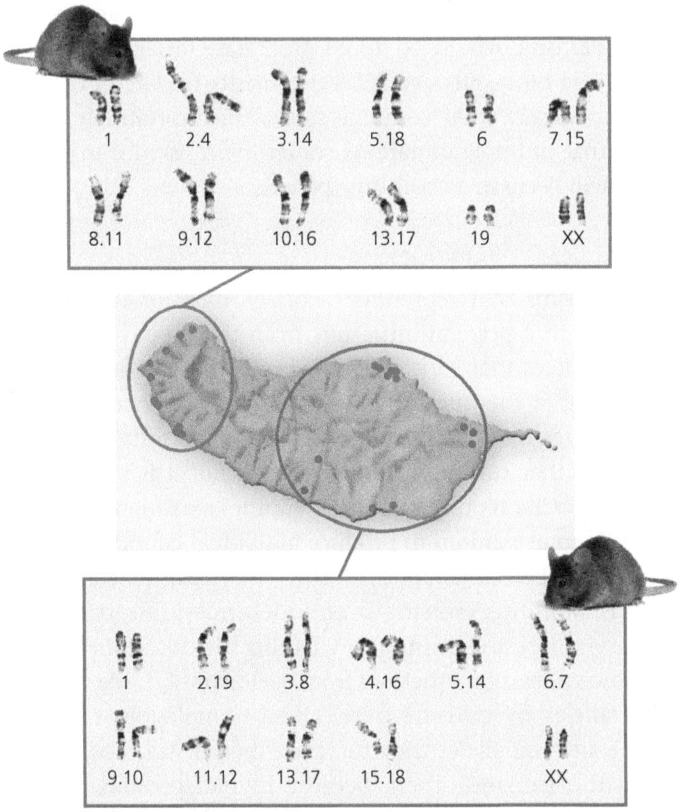

▲ Figure 23.4 **Geographic variation in isolated mouse populations on Madeira.** The number pairs represent fused chromosomes. For example, "2.4" indicates fusion of chromosome 2 and chromosome 4. Mice in the areas indicated by the blue dots have the set of fused chromosomes in the blue box; mice in the red-dot locales have the set of fused chromosomes in the red box.

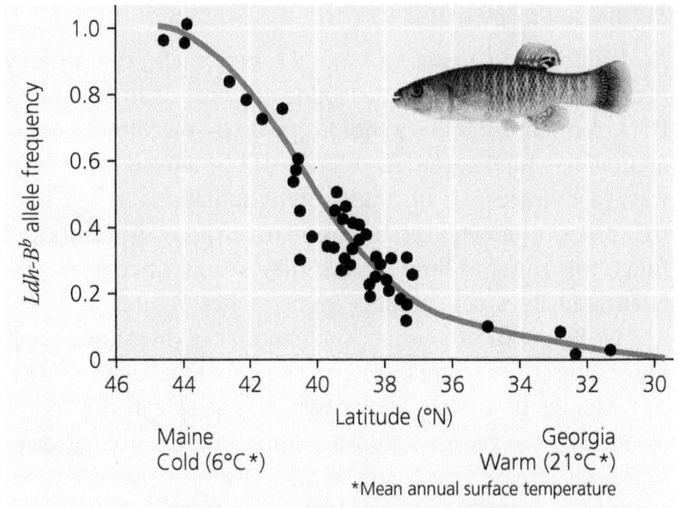

▲ Figure 23.5 **A cline determined by temperature.** In mummichog fish, the frequency of the $Ldh\text{-}B^b$ allele for the enzyme lactate dehydrogenase-B (which functions in metabolism) decreases in fish sampled from Maine to Georgia. The $Ldh\text{-}B^b$ allele codes for a form of the enzyme that is a better catalyst in cold water than are other versions of the enzyme. Individuals with the $Ldh\text{-}B^b$ allele can swim faster in cold water than can individuals with other alleles.

Other examples of geographic variation occur as a **cline**, a graded change in a character along a geographic axis. Some clines are produced by a gradation in an environmental variable, as illustrated by the impact of temperature on the frequency of a cold-adaptive allele in mummichog fish (*Fundulus heteroclitus*). Clines such as the one depicted in Figure 23.5 probably result from natural selection—otherwise there would be no reason to expect a close association between the environmental variable and the frequency of the allele. But selection can only operate if multiple alleles exist for a given locus. Such variation in alleles can arise in several ways.

Sources of Genetic Variation

The genetic variation on which evolution depends originates when mutation, gene duplication, or other processes produce new alleles and new genes. Many new genetic variants can be produced in short periods of time in organisms that reproduce rapidly. Sexual reproduction can also result in genetic variation as existing genes are arranged in new ways.

Formation of New Alleles

As described in Chapters 17 and 21, new alleles can arise by *mutation*, a change in the nucleotide sequence of an organism's DNA. A mutation is like a shot in the dark—we cannot predict accurately which segments of DNA will be altered or in what way. In multicellular organisms, only mutations in cell lines that produce gametes can be passed to offspring. In plants and fungi, this is not as limiting as it may sound, since many different cell lines can produce gametes (see Figures 30.6 and 31.17). But in most animals, the majority of mutations occur in somatic cells and are lost when the individual dies.

A change of as little as one base in a gene, called a "point mutation," can have a significant impact on phenotype, as in sickle-cell disease (see Figure 17.23). Organisms reflect thousands of generations of past selection, and hence their phenotypes generally provide a close match to their environment. As a result, it's unlikely that a new mutation that alters a phenotype will improve it. In fact, most such mutations are at least slightly harmful. But much of the DNA in eukaryotic genomes does not code for protein products, and point mutations in these noncoding regions are often harmless. Also, because of the redundancy in the genetic code, even a point mutation in a gene that encodes a protein will have no effect on the protein's function if the amino acid composition is not changed. And even where there is a change in the amino acid, it may not affect the protein's shape and function. However, as will be discussed later in this chapter, a mutant allele may on rare occasions actually make its bearer better suited to the environment, enhancing reproductive success.

Altering Gene Number or Position

Chromosomal changes that delete, disrupt, or rearrange many loci at once are usually harmful. However, when such large-scale changes leave genes intact, their effects on organisms may be neutral (as in the case of the Madeira mice described in Figure 23.4). In rare cases, chromosomal rearrangements may even be beneficial. For example, the translocation of part of one chromosome to a different chromosome could link DNA segments in a way that results in a positive effect.

An important source of variation begins when genes are duplicated due to errors in meiosis (such as unequal crossing over), slippage during DNA replication, or the activities of transposable elements (see Chapters 15 and 21). Duplications of large chromosome segments, like other chromosomal aberrations, are often harmful, but the duplication of smaller pieces of DNA may not be. Gene duplications that do not have severe effects can persist over generations, allowing mutations to accumulate. The result is an expanded genome with new genes that may take on new functions.

Such beneficial increases in gene number appear to have played a major role in evolution. For example, the remote ancestors of mammals had a single gene for detecting odors that has since been duplicated many times. As a result, humans today have about 1,000 olfactory receptor genes, and mice have 1,300. This dramatic proliferation of olfactory genes probably helped early mammals, enabling them to detect faint odors and to distinguish among many different smells. More recently, about 60% of human olfactory receptor genes have been inactivated by mutations, whereas mice have lost only 20% of theirs. Since mutation rates in humans and mice are similar, this difference is likely due to strong selection against mice with mutations that inactivate their olfactory genes. A versatile sense of smell appears to be much more important to mice than to humans!

Rapid Reproduction

Mutation rates tend to be low in plants and animals, averaging about one mutation in every 100,000 genes per generation, and they are often even lower in prokaryotes. But prokaryotes typically have short generation spans, so mutations can quickly generate genetic variation in populations of these organisms. The same is true of viruses. For instance, HIV has a generation span of about two days. It also has an RNA genome, which has a much higher mutation rate than a typical DNA genome because of the lack of RNA repair mechanisms in host cells (see Chapter 19). For this reason, it is unlikely that a single-drug treatment would ever be effective against HIV; mutant forms of the virus that are resistant to a particular drug would no doubt proliferate in relatively short order. The most effective AIDS treatments to date have been drug "cocktails" that combine several medications. It is less likely that multiple mutations conferring resistance to *all* the drugs will occur in a short time period.

Sexual Reproduction

In organisms that reproduce sexually, most of the genetic variation in a population results from the unique combination of alleles that each individual receives from its parents. Of course, at the nucleotide level, all the differences among these alleles have originated from past mutations and other processes that can produce new alleles. But it is the mechanism of sexual reproduction that shuffles existing alleles and deals them at random to produce individual genotypes.

As described in Chapter 13, three mechanisms contribute to this shuffling: crossing over, independent assortment of chromosomes, and fertilization. During meiosis, homologous chromosomes, one inherited from each parent, trade some of their alleles by crossing over. These homologous chromosomes and the alleles they carry are then distributed at random into gametes. Then, because myriad possible mating combinations exist in a population, fertilization brings together gametes that are likely to have different genetic backgrounds. The combined effects of these three mechanisms ensure that sexual reproduction rearranges existing alleles into fresh combinations each generation, providing much of the genetic variation that makes evolution possible.

CONCEPT CHECK 23.1

1. (a) Explain why genetic variation within a population is a prerequisite for evolution. (b) What factors can produce genetic differences between populations?
2. Of all the mutations that occur in a population, why do only a small fraction become widespread?
3. **MAKE CONNECTIONS** If a population stopped reproducing sexually (but still reproduced asexually), how would its genetic variation be affected over time? Explain. (See Concept 13.4, pp. 257–259.)

For suggested answers, see Appendix A.

CONCEPT 23.2

The Hardy-Weinberg equation can be used to test whether a population is evolving

Although the individuals in a population must differ genetically for evolution to occur, the presence of genetic variation does not guarantee that a population will evolve. For that to happen, one of the factors that cause evolution must be at work. In this section, we'll explore one way to test whether evolution is occurring in a population. The first step in this process is to clarify what we mean by a population.

Gene Pools and Allele Frequencies

A **population** is a group of individuals of the same species that live in the same area and interbreed, producing fertile offspring. Different populations of a single species may be isolated geographically from one another, thus exchanging genetic material only rarely. Such isolation is common for species that live on widely separated islands or in different lakes. But not all populations are isolated, nor must populations have sharp boundaries (Figure 23.6). Still, members of a population typically breed with one another and thus on average are more closely related to each other than to members of other populations.

We can characterize a population's genetic makeup by describing its **gene pool**, which consists of all copies of every type of allele at every locus in all members of the population. If only one allele exists for a particular locus in a population, that allele is said to be *fixed* in the gene pool, and all individuals are homozygous for that allele. But if there are two or more alleles for a particular locus in a population, individuals may be either homozygous or heterozygous.

Each allele has a frequency (proportion) in the population. For example, imagine a population of 500 wildflower plants with two alleles, C^R and C^W, for a locus that codes for flower pigment. These alleles show incomplete dominance (see Figure 14.10); thus, each genotype has a distinct phenotype.

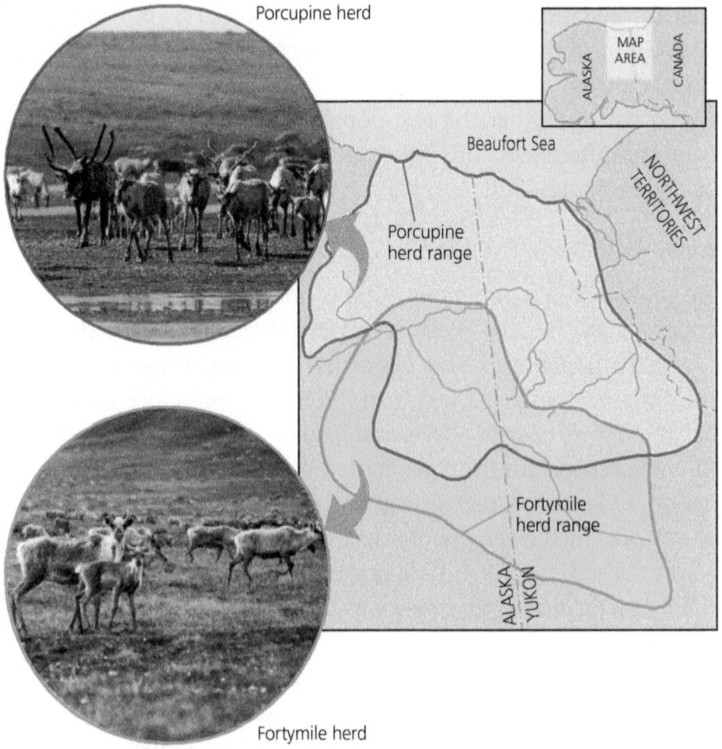

▲ **Figure 23.6 One species, two populations.** These two caribou populations in the Yukon are not totally isolated; they sometimes share the same area. Still, members of either population are most likely to breed within their own population.

Plants homozygous for the C^R allele (C^RC^R) produce red pigment and have red flowers; plants homozygous for the C^W allele (C^WC^W) produce no red pigment and have white flowers; and heterozygotes (C^RC^W) produce some red pigment and have pink flowers.

In our population, suppose there are 320 plants with red flowers, 160 with pink flowers, and 20 with white flowers. Because these are diploid organisms, there are a total of 1,000 copies of the gene for flower color in the population of 500 individuals. The C^R allele accounts for 800 of these copies ($320 \times 2 = 640$ for C^RC^R plants, plus $160 \times 1 = 160$ for C^RC^W plants).

When studying a locus with two alleles, the convention is to use p to represent the frequency of one allele and q to represent the frequency of the other allele. Thus, p, the frequency of the C^R allele in the gene pool of this population, is $800/1{,}000 = 0.8 = 80\%$. And because there are only two alleles for this gene, the frequency of the C^W allele, represented by q, must be $200/1{,}000 = 0.2 = 20\%$. For loci that have more than two alleles, the sum of all allele frequencies must still equal 1 (100%).

Next we'll see how allele and genotype frequencies can be used to test whether evolution is occurring in a population.

The Hardy-Weinberg Principle

One way to assess whether natural selection or other factors are causing evolution at a particular locus is to determine what the genetic makeup of a population would be if it were *not* evolving at that locus. We can then compare that scenario with data from a real population. If there are no differences, we can conclude that the real population is not evolving. If there are differences, this suggests that the real population may be evolving—and then we can try to figure out why.

Hardy-Weinberg Equilibrium

The gene pool of a population that is not evolving can be described by the **Hardy-Weinberg principle**, named for the British mathematician and German physician, respectively, who independently derived it in 1908. This principle states that the frequencies of alleles and genotypes in a population will remain constant from generation to generation, provided that only Mendelian segregation and recombination of alleles are at work. Such a gene pool is in *Hardy-Weinberg equilibrium*.

To use the Hardy-Weinberg principle, it is helpful to think about genetic crosses in a new way. Previously, we used Punnett squares to determine the genotypes of offspring in a genetic cross (see Figure 14.5). Here, instead of considering the possible allele combinations from one cross, consider the combination of alleles in *all* of the crosses in a population.

Imagine that all the alleles for a given locus from all the individuals in a population were placed in a large bin (**Figure 23.7**).

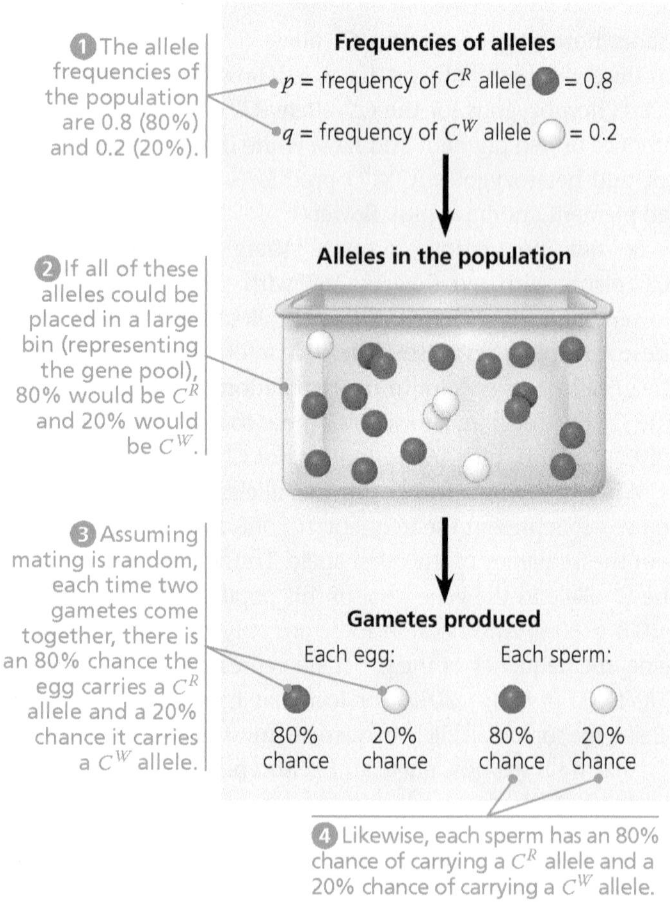

▲ **Figure 23.7 Selecting alleles at random from a gene pool.**

We can think of this bin as holding the population's gene pool for that locus. "Reproduction" occurs by selecting alleles at random from the bin; somewhat similar events occur in nature when fish release sperm and eggs into the water or when pollen (containing plant sperm) is blown about by the wind. By viewing reproduction as a process of randomly selecting and combining alleles from the bin (the gene pool), we are in effect assuming that mating occurs at random—that is, that all male-female matings are equally likely.

Let's apply the bin analogy to the hypothetical wildflower population discussed earlier. In that population of 500 flowers, the frequency of the allele for red flowers (C^R) is $p = 0.8$, and the frequency of the allele for white flowers (C^W) is $q = 0.2$. Thus, a bin holding all 1,000 copies of the flower-color gene in the population contains 800 C^R alleles and 200 C^W alleles. Assuming that gametes are formed by selecting alleles at random from the bin, the probability that an egg or sperm contains a C^R or C^W allele is equal to the frequency of these alleles in the bin. Thus, as shown in Figure 23.7, each egg has an 80% chance of containing a C^R allele and a 20% chance of containing a C^W allele; the same is true for each sperm.

Using the rule of multiplication (see Figure 14.9), we can now calculate the frequencies of the three possible genotypes, assuming random unions of sperm and eggs. The probability that two C^R alleles will come together is $p \times p = p^2 = 0.8 \times 0.8 = 0.64$. Thus, about 64% of the plants in the next generation will have the genotype C^RC^R. The frequency of C^WC^W individuals is expected to be about $q \times q = q^2 = 0.2 \times 0.2 = 0.04$, or 4%. C^RC^W heterozygotes can arise in two different ways. If the sperm provides the C^R allele and the egg provides the C^W allele, the resulting heterozygotes will be $p \times q = 0.8 \times 0.2 = 0.16$, or 16% of the total. If the sperm provides the C^W allele and the egg the C^R allele, the heterozygous offspring will make up $q \times p = 0.2 \times 0.8 = 0.16$, or 16%. The frequency of heterozygotes is thus the sum of these possibilities: $pq + qp = 2pq = 0.16 + 0.16 = 0.32$, or 32%.

As shown in **Figure 23.8** on the facing page, the genotype frequencies in the next generation must add up to 1 (100%). Thus, the equation for Hardy-Weinberg equilibrium states that at a locus with two alleles, the three genotypes will appear in the following proportions:

p^2	+	$2pq$	+	q^2	=	1
Expected frequency of genotype C^RC^R		Expected frequency of genotype C^RC^W		Expected frequency of genotype C^WC^W		

Note that for a locus with two alleles, only three genotypes are possible (in this case, C^RC^R, C^RC^W, and C^WC^W). As a result, the sum of the frequencies of the three genotypes must equal 1 (100%) in *any* population—regardless of whether the population is in Hardy-Weinberg equilibrium. A population is in Hardy-Weinberg equilibrium only if the genotype frequencies are such that the actual frequency of

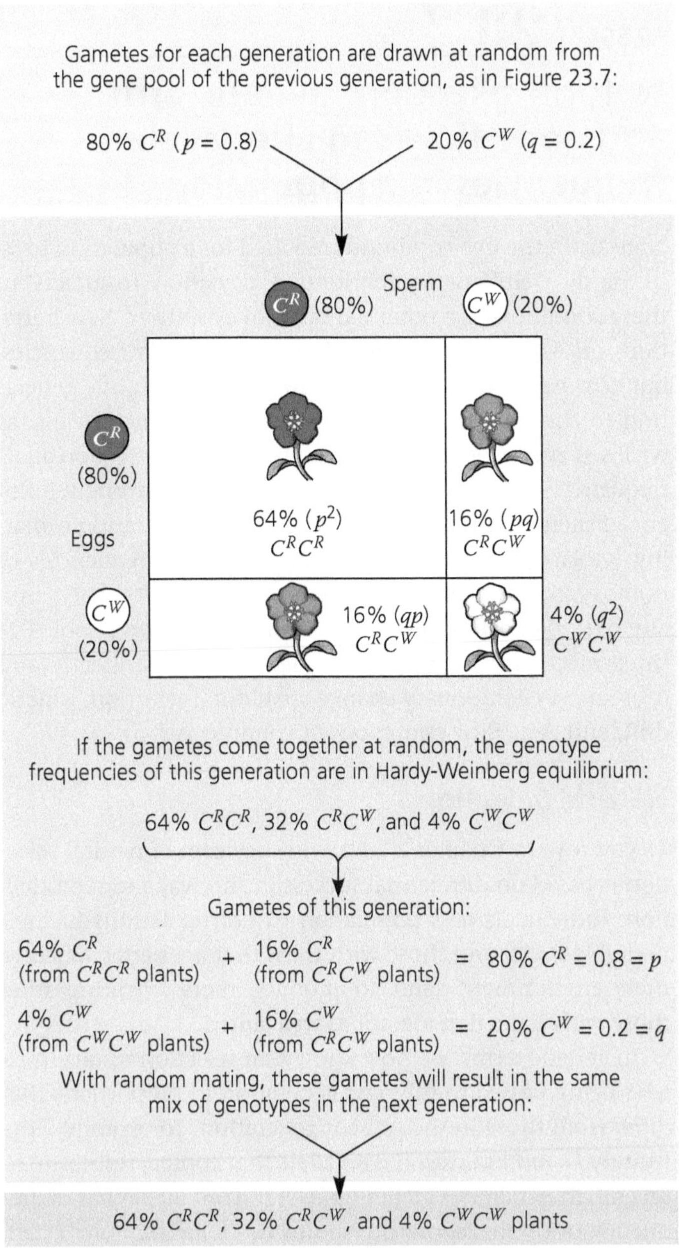

▲ **Figure 23.8 The Hardy-Weinberg principle.** In our wildflower population, the gene pool remains constant from one generation to the next. Mendelian processes alone do not alter frequencies of alleles or genotypes.

? *If the frequency of the C^R allele is 60%, predict the frequencies of the C^RC^R, C^RC^W, and C^WC^W genotypes.*

one homozygote is p^2, the actual frequency of the other homozygote is q^2, and the actual frequency of heterozygotes is $2pq$. Finally, as suggested by Figure 23.8, if a population such as our wildflowers is in Hardy-Weinberg equilibrium and its members continue to mate randomly generation after generation, allele and genotype frequencies will remain constant. The system operates somewhat like a deck of cards: No matter how many times the deck is reshuffled to deal out new hands, the deck itself remains the same. Aces do not grow more numerous than jacks. And the repeated shuffling of a population's gene pool over the generations cannot, in itself, change the frequency of one allele relative to another.

Conditions for Hardy-Weinberg Equilibrium

The Hardy-Weinberg principle describes a hypothetical population that is not evolving. But in real populations, the allele and genotype frequencies often *do* change over time. Such changes can occur when at least one of the following five conditions of Hardy-Weinberg equilibrium is not met:

1. **No mutations.** The gene pool is modified if mutations alter alleles or if entire genes are deleted or duplicated.
2. **Random mating.** If individuals mate preferentially within a subset of the population, such as their close relatives (inbreeding), random mixing of gametes does not occur, and genotype frequencies change.
3. **No natural selection.** Differences in the survival and reproductive success of individuals carrying different genotypes can alter allele frequencies.
4. **Extremely large population size.** The smaller the population, the more likely it is that allele frequencies will fluctuate by chance from one generation to the next (a process called genetic drift).
5. **No gene flow.** By moving alleles into or out of populations, gene flow can alter allele frequencies.

Departure from these conditions usually results in evolutionary change, which, as we've already described, is common in natural populations. But it is also common for natural populations to be in Hardy-Weinberg equilibrium for specific genes. This apparent contradiction occurs because a population can be evolving at some loci, yet simultaneously be in Hardy-Weinberg equilibrium at other loci. In addition, some populations evolve so slowly that the changes in their allele and genotype frequencies are difficult to distinguish from those predicted for a nonevolving population.

Applying the Hardy-Weinberg Principle

The Hardy-Weinberg equation is often used as an initial test of whether evolution is occurring in a population (you'll encounter an example in Concept Check 23.2, question 3). The equation also has medical applications, such as estimating the percentage of a population carrying the allele for an inherited disease. For example, consider phenylketonuria (PKU), a metabolic disorder that results from homozygosity for a recessive allele and occurs in about one out of every 10,000 babies born in the United States. Left untreated, PKU results in mental disability and other problems. (Newborns are now tested for PKU, and symptoms can be largely avoided with a diet very low in phenylalanine. For this reason, products that contain phenylalanine, such as diet colas, carry warning labels.)

To apply the Hardy-Weinberg equation, we must assume that no new PKU mutations are being introduced into the population (condition 1), and that people neither choose their mates on the basis of whether or not they carry this gene nor generally mate with close relatives (condition 2). We must also ignore any effects of differential survival and reproductive success among PKU genotypes (condition 3) and assume that there are no effects of genetic drift (condition 4) or of gene flow from other populations into the United States (condition 5). These assumptions are reasonable: The mutation rate for the PKU gene is low, inbreeding is not common in the United States, selection occurs only against the rare homozygotes (and then only if dietary restrictions are not followed), the U.S. population is very large, and populations outside the country have PKU allele frequencies similar to those seen in the United States. If all these assumptions hold, then the frequency of individuals in the population born with PKU will correspond to q^2 in the Hardy-Weinberg equation (q^2 = frequency of homozygotes). Because the allele is recessive, we must estimate the number of heterozygotes rather than counting them directly as we did with the pink flowers. Since we know there is one PKU occurrence per 10,000 births ($q^2 = 0.0001$), the frequency of the recessive allele for PKU is

$$q = \sqrt{0.0001} = 0.01$$

and the frequency of the dominant allele is

$$p = 1 - q = 1 - 0.01 = 0.99$$

The frequency of carriers, heterozygous people who do not have PKU but may pass the PKU allele to offspring, is

$$2pq = 2 \times 0.99 \times 0.01 = 0.0198$$
(approximately 2% of the U.S. population)

Remember, the assumption of Hardy-Weinberg equilibrium yields an approximation; the real number of carriers may differ. Still, our calculations suggest that harmful recessive alleles at this and other loci can be concealed in a population because they are carried by healthy heterozygotes.

CONCEPT CHECK 23.2

1. Suppose a population of organisms with 20,000 gene loci is fixed at half of these loci and has two alleles at each of the other loci. How many different types of alleles are found in its entire gene pool? Explain.
2. If p is the frequency of allele A, use the Hardy-Weinberg equation to predict the frequency of individuals that have at least one A allele.
3. **WHAT IF?** A locus that affects susceptibility to a degenerative brain disease has two alleles, A and a. In a population, 16 people have genotype AA, 92 have genotype Aa, and 12 have genotype aa. Is this population evolving? Explain.

For suggested answers, see Appendix A.

CONCEPT 23.3

Natural selection, genetic drift, and gene flow can alter allele frequencies in a population

Note again the five conditions required for a population to be in Hardy-Weinberg equilibrium. A deviation from any of these conditions is a potential cause of evolution. New mutations (violation of condition 1) can alter allele frequencies, but because mutations are rare, the change from one generation to the next is likely to be very small. Nevertheless, as we'll see, mutation ultimately can have a large effect on allele frequencies when it produces new alleles that strongly influence fitness in a positive or negative way. Nonrandom mating (violation of condition 2) can affect the frequencies of homozygous and heterozygous genotypes but by itself usually has no effect on allele frequencies in the gene pool. The three mechanisms that alter allele frequencies directly and cause most evolutionary change are natural selection, genetic drift, and gene flow (violations of conditions 3–5).

Natural Selection

As you read in Chapter 22, Darwin's concept of natural selection is based on differential success in survival and reproduction: Individuals in a population exhibit variations in their heritable traits, and those with traits that are better suited to their environment tend to produce more offspring than those with traits that are not as well suited.

In genetic terms, we now know that selection results in alleles being passed to the next generation in proportions that differ from those in the present generation. For example, the fruit fly *D. melanogaster* has an allele that confers resistance to several insecticides, including DDT. This allele has a frequency of 0% in laboratory strains of *D. melanogaster* established from flies collected in the wild in the early 1930s, prior to DDT use. However, in strains established from flies collected after 1960 (following 20 or more years of DDT use), the allele frequency is 37%. We can infer that this allele either arose by mutation between 1930 and 1960 or that it was present in 1930, but very rare. In any case, the rise in frequency of this allele most likely occurred because DDT is a powerful poison that is a strong selective force in exposed fly populations.

As the *D. melanogaster* example shows, an allele that confers insecticide resistance will increase in frequency in a population exposed to that insecticide. Such changes are not coincidental. By consistently favoring some alleles over others, natural selection can cause *adaptive evolution* (evolution that results in a better match between organisms and their environment). We'll explore this process in more detail a little later in this chapter.

Genetic Drift

If you flip a coin 1,000 times, a result of 700 heads and 300 tails might make you suspicious about that coin. But if you flip a coin only 10 times, an outcome of 7 heads and 3 tails would not be surprising. The smaller the number of coin flips, the more likely it is that chance alone will cause a deviation from the predicted result. (In this case, the prediction is an equal number of heads and tails.) Chance events can also cause allele frequencies to fluctuate unpredictably from one generation to the next, especially in small populations—a process called **genetic drift**.

Figure 23.9 models how genetic drift might affect a small population of our wildflowers. In this example, an allele is lost from the gene pool, but it is a matter of chance that the C^W allele is lost and not the C^R allele. Such unpredictable changes in allele frequencies can be caused by chance events associated with survival and reproduction. Perhaps a large animal such as a moose stepped on the three C^WC^W individuals in generation 2, killing them and increasing the chance that only the C^R allele would be passed to the next generation. Allele frequencies can also be affected by chance events that occur during fertilization. For example, suppose two individuals of genotype C^RC^W had a small number of offspring. By chance alone, every egg and sperm pair that generated offspring could happen to have carried the C^R allele and not the C^W allele.

Certain circumstances can result in genetic drift having a significant impact on a population. Two examples are the founder effect and the bottleneck effect.

The Founder Effect

When a few individuals become isolated from a larger population, this smaller group may establish a new population whose gene pool differs from the source population; this is called the **founder effect**. The founder effect might occur, for example, when a few members of a population are blown by a storm to a new island. Genetic drift, in which chance events alter allele frequencies, will occur in such a case if the storm indiscriminately transports some individuals (and their alleles), but not others, from the source population.

The founder effect probably accounts for the relatively high frequency of certain inherited disorders among isolated human populations. For example, in 1814, 15 British colonists founded a settlement on Tristan da Cunha, a group of small islands in the Atlantic Ocean midway between Africa and South America. Apparently, one of the colonists carried a recessive allele for retinitis pigmentosa, a progressive form of blindness that afflicts homozygous individuals. Of the founding colonists' 240 descendants on the island in the late 1960s, 4 had retinitis pigmentosa. The frequency of the allele that causes this disease is ten times

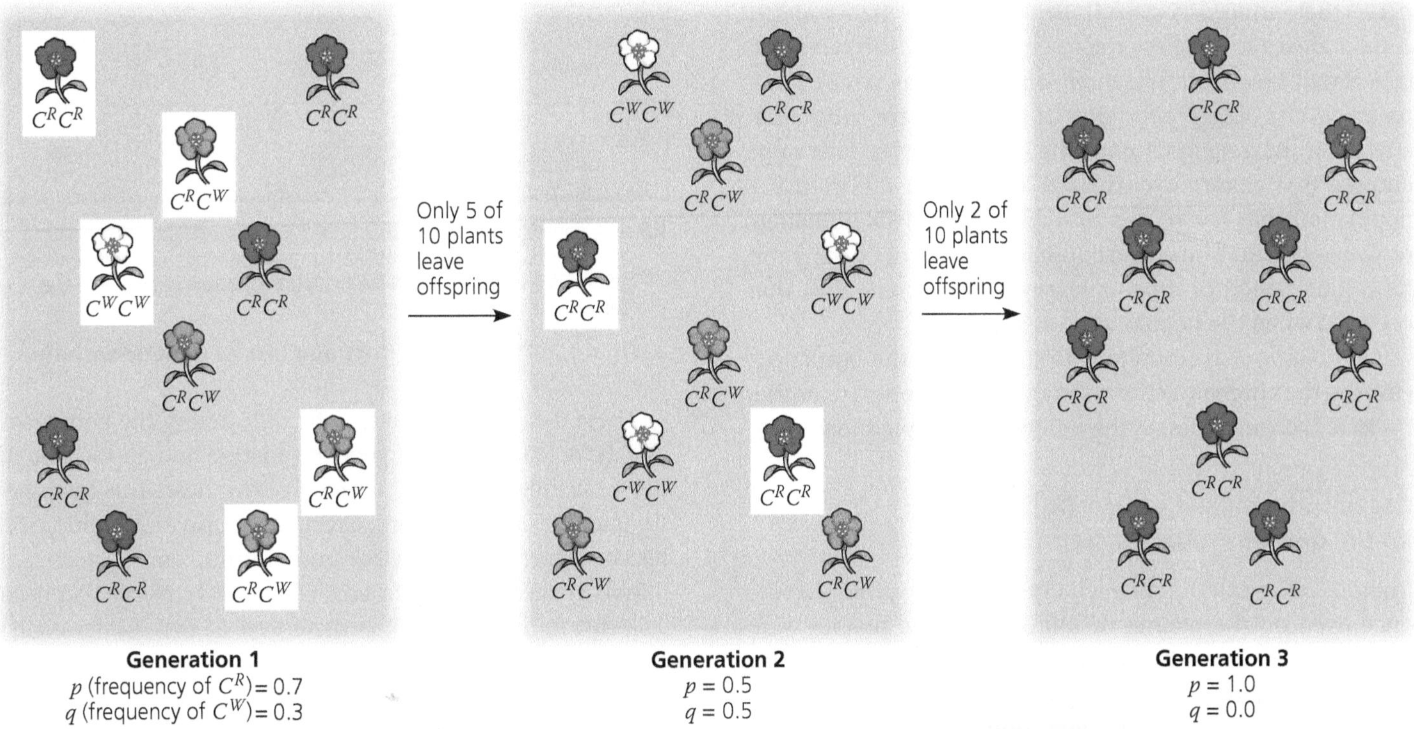

▲ **Figure 23.9 Genetic drift.** This small wildflower population has a stable size of ten plants. Suppose that by chance only five plants of generation 1 (those in white boxes) produce fertile offspring. (This could occur, for example, if only those plants happened to grow in a location that provided enough nutrients to support the production of offspring.) Again by chance, only two plants of generation 2 leave fertile offspring. As a result, by chance the frequency of the C^W allele first increases in generation 2, then falls to zero in generation 3.

BioFlix Visit the Study Area at **www.masteringbiology.com** for the BioFlix® 3-D Animation on Mechanisms of Evolution.

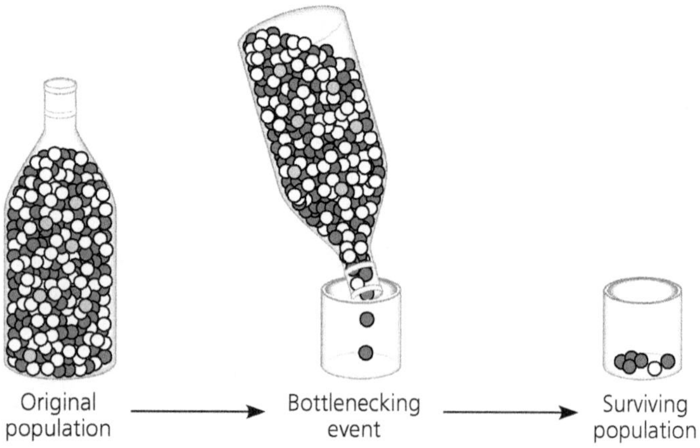

▲ **Figure 23.10 The bottleneck effect.** Shaking just a few marbles through the narrow neck of a bottle is analogous to a drastic reduction in the size of a population. By chance, blue marbles are overrepresented in the surviving population and gold marbles are absent.

higher on Tristan da Cunha than in the populations from which the founders came.

The Bottleneck Effect

A sudden change in the environment, such as a fire or flood, may drastically reduce the size of a population. A severe drop in population size can cause the **bottleneck effect**, so named because the population has passed through a "bottleneck" that reduces its size (Figure 23.10). By chance alone, certain alleles may be overrepresented among the survivors, others may be underrepresented, and some may be absent altogether. Ongoing genetic drift is likely to have substantial effects on the gene pool until the population becomes large enough that chance events have less impact. But even if a population that has passed through a bottleneck ultimately recovers in size, it may have low levels of genetic variation for a long period of time—a legacy of the genetic drift that occurred when the population was small.

One reason it is important to understand the bottleneck effect is that human actions sometimes create severe bottlenecks for other species, as the following example shows.

Case Study: *Impact of Genetic Drift on the Greater Prairie Chicken*

Millions of greater prairie chickens (*Tympanuchus cupido*) once lived on the prairies of Illinois. As these prairies were converted to farmland and other uses during the 19th and 20th centuries, the number of greater prairie chickens plummeted (Figure 23.11a). By 1993, only two Illinois populations remained, which together harbored fewer than 50 birds. The few surviving birds had low levels of genetic variation, and less than 50% of their eggs hatched, compared with much higher hatching rates of the larger populations in Kansas and Nebraska (Figure 23.11b).

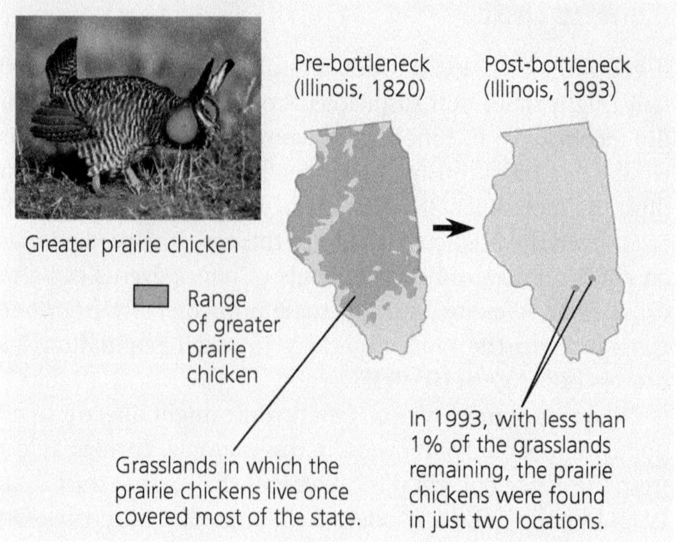

(a) The Illinois population of greater prairie chickens dropped from millions of birds in the 1800s to fewer than 50 birds in 1993.

Location	Population size	Number of alleles per locus	Percentage of eggs hatched
Illinois			
1930–1960s	1,000–25,000	5.2	93
1993	<50	3.7	<50
Kansas, 1998 (no bottleneck)	750,000	5.8	99
Nebraska, 1998 (no bottleneck)	75,000–200,000	5.8	96

(b) As a consequence of the drastic reduction in the size of the Illinois population, genetic drift resulted in a drop in the number of alleles per locus (averaged across six loci studied) and a decrease in the percentage of eggs that hatched.

▲ **Figure 23.11 Genetic drift and loss of genetic variation.**

These data suggest that genetic drift during the bottleneck may have led to a loss of genetic variation and an increase in the frequency of harmful alleles. To investigate this hypothesis, Juan Bouzat, of Bowling Green State University, Ohio, and his colleagues extracted DNA from 15 museum specimens of Illinois greater prairie chickens. Of the 15 birds, 10 had been collected in the 1930s, when there were 25,000 greater prairie chickens in Illinois, and 5 had been collected in the 1960s, when there were 1,000 greater prairie chickens in Illinois. By studying the DNA of these specimens, the researchers were able to obtain a minimum, baseline estimate of how much genetic variation was present in the Illinois population *before* the population shrank to extremely low numbers. This baseline estimate is a key piece of information that is not usually available in cases of population bottlenecks.

The researchers surveyed six loci and found that the 1993 Illinois greater prairie chicken population had lost nine alleles that were present in the museum specimens. The 1993 population also had fewer alleles per locus than the pre-bottleneck Illinois or the current Kansas and Nebraska populations (see Figure 23.11b). Thus, as predicted, drift had reduced the genetic variation of the small 1993 population. Drift may also have increased the frequency of harmful alleles, leading to the low egg-hatching rate. To counteract these negative effects, 271 birds from neighboring states were added to the Illinois population over four years. This strategy succeeded: New alleles entered the population, and the egg-hatching rate improved to over 90%. Overall, studies on the Illinois greater prairie chicken illustrate the powerful effects of genetic drift in small populations and provide hope that in at least some populations, these effects can be reversed.

Effects of Genetic Drift: A Summary

The examples we've described highlight four key points:

1. **Genetic drift is significant in small populations.** Chance events can cause an allele to be disproportionately over- or underrepresented in the next generation. Although chance events occur in populations of all sizes, they tend to alter allele frequencies substantially only in small populations.
2. **Genetic drift can cause allele frequencies to change at random.** Because of genetic drift, an allele may increase in frequency one year, then decrease the next; the change from year to year is not predictable. Thus, unlike natural selection, which in a given environment consistently favors some alleles over others, genetic drift causes allele frequencies to change at random over time.
3. **Genetic drift can lead to a loss of genetic variation within populations.** By causing allele frequencies to fluctuate randomly over time, genetic drift can eliminate alleles from a population. Because evolution depends on genetic variation, such losses can influence how effectively a population can adapt to a change in the environment.
4. **Genetic drift can cause harmful alleles to become fixed.** Alleles that are neither harmful nor beneficial can be lost or become fixed entirely by chance through genetic drift. In very small populations, genetic drift can also cause alleles that are slightly harmful to become fixed. When this occurs, the population's survival can be threatened (as for the greater prairie chicken).

Gene Flow

Natural selection and genetic drift are not the only phenomena affecting allele frequencies. Allele frequencies can also change by **gene flow**, the transfer of alleles into or out of a population due to the movement of fertile individuals or their gametes. For example, suppose that near our original hypothetical wildflower population there is another population consisting primarily of white-flowered individuals (C^WC^W). Insects carrying pollen from these plants may fly to and pollinate plants in our original population. The introduced C^W alleles would modify our original population's allele frequencies in the next generation. Because alleles are exchanged between populations, gene flow tends to reduce the genetic differences between populations. In fact, if it is extensive enough, gene flow can result in two populations combining into a single population with a common gene pool.

Alleles transferred by gene flow can also affect how well populations are adapted to local environmental conditions. Researchers studying the songbird *Parus major* (great tit) on the small Dutch island of Vlieland noted survival differences between two populations on the island. Females born in the eastern population survive twice as well as females born in the central population, regardless of where the females eventually settle and raise offspring (Figure 23.12). This finding suggests that females born in the eastern population are better adapted to life on the island than females born in the

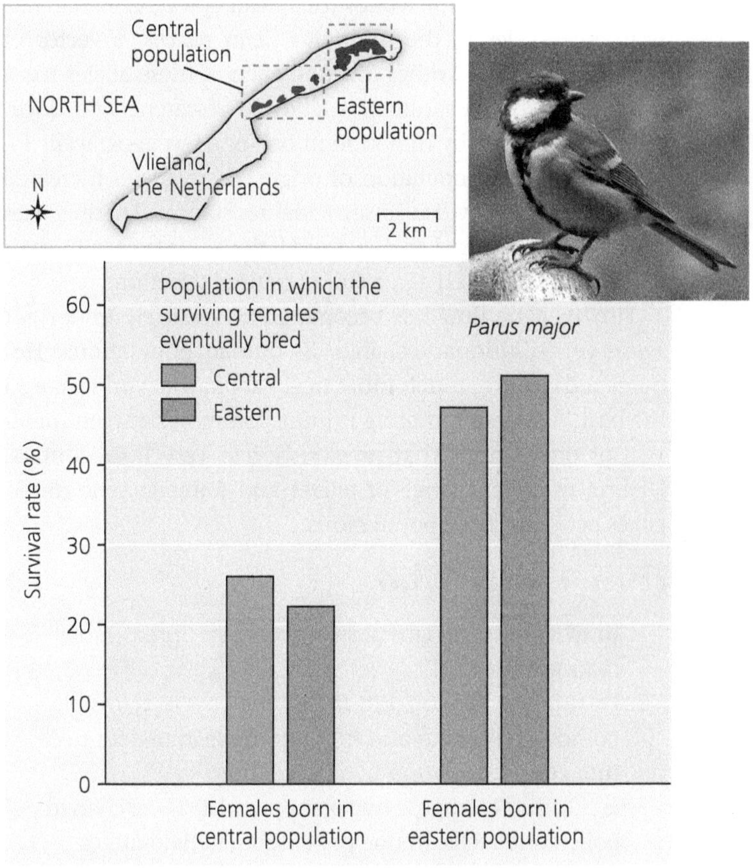

▲ **Figure 23.12 Gene flow and local adaptation.** In *Parus major* populations on Vlieland, the yearly survival rate of females born in the eastern population is higher than that of females born in the central population. Gene flow from the mainland to the central population is 3.3 times higher than it is to the eastern population, and birds from the mainland are selected against in both populations. These data suggest that gene flow from the mainland has prevented the central population from adapting fully to its local conditions.

central population. But extensive field studies also showed that the two populations are connected by high levels of gene flow (mating), which should reduce genetic differences between them. So how can the eastern population be better adapted to life on Vlieland than the central population? The answer lies in the unequal amounts of gene flow from the mainland. In any given year, 43% of the first-time breeders in the central population are immigrants from the mainland, compared with only 13% in the eastern population. Birds with mainland genotypes survive and reproduce poorly on Vlieland, and in the eastern population, selection reduces the frequency of these genotypes. In the central population, however, gene flow from the mainland is so high that it overwhelms the effects of selection. As a result, females born in the central population have many immigrant genes, reducing the degree to which members of that population are adapted to life on the island. Researchers are currently investigating why gene flow is so much higher in the central population and why birds with mainland genotypes have low fitness on Vlieland.

Gene flow can also transfer alleles that improve the ability of populations to adapt to local conditions. For example, gene flow has resulted in the worldwide spread of several insecticide-resistance alleles in the mosquito *Culex pipiens*, a vector of West Nile virus and other diseases. Each of these alleles has a unique genetic signature that allowed researchers to document that it arose by mutation in one or a few geographic locations. In their population of origin, these alleles increased because they provided insecticide resistance. These alleles were then transferred to new populations, where again, their frequencies increased as a result of natural selection.

Finally, gene flow has become an increasingly important agent of evolutionary change in human populations. Humans today move much more freely about the world than in the past. As a result, mating is more common between members of populations that previously had very little contact, leading to an exchange of alleles and fewer genetic differences between those populations.

CONCEPT CHECK 23.3

1. In what sense is natural selection more "predictable" than genetic drift?
2. Distinguish genetic drift from gene flow in terms of (a) how they occur and (b) their implications for future genetic variation in a population.
3. **WHAT IF?** Suppose two plant populations exchange pollen and seeds. In one population, individuals of genotype *AA* are most common (9,000 *AA*, 900 *Aa*, 100 *aa*), while the opposite is true in the other population (100 *AA*, 900 *Aa*, 9,000 *aa*). If neither allele has a selective advantage, what will happen over time to the allele and genotype frequencies of these populations?

For suggested answers, see Appendix A.

CONCEPT 23.4

Natural selection is the only mechanism that consistently causes adaptive evolution

Evolution by natural selection is a blend of chance and "sorting": chance in the creation of new genetic variations (as in mutation) and sorting as natural selection favors some alleles over others. Because of this favoring process, the outcome of natural selection is *not* random. Instead, natural selection consistently increases the frequencies of alleles that provide reproductive advantage and thus leads to adaptive evolution.

A Closer Look at Natural Selection

In examining how natural selection brings about adaptive evolution, we'll begin with the concept of relative fitness and the different ways that an organism's phenotype is subject to natural selection.

Relative Fitness

The phrases "struggle for existence" and "survival of the fittest" are commonly used to describe natural selection, but these expressions are misleading if taken to mean direct competitive contests among individuals. There *are* animal species in which individuals, usually the males, lock horns or otherwise do combat to determine mating privilege. But reproductive success is generally more subtle and depends on many factors besides outright battle. For example, a barnacle that is more efficient at collecting food than its neighbors may have greater stores of energy and hence be able to produce a larger number of eggs. A moth may have more offspring than other moths in the same population because its body colors more effectively conceal it from predators, improving its chance of surviving long enough to produce more offspring. These examples illustrate how in a given environment, certain traits can lead to greater **relative fitness**: the contribution an individual makes to the gene pool of the next generation *relative to* the contributions of other individuals.

Although we often refer to the relative fitness of a genotype, remember that the entity that is subjected to natural selection is the whole organism, not the underlying genotype. Thus, selection acts more directly on the phenotype than on the genotype; it acts on the genotype indirectly, via how the genotype affects the phenotype.

Directional, Disruptive, and Stabilizing Selection

Natural selection can alter the frequency distribution of heritable traits in three ways, depending on which phenotypes in a population are favored. These three modes of selection are called directional selection, disruptive selection, and stabilizing selection.

Directional selection occurs when conditions favor individuals exhibiting one extreme of a phenotypic range, thereby shifting a population's frequency curve for the phenotypic character in one direction or the other (Figure 23.13a). Directional selection is common when a population's environment changes or when members of a population migrate to a new (and different) habitat. For instance, an increase in the relative abundance of large seeds over small seeds led to an increase in beak depth in a population of Galápagos finches (see Figure 23.2).

Disruptive selection (Figure 23.13b) occurs when conditions favor individuals at both extremes of a phenotypic range over individuals with intermediate phenotypes. One example is a population of black-bellied seedcracker finches in Cameroon whose members display two distinctly different beak sizes. Small-billed birds feed mainly on soft seeds, whereas large-billed birds specialize in cracking hard seeds. It appears that birds with intermediate-sized bills are relatively inefficient at cracking both types of seeds and thus have lower relative fitness.

Stabilizing selection (Figure 23.13c) acts against both extreme phenotypes and favors intermediate variants. This mode of selection reduces variation and tends to maintain the status quo for a particular phenotypic character. For example, the birth weights of most human babies lie in the range of 3–4 kg (6.6–8.8 pounds); babies who are either much smaller or much larger suffer higher rates of mortality.

Regardless of the mode of selection, however, the basic mechanism remains the same. Selection favors individuals whose heritable phenotypic traits provide higher reproductive success than do the traits of other individuals.

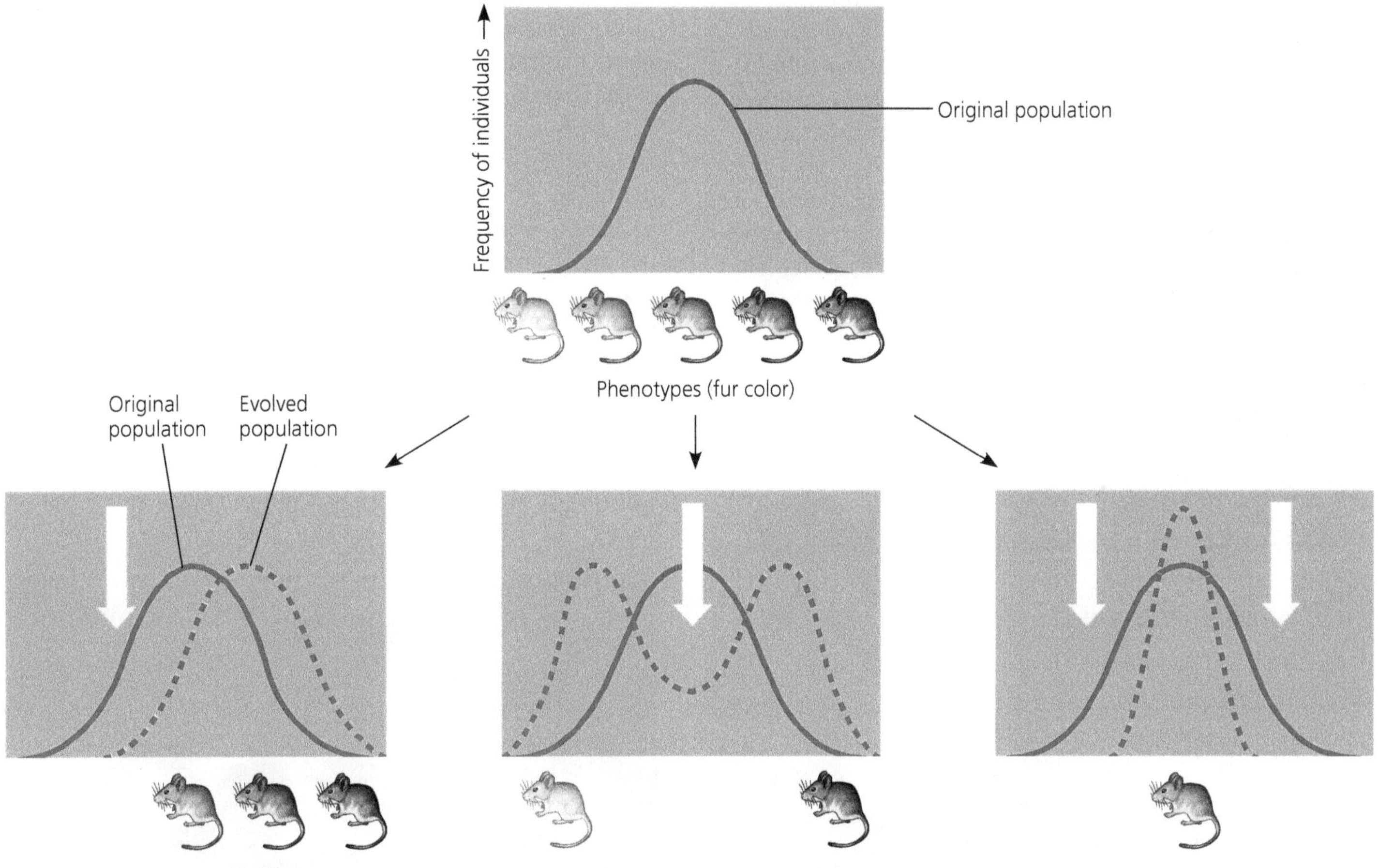

(a) Directional selection shifts the overall makeup of the population by favoring variants that are at one extreme of the distribution. In this case, lighter mice are selected against because they live among dark rocks, making it harder for them to hide from predators.

(b) Disruptive selection favors variants at both ends of the distribution. These mice have colonized a patchy habitat made up of light and dark rocks, with the result that mice of an intermediate color are selected against.

(c) Stabilizing selection removes extreme variants from the population and preserves intermediate types. If the environment consists of rocks of an intermediate color, both light and dark mice will be selected against.

▲ **Figure 23.13 Modes of selection.** These cases describe three ways in which a hypothetical deer mouse population with heritable variation in fur coloration from light to dark might evolve. The graphs show how the frequencies of individuals with different fur colors change over time. The large white arrows symbolize selective pressures against certain phenotypes.

MAKE CONNECTIONS *Review Figure 22.13 on p. 461. Which mode of selection has occurred in soapberry bug populations that feed on the introduced goldenrain tree? Explain.*

The Key Role of Natural Selection in Adaptive Evolution

The adaptations of organisms include many striking examples. Cuttlefish, for example, have the ability to change color rapidly, enabling them to blend into different backgrounds. Another example is the remarkable jaws of snakes (Figure 23.14), which allow them to swallow prey much larger than their own head (a feat analogous to a person swallowing a whole watermelon). Other adaptations, such as a version of an enzyme that shows improved function in cold environments (see Figure 23.5), may be less visually dramatic but just as important for survival and reproduction.

Such adaptations can arise gradually over time as natural selection increases the frequencies of alleles that enhance survival and reproduction. As the proportion of individuals that have favorable traits increases, the match between a species and its environment improves; that is, adaptive evolution occurs. However, as we saw in Chapter 22, the physical and biological components of an organism's environment may change over time. As a result, what constitutes a "good match" between an organism and its environment can be a moving target, making adaptive evolution a continuous, dynamic process.

And what about the two other important mechanisms of evolutionary change in populations, genetic drift and gene flow? Both can, in fact, increase the frequencies of alleles that improve the match between organisms and their environment, but neither does so consistently. Genetic drift can cause the frequency of a slightly beneficial allele to increase, but it also can cause the frequency of such an allele to decrease. Similarly, gene flow may introduce alleles that are advantageous or ones that are disadvantageous. Natural selection is the only evolutionary mechanism that consistently leads to adaptive evolution.

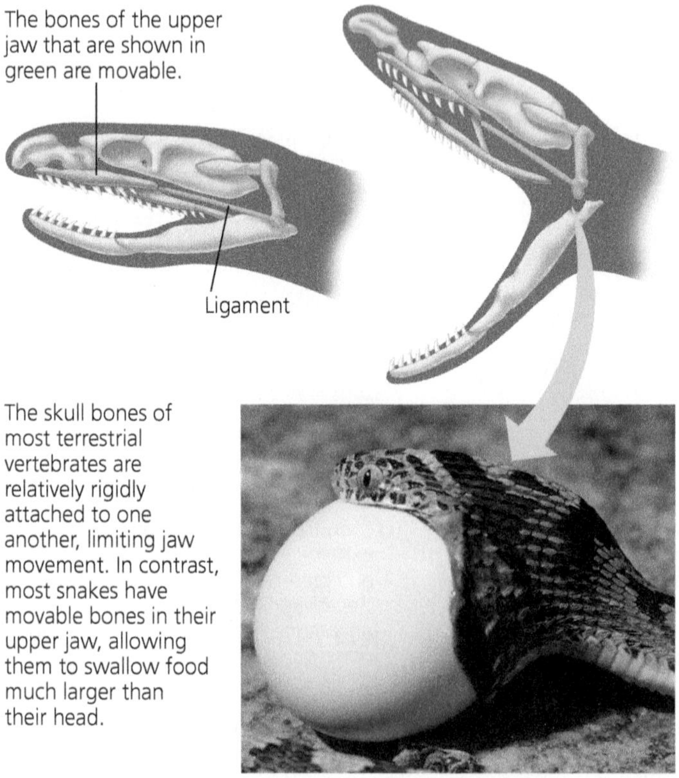

▲ Figure 23.14 **Movable jaw bones in snakes.**

Sexual Selection

Charles Darwin was the first to explore the implications of **sexual selection**, a form of selection in which individuals with certain inherited characteristics are more likely than other individuals to obtain mates. Sexual selection can result in **sexual dimorphism**, a difference between the two sexes in secondary sexual characteristics (Figure 23.15). These distinctions include differences in size, color, ornamentation, and behavior.

How does sexual selection operate? There are several ways. In **intrasexual selection**, meaning selection within the same sex, individuals of one sex compete directly for mates of the opposite sex. In many species, intrasexual selection occurs among males. For example, a single male may patrol a group of females and prevent other males from mating with them. The patrolling male may defend his status by defeating smaller, weaker, or less fierce males in combat. More often, this male is the psychological victor in ritualized displays that discourage would-be competitors but do not risk injury that would reduce his own fitness (see Figure 51.17). Intrasexual selection has also been observed among females in a variety of species, including ring-tailed lemurs and broad-nosed pipefish.

In **intersexual selection**, also called *mate choice*, individuals of one sex (usually the females) are choosy in selecting

▲ Figure 23.15 **Sexual dimorphism and sexual selection.** Peacocks (above left) and peahens (above right) show extreme sexual dimorphism. There is intrasexual selection between competing males, followed by intersexual selection when the females choose among the showiest males.

their mates from the other sex. In many cases, the female's choice depends on the showiness of the male's appearance or behavior (see Figure 23.15). What intrigued Darwin about mate choice is that male showiness may not seem adaptive in any other way and may in fact pose some risk. For example, bright plumage may make male birds more visible to predators. But if such characteristics help a male gain a mate, and if this benefit outweighs the risk from predation, then both the bright plumage and the female preference for it will be reinforced because they enhance overall reproductive success.

How do female preferences for certain male characteristics evolve in the first place? One hypothesis is that females prefer male traits that are correlated with "good genes." If the trait preferred by females is indicative of a male's overall genetic quality, both the male trait and female preference for it should increase in frequency. Figure 23.16 describes one experiment testing this hypothesis in gray tree frogs (*Hyla versicolor*).

Other researchers have shown that in several bird species, the traits preferred by females are related to overall male health. Here, too, female preference appears to be based on traits that reflect "good genes," in this case alleles indicative of a robust immune system.

The Preservation of Genetic Variation

Some of the genetic variation in populations represents **neutral variation**, differences in DNA sequence that do not confer a selective advantage or disadvantage. But variation is also found at loci affected by selection. What prevents natural selection from reducing genetic variation at those loci by culling all unfavorable alleles? The tendency for directional and stabilizing selection to reduce variation is countered by mechanisms that preserve or restore it.

Diploidy

In diploid eukaryotes, a considerable amount of genetic variation is hidden from selection in the form of recessive alleles. Recessive alleles that are less favorable than their dominant counterparts, or even harmful in the current environment, can persist by propagation in heterozygous individuals. This latent variation is exposed to natural selection only when both parents carry the same recessive allele and two copies end up in the same zygote. This happens only rarely if the frequency of the recessive allele is very low. Heterozygote protection maintains a huge pool of alleles that might not be favored under present conditions, but which could bring new benefits if the environment changes.

Balancing Selection

Selection itself may preserve variation at some loci. **Balancing selection** occurs when natural selection maintains two or

▼ **Figure 23.16** **INQUIRY**

Do females select mates based on traits indicative of "good genes"?

EXPERIMENT Female gray tree frogs (*Hyla versicolor*) prefer to mate with males that give long mating calls. Allison Welch and colleagues, at the University of Missouri, tested whether the genetic makeup of long-calling (LC) males is superior to that of short-calling (SC) males. The researchers fertilized half the eggs of each female with sperm from an LC male and fertilized the remaining eggs with sperm from an SC male. The resulting half-sibling offspring were raised in a common environment, and several measures of their "performance" were tracked for two years.

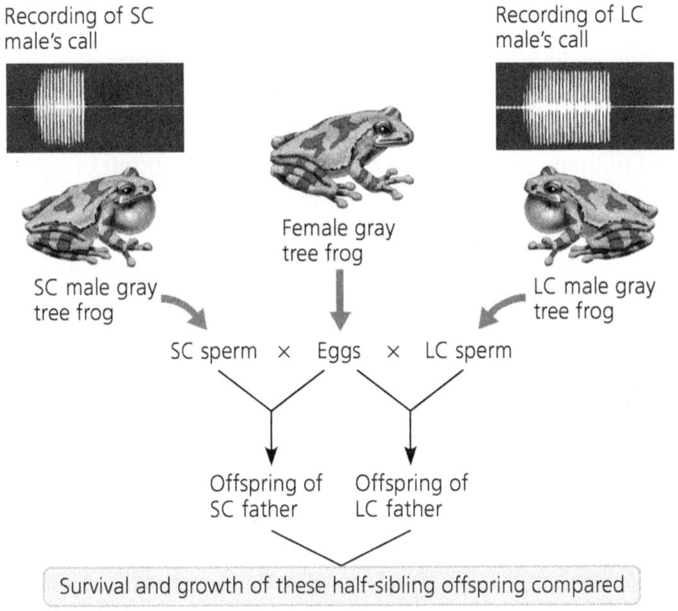

RESULTS

Offspring Performance	1995	1996
Larval survival	LC better	NSD
Larval growth	NSD	LC better
Time to metamorphosis	LC better (shorter)	LC better (shorter)

NSD = no significant difference; LC better = offspring of LC males superior to offspring of SC males.

CONCLUSION Because offspring fathered by an LC male outperformed their half-siblings fathered by an SC male, the team concluded that the duration of a male's mating call is indicative of the male's overall genetic quality. This result supports the hypothesis that female mate choice can be based on a trait that indicates whether the male has "good genes."

SOURCE A. M. Welch et al., Call duration as an indicator of genetic quality in male gray tree frogs, *Science* 280:1928–1930 (1998).

INQUIRY IN ACTION Read and analyze the original paper in *Inquiry in Action: Interpreting Scientific Papers.*

WHAT IF? Why did the researchers split each female frog's eggs into two batches for fertilization by different males? Why didn't they mate each female with a single male frog?

more forms in a population. This type of selection includes heterozygote advantage and frequency-dependent selection.

Heterozygote Advantage If individuals who are heterozygous at a particular locus have greater fitness than do both kinds of homozygotes, they exhibit **heterozygote advantage**. In such a case, natural selection tends to maintain two or more alleles at that locus. Note that heterozygote advantage is defined in terms of *genotype*, not phenotype. Thus, whether heterozygote advantage represents stabilizing or directional selection depends on the relationship between the genotype and the phenotype. For example, if the phenotype of a heterozygote is intermediate to the phenotypes of both homozygotes, heterozygote advantage is a form of stabilizing selection.

An example of heterozygote advantage occurs at the locus in humans that codes for the β polypeptide subunit of hemoglobin, the oxygen-carrying protein of red blood cells. In homozygous individuals, a certain recessive allele at that locus causes sickle-cell disease. The red blood cells of people with sickle-cell disease become distorted in shape, or *sickled*, under low-oxygen conditions (see Figure 5.21), as occurs in the capillaries. These sickled cells can clump together and block the flow of blood in the capillaries, resulting in serious damage to organs such as the kidney, heart, and brain. Although some red blood cells become sickled in heterozygotes, not enough become sickled to cause sickle-cell disease.

Heterozygotes for the sickle-cell allele are protected against the most severe effects of malaria, a disease caused by a parasite that infects red blood cells (see Figure 28.10). This partial protection occurs because the body destroys sickled red blood cells rapidly, killing the parasites they harbor (but not affecting parasites inside normal red blood cells). Protection against malaria is important in tropical regions where the disease is a major killer. In such regions, selection favors heterozygotes over homozygous dominant individuals, who are more vulnerable to the effects of malaria, and also over homozygous recessive individuals, who develop sickle-cell disease. The frequency of the sickle-cell allele in Africa is generally highest in areas where the malaria parasite is most common (Figure 23.17). In some populations, it accounts for 20% of the hemoglobin alleles in the gene pool, a very high frequency for such a harmful allele.

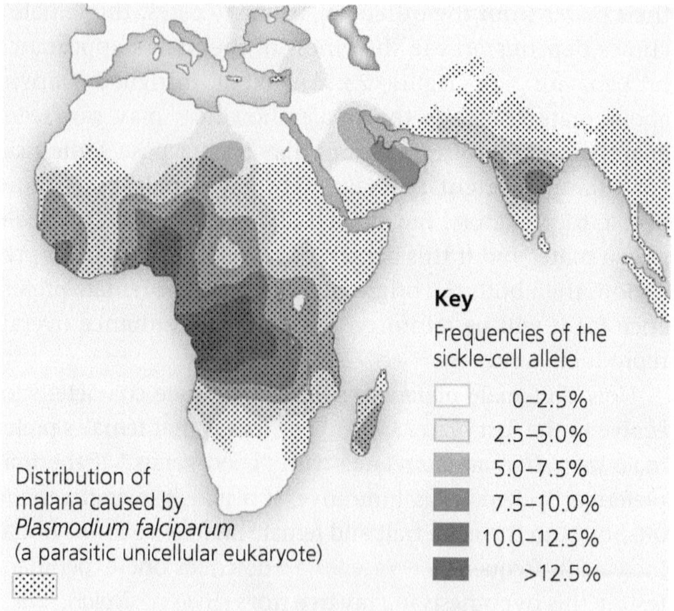

▲ **Figure 23.17 Mapping malaria and the sickle-cell allele.** The sickle-cell allele is most common in Africa, but it is not the only case of heterozygote advantage providing protection against malaria. Alleles at other loci (not shown on this map) are also favored by heterozygote advantage in populations near the Mediterranean Sea and in southeast Asia where malaria is widespread.

Frequency-Dependent Selection In **frequency-dependent selection**, the fitness of a phenotype depends on how common it is in the population. Consider the scale-eating fish (*Perissodus microlepis*) of Lake Tanganyika, in Africa. These fish attack other fish from behind, darting in to remove a few scales from the flank of their prey. Of interest here is a peculiar feature of the scale-eating fish: Some are "left-mouthed" and some are "right-mouthed." Simple Mendelian inheritance determines these phenotypes, with the right-mouthed allele being dominant to the left-mouthed allele. Because their mouth twists to the left, left-mouthed fish always attack their prey's right flank (Figure 23.18). (To see why, twist your lower jaw and lips to the left and imagine trying to take a bite from the left side of a fish, approaching it from behind.) Similarly, right-mouthed fish always attack from the left. Prey species guard against attack from whatever phenotype of scale-eating fish is most common in the lake. Thus, from year to year, selection favors whichever mouth phenotype is least common. As a result, the frequency of left- and right-mouthed fish oscillates over time, and balancing selection (due to frequency dependence) keeps the frequency of each phenotype close to 50%.

Why Natural Selection Cannot Fashion Perfect Organisms

Though natural selection leads to adaptation, nature abounds with examples of organisms that are less than ideally "engineered" for their lifestyles. There are several reasons why.

1. **Selection can act only on existing variations.** Natural selection favors only the fittest phenotypes among those currently in the population, which may not be the ideal traits. New advantageous alleles do not arise on demand.
2. **Evolution is limited by historical constraints.** Each species has a legacy of descent with modification from ancestral forms. Evolution does not scrap the

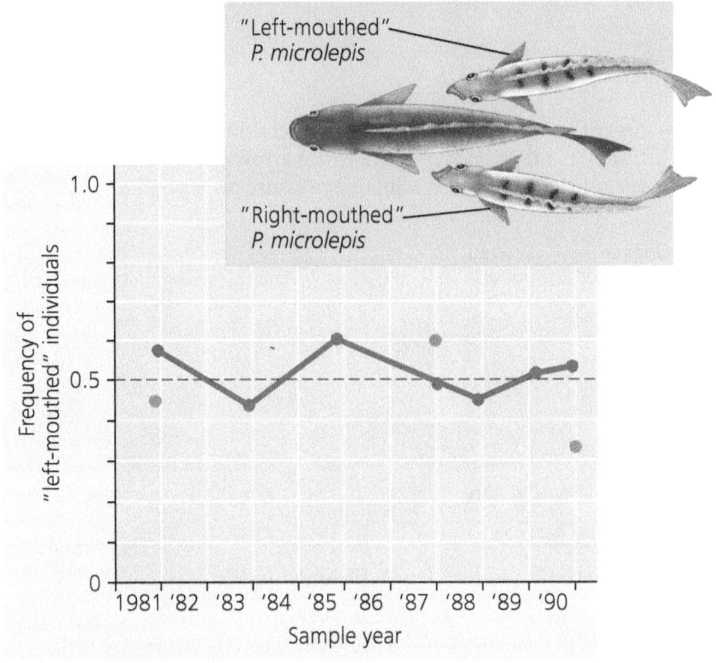

▲ **Figure 23.18 Frequency-dependent selection in scale-eating fish (*Perissodus microlepis*).** Michio Hori, of Kyoto University, Japan, noted that the frequency of left-mouthed individuals rises and falls in a regular manner. At each of three time periods when the phenotypes of breeding adults were assessed, adults that reproduced (represented by green dots) had the opposite phenotype of that which was most common in the population. Thus, it appeared that right-mouthed individuals were favored by selection when left-mouthed individuals were more common, and vice versa.

? *What did the researchers measure to determine which phenotype was favored by selection? Are any assumptions implied by this choice? Explain.*

ancestral anatomy and build each new complex structure from scratch; rather, evolution co-opts existing structures and adapts them to new situations. We could imagine that if a terrestrial animal were to adapt to an environment in which flight would be advantageous, it might be best just to grow an extra pair of limbs that would serve as wings. However, evolution does not work this way; instead, it operates on the traits an organism already has. Thus, in birds and bats, an existing pair of limbs took on new functions for flight as these organisms evolved from nonflying ancestors.

3. **Adaptations are often compromises.** Each organism must do many different things. A seal spends part of its time on rocks; it could probably walk better if it had legs instead of flippers, but then it would not swim nearly as well. We humans owe much of our versatility and athleticism to our prehensile hands and flexible limbs, but these also make us prone to sprains, torn ligaments, and dislocations: Structural reinforcement has been compromised for agility. Figure 23.19 depicts another example of evolutionary compromise.

▲ **Figure 23.19 Evolutionary compromise.** The loud call that enables a Túngara frog to attract mates also attracts more dangerous characters in the neighborhood—in this case, a bat about to seize a meal.

4. **Chance, natural selection, and the environment interact.** Chance events can affect the subsequent evolutionary history of populations. For instance, when a storm blows insects or birds hundreds of kilometers over an ocean to an island, the wind does not necessarily transport those individuals that are best suited to the new environment. Thus, not all alleles present in the founding population's gene pool are better suited to the new environment than the alleles that are "left behind." In addition, the environment at a particular location may change unpredictably from year to year, again limiting the extent to which adaptive evolution results in a close match between the organism and current environmental conditions.

With these four constraints, evolution does not tend to craft perfect organisms. Natural selection operates on a "better than" basis. We can, in fact, see evidence for evolution in the many imperfections of the organisms it produces.

CONCEPT CHECK 23.4

1. What is the relative fitness of a sterile mule? Explain.
2. Explain why natural selection is the only evolutionary mechanism that consistently leads to adaptive evolution.
3. WHAT IF? Consider a population in which heterozygotes at a certain locus have an extreme phenotype (such as being larger than homozygotes) that confers a selective advantage. Does such a situation represent directional, disruptive, or stabilizing selection? Explain your answer.
4. WHAT IF? Would individuals who are heterozygous for the sickle-cell allele be selected for or against in a region free from malaria? Explain.

For suggested answers, see Appendix A.

23 CHAPTER REVIEW

SUMMARY OF KEY CONCEPTS

CONCEPT 23.1

Genetic variation makes evolution possible (pp. 469–473)

- **Genetic variation** refers to genetic differences among individuals within a population.
- The nucleotide differences that provide the basis of genetic variation arise by mutation and other processes that produce new alleles and new genes.
- New genetic variants are produced rapidly in organisms with short generation times. In sexually reproducing organisms, most of the genetic differences among individuals result from crossing over, the independent assortment of chromosomes, and fertilization.

? *Why do biologists estimate gene variability and nucleotide variability, and what do these estimates represent?*

CONCEPT 23.2

The Hardy-Weinberg equation can be used to test whether a population is evolving (pp. 473–476)

- A **population**, a localized group of organisms belonging to one species, is united by its **gene pool**, the aggregate of all the alleles in the population.
- The **Hardy-Weinberg principle** states that the allele and genotype frequencies of a population will remain constant if the population is large, mating is random, mutation is negligible, there is no gene flow, and there is no natural selection. For such a population, if p and q represent the frequencies of the only two possible alleles at a particular locus, then p^2 is the frequency of one kind of homozygote, q^2 is the frequency of the other kind of homozygote, and $2pq$ is the frequency of the heterozygous genotype.

? *Is it circular reasoning to calculate* p *and* q *from observed genotype frequencies and then use those values of* p *and* q *to test if the population is in Hardy-Weinberg equilibrium? Explain your answer. (Hint: Consider a specific case, such as a population with 195 individuals of genotype* AA, *10 of genotype* Aa, *and 195 of genotype* aa.)

CONCEPT 23.3

Natural selection, genetic drift, and gene flow can alter allele frequencies in a population (pp. 476–480)

- In natural selection, individuals that have certain inherited traits tend to survive and reproduce at higher rates than other individuals *because of* those traits.
- In **genetic drift**, chance fluctuations in allele frequencies over generations tend to reduce genetic variation.
- **Gene flow**, the transfer of alleles between populations, tends to reduce genetic differences between populations over time.

? *Would two small, geographically isolated populations in very different environments be likely to evolve in similar ways? Explain.*

CONCEPT 23.4

Natural selection is the only mechanism that consistently causes adaptive evolution (pp. 480–485)

- One organism has greater **relative fitness** than a second organism if it leaves more fertile descendants than the second organism. The modes of natural selection differ in how selection acts on phenotype (the white arrows in the summary diagram below represent selective pressure on a population).

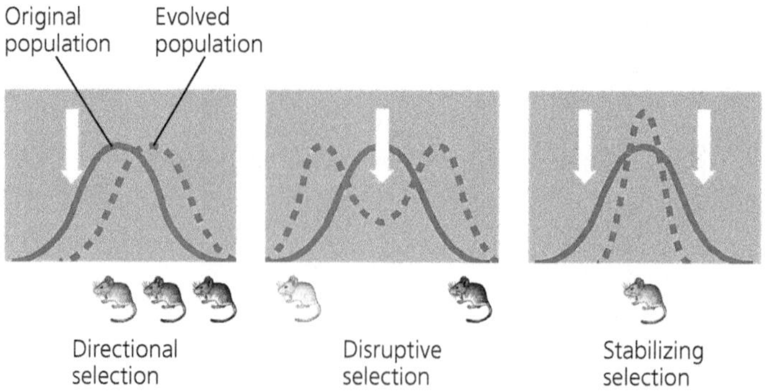

- Unlike genetic drift and gene flow, natural selection consistently increases the frequencies of alleles that enhance survival and reproduction, thus improving the match between organisms and their environment.
- **Sexual selection** influences evolutionary change in secondary sex characteristics that can give individuals advantages in mating.
- Despite the winnowing effects of selection, populations have considerable genetic variation. Some of this variation represents **neutral variation**; additional variation can be maintained by diploidy and balancing selection.
- There are constraints to evolution: Natural selection can act only on available variation; structures result from modified ancestral anatomy; adaptations are often compromises; and chance, natural selection, and the environment interact.

? *How might secondary sex characteristics differ between males and females in a species in which females compete for mates?*

TEST YOUR UNDERSTANDING

LEVEL 1: KNOWLEDGE/COMPREHENSION

1. Natural selection changes allele frequencies because some ______ survive and reproduce more successfully than others.
   a. alleles
   b. loci
   c. gene pools
   d. species
   e. individuals

2. No two people are genetically identical, except for identical twins. The main source of genetic variation among human individuals is
   a. new mutations that occurred in the preceding generation.
   b. genetic drift due to the small size of the population.
   c. the reshuffling of alleles in sexual reproduction.
   d. geographic variation within the population.
   e. environmental effects.

3. Sparrows with average-sized wings survive severe storms better than those with longer or shorter wings, illustrating
   a. the bottleneck effect.
   b. disruptive selection.
   c. frequency-dependent selection.
   d. neutral variation.
   e. stabilizing selection.

LEVEL 2: APPLICATION/ANALYSIS

4. If the nucleotide variability of a locus equals 0%, what is the gene variability and number of alleles at that locus?
   a. gene variability = 0%; number of alleles = 0
   b. gene variability = 0%; number of alleles = 1
   c. gene variability = 0%; number of alleles = 2
   d. gene variability > 0%; number of alleles = 2
   e. Without more information, gene variability and number of alleles cannot be determined.

5. There are 40 individuals in population 1, all with genotype *A1A1*, and there are 25 individuals in population 2, all with genotype *A2A2*. Assume that these populations are located far from each other and that their environmental conditions are very similar. Based on the information given here, the observed genetic variation is most likely an example of
   a. genetic drift.
   b. gene flow.
   c. disruptive selection.
   d. discrete variation.
   e. directional selection.

6. A fruit fly population has a gene with two alleles, *A1* and *A2*. Tests show that 70% of the gametes produced in the population contain the *A1* allele. If the population is in Hardy-Weinberg equilibrium, what proportion of the flies carry both *A1* and *A2*?
   a. 0.7 b. 0.49 c. 0.21 d. 0.42 e. 0.09

LEVEL 3: SYNTHESIS/EVALUATION

7. **EVOLUTION CONNECTION**
   How is the process of evolution revealed by the imperfections of living organisms?

8. **SCIENTIFIC INQUIRY**
   DRAW IT Richard Koehn, of the State University of New York, Stony Brook, and Thomas Hilbish, of the University of South Carolina, studied genetic variation in the marine mussel *Mytilus edulis* around Long Island, New York. They measured the frequency of a particular allele (*lap*^{94}) for an enzyme involved in regulating the mussel's internal saltwater balance. The researchers presented their data as a series of pie charts linked to sampling sites within Long Island Sound, where the salinity is highly variable, and along the coast of the open ocean, where salinity is constant:

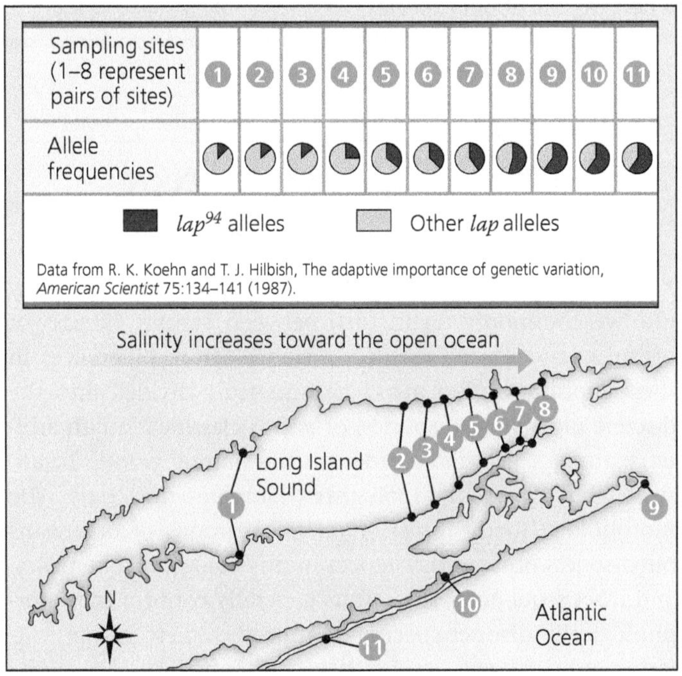

(*Question 8, continued*)
Create a data table for the 11 sampling sites by estimating the frequency of *lap*^{94} from the pie charts. (*Hint*: Think of each pie chart as a clock face to help you estimate the proportion of the shaded area.) Then graph the frequencies for sites 1–8 to show how the frequency of this allele changes with increasing salinity in Long Island Sound (from southwest to northeast). How do the data from sites 9–11 compare with the data from the sites within the Sound?

Construct a hypothesis that explains the patterns you observe in the data and that accounts for the following observations: (1) the *lap*^{94} allele helps mussels maintain osmotic balance in water with a high salt concentration but is costly to use in less salty water; and (2) mussels produce larvae that can disperse long distances before they settle on rocks and grow into adults.

9. **WRITE ABOUT A THEME**
   Emergent Properties Heterozygotes at the sickle-cell locus produce both normal and abnormal (sickle-cell) hemoglobin (see Concept 14.4). When hemoglobin molecules are packed into a heterozygote's red blood cells, some cells receive relatively large quantities of abnormal hemoglobin, making these cells prone to sickling. In a short essay (approximately 100–150 words), explain how these molecular and cellular events lead to emergent properties at the individual and population levels of biological organization.

For selected answers, see Appendix A.

24

The Origin of Species

▲ **Figure 24.1 How did this flightless bird come to live on the isolated Galápagos Islands?**

EVOLUTION

KEY CONCEPTS

24.1 The biological species concept emphasizes reproductive isolation

24.2 Speciation can take place with or without geographic separation

24.3 Hybrid zones reveal factors that cause reproductive isolation

24.4 Speciation can occur rapidly or slowly and can result from changes in few or many genes

OVERVIEW

That "Mystery of Mysteries"

Darwin came to the Galápagos Islands eager to explore landforms newly emerged from the sea. He noted that these volcanic islands, despite their geologic youth, were teeming with plants and animals found nowhere else in the world (Figure 24.1). Later he realized that these species, like the islands, were relatively new. He wrote in his diary: "Both in space and time, we seem to be brought somewhat near to that great fact—that mystery of mysteries—the first appearance of new beings on this Earth."

The "mystery of mysteries" that captivated Darwin is **speciation**, the process by which one species splits into two or more species. Speciation fascinated Darwin (and many biologists since) because it is responsible for the tremendous diversity of life, repeatedly yielding new species that differ from existing ones. Speciation explains not only differences between species, but also similarities between them (the unity of life). When one species splits into two, the species that result share many characteristics because they are descended from this common ancestral species. For example, DNA similarities indicate that the flightless cormorant (*Phalacrocorax harrisi*) in Figure 24.1 is closely related to flying cormorants found in the Americas. This suggests that the flightless cormorant may have originated from an ancestral cormorant species that migrated from the mainland to the Galápagos.

Speciation also forms a conceptual bridge between **microevolution**, changes over time in allele frequencies in a population, and **macroevolution**, the broad pattern of evolution above the species level. An example of macroevolutionary change is the origin of new groups of organisms, such as mammals or flowering plants, through a series of speciation events. We examined microevolutionary mechanisms (mutation, natural selection, genetic drift, and gene flow) in Chapter 23, and we'll turn to macroevolution in Chapter 25. In this chapter, we will explore the "bridge"—the mechanisms by which new species originate from existing ones. First, however, we need to establish what we actually mean when we talk about "species."

CONCEPT 24.1

The biological species concept emphasizes reproductive isolation

The word *species* is Latin for "kind" or "appearance." In daily life, we commonly distinguish between various "kinds" of organisms—dogs and cats, for instance—from differences in their appearance. But are organisms truly divided into the discrete units we call species, or is this classification an arbitrary attempt to impose order on the natural world? To answer this question, biologists compare not only the morphology (body form) of different groups of organisms but also less obvious differences in physiology, biochemistry, and DNA sequences. The results generally confirm that morphologically distinct species are indeed discrete groups, differing in many ways besides their body forms.

The Biological Species Concept

The primary definition of species used in this textbook is the **biological species concept**. According to this concept, a **species** is a group of populations whose members have the potential to interbreed in nature and produce viable, fertile offspring—but do not produce viable, fertile offspring with members of other such groups (Figure 24.2). Thus, the members of a biological species are united by being reproductively compatible, at least potentially. All human beings, for example, belong to the same species. A businesswoman in Manhattan may be unlikely to meet a dairy farmer in Mongolia, but if the two should happen to meet and mate, they could have viable babies that develop into fertile adults. In contrast, humans and chimpanzees remain distinct biological species even where they share territory, because many factors keep them from interbreeding and producing fertile offspring.

(a) Similarity between different species. The eastern meadowlark (*Sturnella magna*, left) and the western meadowlark (*Sturnella neglecta*, right) have similar body shapes and colorations. Nevertheless, they are distinct biological species because their songs and other behaviors are different enough to prevent interbreeding should they meet in the wild.

(b) Diversity within a species. As diverse as we may be in appearance, all humans belong to a single biological species (*Homo sapiens*), defined by our capacity to interbreed successfully.

▲ Figure 24.2 **The biological species concept is based on the potential to interbreed rather than on physical similarity.**

What holds the gene pool of a species together, causing its members to resemble each other more than they resemble other species? To answer this question, we need to return to the evolutionary mechanism called *gene flow*, the transfer of alleles between populations (see Chapter 23). Typically, gene flow occurs between the different populations of a species. This ongoing exchange of alleles tends to hold the populations together genetically. As we'll explore in the following sections, the absence of gene flow plays a key role in the formation of new species, as well as in keeping them apart once their potential to interbreed has been reduced.

Reproductive Isolation

Because biological species are defined in terms of reproductive compatibility, the formation of a new species hinges on **reproductive isolation**—the existence of biological factors (barriers) that impede members of two species from interbreeding and producing viable, fertile offspring. Such barriers block gene flow between the species and limit the formation of **hybrids**, offspring that result from an interspecific mating. Although a single barrier may not prevent all gene flow, a combination of several barriers can effectively isolate a species' gene pool.

Clearly, a fly cannot mate with a frog or a fern, but the reproductive barriers between more closely related species are not so obvious. These barriers can be classified according to whether they contribute to reproductive isolation before or after fertilization. **Prezygotic barriers** ("before the zygote") block fertilization from occurring. Such barriers typically act in one of three ways: by impeding members of different species from attempting to mate, by preventing an attempted mating from being completed successfully, or by hindering fertilization if mating is completed successfully. If a sperm cell from one species overcomes prezygotic barriers and fertilizes an ovum from another species, a variety of **postzygotic barriers** ("after the zygote") may contribute to reproductive isolation after the hybrid zygote is formed. For example, developmental errors may reduce survival among hybrid embryos. Or problems after birth may cause hybrids to be infertile or may decrease their chance of surviving long enough to reproduce. Figure 24.3, on the next two pages, describes prezygotic and postzygotic barriers in more detail.

▼ Figure 24.3

Exploring Reproductive Barriers

Prezygotic barriers impede mating or hinder fertilization if mating does occur

Habitat Isolation

Two species that occupy different habitats within the same area may encounter each other rarely, if at all, even though they are not isolated by obvious physical barriers, such as mountain ranges.

Example: Two species of garter snakes in the genus *Thamnophis* occur in the same geographic areas, but one lives mainly in water (a) while the other is primarily terrestrial (b).

Temporal Isolation

Species that breed during different times of the day, different seasons, or different years cannot mix their gametes.

Example: In North America, the geographic ranges of the western spotted skunk (*Spilogale gracilis*) (c) and the eastern spotted skunk (*Spilogale putorius*) (d) overlap, but *S. gracilis* mates in late summer and *S. putorius* mates in late winter.

Behavioral Isolation

Courtship rituals that attract mates and other behaviors unique to a species are effective reproductive barriers, even between closely related species. Such behavioral rituals enable *mate recognition*—a way to identify potential mates of the same species.

Example: Blue-footed boobies, inhabitants of the Galápagos, mate only after a courtship display unique to their species. Part of the "script" calls for the male to high-step (e), a behavior that calls the female's attention to his bright blue feet.

Mechanical Isolation

Mating is attempted, but morphological differences prevent its successful completion.

Example: The shells of two species of snails in the genus *Bradybaena* spiral in different directions: Moving inward to the center, one spirals in a counterclockwise direction (f, left), the other in a clockwise direction (f, right). As a result, the snails' genital openings (indicated by arrows) are not aligned, and mating cannot be completed.

Postzygotic barriers prevent a hybrid zygote from developing into a viable, fertile adult

Gametic Isolation

Sperm of one species may not be able to fertilize the eggs of another species. For instance, sperm may not be able to survive in the reproductive tract of females of the other species, or biochemical mechanisms may prevent the sperm from penetrating the membrane surrounding the other species' eggs.

Example: Gametic isolation separates certain closely related species of aquatic animals, such as sea urchins (g). Sea urchins release their sperm and eggs into the surrounding water, where they fuse and form zygotes. It is difficult for gametes of different species, such as the red and purple urchins shown here, to fuse because proteins on the surfaces of the eggs and sperm bind very poorly to each other.

Reduced Hybrid Viability

The genes of different parent species may interact in ways that impair the hybrid's development or survival in its environment.

Example: Some salamander subspecies of the genus *Ensatina* live in the same regions and habitats, where they may occasionally hybridize. But most of the hybrids do not complete development, and those that do are frail (h).

Reduced Hybrid Fertility

Even if hybrids are vigorous, they may be sterile. If the chromosomes of the two parent species differ in number or structure, meiosis in the hybrids may fail to produce normal gametes. Since the infertile hybrids cannot produce offspring when they mate with either parent species, genes cannot flow freely between the species.

Example: The hybrid offspring of a male donkey (i) and a female horse (j) is a mule (k), which is robust but sterile. A "hinny" (not shown), the offspring of a female donkey and a male horse, is also sterile.

Hybrid Breakdown

Some first-generation hybrids are viable and fertile, but when they mate with one another or with either parent species, offspring of the next generation are feeble or sterile.

Example: Strains of cultivated rice have accumulated different mutant recessive alleles at two loci in the course of their divergence from a common ancestor. Hybrids between them are vigorous and fertile (l, left and right), but plants in the next generation that carry too many of these recessive alleles are small and sterile (l, center). Although these rice strains are not yet considered different species, they have begun to be separated by postzygotic barriers.

Limitations of the Biological Species Concept

One strength of the biological species concept is that it directs our attention to a way by which speciation can occur: by the evolution of reproductive isolation. However, the number of species to which this concept can be usefully applied is limited. There is, for example, no way to evaluate the reproductive isolation of fossils. The biological species concept also does not apply to organisms that reproduce asexually all or most of the time, such as prokaryotes. (Many prokaryotes do transfer genes among themselves, as we will discuss in Chapter 27, but this is not part of their reproductive process.) Furthermore, in the biological species concept, species are designated by the *absence* of gene flow. But there are many pairs of species that are morphologically and ecologically distinct, and yet gene flow occurs between them. An example is the grizzly bear (*Ursus arctos*) and polar bear (*Ursus maritimus*), whose hybrid offspring have been dubbed "grolar bears" (**Figure 24.4**). As we'll discuss, natural selection can cause such species to remain distinct even though some gene flow occurs between them. This observation has led some researchers to argue that the biological species concept overemphasizes gene flow and downplays the role of natural selection. Because of the limitations to the biological species concept, alternative species concepts are useful in certain situations.

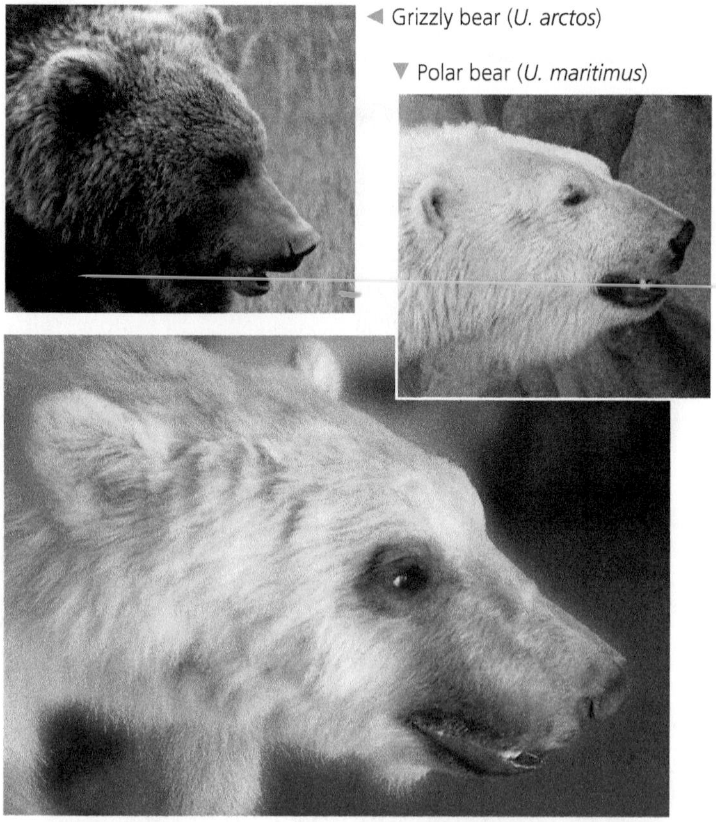

◄ Grizzly bear (*U. arctos*)

▼ Polar bear (*U. maritimus*)

▲ Hybrid "grolar bear"

▲ **Figure 24.4 Hybridization between two species of bears in the genus *Ursus*.**

Other Definitions of Species

While the biological species concept emphasizes the *separateness* of species from one another due to reproductive barriers, several other definitions emphasize the *unity within* a species. For example, the **morphological species concept** characterizes a species by body shape and other structural features. The morphological species concept can be applied to asexual and sexual organisms, and it can be useful even without information on the extent of gene flow. In practice, this is how scientists distinguish most species. One disadvantage, however, is that this definition relies on subjective criteria; researchers may disagree on which structural features distinguish a species.

The **ecological species concept** views a species in terms of its ecological niche, the sum of how members of the species interact with the nonliving and living parts of their environment (see Chapter 54). For example, two species of salamanders might be similar in appearance but differ in the foods they eat or in their ability to tolerate dry conditions. Unlike the biological species concept, the ecological species concept can accommodate asexual as well as sexual species. It also emphasizes the role of disruptive natural selection as organisms adapt to different environmental conditions.

The **phylogenetic species concept** defines a species as the smallest group of individuals that share a common ancestor, forming one branch on the tree of life. Biologists trace the phylogenetic history of a species by comparing its characteristics, such as morphology or molecular sequences, with those of other organisms. Such analyses can distinguish groups of individuals that are sufficiently different to be considered separate species. Of course, the difficulty with this species concept is determining the degree of difference required to indicate separate species.

In addition to those discussed here, more than 20 other species definitions have been proposed. The usefulness of each definition depends on the situation and the research questions being asked. For our purposes of studying how species originate, the biological species concept, with its focus on reproductive barriers, is particularly helpful.

CONCEPT CHECK 24.1

1. (a) Which species concept(s) could you apply to both asexual and sexual species? (b) Which would be most useful for identifying species in the field? Explain.
2. **WHAT IF?** Suppose you are studying two bird species that live in a forest and are not known to interbreed. One species feeds and mates in the treetops and the other on the ground. But in captivity, the birds can interbreed and produce viable, fertile offspring. What type of reproductive barrier most likely keeps these species separate in nature? Explain.

For suggested answers, see Appendix A.

CONCEPT 24.2

Speciation can take place with or without geographic separation

Now that we have a clearer sense of what constitutes a unique species, let's return to our discussion of the process by which such species arise from existing species. Speciation can occur in two main ways, depending on how gene flow is interrupted between populations of the existing species (Figure 24.5).

Allopatric ("Other Country") Speciation

In **allopatric speciation** (from the Greek *allos*, other, and *patra*, homeland), gene flow is interrupted when a population is divided into geographically isolated subpopulations. For example, the water level in a lake may subside, resulting in two or more smaller lakes that are now home to separated populations (see Figure 24.5a). Or a river may change course and divide a population of animals that cannot cross it. Allopatric speciation can also occur without geologic remodeling, such as when individuals colonize a remote area and their descendants become geographically isolated from the parent population. The flightless cormorant shown in Figure 24.1 most likely originated in this way from an ancestral flying species that reached the Galápagos Islands.

The Process of Allopatric Speciation

How formidable must a geographic barrier be to promote allopatric speciation? The answer depends on the ability of the organisms to move about. Birds, mountain lions, and coyotes can cross rivers and canyons—as can the windblown pollen of pine trees and the seeds of many flowering plants. In contrast, small rodents may find a wide river or deep canyon a formidable barrier (Figure 24.6).

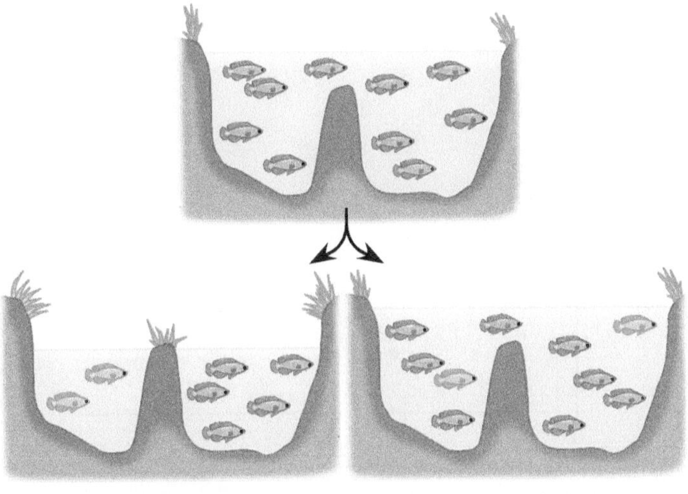

(a) **Allopatric speciation.** A population forms a new species while geographically isolated from its parent population.

(b) **Sympatric speciation.** A subset of a population forms a new species without geographic separation.

▲ Figure 24.5 **Two main modes of speciation.**

▲ Figure 24.6 **Allopatric speciation of antelope squirrels on opposite rims of the Grand Canyon.** Harris's antelope squirrel (*Ammospermophilus harrisii*) inhabits the canyon's south rim (left). Just a few kilometers away on the north rim (right) lives the closely related white-tailed antelope squirrel (*Ammospermophilus leucurus*). Birds and other organisms that can disperse easily across the canyon have not diverged into different species on the two rims.

Once geographic separation has occurred, the separated gene pools may diverge. Different mutations arise, and natural selection and genetic drift may alter allele frequencies in different ways in the separated populations. Reproductive isolation may then arise as a by-product of selection or drift having caused the populations to diverge genetically. For example, on Andros Island, in the Bahamas, populations of the mosquitofish *Gambusia hubbsi* colonized a series of ponds that later became isolated from one another. Genetic analyses indicate that little or no gene flow currently occurs between the ponds. The environments of these ponds are very similar except that some contain many predatory fishes, while others do not. In the "high-predation" ponds, selection has favored the evolution of a mosquitofish body shape that enables rapid bursts of speed (Figure 24.7). In ponds lacking

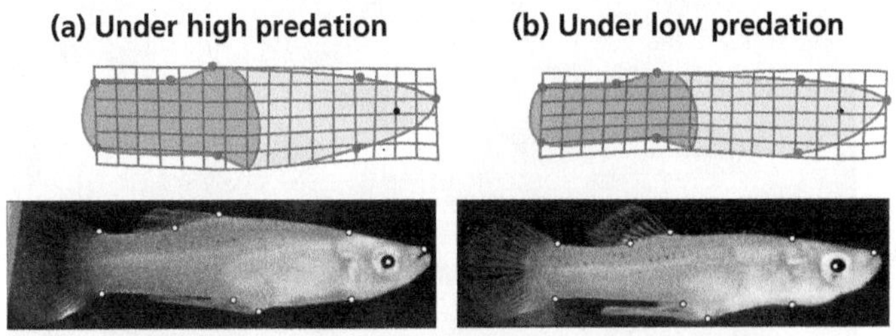

In ponds with predatory fishes, the head region of the mosquitofish is streamlined and the tail region is powerful, enabling rapid bursts of speed.

In ponds without predatory fishes, mosquitofish have a different body shape that favors long, steady swimming.

▲ Figure 24.7 **Reproductive isolation as a by-product of selection.** After bringing together mosquitofish from different ponds, researchers concluded that selection for traits that enable mosquitofish in high-predation ponds to avoid predators has isolated them reproductively from mosquitofish in low-predation ponds.

predatory fishes, selection has favored a different body shape, one that improves the ability to swim for long periods of time. How have these different selective pressures affected the evolution of reproductive barriers? Researchers answered this question by bringing together mosquitofish from the two types of ponds. They found that female mosquitofish prefer to mate with males whose body shape is similar to their own. This preference establishes a barrier to reproduction between mosquitofish from ponds with predators and those from ponds without predators. Thus, as a by-product of selection for avoiding predators, reproductive barriers have started to form in these allopatric populations.

Evidence of Allopatric Speciation

Many studies provide evidence that speciation can occur in allopatric populations. Consider the 30 species of snapping shrimp in the genus *Alpheus* that live off the Isthmus of Panama, the land bridge that connects South and North America (Figure 24.8). Fifteen of these species live on the Atlantic side of the isthmus, while the other 15 live on the Pacific side. Before the isthmus formed, gene flow could occur between the Atlantic and Pacific populations of snapping shrimp. Did the species on different sides of the isthmus originate by allopatric speciation? Morphological and genetic data group these shrimp into 15 pairs of *sibling species*, pairs whose member species are each other's closest relative. In each of these 15 pairs, one of the sibling species lives on the Atlantic side of the isthmus, while the other lives on the Pacific side, strongly suggesting that the two species arose as a consequence of geographic separation. Furthermore, genetic analyses indicate that the *Alpheus* species originated from 9 to 3 million years ago, with the sibling species that live in the deepest water diverging first. These divergence times are consistent with geologic evidence that the isthmus formed gradually, starting 10 million years ago, and closing completely about 3 million years ago.

The importance of allopatric speciation is also suggested by the fact that regions that are isolated or highly subdivided by barriers typically have more species than do otherwise similar regions that lack such features. For example, many unique plants and animals are found on the geographically isolated Hawaiian Islands (we'll return to the origin of Hawaiian species in Chapter 25). Similarly, unusually high numbers of butterfly species are found in South American regions that are subdivided by many rivers.

Laboratory and field tests also provide evidence that reproductive isolation between two populations generally increases as the distance between them increases. In a study of dusky salamanders (*Desmognathus ochrophaeus*), biologists brought individuals from different populations into the laboratory and tested their ability to produce viable, fertile offspring (Figure 24.9). The researchers observed little reproductive isolation in salamanders from neighboring populations. In contrast, salamanders from widely separated populations often failed to reproduce, a result consistent with allopatric speciation. In other studies, researchers have tested whether intrinsic reproductive barriers develop when populations are isolated

▼ **Figure 24.8 Allopatric speciation in snapping shrimp (*Alpheus*).** The shrimp pictured are just 2 of the 15 pairs of sibling species that arose as populations were divided by the formation of the Isthmus of Panama. The color-coded type indicates the sibling species.

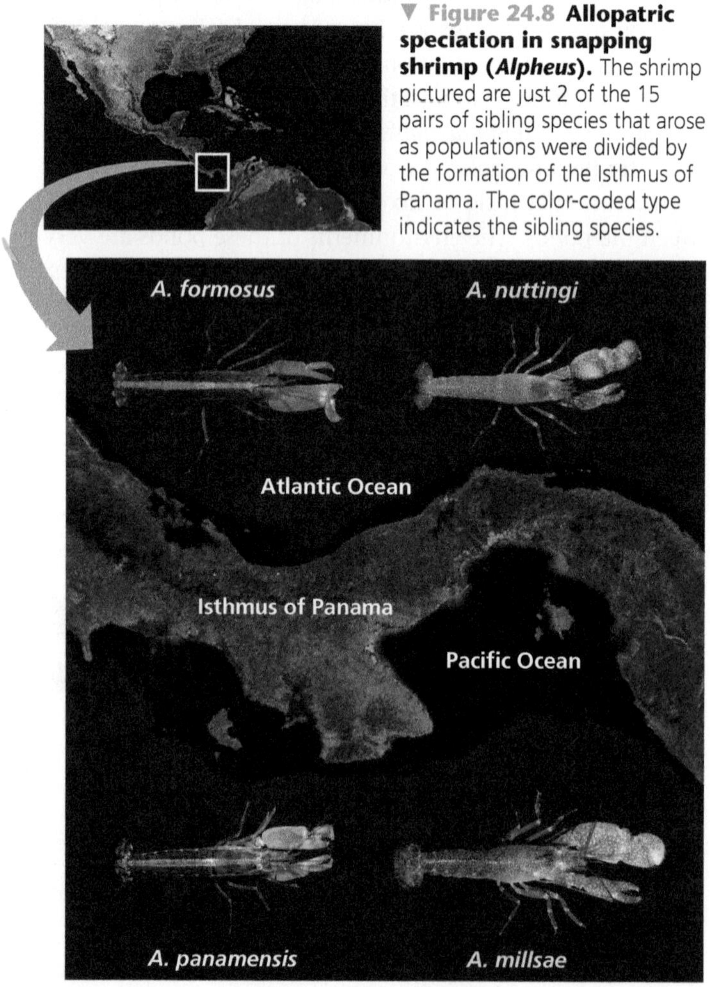

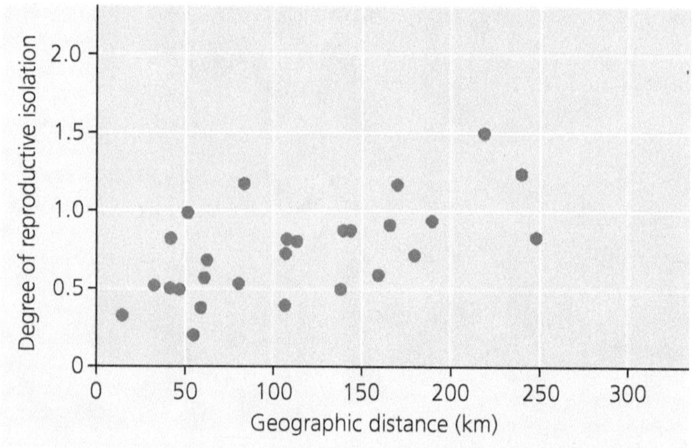

▲ **Figure 24.9 Reproductive isolation increases with distance in populations of dusky salamanders.** The degree of reproductive isolation is represented here by an index ranging from 0 (no isolation) to 2 (complete isolation).

▼ **Figure 24.10** **INQUIRY**

Can divergence of allopatric populations lead to reproductive isolation?

EXPERIMENT Diane Dodd, then at Yale University, divided a laboratory population of the fruit fly *Drosophila pseudoobscura*, raising some flies on a starch medium and others on a maltose medium. After one year (about 40 generations), natural selection resulted in divergent evolution: Populations raised on starch digested starch more efficiently, while those raised on maltose digested maltose more efficiently. Dodd then put flies from the same or different populations in mating cages and measured mating frequencies. All flies used in the mating preference tests were reared for one generation on a standard cornmeal medium.

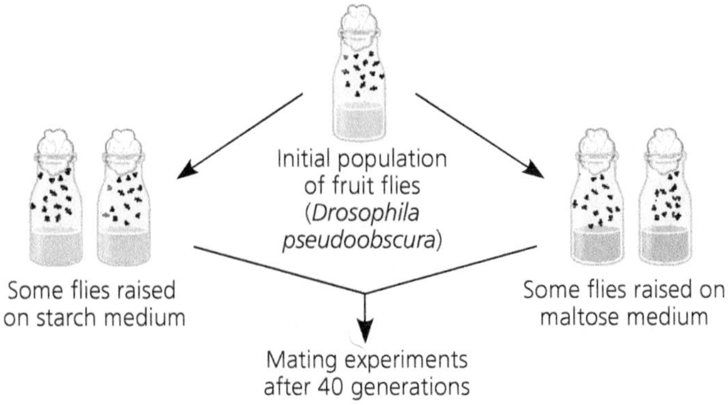

RESULTS Mating patterns among populations of flies raised on different media are shown below. When flies from "starch populations" were mixed with flies from "maltose populations," the flies tended to mate with like partners. But in the control group (shown on the right), flies from different populations adapted to starch were about as likely to mate with each other as with flies from their own population; similar results were obtained for control groups adapted to maltose.

		Female	
		Starch	Maltose
Male	Starch	22	9
	Maltose	8	20

Number of matings in experimental group

		Female	
		Starch population 1	Starch population 2
Male	Starch population 1	18	15
	Starch population 2	12	15

Number of matings in control group

CONCLUSION In the experimental group, the strong preference of "starch flies" and "maltose flies" to mate with like-adapted flies indicates that a reproductive barrier was forming between these fly populations. Although this reproductive barrier was not absolute (some mating between starch flies and maltose flies did occur), after 40 generations it appeared to be under way. This barrier may have been caused by differences in courtship behavior that arose as an incidental by-product of differing selective pressures as these allopatric populations adapted to different sources of food.

SOURCE D. M. B. Dodd, Reproductive isolation as a consequence of adaptive divergence in *Drosophila pseudoobscura*, *Evolution* 43:1308–1311 (1989).

WHAT IF? Why were all flies used in the mating preference tests reared on a standard medium (rather than on a starch or maltose medium)?

experimentally and subjected to different environmental conditions. In such cases, too, the results provide strong support for allopatric speciation (Figure 24.10).

We need to emphasize here that although geographic isolation prevents interbreeding between allopatric populations, physical separation is not a biological barrier to reproduction. Biological reproductive barriers such as those described in Figure 24.3 are intrinsic to the organisms themselves. Hence, it is biological barriers that can prevent interbreeding when members of different populations come into contact with one another.

Sympatric ("Same Country") Speciation

In **sympatric speciation** (from the Greek *syn*, together), speciation occurs in populations that live in the same geographic area. How can reproductive barriers form between sympatric populations while their members remain in contact with each other? Although such contact (and the ongoing gene flow that results) makes sympatric speciation less common than allopatric speciation, sympatric speciation can occur if gene flow is reduced by such factors as polyploidy, habitat differentiation, and sexual selection. (Note that these factors can also promote allopatric speciation.)

Polyploidy

A species may originate from an accident during cell division that results in extra sets of chromosomes, a condition called **polyploidy**. Polyploid speciation occasionally occurs in animals; for example, the gray tree frog *Hyla versicolor* (see Figure 23.16) is thought to have originated in this way. However, polyploidy is far more common in plants. Botanists estimate that more than 80% of the plant species alive today are descended from ancestors that formed by polyploid speciation.

Two distinct forms of polyploidy have been observed in plant (and a few animal) populations. An **autopolyploid** (from the Greek *autos*, self) is an individual that has more than two chromosome sets that are all derived from a single species. In plants, for example, a failure of cell division could double a cell's chromosome number from the diploid number ($2n$) to a tetraploid number ($4n$).

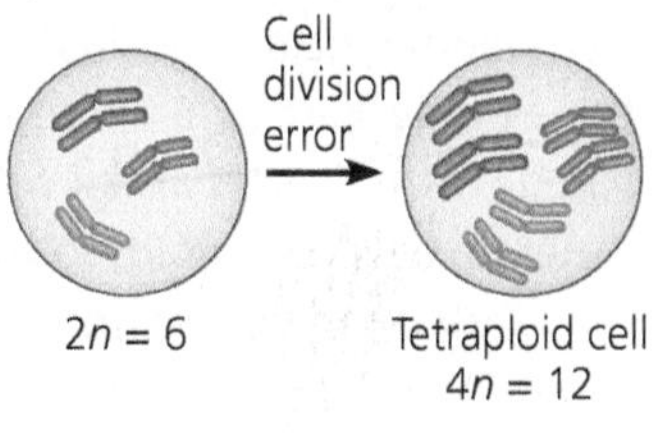

A tetraploid can produce fertile tetraploid offspring by self-pollinating or by mating with other tetraploids. In addition, the tetraploids are reproductively isolated from diploid plants of the original population, because the

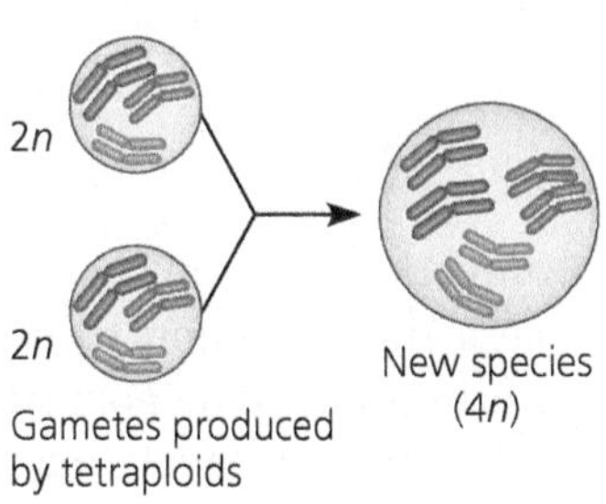

triploid (3*n*) offspring of such unions have reduced fertility. Thus, in just one generation, autopolyploidy can generate reproductive isolation without any geographic separation.

A second form of polyploidy can occur when two different species interbreed and produce hybrid offspring. Most such hybrids are sterile because the set of chromosomes from one species cannot pair during meiosis with the set of chromosomes from the other species. However, an infertile hybrid may be able to propagate itself asexually (as many plants can do). In subsequent generations, various mechanisms can change a sterile hybrid into a fertile polyploid called an **allopolyploid** (Figure 24.11). The allopolyploids are fertile when mating with each other but cannot interbreed with either parent species; thus, they represent a new biological species.

Although polyploid speciation is relatively rare, even in plants, scientists have documented that at least five new plant species have originated in this way since 1850. One of these examples involves the origin of a new species of goatsbeard plant (genus *Tragopogon*) in the Pacific Northwest. *Tragopogon* first arrived in the region when humans introduced three European species in the early 1900s. These three species are now common weeds in abandoned parking lots and other urban sites. In 1950, a new *Tragopogon* species was discovered near the Idaho-Washington border, a region where all three European species also were found. Genetic analyses revealed that this new species, *Tragopogon miscellus*, is a tetraploid hybrid of two of the European species. Although the *T. miscellus* population grows mainly by reproduction of its own members, additional episodes of hybridization between the parent species continue to add new members to the *T. miscellus* population—just one of many examples in which scientists have observed speciation in progress.

Many important agricultural crops—such as oats, cotton, potatoes, tobacco, and wheat—are polyploids. The wheat used for bread, *Triticum aestivum*, is an allohexaploid (six sets of chromosomes, two sets from each of three different species). The first of the polyploidy events that eventually led to modern wheat probably occurred about 8,000 years ago in the Middle East as a spontaneous hybrid of an early cultivated wheat species and a wild grass. Today, plant geneticists generate new polyploids in the laboratory by using chemicals that induce meiotic and mitotic errors. By harnessing the evolutionary process, researchers can produce new hybrid species with desired qualities, such as a hybrid that combines the high yield of wheat with the hardiness of rye.

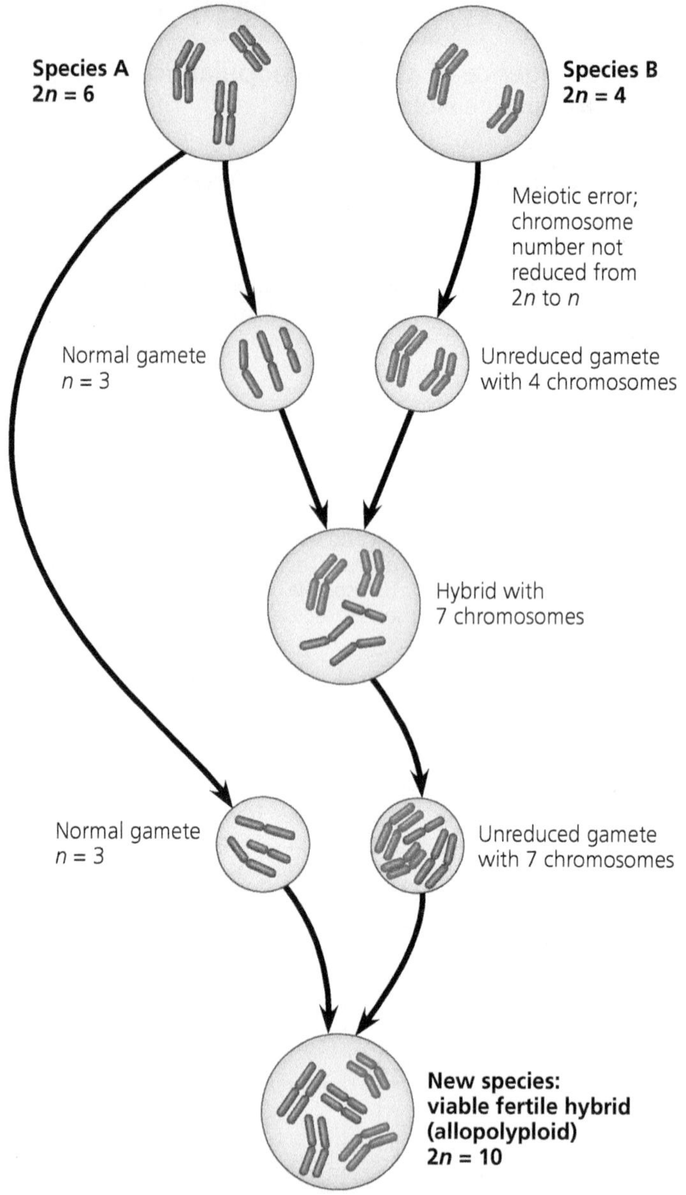

▲ Figure 24.11 **One mechanism for allopolyploid speciation in plants.** Most hybrids are sterile because their chromosomes are not homologous and cannot pair during meiosis. However, such a hybrid may be able to reproduce asexually. This diagram traces one mechanism that can produce fertile hybrids (allopolyploids) as new species. The new species has a diploid chromosome number equal to the sum of the diploid chromosome numbers of the two parent species.

Habitat Differentiation

Sympatric speciation can also occur when genetic factors enable a subpopulation to exploit a habitat or resource not used by the parent population. Such is the case with the North American apple maggot fly (*Rhagoletis pomonella*), a pest of apples. The fly's original habitat was the native hawthorn tree, but about 200 years ago, some populations colonized apple trees that had been introduced by European settlers. As apples mature more quickly than hawthorn fruit, natural selection has favored apple-feeding flies with rapid development. These apple-feeding populations now show temporal isolation from the hawthorn-feeding *R. pomonella*, providing a prezygotic restriction to gene flow between the two populations. Researchers also have identified alleles that benefit the flies that use one host plant but harm the flies that use the other host plant. As a result, natural selection operating on these alleles provides a postzygotic barrier to reproduction, further limiting gene flow. Altogether, although the two populations are still classified as subspecies rather than separate species, sympatric speciation appears to be well under way.

Sexual Selection

There is evidence that sympatric speciation can also be driven by sexual selection. Clues to how this can occur have been found in cichlid fish from one of Earth's hot spots of animal speciation, East Africa's Lake Victoria. This lake was once home to as many as 600 species of cichlids. Genetic data indicate that these species originated within the last 100,000 years from a small number of colonizing species that arrived from rivers and lakes located elsewhere. How did so many species—more than double the number of freshwater fish species known in all of Europe—originate within a single lake?

One hypothesis is that subgroups of the original cichlid populations adapted to different food sources and that the resulting genetic divergence contributed to speciation in Lake Victoria. But sexual selection, in which (typically) females select males based on their appearance (see Chapter 23), may also have been a factor. Researchers have studied two closely related sympatric species of cichlids that differ mainly in the coloration of breeding males: Breeding *Pundamilia pundamilia* males have a blue-tinged back, whereas breeding *Pundamilia nyererei* males have a red-tinged back (**Figure 24.12**). Their results suggest that mate choice based on male breeding coloration is the main reproductive barrier that normally keeps the gene pools of these two species separate.

▼ **Figure 24.12** **INQUIRY**

Does sexual selection in cichlids result in reproductive isolation?

EXPERIMENT Ole Seehausen and Jacques van Alphen, then at the University of Leiden, placed males and females of *Pundamilia pundamilia* and *P. nyererei* together in two aquarium tanks, one with natural light and one with a monochromatic orange lamp. Under normal light, the two species are noticeably different in male breeding coloration; under monochromatic orange light, the two species are very similar in color. The researchers then observed the mate choices of the females in each tank.

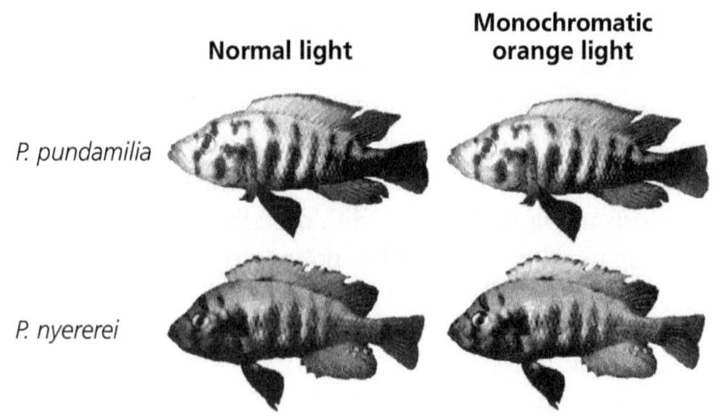

RESULTS Under normal light, females of each species strongly preferred males of their own species. But under orange light, females of each species responded indiscriminately to males of both species. The resulting hybrids were viable and fertile.

CONCLUSION Seehausen and van Alphen concluded that mate choice by females based on male breeding coloration is the main reproductive barrier that normally keeps the gene pools of these two species separate. Since the species can still interbreed when this prezygotic behavioral barrier is breached in the laboratory, the genetic divergence between the species is likely to be small. This suggests that speciation in nature has occurred relatively recently.

SOURCE O. Seehausen and J. J. M. van Alphen, The effect of male coloration on female mate choice in closely related Lake Victoria cichlids (*Haplochromis nyererei* complex), *Behavioral Ecology and Sociobiology* 42:1–8 (1998).

WHAT IF? If changing the light to orange had not affected the mating behavior of the cichlids, how might the researchers' conclusion have been different?

Allopatric and Sympatric Speciation: *A Review*

Now let's recap the two main modes by which new species form. In allopatric speciation, a new species forms in geographic isolation from its parent population. Geographic isolation severely restricts gene flow. As a result, other reproductive barriers from the ancestral species may arise as a byproduct of genetic changes that occur within the isolated population. Many different processes can produce such genetic changes, including natural selection under different environmental conditions, genetic drift, and sexual selection. Once formed, intrinsic reproductive barriers that arise in allopatric populations can prevent interbreeding with the parent population even if the populations come back into contact.

Sympatric speciation, in contrast, requires the emergence of a reproductive barrier that isolates a subset of a population from the remainder of the population in the same area. Though rarer than allopatric speciation, sympatric speciation can occur when gene flow to and from the isolated subpopulation is blocked. This can occur as a result of polyploidy, a condition in which an organism has extra sets of chromosomes. Sympatric speciation also can occur when a subset of a population becomes reproductively isolated because of natural selection that results from a switch to a habitat or food source not used by the parent population. Finally, sympatric speciation can result from sexual selection.

Having reviewed the geographic context in which species originate, we'll next explore in more detail what can happen when new or partially formed species come into contact.

CONCEPT CHECK 24.2

1. Summarize key differences between allopatric and sympatric speciation. Which type of speciation is more common, and why?
2. Describe two mechanisms that can decrease gene flow in sympatric populations, thereby making sympatric speciation more likely to occur.
3. **WHAT IF?** Is allopatric speciation more likely to occur on an island close to a mainland or on a more isolated island of the same size? Explain your prediction.
4. **MAKE CONNECTIONS** After reviewing the process of meiosis in Figure 13.8 (p. 254), describe how an error during meiosis could lead to polyploidy.

For suggested answers, see Appendix A.

CONCEPT 24.3

Hybrid zones reveal factors that cause reproductive isolation

What happens if species with incomplete reproductive barriers come into contact with one another? One possible outcome is the formation of a **hybrid zone**, a region in which members of different species meet and mate, producing at least some offspring of mixed ancestry. In this section, we'll explore hybrid zones and what they reveal about factors that cause the evolution of reproductive isolation.

Patterns Within Hybrid Zones

Some hybrid zones form as narrow bands, such as the one depicted in Figure 24.13 for two species of toads in the genus *Bombina*, the yellow-bellied toad (*B. variegata*) and the fire-bellied toad (*B. bombina*). This hybrid zone, represented by the red line on the map, extends for 4,000 km but is less than 10 km wide in most places. The hybrid zone occurs where the

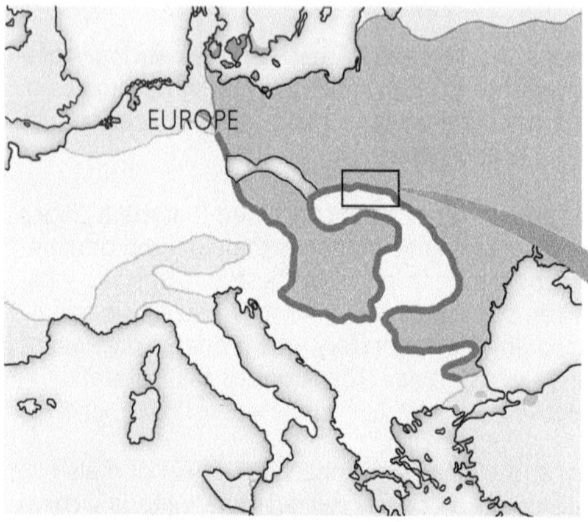

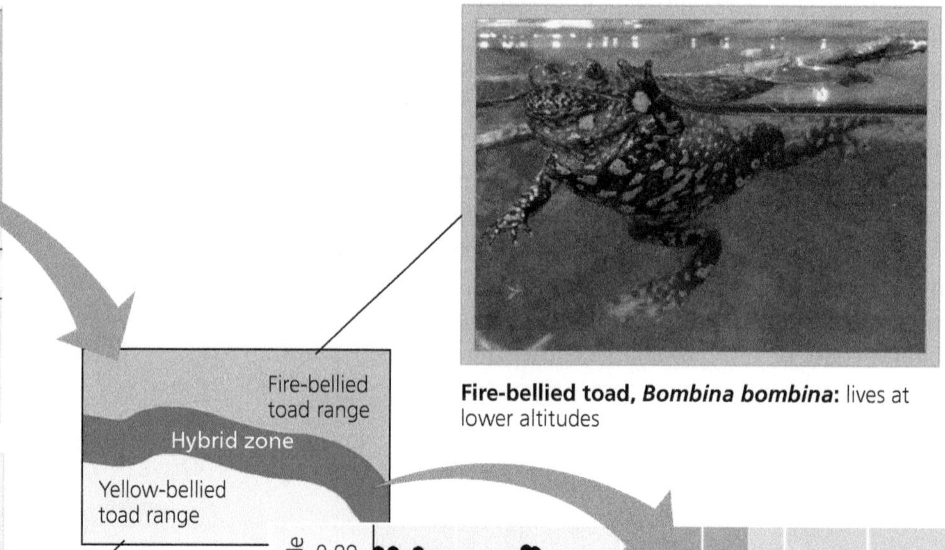

Fire-bellied toad, *Bombina bombina*: lives at lower altitudes

Yellow-bellied toad, *Bombina variegata*: lives at higher altitudes

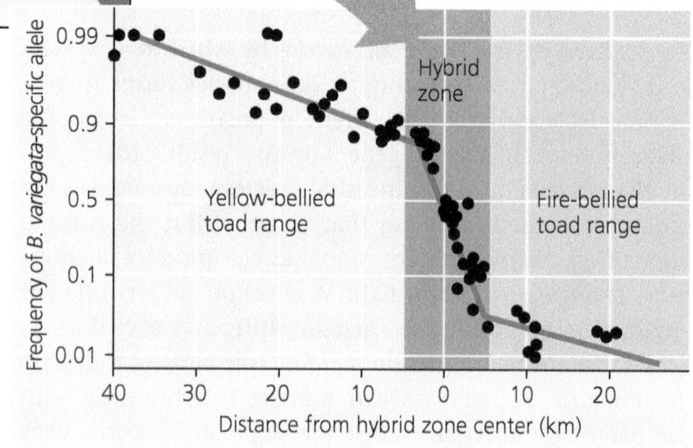

▲ **Figure 24.13 A narrow hybrid zone for *Bombina* toads in Europe.** The graph shows the pattern of species-specific allele frequencies across the width of the zone near Krakow, Poland. Individuals with frequencies close to 1.0 are yellow-bellied toads, individuals with frequencies close to 0.0 are fire-bellied toads, and individuals with intermediate frequencies are considered hybrids.

? *Does the graph indicate that gene flow is spreading fire-bellied toad alleles into the range of the yellow-bellied toad? Explain.*

higher-altitude habitat of the yellow-bellied toad meets the lowland habitat of the fire-bellied toad. Across a given "slice" of the zone, the frequency of alleles specific to yellow-bellied toads typically decreases from close to 100% at the edge where only yellow-bellied toads are found, to 50% in the central portion of the zone, to 0% at the edge where only fire-bellied toads are found.

What causes such a pattern of allele frequencies across a hybrid zone? We can infer that there is an obstacle to gene flow—otherwise, alleles from one parent species would also be common in the gene pool of the other parent species. Are geographic barriers reducing gene flow? Not in this case, since the toads can move throughout the hybrid zone. A more important factor is that hybrid toads have increased rates of embryonic mortality and a variety of morphological abnormalities, including ribs that are fused to the spine and malformed tadpole mouthparts. Because the hybrids have poor survival and reproduction, they produce few viable offspring with members of the parent species. As a result, hybrid individuals rarely serve as a stepping-stone from which alleles are passed from one species to the other. Outside the hybrid zone, additional obstacles to gene flow may be provided by natural selection in the different environments in which the parent species live.

Other hybrid zones have more complicated spatial patterns. For example, many plant species only occur in locations that have a very particular set of environmental conditions. Favorable "patches" that have such conditions are often scattered irregularly across the landscape and are isolated from one another. When two such plant species interbreed, the hybrid zone occurs in a group of disconnected patches, a more complex spatial pattern than the continuous band shown in Figure 24.13. But regardless of whether they have complex or simple spatial patterns, hybrid zones form when two species lacking complete barriers to reproduction come into contact. Once formed, how does a hybrid zone change over time?

Hybrid Zones over Time

Studying a hybrid zone is like observing a natural experiment on speciation. Will the hybrids become reproductively isolated from their parents and form a new species, as occurred by polyploidy in the goatsbeard plant of the Pacific Northwest? If not, there are three possible outcomes for the hybrid zone over time: reinforcement of barriers, fusion of species, or stability (**Figure 24.14**). Reproductive barriers between species may be reinforced over time (limiting the formation of hybrids) or weakened over time (causing the separating species to fuse into one species). Or hybrids may continue to be produced, creating a long-term and stable hybrid zone. Let's examine what studies in the field suggest about these three possibilities.

Reinforcement: Strengthening Reproductive Barriers

When hybrids are less fit than members of their parent species, as in the *Bombina* example, we might expect natural selection to strengthen prezygotic barriers to reproduction, thus reducing

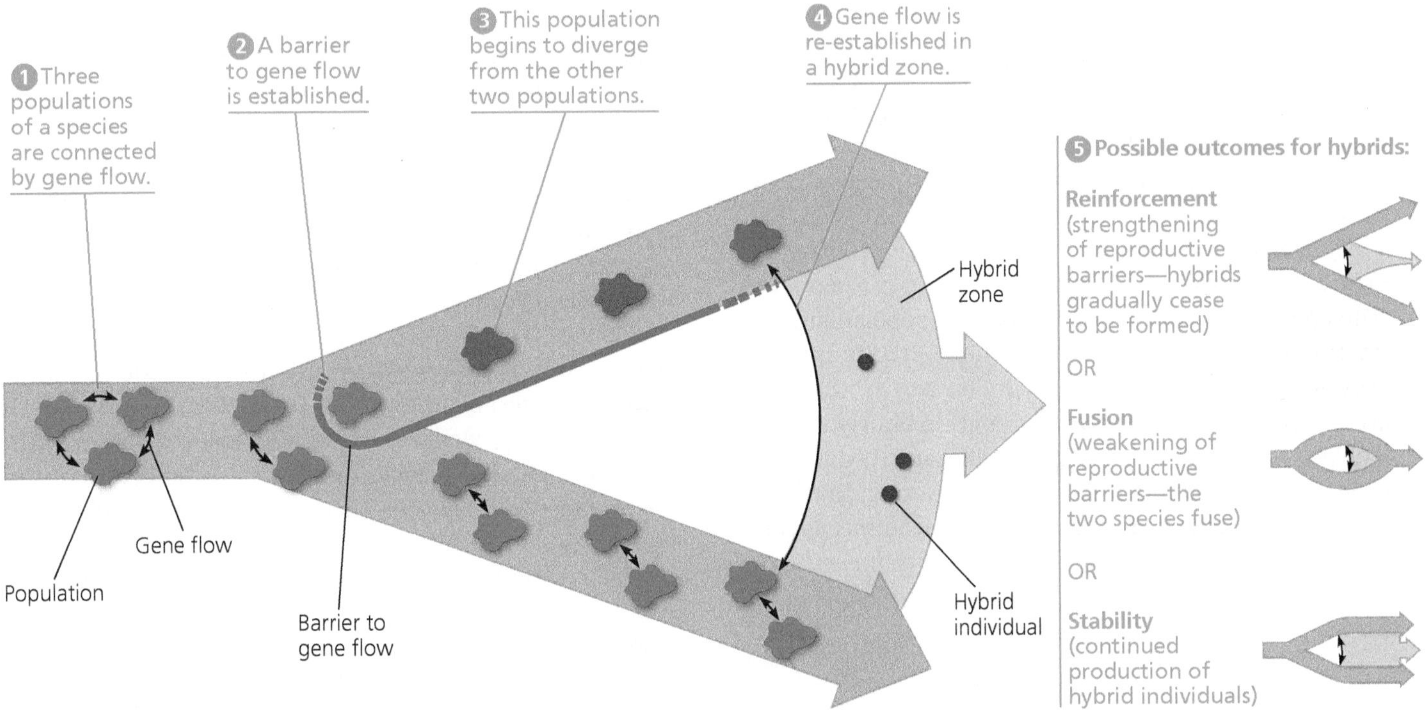

▲ **Figure 24.14 Formation of a hybrid zone and possible outcomes for hybrids over time.** The thick colored arrows represent the passage of time.

WHAT IF? *Predict what might happen if gene flow were re-established at step 3 in this process.*

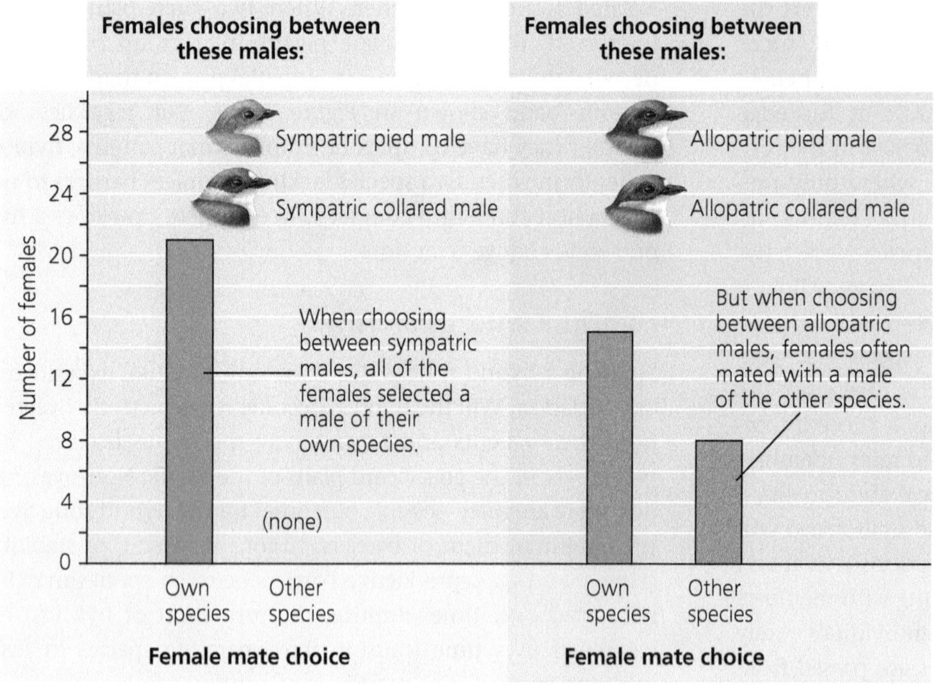

▲ **Figure 24.15 Reinforcement of barriers to reproduction in closely related species of European flycatchers.**

the formation of unfit hybrids. Because this process involves *reinforcing* reproductive barriers, it is called **reinforcement**. If reinforcement is occurring, a logical prediction is that barriers to reproduction between species should be stronger for sympatric populations than for allopatric populations.

As an example, let's consider the evidence for reinforcement in two closely related species of European flycatcher, the pied flycatcher and the collared flycatcher. In allopatric populations of these birds, males of the two species closely resemble one another. But in sympatric populations, the males of the two species look very different: Male pied flycatchers are a dull brown, whereas male collared flycatchers have enlarged patches of white. Female pied and collared flycatchers do not select males of the other species when given a choice between males from sympatric populations, but they frequently do make mistakes when selecting between males from allopatric populations (Figure 24.15). Thus, barriers to reproduction appear to be stronger in birds from sympatric populations than in birds from allopatric populations, as you would predict if reinforcement is occurring. Similar results have been observed in a number of organisms, including fishes, insects, plants, and other birds. But interestingly, reinforcement does *not* appear to be at work in the case of the *Bombina* toads, as we'll discuss shortly.

Fusion: Weakening Reproductive Barriers

Next let's consider the case in which two species contact one another in a hybrid zone, but the barriers to reproduction are not strong. So much gene flow may occur that reproductive barriers weaken further and the gene pools of the two species become increasingly alike. In effect, the speciation process reverses, eventually causing the two hybridizing species to fuse into a single species.

Such a situation may be occurring among some of the Lake Victoria cichlids we discussed earlier. In the past 30 years, about 200 of the former 600 species of Lake Victoria cichlids have vanished. Some of these species were driven to extinction by an introduced predator, the Nile perch. But many species not eaten by Nile perch also have disappeared—perhaps in some cases by species fusion. Many pairs of ecologically similar cichlid species are reproductively isolated because the females of one species prefer to mate with males of one color, while females of the other species prefer to mate with males of a different color (see Figure 24.12). Researchers think that murky waters caused by pollution may have reduced the ability of females to use color to distinguish males of their own species from males of closely related species. If further evidence supports this hypothesis, it would seem that pollution in Lake Victoria has produced a cascade of related effects. First, by decreasing the ability of females to distinguish males of their own species, pollution has increased the frequency of mating between members of species that had been isolated reproductively from one another. Second, as a result of these matings, many hybrids have been produced, leading to fusion of the parent species' gene pools and a loss of species (Figure 24.16).

Similar events may be affecting the polar bear (*Ursus maritimus*). Fossils and genetic analyses indicate that polar bears evolved from North American populations of grizzly bears (*U. arctos*) between 100,000 and 200,000 years ago. In recent decades, global warming has reduced the extent of the Arctic Ocean ice packs from which polar bears hunt for seals and other prey. As their ice-pack habitat disappears (placing them at risk of extinction), polar bears are more likely to be found on land, where they may encounter grizzly bears. Hybrid offspring of polar bears and grizzly bears in the wild have been documented (see Figure 24.4). As polar bear habitat continues to disappear, increasing numbers of such hybrids may cause the gene pools of these species to begin to fuse, thus contributing to the possible eventual extinction of the polar bear.

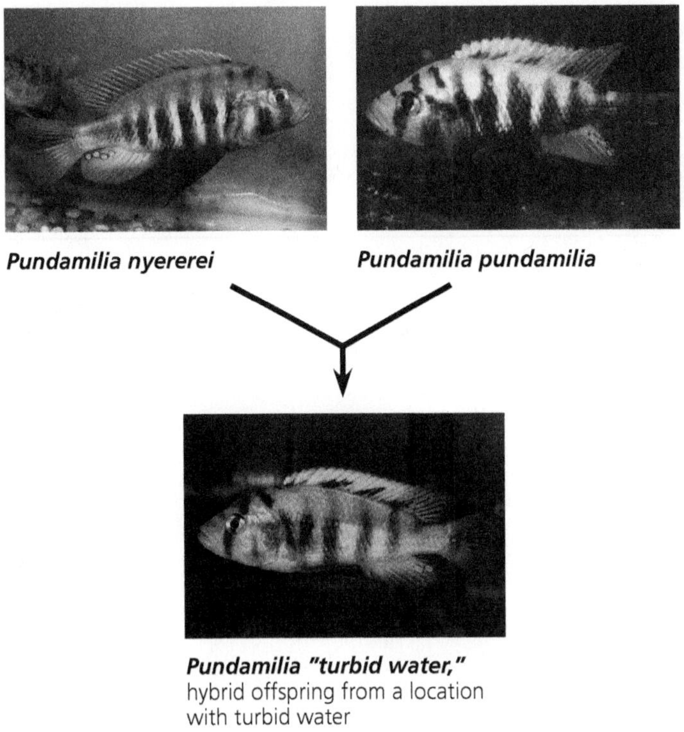

▲ **Figure 24.16 Fusion: The breakdown of reproductive barriers.** Increasingly cloudy water in Lake Victoria over the past 30 years may have weakened reproductive barriers between *P. nyererei* and *P. pundamilia*. In areas of cloudy water, the two species have hybridized extensively, causing their gene pools to fuse.

Stability: Continued Formation of Hybrid Individuals

Many hybrid zones are stable in the sense that hybrids continue to be produced. In some cases, this occurs because the hybrids survive or reproduce better than members of either parent species, at least in certain habitats or years. But stable hybrid zones have also been observed in cases where the hybrids are selected *against*—an unexpected result.

Recall that hybrids are at a strong disadvantage in the *Bombina* hybrid zone. As a result, the offspring of individuals that prefer to mate with members of their own species should survive or reproduce better than the unfit hybrid offspring of individuals that mate indiscriminately with members of the other species. This suggests that reinforcement should occur, strengthening reproductive barriers and thereby limiting the production of hybrid toads. But in more than 20 years of study, no evidence for reinforcement has been found, and hybrids continue to be produced.

What could explain this finding? One possibility relates to the narrowness of the *Bombina* hybrid zone (see Figure 24.13). Evidence suggests that members of both parent species migrate into the zone from the parent populations located outside the zone. Such movements lead to the continued production of hybrids, potentially overwhelming the selection for increased reproductive isolation inside the zone. If the hybrid zone were wider, this would be less likely to occur, since the center of the zone would receive little gene flow from distant parent populations located outside the hybrid zone.

In short, sometimes the outcomes in hybrid zones match our predictions (European flycatchers and cichlid fishes), and sometimes they don't (*Bombina*). But whether our predictions are upheld or not, events in hybrid zones can shed light on how barriers to reproduction between closely related species change over time. In the next section, we'll examine how interactions between hybridizing species can also provide a glimpse into the speed and genetic control of speciation.

CONCEPT CHECK 24.3

1. What are hybrid zones, and why can they be viewed as "natural laboratories" in which to study speciation?
2. **WHAT IF?** Consider two species that diverged while geographically separated but resumed contact before reproductive isolation was complete. Predict what would happen over time if the two species mated indiscriminately and (a) hybrid offspring survived and reproduced more poorly than offspring from intraspecific matings or (b) hybrid offspring survived and reproduced as well as offspring from intraspecific matings.

For suggested answers, see Appendix A.

CONCEPT 24.4

Speciation can occur rapidly or slowly and can result from changes in few or many genes

Darwin faced many unanswered questions when he began to ponder that "mystery of mysteries"—speciation. As you read in Chapter 22, he found answers to some of those questions when he realized that evolution by natural selection helped explain both the diversity of life and the adaptations of organisms. But biologists since Darwin have continued to ask fundamental questions about speciation. For example, how long does it take for new species to form? And how many genes change when one species splits into two? Answers to these questions are also beginning to emerge.

The Time Course of Speciation

We can gather information about how long it takes new species to form from broad patterns in the fossil record and from studies that use morphological data (including fossils) or molecular data to assess the time interval between speciation events in particular groups of organisms.

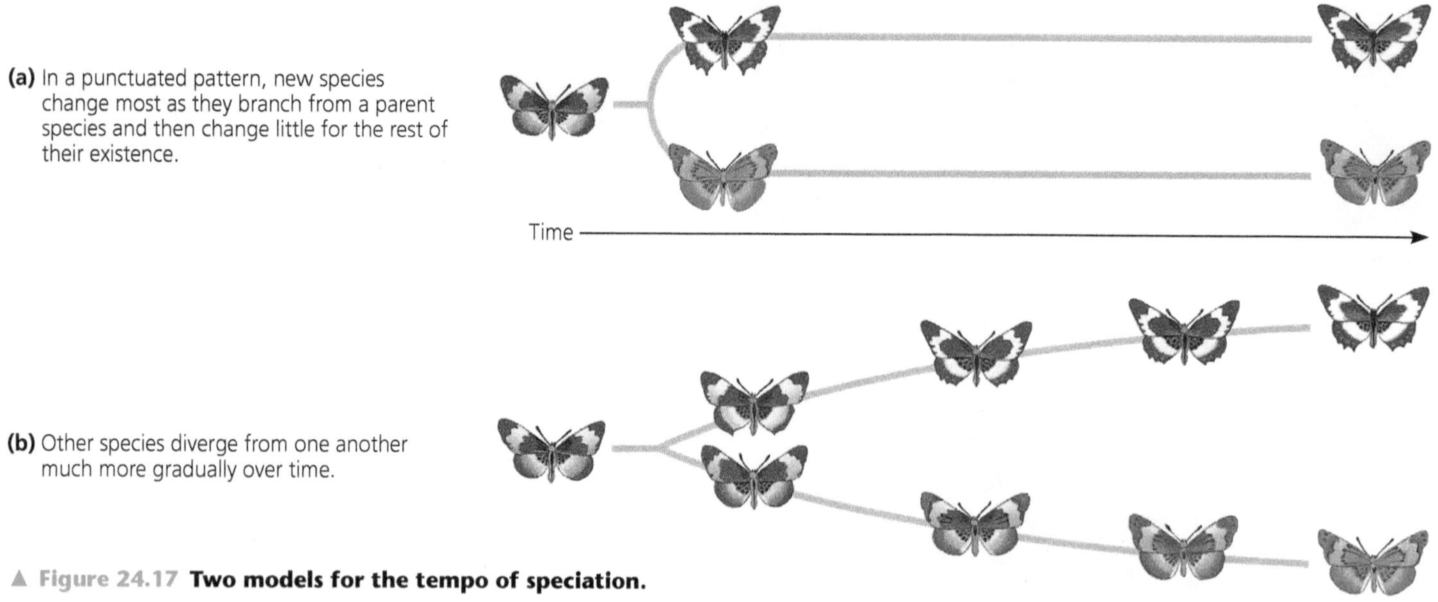

▲ **Figure 24.17 Two models for the tempo of speciation.**

Patterns in the Fossil Record

The fossil record includes many episodes in which new species appear suddenly in a geologic stratum, persist essentially unchanged through several strata, and then disappear. For example, there are dozens of species of marine invertebrates that make their debut in the fossil record with novel morphologies, but then change little for millions of years before becoming extinct. Paleontologists Niles Eldredge, of the American Museum of Natural History, and Stephen Jay Gould, of Harvard University, coined the term **punctuated equilibria** to describe these periods of apparent stasis punctuated by sudden change (Figure 24.17a). Other species do not show a punctuated pattern; instead, they change more gradually over long periods of time (Figure 24.17b).

What do punctuated and gradual patterns tell us about how long it takes new species to form? Suppose that a species survived for 5 million years, but most of the morphological changes that caused it to be designated a new species occurred during the first 50,000 years of its existence—just 1% of its total lifetime. Time periods this short (in geologic terms) often cannot be distinguished in fossil strata, in part because the rate of sediment accumulation is too slow to separate layers this close in time. Thus, based on its fossils, the species would seem to have appeared suddenly and then lingered with little or no change before becoming extinct. Even though such a species may have originated more slowly than its fossils suggest (in this case taking 50,000 years), a punctuated pattern indicates that speciation occurred relatively rapidly. For species whose fossils changed much more gradually, we also cannot tell exactly when a new biological species formed, since information about reproductive isolation does not fossilize. However, it is likely that speciation in such groups occurred relatively slowly, perhaps taking millions of years.

Speciation Rates

The punctuated pattern suggests that once the process of speciation begins, it can be completed relatively rapidly—a suggestion supported by a growing number of studies.

For example, research conducted at Indiana University suggests that rapid speciation produced the wild sunflower *Helianthus anomalus*. Genetic evidence indicates that this species originated by the hybridization of two other sunflower species, *H. annuus* and *H. petiolaris*. The hybrid species *H. anomalus* is ecologically distinct and reproductively isolated from both parent species (Figure 24.18). Unlike the outcome of allopolyploid speciation, in which there is a change in chromosome number after hybridization, in these sunflowers the two parent species and the hybrid all have the same number of chromosomes ($2n = 34$). How, then, did speciation occur? To answer this question, the researchers performed an

▲ **Figure 24.18 A hybrid sunflower species and its dry sand dune habitat.** The wild sunflower *Helianthus anomalus* originated via the hybridization of two other sunflowers, *H. annuus* and *H. petiolaris*, which live in nearby but moister environments.

▼ Figure 24.19 **INQUIRY**

How does hybridization lead to speciation in sunflowers?

EXPERIMENT At Indiana University, Loren Rieseberg and his colleagues crossed the two parent sunflower species, *H. annuus* and *H. petiolaris*, to produce experimental hybrids in the laboratory (for each gamete, only two of the $n = 17$ chromosomes are shown).

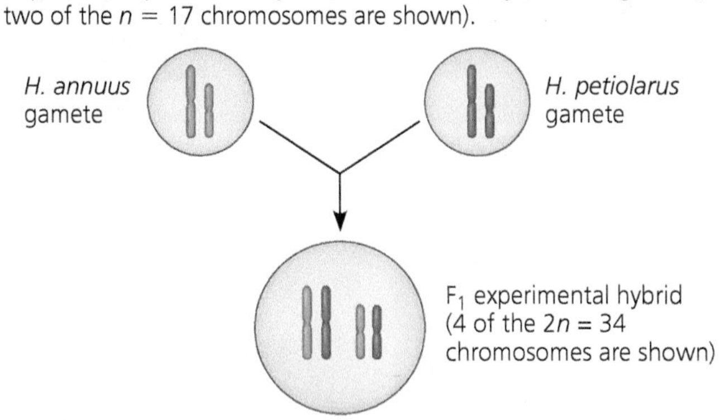

Note that in the first (F_1) generation, each chromosome of the experimental hybrids consisted entirely of DNA from one or the other parent species. The researchers then tested whether the F_1 and subsequent generations of experimental hybrids were fertile. They also used species-specific genetic markers to compare the chromosomes in the experimental hybrids with the chromosomes in the naturally occurring hybrid *H. anomalus*.

RESULTS Although only 5% of the F_1 experimental hybrids were fertile, after just four more generations the hybrid fertility rose to more than 90%. The chromosomes of individuals from this fifth hybrid generation differed from those in the F_1 generation but were similar to those in *H. anomalus* individuals from natural populations:

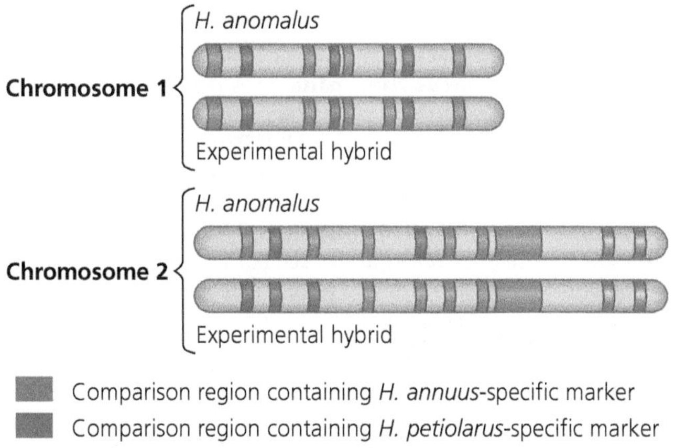

CONCLUSION Over time, the chromosomes in the population of experimental hybrids became similar to the chromosomes of *H. anomalus* individuals from natural populations. This suggests that the observed rise in the fertility of the experimental hybrids occurred as selection eliminated regions of DNA from the parent species that were not compatible with one another. Overall, it appeared that the initial steps of the speciation process occurred rapidly and could be mimicked in a laboratory experiment.

SOURCE L. H. Rieseberg et al., Role of gene interactions in hybrid speciation: evidence from ancient and experimental hybrids, *Science* 272:741–745 (1996).

WHAT IF? *The increased fertility of the experimental hybrids could have resulted from natural selection for thriving under laboratory conditions. Evaluate this alternative explanation for the results.*

experiment designed to mimic events in nature (Figure 24.19). Their results indicated that natural selection could produce extensive genetic changes in hybrid populations over short periods of time. These changes appear to have caused the hybrids to diverge reproductively from their parents and form a new species, *H. anomalus*.

The sunflower example, along with the apple maggot fly, Lake Victoria cichlid, and fruit fly examples discussed earlier, suggests that new species can arise rapidly *once divergence begins*. But what is the total length of time between speciation events? This interval consists of the time that elapses before populations of a newly formed species start to diverge from one another plus the time it takes for speciation to be complete once divergence begins. It turns out that the total time between speciation events varies considerably. For example, in a survey of data from 84 groups of plants and animals, the interval between speciation events ranged from 4,000 years (in cichlids of Lake Nabugabo, Uganda) to 40 million years (in some beetles). Overall, the time between speciation events averaged 6.5 million years and rarely took less than 500,000 years.

What can we learn from such data? First, the data suggest that on average, millions of years may pass before a newly formed species will itself give rise to another new species. As we'll see in Chapter 25, this result has implications for how long it takes life on Earth to recover from mass extinction events. Second, the extreme variability in the time it takes new species to form indicates that organisms do not have a "speciation clock" ticking inside them, causing them to produce new species at regular time intervals. Instead, speciation begins only after gene flow between populations is interrupted, perhaps by changing environmental conditions or by unpredictable events, such as a storm that transports a few individuals to an isolated area. Furthermore, once gene flow is interrupted, the populations must diverge genetically to such an extent that they become reproductively isolated—all before other events cause gene flow to resume, possibly reversing the speciation process (see Figure 24.16).

Studying the Genetics of Speciation

Studies of ongoing speciation (as in hybrid zones) can reveal traits that cause reproductive isolation. By identifying the genes that control those traits, scientists can explore a fundamental question of evolutionary biology: How many genes change when a new species forms?

In a few cases, the evolution of reproductive isolation is due to a change in a single gene. For example, in Japanese snails of the genus *Euhadra*, a change in a single gene can result in a mechanical barrier to reproduction. This gene controls the direction in which the shells spiral. When their shells spiral in different directions, the snails' genitalia are oriented in a manner that prevents mating (Figure 24.3f shows a similar example).

A major barrier to reproduction between two closely related species of monkey flower, *Mimulus cardinalis* and *M. lewisii*, also appears to be influenced by a relatively small number of genes. These two species are isolated by several prezygotic and postzygotic barriers. Of these, one prezygotic barrier, pollinator choice, accounts for most of the isolation: In a hybrid zone between *M. cardinalis* and *M. lewisii*, nearly 98% of pollinator visits were restricted to one species or the other.

The two monkey flower species are visited by different pollinators: Hummingbirds prefer the red-flowered *M. cardinalis*, and bumblebees prefer the pink-flowered *M. lewisii*. Douglas Schemske, of Michigan State University, and colleagues have shown that pollinator choice is affected by at least two loci in the monkey flowers, one of which, the "yellow upper," or *yup*, locus, influences flower color (Figure 24.20). By crossing the two parent species to produce F_1 hybrids and then performing repeated backcrosses of these F_1 hybrids to each parent species, Schemske and colleagues succeeded in transferring the *M. cardinalis* allele at this locus into *M. lewisii*, and vice versa. In a field experiment, *M. lewisii* plants with the *M. cardinalis yup* allele received 68-fold more visits from hummingbirds than did wild-type *M. lewisii*. Similarly, *M. cardinalis* plants with the *M. lewisii yup* allele received 74-fold more visits from bumblebees than did wild-type *M. cardinalis*. Thus, a mutation at a single locus can influence pollinator preference and hence contribute to reproductive isolation in monkey flowers.

In other organisms, the speciation process is influenced by larger numbers of genes and gene interactions. For example, hybrid sterility between two subspecies of the fruit fly *Drosophila pseudoobscura* results from gene interactions among at least four loci, and postzygotic isolation in the sunflower hybrid zone discussed earlier is influenced by at least 26 chromosome segments (and an unknown number of genes). Overall, studies suggest that few or many genes can influence the evolution of reproductive isolation and hence the emergence of a new species.

From Speciation to Macroevolution

As you've seen, speciation may begin with differences as seemingly small as the color on a cichlid's back. However, as speciation occurs again and again, such differences can accumulate and become more pronounced, eventually leading to the formation of new groups of organisms that differ greatly from their ancestors (as in the origin of whales from land-dwelling mammals; see Figure 22.20). Furthermore, as one group of organisms increases in size by producing many new species, another group of organisms may shrink, losing species to extinction. The cumulative effects of many such speciation and extinction events have helped shape the sweeping evolutionary changes that are documented in the fossil record. In the next chapter, we turn to such large-scale evolutionary changes as we begin our study of macroevolution.

(a) Typical *Mimulus lewisii*

(b) *M. lewisii* with an *M. cardinalis* flower-color allele

(c) Typical *Mimulus cardinalis*

(d) *M. cardinalis* with an *M. lewisii* flower-color allele

▲ **Figure 24.20 A locus that influences pollinator choice.** Pollinator preferences provide a strong barrier to reproduction between *Mimulus lewisii* and *M. cardinalis*. After transferring the *M. lewisii* allele for a flower-color locus into *M. cardinalis* and vice versa, researchers observed a shift in some pollinators' preferences.

WHAT IF? *If* M. cardinalis *individuals that had the* M. lewisii yup *allele were planted in an area that housed both monkey flower species, how might the production of hybrid offspring be affected?*

CONCEPT CHECK 24.4

1. Speciation can occur rapidly between diverging populations, yet the length of time between speciation events is often more than a million years. Explain this apparent contradiction.
2. Summarize evidence that the *yup* locus acts as a prezygotic barrier to reproduction in two species of monkey flowers. Do these results demonstrate that the *yup* locus alone controls barriers to reproduction between these species? Explain.
3. **MAKE CONNECTIONS** Compare Figure 13.11 (p. 259) with Figure 24.19 (p. 503). What cellular process could cause the hybrid chromosomes to contain DNA from both parent species? Explain.

For suggested answers, see Appendix A.

24 CHAPTER REVIEW

SUMMARY OF KEY CONCEPTS

CONCEPT 24.1

The biological species concept emphasizes reproductive isolation (pp. 488–492)

- A biological **species** is a group of populations whose individuals have the potential to interbreed and produce viable, fertile offspring with each other but not with members of other species. The **biological species concept** emphasizes reproductive isolation through prezygotic and postzygotic barriers that separate gene pools.
- Although helpful in thinking about how speciation occurs, the biological species concept has limitations. For instance, it cannot be applied to organisms known only as fossils or to organisms that reproduce only asexually. Thus, scientists use other species concepts, such as the **morphological species concept**, in certain circumstances.

? *Explain the importance of gene flow to the biological species concept.*

CONCEPT 24.2

Speciation can take place with or without geographic separation (pp. 493–498)

- In **allopatric speciation**, gene flow is reduced when two populations of one species become geographically separated from each other. One or both populations may undergo evolutionary change during the period of separation, resulting in the establishment of prezygotic or postzygotic barriers to reproduction.
- In **sympatric speciation**, a new species originates while remaining in the same geographic area as the parent species. Plant species (and, more rarely, animal species) have evolved sympatrically through polyploidy. Sympatric speciation can also result from habitat shifts and sexual selection.

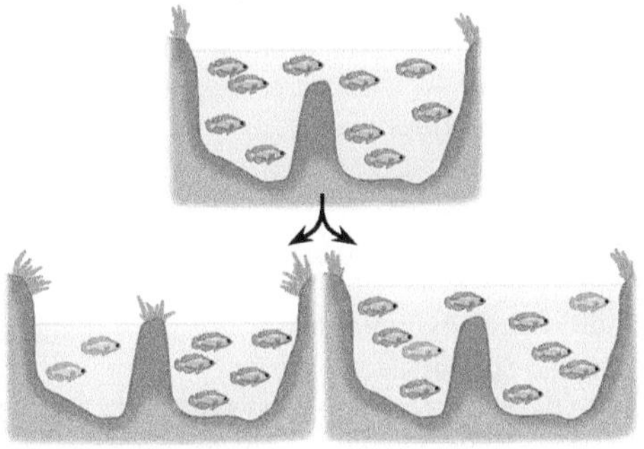

? *Can factors that cause sympatric speciation also cause allopatric speciation? Explain.*

CONCEPT 24.3

Hybrid zones reveal factors that cause reproductive isolation (pp. 498–501)

- Many groups of organisms form **hybrid zones** in which members of different species meet and mate, producing at least some offspring of mixed ancestry.
- Many hybrid zones are *stable* in that hybrid offspring continue to be produced over time. In others, **reinforcement** strengthens prezygotic barriers to reproduction, thus decreasing the formation of unfit hybrids. In still other hybrid zones, barriers to reproduction may weaken over time, resulting in the *fusion* of the species' gene pools (reversing the speciation process).

? *What factors can support the long-term stability of a hybrid zone if the parent species live in different environments?*

CONCEPT 24.4

Speciation can occur rapidly or slowly and can result from changes in few or many genes (pp. 501–504)

- New species can form rapidly once divergence begins—but it can take millions of years for that to happen. The time interval between speciation events varies considerably, from a few thousand years to tens of millions of years.
- New developments in genetics have enabled researchers to identify specific genes involved in some cases of speciation. Results show that speciation can be driven by few or many genes.

? *Is speciation something that happened only in the distant past, or are new species continuing to arise today? Explain.*

TEST YOUR UNDERSTANDING

LEVEL 1: KNOWLEDGE/COMPREHENSION

1. The *largest* unit within which gene flow can readily occur is a
   a. population.
   b. species.
   c. genus.
   d. hybrid.
   e. phylum.

2. Males of different species of the fruit fly *Drosophila* that live in the same parts of the Hawaiian Islands have different elaborate courtship rituals. These rituals involve fighting other males and making stylized movements that attract females. What type of reproductive isolation does this represent?
   a. habitat isolation
   b. temporal isolation
   c. behavioral isolation
   d. gametic isolation
   e. postzygotic barriers

3. According to the punctuated equilibria model,
   a. natural selection is unimportant as a mechanism of evolution.
   b. given enough time, most existing species will branch gradually into new species.
   c. most new species accumulate their unique features relatively rapidly as they come into existence, then change little for the rest of their duration as a species.
   d. most evolution occurs in sympatric populations.
   e. speciation is usually due to a single mutation.

LEVEL 2: APPLICATION/ANALYSIS

4. Bird guides once listed the myrtle warbler and Audubon's warbler as distinct species. Recently, these birds have been classified as eastern and western forms of a single species, the

yellow-rumped warbler. Which of the following pieces of evidence, if true, would be cause for this reclassification?

a. The two forms interbreed often in nature, and their offspring have good survival and reproduction.
b. The two forms live in similar habitats.
c. The two forms have many genes in common.
d. The two forms have similar food requirements.
e. The two forms are very similar in coloration.

5. Which of the following factors would *not* contribute to allopatric speciation?
   a. A population becomes geographically isolated from the parent population.
   b. The separated population is small, and genetic drift occurs.
   c. The isolated population is exposed to different selection pressures than the ancestral population.
   d. Different mutations begin to distinguish the gene pools of the separated populations.
   e. Gene flow between the two populations is extensive.

6. Plant species A has a diploid number of 12. Plant species B has a diploid number of 16. A new species, C, arises as an allopolyploid from A and B. The diploid number for species C would probably be
   a. 12. b. 14. c. 16. d. 28. e. 56.

LEVEL 3: SYNTHESIS/EVALUATION

7. Suppose that a group of male pied flycatchers migrated from a region where there were no collared flycatchers to a region where both species were present (see Figure 24.15). Assuming events like this are very rare, which of the following scenarios is *least* likely?
   a. The frequency of hybrid offspring would increase.
   b. Migrant pied males would produce fewer offspring than would resident pied males.
   c. Pied females would rarely mate with collared males.
   d. Migrant males would mate with collared females more often than with pied females.
   e. The frequency of hybrid offspring would decrease.

8. **EVOLUTION CONNECTION**
   What is the biological basis for assigning all human populations to a single species? Can you think of a scenario by which a second human species could originate in the future?

9. **SCIENCE, TECHNOLOGY, AND SOCIETY**
   In the United States, the rare red wolf (*Canis lupus*) has been known to hybridize with coyotes (*Canis latrans*), which are much more numerous. Although red wolves and coyotes differ in terms of morphology, DNA, and behavior, genetic evidence suggests that living red wolf individuals are actually hybrids. Red wolves are designated as an endangered species and hence receive legal protection under the Endangered Species Act. Some people think that their endangered status should be withdrawn because the remaining red wolves are hybrids, not members of a "pure" species. Do you agree? Why or why not?

10. **SCIENTIFIC INQUIRY**
    DRAW IT In this chapter, you read that bread wheat (*Triticum aestivum*) is an allohexaploid, containing two sets of chromosomes from each of three different parent species. Genetic analysis suggests that the three species pictured following this question each contributed chromosome sets to *T. aestivum*. (The capital letters here represent sets of chromosomes rather than individual genes.) Evidence also indicates that the first polyploidy event was a spontaneous hybridization of the early cultivated wheat species *T. monococcum* and a wild *Triticum* grass species. Based on this information, draw a diagram of one possible chain of events that could have produced the allohexaploid *T. aestivum*.

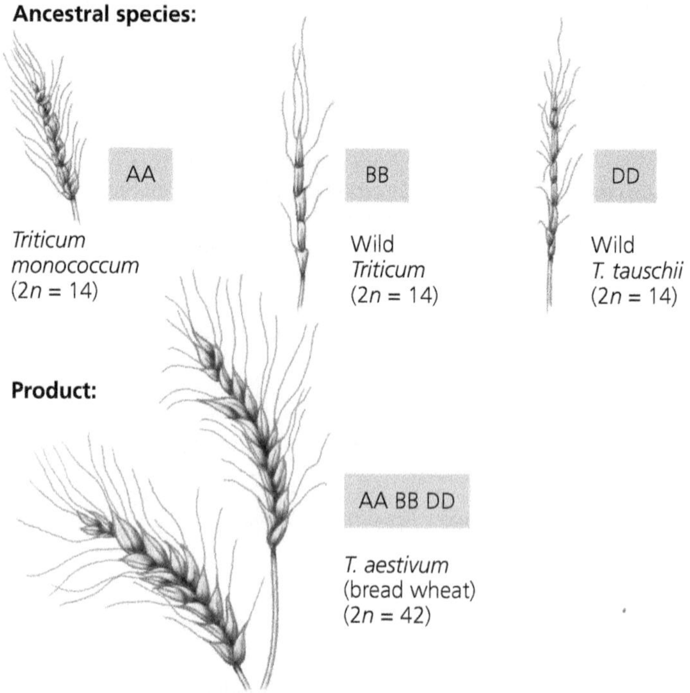

11. **WRITE ABOUT A THEME**
    The Genetic Basis of Life In sexually reproducing species, each individual begins life with DNA inherited from both parent organisms. In a short essay (100–150 words), apply this idea to what occurs when organisms of two species that have homologous chromosomes mate and produce (F_1) hybrid offspring. What percentage of the DNA in the F_1 hybrids' chromosomes comes from each parent species? As the hybrids mate and produce F_2 and later-generation hybrid offspring, describe how recombination and natural selection may affect whether the DNA in hybrid chromosomes is derived from one parent species or the other.

For selected answers, see Appendix A.

25

The History of Life on Earth

▲ **Figure 25.1 What does fossil evidence say about where these dinosaurs lived?**

EVOLUTION

KEY CONCEPTS

25.1 Conditions on early Earth made the origin of life possible
25.2 The fossil record documents the history of life
25.3 Key events in life's history include the origins of single-celled and multicelled organisms and the colonization of land
25.4 The rise and fall of groups of organisms reflect differences in speciation and extinction rates
25.5 Major changes in body form can result from changes in the sequences and regulation of developmental genes
25.6 Evolution is not goal oriented

OVERVIEW

Lost Worlds

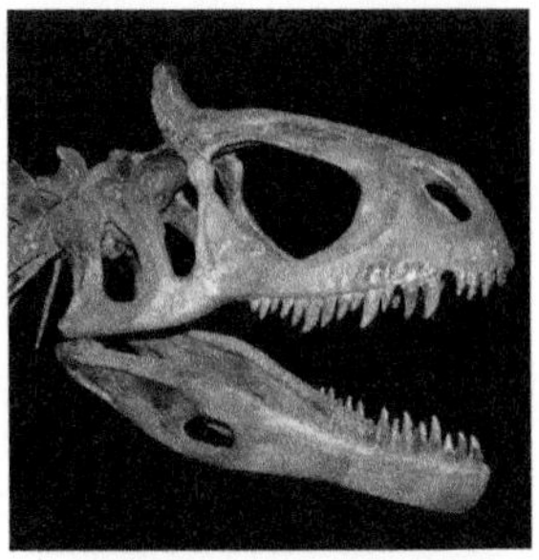

▲ ***Cryolophosaurus* skull**

Visitors to Antarctica today encounter one of Earth's harshest, most barren environments. In this land of extreme cold where there is almost no liquid water, life is sparse and small—the largest fully terrestrial animal is a fly that is 5 mm long. But even as early Antarctic explorers struggled to survive, some of them made an astonishing discovery: fossil evidence that life once thrived where it now barely exists. Fossils reveal that 500 million years ago, the ocean waters surrounding Antarctica were warm and teeming with tropical invertebrates. Later, the continent was covered in forests for hundreds of millions of years. At various times, a wide range of animals stalked through these forests, including 3-m-tall predatory "terror birds" and giant dinosaurs such as the voracious *Cryolophosaurus* (Figure 25.1), a 7-m-long relative of *Tyrannosaurus rex*.

Fossils discovered in other parts of the world tell a similar, if not quite as surprising, story: Past organisms were very different from those presently living. The sweeping changes in life on Earth as revealed by fossils illustrate **macroevolution**, the broad pattern of evolution above the species level. Examples of macroevolutionary change include the emergence of terrestrial vertebrates through a series of speciation events, the impact of mass extinctions on the diversity of life, and the origin of key adaptations such as flight in birds.

Taken together, such changes provide a grand view of the evolutionary history of life on Earth. We'll examine that history in this chapter, beginning with hypotheses regarding the origin of life. The origin of life is the most speculative topic of the entire unit, for no fossil evidence of that seminal episode exists. We will then turn to evidence from the fossil record and what it tells us about major events in the history of life, paying particular attention to factors that have helped to shape the rise and fall of different groups of organisms over time.

CONCEPT 25.1

Conditions on early Earth made the origin of life possible

Direct evidence of life on early Earth comes from fossils of microorganisms that are about 3.5 billion years old. But when and how did the first living cells appear? Observations and experiments in chemistry, geology, and physics have led scientists to propose one scenario that we'll examine here. They hypothesize that chemical and physical processes on early Earth, aided by the emerging force of natural selection, could have produced very simple cells through a sequence of four main stages:

1. The abiotic (nonliving) synthesis of small organic molecules, such as amino acids and nitrogenous bases
2. The joining of these small molecules into macromolecules, such as proteins and nucleic acids
3. The packaging of these molecules into **protocells**, droplets with membranes that maintained an internal chemistry different from that of their surroundings
4. The origin of self-replicating molecules that eventually made inheritance possible

Though speculative, this scenario leads to predictions that can be tested in the laboratory. In this section, we will examine some of the evidence for each stage.

Synthesis of Organic Compounds on Early Earth

There is scientific evidence that Earth and the other planets of the solar system formed about 4.6 billion years ago, condensing from a vast cloud of dust and rocks that surrounded the young sun. For the first few hundred million years, life probably could not have originated or survived on Earth because the planet was still being bombarded by huge chunks of rock and ice left over from the formation of the solar system. The collisions generated enough heat to vaporize the available water and prevent seas from forming. This early phase likely ended about 4.2–3.9 billion years ago.

As the bombardment of early Earth slowed, conditions on the planet were extremely different from those of today. The first atmosphere was probably thick with water vapor, along with various compounds released by volcanic eruptions, including nitrogen and its oxides, carbon dioxide, methane, ammonia, hydrogen, and hydrogen sulfide. As Earth cooled, the water vapor condensed into oceans, and much of the hydrogen escaped into space.

During the 1920s, Russian chemist A. I. Oparin and British scientist J. B. S. Haldane independently hypothesized that Earth's early atmosphere was a reducing (electron-adding) environment, in which organic compounds could have formed from simpler molecules. The energy for this organic synthesis could have come from lightning and intense UV radiation. Haldane suggested that the early oceans were a solution of organic molecules, a "primitive soup" from which life arose.

During 1953, Stanley Miller, working under the guidance of Harold Urey at the University of Chicago, tested the Oparin-Haldane hypothesis by creating laboratory conditions comparable to those that scientists at the time thought existed on early Earth (see Figure 4.2). His apparatus yielded a variety of amino acids found in organisms today, along with other organic compounds. Many laboratories have since repeated Miller's classic experiment using different recipes for the atmosphere, some of which also produced organic compounds.

However, it is unclear whether the atmosphere of early Earth contained enough methane and ammonia to be reducing. Some evidence suggests that the early atmosphere was made up primarily of nitrogen and carbon dioxide and was neither reducing nor oxidizing (electron-removing). Recent Miller-Urey-type experiments using such "neutral" atmospheres have also produced organic molecules. In addition, it is likely that small pockets of the early atmosphere—perhaps near the openings of volcanoes—were reducing. Perhaps the first organic compounds formed near volcanoes or deep-sea vents, where hot water and minerals gush into the ocean from Earth's interior. In a 2008 test of this volcanic-atmosphere hypothesis, researchers used modern equipment to reanalyze molecules that Miller had saved from one of his experiments. The study found that numerous amino acids had formed under conditions that simulated a volcanic eruption (Figure 25.2).

Miller-Urey-type experiments demonstrate that the abiotic synthesis of organic molecules is possible under various assumptions about the composition of the early atmosphere. A second source of organic molecules may have been meteorites. Among the meteorites that land on Earth are carbonaceous chondrites, rocks that are 1–2% carbon compounds by mass. Fragments of the Murchison meteorite, a 4.5-billion-year-old chondrite that fell to Australia in 1969, contain more than 80 amino acids, some in large amounts. These amino acids cannot be contaminants from Earth because they consist of an equal mix of D and L isomers (see Chapter 4). Organisms make and use only L isomers, with a few rare exceptions. Recent studies have shown that the Murchison meteorite also contained other key organic molecules, including lipids, simple sugars, and nitrogenous bases such as uracil.

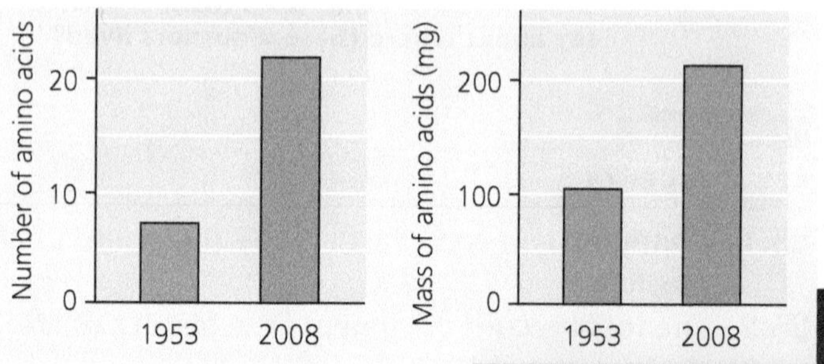

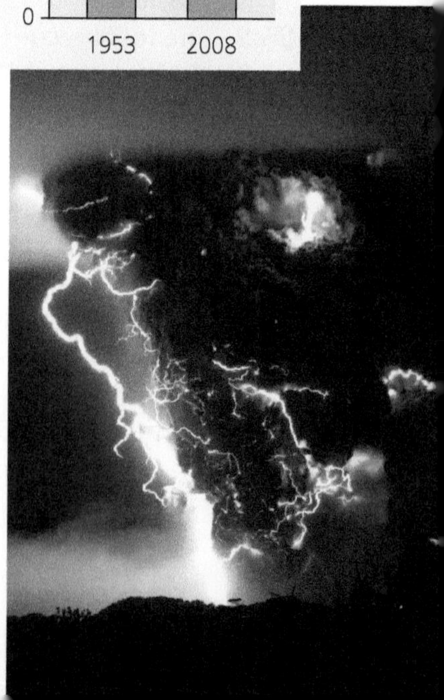

▲ **Figure 25.2 Amino acid synthesis in a simulated volcanic eruption.** In addition to his classic 1953 study, Miller also conducted an experiment simulating a volcanic eruption. In a 2008 reanalysis of those results, researchers found that far more amino acids were produced under simulated volcanic conditions than were produced in the conditions of the original 1953 experiment.

MAKE CONNECTIONS *After reviewing Concept 5.4 (pp. 78–80), explain how more than 20 amino acids could have been produced in the 2008 experiment.*

Abiotic Synthesis of Macromolecules

The presence of small organic molecules, such as amino acids and nitrogenous bases, is not sufficient for the emergence of life as we know it. Every cell has a vast assortment of macromolecules, including enzymes and other proteins and the nucleic acids that are essential for self-replication. Could such macromolecules have formed on early Earth? A 2009 study demonstrated that one key step, the abiotic synthesis of RNA monomers, can occur spontaneously from simple precursor molecules. In addition, by dripping solutions of amino acids or RNA nucleotides onto hot sand, clay, or rock, researchers have produced polymers of these molecules. The polymers formed spontaneously, without the help of enzymes or ribosomes. Unlike proteins, the amino acid polymers are a complex mix of linked and cross-linked amino acids. Nevertheless, it is possible that such polymers may have acted as weak catalysts for a variety of chemical reactions on early Earth.

Protocells

All organisms must be able to carry out reproduction and energy processing (metabolism). Life cannot persist without both of these functions. DNA molecules carry genetic information, including the instructions needed to replicate themselves accurately during reproduction. But the replication of DNA requires elaborate enzymatic machinery, along with a copious supply of nucleotide building blocks that are provided by the cell's metabolism (see Chapter 16). This suggests that self-replicating molecules and a metabolism-like source of the building blocks may have appeared together in early protocells. How did that happen?

The necessary conditions may have been met in *vesicles*, fluid-filled compartments bounded by a membrane-like structure. Recent experiments show that abiotically produced vesicles can exhibit certain properties of life, including simple reproduction and metabolism, as well as the maintenance of an internal chemical environment different from that of their surroundings.

For example, vesicles can form spontaneously when lipids or other organic molecules are added to water. When this occurs, the hydrophobic molecules in the mixture organize into a bilayer similar to the lipid bilayer of a plasma membrane. Adding substances such as *montmorillonite*, a soft mineral clay produced by the weathering of volcanic ash, greatly increases the rate of vesicle self-assembly (Figure 25.3a). This clay, which is thought to have been common on early Earth, provides surfaces on which organic molecules become concentrated, increasing the likelihood that the molecules will react with each other and form vesicles. Abiotically produced vesicles can "reproduce" on their own (Figure 25.3b), and they can increase in size ("grow") without dilution of their contents. Vesicles also can absorb montmorillonite particles, including those on which RNA and other organic molecules have become attached

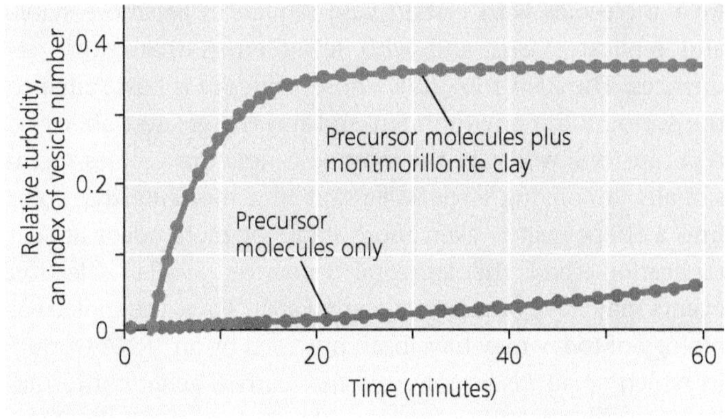

(a) Self-assembly. The presence of montmorillonite clay greatly increases the rate of vesicle self-assembly.

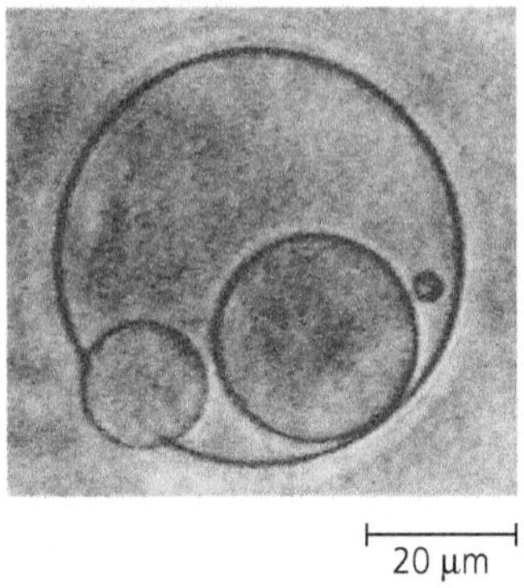

(b) Reproduction. Vesicles can divide on their own, as in this vesicle "giving birth" to smaller vesicles (LM).

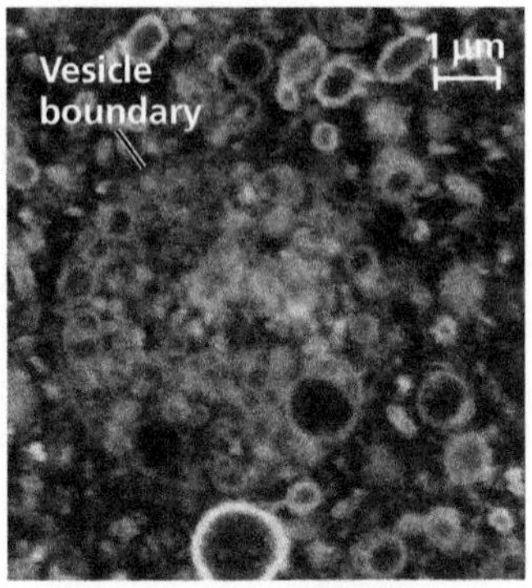

(c) Absorption of RNA. This vesicle has incorporated montmorillonite clay particles coated with RNA (orange).

▲ Figure 25.3 **Features of abiotically produced vesicles.**

(Figure 25.3c). Finally, experiments have shown that some vesicles have a selectively permeable bilayer and can perform metabolic reactions using an external source of reagents—another important prerequisite for life.

Self-Replicating RNA and the Dawn of Natural Selection

The first genetic material was most likely RNA, not DNA. Thomas Cech, of the University of Colorado, and Sidney Altman, of Yale University, found that RNA, which plays a central role in protein synthesis, can also carry out a number of enzyme-like catalytic functions. Cech called these RNA catalysts **ribozymes**. Some ribozymes can make complementary copies of short pieces of RNA, provided that they are supplied with nucleotide building blocks.

Natural selection on the molecular level has produced ribozymes capable of self-replication in the laboratory. How does this occur? Unlike double-stranded DNA, which takes the form of a uniform helix, single-stranded RNA molecules assume a variety of specific three-dimensional shapes mandated by their nucleotide sequences. In a particular environment,

RNA molecules with certain base sequences are more stable and replicate faster and with fewer errors than other sequences. The RNA molecule whose sequence is best suited to the surrounding environment and has the greatest ability to replicate itself will leave the most descendant molecules. Occasionally, a copying error will result in a molecule that folds into a shape that is even more stable or more adept at self-replication than the ancestral sequence. Similar selection events may have occurred on early Earth. Thus, the molecular biology of today may have been preceded by an "RNA world," in which small RNA molecules that carried genetic information were able to replicate and to store information about the vesicles that carried them.

A vesicle with self-replicating, catalytic RNA would differ from its many neighbors that did not carry RNA or that carried RNA without such capabilities. If that vesicle could grow, split, and pass its RNA molecules to its daughters, the daughters would be protocells that had some of the properties of their parent. Although the first such protocells must have carried only limited amounts of genetic information, specifying only a few properties, their inherited characteristics could have been acted on by natural selection. The most successful of the early protocells would have increased in number because they could exploit their resources effectively and pass their abilities on to subsequent generations.

Once RNA sequences that carried genetic information appeared in protocells, many further changes would have been possible. For example, RNA could have provided the template on which DNA nucleotides were assembled. Double-stranded DNA is a more stable repository for genetic information than the more fragile single-stranded RNA. DNA also can be replicated more accurately. Accurate replication was advantageous as genomes grew larger through gene duplication and other processes and as more properties of the protocells became coded in genetic information. After DNA appeared, perhaps RNA molecules began to take on their present-day roles as regulators and intermediates in the translation of genes. The stage was now set for a blossoming of diverse life-forms—a change we see documented in the fossil record.

CONCEPT CHECK 25.1

1. What hypothesis did Miller test in his classic experiment?
2. How would the appearance of protocells have represented a key step in the origin of life?
3. **MAKE CONNECTIONS** In changing from an "RNA world" to today's "DNA world," genetic information must have flowed from RNA to DNA. After reviewing Figures 17.3 (p. 329) and 19.8 (p. 389), suggest how this could have occurred. Is such a flow a common occurrence today?

For suggested answers, see Appendix A.

CONCEPT 25.2

The fossil record documents the history of life

Starting with the earliest traces of life, the fossil record opens a window into the world of long ago and provides glimpses of the evolution of life over billions of years. In this section, we'll explore what the fossil record reveals about the major changes in the history of life—what those changes have been and how they may have occurred.

The Fossil Record

Recall from Chapter 22 that sedimentary rocks are the richest source of fossils. As a result, the fossil record is based primarily on the sequence in which fossils have accumulated in sedimentary rock layers, called *strata* (see Figure 22.3). Useful information is also provided by other types of fossils, such as insects preserved in amber (fossilized tree sap) and mammals frozen in ice.

The fossil record shows that there have been great changes in the kinds of organisms on Earth at different points in time (Figure 25.4). Many past organisms were unlike today's organisms, and many organisms that once were common are now extinct. As we'll see later, fossils also document how new groups of organisms arose from previously existing ones.

As substantial and significant as the fossil record is, keep in mind that it is an incomplete chronicle of evolutionary change. Many of Earth's organisms did not die in the right place at the right time to be preserved as fossils. Of those fossils that were formed, many were destroyed by later geologic processes, and only a fraction of the others have been discovered. As a result, the known fossil record is biased in favor of species that existed for a long time, were abundant and widespread in certain kinds of environments, and had hard shells, skeletons, or other parts that facilitated their fossilization. Even with its limitations, however, the fossil record is a remarkably detailed account of biological change over the vast scale of geologic time. Furthermore, as shown by the recently unearthed fossils of whale ancestors with hind limbs (see Figures 22.19 and 22.20), gaps in the fossil record continue to be filled by new discoveries.

Although some of these new discoveries are fortuitous, others illustrate the predictive nature of paleontology. For instance, researchers seeking to discover a close ancestor of early terrestrial vertebrates predicted that such a fossil would most likely be located in a river bed (which would have sedimentary rocks) containing rocks that were 375 million years old (an age based on previously known fossils). After digging for several years in one of the few such places on Earth, their predictions bore fruit with the discovery of *Tiktaalik*, an aquatic organism closely related to the first vertebrates to walk on land (see Figures 25.4 and 34.20).

Figure 25.4 Documenting the history of life. These fossils illustrate representative organisms from different points in time. Although prokaryotes and unicellular eukaryotes are only shown at the base of the diagram, these organisms continue to thrive today. In fact, most organisms on Earth are unicellular.

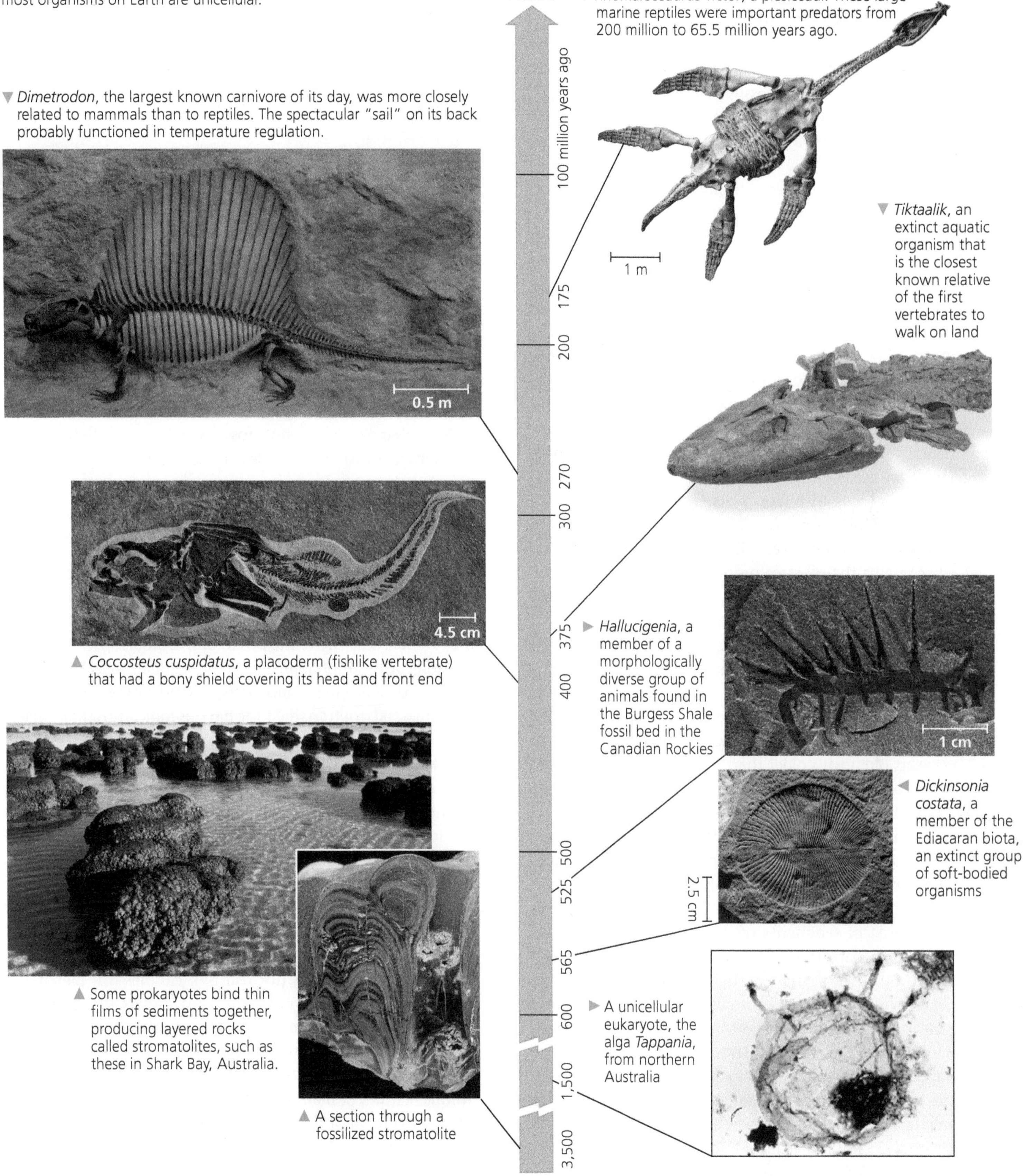

Rhomaleosaurus victor, a plesiosaur. These large marine reptiles were important predators from 200 million to 65.5 million years ago.

Dimetrodon, the largest known carnivore of its day, was more closely related to mammals than to reptiles. The spectacular "sail" on its back probably functioned in temperature regulation.

Tiktaalik, an extinct aquatic organism that is the closest known relative of the first vertebrates to walk on land

Coccosteus cuspidatus, a placoderm (fishlike vertebrate) that had a bony shield covering its head and front end

Hallucigenia, a member of a morphologically diverse group of animals found in the Burgess Shale fossil bed in the Canadian Rockies

Dickinsonia costata, a member of the Ediacaran biota, an extinct group of soft-bodied organisms

Some prokaryotes bind thin films of sediments together, producing layered rocks called stromatolites, such as these in Shark Bay, Australia.

A section through a fossilized stromatolite

A unicellular eukaryote, the alga *Tappania*, from northern Australia

How Rocks and Fossils Are Dated

Fossils are valuable data for reconstructing the history of life, but only if we can determine where they fit in that unfolding story. While the order of fossils in rock strata tells us the sequence in which the fossils were laid down—their relative ages—it does not tell us their actual (absolute) ages. Examining the relative positions of fossils in strata is like peeling off layers of wallpaper in an old house. You can determine the sequence in which the layers were applied, but not the year each layer was added.

How can we determine the absolute age of a fossil? (Note that "absolute" dating does not mean errorless dating, but only that an age is given in years rather than relative terms such as *before* and *after*.) One of the most common techniques is **radiometric dating**, which is based on the decay of radioactive isotopes (see Chapter 2). In this process, a radioactive "parent" isotope decays to a "daughter" isotope at a fixed rate. The rate of decay is expressed by the **half-life**, the time required for 50% of the parent isotope to decay (Figure 25.5). Each type of radioactive isotope has a characteristic half-life, which is not affected by temperature, pressure, or other environmental variables. For example, carbon-14 decays relatively quickly; it has a half-life of 5,730 years. Uranium-238 decays slowly; its half-life is 4.5 billion years.

Fossils contain isotopes of elements that accumulated in the organisms when they were alive. For example, a living organism contains the most common carbon isotope, carbon-12, as well as a radioactive isotope, carbon-14. When the organism dies, it stops accumulating carbon, and the amount of carbon-12 in its tissues does not change over time. However, the carbon-14 that it contains at the time of death slowly decays into another element, nitrogen-14. Thus, by measuring the ratio of carbon-14 to carbon-12 in a fossil, we can determine the fossil's age. This method works for fossils up to about 75,000 years old; fossils older than that contain too little carbon-14 to be detected with current techniques. Radioactive isotopes with longer half-lives are used to date older fossils.

Determining the age of these older fossils in sedimentary rocks is challenging. Organisms do not use radioisotopes with long half-lives, such as uranium-238, to build their bones or shells. Moreover, the sedimentary rocks themselves tend to consist of sediments of differing ages. Though we usually cannot date these old fossils directly, an indirect method can be used to infer the age of fossils that are sandwiched between two layers of volcanic rocks. As lava cools into volcanic rock, radioisotopes from the surrounding environment become trapped in the newly formed rock. Some of the trapped radioisotopes have long half-lives, allowing geologists to estimate the ages of ancient volcanic rocks. If two volcanic layers surrounding fossils are determined to be 525 million and 535 million years old, for example, then the fossils are roughly 530 million years old.

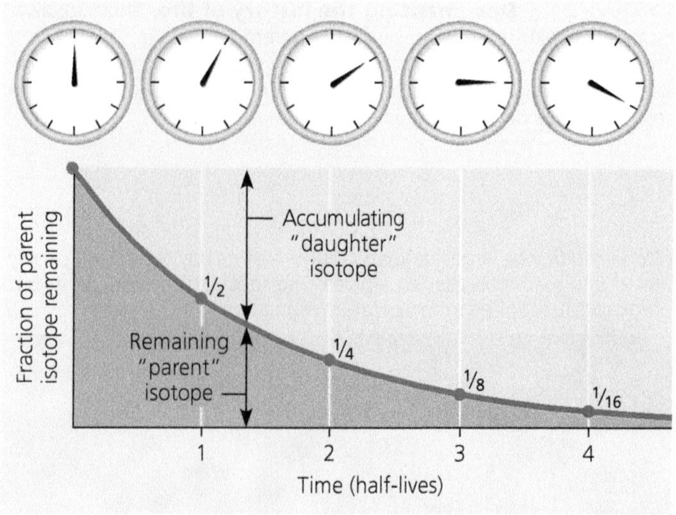

▲ **Figure 25.5 Radiometric dating.** In this diagram, each division of the clock face represents a half-life.

DRAW IT *Relabel the x-axis of this graph with time measurements in years to illustrate the radioactive decay of uranium-238 (half-life = 4.5 billion years).*

Now that we've seen how fossils can be dated, let's turn to an example of what we can learn from them.

The Origin of New Groups of Organisms

Some fossils provide a detailed look at the origin of new groups of organisms. Such fossils are central to our understanding of evolution; they illustrate how new features arise and how long it takes for such changes to occur. We'll examine one such case here: the origin of mammals.

Along with amphibians and reptiles, mammals belong to the group of animals called *tetrapods* (from the Greek *tetra*, four, and *pod*, foot), named for having four limbs. Mammals have a number of unique anatomical features that fossilize readily, allowing scientists to trace their origin. For example, the lower jaw is composed of one bone (the dentary) in mammals but several bones in other tetrapods. In addition, the lower and upper jaws hinge between a different set of bones in mammals than in other tetrapods. As we'll explore in Chapter 34, mammals also have a unique set of three bones that transmit sound in the middle ear (the hammer, anvil, and stirrup), whereas other tetrapods have only one such bone (the stirrup). Finally, the teeth of mammals are differentiated into incisors (for tearing), canines (for piercing), and the multi-pointed premolars and molars (for crushing and grinding). In contrast, the teeth of other tetrapods usually consist of a row of undifferentiated, single-pointed teeth.

As detailed in Figure 25.6, the fossil record shows that the unique features of mammalian jaws and teeth evolved gradually over time, in a series of steps. As you study Figure 25.6, bear in mind that it includes just a few examples of the fossil skulls that document the origin of mammals. If all the

▼ Figure 25.6

Exploring The Origin of Mammals

Over the course of 120 million years, mammals originated gradually from a group of tetrapods called synapsids. Shown here are a few of the many fossil organisms whose morphological features represent intermediate steps between living mammals and their synapsid ancestors. The evolutionary context of the origin of mammals is shown in the tree diagram at right (the dagger symbol † indicates extinct lineages).

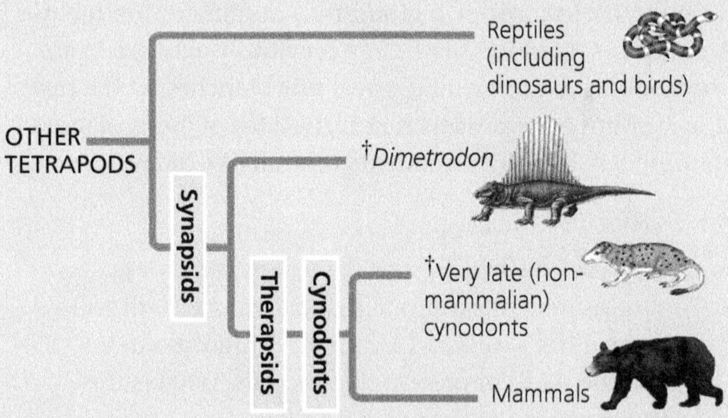

Key to skull bones

- Articular
- Quadrate
- Dentary
- Squamosal

Synapsid (300 mya)

Synapsids had multiple bones in the lower jaw and single-pointed teeth. The jaw hinge was formed by the articular and quadrate bones. Synapsids also had an opening called the *temporal fenestra* behind the eye socket. Powerful cheek muscles for closing the jaws probably passed through the temporal fenestra. Over time, this opening enlarged and moved in front of the hinge between the lower and upper jaws, thereby increasing the power and precision with which the jaws could be closed (much as moving a doorknob away from the hinge makes a door easier to close).

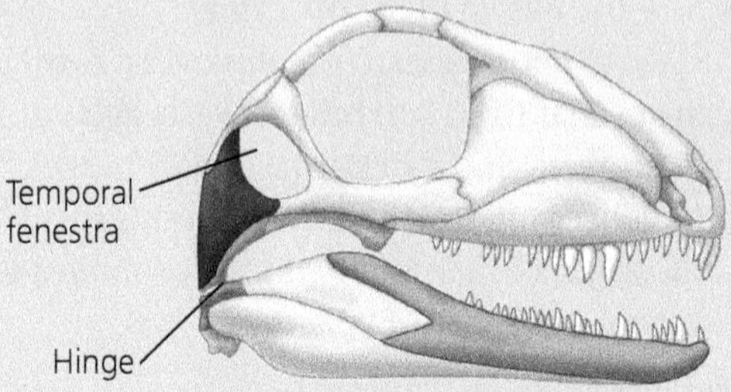

Therapsid (280 mya)

Later, a group of synapsids called therapsids appeared. Therapsids had large dentary bones, long faces, and the first examples of specialized teeth, large canines. These trends continued in a group of therapsids called cynodonts.

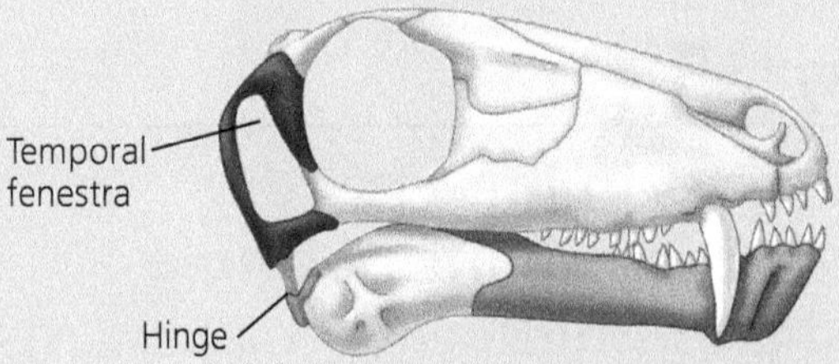

Early cynodont (260 mya)

In early cynodont therapsids, the dentary was the largest bone in the lower jaw, the temporal fenestra was large and positioned forward of the jaw hinge, and teeth with several cusps first appeared (not visible in the diagram). As in earlier synapsids, the jaw had an articular-quadrate hinge.

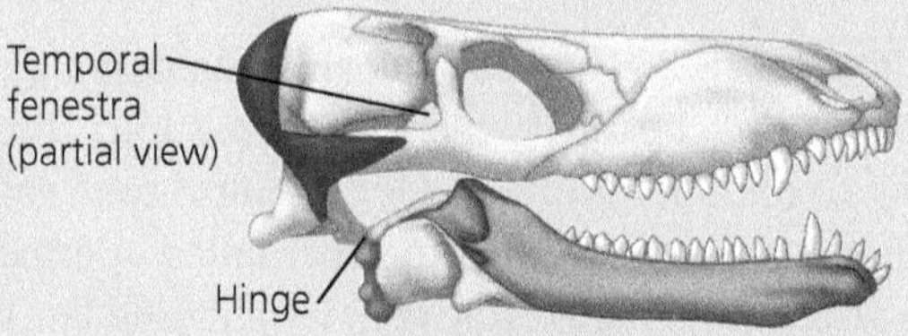

Later cynodont (220 mya)

Later cynodonts had teeth with complex cusp patterns and their lower and upper jaws hinged in two locations: They retained the original articular-quadrate hinge and formed a new, second hinge between the dentary and squamosal bones. (The temporal fenestra is not visible in this or the below cynodont skull at the angles shown.)

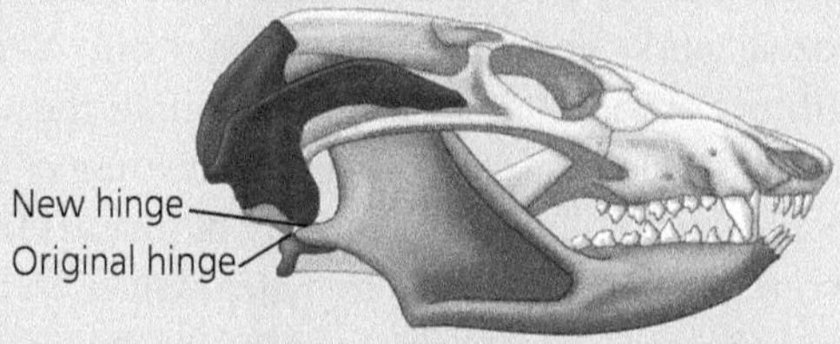

Very late cynodont (195 mya)

In some very late (non-mammalian) cynodonts and early mammals, the original articular-quadrate hinge was lost, leaving the dentary-squamosal hinge as the only hinge between the lower and upper jaws, as in living mammals. The articular and quadrate bones migrated into the ear region (not shown), where they functioned in transmitting sound. In the mammal lineage, these two bones later evolved into the familiar hammer (malleus) and anvil (incus) shown in Figure 34.31.

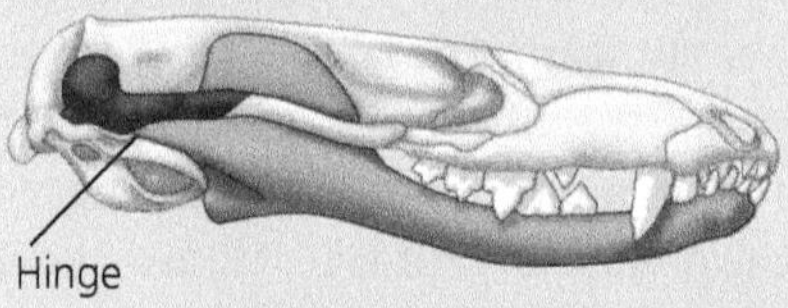

known fossils in the sequence were arranged by shape and placed side by side, their features would blend smoothly from one group to the next. Some of these fossils would reflect how the features of a group that dominates life today, the mammals, gradually arose in a previously existing group, the cynodonts. Others would reveal side branches on the tree of life—groups of organisms that thrived for millions of years but ultimately left no descendants that survive today.

CONCEPT CHECK 25.2

1. Your measurements indicate that a fossilized skull you unearthed has a carbon-14/carbon-12 ratio about 1/16 that of the skulls of present-day animals. What is the approximate age of the fossilized skull?
2. Describe an example from the fossil record that shows how life has changed over time.
3. **WHAT IF?** Suppose researchers discover a fossil of an organism that lived 300 million years ago but had mammalian teeth and a mammalian jaw hinge. What inferences might you draw from this fossil about the origin of mammals and the evolution of novel skeletal structures? Explain.

For suggested answers, see Appendix A.

CONCEPT **25.3**

Key events in life's history include the origins of single-celled and multicelled organisms and the colonization of land

The study of fossils has helped geologists establish a **geologic record** of Earth's history, which is divided into three eons (Table 25.1, on the facing page). The first two eons—the Archaean and the Proterozoic—together lasted approximately 4 billion years. The Phanerozoic eon, roughly the last half billion years, encompasses most of the time that animals have existed on Earth. It is divided into three eras: the Paleozoic, Mesozoic, and Cenozoic. Each era represents a distinct age in the history of Earth and its life. For example, the Mesozoic era is sometimes called the "age of reptiles" because of its abundance of reptilian fossils, including those of dinosaurs. The boundaries between the eras correspond to major extinction events seen in the fossil record, when many forms of life disappeared and were replaced by forms that evolved from the survivors.

As we've seen, the fossil record provides a sweeping overview of the history of life over geologic time. Here we will focus on a few major events in that history, returning to study the details in Unit Five. Figure 25.7 uses the analogy of a clock to place these events in the context of the geologic record. This clock will reappear at various points in this section as a quick visual reminder of when the events we are discussing took place.

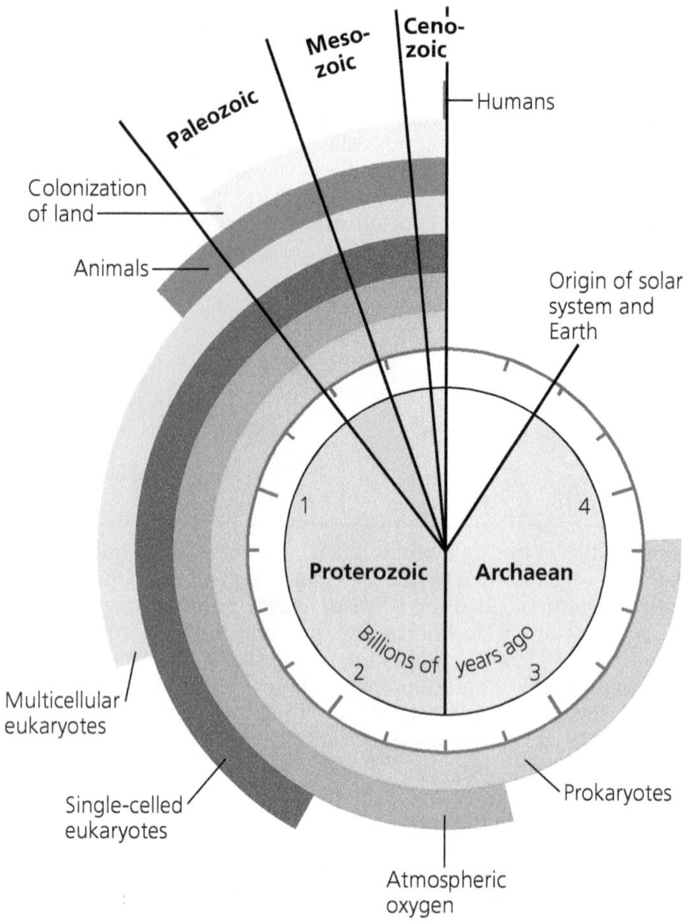

▲ **Figure 25.7 Clock analogy for some key events in Earth's history.** The clock ticks down from the origin of Earth 4.6 billion years ago to the present.

The First Single-Celled Organisms

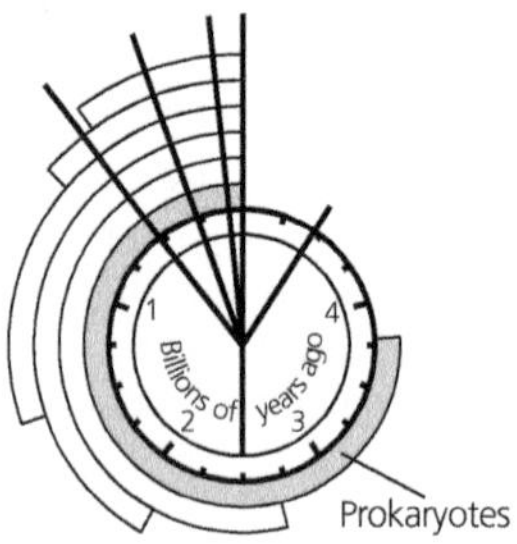

The earliest direct evidence of life, dating from 3.5 billion years ago, comes from fossilized stromatolites (see Figure 25.4). **Stromatolites** are layered rocks that form when certain prokaryotes bind thin films of sediment together. Present-day stromatolites are found in a few warm, shallow, salty bays. If microbial communities complex enough to form stromatolites existed 3.5 billion years ago, it is a reasonable hypothesis that single-celled organisms originated much earlier, perhaps as early as 3.9 billion years ago.

Early prokaryotes were Earth's sole inhabitants from at least 3.5 billion years ago to about 2.1 billion years ago. As we will see, these prokaryotes transformed life on our planet.

Table 25.1 The Geologic Record

Relative Duration of Eons	Era	Period	Epoch	Age (Millions of Years Ago)	Some Important Events in the History of Life
Phan-erozoic	Cenozoic	Quaternary	Holocene		Historical time
				0.01	
			Pleistocene		Ice ages; origin of genus *Homo*
				2.6	
		Neogene	Pliocene		Appearance of bipedal human ancestors
				5.3	
			Miocene		Continued radiation of mammals and angiosperms; earliest direct human ancestors
				23	
		Paleogene	Oligocene		Origins of many primate groups
				33.9	
			Eocene		Angiosperm dominance increases; continued radiation of most present-day mammalian orders
				55.8	
			Paleocene		Major radiation of mammals, birds, and pollinating insects
				65.5	
	Mesozoic	Cretaceous			Flowering plants (angiosperms) appear and diversify; many groups of organisms, including most dinosaurs, become extinct at end of period
				145.5	
		Jurassic			Gymnosperms continue as dominant plants; dinosaurs abundant and diverse
				199.6	
		Triassic			Cone-bearing plants (gymnosperms) dominate landscape; dinosaurs evolve and radiate; origin of mammals
				251	
	Paleozoic	Permian			Radiation of reptiles; origin of most present-day groups of insects; extinction of many marine and terrestrial organisms at end of period
				299	
		Carboniferous			Extensive forests of vascular plants form; first seed plants appear; origin of reptiles; amphibians dominant
				359	
		Devonian			Diversification of bony fishes; first tetrapods and insects appear
				416	
		Silurian			Diversification of early vascular plants
				444	
		Ordovician			Marine algae abundant; colonization of land by diverse fungi, plants, and animals
				488	
		Cambrian			Sudden increase in diversity of many animal phyla (Cambrian explosion)
				542	
Proter-ozoic		Ediacaran			Diverse algae and soft-bodied invertebrate animals appear
				635	
				2,100	Oldest fossils of eukaryotic cells appear
				2,500	
Archaean				2,700	Concentration of atmospheric oxygen begins to increase
				3,500	Oldest fossils of cells (prokaryotes) appear
				3,800	Oldest known rocks on Earth's surface
				Approx. 4,600	Origin of Earth

Photosynthesis and the Oxygen Revolution

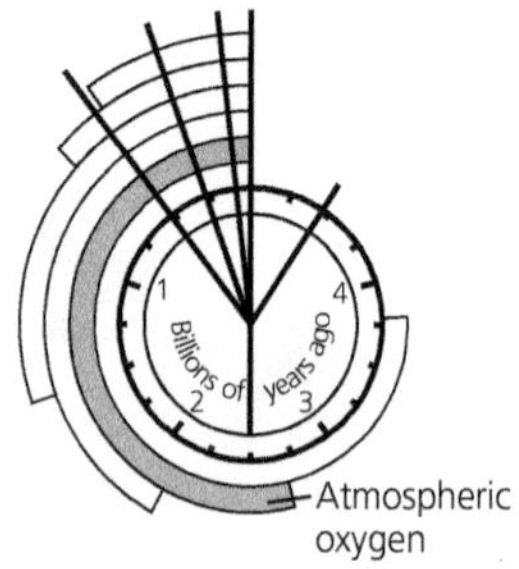

Most atmospheric oxygen gas (O_2) is of biological origin, produced during the water-splitting step of photosynthesis. When oxygenic photosynthesis first evolved, the free O_2 it produced probably dissolved in the surrounding water until it reached a high enough concentration to react with dissolved iron. This would have caused the iron to precipitate as iron oxide, which accumulated as sediments. These sediments were compressed into banded iron formations, red layers of rock containing iron oxide that are a source of iron ore today. Once all of the dissolved iron had precipitated, additional O_2 dissolved in the water until the seas and lakes became saturated with O_2. After this occurred, the O_2 finally began to "gas out" of the water and enter the atmosphere. This change left its mark in the rusting of iron-rich terrestrial rocks, a process that began about 2.7 billion years ago. This chronology implies that bacteria similar to today's cyanobacteria (oxygen-releasing, photosynthetic bacteria) originated well before 2.7 billion years ago.

The amount of atmospheric O_2 increased gradually from about 2.7 to 2.3 billion years ago, but then shot up relatively rapidly to between 1% and 10% of its present level (**Figure 25.8**). This "oxygen revolution" had an enormous impact on life. In certain of its chemical forms, oxygen attacks chemical bonds and can inhibit enzymes and damage cells. As a result, the rising concentration of atmospheric O_2 probably doomed many prokaryotic groups. Some species survived in habitats that remained anaerobic, where we find their descendants living today (see Chapter 27). Among other survivors, diverse adaptations to the changing atmosphere evolved, including cellular respiration, which uses O_2 in the process of harvesting the energy stored in organic molecules.

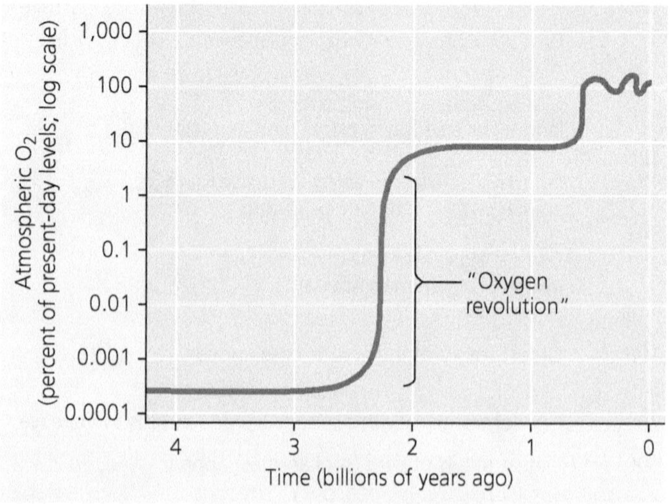

▲ **Figure 25.8 The rise of atmospheric oxygen.** Chemical analyses of ancient rocks have enabled this reconstruction of atmospheric oxygen levels during Earth's history.

As mentioned previously, the early, gradual rise in atmospheric O_2 levels was probably brought about by ancient cyanobacteria. A few hundred million years later, the rise in O_2 accelerated. What caused this acceleration? One hypothesis is that this rise followed the evolution of eukaryotic cells containing chloroplasts, as we will discuss next.

The First Eukaryotes

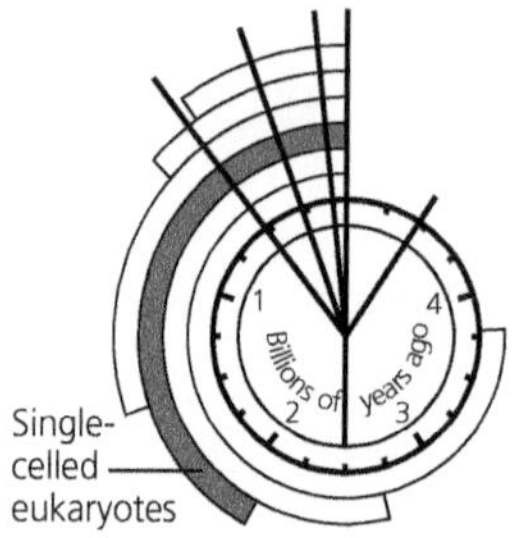

The oldest widely accepted fossils of eukaryotic organisms are about 2.1 billion years old. Recall that eukaryotic cells have more complex organization than prokaryotic cells: Eukaryotic cells have a nuclear envelope, mitochondria, endoplasmic reticulum, and other internal structures that prokaryotes lack. Also, unlike prokaryotic cells, eukaryotic cells have a cytoskeleton, a feature that enables eukaryotic cells to change their shape and thereby surround and engulf other cells.

How did these eukaryotic features evolve from prokaryotic cells? A range of evidence supports the **endosymbiont theory**, which posits that mitochondria and plastids (a general term for chloroplasts and related organelles) were formerly small prokaryotes that began living within larger cells. The term *endosymbiont* refers to a cell that lives within another cell, called the *host cell*. The prokaryotic ancestors of mitochondria and plastids probably gained entry to the host cell as undigested prey or internal parasites. Though such a process may seem unlikely, scientists have directly observed cases in which endosymbionts that began as prey or parasites came to have a mutually beneficial relationship with the host in as little as five years.

By whatever means the relationships began, we can hypothesize how the symbiosis could have become mutually beneficial. A host that is a heterotroph (an organism that eats other organisms or substances derived from them) could use nutrients released from photosynthetic endosymbionts. And in a world that was becoming increasingly aerobic, a host that was itself an anaerobe would have benefited from endosymbionts that turned the oxygen to advantage. Over time, the host and endosymbionts would have become a single organism, its parts inseparable. Although all eukaryotes have mitochondria or remnants of these organelles, they do not all have plastids. Thus, the hypothesis of **serial endosymbiosis** supposes that mitochondria evolved before plastids through a sequence of endosymbiotic events (**Figure 25.9**).

A great deal of evidence supports the endosymbiotic origin of mitochondria and plastids. The inner membranes of both organelles have enzymes and transport systems that are homologous to those found in the plasma membranes of living prokaryotes. Mitochondria and plastids replicate by a splitting process that is similar to that of certain prokaryotes. In addition, each of these organelles contains a single, circular DNA molecule that, like the chromosomes of bacteria, is not associated with histones or large amounts of other proteins. As might be expected of organelles descended from free-living organisms, mitochondria and plastids also have the cellular machinery (including ribosomes) needed to transcribe and translate their DNA into proteins. Finally, in terms of size, RNA sequences, and sensitivity to certain antibiotics, the ribosomes of mitochondria and plastids are more similar to prokaryotic ribosomes than they are to the cytoplasmic ribosomes of eukaryotic cells.

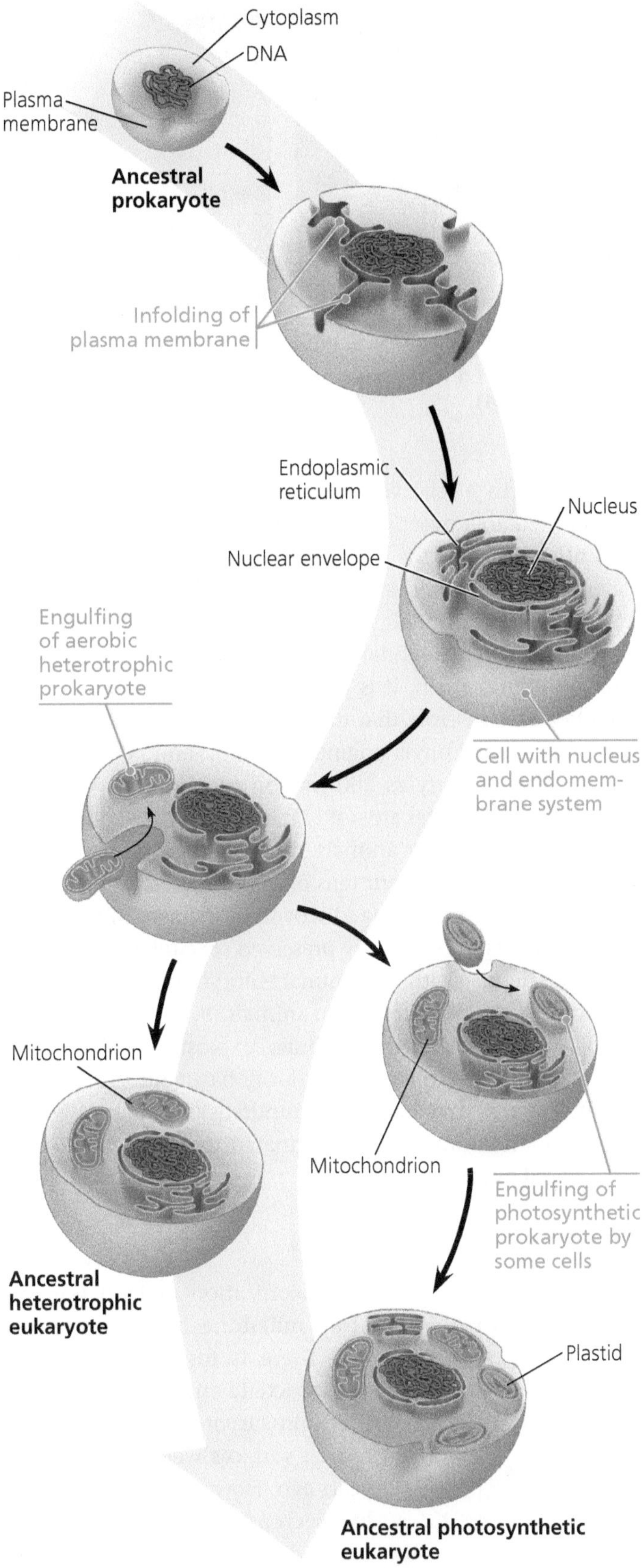

▲ **Figure 25.9 A hypothesis for the origin of eukaryotes through serial endosymbiosis.** The proposed ancestors of mitochondria were aerobic, heterotrophic prokaryotes (meaning they used oxygen to metabolize organic molecules obtained from other organisms). The proposed ancestors of plastids were photosynthetic prokaryotes. In this figure, the arrows represent change over evolutionary time.

The Origin of Multicellularity

An orchestra can play a greater variety of musical compositions than a violin soloist can; the increased complexity of the orchestra makes more variations possible. Likewise, the appearance of structurally complex eukaryotic cells sparked the evolution of greater morphological diversity than was possible for the simpler prokaryotic cells. After the first eukaryotes appeared, a great range of unicellular forms evolved, giving rise to the diversity of single-celled eukaryotes that continue to flourish today. Another wave of diversification also occurred: Some single-celled eukaryotes gave rise to multicellular forms, whose descendants include a variety of algae, plants, fungi, and animals.

The Earliest Multicellular Eukaryotes

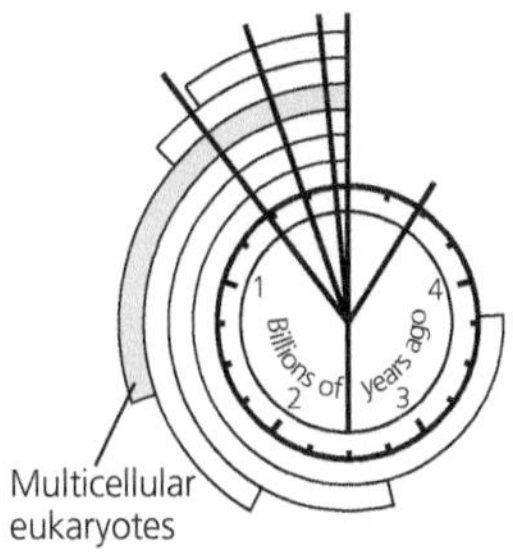

Based on comparisons of DNA sequences, researchers have suggested that the common ancestor of multicellular eukaryotes lived 1.5 billion years ago. This result is in rough agreement with the fossil record; the oldest known fossils of multicellular eukaryotes are of relatively small algae that lived about 1.2 billion years ago. Larger and more diverse multicellular eukaryotes do not appear in the fossil record until about 575 million years ago (see Figure 25.4). These fossils, referred to as the Ediacaran biota, were of soft-bodied organisms—some over 1 m long—that lived from 575 to 535 million years ago.

Why were multicellular eukaryotes limited in size and diversity until the late Proterozoic? One hypothesis stems from geologic evidence indicating that a series of severe ice ages occurred from 750 to 580 million years ago. At various times during this period, glaciers covered all of the planet's landmasses, and the seas were largely iced over. The "snowball Earth" hypothesis suggests that most life would have been confined to areas near deep-sea vents and hot springs or to equatorial regions of the ocean that lacked ice cover. The fossil record of the first major diversification of multicellular eukaryotes (beginning about 575 million years ago) corresponds roughly to the time when snowball Earth thawed. As that diversification came to a close about 40 million years later, the stage was set for another, even more spectacular burst of evolutionary change.

The Cambrian Explosion

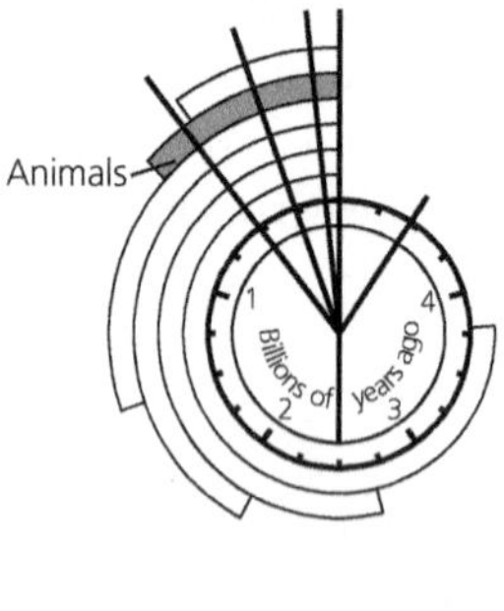

Many present-day animal phyla appear suddenly in fossils formed early in the Cambrian period (535–525 million years ago), a phenomenon referred to as the **Cambrian explosion**. Fossils of several animal groups—sponges, cnidarians (sea anemones and their relatives), and molluscs—appear in even older rocks dating from the late Proterozoic (Figure 25.10).

Prior to the Cambrian explosion, all large animals were soft-bodied. The fossils of large pre-Cambrian animals reveal little evidence of predation. Instead, these animals appear to have been grazers (feeding on algae), suspension feeders, or scavengers, not hunters. The Cambrian explosion changed all of that. In a relatively short period of time (10 million years), predators over 1 m in length emerged that had claws and other features for capturing prey; simultaneously, new defensive adaptations, such as sharp spines and heavy body armor, appeared in their prey (see Figure 25.4).

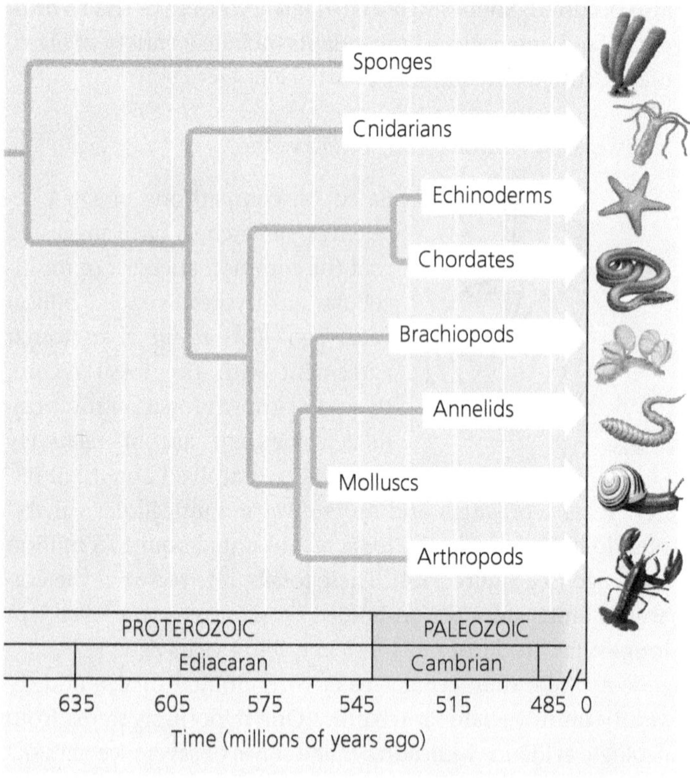

▲ **Figure 25.10 Appearance of selected animal groups.** The white bars indicate earliest appearances of these animal groups in the fossil record.

DRAW IT *Circle the branch point that represents the most recent common ancestor of chordates and annelids. What is a minimum estimate of that ancestor's age?*

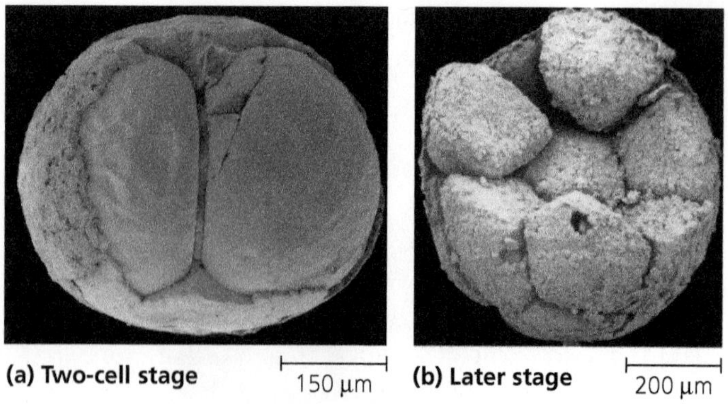

▲ **Figure 25.11 Proterozoic fossils that may be animal embryos (SEM).**

Although the Cambrian explosion had an enormous impact on life on Earth, it is possible that many animal phyla originated long before that time. Some DNA analyses suggest that most animal phyla originated and began to diverge from one another as early as 700 million to 1 billion years ago. Even if these estimates are not correct, recent fossil discoveries in China suggest that animals similar to members of living animal phyla were present tens of millions of years before the Cambrian explosion. The discoveries include 575-million-year-old fossils of beautifully preserved specimens interpreted by most scientists either as animal embryos or as members of extinct groups closely related to animals (Figure 25.11). Overall, it appears that the Cambrian explosion had a "long fuse"—at least 40 million years long, based on the Chinese fossils. The fuse may have been hundreds of millions of years long if some animal phyla originated as far back as some DNA-based estimates suggest.

The Colonization of Land

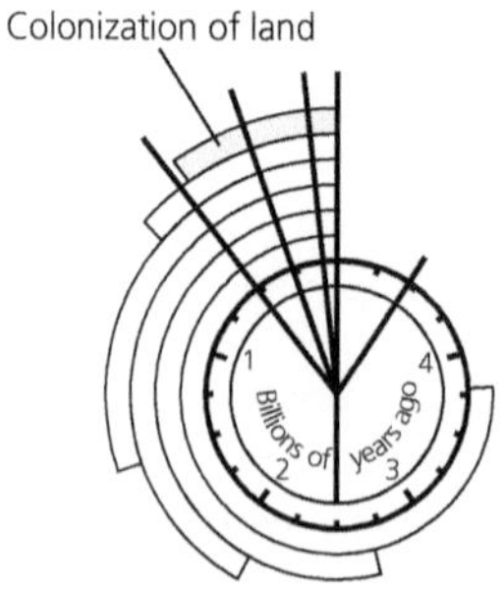

The colonization of land was another milestone in the history of life. There is fossil evidence that cyanobacteria and other photosynthetic prokaryotes coated damp terrestrial surfaces well over a billion years ago. However, larger forms of life, such as fungi, plants, and animals, did not begin to colonize land until about 500 million years ago. This gradual evolutionary venture out of aquatic environments was associated with adaptations that made it possible to reproduce on land and that helped prevent dehydration. For example, many land plants today have a vascular system for transporting materials internally and a waterproof coating of wax on their leaves that slows the loss of water to the air. Early signs of these adaptations were present 420 million years ago, at which time small plants (about 10 cm high) existed that had a vascular system but lacked true roots or leaves. By about 50 million years later, plants had diversified greatly and included reeds and treelike plants with true roots and leaves.

Plants colonized land in the company of fungi. Even today, the roots of most plants are associated with fungi that aid in the absorption of water and minerals from the soil (see Chapter 31). These root fungi, in turn, obtain their organic nutrients from the plants. Such mutually beneficial associations of plants and fungi are evident in some of the oldest fossilized roots, dating this relationship back to the early spread of life onto land.

Although many animal groups are now represented in terrestrial environments, the most widespread and diverse land animals are arthropods (particularly insects and spiders) and tetrapods. Arthropods were the first animals to colonize land, roughly 420 million years ago. The earliest tetrapods found in the fossil record lived about 365 million years ago and appear to have evolved from a group of lobe-finned fishes (see Chapter 34). Tetrapods include humans, although we are late arrivals on the scene. The human lineage diverged from other primates around 6–7 million years ago, and our species originated only about 195,000 years ago. If the clock of Earth's history were rescaled to represent an hour, humans appeared less than 0.2 second ago.

CONCEPT CHECK 25.3

1. The first appearance of free oxygen in the atmosphere likely triggered a massive wave of extinctions among the prokaryotes of the time. Why?
2. What evidence supports the hypothesis that mitochondria preceded plastids in the evolution of eukaryotic cells?
3. **WHAT IF?** What would a fossil record of life today look like?

For suggested answers, see Appendix A.

CONCEPT 25.4

The rise and fall of groups of organisms reflect differences in speciation and extinction rates

From its beginnings, life on Earth has seen the rise and fall of groups of organisms. Anaerobic prokaryotes originated, flourished, and then declined as the oxygen content of the atmosphere rose. Billions of years later, the first tetrapods emerged from the sea, giving rise to several major new groups of organisms. One of these, the amphibians, went on to dominate life on land for 100 million years, until other tetrapods (including dinosaurs and, later, mammals) replaced them as the dominant terrestrial vertebrates.

The rise and fall of these and other major groups of organisms have shaped the history of life. Narrowing our focus, we can also see that the rise or fall of any particular group is related to the speciation and extinction rates of its member species. Just as a population increases in size when there are more births than deaths, the rise of a group of organisms occurs when it produces more new species than are lost to extinction. The reverse occurs when a group is in decline. As we'll see, such changes in the fates of groups of organisms have been influenced by large-scale processes such as plate tectonics, mass extinctions, and adaptive radiations.

Plate Tectonics

If photographs of Earth were taken from space every 10,000 years and spliced together to make a movie, it would show something many of us find hard to imagine: The seemingly "rock solid" continents we live on move over time. Since the origin of multicellular eukaryotes roughly 1.5 billion years ago, there have been three occasions (1.1 billion, 600 million, and 250 million years ago) when most of the landmasses of Earth came together to form a supercontinent, then later broke apart. Each time they yielded a different configuration of continents. Looking into the future, some geologists have estimated that the continents will come together again and form a new supercontinent roughly 250 million years from now.

According to the theory of **plate tectonics**, the continents are part of great plates of Earth's crust that essentially float on the hot, underlying portion of the mantle (Figure 25.12). Movements in the mantle cause the plates to move over time in a process called *continental drift*. Geologists can measure the rate at which the plates are moving now, usually only a few centimeters per year. They can also infer the past locations of the continents using the magnetic signal recorded in rocks at the time of their formation. This method works because as a continent shifts its position over time, the direction of magnetic north recorded in its newly formed rocks also changes.

▶ **Figure 25.12 Cutaway view of Earth.** The thickness of the crust is exaggerated here.

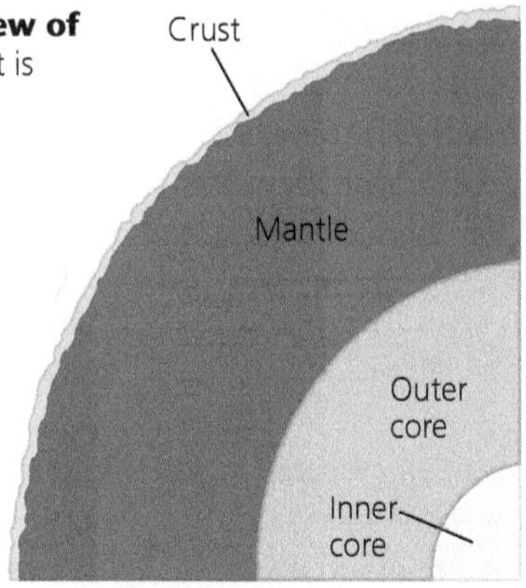

Earth's major tectonic plates are shown in Figure 25.13. Many important geologic processes, including the formation of mountains and islands, occur at plate boundaries. In some cases, two plates are moving away from each other, as are the North American and Eurasian plates, which are currently drifting apart at a rate of about 2 cm per year. In other cases, two plates are sliding past each other, forming regions where earthquakes are common. California's infamous San Andreas Fault is part of a border where two plates slide past each other. In still other cases, two plates are colliding. Typically, oceanic plates (those found on the bottom of the ocean) are more dense than terrestrial plates. As a result, when an oceanic plate collides with a terrestrial plate, the oceanic plate usually sinks below the terrestrial plate. When two oceanic plates or two terrestrial plates collide with each other, violent upheavals occur and mountains form along the plate boundaries. One spectacular example of this occurred 45 million years ago, when the Indian plate crashed into the Eurasian plate, starting the formation of the Himalayan mountains.

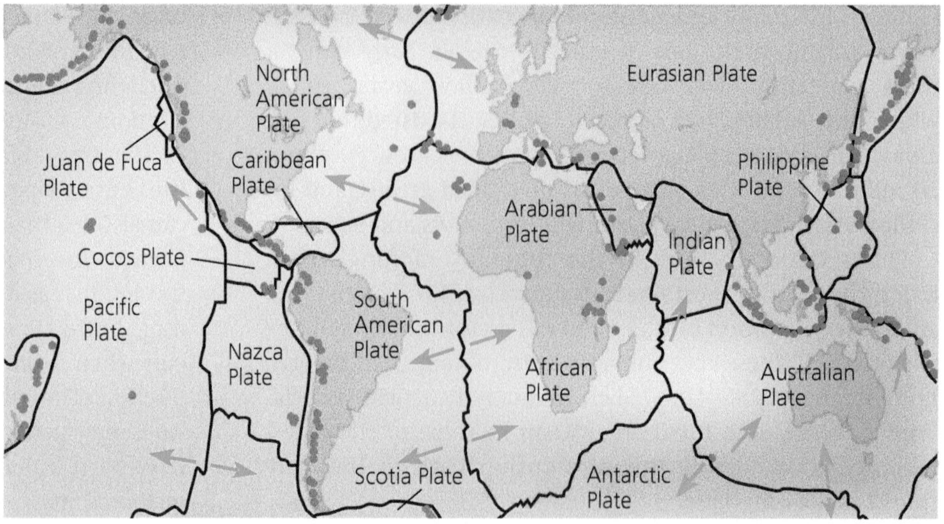

▲ Figure 25.13 **Earth's major tectonic plates.** The arrows indicate direction of movement. The reddish orange dots represent zones of violent tectonic activity.

Consequences of Continental Drift

Plate movements rearrange geography slowly, but their cumulative effects are dramatic. In addition to reshaping the physical features of our planet, continental drift also has a major impact on life on Earth.

One reason for its great impact on life is that continental drift alters the habitats in which organisms live. Consider the changes shown in Figure 25.14. About 250 million years ago, plate movements brought all the previously separated landmasses together into a supercontinent named **Pangaea**. Ocean basins became deeper, which lowered sea level and drained shallow coastal seas. At that time, as now, most marine species inhabited shallow waters, and the formation of Pangaea destroyed a considerable amount of that habitat. The interior of the vast continent was cold and dry, probably an even more severe environment than that of central Asia today. Overall, the formation of Pangaea had a tremendous impact on the physical environment and climate, which drove some species to extinction and provided new opportunities for groups of organisms that survived the crisis.

Another aspect of continental drift that affects organisms is the climate change that results when a continent shifts its location. The southern tip of Labrador, Canada, for example, once was located in the tropics but has moved 40° to the north over the last 200 million years. When faced with the changes in climate that such shifts in position entail, organisms adapt,

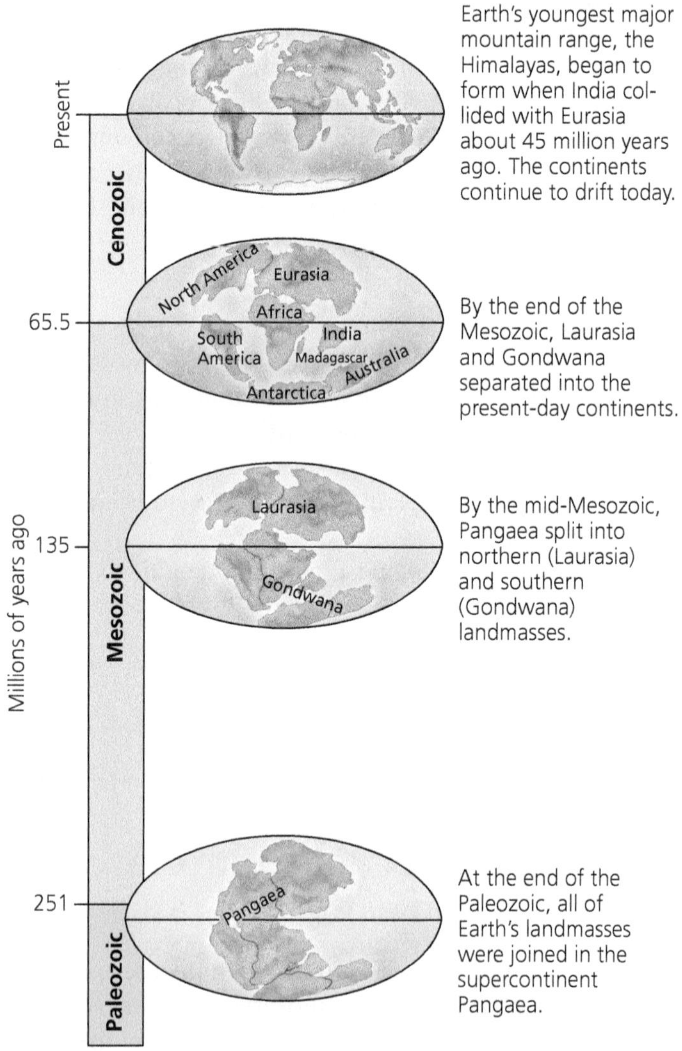

▲ Figure 25.14 **The history of continental drift during the Phanerozoic eon.**

move to a new location, or become extinct (this last outcome occurred for many organisms stranded on Antarctica).

Continental drift also promotes allopatric speciation on a grand scale. When supercontinents break apart, regions that once were connected become geographically isolated. As the continents drifted apart over the last 200 million years, each became a separate evolutionary arena, with lineages of plants and animals that diverged from those on other continents.

Finally, continental drift can help explain puzzles about the geographic distribution of extinct organisms, such as why fossils of the same species of Permian freshwater reptiles have been discovered in both Brazil and the West African nation of Ghana. These two parts of the world, now separated by 3,000 km of ocean, were joined together when these reptiles were living. Continental drift also explains much about the current distributions of organisms, such as why Australian fauna and flora contrast so sharply with those of the rest of the world. Marsupial mammals fill ecological roles in Australia analogous to those filled by eutherians (placental mammals) on other continents (see Figure 22.18). Fossil evidence suggests that marsupials originated in what is now Asia and reached Australia via South America and Antarctica while the continents were still joined. The subsequent breakup of the southern continents set Australia "afloat" like a giant raft of marsupials. In Australia, marsupials diversified, and the few eutherians that lived there became extinct; on other continents, most marsupials became extinct, and the eutherians diversified.

Mass Extinctions

The fossil record shows that the overwhelming majority of species that ever lived are now extinct. A species may become extinct for many reasons. Its habitat may have been destroyed, or its environment may have changed in a manner unfavorable to the species. For example, if ocean temperatures fall by even a few degrees, species that are otherwise well adapted may perish. Even if physical factors in the environment remain stable, biological factors may change—the origin of one species can spell doom for another.

Although extinction occurs on a regular basis, at certain times disruptive global environmental changes have caused the rate of extinction to increase dramatically. When this occurs, a **mass extinction** results, in which large numbers of species become extinct throughout Earth.

The "Big Five" Mass Extinction Events

Five mass extinctions are documented in the fossil record over the past 500 million years (**Figure 25.15**). These events are particularly well documented for the decimation of hard-bodied animals that lived in shallow seas, the organisms for which the fossil record is most complete. In each mass extinction, 50% or more of Earth's marine species became extinct.

Two mass extinctions—the Permian and the Cretaceous—have received the most attention. The Permian mass extinction, which defines the boundary between the Paleozoic and Mesozoic eras (251 million years ago), claimed about 96% of marine animal species and drastically altered life in the ocean.

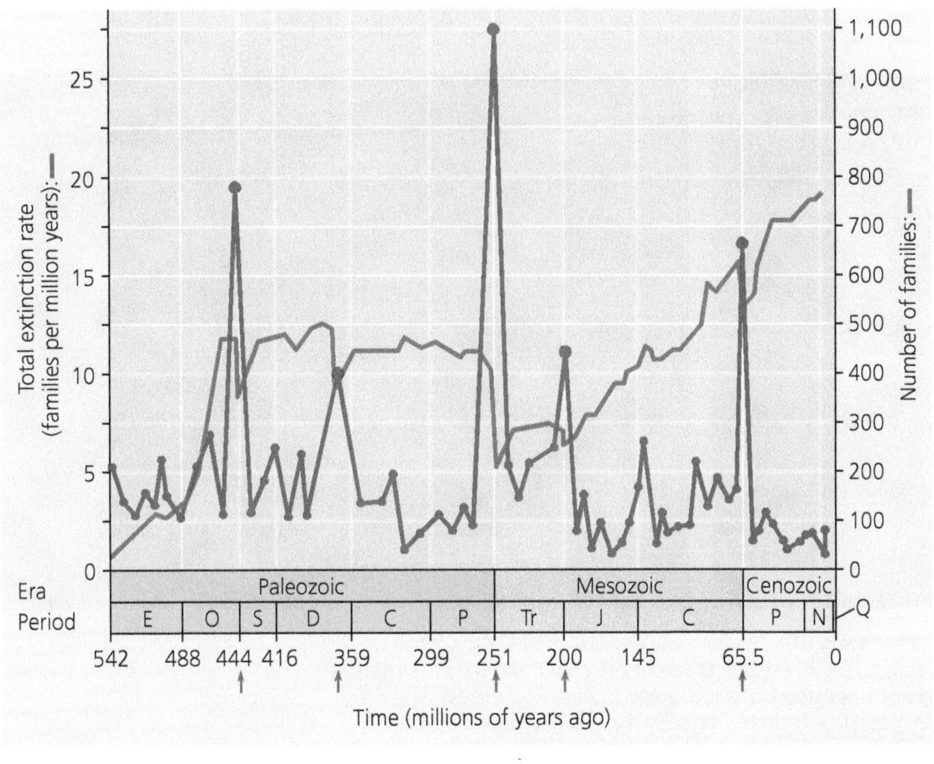

◄ **Figure 25.15 Mass extinction and the diversity of life.** The five generally recognized mass extinction events, indicated by red arrows, represent peaks in the extinction rate of marine animal families (red line and left vertical axis). These mass extinctions interrupted the overall increase in the number of marine animal families over time (blue line and right vertical axis).

? *96% of marine animal species became extinct in the Permian mass extinction. Explain why the blue curve shows only a 50% drop at that time.*

Terrestrial life was also affected. For example, 8 out of 27 known orders of insects were wiped out. This mass extinction occurred in less than 500,000 years, possibly in just a few thousand years—an instant in the context of geologic time.

The Permian mass extinction occurred at the time of enormous volcanic eruptions in what is now Siberia. This period was the most extreme episode of volcanism to have occurred during the past half billion years. Geologic data indicate that an area of 1.6 million km^2 (roughly half the size of western Europe) was covered with a layer of lava hundreds to thousands of meters thick. Besides spewing enormous amounts of lava and ash, the eruptions may have produced enough carbon dioxide to warm the global climate by an estimated 6°C. Reduced temperature differences between the equator and the poles could have slowed the mixing of ocean water, which in turn could have led to a widespread drop in oxygen concentrations. The resulting low-oxygen condition, called *ocean anoxia*, would have suffocated oxygen-breathers and promoted the growth of anaerobic bacteria that emit a poisonous metabolic by-product, hydrogen sulfide (H_2S) gas. As this gas bubbled into the atmosphere, it could have caused further extinctions by directly killing land plants and animals and by initiating chemical reactions that destroy the ozone layer, a "shield" that ordinarily protects organisms from life-threatening levels of UV radiation.

The Cretaceous mass extinction occurred about 65.5 million years ago and marks the boundary between the Mesozoic and Cenozoic eras. This event extinguished more than half of all marine species and eliminated many families of terrestrial plants and animals, including all dinosaurs (except birds, which are members of the same group; see Chapter 34). One clue to a possible cause of the Cretaceous mass extinction is a thin layer of clay enriched in iridium that separates sediments from the Mesozoic and Cenozoic eras. Iridium is an element that is very rare on Earth but common in many of the meteorites and other extraterrestrial objects that occasionally fall to Earth. Walter Alvarez and the late Luis Alvarez, of the University of California, Berkeley, and their colleagues proposed that this clay is fallout from a huge cloud of debris that billowed into the atmosphere when an asteroid or large comet collided with Earth. This cloud would have blocked sunlight and severely disturbed the global climate for several months.

Is there evidence of such an asteroid or comet? Research has focused on the Chicxulub crater, a 65-million-year-old scar beneath sediments off the Yucatán coast of Mexico (**Figure 25.16**). The crater is the right size to have been caused by an object with a diameter of 10 km. Critical evaluation of this and other hypotheses for mass extinctions continues.

Is a Sixth Mass Extinction Under Way?

As we will explore in Chapter 56, human actions, such as habitat destruction, are modifying the global environment to such an extent that many species are threatened with extinction. More than a thousand species have become extinct in the last 400 years. Scientists estimate that this rate is 100 to 1,000 times the typical background rate seen in the fossil record. Is a sixth mass extinction now in progress?

This question is difficult to answer, in part because it is hard to document the total number of extinctions occurring today. Tropical rain forests, for example, harbor many undiscovered

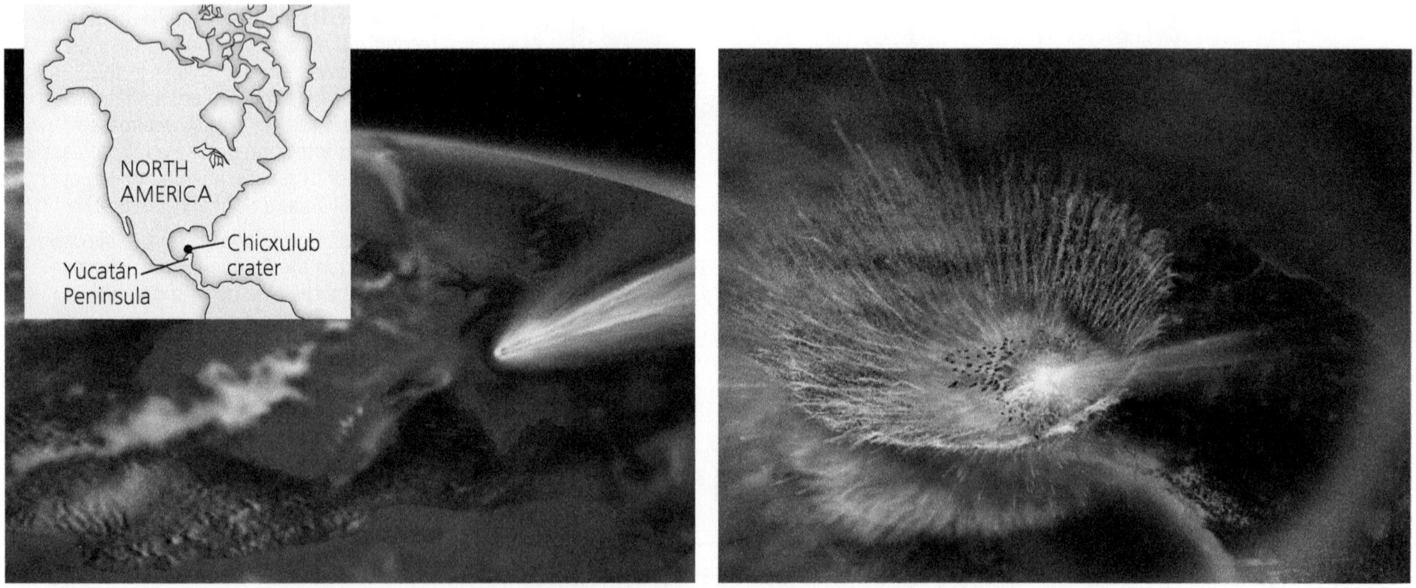

▲ **Figure 25.16 Trauma for Earth and its Cretaceous life.** Beneath the Caribbean Sea, the 65-million-year-old Chicxulub impact crater measures 180 km across. The horseshoe shape of the crater and the pattern of debris in sedimentary rocks indicate that an asteroid or comet struck at a low angle from the southeast. This artist's interpretation represents the impact and its immediate effect: a cloud of hot vapor and debris that could have killed many of the plants and animals in North America within hours.

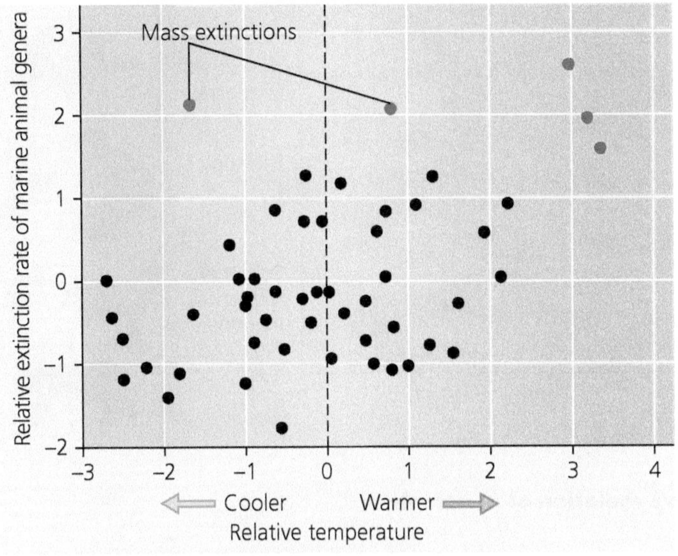

▲ **Figure 25.17 Fossil extinctions and temperature.** Extinction rates increased when global temperatures were high. Temperatures were estimated using ratios of oxygen isotopes and converted to an index in which 0 is the overall average temperature.

species. As a result, destroying tropical forest may drive species to extinction before we even learn of their existence. Such uncertainties make it hard to assess the full extent of the current extinction crisis. Even so, it is clear that losses to date have not reached those of the "big five" mass extinctions, in which large percentages of Earth's species became extinct. This does not in any way discount the seriousness of today's situation. Monitoring programs show that many species are declining at an alarming rate, and studies on polar bears, pine trees, and other species suggest that climate change may hasten some of these declines. Indeed, the fossil record indicates that over the last 500 million years, extinction rates have tended to increase when global temperatures were high (Figure 25.17). Overall, present-day and fossil evidence both suggest that unless dramatic actions are taken, a sixth, human-caused mass extinction is likely to occur within the next few centuries or millennia.

Consequences of Mass Extinctions

Mass extinctions have significant and long-term effects. By eliminating large numbers of species, a mass extinction can reduce a thriving and complex ecological community to a pale shadow of its former self. And once an evolutionary lineage disappears, it cannot reappear. The course of evolution is changed forever. Consider what would have happened if the early primates living 66 million years ago had died out in the Cretaceous mass extinction. Humans would not exist, and life on Earth would differ greatly from what it is today.

The fossil record shows that it typically takes 5–10 million years for the diversity of life to recover to previous levels after a mass extinction. In some cases, it has taken much longer than that: It took about 100 million years for the number of marine families to recover after the Permian mass extinction (see Figure 25.15). These data have sobering implications. If current trends continue and a sixth mass extinction occurs, it will take millions of years for life on Earth to recover.

Mass extinctions can also alter ecological communities by changing the types of organisms found in them. For example, after the Permian and Cretaceous mass extinctions, the percentage of marine organisms that were predators increased substantially (Figure 25.18). A rise in the number of predator species can increase both the pressures faced by prey and the competition among predators for food. In addition, mass extinctions can curtail lineages with highly advantageous features. For example, in the late Triassic a group of gastropods (snails and their relatives) arose that could drill through the shells of bivalves (such as clams) and feed on the animals inside. Although shell drilling provided access to a new and abundant source of food, this newly formed group was wiped out during the mass extinction at the end of the Triassic (about 200 million years ago). Another 120 million years passed before another group of gastropods (the oyster drills) exhibited the ability to drill through shells. As their predecessors might have done if they had not originated at an unfortunate time, oyster

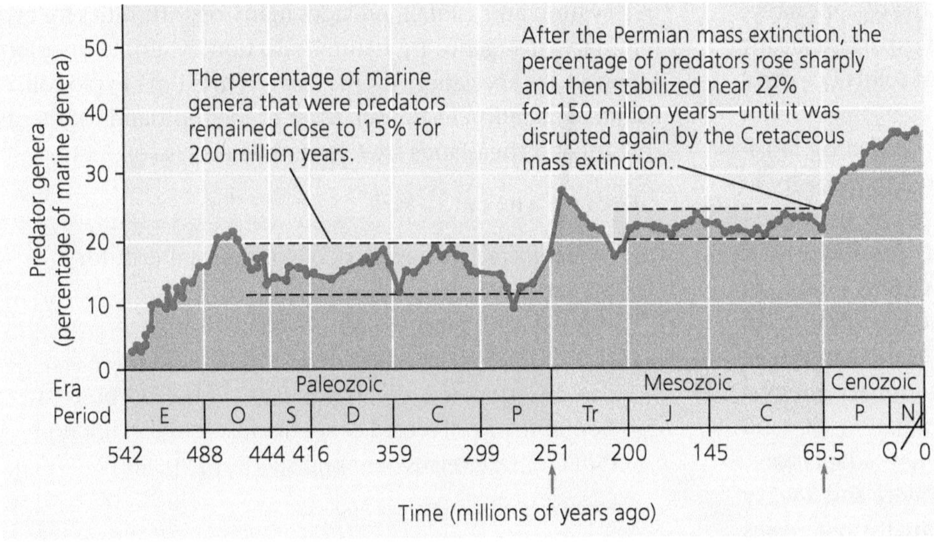

◀ **Figure 25.18 Mass extinctions and ecology.** The Permian and Cretaceous mass extinctions (indicated by red arrows) altered the ecology of the oceans by increasing the percentage of marine genera that were predators.

drills have since diversified into many new species. Finally, by eliminating so many species, mass extinctions can pave the way for adaptive radiations, in which new groups of organisms proliferate.

Adaptive Radiations

The fossil record indicates that the diversity of life has increased over the past 250 million years (see blue line in Figure 25.15). This increase has been fueled by **adaptive radiations**, periods of evolutionary change in which groups of organisms form many new species whose adaptations allow them to fill different ecological roles, or niches, in their communities. Large-scale adaptive radiations occurred after each of the big five mass extinctions, when survivors became adapted to the many vacant ecological niches. Adaptive radiations have also occurred in groups of organisms that possessed major evolutionary innovations, such as seeds or armored body coverings, or that colonized regions in which they faced little competition from other species.

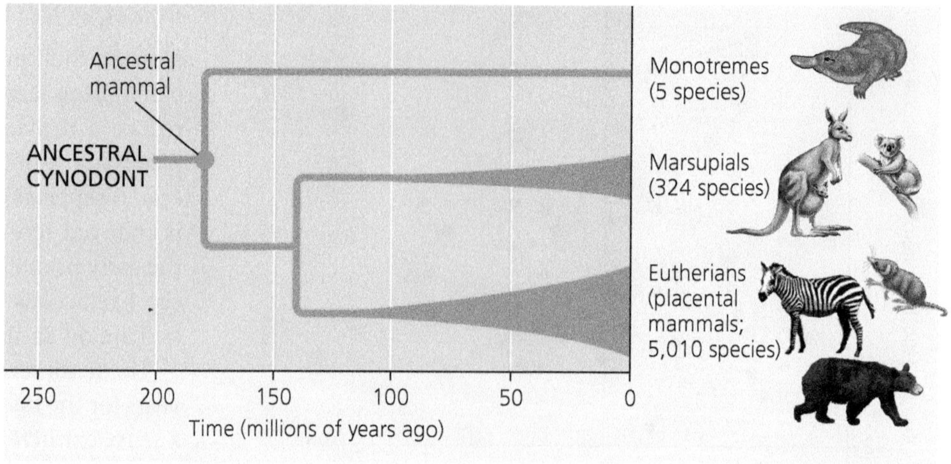

▲ **Figure 25.19 Adaptive radiation of mammals.**

Worldwide Adaptive Radiations

Fossil evidence indicates that mammals underwent a dramatic adaptive radiation after the extinction of terrestrial dinosaurs 65.5 million years ago (Figure 25.19). Although mammals originated about 180 million years ago, the mammal fossils older than 65.5 million years are mostly small and not morphologically diverse. Many species appear to have been nocturnal based on their large eye sockets, similar to those in living nocturnal mammals. A few early mammals were intermediate in size, such as *Repenomamus giganticus*, a 1-m-long predator that lived 130 million years ago—but none approached the size of many dinosaurs. Early mammals may have been restricted in size and diversity because they were eaten or outcompeted by the larger and more diverse dinosaurs. With the disappearance of the dinosaurs (except for birds), mammals expanded greatly in both diversity and size, filling the ecological roles once occupied by terrestrial dinosaurs.

The history of life has also been greatly altered by radiations in which groups of organisms increased in diversity as they came to play entirely new ecological roles in their communities. Examples include the rise of photosynthetic prokaryotes, the evolution of large predators in the Cambrian explosion, and the radiations following the colonization of land by plants, insects, and tetrapods. Each of these last three radiations was associated with major evolutionary innovations that facilitated life on land. The radiation of land plants, for example, was associated with key adaptations, such as stems that support plants against gravity and a waxy coat that protects leaves from water loss. Finally, organisms that arise in an adaptive radiation can serve as a new source of food for still other organisms. In fact, the diversification of land plants stimulated a series of adaptive radiations in insects that ate or pollinated plants, one reason that insects are the most diverse group of animals on Earth today.

Regional Adaptive Radiations

Striking adaptive radiations have also occurred over more limited geographic areas. Such radiations can be initiated when a few organisms make their way to a new, often distant location in which they face relatively little competition from other organisms. The Hawaiian archipelago is one of the world's great showcases of this type of adaptive radiation (Figure 25.20). Located about 3,500 km from the nearest continent, the volcanic islands are progressively older as one follows the chain toward the northwest; the youngest island, Hawaii, is less than a million years old and still has active volcanoes. Each island was born "naked" and was gradually populated by stray organisms that rode the ocean currents and winds either from far-distant land areas or from older islands of the archipelago itself. The physical diversity of each island, including immense variation in elevation and rainfall, provides many opportunities for evolutionary divergence by natural selection. Multiple invasions followed by speciation events have ignited an explosion of adaptive radiation in Hawaii. Most of the thousands of species that inhabit the islands are found nowhere else on Earth.

CONCEPT CHECK 25.4

1. Explain the consequences of continental drift for life on Earth.
2. What factors promote adaptive radiations?
3. **WHAT IF?** If a mass extinction were caused by a sudden catastrophic event, would dates of the last observation in the fossil record of species lost in the extinction differ for rare versus common species? Explain.

For suggested answers, see Appendix A.

▲ **Figure 25.20 Adaptive radiation on the Hawaiian Islands.** Molecular analysis indicates that these remarkably varied Hawaiian plants, known collectively as the "silversword alliance," are all descended from an ancestral tarweed that arrived on the islands about 5 million years ago from North America. Members of the silversword alliance have since spread into different habitats and formed new species with strikingly different adaptations.

CONCEPT 25.5

Major changes in body form can result from changes in the sequences and regulation of developmental genes

The fossil record tells us what the great changes in the history of life have been and when they occurred. Moreover, an understanding of plate tectonics, mass extinction, and adaptive radiation provides a picture of how those changes came about. But we can also seek to understand the intrinsic biological mechanisms that underlie changes seen in the fossil record. For this, we turn to genetic mechanisms of change, paying particular attention to genes that influence development.

Effects of Developmental Genes

As you read in Chapter 21, "evo-devo"—research at the interface between evolutionary biology and developmental biology—is illuminating how slight genetic divergences can produce major morphological differences between species. Genes that control development influence the rate, timing, and spatial pattern of change in an organism's form as it develops from a zygote into an adult.

Changes in Rate and Timing

Many striking evolutionary transformations are the result of **heterochrony** (from the Greek *hetero*, different, and *chronos*, time), an evolutionary change in the rate or timing of developmental events. For example, an organism's shape depends in part on the relative growth rates of different body parts

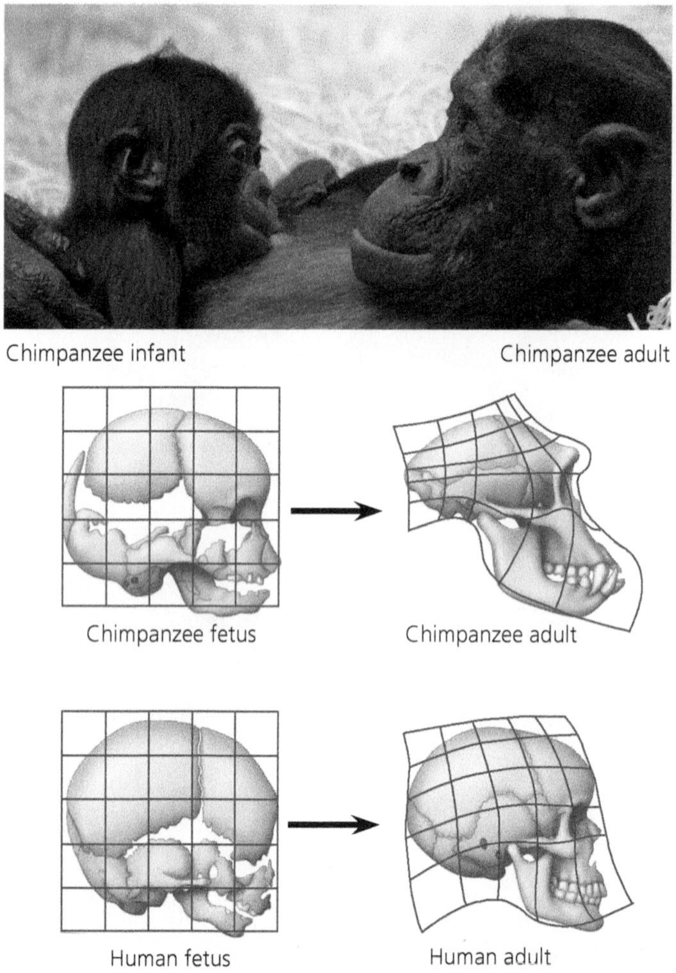

▲ **Figure 25.21 Relative skull growth rates.** In the human evolutionary lineage, mutations that slowed the growth of the jaw relative to other parts of the skull produced an adult whose head resembles that of a chimpanzee infant.

▲ **Figure 25.22 Paedomorphosis.** The adults of some species retain features that were juvenile in ancestors. This salamander is an axolotl, an aquatic species that grows to full size, becomes sexually mature, and reproduces while retaining certain larval (tadpole) characteristics, including gills.

during development. Changes to these rates can alter the adult form substantially, as seen in the contrasting shapes of human and chimpanzee skulls (Figure 25.21). Other examples of the dramatic evolutionary effects of heterochrony include how increased growth rates of finger bones yielded the skeletal structure of wings in bats (see Figure 22.15) and how slowed growth of leg and pelvic bones led to the reduction and eventual loss of hind limbs in whales (see Figure 22.20).

Heterochrony can also alter the timing of reproductive development relative to the development of nonreproductive organs. If reproductive organ development accelerates compared to other organs, the sexually mature stage of a species may retain body features that were juvenile structures in an ancestral species, a condition called **paedomorphosis** (from the Greek *paedos*, of a child, and *morphosis*, formation). For example, most salamander species have aquatic larvae that undergo metamorphosis in becoming adults. But some species grow to adult size and become sexually mature while retaining gills and other larval features (Figure 25.22). Such an evolutionary alteration of developmental timing can produce animals that appear very different from their ancestors, even though the overall genetic change may be small. Indeed, recent evidence indicates that a change at a single locus was probably sufficient to bring about paedomorphosis in the axolotl salamander, although other genes may have contributed as well.

Changes in Spatial Pattern

Substantial evolutionary changes can also result from alterations in genes that control the placement and spatial organization of body parts. For example, master regulatory genes called **homeotic genes** (described in Chapters 18 and 21) determine such basic features as where a pair of wings and a pair of legs will develop on a bird or how a plant's flower parts are arranged.

The products of one class of homeotic genes, the *Hox* genes, provide positional information in an animal embryo. This information prompts cells to develop into structures appropriate for a particular location. Changes in *Hox* genes or in how they are expressed can have a profound impact on morphology. For example, among crustaceans, a change in the location where two *Hox* genes (*Ubx* and *Scr*) are expressed correlates with the conversion of a swimming appendage to a feeding appendage. Large effects are also seen in snakes, where changes in how two *Hox* genes (*HoxC6* and *HoxC8*) are expressed suppresses limb formation (Figure 25.23). Similarly, when comparing plant species, changes to the expression of homeotic genes known as *MADS-box* genes can produce flowers that differ dramatically in form (see Chapter 35).

The Evolution of Development

The 565-million-year-old fossils of Ediacaran animals in Figure 25.4 suggest that a set of genes sufficient to produce complex animals existed at least 30 million years *before* the Cambrian explosion. If such genes have existed for so long,

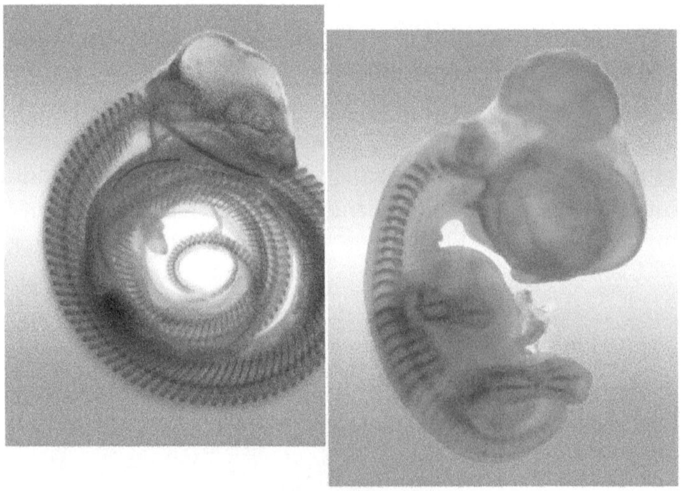

▲ **Figure 25.23** ***Hox*** **gene expression and limb development.** Regions of *HoxC6* gene expression (purple) correlate with limbless regions in the torsos of a snake embryo (left) and a chicken embryo (right).

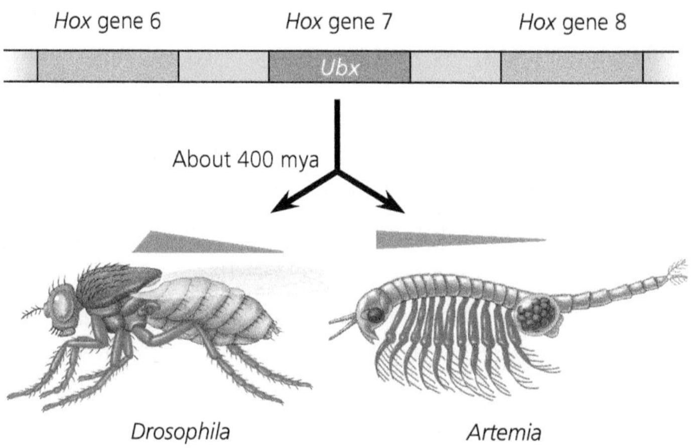

▲ **Figure 25.24 Origin of the insect body plan.** Expression of the *Hox* gene *Ubx* suppresses the formation of legs in fruit flies (*Drosophila*) but not in brine shrimp (*Artemia*), thus helping to build the insect body plan. Fruit fly and brine shrimp *Hox* genes have evolved independently for 400 million years. The green triangles indicate the relative amounts of *Ubx* expression in different body regions.

how can we explain the astonishing increases in diversity seen during and since the Cambrian explosion?

Adaptive evolution by natural selection provides one answer to this question. As we've seen throughout this unit, by sorting among differences in the sequences of protein-encoding genes, selection can improve adaptations rapidly. In addition, new genes (created by gene duplication events) can take on a wide range of new metabolic and structural functions. Thus, adaptive evolution of both new and existing genes may have played a key role in shaping the great diversity of life.

Examples in the previous section suggest that developmental genes may play a critical role. Next we'll examine how new morphological forms arise from changes in the nucleotide sequences or regulation of developmental genes.

Changes in Genes

New developmental genes arising after gene duplication events very likely facilitated the origin of novel morphological forms. But since other genetic changes also may have occurred at such times, it can be difficult to establish causal links between genetic and morphological changes that occurred in the past.

This difficulty was sidestepped in a recent study of developmental changes associated with the divergence of six-legged insects from crustacean-like ancestors that had more than six legs. In insects, such as *Drosophila*, the *Ubx* gene is expressed in the abdomen, while in crustaceans, such as *Artemia*, it is expressed in the main trunk of the body (**Figure 25.24**). When expressed, the *Ubx* gene suppresses leg formation in insects but not in crustaceans. To examine the workings of this gene, researchers cloned the *Ubx* gene from *Drosophila* and *Artemia*. Next, they genetically engineered fruit fly embryos to express either the *Drosophila Ubx* gene or the *Artemia Ubx* gene throughout their bodies. The *Drosophila* gene suppressed 100% of the limbs in the embryos, as expected, whereas the *Artemia* gene suppressed only 15%.

The researchers then sought to uncover key steps involved in the evolutionary transition from a crustacean *Ubx* gene to an insect *Ubx* gene. Their approach was to identify mutations that would cause the *Artemia Ubx* gene to suppress leg formation, thus making the crustacean gene act more like an insect *Ubx* gene. To do this, they constructed a series of "hybrid" *Ubx* genes, each of which contained known segments of the *Drosophila Ubx* gene and known segments of the *Artemia Ubx* gene. By inserting these hybrid genes into fruit fly embryos (one hybrid gene per embryo) and observing their effects on leg development, the researchers were able to pinpoint the exact amino acid changes responsible for the suppression of additional limbs in insects. In so doing, this study provided evidence linking a particular change in the nucleotide sequence of a developmental gene to a major evolutionary change: the origin of the six-legged insect body plan.

Changes in Gene Regulation

Changes in the nucleotide sequence or regulation of developmental genes can result in morphological changes that harm the organism (see Chapter 18). Moreover, a change in the nucleotide sequence of a gene may affect its function wherever the gene is expressed. In contrast, changes in the regulation of gene expression can be limited to a single cell type (see Chapter 18). Thus, a change in the regulation of a developmental gene may have fewer harmful side effects than a change to the sequence of the gene. This line of reasoning has prompted researchers to suggest that changes in the form of organisms may often be caused by mutations that affect the regulation of developmental genes—not their sequences.

This idea is supported by studies in a variety of species, including threespine stickleback fish. These fish live in the open ocean and in shallow, coastal waters. In western Canada, they also live in lakes formed when the coastline receded during the past 12,000 years. Marine stickleback fish have a pair of spines on their ventral (lower) surface, which deter some predators. These spines are often reduced or absent in stickleback fish living in lakes that lack predatory fishes and that are also low in calcium. Spines may have been lost because they are not advantageous in the absence of predators, and the limited calcium is needed for purposes other than constructing spines.

At the genetic level, the developmental gene, *Pitx1*, was known to influence whether stickleback fish have ventral spines. Was the reduction of spines in some lake populations due to changes in the *Pitx1* gene or to changes in how the gene is expressed (**Figure 25.25**)? The researchers' results indicate that the regulation of gene expression has changed, not the DNA sequence of the gene. Furthermore, lake stickleback

▼ Figure 25.25 **INQUIRY**

What causes the loss of spines in lake stickleback fish?

EXPERIMENT Marine populations of the threespine stickleback fish (*Gasterosteus aculeatus*) have a set of protective spines on their lower (ventral) surface; however, these spines have been lost or reduced in some lake populations of this fish. Working at Stanford University, Michael Shapiro, David Kingsley, and colleagues performed genetic crosses and found that most of the reduction in spine size resulted from the effects of a single developmental gene, *Pitx1*. The researchers then tested two hypotheses about how *Pitx1* causes this morphological change.

Threespine stickleback
(*Gasterosteus aculeatus*)

Hypothesis A: A change in the DNA sequence of *Pitx1* had caused spine reduction in lake populations. To test this idea, the team used DNA sequencing to compare the coding sequence of the *Pitx1* gene between marine and lake stickleback populations.

Hypothesis B: A change in the regulation of the expression of *Pitx1* had caused spine reduction. To test this idea, the researchers monitored where in the developing embryo the *Pitx1* gene was expressed. They conducted whole-body *in situ* hybridization experiments (see Chapter 20) using *Pitx1* DNA as a probe to detect *Pitx1* mRNA in the fish.

RESULTS

Test of Hypothesis A: Are there differences in the coding sequence of the *Pitx1* gene in marine and lake stickleback fish? **Result: No** → The 283 amino acids of the *Pitx1* protein are identical in marine and lake stickleback populations.

Test of Hypothesis B: Are there any differences in the regulation of expression of *Pitx1*? **Result: Yes** → Red arrows (→) indicate regions of *Pitx1* gene expression in the photographs below. *Pitx1* is expressed in the ventral spine and mouth regions of developing marine stickleback fish but only in the mouth region of developing lake stickleback fish.

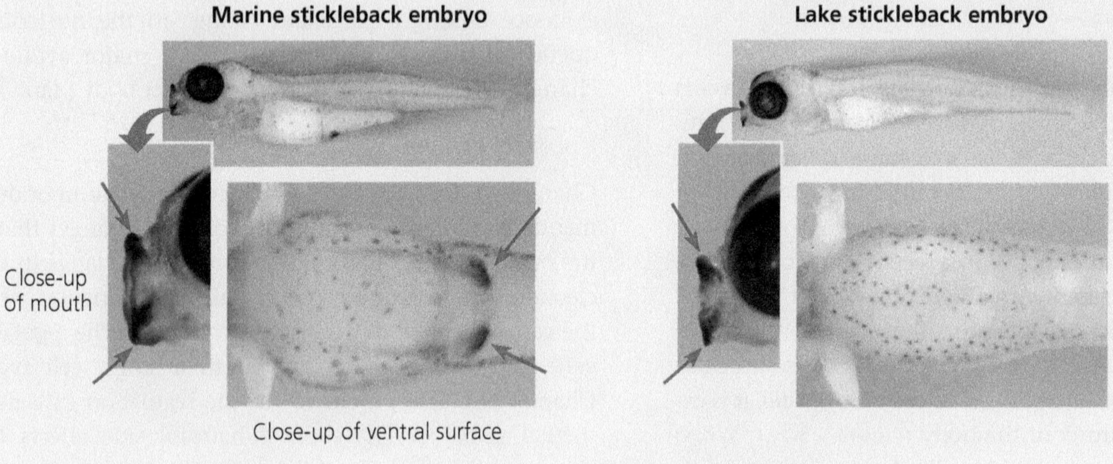

CONCLUSION The loss or reduction of ventral spines in lake populations of threespine stickleback fish appears to have resulted primarily from a change in the regulation of *Pitx1* gene expression, not from a change in the gene's sequence.

SOURCE M. D. Shapiro et al., Genetic and developmental basis of evolutionary pelvic reduction in three-spine sticklebacks, *Nature* 428:717–723 (2004).

WHAT IF? Describe the set of results that would have led researchers to the conclusion that a change in the coding sequence of the *Pitx1* gene was more important than a change in regulation of gene expression.

fish do express the *Pitx1* gene in tissues not related to the production of spines (for example, the mouth), illustrating how morphological change can be caused by altering the expression of a developmental gene in some parts of the body but not others.

CONCEPT CHECK 25.5

1. How can heterochrony cause the evolution of different body forms?
2. Why is it likely that *Hox* genes have played a major role in the evolution of novel morphological forms?
3. **MAKE CONNECTIONS** Given that changes in morphology are often caused by changes in the regulation of gene expression, predict whether noncoding DNA is likely to be affected by natural selection. See Concept 18.3 (pp. 364–366) to review noncoding DNA and regulation of gene expression.

For suggested answers, see Appendix A.

CONCEPT 25.6

Evolution is not goal oriented

What does our study of macroevolution tell us about how evolution works? One lesson is that throughout the history of life, the origin of new species has been affected by both the bottom-up factors described in Chapter 24 (such as natural selection operating in populations) and the top-down factors described here (such as continental drift promoting bursts of speciation throughout the globe). Moreover, to paraphrase the Nobel Prize–winning geneticist François Jacob, evolution is like tinkering—a process in which new forms arise by the slight modification of existing forms. Even large changes, like the ones that produced the first mammals or the six-legged body plan of insects, can result from the modification of existing structures or existing developmental genes. Over time, such tinkering has led to three key features of the natural world described in Chapter 22: the striking ways in which organisms are suited for life in their environments; the many shared characteristics of life; and the rich diversity of life.

Evolutionary Novelties

François Jacob's view of evolution harkens back to Darwin's concept of descent with modification. As new species form, novel and complex structures can arise as gradual modifications of ancestral structures. In many cases, complex structures have evolved in increments from simpler versions that performed the same basic function. For example, consider the human eye, an intricate organ constructed from numerous parts that work together in forming an image and transmitting it to the brain. How could the human eye have evolved in gradual increments? Some argue that if the eye needs all of its components to function, a partial eye could not have been of use to our ancestors.

The flaw in this argument, as Darwin himself noted, lies in the assumption that only complicated eyes are useful. In fact, many animals depend on eyes that are far less complex than our own (**Figure 25.26**). The simplest eyes that we know of are patches of light-sensitive photoreceptor cells. These simple eyes appear to have had a single evolutionary origin and are now found in a variety of animals, including small molluscs called limpets. Such eyes have no equipment for focusing images, but they do enable the animal to distinguish light from dark. Limpets cling more tightly to their rock when a shadow falls on them, a behavioral adaptation that reduces the risk of being eaten. Because limpets have had a long evolutionary history, we can conclude that their "simple" eyes are quite adequate to support their survival and reproduction.

▼ Figure 25.26 A range of eye complexity among molluscs.

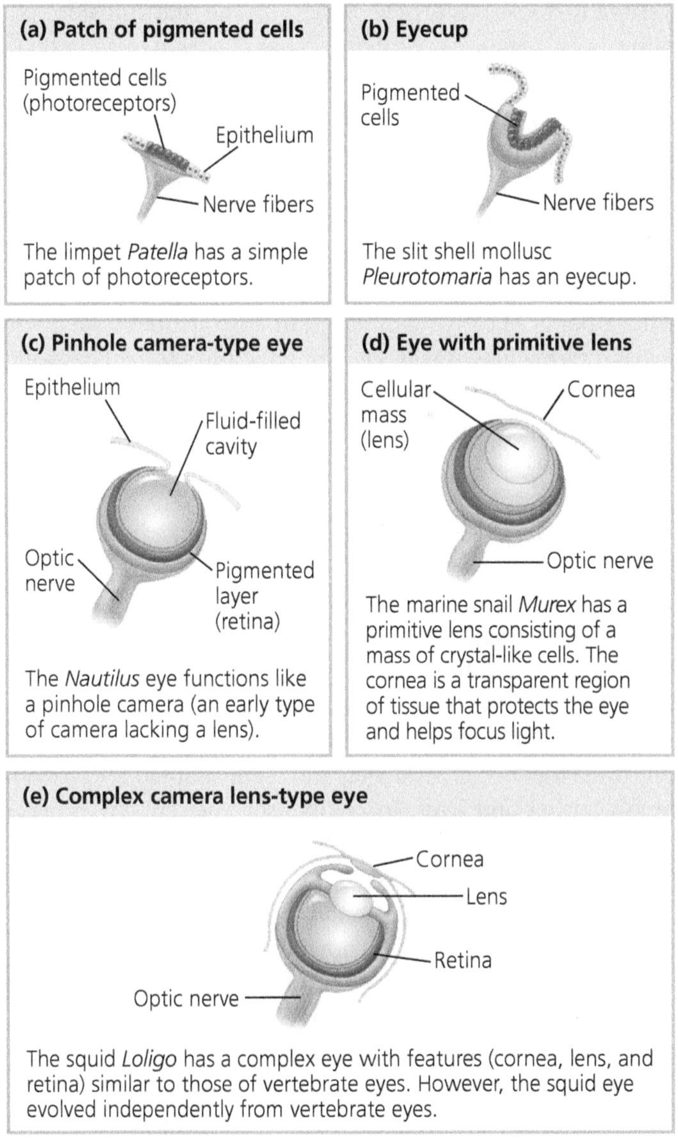

(a) The limpet *Patella* has a simple patch of photoreceptors.

(b) The slit shell mollusc *Pleurotomaria* has an eyecup.

(c) The *Nautilus* eye functions like a pinhole camera (an early type of camera lacking a lens).

(d) The marine snail *Murex* has a primitive lens consisting of a mass of crystal-like cells. The cornea is a transparent region of tissue that protects the eye and helps focus light.

(e) The squid *Loligo* has a complex eye with features (cornea, lens, and retina) similar to those of vertebrate eyes. However, the squid eye evolved independently from vertebrate eyes.

In the animal kingdom, complex eyes have evolved independently from such basic structures many times. Some molluscs, such as squids and octopuses, have eyes as complex as those of humans and other vertebrates (see Figure 25.26). Although complex mollusc eyes evolved independently of vertebrate eyes, both evolved from a simple cluster of photoreceptor cells present in a common ancestor. In each case, the complex eye evolved through a series of incremental modifications that benefited the eyes' owners at every stage. Evidence of their independent evolution may also be found in their structure: Vertebrate eyes detect light at the back layer of the retina and conduct nerve impulses toward the front, while complex mollusc eyes do the reverse.

Throughout their evolutionary history, eyes retained their basic function of vision. But evolutionary novelties can also arise when structures that originally played one role gradually acquire a different one. For example, as cynodonts gave rise to early mammals, bones that formerly comprised the jaw hinge (the articular and quadrate; see Figure 25.6) were incorporated into the ear region of mammals, where they eventually took on a new function: the transmission of sound (see Chapter 34). Structures that evolve in one context but become co-opted for another function are sometimes called *exaptations* to distinguish them from the adaptive origin of the original structure. Note that the concept of exaptation does not imply that a structure somehow evolves in anticipation of future use. Natural selection cannot predict the future; it can only improve a structure in the context of its *current* utility. Novel features, such as the new jaw hinge and ear bones of early mammals, can arise gradually via a series of intermediate stages, each of which has some function in the organism's current context.

Evolutionary Trends

What else can we learn from patterns of macroevolution? Consider evolutionary "trends" observed in the fossil record. For instance, some evolutionary lineages exhibit a trend toward larger or smaller body size. An example is the evolution of the present-day horse (genus *Equus*), a descendant of the 55-million-year-old *Hyracotherium* (**Figure 25.27**). About the size of a large dog, *Hyracotherium* had four toes on its front feet, three toes on its hind feet, and teeth adapted for browsing on bushes and trees. In comparison, present-day horses are larger, have only one toe on each foot, and possess teeth modified for grazing on grasses.

Extracting a single evolutionary progression from the fossil record can be misleading, however; it is like describing a bush as growing toward a single point by tracing only the branches that lead to that twig. For example, by selecting certain species from the available fossils, it is possible to arrange a succession of animals intermediate between *Hyracotherium* and living horses that shows a trend toward large, single-toed species (follow the yellow highlighting in Figure 25.27). However, if we consider *all* fossil horses known today, this apparent trend vanishes. The genus *Equus* did not evolve in a straight line; it is the only surviving twig of an evolutionary tree that is so branched that it is more like a bush. *Equus* actually descended through a series of speciation episodes that included several adaptive radiations, not all of which led to large, one-toed, grazing horses. In fact, phylogenetic analyses suggest that all lineages that include grazers are closely related to *Parahippus*; the many other horse lineages, all of which are now extinct, remained multi-toed browsers for 35 million years.

Branching evolution *can* result in a real evolutionary trend even if some species counter the trend. One model of long-term trends proposed by Steven Stanley, of Johns Hopkins University, views species as analogous to individuals: Speciation is their birth, extinction is their death, and new species that diverge from them are their offspring. In this model, Stanley suggests that just as populations of individual organisms undergo natural selection, species undergo *species selection*. The species that endure the longest and generate the most new offspring species determine the direction of major evolutionary trends. The species selection model suggests that "differential speciation success" plays a role in macroevolution similar to the role of differential reproductive success in microevolution. Evolutionary trends can also result directly from natural selection. For example, when horse ancestors invaded the grasslands that spread during the mid-Cenozoic, there was strong selection for grazers that could escape predators by running faster. This trend would not have occurred without open grasslands.

Whatever its cause, an evolutionary trend does not imply that there is some intrinsic drive toward a particular phenotype. Evolution is the result of the interactions between organisms and their current environments; if environmental conditions change, an evolutionary trend may cease or even reverse itself. The cumulative effect of these ongoing interactions between organisms and their environments is enormous: It is through them that the staggering diversity of life—Darwin's "endless forms most beautiful"—has arisen.

CONCEPT CHECK 25.6

1. How can the Darwinian concept of descent with modification explain the evolution of such complex structures as the vertebrate eye?
2. **WHAT IF?** The myxoma virus kills up to 99.8% of infected European rabbits in populations with no previous exposure to the virus. The virus is transmitted between living rabbits by mosquitoes. Describe an evolutionary trend (in either the rabbit or virus) that might occur after a rabbit population first encounters the virus.

For suggested answers, see Appendix A.

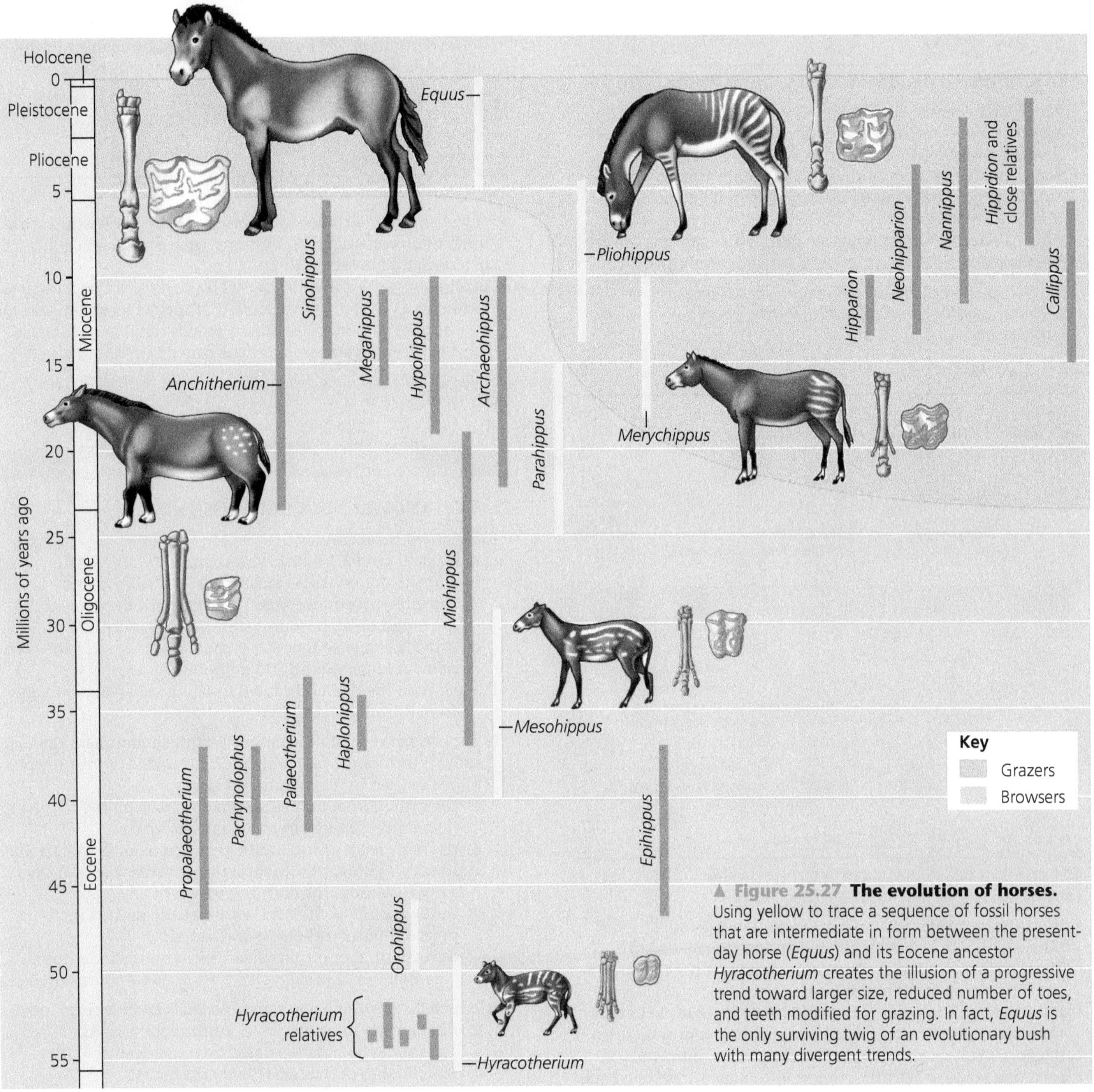

▲ **Figure 25.27 The evolution of horses.** Using yellow to trace a sequence of fossil horses that are intermediate in form between the present-day horse (*Equus*) and its Eocene ancestor *Hyracotherium* creates the illusion of a progressive trend toward larger size, reduced number of toes, and teeth modified for grazing. In fact, *Equus* is the only surviving twig of an evolutionary bush with many divergent trends.

25 CHAPTER REVIEW

SUMMARY OF KEY CONCEPTS

CONCEPT 25.1

Conditions on early Earth made the origin of life possible (pp. 507–510)

- Earth formed 4.6 billion years ago. Experiments simulating possible early atmospheres have produced organic molecules from inorganic precursors. Amino acids, lipids, sugars, and nitrogenous bases have also been found in meteorites.
- Amino acids and RNA nucleotides polymerize when dripped onto hot sand, clay, or rock. Organic compounds can spontaneously assemble into **protocells**, membrane-bounded droplets that have some properties of cells.
- The first genetic material may have been short pieces of RNA capable of guiding polypeptide synthesis and self-replication. Early protocells containing such RNA would have increased through natural selection.

? *Describe the roles that montmorillonite clay and vesicles may have played in the origin of life.*

CONCEPT 25.2

The fossil record documents the history of life (pp. 510–514)

- The **fossil record**, based largely on fossils found in sedimentary rocks, documents the rise and fall of different groups of organisms over time.
- Sedimentary strata reveal the relative ages of **fossils**. The absolute ages of fossils can be estimated by radiometric dating and other methods.
- The fossil record shows how new groups of organisms can arise via the gradual modification of preexisting organisms.

? *What are the challenges of estimating the absolute ages of old fossils? Explain how these challenges may be overcome in some circumstances.*

CONCEPT 25.3

Key events in life's history include the origins of single-celled and multicelled organisms and the colonization of land (pp. 514–519)

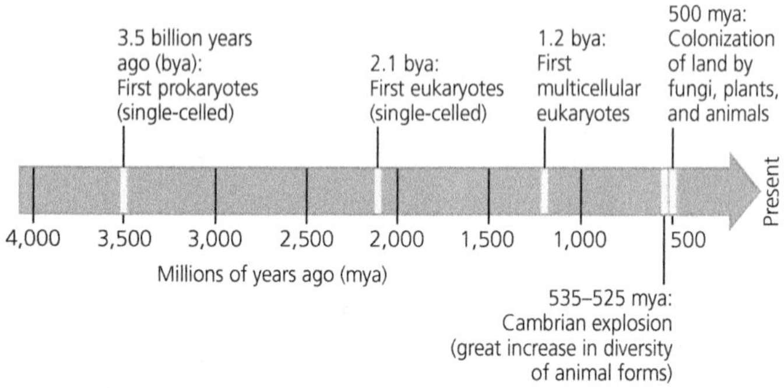

? *What is the "Cambrian explosion," and why is it significant?*

CONCEPT 25.4

The rise and fall of groups of organisms reflect differences in speciation and extinction rates (pp. 519–524)

- In **plate tectonics**, continental plates move gradually over time, altering the physical geography and climate of Earth. These changes lead to extinctions in some groups of organisms and bursts of speciation in others.
- Evolutionary history has been punctuated by five **mass extinctions** that radically altered the history of life. Some of these extinctions may have been caused by changes in continent positions, volcanic activity, or impacts from meteorites or comets.
- Large increases in the diversity of life have resulted from **adaptive radiations** that followed mass extinctions. Adaptive radiations have also occurred in groups of organisms that possessed major evolutionary innovations or that colonized new regions in which there was little competition from other organisms.

? *Explain how the broad evolutionary changes seen in the fossil record are the cumulative result of speciation and extinction events.*

CONCEPT 25.5

Major changes in body form can result from changes in the sequences and regulation of developmental genes (pp. 525–529)

- Developmental genes affect morphological differences between species by influencing the rate, timing, and spatial patterns of change in an organism's form as it develops into an adult.
- The evolution of new forms can be caused by changes in the nucleotide sequences or regulation of developmental genes.

? *How could changes in a single gene or DNA region ultimately lead to the origin of a new group of organisms?*

CONCEPT 25.6

Evolution is not goal oriented (pp. 529–531)

- Novel and complex biological structures can evolve through a series of incremental modifications, each of which benefits the organism that possesses it.
- Evolutionary trends can be caused by factors such as natural selection in a changing environment or species selection. Like all aspects of evolution, evolutionary trends result from interactions between organisms and their current environments.

? *Explain the reasoning behind the statement "Evolution is not goal oriented."*

TEST YOUR UNDERSTANDING

LEVEL 1: KNOWLEDGE/COMPREHENSION

1. Fossilized stromatolites
   a. all date from 2.7 billion years ago.
   b. formed around deep-sea vents.
   c. resemble structures formed by bacterial communities that are found today in some warm, shallow, salty bays.
   d. provide evidence that plants moved onto land in the company of fungi around 500 million years ago.
   e. contain the first undisputed fossils of eukaryotes and date from 2.1 billion years ago.

2. The oxygen revolution changed Earth's environment dramatically. Which of the following took advantage of the presence of free oxygen in the oceans and atmosphere?
   a. the evolution of cellular respiration, which used oxygen to help harvest energy from organic molecules
   b. the persistence of some animal groups in anaerobic habitats
   c. the evolution of photosynthetic pigments that protected early algae from the corrosive effects of oxygen
   d. the evolution of chloroplasts after early protists incorporated photosynthetic cyanobacteria
   e. the evolution of multicellular eukaryotic colonies from communities of prokaryotes

3. Which factor most likely caused animals and plants in India to differ greatly from species in nearby southeast Asia?
   a. The species became separated by convergent evolution.
   b. The climates of the two regions are similar.
   c. India is in the process of separating from the rest of Asia.
   d. Life in India was wiped out by ancient volcanic eruptions.
   e. India was a separate continent until 45 million years ago.

4. Adaptive radiations can be a direct consequence of four of the following five factors. Select the exception.
   a. vacant ecological niches
   b. genetic drift
   c. colonization of an isolated region that contains suitable habitat and few competitor species
   d. evolutionary innovation
   e. an adaptive radiation in a group of organisms (such as plants) that another group uses as food

5. Which of the following steps has *not* yet been accomplished by scientists studying the origin of life?
   a. synthesis of small RNA polymers by ribozymes
   b. abiotic synthesis of polypeptides

c. formation of molecular aggregates with selectively permeable membranes
d. formation of protocells that use DNA to direct the polymerization of amino acids
e. abiotic synthesis of organic molecules

6. **DRAW IT** Use the unlabeled clock diagram below to test your memory of the sequence of key events in the history of life described in this chapter by labeling the colored bars. As a visual aid to help you study, add labels that represent other significant events, including the Cambrian explosion, origin of mammals, and Permian and Cretaceous mass extinctions.

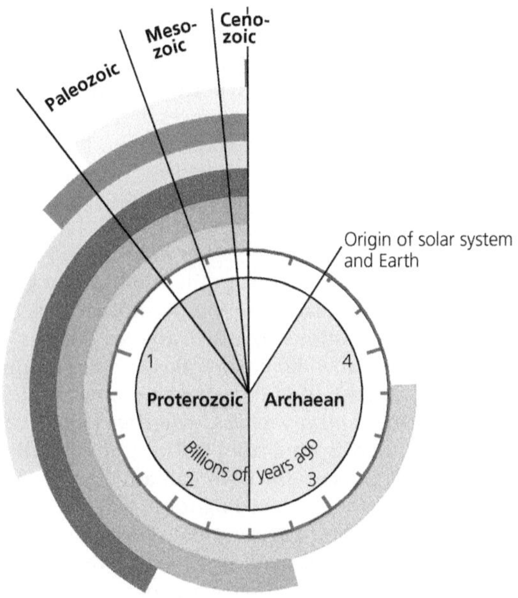

LEVEL 2: APPLICATION/ANALYSIS

7. A genetic change that caused a certain *Hox* gene to be expressed along the tip of a vertebrate limb bud instead of farther back helped make possible the evolution of the tetrapod limb. This type of change is illustrative of
a. the influence of environment on development.
b. paedomorphosis.
c. a change in a developmental gene or in its regulation that altered the spatial organization of body parts.
d. heterochrony.
e. gene duplication.

8. A swim bladder is a gas-filled sac that helps fish maintain buoyancy. The evolution of the swim bladder from lungs of an ancestral fish is an example of
a. an evolutionary trend.
b. exaptation.
c. changes in *Hox* gene expression.
d. paedomorphosis.
e. adaptive radiation.

LEVEL 3: SYNTHESIS/EVALUATION

9. **EVOLUTION CONNECTION**
Describe how gene flow, genetic drift, and natural selection all can influence macroevolution.

10. **SCIENTIFIC INQUIRY**
Herbivory (plant eating) has evolved repeatedly in insects, typically from meat-eating or detritus-feeding ancestors (detritus is dead organic matter). Moths and butterflies, for example, eat plants, whereas their "sister group" (the insect group to which they are most closely related), the caddisflies, feed on animals, fungi, or detritus. As illustrated in the phylogenetic tree below, the combined moth/butterfly and caddisfly group shares a common ancestor with flies and fleas. Like caddisflies, flies and fleas are thought to have evolved from ancestors that did not eat plants.
There are 140,000 species of moths and butterflies and 7,000 species of caddisflies. State a hypothesis about the impact of herbivory on adaptive radiations in insects. How could this hypothesis be tested?

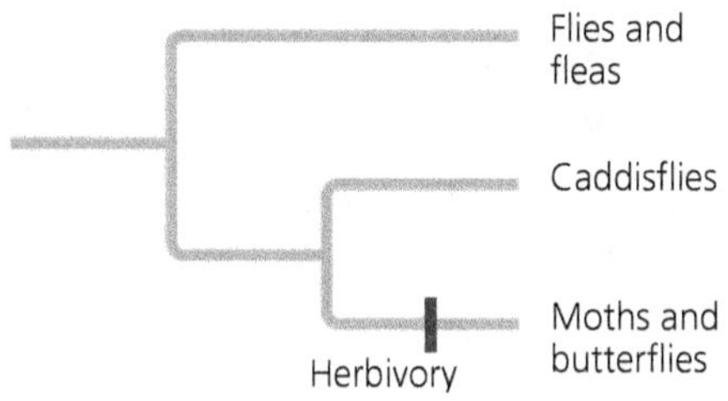

11. **SCIENCE, TECHNOLOGY, AND SOCIETY**
Experts estimate that human activities cause the extinction of hundreds of species every year. In contrast, the natural rate of extinction is thought to average only a few species per year. If human actions continue to alter the global environment, especially by destroying tropical rain forests and changing Earth's climate, the likely result will be a wave of extinctions that could rival those at the end of the Cretaceous period. Considering that life has endured five mass extinctions, should we be concerned that we may cause a sixth mass extinction? How would such an extinction differ from previous extinctions? What might be some of the consequences?

12. **WRITE ABOUT A THEME**
Structure and Function You have seen many examples of how form fits function at all levels of the biological hierarchy. However, we can imagine forms that would function better than some forms actually found in nature. For example, if the wings of a bird were not formed from its forelimbs, such a hypothetical bird could fly yet also hold objects with its forelimbs. In a short essay (100–150 words), use the concept of "evolution as tinkering" to explain why there are limits to the functionality of forms in nature.

For selected answers, see Appendix A.

MasteringBIOLOGY www.masteringbiology.com

1. MasteringBiology® Assignments
Tutorial Fossil Record
Activities Discovery Channel Video: Early Life • The History of Life • A Scrolling Geologic Record • Discovery Channel Video: Mass Extinctions • Adaptive Radiation
Questions Student Misconceptions • Reading Quiz • Multiple Choice • End-of-Chapter

2. eText
Read your book online, search, take notes, highlight text, and more.

3. The Study Area
Practice Tests • Cumulative Test • *BioFlix* 3-D Animations • MP3 Tutor Sessions • Videos • Activities • Investigations • Lab Media • Audio Glossary • Word Study Tools • Art

UNIT 5 The Evolutionary History of Biological Diversity

An Interview with

W. Ford Doolittle

Brimming with curiosity about nature, W. Ford Doolittle is a passionate advocate for both science and scientists. Dr. Doolittle holds degrees in molecular biology from Harvard and Stanford Universities. Since 1971 he has worked at Dalhousie University in Halifax, Canada, where he is now a Professor Emeritus. The author of more than 270 scientific articles, Dr. Doolittle is well known for his work on the molecular biology of cyanobacteria and archaea, early steps in the evolution of eukaryotes, and the importance of horizontal gene transfer in prokaryotes. He has also nurtured dozens of young scientists, making Dalhousie a world-renowned center for the study of evolution. The recipient of numerous awards and honorary degrees, Dr. Doolittle is an elected member of the Royal Society of Canada and the U.S. National Academy of Sciences. He is also an avid photographer, and in 2011 he will receive a B.F.A. in photography from the Nova Scotia College of Art and Design. Surrounded by stacks of journal articles, photography projects, and the bustle of a busy laboratory, Michael Cain and Jane Reece spoke with Dr. Doolittle in his office at Dalhousie.

How did you get started in science?

I hadn't planned on studying science until, as a high school student, I got a job washing glassware in Sol Spiegelman's lab at the University of Illinois. [Spiegelman was a molecular biologist whose work on RNA played a key role in developing understanding of biology's "central dogma" (see Chapter 17).] In college, I continued working in Sol's lab during the summer. It was a very exciting place to be, kind of like a hospital emergency ward where everything was important, everything was urgent. Some people worked all day, some people worked all night, some people worked all day and night! The lab was abuzz with simple and elegant experiments in molecular biology. I got the feeling that science was important, which I have never lost. And I got the feeling that science was important for its own sake, which I also have never lost. Doing science seems to fill our human need to know, to understand what the universe is like.

Did you become interested in evolution while working in Sol's lab?

Well, that came a little later. When I arrived at Dalhousie in 1971, I began studying blue-green algae (now called cyanobacteria) because they were a pretty color and few people were working on them. So the field was wide open. Lynn Margulis had just published her book *Origin of Eukaryotic Cells*, which put forward a startling idea—the endosymbiont hypothesis—positing that mitochondria and chloroplasts were formerly aerobic bacteria and cyanobacteria, respectively, that began living within larger cells, ultimately leading to the origin of eukaryotes. Then a fortuitous thing happened: I hired Linda Bonen, who brought a new technique to our lab, called RNA cataloging, from which you could get RNA sequence information. It's not a full sequence, but it was enough to start comparing ribosomal RNA molecules (rRNAs). I realized that we could use this technique to test the endosymbiont hypothesis for the origin of chloroplasts. We compared the sequences of rRNAs from chloroplasts with those from cyanobacteria and found they were similar, just as Margulis had predicted! From there, I became more and more interested in evolution, which continues to fascinate me today.

What are the main questions you are asking in your research?

I've had a long-standing interest in the evolution of genes and genomes. Most of my current work is on prokaryotes, but I've also been interested in questions about eukaryotes, such as, Where did introns come from? How did eukaryotic genomes originate? In recent years, my students and I have been occupied with two main research areas. One is *metagenomics*, where we collect environmental samples, such as mud from the bottom of harbors, and then sequence the prokaryotic DNA contained in the samples. We use these DNA sequences to shed light on how microbes interact with each other and their environment. The other main area of my current research is *horizontal gene transfer*, the transfer of genetic information—usually whole genes but not necessarily—from one species to another.

How can genes move from one prokaryotic species to another?

This can happen in a variety of ways, and such transfers turn out to be surprisingly common. Mechanisms have evolved in some bacteria enabling them to take up DNA molecules directly from the environment—and these DNA molecules may have come from individuals of other species that have died and broken apart. When this happens, sometimes the DNA is incorporated into the bacterial chromosomes and hence becomes part of their own genetic heritage. Many prokaryotes can also form temporary bridges that connect two or more individuals to one another, enabling genes to move from one species to another. And as we mentioned earlier, sometimes entire genomes are transferred in endosymbiosis. These and other processes that result in horizontal gene transfer have occurred throughout the nearly 4 billion years of life on Earth—and they continue to occur today.

What impact has horizontal gene transfer had on the evolutionary history of life?

Horizontal gene transfer, or HGT for short, has been a major force in the history of life. For instance, the endosymbiotic origins of mitochondria and chloroplasts were profoundly important events in the origin of eukaryotic cells. We humans wouldn't be here if it weren't for mitochondria, and of course without chloroplasts there wouldn't be any plants. Furthermore, HGT has been a dominant force in prokaryotic evolution—probably *the* dominant force. Genes that control key metabolic processes, such as photosynthesis and nitrogen fixation, can be transferred readily between species, and this has had an enormous impact on the ecological and evolutionary success of prokaryotes. And while one can construct evolutionary trees that identify major groups of prokaryotes, such trees can obscure the fact that there has been a tremendous amount of HGT, affecting the majority of the genes.

Tell us more about evolutionary trees.

An evolutionary tree (or *phylogenetic tree*) is a branching diagram that represents the evolutionary history of a group of organisms. For example, we might use morphological and genetic data to figure out a phylogenetic tree of animals. Such a tree can provide a huge amount of information. For any particular group of animals, whether they be weevils, whales, or worms, our tree could identify the ancestors and closest relatives of the group. If we traced the history of animals all the way back, we could use the tree to help us answer questions such as, What did the earliest animals look like? What features did they pass on to all their descendants, including us? Phylogenetic trees also have great practical value. The same techniques we use to reconstruct evolutionary history have been used in forensics, where phylogenetic trees have helped solve criminal cases, and epidemiology, where trees have been used to estimate when and where diseases such as AIDS originated.

What have you learned during your career about the pattern and process of evolution?

We can document the *pattern* of evolution, the "what happened" part, with data from many scientific disciplines. For example, if we measure genetic change in a population, we are documenting an evolutionary pattern. The *process* of evolution is the "what caused it" part, which focuses on the mechanisms that produce the observed pattern. Sixty years ago, many scientists thought that natural selection was *the* mechanism that explained most evolutionary patterns. But we don't think that anymore; we now know that genetic drift and catastrophic events such as an asteroid striking Earth can explain many observed evolutionary patterns. I call this "process pluralism" to indicate that evolutionary patterns can result from many processes. Results from my research suggest that we should be considering "pattern pluralism" as well. Consider the tree of life, a phylogenetic tree that represents the history of all life as a series of branching events, in which a common ancestor gives rise to two descendant groups of organisms. This approach works well for organisms such as animals, but for prokaryotes the importance of HGT leads me to question whether the tree of life pattern is real. For prokaryotes, the pattern of evolution may be more like a tangled network of organisms exchanging DNA, not a simple branching tree.

Does this mean that Charles Darwin was wrong when he introduced the idea of a tree of life in *The Origin of Species*?

Darwin set out in his book to document the fact of evolution—the pattern of evolutionary change over time—and to show that natural selection could account for observed patterns of change. He did a great job on both accounts. We now recognize that well-understood genetic and ecological processes operating over nearly 4 billion years of evolution are adequate to explain diversity and adaptation in the living world. As for his ideas about the tree of life, Darwin was focused on plants and animals, two groups for which the tree of life idea works well. Remember, when Darwin formulated his ideas, many scientists still thought that bacteria formed spontaneously from rotten meat. It wasn't even clear that bacteria were organisms. So I would say that Darwin's idea about the tree of life is still true, but that certain restrictions apply. It is similar to the situation in physics: Newton's laws work well under certain conditions, but not as well under other conditions. The tree of life still works well for plants and animals, but less well for prokaryotes due to HGT. And after all, most of life is prokaryotic.

Have recent discoveries altered our understanding of the evolutionary history of life?

Certainly. For one thing, our view of genomes and genome evolution has changed greatly in recent years. Who would have thought that we humans only have about the same number of genes as a 1-mm-long worm? It's astonishing. Not that long ago, little was known about endosymbiosis or HGT or the astoundingly rapid rates at which bacterial populations can evolve. Overall, the importance of prokaryotes and protists (single-celled eukaryotes) has really become clear. I mentioned metagenomics earlier, an approach that has already revealed previously unsuspected levels of microbial diversity. I think metagenomics will play an increasingly important role in future discoveries. It might even help us understand the consequences of increased atmospheric carbon dioxide (CO_2) and global warming, among the most important problems we face today. Microorganisms absorb vast amounts of CO_2 from the atmosphere. How will ongoing global warming affect microorganisms? Will they absorb even more CO_2, thus reducing effects of global warming? Or will the opposite occur? We don't know, but we can use metagenomics to figure out how climate change is currently affecting microbial communities. Once we understand what is going on, perhaps that can help us fix it.

You've devoted much time and effort to mentoring others. Can you comment on that?

Working in Sol Spiegelman's lab when I was young was a big turning point in my life. And as I gained experience, I tried to provide similar opportunities for others. One way I've done that is to establish programs that provide opportunities for young scientists to work together and to learn from each other and from more experienced scientists. I've always thought that it really helps to get experience early in your career, so I welcome people seeking such experience. One of the best ways to find what you really love doing is to try different things and see what most excites you. I did not plan to be a scientist, but I started doing science and I loved it. I'm a big believer in hands-on experience as a way of learning.

"For prokaryotes, the pattern of evolution may be more like a tangled network of organisms exchanging DNA, not a simple branching tree."

W. Ford Doolittle (center) with Michael Cain (left) and Jane Reece

26

Phylogeny and the Tree of Life

▲ **Figure 26.1 What is this organism?**

EVOLUTION

KEY CONCEPTS

26.1 Phylogenies show evolutionary relationships
26.2 Phylogenies are inferred from morphological and molecular data
26.3 Shared characters are used to construct phylogenetic trees
26.4 An organism's evolutionary history is documented in its genome
26.5 Molecular clocks help track evolutionary time
26.6 New information continues to revise our understanding of the tree of life

OVERVIEW

Investigating the Tree of Life

Look closely at the organism in Figure 26.1. Although it resembles a snake, this animal is actually an Australian legless lizard known as the common scaly-foot (*Pygopus lepidopodus*). Why isn't the scaly-foot considered a snake? More generally, how do biologists distinguish and categorize the millions of species on Earth?

An understanding of evolutionary relationships suggests one way to address these questions: We can decide in which "container" to place a species by comparing its traits with those of potential close relatives. For example, the scaly-foot does not have a fused eyelid, a highly mobile jaw, or a short tail posterior to the anus, three traits shared by all snakes. These and other characteristics suggest that despite a superficial resemblance, the scaly-foot is not a snake. Furthermore, a survey of the lizards reveals that the scaly-foot is not alone; the legless condition has evolved independently in several different groups of lizards. Most legless lizards are burrowers or live in grasslands, and like snakes, these species lost their legs over generations as they adapted to their environments.

Snakes and lizards are part of the continuum of life extending from the earliest organisms to the great variety of species alive today. In this unit, we will survey this diversity and describe hypotheses regarding how it evolved. As we do so, our emphasis will shift from the *process* of evolution (the evolutionary mechanisms described in Unit Four) to its *pattern* (observations of evolution's products over time).

To set the stage for surveying life's diversity, in this chapter we consider how biologists trace **phylogeny**, the evolutionary history of a species or group of species. A phylogeny of lizards and snakes, for example, indicates that both the scaly-foot and snakes evolved from lizards with legs—but that they evolved from different lineages of legged lizards. Thus, it appears that their legless conditions evolved independently.

To construct phylogenies, biologists utilize **systematics**, a discipline focused on classifying organisms and determining their evolutionary relationships. Systematists use data ranging from fossils to molecules and genes to infer evolutionary relationships (Figure 26.2). This information is enabling biologists to construct a tree of all life, which will continue to be refined as additional data are collected.

▲ Figure 26.2 **An unexpected family tree.** What are the evolutionary relationships between a human, a mushroom, and a tulip? A phylogeny based on DNA data reveals that—despite appearances—animals (including humans) and fungi (including mushrooms) are more closely related to each other than either is to plants.

CONCEPT 26.1

Phylogenies show evolutionary relationships

As we discussed in Chapter 22, organisms share many characteristics because of common ancestry. As a result, we can learn a great deal about a species if we know its evolutionary history. For example, an organism is likely to share many of its genes, metabolic pathways, and structural proteins with its close relatives. We'll consider practical applications of such information at the close of this section, but first we'll examine how organisms are named and classified, the scientific discipline of **taxonomy**. We'll also look at how we can interpret and use diagrams that represent evolutionary history.

Binomial Nomenclature

Common names for organisms—such as monkey, finch, and lilac—convey meaning in casual usage, but they can also cause confusion. Each of these names, for example, refers to more than one species. Moreover, some common names do not accurately reflect the kind of organism they signify. Consider these three "fishes": jellyfish (a cnidarian), crayfish (a small lobsterlike crustacean), and silverfish (an insect). And of course, a given organism has different names in different languages.

To avoid ambiguity when communicating about their research, biologists refer to organisms by Latin scientific names. The two-part format of the scientific name, commonly called a **binomial**, was instituted in the 18th century by Carolus Linnaeus (see Chapter 22). The first part of a binomial is the name of the **genus** (plural, *genera*) to which the species belongs. The second part, called the specific epithet, is unique for each species within the genus. An example of a binomial is *Panthera pardus*, the scientific name for the large cat commonly called the leopard. Notice that the first letter of the genus is capitalized and the entire binomial is italicized. (Newly created scientific names are also "latinized": You can name an insect you discover after a friend, but you must add a Latin ending.) Many of the more than 11,000 binomials assigned by Linnaeus are still used today, including the optimistic name he gave our own species—*Homo sapiens*, meaning "wise man."

Hierarchical Classification

In addition to naming species, Linnaeus also grouped them into a hierarchy of increasingly inclusive categories. The first grouping is built into the binomial: Species that appear to be closely related are grouped into the same genus. For example, the leopard (*Panthera pardus*) belongs to a genus that also includes the African lion (*Panthera leo*), the tiger (*Panthera tigris*), and the jaguar (*Panthera onca*). Beyond genera, taxonomists employ progressively more comprehensive categories of classification. The taxonomic system named after Linnaeus, the Linnaean system, places related genera in the same **family**, families into **orders**, orders into **classes**, classes into **phyla** (singular, *phylum*), phyla into **kingdoms**, and, more recently, kingdoms into **domains** (Figure 26.3). The resulting biological classification of a particular organism is somewhat like a postal address identifying a person in a particular apartment, in a building with many apartments, on a street with many apartment buildings, in a city with many streets, and so on.

The named taxonomic unit at any level of the hierarchy is called a **taxon** (plural, *taxa*). In the leopard example, *Panthera* is a taxon at the genus level, and Mammalia is a taxon at the class level that includes all the many orders of mammals. Note that in the Linnaean system, taxa broader than the genus are not italicized, though they are capitalized.

Classifying species is a way to structure our human view of the world. We lump together various species of trees to which we give the common name of pines and distinguish them from other trees that we call firs. Taxonomists have decided

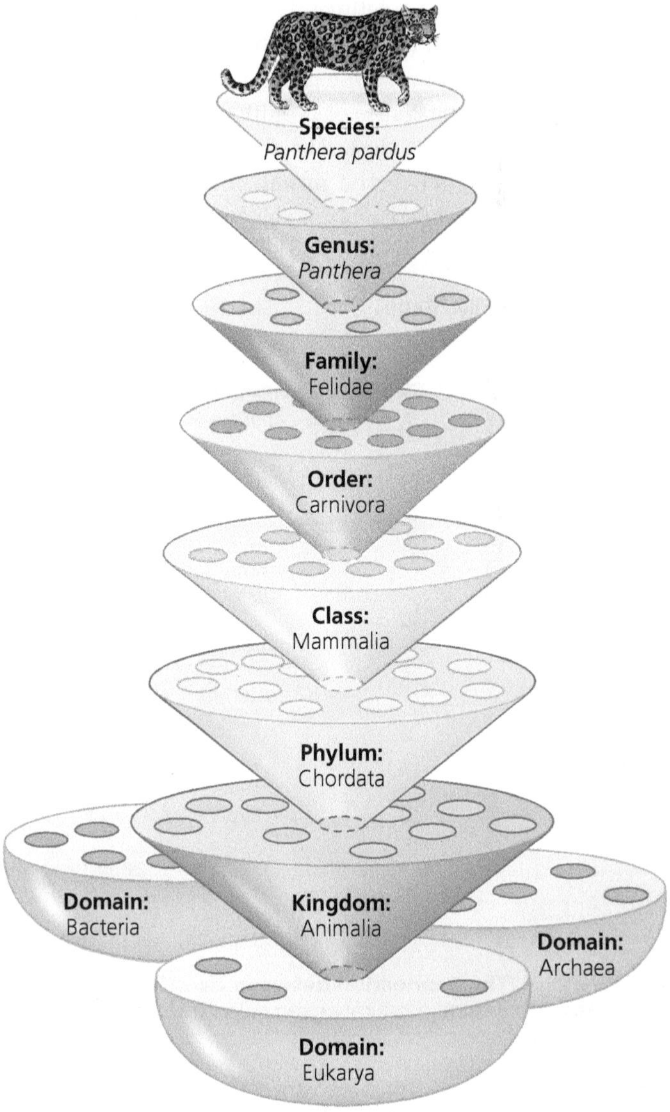

▲ **Figure 26.3 Linnaean classification.** At each level, or "rank," species are placed in groups within more inclusive groups.

that pines and firs are different enough to be placed in separate genera, yet similar enough to be grouped into the same family, Pinaceae. As with pines and firs, higher levels of classification are usually defined by particular characters chosen by taxonomists. However, characters that are useful for classifying one group of organisms may not be appropriate for other organisms. For this reason, the larger categories often are not comparable between lineages; that is, an order of snails does not exhibit the same degree of morphological or genetic diversity as an order of mammals. Furthermore, as we'll see, the placement of species into orders, classes, and so on, does not necessarily reflect evolutionary history.

Linking Classification and Phylogeny

The evolutionary history of a group of organisms can be represented in a branching diagram called a **phylogenetic tree**. As in Figure 26.4, the branching pattern often matches how taxonomists have classified groups of organisms nested within more inclusive groups. Sometimes, however, taxonomists have placed a species within a genus (or other group) to which it is *not* most closely related. One reason for misclassification might be that over the course of evolution, a species has lost a key feature shared by its close relatives. If DNA or other new evidence indicates that such a mistake has occurred, the organism may be reclassified to accurately reflect its evolutionary history. Another issue is that while the Linnaean system may distinguish groups, such as mammals, reptiles, birds, and other classes of vertebrates, it tells us nothing about these groups' evolutionary relationships to one another.

In fact, such difficulties in aligning Linnaean classification with phylogeny have led some systematists to propose that classification be based entirely on evolutionary relationships. A system called **PhyloCode**, for example, only names groups that include a common ancestor and all of its descendants. While PhyloCode would change the way taxa are defined and recognized, the taxonomic names of most species would remain the same. But groups would no longer have "ranks" attached to them, such as family or class. Also, some commonly recognized groups would become part of other groups previously of the same rank. For example, because birds evolved from a group of reptiles, Aves (the Linnaean class to which birds are assigned) would be considered a subgroup of Reptilia (also a class in the Linnaean system). Although PhyloCode is controversial, many systematists are adopting the phylogenetic approach on which it is based.

Whether groups are named according to PhyloCode or according to Linnaean classification, a phylogenetic tree represents a hypothesis about evolutionary relationships. These relationships often are depicted as a series of dichotomies, or two-way **branch points**. Each branch point represents the divergence of two evolutionary lineages from a common ancestor. In Figure 26.5, for example, branch point 3 represents the common ancestor of taxa A, B, and C. The position of branch point 4 to the right of 3 indicates that taxa B and C diverged after their shared lineage split from that of taxon A. (Tree branches can be rotated around a branch point without changing their evolutionary relationships.)

In Figure 26.5, taxa B and C are **sister taxa**, groups of organisms that share an immediate common ancestor (branch

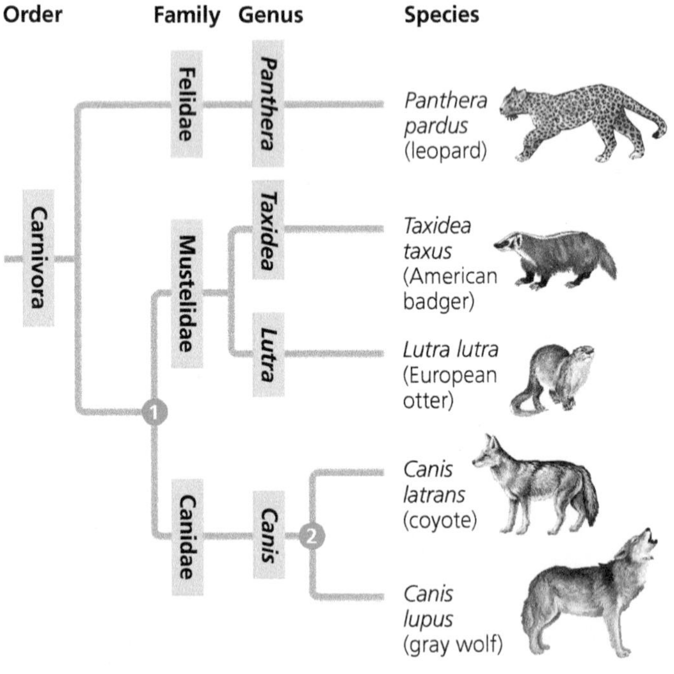

▲ **Figure 26.4 The connection between classification and phylogeny.** Hierarchical classification can reflect the branching patterns of phylogenetic trees. This tree traces possible evolutionary relationships between some of the taxa within order Carnivora, itself a branch of class Mammalia. The branch point 1 represents the most recent common ancestor of all members of the weasel (Mustelidae) and dog (Canidae) families. The branch point 2 represents the most recent common ancestor of coyotes and gray wolves.

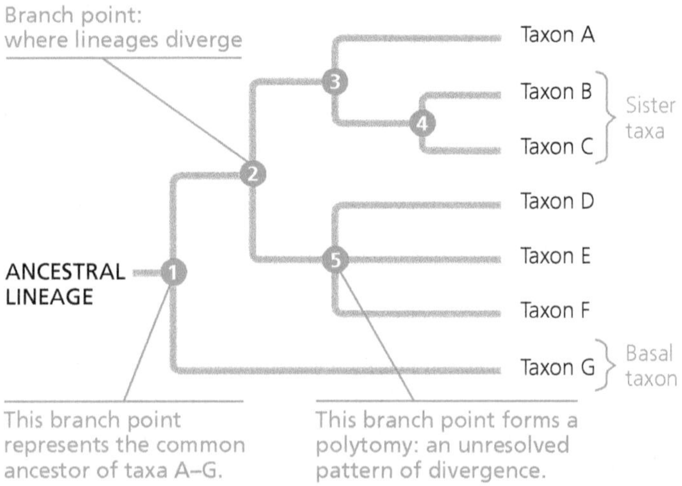

▲ **Figure 26.5 How to read a phylogenetic tree.**

DRAW IT *Redraw this tree, rotating the branches around branch points 2 and 4. Does your new version tell a different story about the evolutionary relationships between the taxa? Explain.*

point 4) and hence are each other's closest relatives. Note also that this tree, like most of the phylogenetic trees in this book, is **rooted**, which means that a branch point within the tree (often drawn farthest to the left) represents the most recent common ancestor of all taxa in the tree. The term **basal taxon** refers to a lineage that diverges early in the history of a group and hence, like taxon G in Figure 26.5, lies on a branch that originates near the common ancestor of the group. Finally, the lineage leading to taxa D–F includes a **polytomy**, a branch point from which more than two descendant groups emerge. A polytomy signifies that evolutionary relationships among the taxa are not yet clear.

What We Can and Cannot Learn from Phylogenetic Trees

Let's summarize three key points about phylogenetic trees. First, they are intended to show patterns of descent, not phenotypic similarity. Although closely related organisms often resemble one another due to their common ancestry, they may not if their lineages have evolved at different rates or faced very different environmental conditions. For example, even though crocodiles are more closely related to birds than to lizards (see Figure 22.17), they look more like lizards because morphology has changed dramatically in the bird lineage.

Second, the sequence of branching in a tree does not necessarily indicate the actual (absolute) ages of the particular species. For example, the tree in Figure 26.4 does not indicate that the wolf evolved more recently than the European otter; rather, the tree shows only that the most recent common ancestor of the wolf and otter (branch point 1) lived before the most recent common ancestor of the wolf and coyote (2). To indicate when wolves and otters evolved, the tree would need to include additional divergences in each evolutionary lineage, as well as the dates when those splits occurred. Generally, unless given specific information about what the branch lengths in a phylogenetic tree mean—for example, that they are proportional to time—we should interpret the diagram solely in terms of patterns of descent. No assumptions should be made about when particular species evolved or how much change occurred in each lineage.

Third, we should not assume that a taxon on a phylogenetic tree evolved from the taxon next to it. Figure 26.4 does not indicate that wolves evolved from coyotes or vice versa. We can infer only that the lineage leading to wolves and the lineage leading to coyotes both evolved from the common ancestor 2. That ancestor, which is now extinct, was neither a wolf nor a coyote. However, its descendants include the two *extant* (living) species shown here, wolves and coyotes.

Applying Phylogenies

Understanding phylogeny can have practical applications. Consider maize (corn), which originated in the Americas and is now an important food crop worldwide. From a phylogeny of maize based on DNA data, researchers have been able to identify two species of wild grasses that may be maize's closest living relatives. These two close relatives may be useful as "reservoirs" of beneficial alleles that can be transferred to cultivated maize by cross-breeding or genetic engineering (see Chapter 20).

A different use of phylogenetic trees is described in Figure 26.6: investigating whether whale meat samples had

▼ **Figure 26.6** **INQUIRY**

What is the species identity of food being sold as whale meat?

EXPERIMENT C. S. Baker, then at the University of Auckland, New Zealand, and S. R. Palumbi, then at the University of Hawaii, purchased 13 samples of "whale meat" from Japanese fish markets. They sequenced a specific part of the mitochondrial DNA from each sample and compared their results with the comparable DNA sequence from known whale species. To infer the species identity of each sample, Baker and Palumbi constructed a *gene tree*, a phylogenetic tree that shows patterns of relatedness among DNA sequences rather than among taxa.

RESULTS The analysis yielded the following gene tree:

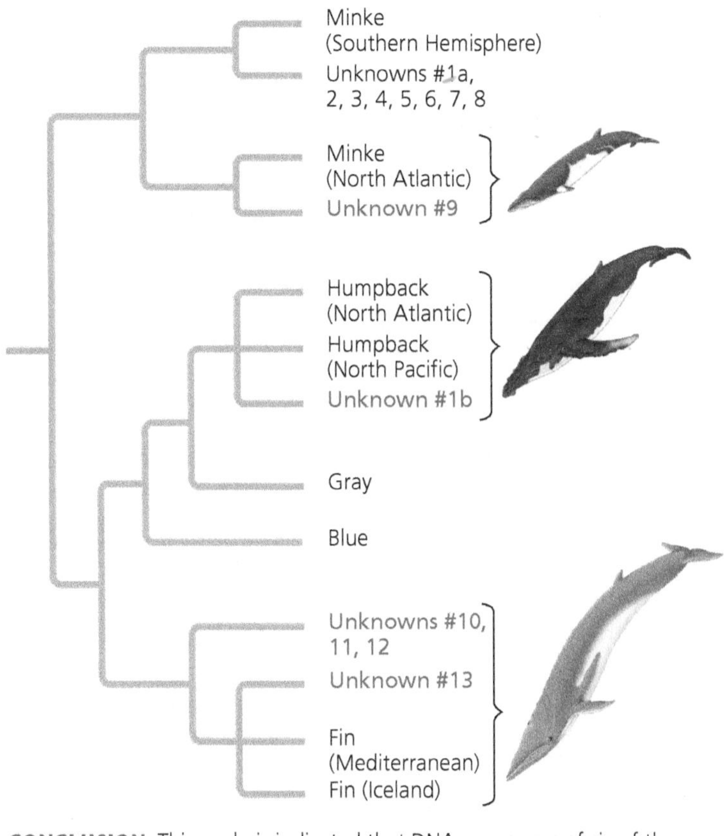

CONCLUSION This analysis indicated that DNA sequences of six of the unknown samples (in red) were most closely related to DNA sequences of whales that are not legal to harvest.

SOURCE C. S. Baker and S. R. Palumbi, Which whales are hunted? A molecular genetic approach to monitoring whaling, *Science* 265:1538–1539 (1994).

WHAT IF? What different results would have indicated that the whale meat had *not* been illegally harvested?

been illegally harvested from whale species protected under international law—rather than from species that can be harvested legally, such as Minke whales caught in the Southern Hemisphere. This phylogeny indicated that meat from humpback, fin, and Minke whales caught in the Northern Hemisphere was being sold illegally in some Japanese fish markets.

How do researchers construct trees like those we've considered here? In the next section, we'll begin to answer that question by examining the data used to determine phylogenies.

CONCEPT CHECK 26.1

1. Which levels of the classification in Figure 26.3 do humans share with leopards?
2. What does the phylogenetic tree in Figure 26.4 indicate about the evolutionary relationships of the leopard, badger, and wolf?
3. Which of the trees shown here depicts an evolutionary history different from the other two? Explain.

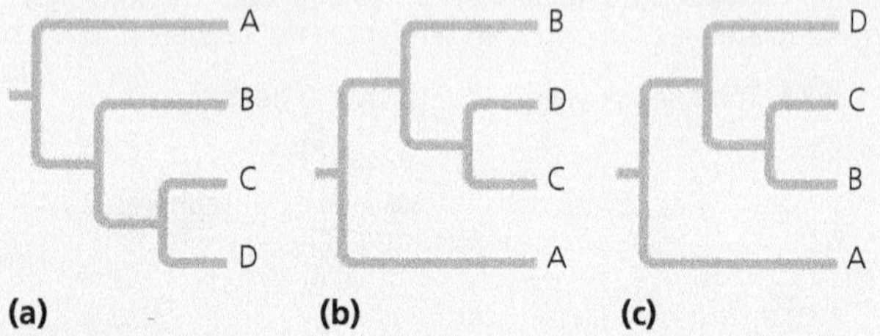

4. **WHAT IF?** Suppose new evidence indicates that taxon E in Figure 26.5 is the sister taxon of a group consisting of taxa D and F. Redraw the tree to accommodate this new finding.

For suggested answers, see Appendix A.

CONCEPT 26.2

Phylogenies are inferred from morphological and molecular data

To infer phylogeny, systematists must gather as much information as possible about the morphology, genes, and biochemistry of the relevant organisms. It is important to focus on features that result from common ancestry, because only such features reflect evolutionary relationships.

Morphological and Molecular Homologies

Recall that phenotypic and genetic similarities due to shared ancestry are called *homologies*. For example, the similarity in the number and arrangement of bones in the forelimbs of mammals is due to their descent from a common ancestor with the same bone structure; this is an example of a morphological homology (see Figure 22.15). In the same way, genes or other DNA sequences are homologous if they are descended from sequences carried by a common ancestor.

In general, organisms that share very similar morphologies or similar DNA sequences are likely to be more closely related than organisms with vastly different structures or sequences. In some cases, however, the morphological divergence between related species can be great and their genetic divergence small (or vice versa). Consider the Hawaiian silversword plants discussed in Chapter 25. These species vary dramatically in appearance throughout the islands. Some are tall, twiggy trees, and others are dense, ground-hugging shrubs (see Figure 25.20). But despite these striking phenotypic differences, the silverswords' genes are very similar. Based on these small molecular divergences, scientists estimate that the silversword group began to diverge 5 million years ago, which is also about the time when the oldest of the current islands formed. We'll discuss how scientists use molecular data to estimate such divergence times later in this chapter.

Sorting Homology from Analogy

A potential red herring in constructing a phylogeny is similarity due to convergent evolution—called **analogy**—rather than to shared ancestry (homology). As you read in Chapter 22, convergent evolution occurs when similar environmental pressures and natural selection produce similar (analogous) adaptations in organisms from different evolutionary lineages. For example, the two mole-like animals illustrated in Figure 26.7 are very similar in their external appearance. However, their internal anatomy, physiology, and reproductive systems are very dissimilar. Australian "moles" are marsupials; their young complete their embryonic development in a pouch on the outside of the mother's body. North American moles, in contrast, are eutherians; their young complete

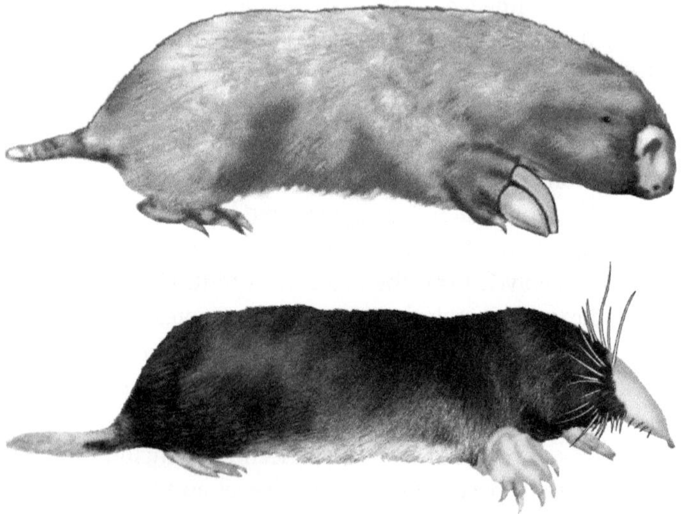

▲ Figure 26.7 **Convergent evolution of analogous burrowing characteristics.** An elongated body, enlarged front paws, small eyes, and a pad of thickened skin that protects a tapered nose all evolved independently in the marsupial Australian "mole" (top) and a eutherian North American mole (bottom).

their embryonic development in the uterus within the mother's body. Indeed, genetic comparisons and the fossil record provide evidence that the common ancestor of these moles lived 140 million years ago, about the time the marsupial and eutherian mammals diverged. This common ancestor and most of its descendants were not mole-like, but analogous characteristics evolved independently in these two mole lineages as they became adapted to similar lifestyles.

Distinguishing between homology and analogy is critical in reconstructing phylogenies. To see why, consider bats and birds, both of which have adaptations that enable flight. This superficial resemblance might imply that bats are more closely related to birds than they are to cats, which cannot fly. But a closer examination reveals that a bat's wing is far more similar to the forelimbs of cats and other mammals than to a bird's wing. Bats and birds descended from a common tetrapod ancestor that lived about 320 million years ago. This common ancestor could not fly. Thus, although the underlying skeletal systems of bats and birds are homologous, their *wings* are not. Flight is enabled in different ways—stretched membranes in the bat wing versus feathers in the bird wing. Fossil evidence also documents that bat wings and bird wings arose independently from the forelimbs of different tetrapod ancestors. Thus, with respect to flight, a bat's wing is *analogous*, not homologous, to a bird's wing. Analogous structures that arose independently are also called **homoplasies** (from the Greek, meaning "to mold in the same way").

Besides corroborative similarities and fossil evidence, another clue to distinguishing between homology and analogy is the complexity of the characters being compared. The more elements that are similar in two complex structures, the more likely it is that they evolved from a common ancestor. For instance, the skulls of an adult human and an adult chimpanzee both consist of many bones fused together. The compositions of the skulls match almost perfectly, bone for bone. It is highly improbable that such complex structures, matching in so many details, have separate origins. More likely, the genes involved in the development of both skulls were inherited from a common ancestor. The same argument applies to comparisons at the gene level. Genes are sequences of thousands of nucleotides, each of which represents an inherited character in the form of one of the four DNA bases: A (adenine), G (guanine), C (cytosine), or T (thymine). If genes in two organisms share many portions of their nucleotide sequences, it is likely that the genes are homologous.

Evaluating Molecular Homologies

Comparisons of DNA molecules often pose technical challenges for researchers. The first step after sequencing the molecules is to align comparable sequences from the species being studied. If the species are very closely related, the sequences probably differ at only one or a few sites. In contrast, comparable nucleic acid sequences in distantly related species usually have different bases at many sites and may have different lengths. This is because insertions and deletions accumulate over long periods of time.

Suppose, for example, that certain noncoding DNA sequences near a particular gene are very similar in two species, except that the first base of the sequence has been deleted in one of the species. The effect is that the remaining sequence shifts back one notch. A comparison of the two sequences that does not take this deletion into account would overlook what in fact is a very good match. To address such problems, researchers have developed computer programs that estimate the best way to align comparable DNA segments of differing lengths (Figure 26.8).

Such molecular comparisons reveal that many base substitutions and other differences have accumulated in the comparable genes of an Australian mole and a North American mole. The many differences indicate that their lineages have diverged greatly since their common ancestor; thus, we say that the living species are not closely related. In contrast, the high degree of gene sequence similarity among the silverswords indicates that they are all very closely related, in spite of their considerable morphological differences.

Just as with morphological characters, it is necessary to distinguish homology from analogy in evaluating molecular similarities for evolutionary studies. Two sequences that resemble each other at many points along their length most likely are

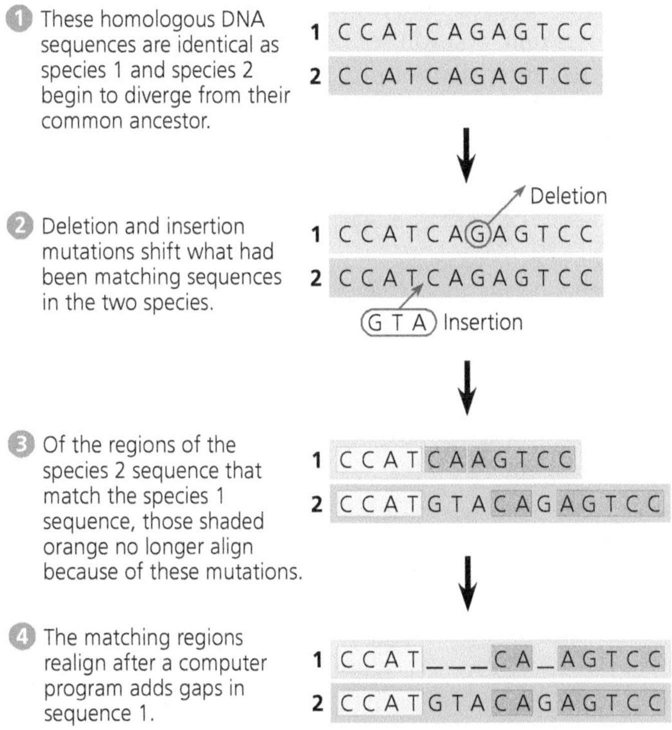

▲ **Figure 26.8 Aligning segments of DNA.** Systematists search for similar sequences along DNA segments from two species (only one DNA strand is shown for each species). In this example, 11 of the original 12 bases have not changed since the species diverged. Hence, those portions of the sequences still align once the length is adjusted.

ACGGATAGTCCACTAGGCACTA

TCACCGACAGGTCTTTGACTAG

▲ **Figure 26.9 A molecular homoplasy.** These two DNA sequences from organisms that are not closely related coincidentally share 25% of their bases. Statistical tools have been developed to determine whether DNA sequences that share more than 25% of their bases do so because they are homologous.

? *Why might you expect organisms that are not closely related to nevertheless share roughly 25% of their bases?*

homologous (see Figure 26.8). But in organisms that do not appear to be closely related, the bases that their otherwise very different sequences happen to share may simply be coincidental matches, called molecular homoplasies (Figure 26.9). Scientists have developed statistical tools that can help distinguish "distant" homologies from such coincidental matches in extremely divergent sequences.

To date, researchers have sequenced more than 110 billion bases of DNA from thousands of species. This enormous collection of data has fueled a boom in the study of phylogeny. The new data have supported earlier hypotheses regarding many evolutionary relationships, such as that between Australian and North American moles, and have clarified other relationships, such as those between the various silverswords. In the rest of this unit, you will see how our understanding of phylogeny has been transformed by **molecular systematics**, the discipline that uses data from DNA and other molecules to determine evolutionary relationships.

CONCEPT CHECK 26.2

1. Decide whether each of the following pairs of structures more likely represents analogy or homology, and explain your reasoning: (a) a porcupine's quills and a cactus's spines; (b) a cat's paw and a human's hand; (c) an owl's wing and a hornet's wing.
2. **WHAT IF?** Suppose that species 1 and species 2 have similar appearances but very divergent gene sequences and that species 2 and species 3 have very different appearances but similar gene sequences. Which pair of species is more likely to be closely related: 1 and 2, or 2 and 3? Explain.

For suggested answers, see Appendix A.

CONCEPT 26.3

Shared characters are used to construct phylogenetic trees

In reconstructing phylogenies, the first step is to distinguish homologous features from analogous ones (since only homology reflects evolutionary history). Next we must choose a method of inferring phylogeny from these homologous characters. A widely used set of methods is known as cladistics.

Cladistics

In the approach to systematics called **cladistics**, common ancestry is the primary criterion used to classify organisms. Using this methodology, biologists attempt to place species into groups called **clades**, each of which includes an ancestral species and all of its descendants (Figure 26.10a). Clades, like

▼ **Figure 26.10 Monophyletic, paraphyletic, and polyphyletic groups.**

(a) Monophyletic group (clade) | **(b) Paraphyletic group** | **(c) Polyphyletic group**

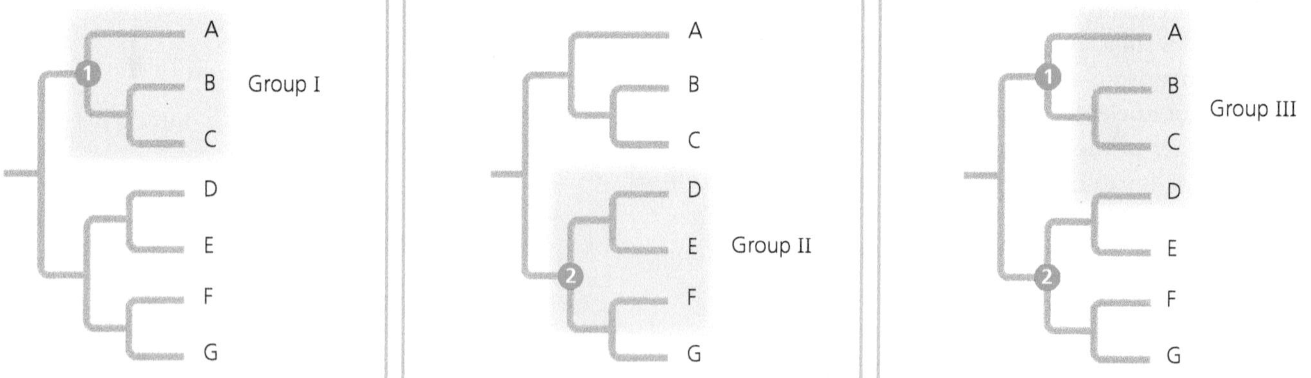

Group I, consisting of three species (A, B, C) and their common ancestor ①, is a clade, also called a monophyletic group. A monophyletic group consists of an ancestral species and *all* of its descendants.

Group II is paraphyletic, meaning that it consists of an ancestral species ② and some of its descendants (species D, E, F) but not all of them (missing species G).

Group III is polyphyletic, meaning that some of its members have different ancestors. In this case, species A, B, and C share common ancestor ①, but species D has a different ancestor: ②.

taxonomic ranks, are nested within larger clades. In Figure 26.4, for example, the cat group (Felidae) represents a clade within a larger clade (Carnivora) that also includes the dog group (Canidae). However, a taxon is equivalent to a clade only if it is **monophyletic** (from the Greek, meaning "single tribe"), signifying that it consists of an ancestral species and all of its descendants (see Figure 26.10a). Contrast this with a **paraphyletic** ("beside the tribe") group, which consists of an ancestral species and some, but not all, of its descendants (Figure 26.10b), or a **polyphyletic** ("many tribes") group, which includes taxa with different ancestors (Figure 26.10c). Next we'll discuss how clades are identified using shared derived characters.

Shared Ancestral and Shared Derived Characters

As a result of descent with modification, organisms both share characteristics with their ancestors and differ from them. For example, all mammals have backbones, but a backbone does not distinguish mammals from other vertebrates because *all* vertebrates have backbones. The backbone predates the branching of mammals from other vertebrates. Thus for mammals, the backbone is a **shared ancestral character**, a character that originated in an ancestor of the taxon. In contrast, hair is a character shared by all mammals but *not* found in their ancestors. Thus, in mammals, hair is considered a **shared derived character**, an evolutionary novelty unique to a clade.

Note that it is a relative matter whether a particular character is considered ancestral or derived. A backbone can also qualify as a shared derived character, but only at a deeper branch point that distinguishes all vertebrates from other animals. Among mammals, a backbone is considered a shared ancestral character because it was present in the ancestor common to all mammals.

Inferring Phylogenies Using Derived Characters

Shared derived characters are unique to particular clades. Because all features of organisms arose at some point in the history of life, it should be possible to determine the clade in which each shared derived character first appeared and to use that information to infer evolutionary relationships.

To see how this analysis is done, consider the set of characters shown in Figure 26.11a for each of five vertebrates—a leopard, turtle, frog, bass, and lamprey (a jawless aquatic vertebrate). As a basis of comparison, we need to select an outgroup. An **outgroup** is a species or group of species from an evolutionary lineage that is known to have diverged before the lineage that includes the species we are studying (the **ingroup**). A suitable outgroup can be determined based on evidence from morphology, paleontology, embryonic development, and gene sequences. An appropriate outgroup for our example is the lancelet, a small animal that lives in mudflats and (like vertebrates) is a member of Chordata. Unlike the vertebrates, however, the lancelet does not have a backbone.

By comparing members of the ingroup with each other and with the outgroup, we can determine which characters were derived at the various branch points of vertebrate evolution. For example, *all* of the vertebrates in the ingroup have backbones: This character was present in the ancestral vertebrate, but not in the outgroup. Now note that hinged jaws are a character absent in lampreys but present in other members of the ingroup; this character helps us to identify an early branch point in the vertebrate clade. Proceeding in this way, we can translate the data in our table of characters into a phylogenetic tree that groups all the ingroup taxa into a hierarchy based on their shared derived characters (Figure 26.11b).

TAXA

CHARACTERS	Lancelet (outgroup)	Lamprey	Bass	Frog	Turtle	Leopard
Vertebral column (backbone)	0	1	1	1	1	1
Hinged jaws	0	0	1	1	1	1
Four walking legs	0	0	0	1	1	1
Amnion	0	0	0	0	1	1
Hair	0	0	0	0	0	1

(a) Character table. A 0 indicates that a character is absent; a 1 indicates that a character is present.

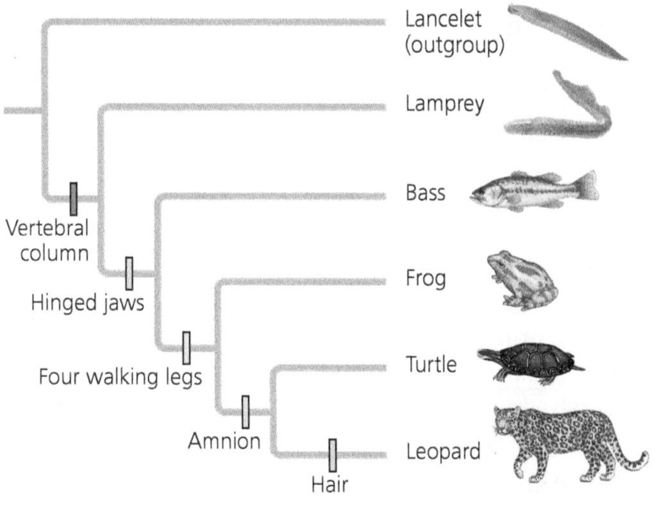

(b) Phylogenetic tree. Analyzing the distribution of these derived characters can provide insight into vertebrate phylogeny.

▲ Figure 26.11 **Constructing a phylogenetic tree.** The characters used here include the amnion, a membrane that encloses the embryo inside a fluid-filled sac (see Figure 34.25).

DRAW IT *In (b), circle the most inclusive clade for which a hinged jaw is a shared ancestral character.*

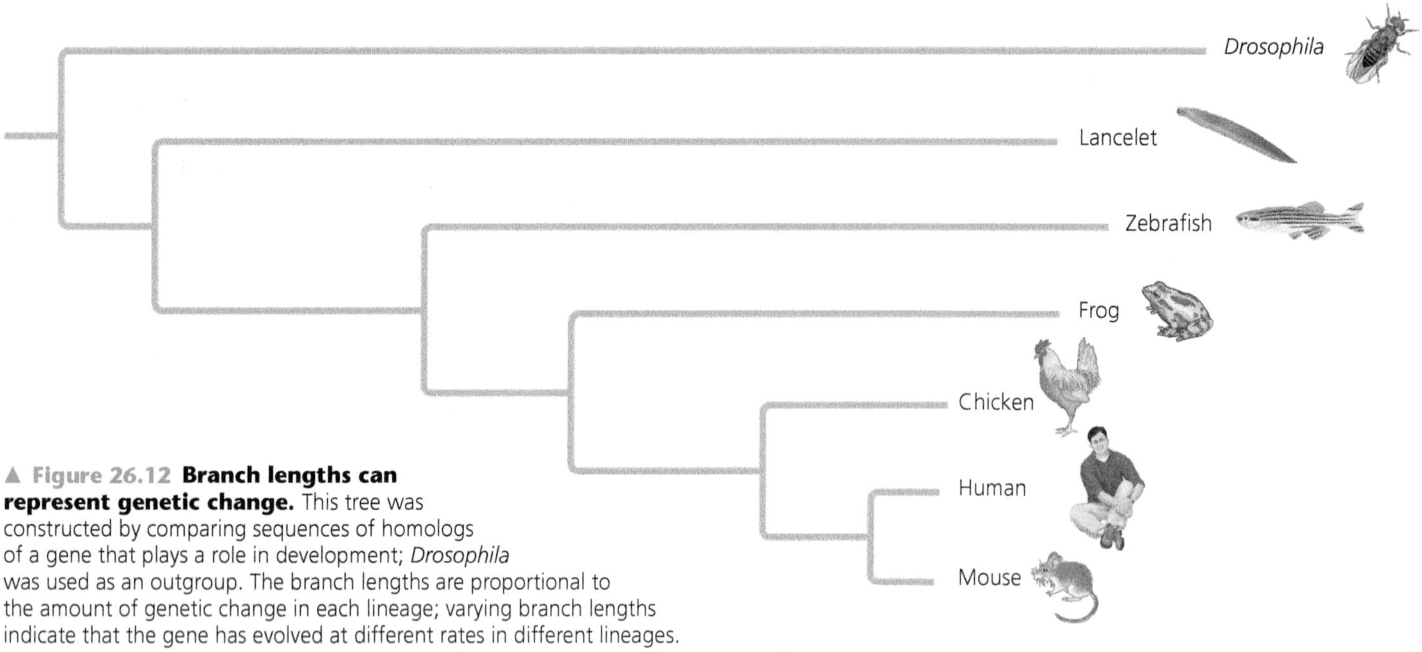

▲ **Figure 26.12 Branch lengths can represent genetic change.** This tree was constructed by comparing sequences of homologs of a gene that plays a role in development; *Drosophila* was used as an outgroup. The branch lengths are proportional to the amount of genetic change in each lineage; varying branch lengths indicate that the gene has evolved at different rates in different lineages.

? *In which vertebrate lineage has the studied gene evolved most rapidly? Explain.*

Phylogenetic Trees with Proportional Branch Lengths

In the phylogenetic trees we have presented so far, the lengths of the tree's branches do not indicate the degree of evolutionary change in each lineage. Furthermore, the chronology represented by the branching pattern of the tree is relative (earlier versus later) rather than absolute (how many millions of years ago). But in some tree diagrams, branch lengths are proportional to amount of evolutionary change or to the times at which particular events occurred.

In Figure 26.12, for example, the branch length of the phylogenetic tree reflects the number of changes that have taken place in a particular DNA sequence in that lineage. Note that the total length of the horizontal lines from the base of the tree to the mouse is less than that of the line leading to the outgroup species, the fruit fly *Drosophila*. This implies that in the time since the mouse and fly diverged from a common ancestor, more genetic changes have occurred in the *Drosophila* lineage than in the mouse lineage.

Even though the branches of a phylogenetic tree may have different lengths, among organisms alive today, all the different lineages that descend from a common ancestor have survived for the same number of years. To take an extreme example, humans and bacteria had a common ancestor that lived over 3 billion years ago. Fossils and genetic evidence indicate that this ancestor was a single-celled prokaryote. Even though bacteria have apparently changed little in their morphology since that common ancestor, there have nonetheless been 3 billion years of evolution in the bacterial lineage, just as there have been 3 billion years of evolution in the eukaryotic lineage that includes humans.

These equal spans of chronological time can be represented in a phylogenetic tree whose branch lengths are proportional to time (Figure 26.13). Such a tree draws on fossil data to place branch points in the context of geologic time. Additionally, it is possible to combine these two types of trees by labeling branch points with information about rates of genetic change or dates of divergence.

Maximum Parsimony and Maximum Likelihood

As the growing database of DNA sequences enables us to study more species, the difficulty of building the phylogenetic tree that best describes their evolutionary history also grows. What if you are analyzing data for 50 species? There are 3×10^{76} different ways to arrange 50 species into a tree! And which tree in this huge forest reflects the true phylogeny? Systematists can never be sure of finding the most accurate tree in such a large data set, but they can narrow the possibilities by applying the principles of maximum parsimony and maximum likelihood.

According to the principle of **maximum parsimony**, we should first investigate the simplest explanation that is consistent with the facts. (The parsimony principle is also called "Occam's razor" after William of Occam, a 14th-century English philosopher who advocated this minimalist problem-solving approach of "shaving away" unnecessary complications.) In the case of trees based on morphology, the most parsimonious tree requires the fewest evolutionary events, as measured by the origin of shared derived morphological characters. For phylogenies based on DNA, the most parsimonious tree requires the fewest base changes.

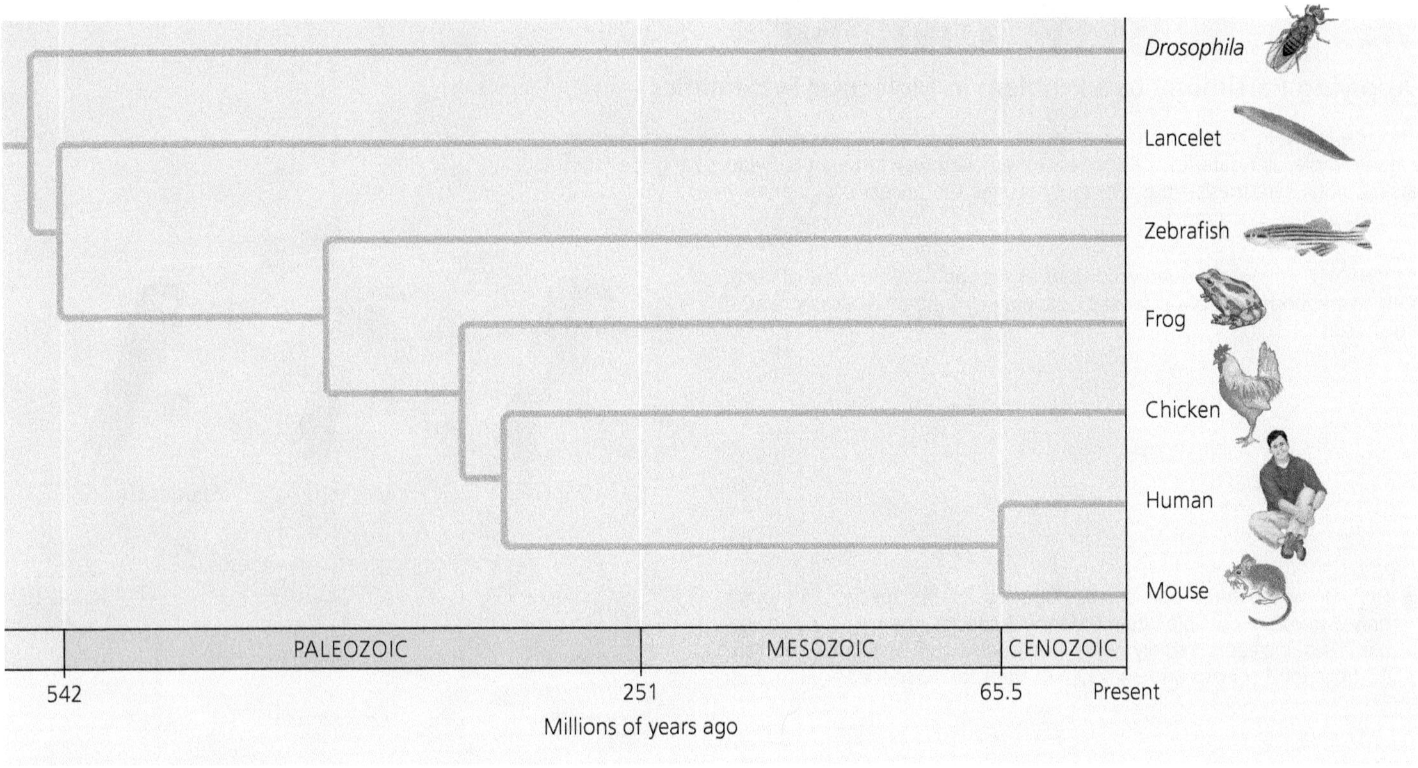

▲ **Figure 26.13 Branch lengths can indicate time.** This tree is based on the same molecular data as the tree in Figure 26.12, but here the branch points are mapped to dates based on fossil evidence. Thus, the branch lengths are proportional to time. Each lineage has the same total length from the base of the tree to the branch tip, indicating that all the lineages have diverged from the common ancestor for equal amounts of time.

The principle of **maximum likelihood** states that given certain probability rules about how DNA sequences change over time, a tree can be found that reflects the most likely sequence of evolutionary events. Maximum-likelihood methods are complex, but as a simple example, let us return to the phylogenetic relationships between a human, a mushroom, and a tulip. Figure 26.14 shows two possible, equally parsimonious trees for this trio. Tree 1 is more likely if we assume that DNA changes have occurred at equal rates along all the branches of the tree from the common ancestor. Tree 2 requires assuming that the rate of evolution slowed greatly in the mushroom lineage and sped up greatly in the tulip lineage. Thus, assuming that equal rates are more common than unequal rates, tree 1 is more likely. We will soon see that many genes do evolve at approximately equal rates in different lineages. But note that if we find new evidence of unequal rates, tree 2 might be more likely! The likelihood of a tree depends on the assumptions on which it is based.

Scientists have developed many computer programs to search for trees that are parsimonious and likely. When a large amount of accurate data is available, the methods used in these programs usually yield similar trees. As an example of one

	Human	Mushroom	Tulip
Human	0	30%	40%
Mushroom		0	40%
Tulip			0

(a) Percentage differences between sequences

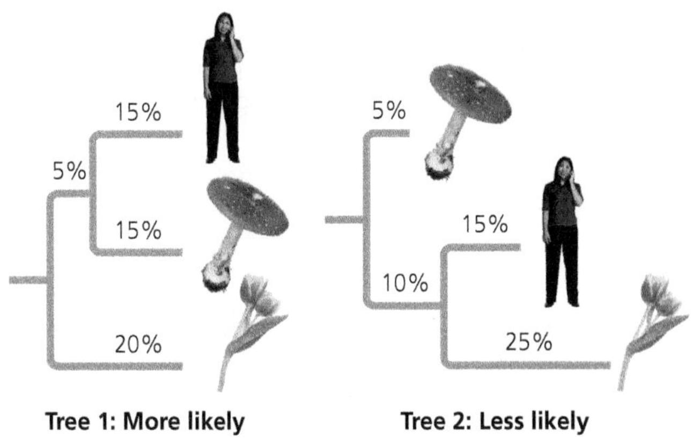

(b) Comparison of possible trees

▲ **Figure 26.14 Trees with different likelihoods.** Based on percentage differences between genes in a human, a mushroom, and a tulip **(a)**, there are two phylogenetic trees with the same total branch length **(b)**. The sum of the percentages from a point of divergence in a tree equals the percentage differences in (a). For example, in tree 1, the human–tulip divergence is 15% + 5% + 20% = 40%. In tree 2, this divergence also equals 40% (15% + 25%). If the genes have evolved at the same rate in the different branches, tree 1 is more likely.

▼ Figure 26.15 **RESEARCH METHOD**

Applying Parsimony to a Problem in Molecular Systematics

APPLICATION In considering possible phylogenies for a group of species, systematists compare molecular data for the species. An efficient way to begin is by identifying the most parsimonious hypothesis—the one that requires the fewest evolutionary events (molecular changes) to have occurred.

TECHNIQUE Follow the numbered steps as we apply the principle of parsimony to a hypothetical phylogenetic problem involving three closely related bird species.

1. First, draw the three possible phylogenies for the species. (Although only 3 trees are possible when ordering 3 species, the number of possible trees increases rapidly with the number of species: There are 15 trees for 4 species and 34,459,425 trees for 10 species.)

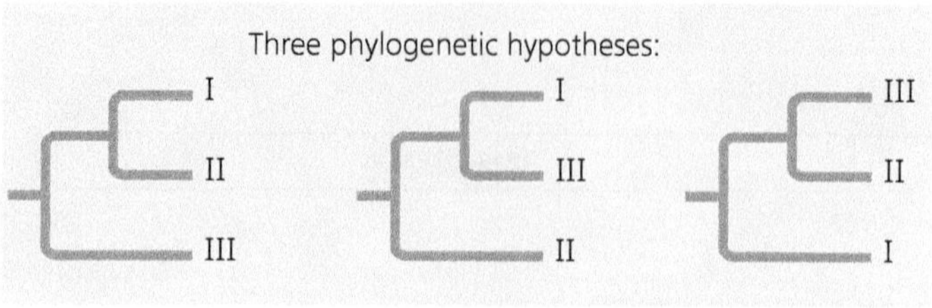

2. Tabulate the molecular data for the species. In this simplified example, the data represent a DNA sequence consisting of just four nucleotide bases. Data from several outgroup species (not shown) were used to infer the ancestral DNA sequence.

	Site 1	2	3	4
Species I	C	T	A	T
Species II	C	T	T	C
Species III	A	G	A	C
Ancestral sequence	A	G	T	T

3. Now focus on site 1 in the DNA sequence. In the tree on the left, a single base-change event, represented by the purple hatchmark on the branch leading to species I and II (and labeled 1/C, indicating a change at site 1 to nucleotide C), is sufficient to account for the site 1 data. In the other two trees, two base-change events are necessary.

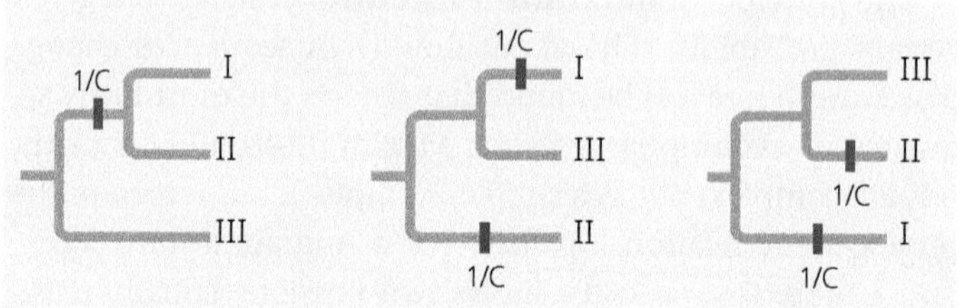

4. Continuing the comparison of bases at sites 2, 3, and 4 reveals that each of the three trees requires a total of five additional base-change events (purple hatchmarks).

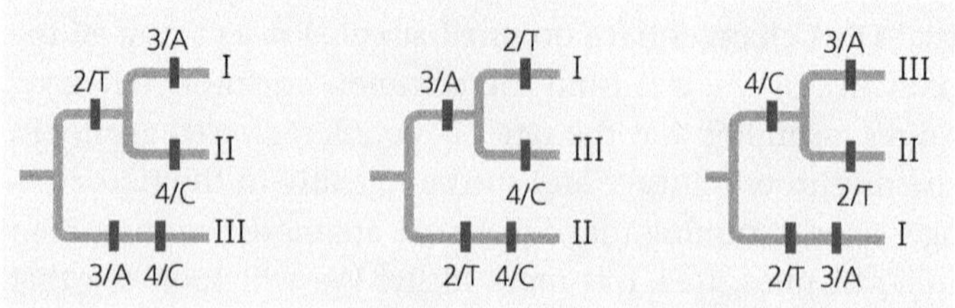

RESULTS To identify the most parsimonious tree, we total all of the base-change events noted in steps 3 and 4. We conclude that the first tree is the most parsimonious of the three possible phylogenies. (In a real example, many more sites would be analyzed. Hence, the trees would often differ by more than one base-change event.)

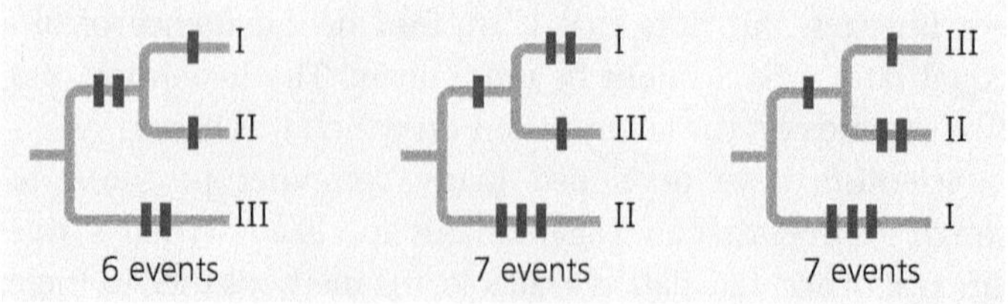

method, Figure 26.15, on the facing page, walks you through the process of identifying the most parsimonious molecular tree for a three-species problem. Computer programs use the principle of parsimony to estimate phylogenies in a similar way: They examine large numbers of possible trees and select the tree or trees that require fewest evolutionary changes.

Phylogenetic Trees as Hypotheses

This is a good place to reiterate that any phylogenetic tree represents a hypothesis about how the various organisms in the tree are related to one another. The best hypothesis is the one that best fits all the available data. A phylogenetic hypothesis may be modified when new evidence compels systematists to revise their trees. Indeed, while many older phylogenetic hypotheses have been supported by new morphological and molecular data, others have been changed or rejected.

Thinking of phylogenies as hypotheses also allows us to use them in a powerful way: We can make and test predictions based on the assumption that a phylogeny—our hypothesis—is correct. For example, in an approach known as *phylogenetic bracketing*, we can predict (by parsimony) that features shared by two groups of closely related organisms are present in their common ancestor and all of its descendants unless independent data indicate otherwise. (Note that "prediction" can refer to unknown past events as well as to evolutionary changes yet to occur.)

This approach has been used to make novel predictions about dinosaurs. For example, there is evidence that birds descended from the theropods, a group of bipedal saurischian dinosaurs. As seen in Figure 26.16, the closest living relatives of birds are crocodiles. Birds and crocodiles share numerous features: They have four-chambered hearts, they "sing" to defend territories and attract mates (although a crocodile's "song" is more like a bellow), and they build nests. Both birds and crocodiles also care for their eggs by *brooding*, a behavior in which a parent warms the eggs with its body. Birds brood by sitting on their eggs, whereas crocodiles cover their eggs with their neck. Reasoning that any feature shared by birds and crocodiles is likely to have been present in their common ancestor (denoted by the blue dot in Figure 26.16) and *all* of its descendants, biologists predicted that dinosaurs had four-chambered hearts, sang, built nests, and exhibited brooding.

Internal organs, such as the heart, rarely fossilize, and it is, of course, difficult to test whether dinosaurs sang to defend territories and attract mates. However, fossilized dinosaur eggs and nests have provided evidence supporting the prediction of brooding in dinosaurs. First, a fossil embryo of an *Oviraptor* dinosaur was found, still inside its egg. This egg was identical to those found in another fossil, one that showed an *Oviraptor* adult crouching over a group of eggs in a posture similar to that in brooding birds today (Figure 26.17). Researchers suggested that the *Oviraptor* dinosaur preserved in this second fossil died while incubating or protecting its eggs. The broader conclusion that emerged from this work—that

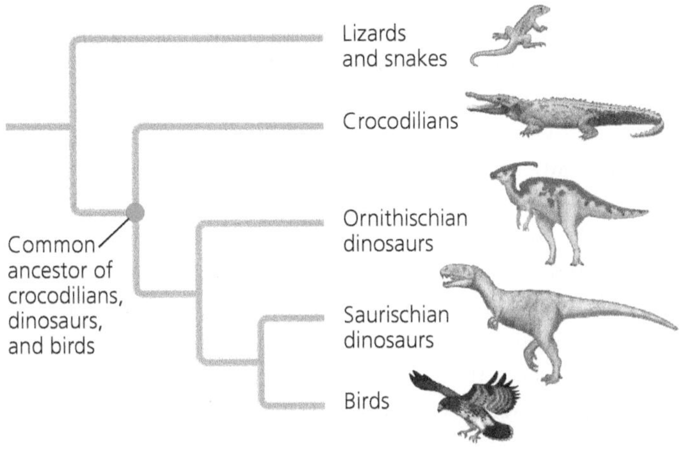

▲ Figure 26.16 **A phylogenetic tree of birds and their close relatives.**

? *What is the most basal taxon represented in this tree?*

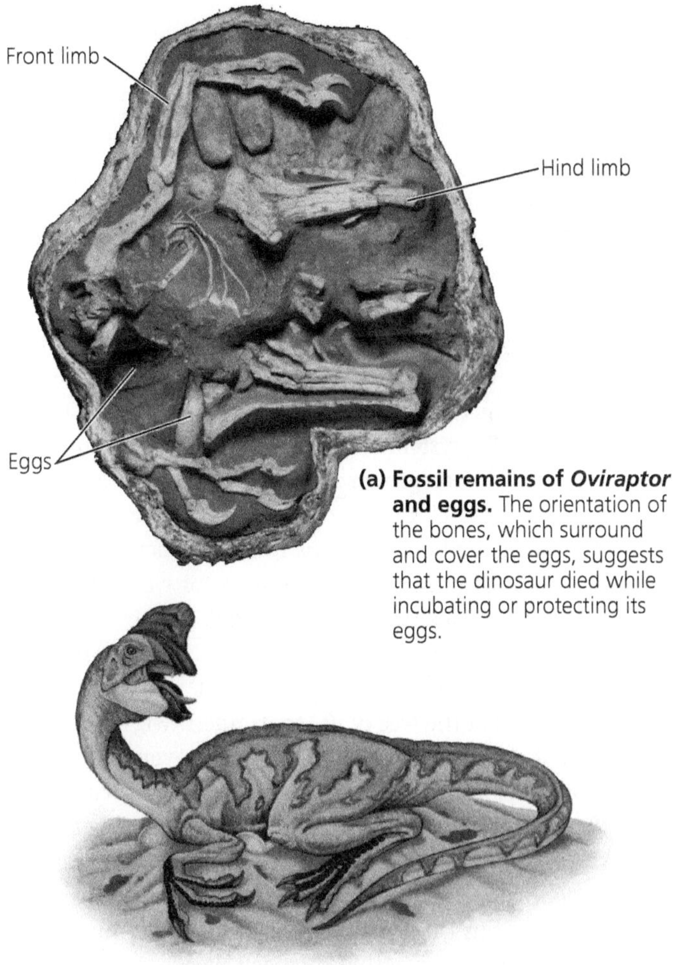

(a) Fossil remains of *Oviraptor* and eggs. The orientation of the bones, which surround and cover the eggs, suggests that the dinosaur died while incubating or protecting its eggs.

(b) Artist's reconstruction of the dinosaur's posture based on the fossil findings.

▲ Figure 26.17 **Fossil support for a phylogenetic prediction: Dinosaurs built nests and brooded their eggs.**

dinosaurs built nests and exhibited brooding—has since been strengthened by additional fossil discoveries that show that other species of dinosaurs built nests and sat on their eggs. Finally, by supporting predictions based on the phylogenetic hypothesis shown in Figure 26.16, fossil discoveries of nests and brooding in dinosaurs provide independent data that suggest that the hypothesis is correct.

CONCEPT CHECK 26.3

1. To distinguish a particular clade of mammals within the larger clade that corresponds to class Mammalia, would hair be a useful character? Why or why not?
2. The most parsimonious tree of evolutionary relationships can be inaccurate. How can this occur?
3. **WHAT IF?** Draw a phylogenetic tree that includes the relationships from both Figure 25.6 and Figure 26.16. Traditionally, all the taxa shown besides birds and mammals were classified as reptiles. Would a cladistic approach support that classification? Explain.

For suggested answers, see Appendix A.

CONCEPT 26.4

An organism's evolutionary history is documented in its genome

As you have seen in this chapter, molecular systematics—using comparisons of nucleic acids or other molecules to deduce relatedness—is a valuable approach for tracing evolutionary history. The molecular approach helps us understand phylogenetic relationships that cannot be determined by nonmolecular methods such as comparative anatomy. For example, molecular systematics helps us uncover evolutionary relationships between groups that have little common ground for morphological comparison, such as animals and fungi. And molecular methods allow us to reconstruct phylogenies among groups of present-day organisms for which the fossil record is poor or lacking entirely. Overall, molecular biology has helped to extend systematics to evolutionary relationships far above and below the species level, ranging from the major branches of the tree of life to its finest twigs.

Different genes evolve at different rates, even in the same evolutionary lineage. As a result, molecular trees can represent short or long periods of time, depending on which genes are used. For example, the DNA that codes for ribosomal RNA (rRNA) changes relatively slowly. Therefore, comparisons of DNA sequences in these genes are useful for investigating relationships between taxa that diverged hundreds of millions of years ago. Studies of rRNA sequences indicate, for instance, that fungi are more closely related to animals than to green plants (see Figure 26.2). In contrast, mitochondrial DNA (mtDNA) evolves relatively rapidly and can be used to explore recent evolutionary events. One research team has traced the relationships among Native American groups through their mtDNA sequences. The molecular findings corroborate other evidence that the Pima of Arizona, the Maya of Mexico, and the Yanomami of Venezuela are closely related, probably descending from the first of three waves of immigrants that crossed the Bering land bridge from Asia to the Americas about 15,000 years ago.

Gene Duplications and Gene Families

What does molecular systematics reveal about the evolutionary history of genome change? Consider gene duplication, which plays a particularly important role in evolution because it increases the number of genes in the genome, providing more opportunities for further evolutionary changes. Molecular techniques now allow us to trace the phylogenies of gene duplications and the influence of these duplications on genome evolution. These molecular phylogenies must account for repeated duplications that have resulted in *gene families*, groups of related genes within an organism's genome (see Figure 21.11). Accounting for such duplications leads us to distinguish two types of homologous genes: orthologous genes and paralogous genes. **Orthologous genes** (from the Greek *orthos*, exact) are those found in different species, and their divergence traces back to the speciation events that produced the species (Figure 26.18a). The cytochrome *c* genes (which code for an electron transport chain protein) in humans and dogs are orthologous. In **paralogous genes** (from the Greek *para*, in parallel), the homology results from gene duplication; hence, multiple copies of these genes have diverged from one another within a species (Figure 26.18b). In Chapter 23, you encountered the example of olfactory receptor genes, which have undergone many gene duplications in vertebrates. Humans and mice both have huge families of more than 1,000 of these paralogous genes.

Note that orthologous genes can only diverge after speciation has taken place, that is, after the genes are found in separate gene pools. For example, although the cytochrome *c* genes in humans and dogs serve the same function, the gene's sequence in humans has diverged from that in dogs in the time since these species last shared a common ancestor. Paralogous genes, on the other hand, can diverge within a species because they are present in more than one copy in the genome. The paralogous genes that make up the olfactory receptor gene family in humans have diverged from each other during our long evolutionary history. They now specify proteins that confer sensitivity to a wide variety of molecules, ranging from food odors to sex pheromones.

Genome Evolution

Now that we can compare the entire genomes of different organisms, including our own, two patterns have emerged. First, lineages that diverged long ago can share orthologous genes. For

Figure 26.18 Two types of homologous genes. Colored bands mark regions of the genes where differences in base sequences have accumulated.

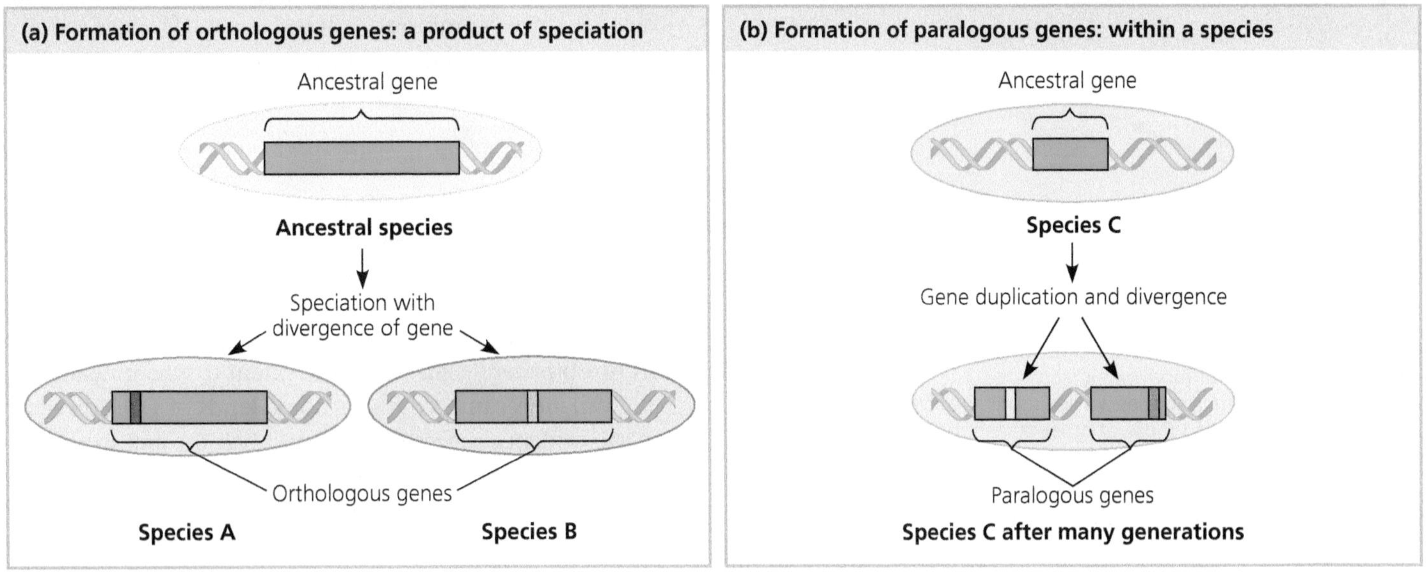

example, though the human and mouse lineages diverged about 65 million years ago, 99% of the genes of humans and mice are orthologous. And 50% of human genes are orthologous with those of yeast, despite 1 billion years of divergent evolution. Such commonalities explain why disparate organisms nevertheless share many biochemical and developmental pathways.

Second, the number of genes a species has doesn't seem to increase through duplication at the same rate as perceived phenotypic complexity. Humans have only about four times as many genes as yeast, a single-celled eukaryote, even though—unlike yeast—we have a large, complex brain and a body with more than 200 different types of tissues. Evidence is emerging that many human genes are more versatile than those of yeast: A single human gene can encode multiple proteins that perform different tasks in various body tissues. Unraveling the mechanisms that cause this genomic versatility and phenotypic variation is an exciting challenge.

CONCEPT CHECK 26.4

1. Explain how comparing proteins of two species can yield data about the species' evolutionary relationship.
2. WHAT IF? Suppose gene A is orthologous in species 1 and species 2, and gene B is paralogous to gene A in species 1. Suggest a sequence of two evolutionary events that could result in the following: Gene A differs considerably between species, yet gene A and gene B show little divergence from each other.
3. MAKE CONNECTIONS Review Figure 18.13 (p. 363); then suggest how a particular gene could have different functions in different tissues within an organism.

For suggested answers, see Appendix A.

CONCEPT 26.5

Molecular clocks help track evolutionary time

One goal of evolutionary biology is to understand the relationships among all organisms, including those for which there is no fossil record. However, if we attempt to determine the timing of molecular phylogenies that extend beyond the fossil record, we must rely on an assumption about how change occurs at the molecular level.

Molecular Clocks

We stated earlier that researchers have estimated that the common ancestor of Hawaiian silversword plants lived about 5 million years ago. How did they make this estimate? They relied on the concept of a **molecular clock**, a yardstick for measuring the absolute time of evolutionary change based on the observation that some genes and other regions of genomes appear to evolve at constant rates. The assumption underlying the molecular clock is that the number of nucleotide substitutions in orthologous genes is proportional to the time that has elapsed since the species branched from their common ancestor (divergence time). In the case of paralogous genes, the number of substitutions is proportional to the time since the ancestral gene was duplicated.

We can calibrate the molecular clock of a gene that has a reliable average rate of evolution by graphing the number of genetic differences—for example, nucleotide, codon, or amino acid differences—against the dates of evolutionary branch points that are known from the fossil record

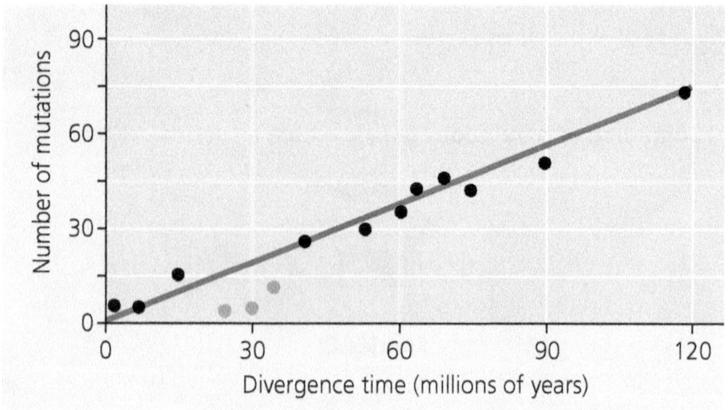

▲ **Figure 26.19 A molecular clock for mammals.** The number of accumulated mutations in seven proteins has increased over time in a consistent manner for most mammal species. The three green data points represent primate species, whose proteins appear to have evolved more slowly than those of other mammals. The divergence time for each data point was based on fossil evidence.

? *Use the graph to estimate the divergence time for a mammal with a total of 30 mutations in the seven proteins.*

(Figure 26.19). The average rates of genetic change inferred from such graphs can then be used to estimate the dates of events that cannot be discerned from the fossil record, such as the origin of the silverswords discussed earlier.

Of course, no gene marks time with complete precision. In fact, some portions of the genome appear to have evolved in irregular bursts that are not at all clocklike. And even those genes that seem to act as reliable molecular clocks are accurate only in the statistical sense of showing a fairly smooth *average* rate of change. Over time, there may still be deviations from that average rate. Furthermore, the same gene may evolve at different rates in different groups of organisms. And even among genes that are clocklike, the rate of the clock may vary greatly from one gene to another; some genes evolve a million times faster than others.

Neutral Theory

The observed regularity of change that enables us to use some genes as molecular clocks raises the possibility that many of the changes in these sequences result from mutations that have become fixed in a population by genetic drift (see Chapter 23) and that the changes are selectively neutral—neither beneficial nor detrimental. In the 1960s, Motoo Kimura, at the Japanese National Institute of Genetics, and Jack King and Thomas Jukes, at the University of California, Berkeley, independently published papers describing this **neutral theory**—that much evolutionary change in genes and proteins has no effect on fitness and therefore is not influenced by natural selection. Kimura pointed out that many new mutations are harmful and are removed quickly. But if most of the rest are neutral and have little or no effect on fitness, then the rate of molecular change should indeed be regular, like a clock. Differences in the clock rate for different genes are a function of how important a gene is. If the exact sequence of amino acids that a gene specifies is essential to survival, most of the mutational changes will be harmful and only a few will be neutral. As a result, such genes change only slowly. But if the exact sequence of amino acids is less critical, fewer of the new mutations will be harmful and more will be neutral. Such genes change more quickly.

Problems with Molecular Clocks

In fact, molecular clocks do not run as smoothly as neutral theory predicts. Many irregularities are likely to be the result of natural selection in which certain DNA changes are favored over others. Consequently, some scientists question the utility of molecular clocks for timing evolution. Their skepticism is part of a broader debate about the extent to which neutral genetic variation can account for some kinds of DNA diversity. Indeed, evidence suggests that almost half the amino acid differences in proteins of two *Drosophila* species, *D. simulans* and *D. yakuba*, are not neutral but have resulted from directional natural selection. But because the direction of natural selection may change repeatedly over long periods of time (and hence may average out), some genes experiencing selection can nevertheless serve as approximate markers of elapsed time.

Another question arises when researchers attempt to extend molecular clocks beyond the time span documented by the fossil record. Although some fossils are more than 3 billion years old, these are very rare. An abundant fossil record extends back only about 550 million years, but molecular clocks have been used to date evolutionary divergences that occurred a billion or more years ago. These estimates assume that the clocks have been constant for all that time. Such estimates are highly uncertain.

In some cases, problems may be avoided by calibrating molecular clocks with many genes rather than just one or a few genes (as is often done). By using many genes, fluctuations in evolutionary rate due to natural selection or other factors that vary over time may average out. For example, one group of researchers constructed molecular clocks of vertebrate evolution from published sequence data for 658 nuclear genes. Despite the broad period of time covered (nearly 600 million years) and the fact that natural selection probably affected some of these genes, their estimates of divergence times agreed closely with fossil-based estimates.

Applying a Molecular Clock: The Origin of HIV

Researchers have used a molecular clock to date the origin of HIV infection in humans. Phylogenetic analysis shows that HIV, the virus that causes AIDS, is descended from viruses that infect chimpanzees and other primates. (Most of these viruses do not cause AIDS-like diseases in their native hosts.) When did HIV jump to humans? There is no simple answer, because the virus has spread to humans more than once. The multiple origins of HIV are reflected in the variety of strains

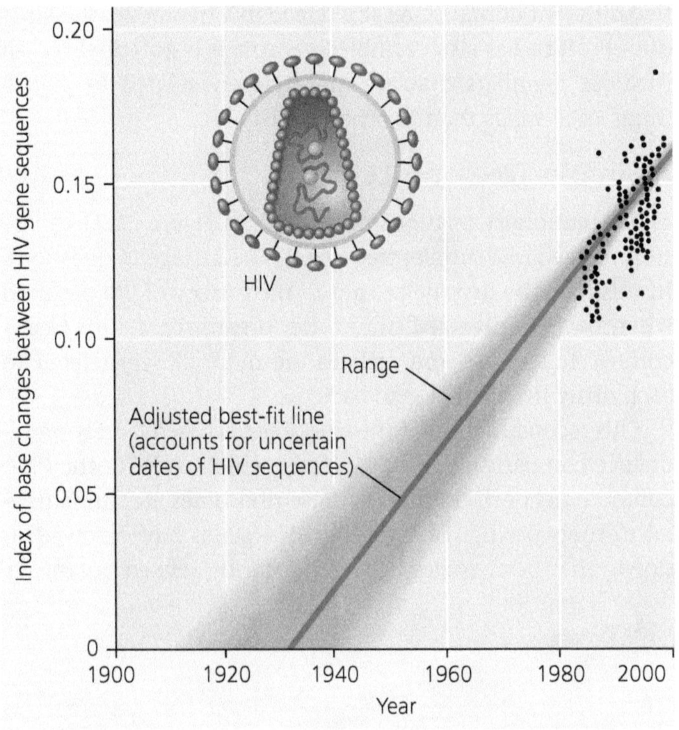

▲ **Figure 26.20 Dating the origin of HIV-1 M with a molecular clock.** The black data points are based on DNA sequences of an HIV gene in blood samples collected from patients. (The dates when these individual HIV gene sequences arose are not known with certainty because a person can harbor the virus for years before symptoms occur.) Projecting the gene's rate of change in the 1980s and 1990s backward in time suggests that the virus originated in the 1930s.

(genetic types) of the virus. HIV's genetic material is made of RNA, and like other RNA viruses, it evolves quickly.

The most widespread strain in humans is HIV-1 M. To pinpoint the earliest HIV-1 M infection, researchers compared samples of the virus from various times during the epidemic, including a sample from 1959. A comparison of gene sequences showed that the virus has evolved in a clocklike fashion (Figure 26.20). Extrapolating backward in time using the molecular clock indicates that the HIV-1 M strain first spread to humans during the 1930s.

CONCEPT CHECK 26.5

1. What is a molecular clock? What assumption underlies the use of a molecular clock?
2. **MAKE CONNECTIONS** Review Concept 17.5 (pp. 344–346). Then explain how numerous base changes could occur in an organism's DNA yet have no effect on its fitness.
3. **WHAT IF?** Suppose a molecular clock dates the divergence of two taxa at 80 million years ago, but new fossil evidence shows that the taxa diverged at least 120 million years ago. Explain how this could happen.

For suggested answers, see Appendix A.

CONCEPT 26.6

New information continues to revise our understanding of the tree of life

The discovery that the scaly-foot in Figure 26.1 evolved from a different lineage of legless lizards than did snakes is one example of how systematics is used to reconstruct the evolutionary relationships of life's diverse forms. In recent decades, we have gained insight into even the very deepest branches of the tree of life through molecular systematics.

From Two Kingdoms to Three Domains

Early taxonomists classified all known species into two kingdoms: plants and animals. Even with the discovery of the diverse microbial world, the two-kingdom system persisted: Noting that bacteria had a rigid cell wall, taxonomists placed them in the plant kingdom. Eukaryotic unicellular organisms with chloroplasts were also considered plants. Fungi, too, were classified as plants, partly because most fungi, like most plants, are unable to move about (never mind the fact that fungi are not photosynthetic and have little in common structurally with plants!). In the two-kingdom system, unicellular eukaryotes that move and ingest food—protozoans—were classified as animals. Those such as *Euglena* that move and are photosynthetic were claimed by both botanists and zoologists and showed up in both kingdoms.

Taxonomic schemes with more than two kingdoms gained broad acceptance in the late 1960s, when many biologists recognized five kingdoms: Monera (prokaryotes), Protista (a diverse kingdom consisting mostly of unicellular organisms), Plantae, Fungi, and Animalia. This system highlighted the two fundamentally different types of cells, prokaryotic and eukaryotic, and set the prokaryotes apart from all eukaryotes by placing them in their own kingdom, Monera.

However, phylogenies based on genetic data soon began to reveal a problem with this system: Some prokaryotes differ as much from each other as they do from eukaryotes. Such difficulties have led biologists to adopt a three-domain system. The three domains—Bacteria, Archaea, and Eukarya—are a taxonomic level higher than the kingdom level. The validity of these domains is supported by many studies, including a recent study that analyzed nearly 100 completely sequenced genomes.

The domain Bacteria contains most of the currently known prokaryotes, including the bacteria closely related to chloroplasts and mitochondria. The second domain, Archaea, consists of a diverse group of prokaryotic organisms that inhabit a wide variety of environments. Some archaea can use hydrogen as an energy source, and others were the chief source of the natural gas deposits that are found throughout Earth's crust. As you will read in Chapter 27, bacteria differ from archaea in many structural, biochemical, and physiological characteristics. The third domain, Eukarya, consists of all the organisms that have cells containing true nuclei. This domain includes many groups of single-celled organisms (see Chapter 28) as well as multicellular plants (Chapters 29 and 30), fungi (Chapter 31), and animals (Chapters 32–34). **Figure 26.21** represents one possible phylogenetic tree for the three domains and the many lineages they encompass.

The three-domain system highlights the fact that much of the history of life has been about single-celled organisms. The two prokaryotic domains consist entirely of single-celled organisms, and even in Eukarya, only the branches shown in red (plants, fungi, and animals) are dominated by multicellular organisms. Of the five kingdoms previously recognized by taxonomists, most biologists continue to recognize Plantae, Fungi, and Animalia, but not Monera and Protista. The kingdom Monera is obsolete because it would have members in two different domains. As you'll read in Chapter 28, the kingdom Protista has also crumbled because it is polyphyletic—it includes members that are more closely related to plants, fungi, or animals than to other protists.

A Simple Tree of All Life

The evolutionary relationships shown in Figure 26.21 can be summarized in a simpler tree (see the figure legend question). In this tree, the first major split in the history of life occurred when bacteria diverged from other organisms. If this tree is correct, eukaryotes and archaea are more closely related to each other than either is to bacteria.

This reconstruction of the tree of life is based largely on sequence comparisons of rRNA genes, which code for the RNA components of ribosomes. Because ribosomes are fundamental to the workings of the cell, rRNA genes have evolved so slowly that homologies between distantly related organisms

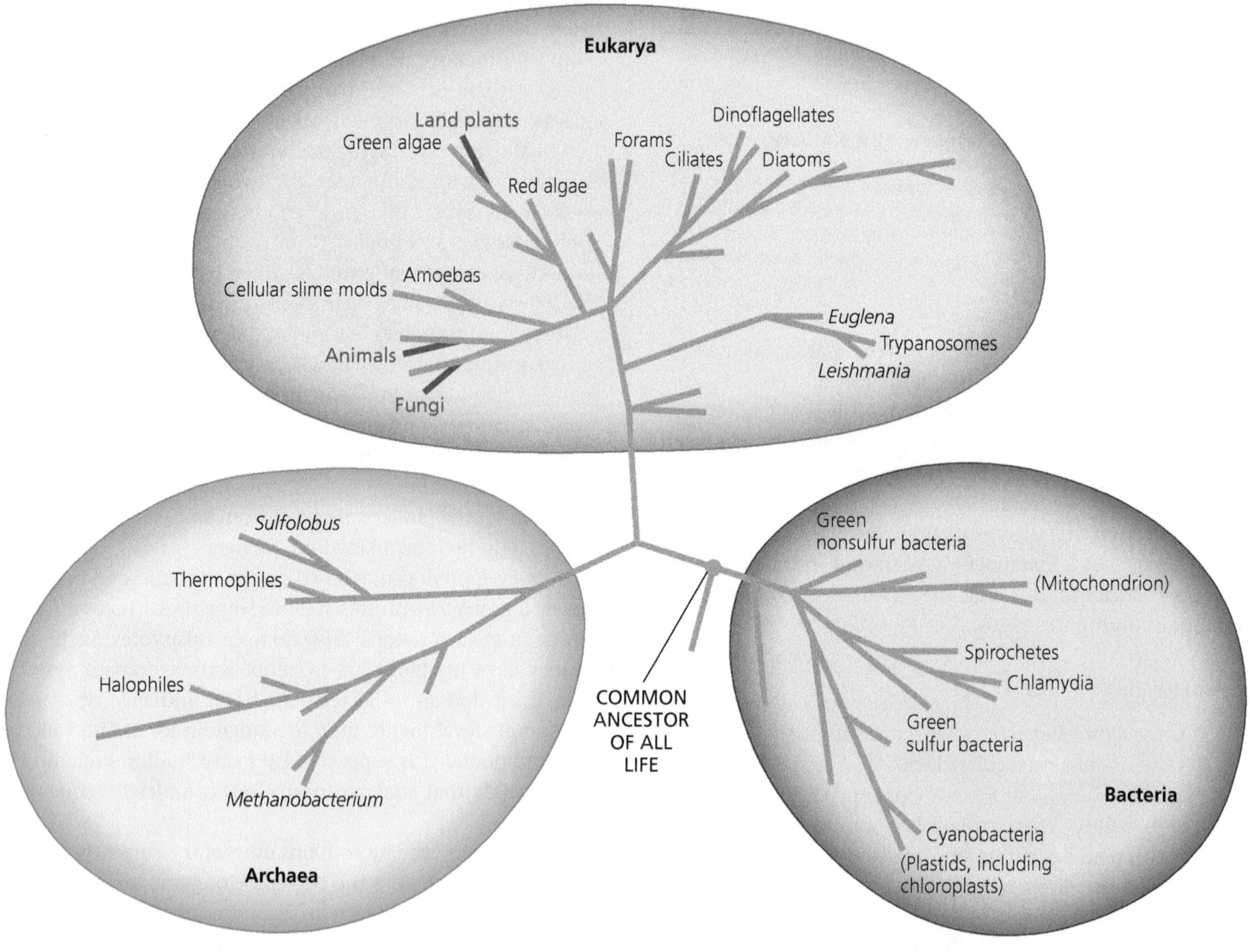

▲ **Figure 26.21 The three domains of life.** The phylogenetic tree shown here is based on rRNA gene sequences. Branch lengths are proportional to the amount of genetic change in each lineage. (To simplify the figure, only some branches are labeled.) In this diagram, the lineages within Eukarya that are dominated by multicellular organisms (plants, fungi, and animals) are shown in red. All other lineages consist solely or primarily of single-celled organisms.

DRAW IT *Redraw this tree as a horizontal tree that has just three branches, one for each domain. Which domain was the first to diverge? Which is the sister domain to Eukarya?*

can still be detected—making these genes very useful for determining evolutionary relationships between deep branches in the history of life. However, other genes reveal a different set of relationships. For example, researchers have found that many of the genes that influence metabolism in yeast (a unicellular eukaryote) are more similar to genes in the domain Bacteria than they are to genes in the domain Archaea—a finding that suggests that the eukaryotes may share a more recent common ancestor with bacteria than with archaea.

Comparisons of complete genomes from the three domains show that there have been substantial movements of genes between organisms in the different domains (**Figure 26.22**). These took place through **horizontal gene transfer**, a process in which genes are transferred from one genome to another through mechanisms such as exchange of transposable elements and plasmids, viral infection (see Chapter 19), and perhaps fusions of organisms. Recent research reinforces the view that horizontal gene transfer is important. For example, a 2008 analysis indicated that, on average, 80% of the genes in 181 prokaryotic genomes had moved between species at some point during the course of evolution. Because phylogenetic trees are based on the assumption that genes are passed vertically from one generation to the next, the occurrence of such horizontal transfer events helps to explain why trees built using different genes can give inconsistent results.

Is the Tree of Life Really a Ring?

Some biologists, including W. Ford Doolittle, interviewed on pages 534–535, have argued that horizontal gene transfer was so common that the early history of life should be represented as a tangled network of connected branches—not a simple, dichotomously branching tree like that in Figure 26.22. Others have suggested that relationships among early organisms are best represented by a ring, not a tree (**Figure 26.23**). In an analysis based on hundreds of genes, these researchers hypothesized that eukaryotes arose as a fusion between an early bacterium and an early archaean. If correct, eukaryotes are simultaneously most closely related to bacteria *and* archaea—an evolutionary relationship that cannot be depicted in a tree of life, but can be depicted in a *ring* of life.

Although scientists continue to debate whether early steps in the history of life are best represented as a tree, a ring, or a tangled web, in recent decades there have been many exciting discoveries about evolutionary events that occurred later in time. We'll explore such discoveries in the rest of this unit's chapters, beginning with Earth's earliest inhabitants, the prokaryotes.

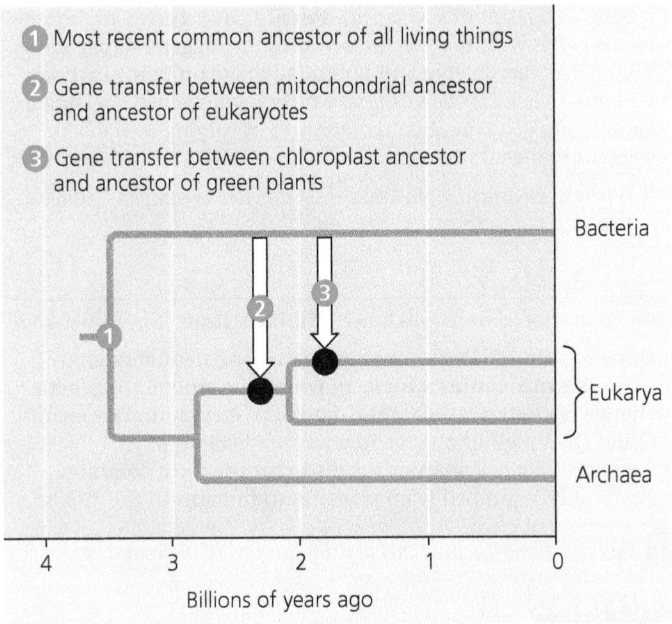

▲ **Figure 26.22 The role of horizontal gene transfer in the history of life.** This tree shows two major episodes of horizontal gene transfer, the dates of which are uncertain. It is known that many more such events occurred. (Because the tree is horizontal, the arrows representing "horizontal" transfer are vertical here.)

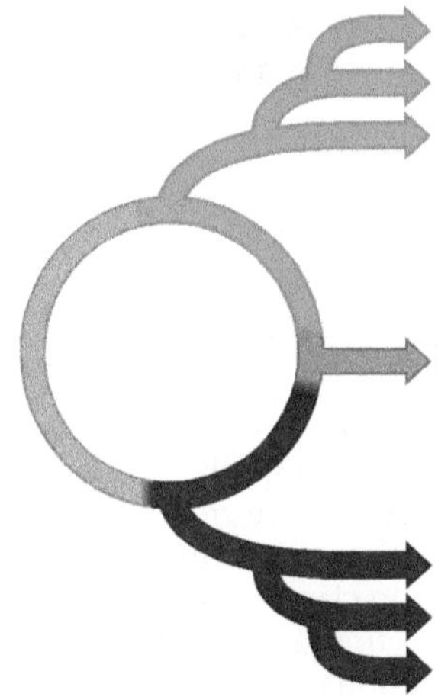

▲ **Figure 26.23 A ring of life.** In this hypothesis, the eukaryote lineage (orange) arose when an early archaean (teal) fused with an early bacterium (purple). Such an event is consistent with a "ring of life" but not with a tree of life. Three great domains (Archaea, Eukarya, and Bacteria) emerged from the ring and gave rise to the tremendous diversity of life we observe today.

CONCEPT CHECK 26.6

1. Why is the kingdom Monera no longer considered a valid taxon?
2. Explain why phylogenies based on different genes can yield different branching patterns for the tree of all life.
3. **WHAT IF?** Draw the three possible dichotomously branching trees showing evolutionary relationships for the domains Bacteria, Archaea, and Eukarya. Two of these trees have been supported by genetic data. Is it likely that the third tree might also receive such support? Explain your answer.

For suggested answers, see Appendix A.

26 CHAPTER REVIEW

SUMMARY OF KEY CONCEPTS

CONCEPT 26.1

Phylogenies show evolutionary relationships (pp. 537–540)

- Linnaeus's **binomial** classification system gives organisms two-part names: a **genus** plus a specific epithet.
- In the Linnaean system, species are grouped in increasingly broad taxa: Related genera are placed in the same family, families in orders, orders in classes, classes in phyla, phyla in kingdoms, and (more recently) kingdoms in domains.
- Systematists depict evolutionary relationships as branching **phylogenetic trees**. Many systematists propose that classification be based entirely on evolutionary relationships.

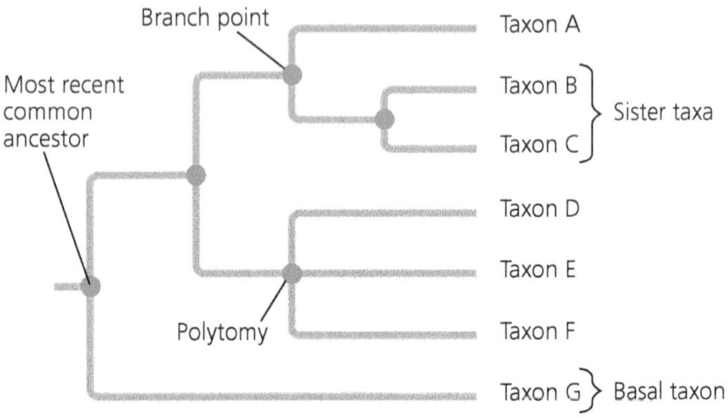

- Unless branch lengths are proportional to time or amount of genetic change, a phylogenetic tree indicates only patterns of descent.
- Much information can be learned about a species from its evolutionary history; hence, phylogenies are useful in a wide range of applications.

? *Humans and chimpanzees are sister species. Explain what that means.*

CONCEPT 26.2

Phylogenies are inferred from morphological and molecular data (pp. 540–542)

- Organisms with similar morphologies or DNA sequences are likely to be more closely related than organisms with very different structures and genetic sequences.
- To infer phylogeny, **homology** (similarity due to shared ancestry) must be distinguished from **analogy** (similarity due to convergent evolution).
- Computer programs are used to align comparable DNA sequences and to distinguish molecular homologies from coincidental matches between taxa that diverged long ago.

? *Why is it necessary to distinguish homology from analogy to infer phylogeny?*

CONCEPT 26.3

Shared characters are used to construct phylogenetic trees (pp. 542–548)

- A **clade** is a monophyletic grouping that includes an ancestral species and all of its descendants.
- Clades can be distinguished by their **shared derived characters.**

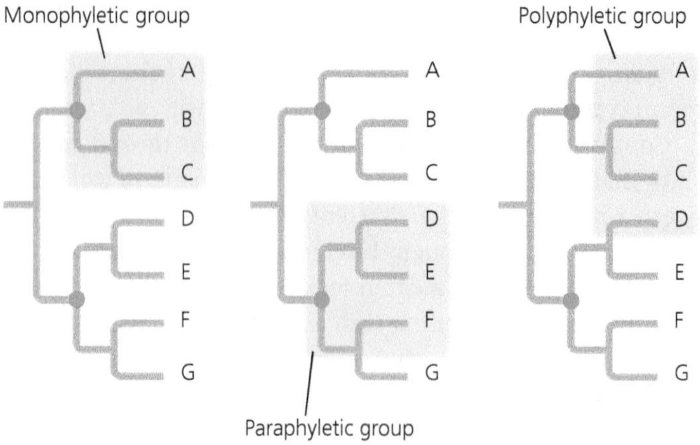

- Branch lengths can be drawn proportional to the amount of evolutionary change or time.
- Among phylogenies, the most parsimonious tree is the one that requires the fewest evolutionary changes. The most likely tree is the one based on the most likely pattern of changes.
- Well-supported phylogenetic hypotheses are consistent with a wide range of data.

? *Explain the logic of using shared derived characters to infer phylogeny.*

CONCEPT 26.4

An organism's evolutionary history is documented in its genome (pp. 548–549)

- **Orthologous genes** are homologous genes found in different species as a result of speciation. **Paralogous genes** are homologous genes within a species that result from gene duplication; such genes can diverge and potentially take on new functions.
- Distantly related species can have orthologous genes. The small variation in gene number in organisms of varying complexity suggests that genes are versatile and may have multiple functions.

? *When reconstructing phylogenies, is it better to compare orthologous or paralogous genes? Explain.*

CONCEPT 26.5

Molecular clocks help track evolutionary time (pp. 549–551)

- Some regions of DNA change at a rate consistent enough to serve as a **molecular clock**, in which the amount of genetic change is used to estimate the date of past evolutionary events. Other DNA regions change in a less predictable way.
- A molecular clock analysis suggests that the most common strain of HIV jumped from primates to humans in the 1930s.

? *Describe some assumptions and limitations of molecular clocks.*

CONCEPT 26.6

New information continues to revise our understanding of the tree of life (pp. 551–553)

- Past classification systems have given way to the current view of the tree of life, which consists of three great **domains**: Bacteria, Archaea, and Eukarya.

- Phylogenies based on rRNA genes suggest that eukaryotes are most closely related to archaea, while data from some other genes suggest a closer relationship to bacteria.
- Other genetic analyses suggest that eukaryotes arose as a fusion between a bacterium and an archaean, leading to a "ring of life" in which eukaryotes are equally closely related to bacteria and archaea.

? *Why was the five-kingdom system abandoned for a three-domain system?*

TESTING YOUR UNDERSTANDING

LEVEL 1: KNOWLEDGE/COMPREHENSION

1. In Figure 26.4, which similarly inclusive taxon descended from the same common ancestor as Canidae?
   a. Felidae
   b. Mustelidae
   c. Carnivora
   d. *Canis*
   e. *Lutra*

2. Three living species X, Y, and Z share a common ancestor T, as do extinct species U and V. A grouping that consists of species T, X, Y, and Z (but not U or V) makes up
   a. a valid taxon.
   b. a monophyletic clade.
   c. an ingroup, with species U as the outgroup.
   d. a paraphyletic group.
   e. a polyphyletic group.

3. In a comparison of birds and mammals, having four limbs is
   a. a shared ancestral character.
   b. a shared derived character.
   c. a character useful for distinguishing birds from mammals.
   d. an example of analogy rather than homology.
   e. a character useful for sorting bird species.

4. To apply parsimony to constructing a phylogenetic tree,
   a. choose the tree that assumes all evolutionary changes are equally probable.
   b. choose the tree in which the branch points are based on as many shared derived characters as possible.
   c. base phylogenetic trees only on the fossil record, as this provides the simplest explanation for evolution.
   d. choose the tree that represents the fewest evolutionary changes, in either DNA sequences or morphology.
   e. choose the tree with the fewest branch points.

LEVEL 2: APPLICATION/ANALYSIS

5. Based on this tree, which statement is *not* correct?

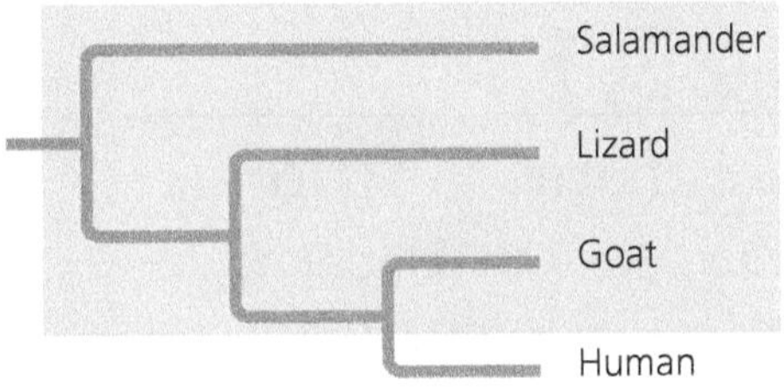

   a. The salamander lineage is a basal taxon.
   b. Salamanders are a sister group to the group containing lizards, goats, and humans.
   c. Salamanders are as closely related to goats as to humans.
   d. Lizards are more closely related to salamanders than to humans.
   e. The group highlighted by shading is paraphyletic.

6. If you were using cladistics to build a phylogenetic tree of cats, which of the following would be the best outgroup?
   a. lion b. domestic cat c. wolf d. leopard e. tiger

7. The relative lengths of the frog and mouse branches in the phylogeny in Figure 26.12 indicate that
   a. frogs evolved before mice.
   b. mice evolved before frogs.
   c. the genes of frogs and mice have only coincidental homoplasies.
   d. the homolog has evolved more slowly in mice.
   e. the homolog has evolved more rapidly in mice.

LEVEL 3: SYNTHESIS/EVALUATION

8. **EVOLUTION CONNECTION**
   Darwin suggested looking at a species' close relatives to learn what its ancestors may have been like. How does his suggestion anticipate recent methods, such as phylogenetic bracketing and the use of outgroups in cladistic analysis?

9. **SCIENTIFIC INQUIRY**
   DRAW IT (a) Draw a phylogenetic tree based on the first five characters in the table below. Place hatch marks on the tree to indicate the origin(s) of each of the six characters.
   (b) Assume that tuna and dolphins are sister species and redraw the phylogenetic tree accordingly. Place hatch marks on the tree to indicate the origin(s) of each of the six characters.
   (c) How many evolutionary changes are required in each tree? Which tree is most parsimonious?

Character	Lancelet (outgroup)	Lamprey	Tuna	Salamander	Turtle	Leopard	Dolphin
Backbone	0	1	1	1	1	1	1
Hinged jaw	0	0	1	1	1	1	1
Four limbs	0	0	0	1	1	1	1*
Amnion	0	0	0	0	1	1	1
Milk	0	0	0	0	0	1	1
Dorsal fin	0	0	1	0	0	0	1

*Although adult dolphins have only two obvious limbs (their flippers), as embryos they have two hind-limb buds, for a total of four limbs.

10. **WRITE ABOUT A THEME**
    The Cellular Basis of Life; The Genetic Basis of Life In a short essay (100–150 words), explain how these two themes—along with the process of descent with modification (see Chapter 22)—enable scientists to construct phylogenies that extend hundreds of millions of years back in time.

For selected answers, see Appendix A.

27

Bacteria and Archaea

▲ Figure 27.1 **Why is this lake's water pink?**

EVOLUTION

KEY CONCEPTS

27.1 Structural and functional adaptations contribute to prokaryotic success
27.2 Rapid reproduction, mutation, and genetic recombination promote genetic diversity in prokaryotes
27.3 Diverse nutritional and metabolic adaptations have evolved in prokaryotes
27.4 Molecular systematics is illuminating prokaryotic phylogeny
27.5 Prokaryotes play crucial roles in the biosphere
27.6 Prokaryotes have both beneficial and harmful impacts on humans

OVERVIEW

Masters of Adaptation

In the heat of summer, parts of Utah's Great Salt Lake turn pink (Figure 27.1), a sign of waters so salty that they would dehydrate your skin if you took a dip. The salt concentration can reach 32%, nearly ten times that of seawater. Yet despite these harsh conditions, the dramatic color of these waters is caused not by minerals or other nonliving sources, but by living things. What organisms can live in such an inhospitable environment, and how do they do it?

The pink color in the Great Salt Lake comes from trillions of prokaryotes in the domains Archaea and Bacteria, including archaea in the genus *Halobacterium*. These archaea have red membrane pigments, some of which capture the light energy that drives ATP synthesis. *Halobacterium* species are among the most salt-tolerant organisms on Earth; they thrive in salinities that dehydrate and kill other cells. *Halobacterium* compensates for water lost through osmosis by pumping potassium ions (K^+) into the cell until the ionic concentration inside the cell matches the concentration outside.

Like *Halobacterium*, many other prokaryotes can tolerate extreme conditions. Examples include *Deinococcus radiodurans*, which can survive 3 million rads of radiation (3,000 times the dose fatal to humans), and *Picrophilus oshimae*, which can grow at a pH of 0.03 (acidic enough to dissolve metal). Other prokaryotes live in environments that are too cold or too hot for most other organisms, and some have even been found living in rocks 3.2 km (2 miles) below Earth's surface.

Prokaryotic species are also very well adapted to more "normal" habitats—the lands and waters in which most other species are found. Their ability to adapt to a broad range of habitats helps explain why prokaryotes are the most abundant organisms on Earth: The number of prokaryotes in a handful of fertile soil is greater than the number of people who have ever lived. In this chapter, we'll examine the adaptations, diversity, and enormous ecological impact of these tiny organisms.

CONCEPT **27.1**

Structural and functional adaptations contribute to prokaryotic success

As you read in Chapter 25, the first organisms to inhabit Earth were likely prokaryotes. Throughout their long evolutionary history, prokaryotic populations have been (and continue to be) subjected to natural selection in all kinds of environments, resulting in their enormous diversity today.

We'll begin by describing prokaryotes. Most prokaryotes are unicellular, although the cells of some species remain attached to each other after cell division. Prokaryotic cells typically have diameters of 0.5–5 μm, much smaller than the

10–100 μm diameter of many eukaryotic cells. (One notable exception, *Thiomargarita namibiensis*, can be 750 μm across—bigger than the dot on this i.) Prokaryotic cells have a variety of shapes (Figure 27.2). Finally, although they are unicellular and small, prokaryotes are well organized, achieving all of an organism's life functions within a single cell.

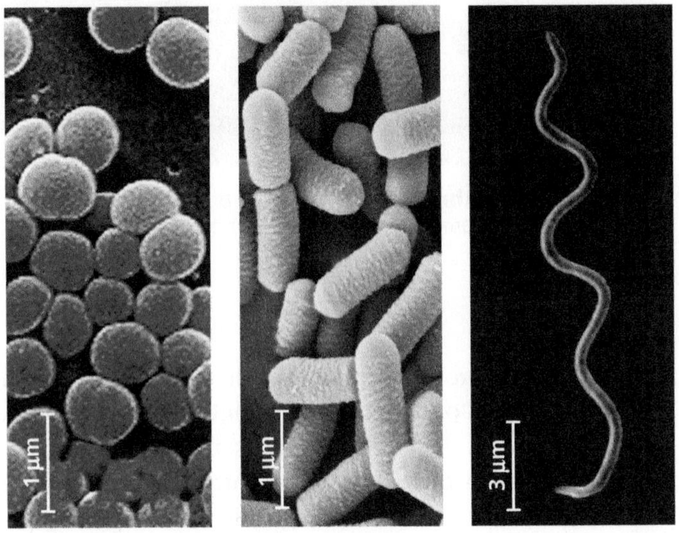

(a) Spherical **(b) Rod-shaped** **(c) Spiral**

▲ Figure 27.2 **The most common shapes of prokaryotes.** **(a)** Cocci (singular, *coccus*) are spherical prokaryotes. They occur singly, in pairs (diplococci), in chains of many cells (streptococci), and in clusters resembling bunches of grapes (staphylococci). **(b)** Bacilli (singular, *bacillus*) are rod-shaped prokaryotes. They are usually solitary, but in some forms the rods are arranged in chains (streptobacilli). **(c)** Spiral prokaryotes include spirilla, which range from comma-like shapes to loose coils, and spirochetes (shown here), which are corkscrew-shaped (colorized SEMs).

Cell-Surface Structures

A key feature of nearly all prokaryotic cells is the cell wall, which maintains cell shape, protects the cell, and prevents it from bursting in a hypotonic environment (see Chapter 7). In a hypertonic environment, most prokaryotes lose water and shrink away from their wall (plasmolyze), like other walled cells. Such water losses can inhibit cell reproduction. Thus, salt can be used to preserve foods because it causes prokaryotes to lose water, preventing them from rapidly multiplying.

The cell walls of prokaryotes differ in structure from those of eukaryotes. In eukaryotes that have cell walls, such as plants and fungi, the walls are usually made of cellulose or chitin (see Chapter 5). In contrast, most bacterial cell walls contain **peptidoglycan**, a polymer composed of modified sugars cross-linked by short polypeptides. This molecular fabric encloses the entire bacterium and anchors other molecules that extend from its surface. Archaeal cell walls contain a variety of polysaccharides and proteins but lack peptidoglycan.

Using a technique called the **Gram stain**, developed by the nineteenth-century Danish physician Hans Christian Gram, scientists can classify many bacterial species into two groups based on differences in cell wall composition. Samples are first stained with crystal violet dye and iodine, then rinsed in alcohol, and finally stained with a red dye such as safranin. The structure of a bacterium's cell wall determines the staining response (Figure 27.3). **Gram-positive** bacteria have simpler walls with a relatively large amount of peptidoglycan. **Gram-negative** bacteria have less peptidoglycan and are structurally more complex, with an outer membrane that contains lipopolysaccharides (carbohydrates bonded to lipids).

▼ Figure 27.3 **Gram staining.**

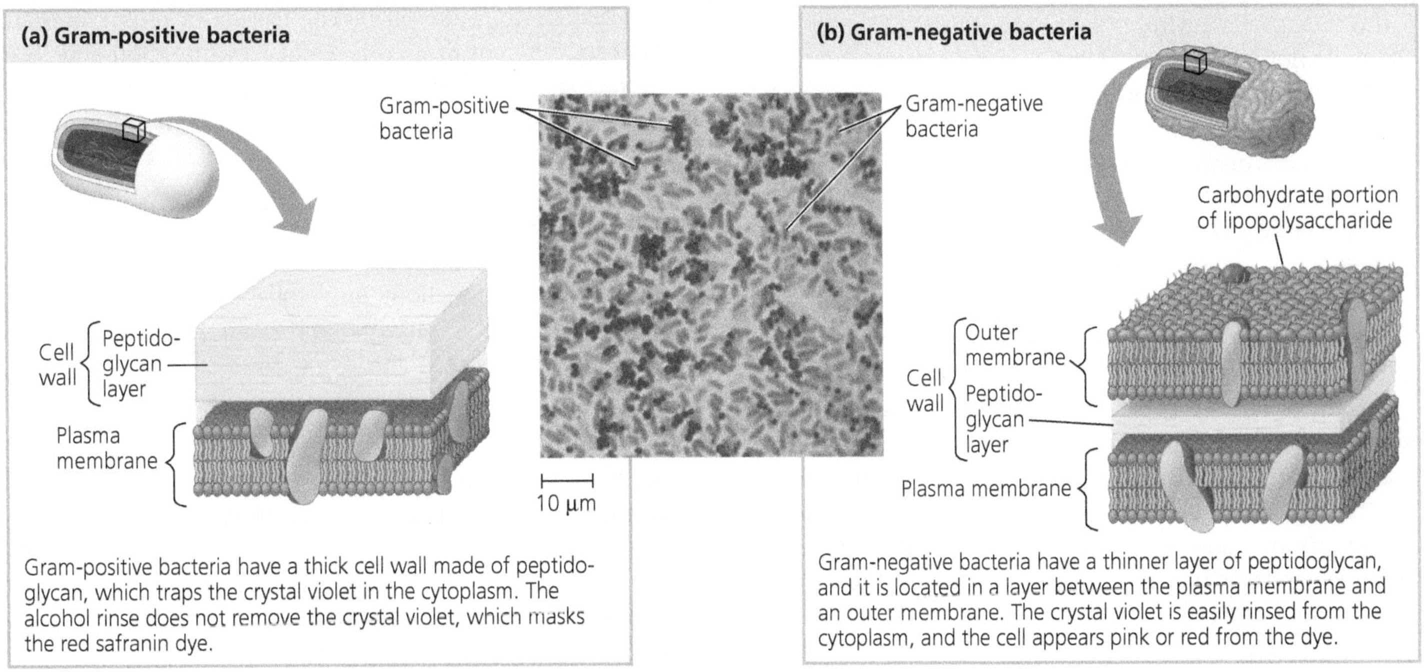

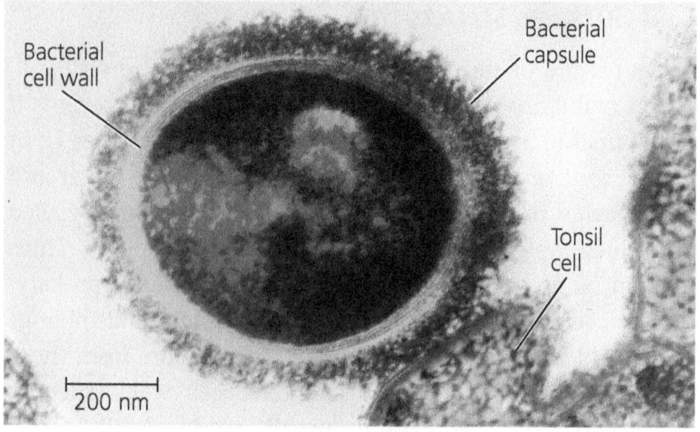

▲ **Figure 27.4 Capsule.** The polysaccharide capsule around this *Streptococcus* bacterium enables the prokaryote to attach to cells in the respiratory tract—in this colorized TEM, a tonsil cell.

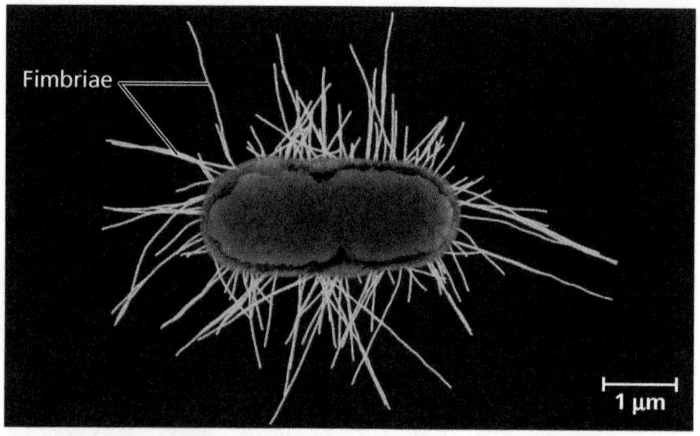

▲ **Figure 27.5 Fimbriae.** These numerous protein-containing appendages enable some prokaryotes to attach to surfaces or to other cells (colorized TEM).

Gram staining is a valuable tool in medicine for quickly determining if a patient's infection is due to gram-negative or to gram-positive bacteria. This information has treatment implications. The lipid portions of the lipopolysaccharides in the walls of many gram-negative bacteria are toxic, causing fever or shock. Furthermore, the outer membrane of a gram-negative bacterium helps protect it from the body's defenses. Gram-negative bacteria also tend to be more resistant than gram-positive species to antibiotics because the outer membrane impedes entry of the drugs. However, certain gram-positive species have virulent strains that are resistant to one or more antibiotics. (Figure 22.14 discusses one example: multidrug-resistant *Staphylococcus aureus*, which can cause lethal skin infections.)

The effectiveness of certain antibiotics, such as penicillin, derives from their inhibition of peptidoglycan cross-linking. The resulting cell wall may not be functional, particularly in gram-positive bacteria. Such drugs destroy many species of pathogenic bacteria without adversely affecting human cells, which do not have peptidoglycan.

The cell wall of many prokaryotes is surrounded by a sticky layer of polysaccharide or protein. This layer is called a **capsule** if it is dense and well-defined (Figure 27.4) or a *slime layer* if it is less well organized. Both kinds of sticky outer layers enable prokaryotes to adhere to their substrate or to other individuals in a colony. Some capsules and slime layers protect against dehydration, and some shield pathogenic prokaryotes from attacks by their host's immune system.

Some prokaryotes stick to their substrate or to one another by means of hairlike appendages called **fimbriae** (singular, *fimbria*) (Figure 27.5). For example, the bacterium that causes gonorrhea, *Neisseria gonorrhoeae*, uses fimbriae to fasten itself to the mucous membranes of its host. Fimbriae are usually shorter and more numerous than **pili** (singular, *pilus*), appendages that pull two cells together prior to DNA transfer from one cell to the other (see Figure 27.12); pili are sometimes referred to as *sex pili*.

Motility

About half of all prokaryotes are capable of **taxis**, a directed movement toward or away from a stimulus (from the Greek *taxis*, to arrange). For example, prokaryotes that exhibit *chemotaxis* change their movement pattern in response to chemicals. They may move *toward* nutrients or oxygen (positive chemotaxis) or *away from* a toxic substance (negative chemotaxis). Some species can move at velocities exceeding 50 µm/sec—up to 50 times their body length per second. For perspective, consider that a person 1.7 m tall moving that fast would be running 306 km (190 miles) per hour!

Of the various structures that enable prokaryotes to move, the most common are flagella (Figure 27.6). Flagella (singular, *flagellum*) may be scattered over the entire surface of the cell or concentrated at one or both ends. Prokaryotic flagella differ greatly from eukaryotic flagella: They are one-tenth the width and are not covered by an extension of the plasma membrane (see Figure 6.24). The flagella of prokaryotes are also very different in their molecular composition and their mechanism of propulsion. Among prokaryotes, bacterial and archaeal flagella are similar in size and rotation mechanism, but they are composed of different proteins. Overall, these structural and molecular comparisons suggest that the flagella of bacteria, archaea, and eukaryotes arose independently. Since the flagella of organisms in the three domains perform similar functions but probably are not related by common descent, it is likely that they are analogous, not homologous, structures.

Evolutionary Origins of Bacterial Flagella

The bacterial flagellum shown in Figure 27.6 has three main parts (the motor, hook, and filament) that are themselves composed of 42 different kinds of proteins. How could such a complex structure evolve? In fact, much evidence indicates that bacterial flagella originated as simpler structures that were modified in a stepwise fashion over time. As in the case of the

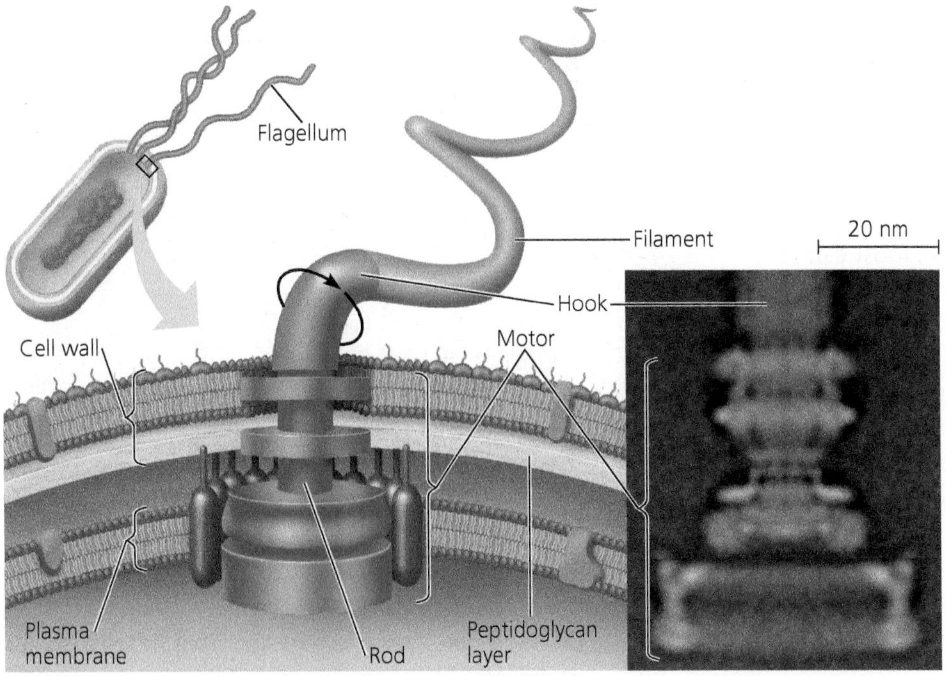

▲ **Figure 27.6 A prokaryotic flagellum.** The motor of a prokaryotic flagellum consists of a system of rings embedded in the cell wall and plasma membrane (TEM). ATP-driven pumps in the motor transport protons out of the cell. The diffusion of protons back into the cell provides the force that turns a curved hook and thereby causes the attached filament to rotate and propel the cell. (This diagram shows flagellar structures characteristic of gram-negative bacteria.)

human eye (see Concept 25.6), biologists asked whether a less complex version of the flagellum could still benefit its owner. Analyses of hundreds of bacterial genomes indicate that only half of the flagellum's protein components appear to be necessary for it to function; the others are inessential or not encoded in the genomes of some species. Of the 21 proteins required by all species studied to date, 19 are modified versions of proteins that perform other tasks in bacteria. For example, a set of 10 proteins in the motor are homologous to 10 similar proteins in a secretory system found in bacteria. (A secretory system is a protein complex that enables a cell to secrete certain macromolecules.) Two other proteins in the motor are homologous to proteins that function in ion transport. The proteins that comprise the rod, hook, and filament are all related to each other and are descended from an ancestral protein that formed a pilus-like tube. These findings suggest that the bacterial flagellum evolved as other proteins were added to an ancestral secretory system. This is an example of *exaptation*, the process in which existing structures take on new functions through descent with modification.

Internal Organization and DNA

The cells of prokaryotes are simpler than those of eukaryotes in both their internal structure and the physical arrangement of their DNA (see Figure 6.5). Prokaryotic cells lack the complex compartmentalization found in eukaryotic cells. However, some prokaryotic cells do have specialized membranes that perform metabolic functions (**Figure 27.7**). These membranes are usually infoldings of the plasma membrane.

The genome of a prokaryote is structurally different from a eukaryotic genome and in most cases has considerably less DNA. In the majority of prokaryotes, the genome consists of a circular chromosome with many fewer proteins than found in the linear chromosomes of eukaryotes (**Figure 27.8**). Also

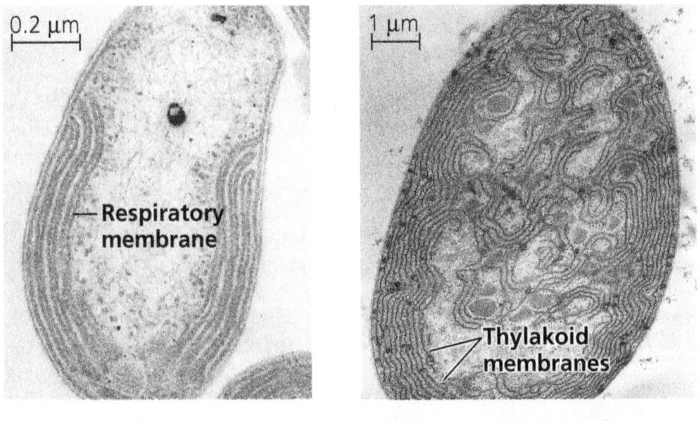

(a) Aerobic prokaryote **(b) Photosynthetic prokaryote**

▲ **Figure 27.7 Specialized membranes of prokaryotes.** **(a)** Infoldings of the plasma membrane, reminiscent of the cristae of mitochondria, function in cellular respiration in some aerobic prokaryotes (TEM). **(b)** Photosynthetic prokaryotes called cyanobacteria have thylakoid membranes, much like those in chloroplasts (TEM).

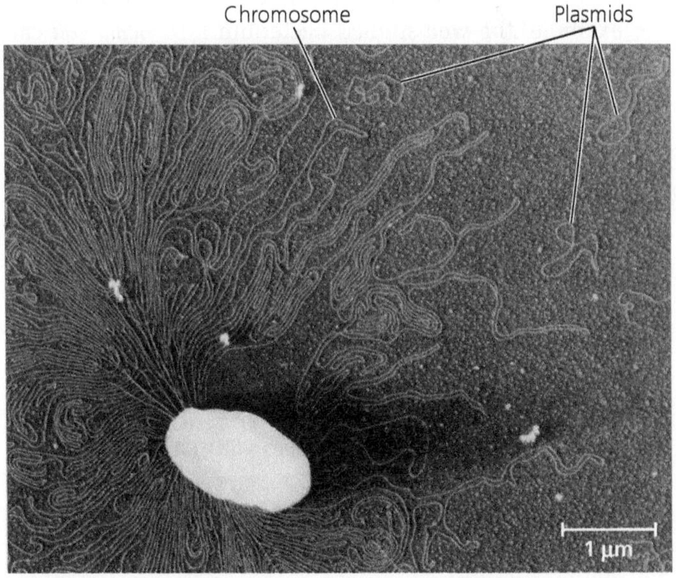

▲ **Figure 27.8 A prokaryotic chromosome and plasmids.** The thin, tangled loops surrounding this ruptured *E. coli* cell are parts of the cell's large, circular chromosome (colorized TEM). Three of the cell's plasmids, the much smaller rings of DNA, are also shown.

unlike eukaryotes, prokaryotes lack a membrane-bounded nucleus; their chromosome is located in the **nucleoid**, a region of cytoplasm that appears lighter than the surrounding cytoplasm in electron micrographs. In addition to its single chromosome, a typical prokaryotic cell may also have much smaller rings of independently replicating DNA molecules called **plasmids** (see Figure 27.8), most carrying only a few genes.

As explained in Chapters 16 and 17, DNA replication, transcription, and translation are fundamentally similar processes in prokaryotes and eukaryotes, although there are some differences. For example, prokaryotic ribosomes are slightly smaller than eukaryotic ribosomes and differ in their protein and RNA content. These differences allow certain antibiotics, such as erythromycin and tetracycline, to bind to ribosomes and block protein synthesis in prokaryotes but not in eukaryotes. As a result, people can use these antibiotics to kill or inhibit the growth of bacteria without harming themselves.

Reproduction and Adaptation

Prokaryotes are highly successful in part because of their potential to reproduce quickly in a favorable environment. By *binary fission* (see Figure 12.12), a single prokaryotic cell divides into 2 cells, which then divide into 4, 8, 16, and so on. Under optimal conditions, many prokaryotes can divide every 1–3 hours; some species can produce a new generation in only 20 minutes. If reproduction continued unchecked at this rate, a single prokaryotic cell could give rise to a colony outweighing Earth in only two days!

In reality, of course, prokaryotic reproduction is limited. The cells eventually exhaust their nutrient supply, poison themselves with metabolic wastes, face competition from other microorganisms, or are consumed by other organisms. For example, the well-studied bacterium *Escherichia coli* can divide every 20 minutes under ideal lab conditions, one reason it is used as a model organism in research. However, when growing in a human intestine, one of its natural environments, *E. coli* cells divide only once every 12–24 hours. But whether cell division occurs every 20 minutes or every few days, reproduction in prokaryotes draws attention to three key features of their biology: *They are small, they reproduce by binary fission, and they have short generation times*. As a result, prokaryotic populations can consist of many trillions of individuals—far more than populations of multicellular eukaryotes, such as plants and animals.

The ability of some prokaryotes to withstand harsh conditions also contributes to their success. Some, like *Halobacterium*, can survive in harsh environments because of particular biochemical adaptations; others, because of particular structural adaptations. Certain bacteria, for example, develop resistant cells called **endospores** when they lack an essential nutrient (**Figure 27.9**). The original cell produces a copy of its chromosome and surrounds it with a tough multilayered structure,

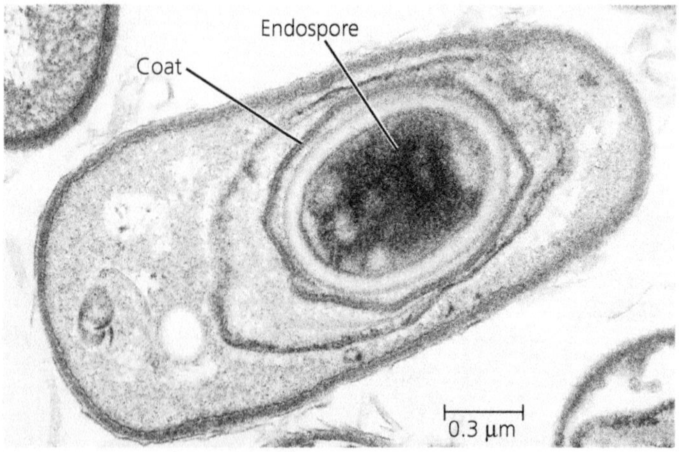

▲ **Figure 27.9 An endospore.** *Bacillus anthracis*, the bacterium that causes the disease anthrax, produces endospores (TEM). An endospore's protective, multilayered coat helps it survive in the soil for years.

forming the endospore. Water is removed from the endospore, and its metabolism halts. The original cell then lyses, releasing the endospore. Most endospores are so durable that they can survive in boiling water; killing them requires heating lab equipment to 121°C under high pressure. In less hostile environments, endospores can remain dormant but viable for centuries, able to rehydrate and resume metabolism when their environment improves.

Finally, in part because of their short generation times, prokaryotic populations can evolve substantially in short periods of time. For example, in a remarkable study that spanned 20,000 generations (roughly eight years) of evolution, researchers at Michigan State University documented adaptive evolution in bacterial populations (**Figure 27.10**). The ability of prokaryotes to adapt rapidly to new conditions highlights the point that although the structure of their cells is simpler than that of eukaryotic cells, prokaryotes are not "primitive" or "inferior" in an evolutionary sense. They are, in fact, highly evolved: For over 3.5 billion years, prokaryotic populations have responded successfully to many different types of environmental challenges. As we will see, one reason for this is that their populations harbor high levels of genetic diversity on which selection can act.

CONCEPT CHECK 27.1

1. Identify and explain at least two adaptations that enable prokaryotes to survive in environments too harsh for other organisms.
2. Contrast the cellular and DNA structures of prokaryotes and eukaryotes.
3. **MAKE CONNECTIONS** Suggest a hypothesis to explain why the thylakoid membranes of chloroplasts resemble those of cyanobacteria. Refer to Figure 6.18 (p. 111) and Figure 26.21 (p. 552).

For suggested answers, see Appendix A.

▼ **Figure 27.10** INQUIRY

Can prokaryotes evolve rapidly in response to environmental change?

EXPERIMENT Vaughn Cooper and Richard Lenski, of Michigan State University, tested the ability of *E. coli* populations to adapt to a new environment. They established 12 populations, each founded by a single cell from an *E. coli* strain, and followed these populations for 20,000 generations (3,000 days). To maintain a continual supply of resources, each day the researchers performed a *serial transfer*: They transferred 0.1 mL of each population to a new tube containing 9.9 mL of fresh growth medium. The growth medium used throughout the experiment provided a challenging environment that contained only low levels of glucose and other resources needed for growth.

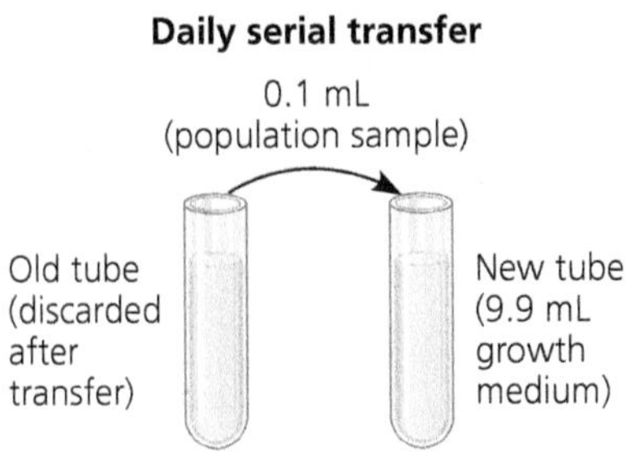

Samples were periodically removed from the 12 populations and grown in competition with the common ancestral strain in the experimental (low-glucose) environment.

RESULTS The fitness of the experimental populations, as measured by the rate at which each population grew, increased rapidly for the first 5,000 generations (two years) and more slowly for the next 15,000 generations. The graph below shows the averages for the 12 populations.

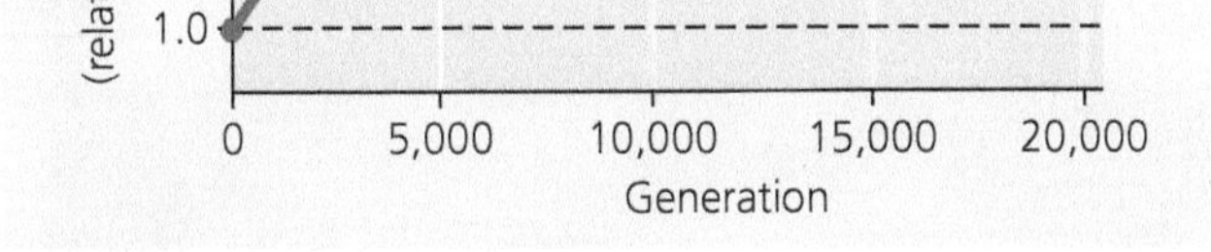

CONCLUSION Populations of *E. coli* continued to accumulate beneficial mutations for 20,000 generations, allowing rapid evolution of improved performance in their new environment.

SOURCE V. S. Cooper and R. E. Lenski, The population genetics of ecological specialization in evolving *Escherichia coli* populations, *Nature* 407:736–739 (2000).

WHAT IF? Suggest possible functions of the genes whose sequence or expression was altered as the experimental populations evolved in the low-glucose environment.

CONCEPT 27.2

Rapid reproduction, mutation, and genetic recombination promote genetic diversity in prokaryotes

As we discussed in Unit Four, genetic variation is a prerequisite for natural selection to occur in a population. The diverse adaptations exhibited by prokaryotes suggest that their populations must have considerable genetic variation—and they do. For example, a ribosomal RNA gene can differ more between two strains of *E. coli* than it does between a human and a platypus. In this section, we'll examine three factors that give rise to high levels of genetic diversity in prokaryotes: rapid reproduction, mutation, and genetic recombination.

Rapid Reproduction and Mutation

In sexually reproducing species, the generation of a novel allele by a new mutation is rare for any particular gene. Instead, most of the genetic variation in sexual populations results from the way existing alleles are arranged in new combinations during meiosis and fertilization (see Chapter 13). Prokaryotes do not reproduce sexually, so at first glance their extensive genetic variation may seem puzzling. In fact, this variation can result from prokaryotes' rapid reproduction and mutation.

Consider a prokaryote reproducing by binary fission. After repeated rounds of division, most of the offspring cells are genetically identical to the original parent cell. However, if errors occur during DNA replication—such as insertions, deletions, or base-pair substitutions—some of the offspring cells may differ genetically. The probability of a spontaneous mutation occurring in a given *E. coli* gene averages only about one in 10 million (1×10^{-7}) per cell division. But among the 2×10^{10} new *E. coli* cells that arise each day in a person's intestine, there will be approximately $(2 \times 10^{10}) \times (1 \times 10^{-7}) = 2{,}000$ bacteria that have a mutation in that gene. The total number of mutations when all 4,300 *E. coli* genes are considered is about $4{,}300 \times 2{,}000 = 9$ million per day per human host.

The key point is that new mutations, though rare, can increase genetic diversity quickly in species with short generation times and large populations. This diversity, in turn, can lead to rapid evolution: Individuals that are genetically better equipped for their environment tend to survive and reproduce more prolifically than less fit individuals (see Figure 27.10).

Genetic Recombination

Although new mutations are a major source of variation in prokaryotic populations, additional diversity arises from *genetic recombination*, the combining of DNA from two sources. In eukaryotes, the sexual processes of meiosis and fertilization combine DNA from two individuals in a single zygote. But meiosis and fertilization do not occur in prokaryotes. Instead, three other mechanisms—transformation, transduction, and conjugation—can bring together prokaryotic DNA from different individuals (that is, cells). When the individuals are members of different species, this movement of genes from one organism to another is called *horizontal gene transfer.* Although scientists have found evidence that each of these mechanisms can transfer DNA within and between species in both domain Bacteria and domain Archaea, to date most of our knowledge comes from research on bacteria.

Transformation and Transduction

In **transformation**, the genotype and possibly phenotype of a prokaryotic cell are altered by the uptake of foreign DNA from its surroundings. For example, a harmless strain of *Streptococcus pneumoniae* can be transformed into pneumonia-causing cells if the cells are placed in a medium containing DNA from a pathogenic strain (see p. 306). This transformation occurs when a nonpathogenic cell takes up a piece of DNA carrying the allele for pathogenicity and replaces its own allele with the foreign allele, an exchange of homologous DNA segments. The cell is now a recombinant: Its chromosome contains DNA derived from two different cells.

For many years after transformation was discovered in laboratory cultures, most biologists thought the process to be too rare and haphazard to play an important role in natural bacterial populations. But researchers have since learned that many bacteria have cell-surface proteins that recognize DNA from closely related species and transport it into the cell. Once inside the cell, the foreign DNA can be incorporated into the genome by homologous DNA exchange.

In **transduction**, phages (from "bacteriophages," the viruses that infect bacteria) carry prokaryotic genes from one host cell to another. In most cases, transduction results from accidents that occur during the phage replicative cycle (**Figure 27.11**). A virus that carries prokaryotic DNA may not be able to replicate because it lacks some or all of its own genetic material. However, the virus can attach to another prokaryotic cell (a recipient) and inject prokaryotic DNA acquired from the first cell (the donor). If some of this DNA is then incorporated into the recipient cell's chromosome by DNA recombination, a recombinant cell is formed.

Conjugation and Plasmids

In a process called **conjugation**, DNA is transferred between two prokaryotic cells (usually of the same species) that are temporarily joined. In bacteria, the DNA transfer is always one-way: One cell donates the DNA, and the other receives it. The best-understood mechanism is that used by *E. coli*, and we will focus on this organism for the rest of this section. In *E. coli*, a pilus of the donor cell attaches to the recipient (**Figure 27.12**). The pilus then retracts, pulling the two cells together, much like a grappling hook. The next step is thought

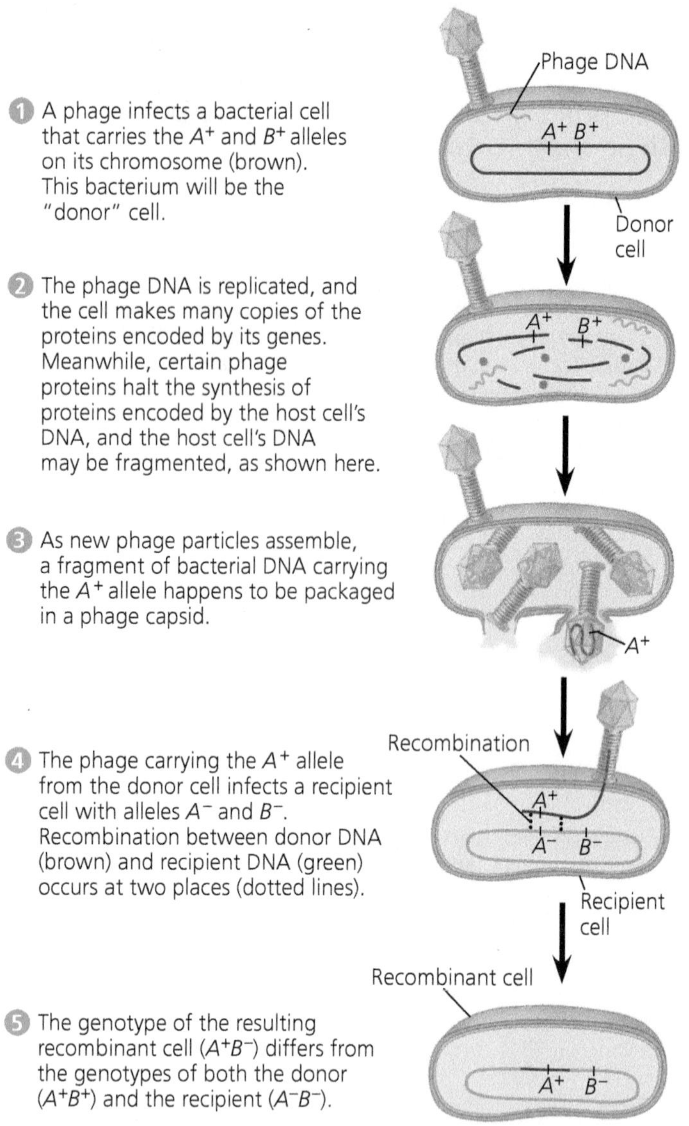

▲ **Figure 27.11 Transduction.** Phages may carry pieces of a bacterial chromosome from one cell (the donor) to another (the recipient). If recombination occurs after the transfer, genes from the donor may be incorporated into the recipient's genome.

? *Under what circumstances would transduction result in horizontal gene transfer?*

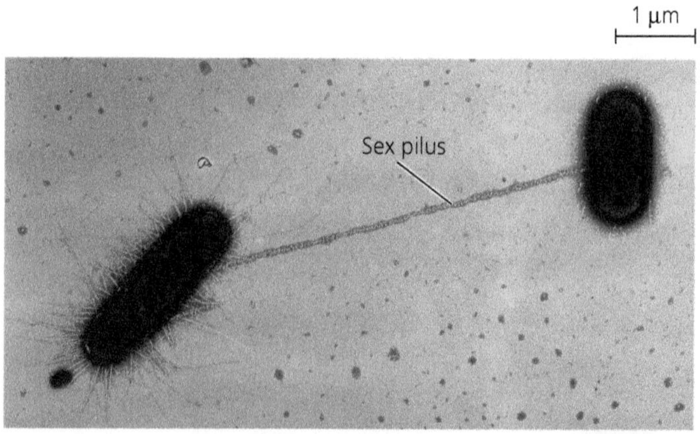

▲ **Figure 27.12 Bacterial conjugation.** The *E. coli* donor cell (left) extends a pilus that attaches to a recipient cell, a key first step in the transfer of DNA. The pilus is a flexible tube of protein subunits (TEM).

to be the formation of a temporary "mating bridge" between the two cells, through which the donor may transfer DNA to the recipient. This is an unsettled issue, however, and recent evidence indicates that DNA may pass directly through the pilus, which is hollow.

In either case, the ability to form pili and donate DNA during conjugation results from the presence of a particular piece of DNA called the **F factor** (F for *f*ertility). The F factor of *E. coli* consists of about 25 genes, most required for the production of pili. The F factor can exist either as a plasmid or as a segment of DNA within the bacterial chromosome.

The F Factor as a Plasmid The F factor in its plasmid form is called the **F plasmid**. Cells containing the F plasmid, designated F^+ cells, function as DNA donors during conjugation. Cells lacking the F factor, designated F^-, function as DNA recipients during conjugation. The F^+ condition is transferable in the sense that an F^+ cell converts an F^- cell to F^+ if a copy of the entire F^+ plasmid is transferred (Figure 27.13a).

The F Factor in the Chromosome Chromosomal genes can be transferred during conjugation when the donor cell's F factor is integrated into the chromosome. A cell with the F factor built into its chromosome is called an *Hfr cell* (for *h*igh *f*requency of *r*ecombination). Like an F^+ cell, an Hfr cell functions as a donor during conjugation with an F^- cell (Figure 27.13b). When chromosomal DNA from an Hfr cell enters an F^- cell, homologous regions of the Hfr and F^- chromosomes may align, allowing segments of their DNA to be exchanged. This results in the production of a recombinant bacterium that has genes derived from two different cells—a new genetic variant on which evolution can act.

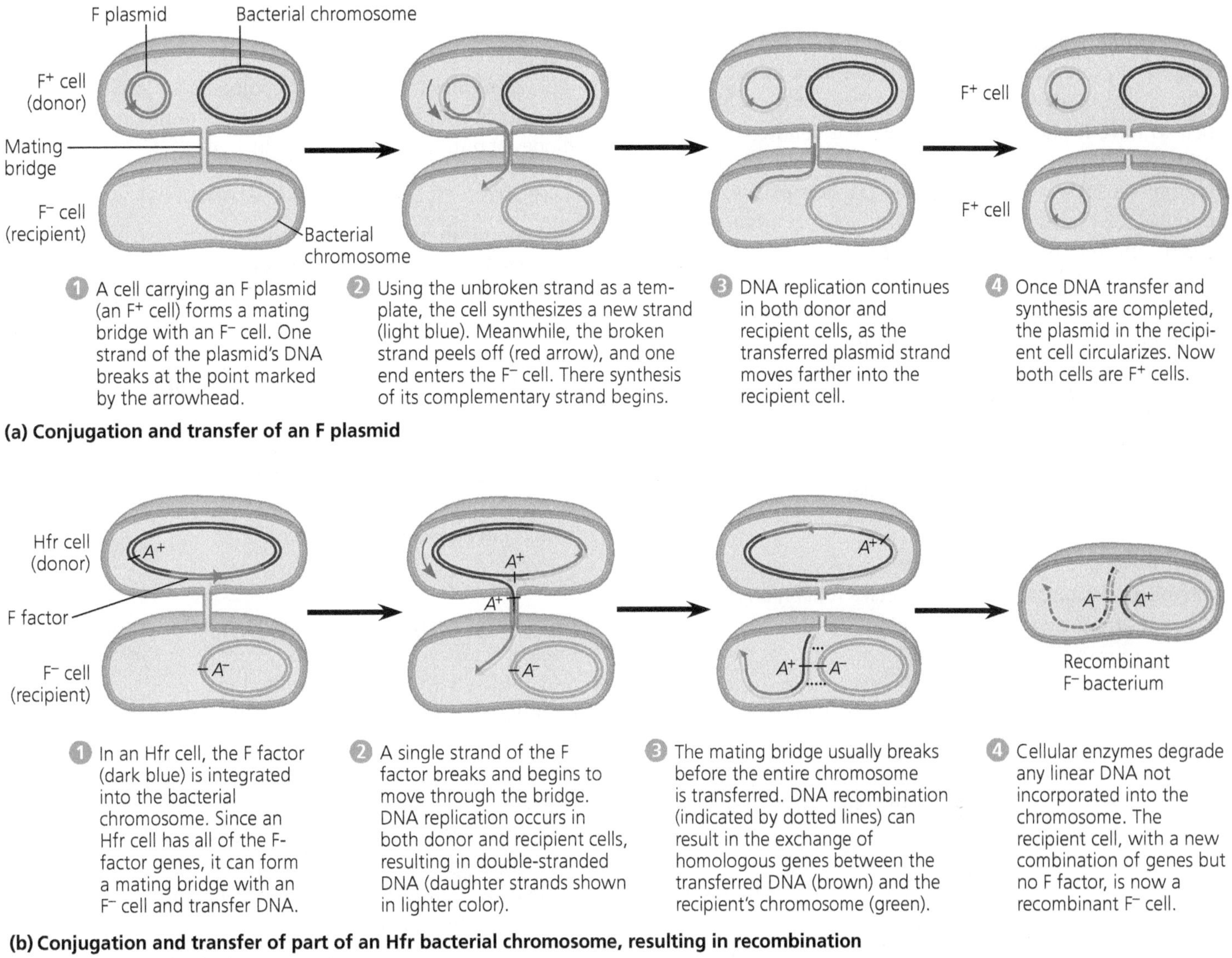

▲ Figure 27.13 **Conjugation and recombination in *E. coli*.** The DNA replication that accompanies transfer of an F plasmid or part of an Hfr bacterial chromosome is called *rolling circle replication*. In effect, the intact circular parental DNA strand "rolls" as its other strand peels off and a new complementary strand is synthesized.

R Plasmids and Antibiotic Resistance During the 1950s in Japan, physicians started noticing that some hospital patients with bacterial dysentery, which produces severe diarrhea, did not respond to antibiotics that had generally been effective in the past. Apparently, resistance to these antibiotics had evolved in certain strains of *Shigella*, the bacterium that causes the disease.

Eventually, researchers began to identify the specific genes that confer antibiotic resistance in *Shigella* and other pathogenic bacteria. Sometimes, mutation in a chromosomal gene of the pathogen can confer resistance. For example, a mutation in one gene may make it less likely that the pathogen will transport a particular antibiotic into its cell. Mutation in a different gene may alter the intracellular target protein for an antibiotic molecule, reducing its inhibitory effect. In other cases, bacteria have "resistance genes," which code for enzymes that specifically destroy or otherwise hinder the effectiveness of certain antibiotics, such as tetracycline or ampicillin. Such resistance genes are carried by plasmids known as **R plasmids** (R for *r*esistance).

Exposing a bacterial population to a specific antibiotic, whether in a laboratory culture or within a host organism, will kill antibiotic-sensitive bacteria but not those that happen to have R plasmids with genes that counter the antibiotic. Under these circumstances, we would predict that natural selection would cause the fraction of the bacterial population carrying genes for antibiotic resistance to increase, and that is exactly what happens. The medical consequences are also predictable: As you've read, resistant strains of pathogens are becoming more common, making the treatment of certain bacterial infections more difficult. The problem is compounded by the fact that many R plasmids, like F plasmids, have genes that encode pili and enable DNA transfer from one bacterial cell to another by conjugation. Making the problem still worse, some R plasmids carry as many as ten genes for resistance to that many antibiotics.

CONCEPT CHECK 27.2

1. What features of prokaryotes make it likely that considerable genetic variation will be added to their populations in each generation?
2. Distinguish between the three mechanisms of transferring DNA from one bacterial cell to another.
3. In a rapidly changing environment, which bacterial population would likely be more successful, one that includes individuals capable of conjugation or one that does not? Explain.
4. WHAT IF? If a nonpathogenic bacterium were to acquire resistance to antibiotics, could this strain pose a health risk to people? Explain. In general, how does DNA transfer among bacteria affect the spread of resistance genes?

For suggested answers, see Appendix A.

CONCEPT 27.3

Diverse nutritional and metabolic adaptations have evolved in prokaryotes

The extensive genetic variation found in prokaryotic populations is reflected in the diverse nutritional adaptations of prokaryotes. Like all organisms, prokaryotes can be categorized by how they obtain energy and the carbon used in building the organic molecules that make up cells. Every type of nutrition observed in eukaryotes is represented among prokaryotes, along with some nutritional modes unique to prokaryotes. In fact, prokaryotes have an astounding range of metabolic adaptations, much broader than that found in eukaryotes.

Organisms that obtain energy from light are called *phototrophs*, and those that obtain energy from chemicals are called *chemotrophs*. Organisms that need only CO_2 in some form as a carbon source are called *autotrophs*. In contrast, *heterotrophs* require at least one organic nutrient, such as glucose, to make other organic compounds. Combining possible energy sources and carbon sources results in four major modes of nutrition, summarized in Table 27.1.

The Role of Oxygen in Metabolism

Prokaryotic metabolism also varies with respect to oxygen (O_2). **Obligate aerobes** must use O_2 for cellular respiration (see Chapter 9) and cannot grow without it. **Obligate anaerobes**, on the other hand, are poisoned by O_2. Some obligate anaerobes live exclusively by fermentation; others extract chemical energy by **anaerobic respiration**, in which substances other than O_2, such as nitrate ions (NO_3^-) or sulfate ions (SO_4^{2-}), accept electrons at the "downhill" end of electron transport chains. **Facultative anaerobes** use O_2 if it is present but can also carry out fermentation or anaerobic respiration in an anaerobic environment.

Nitrogen Metabolism

Nitrogen is essential for the production of amino acids and nucleic acids in all organisms. Whereas eukaryotes can obtain nitrogen from only a limited group of nitrogen compounds, prokaryotes can metabolize nitrogen in a wide variety of forms. For example, some cyanobacteria and some methanogens (a group of archaea) convert atmospheric nitrogen (N_2) to ammonia (NH_3), a process called **nitrogen fixation**. The cells can then incorporate this "fixed" nitrogen into amino acids and other organic molecules. In terms of their nutrition, nitrogen-fixing cyanobacteria are some of the most self-sufficient organisms, since they need only light, CO_2, N_2, water, and some minerals to grow.

Nitrogen fixation by prokaryotes has a large impact on other organisms. For example, nitrogen-fixing prokaryotes can increase the nitrogen available to plants, which cannot use

Table 27.1 Major Nutritional Modes

Mode	Energy Source	Carbon Source	Types of Organisms
AUTOTROPH			
Photoautotroph	Light	CO_2, HCO_3^-, or related compound	Photosynthetic prokaryotes (for example, cyanobacteria); plants; certain protists (for example, algae)
Chemoautotroph	Inorganic chemicals (such as H_2S, NH_3, or Fe^{2+})	CO_2, HCO_3^-, or related compound	Unique to certain prokaryotes (for example, *Sulfolobus*)
HETEROTROPH			
Photoheterotroph	Light	Organic compounds	Unique to certain aquatic and salt-loving prokaryotes (for example, *Rhodobacter, Chloroflexus*)
Chemoheterotroph	Organic compounds	Organic compounds	Many prokaryotes (for example, *Clostridium*) and protists; fungi; animals; some plants

atmospheric nitrogen but can use the nitrogen compounds that the prokaryotes produce from ammonia. Chapter 55 discusses this and other essential roles that prokaryotes play in the nitrogen cycles of ecosystems.

Metabolic Cooperation

Cooperation between prokaryotic cells allows them to use environmental resources they could not use as individual cells. In some cases, this cooperation takes place between specialized cells of a filament. For instance, the cyanobacterium *Anabaena* has genes that encode proteins for photosynthesis and for nitrogen fixation, but a single cell cannot carry out both processes at the same time. The reason is that photosynthesis produces O_2, which inactivates the enzymes involved in nitrogen fixation. Instead of living as isolated cells, *Anabaena* forms filamentous chains (Figure 27.14). Most cells in a filament carry out only photosynthesis, while a few specialized cells called **heterocysts** (sometimes called *heterocytes*) carry out only nitrogen fixation. Each heterocyst is surrounded by a thickened cell wall that restricts entry of O_2 produced by neighboring photosynthetic cells. Intercellular connections allow heterocysts to transport fixed nitrogen to neighboring cells and to receive carbohydrates.

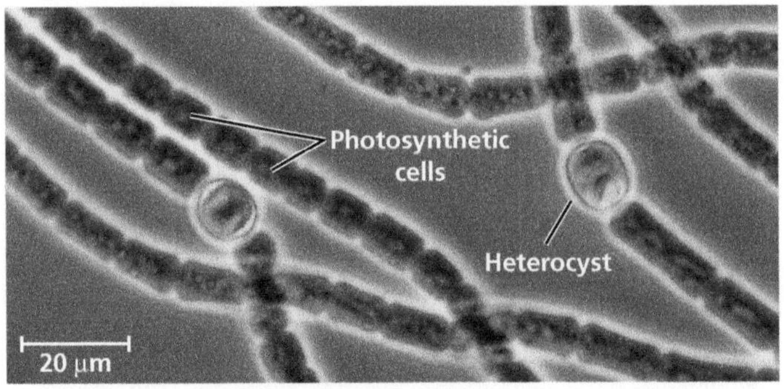

▲ **Figure 27.14 Metabolic cooperation in a prokaryote.** In the filamentous cyanobacterium *Anabaena*, cells called heterocysts fix nitrogen, while the other cells carry out photosynthesis (LM). *Anabaena* is found in many freshwater lakes.

Metabolic cooperation between different prokaryotic species often occurs in surface-coating colonies known as **biofilms**. Cells in a biofilm secrete signaling molecules that recruit nearby cells, causing the colonies to grow. The cells also produce polysaccharides and proteins that stick the cells to the substrate and to one another. Channels in the biofilm allow nutrients to reach cells in the interior and wastes to be expelled. Biofilms are common in nature, but they can cause problems by contaminating industrial products and medical equipment and contributing to tooth decay and more serious health problems. Altogether, damage caused by biofilms costs billions of dollars annually.

In another example of cooperation between prokaryotes, sulfate-consuming bacteria coexist with methane-consuming archaea in ball-shaped aggregates on the ocean floor. The bacteria appear to use the archaea's waste products, such as organic compounds and hydrogen. In turn, the bacteria produce sulfur compounds that the archaea use as oxidizing agents when they consume methane in the absence of oxygen. This partnership has global ramifications: Each year, these archaea consume an estimated 300 billion kilograms of methane, a major contributor to the greenhouse effect (see Chapter 55).

CONCEPT CHECK 27.3

1. Distinguish between the four major modes of nutrition, noting which are unique to prokaryotes.
2. A bacterium requires only the amino acid methionine as an organic nutrient and lives in lightless caves. What mode of nutrition does it employ? Explain.
3. WHAT IF? Describe what you might eat for a typical meal if humans, like cyanobacteria, could fix nitrogen.

For suggested answers, see Appendix A.

CONCEPT 27.4

Molecular systematics is illuminating prokaryotic phylogeny

Until the late 20th century, systematists based prokaryotic taxonomy on phenotypic criteria such as shape, motility, nutritional mode, and response to Gram staining. These criteria are still valuable in certain contexts, such as the rapid identification of pathogenic bacteria cultured from a patient's blood. But when it comes to prokaryotic phylogeny, comparing these characteristics does not reveal a clear evolutionary history. Applying molecular systematics to the investigation of prokaryotic phylogeny, however, has led to some dramatic conclusions.

Lessons from Molecular Systematics

As discussed in Chapter 26, microbiologists began comparing the sequences of prokaryotic genes in the 1970s. Using small-subunit ribosomal RNA as a marker for evolutionary relationships, Carl Woese and his colleagues concluded that many prokaryotes once classified as bacteria are actually more closely related to eukaryotes and belong in a domain of their own: Archaea. Microbiologists have since analyzed larger amounts of genetic data—including hundreds of entire genomes—and have concluded that a few traditional taxonomic groups, such as cyanobacteria, do appear to be monophyletic. However, other groups, such as gram-negative bacteria, are scattered throughout several lineages. **Figure 27.15** shows one phylogenetic hypothesis for some of the major taxa of prokaryotes based on molecular systematics.

One lesson from studying prokaryotic phylogeny is that the genetic diversity of prokaryotes is immense. When researchers began to sequence the genes of prokaryotes, they could investigate only the small fraction of species that could be cultured in the laboratory. In the 1980s, researchers began using the polymerase chain reaction (PCR; see Chapter 20) to analyze the genes of prokaryotes collected from the environment (such as from soil or water samples). Such "genetic prospecting" is now widely used; in fact, today entire prokaryotic genomes can be obtained from environmental samples using *metagenomics* (see Chapter 21). Each year these techniques add new branches to the tree of life. While only about 7,800 prokaryotic species have been assigned scientific names, a single handful of soil could contain 10,000 prokaryotic species by some estimates. Taking full stock of this diversity will require many years of research.

Another important lesson from molecular systematics is the apparent significance of horizontal gene transfer in the evolution of prokaryotes. Over hundreds of millions of years, prokaryotes have acquired genes from even distantly related species, and they continue to do so today. As a result, significant portions of the genomes of many prokaryotes are actually mosaics of genes imported from other species. As we saw in Chapter 26, such gene transfers can make it difficult to determine the root of the tree of life. Still, it is clear that for billions of years, the prokaryotes have evolved in two separate lineages, the archaea and the bacteria (see Figure 27.15).

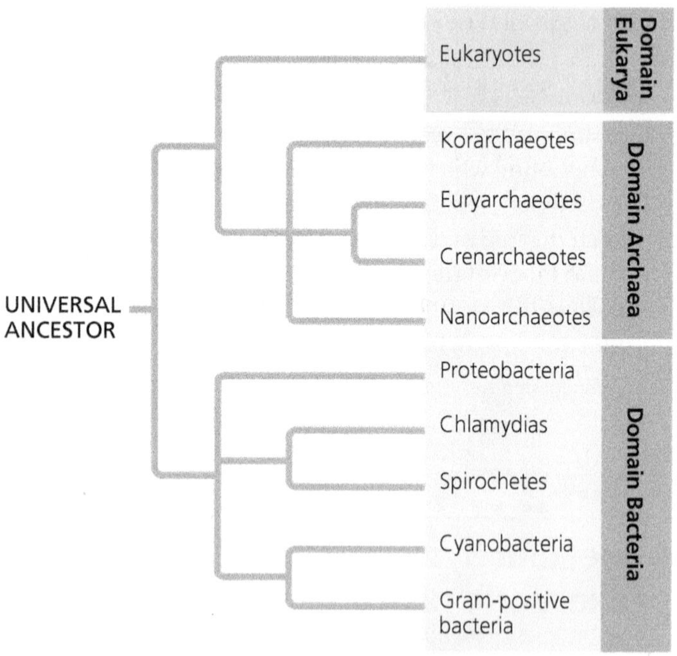

▲ **Figure 27.15 A simplified phylogeny of prokaryotes.** This phylogenetic tree based on molecular data shows one of several debated hypotheses of the relationships between the major prokaryotic groups discussed in this chapter. Within Archaea, the placement of the korarchaeotes and nanoarchaeotes remains unclear.

Archaea

Archaea share certain traits with bacteria and other traits with eukaryotes (**Table 27.2**). However, archaea also have many unique characteristics, as we would expect in a taxon that has followed a separate evolutionary path for so long.

Table 27.2 A Comparison of the Three Domains of Life

CHARACTERISTIC	DOMAIN		
	Bacteria	**Archaea**	**Eukarya**
Nuclear envelope	Absent	Absent	Present
Membrane-enclosed organelles	Absent	Absent	Present
Peptidoglycan in cell wall	Present	Absent	Absent
Membrane lipids	Unbranched hydrocarbons	Some branched hydrocarbons	Unbranched hydrocarbons
RNA polymerase	One kind	Several kinds	Several kinds
Initiator amino acid for protein synthesis	Formyl-methionine	Methionine	Methionine
Introns in genes	Very rare	Present in some genes	Present in many genes
Response to the antibiotics streptomycin and chloramphenicol	Growth inhibited	Growth not inhibited	Growth not inhibited
Histones associated with DNA	Absent	Present in some species	Present
Circular chromosome	Present	Present	Absent
Growth at temperatures > 100°C	No	Some species	No

The first prokaryotes assigned to domain Archaea live in environments so extreme that few other organisms can survive there. Such organisms are called **extremophiles**, meaning "lovers" of extreme conditions (from the Greek *philos*, lover), and include extreme halophiles and extreme thermophiles.

Extreme halophiles (from the Greek *halo*, salt) live in highly saline environments, such as the Great Salt Lake and the Dead Sea (see Figure 27.1). Some species merely tolerate salinity, while others require an environment that is several times saltier than seawater (which has a salinity of 3.5%). For example, the proteins and cell wall of *Halobacterium* have unusual features that improve function in extremely salty environments but render these organisms incapable of survival if the salinity drops below 9%.

Extreme thermophiles (from the Greek *thermos*, hot) thrive in very hot environments (Figure 27.16). For example, archaea in the genus *Sulfolobus* live in sulfur-rich volcanic springs as hot as 90°C. At temperatures this high, the cells of most organisms die because, for example, their DNA does not remain in a double helix and many of their proteins denature. *Sulfolobus* and other extreme thermophiles avoid this fate because their DNA and proteins have adaptations that make them stable at high temperatures. One extreme thermophile that lives near deep-sea hot springs called *hydrothermal vents* is informally known as "strain 121," since it can reproduce even at 121°C. Another extreme thermophile, *Pyrococcus furiosus*, is used in biotechnology as a source of DNA polymerase for the PCR technique (see Chapter 20).

Other archaea live in more moderate environments. Consider the **methanogens**, archaea that release methane as a by-product of their unique ways of obtaining energy. Many methanogens use CO_2 to oxidize H_2, a process that produces

▲ **Figure 27.16 Extreme thermophiles.** Orange and yellow colonies of thermophilic prokaryotes grow in the hot water of a Nevada geyser.

MAKE CONNECTIONS *Review the discussion of enzymes in Concept 8.4 (pp. 155–156). How might the enzymes of thermophiles differ from those of other organisms?*

both energy and methane waste. Among the strictest of anaerobes, methanogens are poisoned by O_2. Although some methanogens live in extreme environments, such as under kilometers of ice in Greenland, others live in swamps and marshes where other microorganisms have consumed all the O_2. The "marsh gas" found in such environments is the methane released by these archaea. Other species of methanogens inhabit the anaerobic environment within the guts of cattle, termites, and other herbivores, playing an essential role in the nutrition of these animals. Methanogens also have an important application as decomposers in sewage treatment facilities.

Many extreme halophiles and all known methanogens are archaea in the clade Euryarchaeota (from the Greek *eurys*, broad, a reference to the habitat range of these prokaryotes). The euryarchaeotes also include some extreme thermophiles, though most thermophilic species belong to a second clade, Crenarchaeota (*cren* means "spring," such as a hydrothermal spring). Recently, genetic prospecting has revealed many species of euryarchaeotes and crenarchaeotes that are not extremophiles. These archaea exist in habitats ranging from farm soils to lake sediments to the surface waters of the open ocean.

New findings continue to update the picture of archaeal phylogeny. In 1996, researchers sampling a hot spring in Yellowstone National Park discovered archaea that do not appear to belong to either Euryarchaeota or Crenarchaeota. They placed these archaea in a new clade, Korarchaeota (from the Greek *koron*, young man). In 2002, researchers exploring hydrothermal vents off the coast of Iceland discovered archaeal cells only 0.4 μm in diameter attached to a much larger crenarchaeote. The genome of the smaller archaean is one of the smallest known of any organism, containing only 500,000 base pairs. Genetic analysis indicates that this prokaryote belongs to a fourth archaeal clade, Nanoarchaeota (from the Greek *nanos*, dwarf). Within a year after this clade was named, three other DNA sequences from nanoarchaeote species were isolated: one from Yellowstone's hot springs, one from hot springs in Siberia, and one from a hydrothermal vent in the Pacific. As prospecting continues, it seems likely that the tree in Figure 27.15 will undergo further changes.

Bacteria

Eukarya
Archaea
Bacteria

Bacteria include the vast majority of prokaryotic species of which most people are aware, from the pathogenic species that cause strep throat and tuberculosis to the beneficial species used to make Swiss cheese and yogurt. Every major mode of nutrition and metabolism is represented among bacteria, and even a small taxonomic group of bacteria may contain species exhibiting many different nutritional modes. As we'll see, the diverse nutritional and metabolic capabilities of bacteria—and archaea—are behind the great impact of these tiny organisms on Earth and its life. Examine Figure 27.17, on the following two pages, for a closer look at several major groups of bacteria.

▼ Figure 27.17

Exploring Major Groups of Bacteria

Proteobacteria

This large and diverse clade of gram-negative bacteria includes photoautotrophs, chemoautotrophs, and heterotrophs. Some proteobacteria are anaerobic, while others are aerobic. Molecular systematists currently recognize five subgroups of proteobacteria; the phylogenetic tree at right shows their relationships based on molecular data.

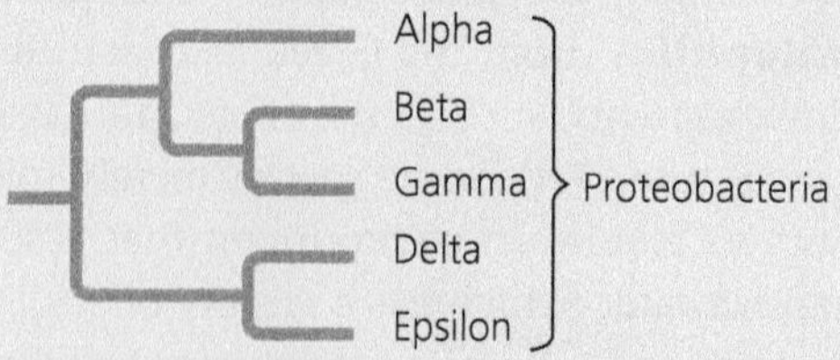

Subgroup: Alpha Proteobacteria

Many of the species in this subgroup are closely associated with eukaryotic hosts. For example, *Rhizobium* species live in nodules within the roots of legumes (plants of the pea/bean family), where the bacteria convert atmospheric N_2 to compounds the host plant can use to make proteins. Species in the genus *Agrobacterium* produce tumors in plants; genetic engineers use these bacteria to carry foreign DNA into the genomes of crop plants (see Figure 20.26). As explained in Chapter 25, scientists hypothesize that mitochondria evolved from aerobic alpha proteobacteria through endosymbiosis.

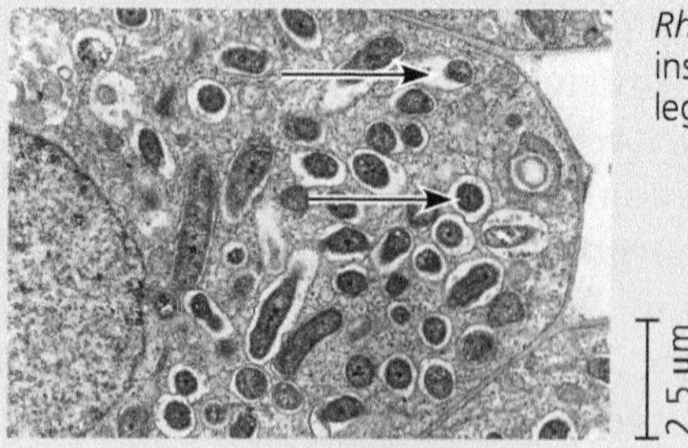

Rhizobium (arrows) inside a root cell of a legume (TEM)

Subgroup: Beta Proteobacteria

This nutritionally diverse subgroup includes *Nitrosomonas*, a genus of soil bacteria that play an important role in nitrogen recycling by oxidizing ammonium (NH_4^+), producing nitrite (NO_2^-) as a waste product.

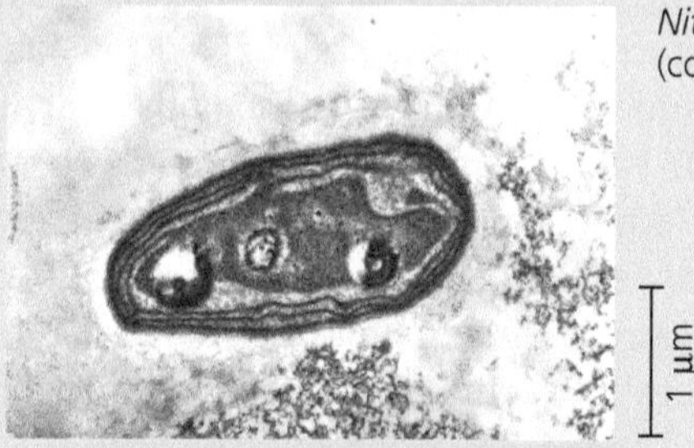

Nitrosomonas (colorized TEM)

Subgroup: Gamma Proteobacteria

This subgroup's autotrophic members include sulfur bacteria such as *Thiomargarita namibiensis* (see p. 557), which obtain energy by oxidizing H_2S, producing sulfur as a waste product (the small globules in the photograph at right). Some heterotrophic gamma proteobacteria are pathogens; for example, *Legionella* causes Legionnaires' disease, *Salmonella* is responsible for some cases of food poisoning, and *Vibrio cholerae* causes cholera. *Escherichia coli*, a common resident of the intestines of humans and other mammals, normally is not pathogenic.

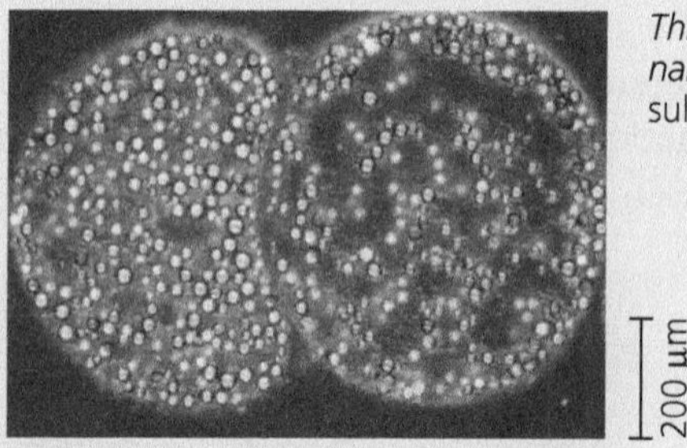

Thiomargarita namibiensis containing sulfur wastes (LM)

Subgroup: Delta Proteobacteria

This subgroup includes the slime-secreting myxobacteria. When the soil dries out or food is scarce, the cells congregate into a fruiting body that releases resistant "myxospores." These cells found new colonies in favorable environments. Another group of delta proteobacteria, the bdellovibrios, attack other bacteria, charging at up to 100 µm/sec (comparable to a human running 240 km/hr). The attack begins when a bdellovibrio attaches to specific molecules found on the outer covering of some bacterial species. The bdellovibrio then drills into its prey by using digestive enzymes and spinning at 100 revolutions per second.

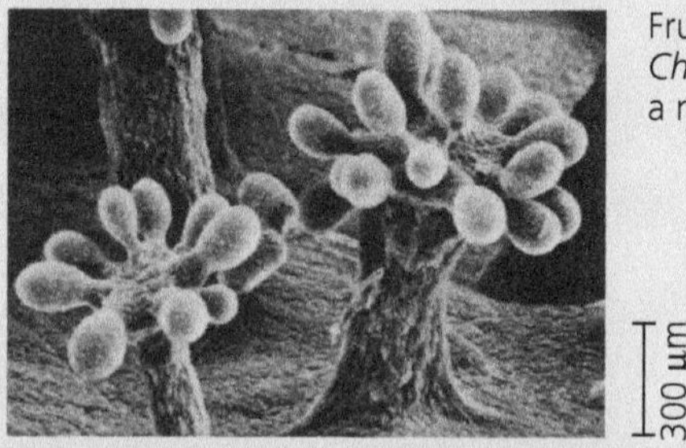

Fruiting bodies of *Chondromyces crocatus*, a myxobacterium (SEM)

Subgroup: Epsilon Proteobacteria

Most species in this subgroup are pathogenic to humans or other animals. Epsilon proteobacteria include *Campylobacter*, which causes blood poisoning and intestinal inflammation, and *Helicobacter pylori*, which causes stomach ulcers.

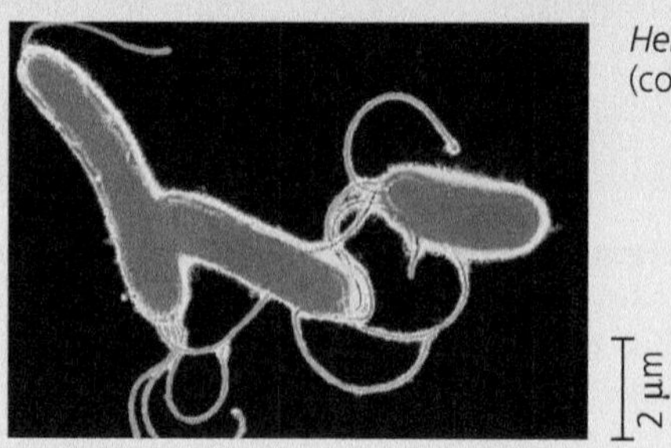

Helicobacter pylori (colorized TEM)

Chlamydias

These parasites can survive only within animal cells, depending on their hosts for resources as basic as ATP. The gram-negative walls of chlamydias are unusual in that they lack peptidoglycan. One species, *Chlamydia trachomatis*, is the most common cause of blindness in the world and also causes nongonococcal urethritis, the most common sexually transmitted disease in the United States.

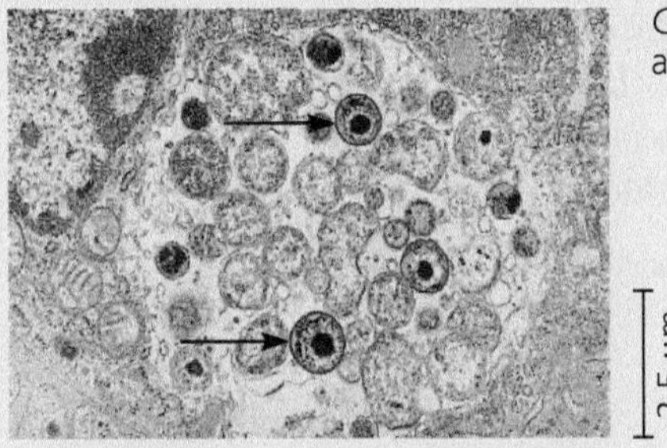

Chlamydia (arrows) inside an animal cell (colorized TEM)

Spirochetes

These helical heterotrophs spiral through their environment by means of rotating, internal, flagellum-like filaments. Many spirochetes are free-living, but others are notorious pathogenic parasites: *Treponema pallidum* causes syphilis, and *Borrelia burgdorferi* causes Lyme disease (see Figure 27.20).

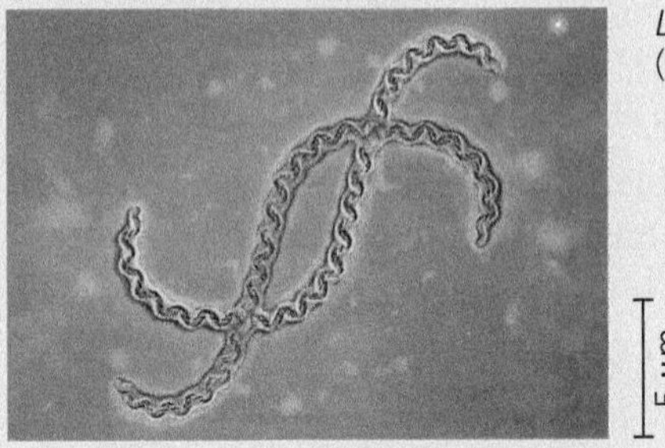

Leptospira, a spirochete (colorized TEM)

Cyanobacteria

These photoautotrophs are the only prokaryotes with plantlike, oxygen-generating photosynthesis. (In fact, as we'll discuss in Chapter 28, chloroplasts likely evolved from an endosymbiotic cyanobacterium.) Both solitary and filamentous cyanobacteria are abundant components of freshwater and marine *phytoplankton*, the collection of photosynthetic organisms that drift near the water's surface. Some filaments have cells specialized for nitrogen fixation, the process that incorporates atmospheric N_2 into inorganic compounds that can be used in the synthesis of amino acids and other organic molecules (see Figure 27.14).

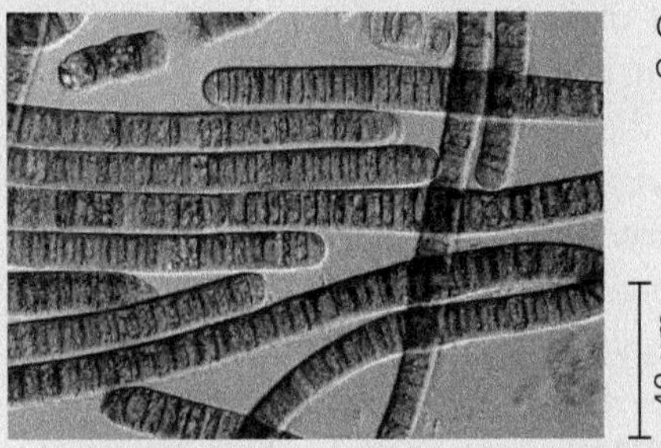

Oscillatoria, a filamentous cyanobacterium

Gram-Positive Bacteria

Gram-positive bacteria rival the proteobacteria in diversity. Species in one subgroup, the actinomycetes (from the Greek *mykes*, fungus, for which these bacteria were once mistaken), form colonies containing branched chains of cells. Two species of actinomycetes cause tuberculosis and leprosy. However, most actinomycetes are free-living species that help decompose the organic matter in soil; their secretions are partly responsible for the "earthy" odor of rich soil. Soil-dwelling species in the genus *Streptomyces* (top) are cultured by pharmaceutical companies as a source of many antibiotics, including streptomycin.

Gram-positive bacteria include many solitary species, such as *Bacillus anthracis* (see Figure 27.9), which causes anthrax, and *Clostridium botulinum*, which causes botulism. The various species of *Staphylococcus* and *Streptococcus* are also gram-positive bacteria.

Mycoplasmas (bottom) are the only bacteria known to lack cell walls. They are also the tiniest known cells, with diameters as small as 0.1 µm, only about five times as large as a ribosome. Mycoplasmas have small genomes—*Mycoplasma genitalium* has only 517 genes, for example. Many mycoplasmas are free-living soil bacteria, but others are pathogens.

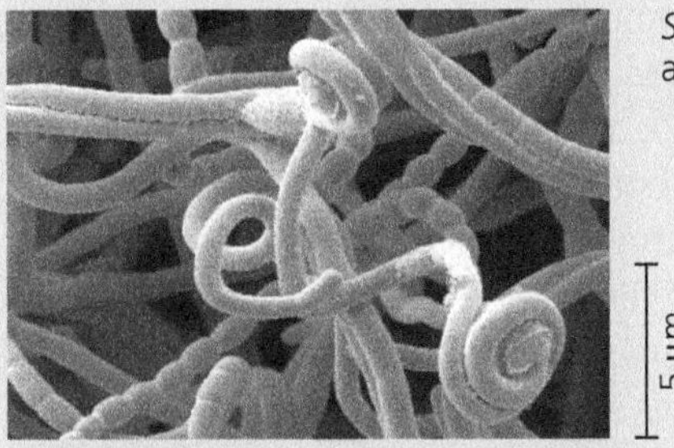

Streptomyces, the source of many antibiotics (SEM)

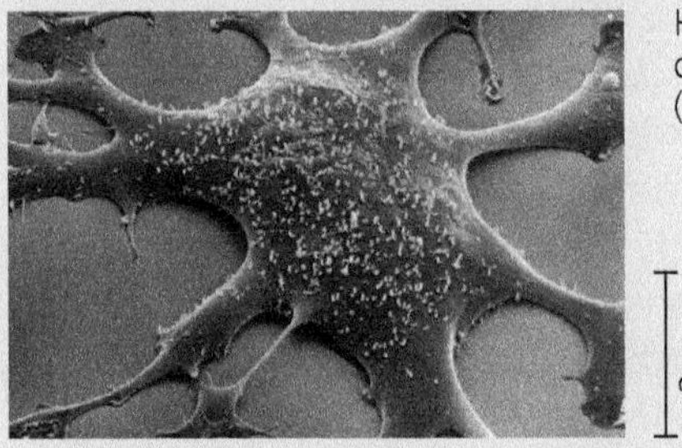

Hundreds of mycoplasmas covering a human fibroblast cell (colorized SEM)

CONCEPT CHECK 27.4

1. Explain how molecular systematics has contributed to our understanding of prokaryotic phylogeny.
2. How has genetic prospecting contributed to our understanding of prokaryotic diversity and phylogeny?
3. **WHAT IF?** What would the discovery of a bacterial species that is a methanogen imply about the evolution of the methane-producing pathway?

For suggested answers, see Appendix A.

CONCEPT **27.5**

Prokaryotes play crucial roles in the biosphere

If humans were to disappear from the planet tomorrow, life on Earth would change for many species, but few would be driven to extinction. In contrast, prokaryotes are so important to the biosphere that if they were to disappear, the prospects of survival for many other species would be dim.

Chemical Recycling

The atoms that make up the organic molecules in all living things were at one time part of inorganic substances in the soil, air, and water. Sooner or later, those atoms will return there. Ecosystems depend on the continual recycling of chemical elements between the living and nonliving components of the environment, and prokaryotes play a major role in this process. For example, chemoheterotrophic prokaryotes function as **decomposers**, breaking down dead organisms as well as waste products and thereby unlocking supplies of carbon, nitrogen, and other elements. Without the actions of prokaryotes and other decomposers such as fungi, all life would cease. (See Chapter 55 for a detailed discussion of chemical cycles.)

Prokaryotes also convert some molecules to forms that can be taken up by other organisms. Cyanobacteria and other autotrophic prokaryotes use CO_2 to make organic compounds such as sugars, which are then passed up through food chains. Cyanobacteria also produce atmospheric O_2, and a variety of prokaryotes fix atmospheric nitrogen (N_2) into forms that other organisms can use to make the building blocks of proteins and nucleic acids. Under some conditions, prokaryotes can increase the availability of nutrients that plants require for growth, such as nitrogen, phosphorus, and potassium (Figure 27.18). Prokaryotes can also *decrease* the availability of key plant nutrients; this occurs when prokaryotes "immobilize" nutrients by using them to synthesize molecules that remain within their cells. Thus, prokaryotes can have complex effects on soil nutrient concentrations. In marine environments, a 2005 study found that an archaean from the clade Crenarchaeota can perform nitrification, a key step in the nitrogen cycle (see Figure 55.14). Crenarchaeotes dominate the oceans by numbers, comprising an estimated 10^{28} cells. The sheer abundance of these organisms suggests that they may have a large impact on the global nitrogen cycle; scientists are investigating this possibility.

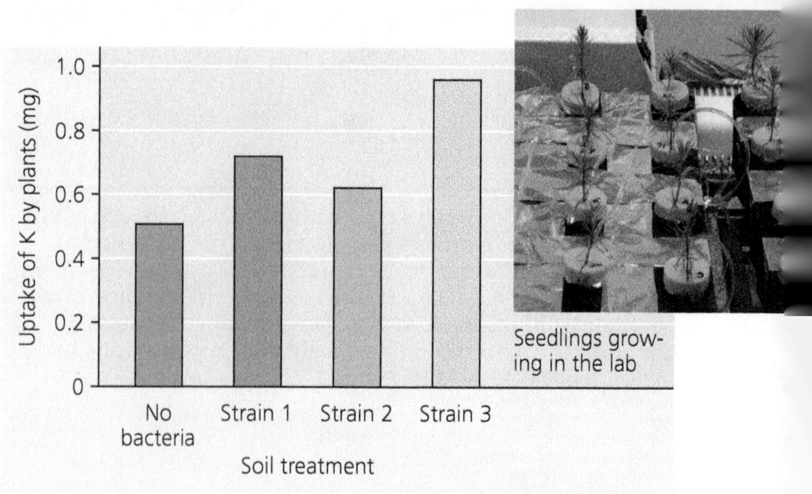

▲ **Figure 27.18 Impact of bacteria on soil nutrient availability.** Pine seedlings grown in sterile soils to which one of three strains of the bacterium *Burkholderia glathei* had been added absorbed more potassium (K) than did seedlings grown in soil without any bacteria. Other results (not shown) demonstrated that strain 3 increased the amount of K released from mineral crystals to the soil.

WHAT IF? *Estimate the average uptake of K for seedlings in soils with bacteria. What would you expect this average to be if bacteria had no effect on nutrient availability?*

Ecological Interactions

Prokaryotes play a central role in many ecological interactions. Consider **symbiosis** (from a Greek word meaning "living together"), an ecological relationship in which two species live in close contact with each other. Prokaryotes often form symbiotic associations with much larger organisms. In general, the larger organism in a symbiotic relationship is known as the **host**, and the smaller is known as the **symbiont**. There are many cases in which a prokaryote and its host participate in **mutualism**, an ecological interaction between two species in which both benefit (Figure 27.19). Other interactions take the form of **commensalism**, an ecological relationship in which one species benefits while the other is not harmed or helped in any significant way. For example, more than 150 bacterial species live on the surface of your body, covering portions of your skin with up to 10 million cells per square centimeter. Some of these species are commensalists: You provide them with food, such as the oils that exude from your pores, and a place to live, while they do not harm or benefit you. Finally, some prokaryotes engage in **parasitism**, an ecological relationship in which a **parasite** eats the cell contents, tissues, or body fluids of its host; as a group, parasites harm but usually do not kill their host, at least not immediately (unlike a predator). Parasites that cause disease are known as **pathogens**, many of which are prokaryotic.

▲ **Figure 27.19 Mutualism: bacterial "headlights."** The glowing oval below the eye of the flashlight fish (*Photoblepharon palpebratus*) is an organ harboring bioluminescent bacteria. The fish uses the light to attract prey and to signal potential mates. The bacteria receive nutrients from the fish.

(We'll discuss mutualism, commensalism, and parasitism in greater detail in Chapter 54.)

The very existence of an ecosystem can depend on prokaryotes. For example, consider the diverse ecological communities found at hydrothermal vents. These communities are densely populated by many different kinds of animals, including worms, clams, crabs, and fishes. But since sunlight does not penetrate to the deep ocean floor, the community does not include photosynthetic organisms. Instead, the energy that supports the community is derived from the metabolic activities of chemoautotrophic bacteria. These bacteria harvest chemical energy from compounds such as hydrogen sulfide (H_2S) that are released from the vent. An active hydrothermal vent may support hundreds of eukaryotic species, but when the vent stops releasing chemicals, the chemoautotrophic bacteria cannot survive. As a result, the entire vent community collapses.

CONCEPT CHECK 27.5

1. Explain how prokaryotes, though small, can be considered giants in their collective impact on Earth and its life.
2. MAKE CONNECTIONS After reviewing photosynthesis in Figure 10.6 (p. 188), summarize the main steps by which cyanobacteria produce O_2 and use CO_2 to make organic compounds.

For suggested answers, see Appendix A.

CONCEPT 27.6

Prokaryotes have both beneficial and harmful impacts on humans

Though the best-known prokaryotes tend to be the bacteria that cause illness in humans, these pathogens represent only a small fraction of prokaryotic species. Many other prokaryotes have positive interactions with humans, and some play essential roles in agriculture and industry.

Mutualistic Bacteria

As is true for many other eukaryotes, human well-being can depend on mutualistic prokaryotes. For example, our intestines are home to an estimated 500–1,000 species of bacteria; their cells outnumber all human cells in the body by a factor of ten. Different species live in different portions of the intestines, and they vary in their ability to process different foods. Many of these species are mutualists, digesting food that our own intestines cannot break down. In 2003, scientists published the first complete genome of one of these gut mutualists, *Bacteroides thetaiotaomicron*. The genome includes a large array of genes involved in synthesizing carbohydrates, vitamins, and other nutrients needed by humans. Signals from the bacterium activate human genes that build the network of intestinal blood vessels necessary to absorb nutrient molecules. Other signals induce human cells to produce antimicrobial compounds to which *B. thetaiotaomicron* is not susceptible. This action may reduce the population sizes of other, competing species, thus potentially benefiting both *B. thetaiotaomicron* and its human host.

Pathogenic Bacteria

All the pathogenic prokaryotes known to date are bacteria, and they deserve their negative reputation. Bacteria cause about half of all human diseases. Roughly 2 million people die each year of the lung disease tuberculosis, caused by *Mycobacterium tuberculosis*. And another 2 million people die each year from diarrheal diseases caused by various bacteria.

Some bacterial diseases are transmitted by other species, such as fleas or ticks. In the United States, the most widespread pest-carried disease is Lyme disease, which infects 15,000 to 20,000 people each year (Figure 27.20). Caused by a bacterium carried by ticks that live on deer and field mice,

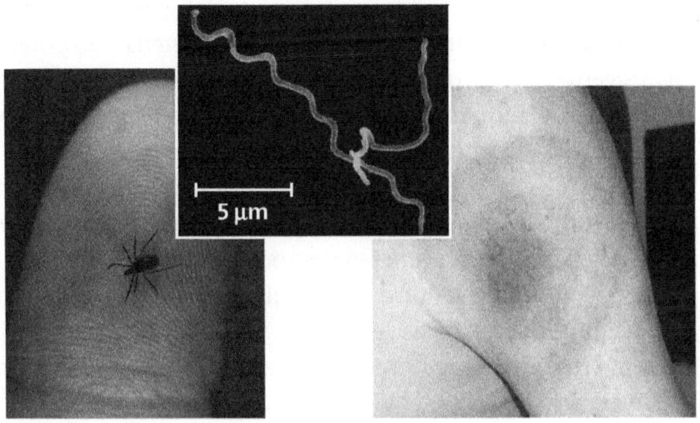

▲ **Figure 27.20 Lyme disease.** Ticks in the genus *Ixodes* spread the disease by transmitting the spirochete *Borrelia burgdorferi* (colorized SEM). A rash may develop at the site of the tick's bite; the rash may be large and ring-shaped (as shown) or much less distinctive.

Lyme disease can result in debilitating arthritis, heart disease, nervous disorders, and death if untreated.

Pathogenic prokaryotes usually cause illness by producing poisons, which are classified as exotoxins or endotoxins. **Exotoxins** are proteins secreted by certain bacteria and other organisms. Cholera, a dangerous diarrheal disease, is caused by an exotoxin secreted by the proteobacterium *Vibrio cholerae*. The exotoxin stimulates intestinal cells to release chloride ions into the gut, and water follows by osmosis. In another example, the potentially fatal disease botulism is caused by botulinum toxin, an exotoxin secreted by the gram-positive bacterium *Clostridium botulinum* as it ferments various foods, including improperly canned meat, seafood, and vegetables. Like other exotoxins, the botulinum toxin can produce disease even if the bacteria that manufacture it are not present. In one such case, eight people contracted botulism after eating salted fish that did not contain any *C. botulinum* bacteria, but did contain the botulinum toxin. Even though the bacterium was no longer present, at some point in the fish preparation process, the bacterium had been able to grow and secrete the toxin.

Endotoxins are lipopolysaccharide components of the outer membrane of gram-negative bacteria. In contrast to exotoxins, endotoxins are released only when the bacteria die and their cell walls break down. Endotoxin-producing bacteria include species in the genus *Salmonella*, such as *Salmonella typhi*, which causes typhoid fever. You might have heard of food poisoning caused by other *Salmonella* species that are frequently found in poultry.

Since the 19th century, improved sanitation systems in the industrialized world have greatly reduced the threat of pathogenic bacteria. Antibiotics have saved a great many lives and reduced the incidence of disease. However, resistance to antibiotics is currently evolving in many bacterial strains. As you read earlier, the rapid reproduction of bacteria enables cells carrying resistance genes to quickly give rise to large populations as a result of natural selection, and these genes can also spread to other species by horizontal gene transfer.

Horizontal gene transfer can also spread genes associated with virulence, turning normally harmless bacteria into potent pathogens. *E. coli*, for instance, is ordinarily a harmless symbiont in the human intestines, but pathogenic strains that cause bloody diarrhea have emerged. One of the most dangerous strains, called O157:H7, is a global threat; in the United States alone, there are 75,000 cases of O157:H7 infection per year, often from contaminated beef or produce. In 2001, scientists sequenced the genome of O157:H7 and compared it with the genome of a harmless strain of *E. coli* called K-12. They discovered that 1,387 out of the 5,416 genes in O157:H7 have no counterpart in K-12. Many of these 1,387 genes are found in chromosomal regions that include phage DNA. This result suggests that at least some of the 1,387 genes were incorporated into the genome of O157:H7 through phage-mediated horizontal gene transfer (transduction). Some of the genes found only in O157:H7 are associated with virulence, including genes that code for adhesive fimbriae that enable O157:H7 to attach itself to the intestinal wall and extract nutrients.

Pathogenic bacteria also pose a potential threat as weapons of bioterrorism. For example, endospores of *Bacillus anthracis* sent through the mail in 2001 caused 18 people to develop inhalation anthrax, which was fatal in 5 of the cases. Such scenarios have stimulated more research on pathogenic prokaryotic species in the hope of developing new vaccines and antibiotics.

Prokaryotes in Research and Technology

On a positive note, we reap many benefits from the metabolic capabilities of both bacteria and archaea. For example, humans have long used bacteria to convert milk to cheese and yogurt. In recent years, our greater understanding of prokaryotes has led to an explosion of new applications in biotechnology; two examples are the use of *E. coli* in gene cloning (see Figure 20.2) and the use of *Agrobacterium tumefaciens* in producing transgenic plants such as Golden Rice (see Figure 20.26 and p. 816).

Bacteria may soon figure prominently in a major industry: plastics. Globally, each year about 350 billion pounds of plastic are produced from petroleum and used to make toys, storage containers, soft drink bottles, and many other items. These products degrade slowly, creating environmental problems. Bacteria can now be used to make natural plastics (**Figure 27.21a**). For example, some bacteria synthesize a type of polymer known as PHA (polyhydroxyalkanoate), which they use to store chemical energy. The PHA they produce can be extracted, formed into pellets, and used to make durable, biodegradable plastics.

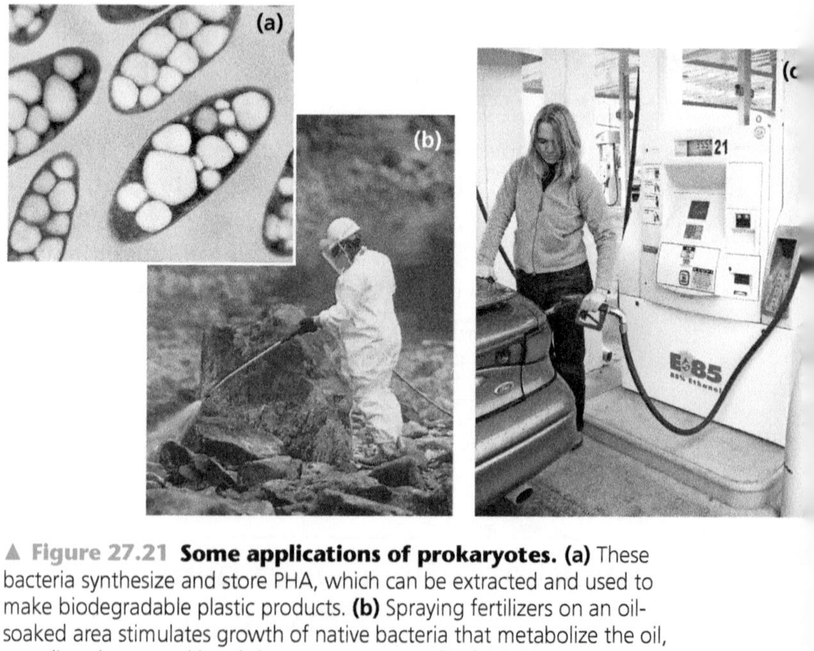

▲ **Figure 27.21 Some applications of prokaryotes. (a)** These bacteria synthesize and store PHA, which can be extracted and used to make biodegradable plastic products. **(b)** Spraying fertilizers on an oil-soaked area stimulates growth of native bacteria that metabolize the oil, speeding the natural breakdown process up to fivefold. **(c)** Current research seeks to develop bacteria that produce ethanol (E-85) fuel efficiently from renewable plant products.

Another way to harness prokaryotes is in **bioremediation**, the use of organisms to remove pollutants from soil, air, or water. For example, anaerobic bacteria and archaea decompose the organic matter in sewage, converting it to material that can be used as landfill or fertilizer after chemical sterilization. Other bioremediation applications include cleaning up oil spills (Figure 27.21b) and precipitating radioactive material (such as uranium) out of groundwater.

Through genetic engineering, humans can now modify bacteria to produce vitamins, antibiotics, hormones, and other products (see Chapter 20). Researchers are seeking to reduce fossil fuel use by engineering bacteria that can produce ethanol from various forms of biomass, including agricultural waste, switchgrass, municipal waste (such as paper products that are not recycled), and corn (Figure 27.21c).

The usefulness of prokaryotes largely derives from their diverse forms of nutrition and metabolism. All this metabolic versatility evolved prior to the appearance of the structural novelties that heralded the evolution of eukaryotic organisms, to which we devote the remainder of this unit.

CONCEPT CHECK 27.6

1. Identify at least two ways that prokaryotes have affected you positively today.
2. A pathogenic bacterium's toxin causes symptoms that increase the bacterium's chance of spreading from host to host. Does this information indicate whether the poison is an exotoxin or endotoxin? Explain.
3. **WHAT IF?** How might a sudden and dramatic change in your diet affect the diversity of prokaryotic species that live in your digestive tract?

For suggested answers, see Appendix A.

27 CHAPTER REVIEW

SUMMARY OF KEY CONCEPTS

CONCEPT 27.1

Structural and functional adaptations contribute to prokaryotic success (pp. 556–561)

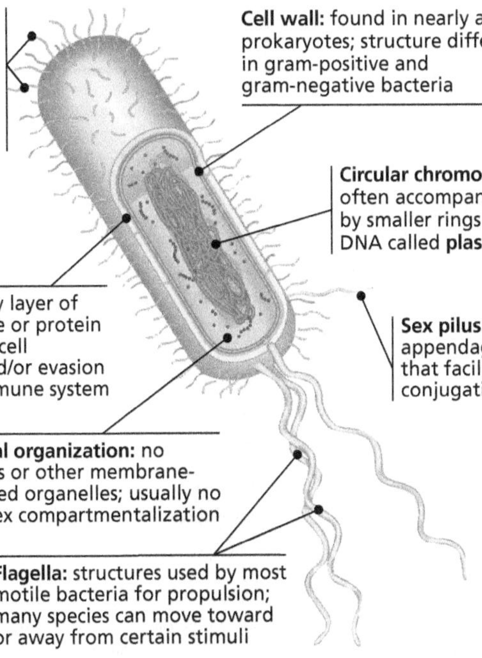

- Prokaryotes can reproduce quickly by binary fission. Some form endospores, which can remain viable in harsh conditions for centuries. Prokaryotic populations can evolve in short periods of time in response to changing environmental conditions.

? *Describe features of prokaryotes that enable them to thrive in many different environments.*

CONCEPT 27.2

Rapid reproduction, mutation, and genetic recombination promote genetic diversity in prokaryotes (pp. 561–564)

- Because prokaryotes can often proliferate rapidly, mutations can quickly increase a population's genetic variation, making adaptive evolution possible.
- Genetic diversity in prokaryotes also can arise by recombination of the DNA from two different cells (via transformation, transduction, or conjugation). By transferring advantageous alleles, such as ones for antibiotic resistance, genetic recombination can promote adaptive evolution in prokaryotic populations.

? *Mutations are rare and prokaryotes reproduce asexually; yet their populations can have high genetic diversity. Explain how this can occur.*

CONCEPT 27.3

Diverse nutritional and metabolic adaptations have evolved in prokaryotes (pp. 564–565)

- Nutritional diversity is much greater in prokaryotes than in eukaryotes. As a group, prokaryotes perform all four modes of nutrition: **photoautotrophy**, **chemoautotrophy**, **photoheterotrophy**, and **chemoheterotrophy**.
- Among prokaryotes, **obligate aerobes** require O_2, **obligate anaerobes** are poisoned by O_2, and **facultative anaerobes** can survive with or without O_2.
- Unlike eukaryotes, prokaryotes can metabolize nitrogen in many different forms. Some can convert atmospheric nitrogen to ammonia, a process called **nitrogen fixation**.
- Prokaryotic cells and even species may cooperate metabolically. In *Anabaena*, photosynthetic cells and nitrogen-fixing cells exchange metabolic products. Metabolic cooperation also occurs in surface-coating **biofilms** that include different species.

? *Describe the range of prokaryotic metabolic adaptations.*

CONCEPT 27.4

Molecular systematics is illuminating prokaryotic phylogeny (pp. 565–570)

- Molecular systematics is leading to a phylogenetic classification of prokaryotes, allowing systematists to identify major new clades.
- Some archaea, such as extreme thermophiles and extreme halophiles, live in extreme environments. Other archaea live in moderate environments such as soils and lakes.
- Diverse nutritional types are scattered among the major groups of bacteria. The two largest groups are the proteobacteria and the gram-positive bacteria.

? *What impact have molecular data had on constructing prokaryotic phylogeny?*

CONCEPT 27.5

Prokaryotes play crucial roles in the biosphere (pp. 570–571)

- Decomposition by heterotrophic prokaryotes and the synthetic activities of autotrophic and nitrogen-fixing prokaryotes contribute to the recycling of elements in ecosystems.
- Many prokaryotes have a symbiotic relationship with a host; the relationships between prokaryotes and their hosts range from mutualism to commensalism to parasitism.

? *In what ways are prokaryotes key to the survival of many species?*

CONCEPT 27.6

Prokaryotes have both beneficial and harmful impacts on humans (pp. 571–573)

- Humans depend on mutualistic prokaryotes, including hundreds of species that live in our intestines and help digest food.
- Pathogenic bacteria typically cause disease by releasing **exotoxins** or **endotoxins** and are potential weapons of bioterrorism. Horizontal gene transfer can spread genes associated with virulence to harmless species or strains.
- Experiments with bacteria such as *E. coli* have led to important advances in DNA technology. Prokaryotes can be used in bioremediation, production of biodegradable plastics, and the synthesis of vitamins, antibiotics, and other products.

? *Describe beneficial and harmful impacts of prokaryotes on humans.*

TEST YOUR UNDERSTANDING

LEVEL 1: KNOWLEDGE/COMPREHENSION

1. Genetic variation in bacterial populations cannot result from
   a. transduction.
   b. transformation.
   c. conjugation.
   d. mutation.
   e. meiosis.

2. Photoautotrophs use
   a. light as an energy source and CO_2 as a carbon source.
   b. light as an energy source and methane as a carbon source.
   c. N_2 as an energy source and CO_2 as a carbon source.
   d. CO_2 as both an energy source and a carbon source.
   e. H_2S as an energy source and CO_2 as a carbon source.

3. Which of the following statements is *not* true?
   a. Archaea and bacteria have different membrane lipids.
   b. Both archaea and bacteria generally lack membrane-enclosed organelles.
   c. The cell walls of archaea lack peptidoglycan.
   d. Only bacteria have histones associated with DNA.
   e. Only some archaea use CO_2 to oxidize H_2, releasing methane.

4. Which of the following involves metabolic cooperation among prokaryotic cells?
   a. binary fission
   b. endospore formation
   c. endotoxin release
   d. biofilms
   e. photoautotrophy

5. Bacteria perform the following ecological roles. Which role typically does *not* involve symbiosis?
   a. skin commensalist
   b. decomposer
   c. aggregate with methane-consuming archaea
   d. gut mutualist
   e. pathogen

6. Plantlike photosynthesis that releases O_2 occurs in
   a. cyanobacteria.
   b. chlamydias.
   c. archaea.
   d. actinomycetes.
   e. chemoautotrophic bacteria.

LEVEL 2: APPLICATION/ANALYSIS

7. **EVOLUTION CONNECTION**
   In patients infected with nonresistant strains of the tuberculosis bacterium, antibiotics can relieve symptoms in a few weeks. However, it takes much longer to halt the infection, and patients may discontinue treatment while bacteria are still present. How might this result in the evolution of drug-resistant pathogens?

LEVEL 3: SYNTHESIS/EVALUATION

8. **SCIENTIFIC INQUIRY**
   DRAW IT The nitrogen-fixing bacterium *Rhizobium* infects the roots of some plant species, forming a mutualism in which the bacterium provides nitrogen, and the plant provides carbohydrates. Scientists measured the 12-week growth of one such plant species (*Acacia irrorata*) when infected by six different *Rhizobium* strains. (a) Graph the data. (b) Interpret your graph.

Rhizobium strain	1	2	3	4	5	6
Plant mass (g)	0.91	0.06	1.56	1.72	0.14	1.03

Source: J. J. Burdon et al., Variation in the effectiveness of symbiotic associations between native rhizobia and temperate Australian *Acacia*: within species interactions, *Journal of Applied Ecology* 36:398–408 (1999).
Note: Without *Rhizobium*, after 12 weeks, *Acacia* plants have a mass of about 0.1 g.

9. **WRITE ABOUT A THEME**
   Energy Transfer In a short essay (about 100–150 words), discuss how prokaryotes and other members of hydrothermal vent communities transfer and transform energy.

For selected answers, see Appendix A.

28

Protists

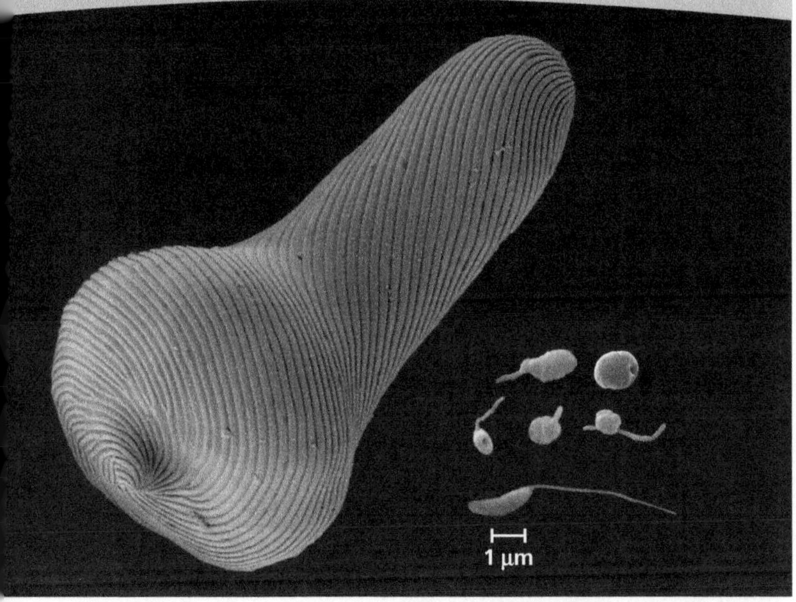

▲ **Figure 28.1 Which of these organisms are prokaryotes and which are eukaryotes?**

EVOLUTION

KEY CONCEPTS

28.1 Most eukaryotes are single-celled organisms
28.2 Excavates include protists with modified mitochondria and protists with unique flagella
28.3 Chromalveolates may have originated by secondary endosymbiosis
28.4 Rhizarians are a diverse group of protists defined by DNA similarities
28.5 Red algae and green algae are the closest relatives of land plants
28.6 Unikonts include protists that are closely related to fungi and animals
28.7 Protists play key roles in ecological communities

OVERVIEW

Living Small

Knowing that most prokaryotes are extremely small organisms, you might assume that Figure 28.1 depicts six prokaryotes and one much larger eukaryote. But in fact, the only prokaryote is the organism immediately above the scale bar. The other six organisms are members of diverse, mostly unicellular groups of eukaryotes informally known as **protists**. Very small eukaryotes have intrigued scientists for more than 300 years, ever since the Dutch microscopist Antoni van Leeuwenhoek first laid eyes on them. As he discovered, viewing a drop of pond water under a light microscope can reveal a fascinating world of unicellular protists and prokaryotes. Some protists propel themselves with whipping flagella, while others creep along by means of blob-like appendages. Some are shaped like tiny trumpets; others resemble miniature jewelry. Recalling his observations, van Leeuwenhoek wrote, "No more pleasant sight has met my eye than this, of so many thousands of living creatures in one small drop of water."

Until recently, biologists thought that 300 years of observation had uncovered a representative sample of living protist species. But in the last decade, genetic prospecting has turned up a treasure trove of previously unknown protists within the world of microscopic life. Many of these newly discovered organisms are just 0.5–2 µm in diameter—as small as many prokaryotes.

The surprising discovery of many species of minuscule protists followed close on the heels of recent findings regarding protist phylogeny. All protists were once classified in a single kingdom, Protista, but advances in eukaryotic systematics have caused the kingdom to crumble. It has become clear that the kingdom Protista is in fact polyphyletic (see Figure 26.10): Some protists are more closely related to plants, fungi, or animals than they are to other protists. As a result, the kingdom Protista has been abandoned, and various lineages of protists are now recognized as kingdoms in their own right. Most biologists still use the term *protist,* but only as a convenient way to refer to eukaryotes that are not plants, animals, or fungi.

In this chapter, you will become acquainted with some of the most significant groups of protists. You will learn about their structural and biochemical adaptations as well as their enormous impact on ecosystems, agriculture, industry, and human health.

CONCEPT **28.1**

Most eukaryotes are single-celled organisms

Protists, along with plants, animals, and fungi, are classified as eukaryotes; they are in domain Eukarya, one of the three domains of life. Unlike the cells of prokaryotes, eukaryotic cells have a nucleus and other membrane-bounded organelles, such as mitochondria and the Golgi apparatus. Such organelles provide specific locations in which particular cellular functions are accomplished, making the structure and organization of eukaryotic cells more complex than those of prokaryotic cells.

We'll survey the diversity of eukaryotes throughout the rest of this unit, beginning in this chapter with the protists. As you explore this material, bear in mind that

- the organisms in most eukaryotic lineages are protists, and
- most protists are unicellular.

Thus, life differs greatly from how most of us commonly think of it. The large, multicellular organisms that we know best (plants, animals, and fungi) are the tips of just a few branches on the great tree of life (see Figure 26.21).

Structural and Functional Diversity in Protists

Given the polyphyletic nature of the group once called Protista, it isn't surprising that few general characteristics of protists can be cited without exceptions. In fact, protists exhibit more structural and functional diversity than any other group of eukaryotes.

Most protists are unicellular, although there are some colonial and multicellular species. Single-celled protists are justifiably considered the simplest eukaryotes, but at the cellular level, many protists are very complex—the most elaborate of all cells. In multicellular organisms, essential biological functions are carried out by organs. Unicellular protists carry out the same essential functions, but they do so using subcellular organelles, not multicellular organs. The organelles that protists use are mostly those discussed in Chapter 6, including the nucleus, endoplasmic reticulum, Golgi apparatus, and lysosomes. Certain protists also rely on organelles not found in most other eukaryotic cells, such as contractile vacuoles that pump excess water from the protistan cell (see Figure 7.16).

Protists are more nutritionally diverse than other eukaryote groups. Some protists are photoautotrophs and contain chloroplasts. Some are heterotrophs, absorbing organic molecules or ingesting larger food particles. Still other protists, called **mixotrophs**, combine photosynthesis *and* heterotrophic nutrition. Photoautotrophy, heterotrophy, and mixotrophy have all arisen independently in many protist lineages.

Reproduction and life cycles also are highly varied among protists. Some protists are only known to reproduce asexually; others can also reproduce sexually or at least employ the sexual processes of meiosis and fertilization. All three basic types of sexual life cycles (see Figure 13.6) are represented among protists, along with some variations that do not quite fit any of these types. We will examine the life cycles of several protist groups later in this chapter.

Endosymbiosis in Eukaryotic Evolution

What gave rise to the enormous diversity of protists that exist today? There is abundant evidence that much of protist diversity has its origins in **endosymbiosis**, the process in which certain unicellular organisms engulf other cells, which become endosymbionts and ultimately organelles in the host cell. For example, as we discussed in Chapter 25, structural, biochemical, and DNA sequence data indicate that the first eukaryotes acquired mitochondria by engulfing an aerobic prokaryote (specifically, an alpha proteobacterium). The early origin of mitochondria is supported by the fact that all eukaryotes studied so far have either mitochondria or modified versions of them.

Much evidence also indicates that later in eukaryotic history, a lineage of heterotrophic eukaryotes acquired an additional endosymbiont—a photosynthetic cyanobacterium—that then evolved into plastids. As the hypothesis illustrated in Figure 28.2 shows, this plastid-bearing lineage gave rise to two lineages of photosynthetic protists, or **algae:** red algae and green algae. This hypothesis is supported by the observation that the DNA of plastid genes in red algae and green algae closely resembles the DNA of cyanobacteria. In addition, plastids in red algae and green algae are surrounded by two membranes. Transport proteins in these membranes are homologous to proteins in the inner and outer membranes of cyanobacterial endosymbionts, providing further support for the hypothesis.

On several occasions during eukaryotic evolution, red algae and green algae underwent **secondary endosymbiosis**: They were ingested in the food vacuoles of heterotrophic eukaryotes and became endosymbionts themselves. For example, protists known as chlorarachniophytes likely evolved when a heterotrophic eukaryote engulfed a green alga. Evidence for this process can be found within the engulfed cell, which contains a tiny vestigial nucleus, called a *nucleomorph*. Genes from the nucleomorph are still transcribed, and their DNA sequences indicate the engulfed cell was a green alga. Also consistent with the hypothesis that chlorarachniophytes evolved from a eukaryote that engulfed another eukaryote, their plastids are surrounded by *four* membranes. The two inner membranes originated as the inner and outer membranes of the ancient cyanobacterium. The third membrane is derived from the engulfed alga's plasma membrane, and the outermost membrane is derived from the heterotrophic eukaryote's food vacuole. In some other protists, plastids acquired by secondary endosymbiosis are surrounded by three membranes, indicating that one of the original four membranes was lost during the course of evolution.

Five Supergroups of Eukaryotes

Our understanding of the evolutionary history of protists has been in a state of flux in recent years. Not only has kingdom Protista been abandoned, but a variety of other hypotheses have been discarded as well. For example, in the early 1990s,

▼ **Figure 28.2 Diversity of plastids produced by endosymbiosis.** Studies of plastid-bearing eukaryotes suggest that plastids evolved from a gram-negative cyanobacterium that was engulfed by an ancestral heterotrophic eukaryote (primary endosymbiosis). That ancestor then diversified into red algae and green algae, some of which were subsequently engulfed by other eukaryotes (secondary endosymbiosis).

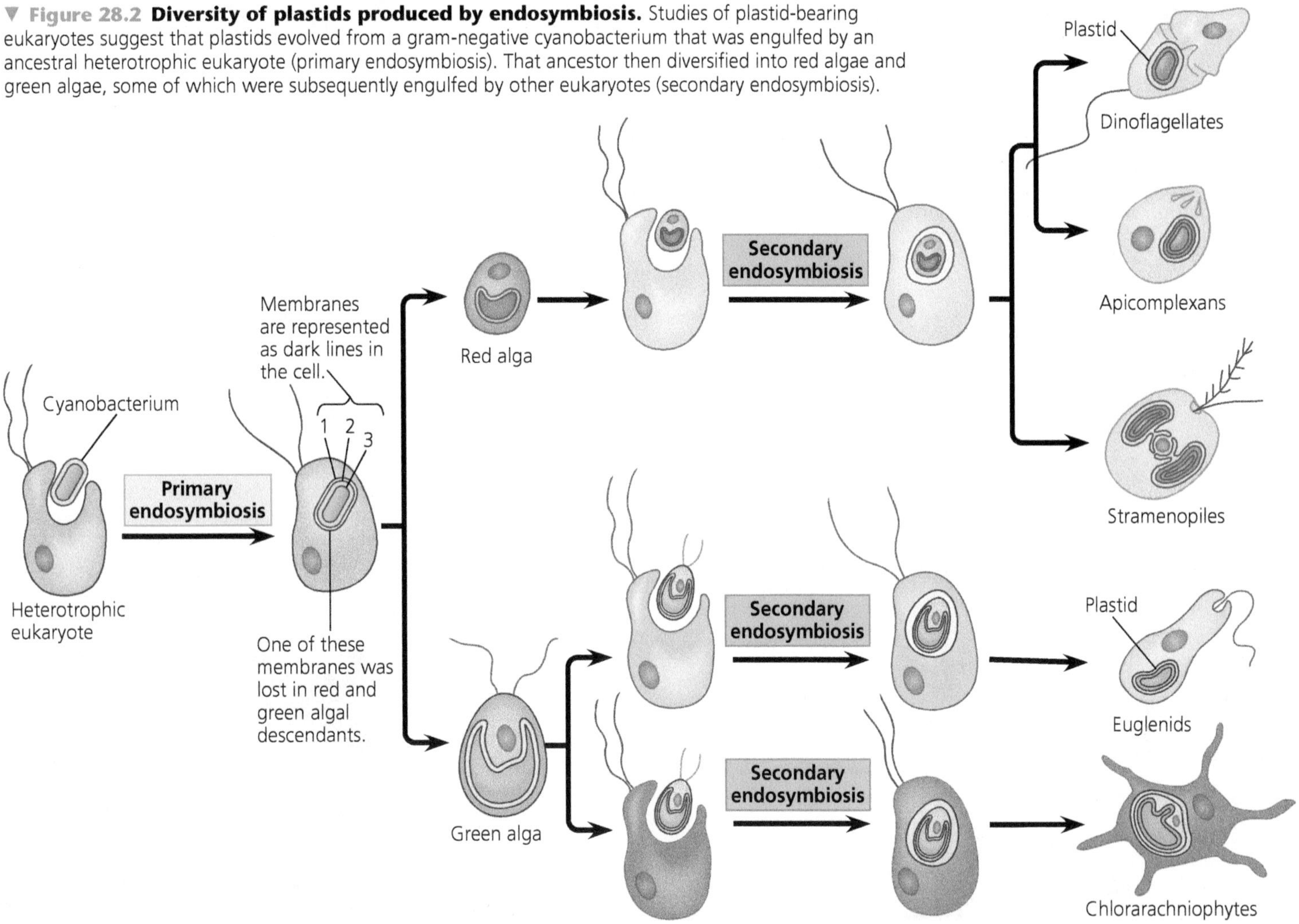

many biologists thought that the oldest lineage of living eukaryotes consisted of the *amitochondriate protists*, organisms without conventional mitochondria and with fewer membrane-bounded organelles than other protist groups. But recent structural and DNA data have undermined this hypothesis. Many of the so-called amitochondriate protists have been shown to have mitochondria—though reduced ones—and some of these organisms are now classified in entirely different groups. For example, microsporidians, once considered amitochondriate protists, are now classified as fungi.

The ongoing changes in our understanding of the phylogeny of protists pose challenges to students and instructors alike. Hypotheses about these relationships are a focus of scientific activity, changing rapidly as new data cause previous ideas to be modified or discarded. In this chapter, our discussion is organized around one current hypothesis: the five supergroups of eukaryotes shown in Figure 28.3, on the next two pages. Because the root of the eukaryotic tree is not known, all five supergroups are shown as diverging simultaneously from a common ancestor. We know that is not correct, but we do not know which organisms were the first to diverge from the others. In addition, while some of the groups in Figure 28.3 are well supported by morphological and DNA data, others are more controversial. As you read this chapter, it may be helpful to focus less on the specific names of groups of organisms and more on why the organisms are important and how ongoing research is elucidating their evolutionary relationships.

CONCEPT CHECK 28.1

1. Cite at least four examples of structural and functional diversity among protists.
2. Summarize the role of endosymbiosis in eukaryotic evolution.
3. **WHAT IF?** After studying Figure 28.3, on the next two pages, draw a simplified version of the phylogenetic tree that shows only the five supergroups of eukaryotes. Now sketch how the tree would look if the unikonts were the first group of eukaryotes to diverge from other eukaryotes.

For suggested answers, see Appendix A.

▼ Figure 28.3

Exploring Protistan Diversity

The tree below represents a phylogenetic hypothesis for the relationships among all the eukaryotes on Earth today. The eukaryotic groups at the branch tips are related in larger "supergroups," labeled vertically at the far right of the tree. The kingdoms Plantae (land plants), Fungi, and Animalia (animals) have survived from the five-kingdom system of classification. Groups that were formerly classified in the kingdom Protista are listed in beige boxes. Dotted lines indicate evolutionary relationships that are uncertain and proposed clades that are under active debate.

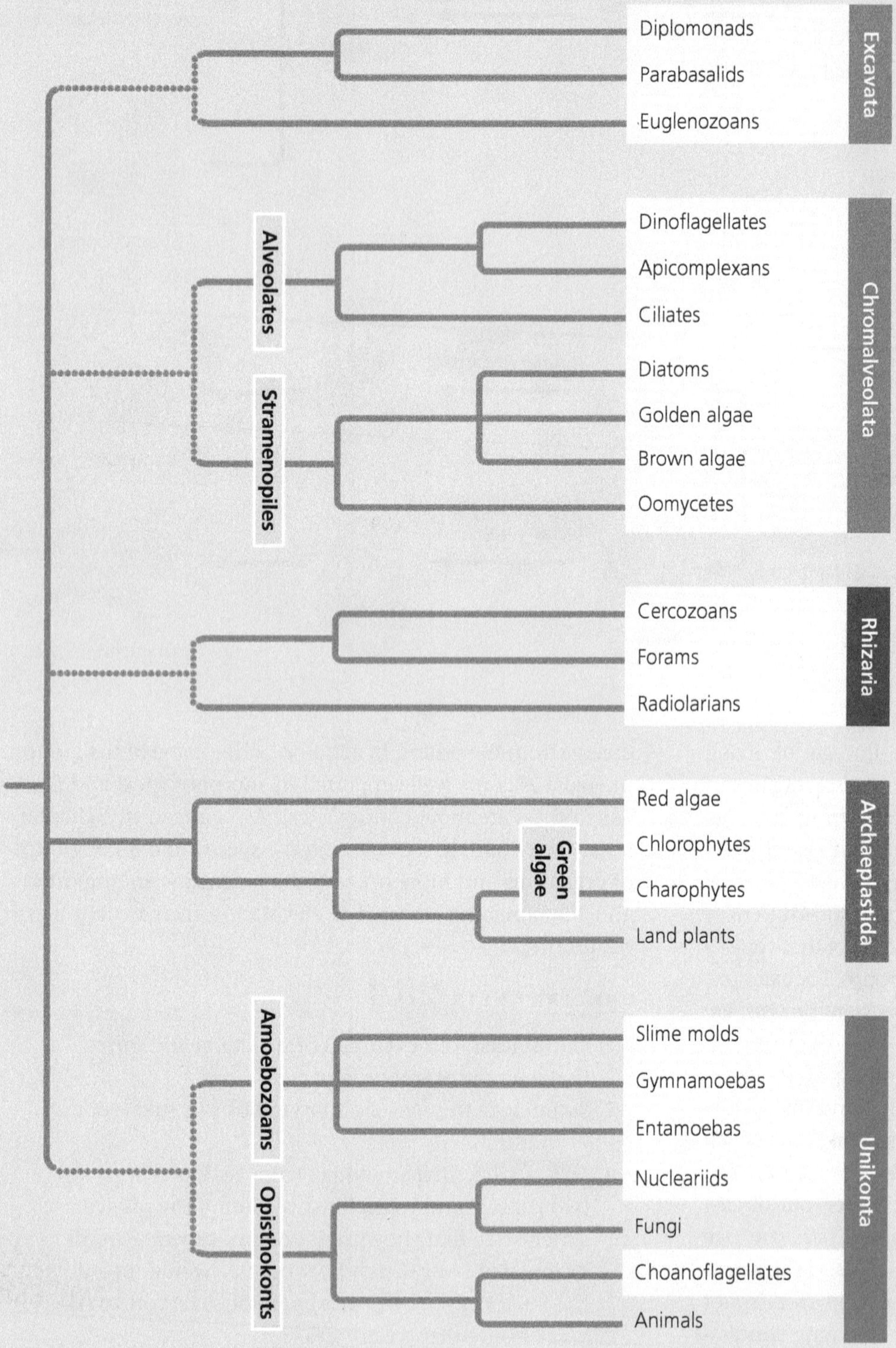

Excavata

Some members of this supergroup have an "excavated" groove on one side of the cell body. Two major clades (the parabasalids and diplomonads) have modified mitochondria; others (the euglenozoans) have flagella that differ in structure from those of other organisms. Excavates include parasites such as *Giardia*, as well as many predatory and photosynthetic species.

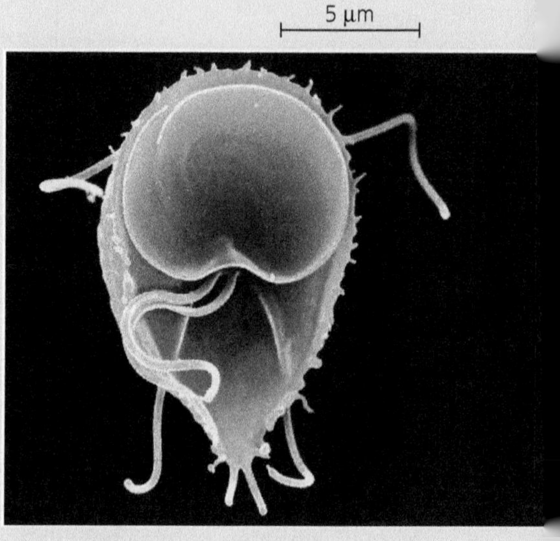

***Giardia intestinalis*, a diplomonad parasite.** This diplomonad (colorized SEM), which lacks the characteristic surface groove of the Excavata, can infect people when they drink water contaminated with feces containing *Giardia* cysts. Drinking such water—even from a seemingly pristine stream—can cause severe diarrhea. Boiling the water kills the parasite.

Chromalveolata

This group may have originated by an ancient secondary endosymbiosis event. Chromalveolates include some of the most important photosynthetic organisms on Earth, such as the diatoms shown here. The group also includes the brown algae that form underwater kelp "forests," as well as important pathogens, such as *Plasmodium*, which causes malaria, and *Phytophthora*, which caused the devastating potato famine in 19th-century Ireland.

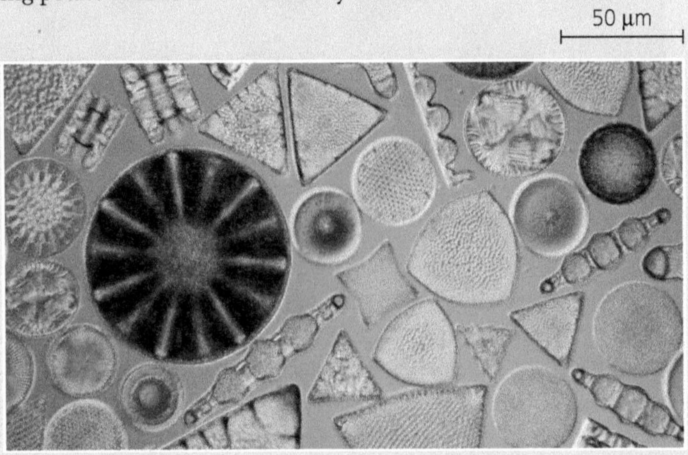

Diatom diversity. These beautiful single-celled protists are important photosynthetic organisms in aquatic communities (LM).

Rhizaria

This group contains many species of amoebas, most of which have pseudopodia that are threadlike in shape. Pseudopodia are extensions that can bulge from any portion of the cell; they are used in movement and in the capture of prey. Several recent molecular phylogenetic studies have suggested that Rhizaria should be nested within Chromalveolata; this hypothesis is currently being tested by other research groups.

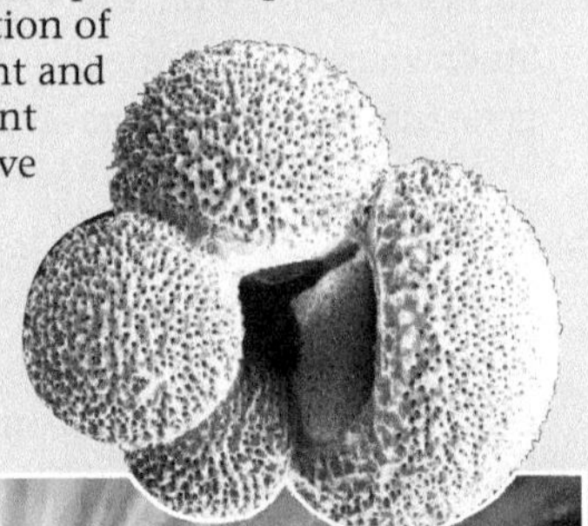

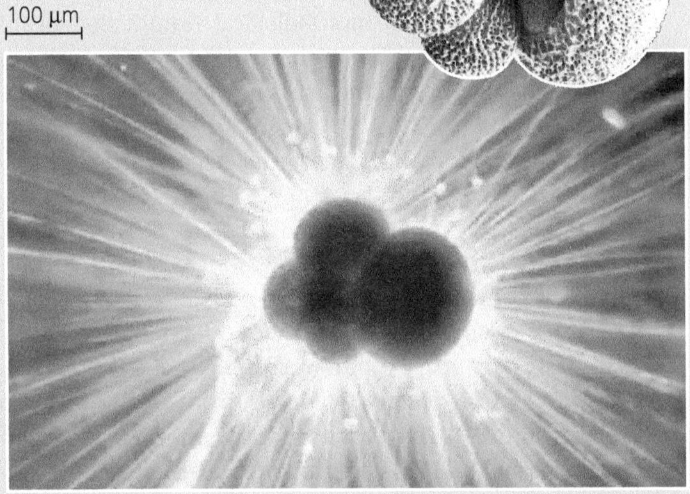

***Globigerina*, a foram in the supergroup Rhizaria.** Threadlike pseudopodia extend through pores in the shell, or *test* (LM). The inset SEM shows a foram test, which is hardened by calcium carbonate.

Archaeplastida

This group of eukaryotes includes red algae and green algae, along with land plants (kingdom Plantae, discussed in Chapters 29 and 30). Red algae and green algae include unicellular species, colonial species (such as the green alga *Volvox*), and multicellular species. Many of the large algae known informally as "seaweeds" are multicellular red or green algae. Protists in Archaeplastida include key photosynthetic species that form the base of the food web in some aquatic communities.

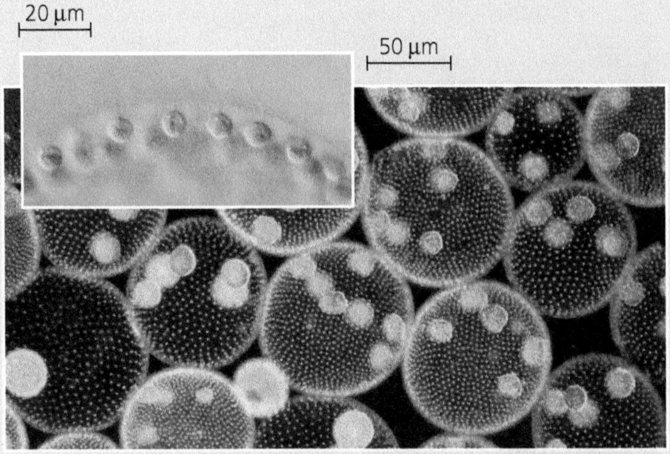

***Volvox*, a colonial freshwater green alga.** The colony is a hollow ball whose wall is composed of hundreds of biflagellated cells (see inset LM) embedded in a gelatinous matrix. The cells are usually connected by cytoplasmic strands; if isolated, these cells cannot reproduce. The large colonies seen here will eventually release the small "daughter" colonies within them (LM).

Unikonta

This group of eukaryotes includes amoebas that have lobe- or tube-shaped pseudopodia, as well as animals, fungi, and non-amoeba protists that are closely related to animals or fungi. According to one current hypothesis, the unikonts may have been the first group of eukaryotes to diverge from other eukaryotes (see Figure 28.23); however, this hypothesis has yet to be widely accepted.

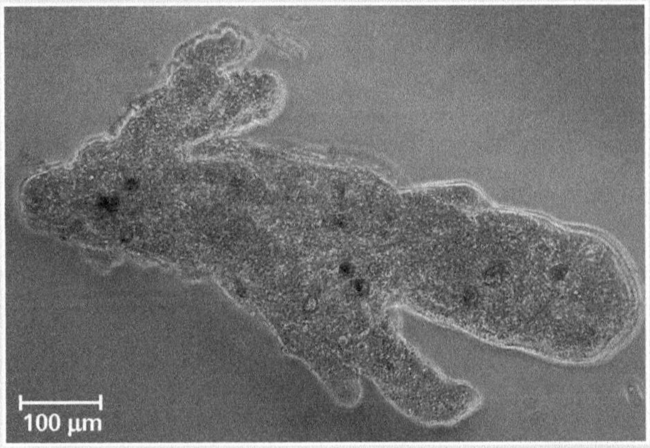

A unikont amoeba. This amoeba (*Amoeba proteus*) is using its pseudopodia to move.

CONCEPT 28.2

Excavates include protists with modified mitochondria and protists with unique flagella

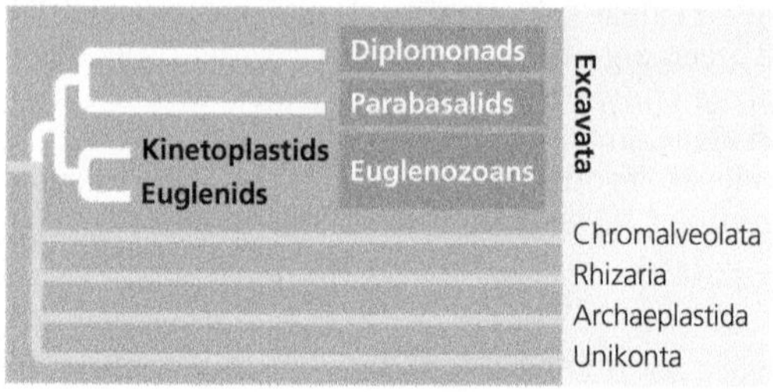

Now that we have examined some of the broad patterns in eukaryotic evolution, we will look more closely at the five main groups of protists shown in Figure 28.3.

We begin this tour with **Excavata** (the excavates), a clade recently proposed based on morphological studies of the cytoskeleton. Some members of this diverse group also have an "excavated" feeding groove on one side of the cell body.

The excavates include the diplomonads, the parabasalids, and the euglenozoans. Molecular data indicate that each of these three groups is monophyletic, but the data have neither confirmed nor strongly refuted the monophyly of the excavate supergroup. Although many excavates share certain unique cytoskeletal features, we cannot yet tell whether that is because the excavates are monophyletic or because the common ancestor of eukaryotes had those features. Overall, support for the excavate clade is relatively weak, making it one of the more controversial of the five supergroups.

Diplomonads and Parabasalids

The protists in these two groups lack plastids and have modified mitochondria (until recently, they were thought to lack mitochondria altogether). Most diplomonads and parabasalids are found in anaerobic environments.

Diplomonads have modified mitochondria called *mitosomes*. These organelles lack functional electron transport chains and hence cannot use oxygen to help extract energy from carbohydrates and other organic molecules. Instead, diplomonads get the energy they need from anaerobic biochemical pathways.

Structurally, diplomonads have two equal-sized nuclei and multiple flagella. Recall that eukaryotic flagella are extensions of the cytoplasm, consisting of bundles of microtubules covered by the cell's plasma membrane (see Figure 6.24). They are quite different from prokaryotic flagella, which are filaments composed of the globular protein flagellin attached to the cell surface (see Figure 27.6).

Many diplomonads are parasites. An infamous example is *Giardia intestinalis* (also known as *Giardia lamblia*; see Figure 28.3), which inhabits the intestines of mammals.

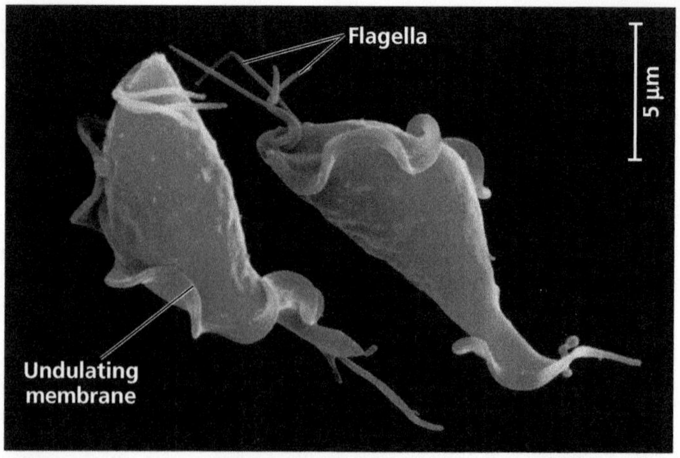

▲ **Figure 28.4 The parabasalid *Trichomonas vaginalis*** (colorized SEM).

Parabasalids also have reduced mitochondria; called *hydrogenosomes*, these organelles generate some energy anaerobically, releasing hydrogen gas as a by-product. The best-known parabasalid is *Trichomonas vaginalis*, a sexually transmitted parasite that infects some 5 million people each year. *T. vaginalis* travels along the mucus-coated lining of the human reproductive and urinary tracts by moving its flagella and by undulating part of its plasma membrane (Figure 28.4). In females, if the vagina's normal acidity is disturbed, *T. vaginalis* can outcompete beneficial microorganisms there and infect the vagina. (*Trichomonas* infections also can occur in the urethra of males, though often without symptoms.) *T. vaginalis* has a gene that allows it to feed on the vaginal lining, promoting infection. Studies suggest that the protist acquired this gene by horizontal gene transfer from bacterial parasites in the vagina.

Euglenozoans

Protists called **euglenozoans** belong to a diverse clade that includes predatory heterotrophs, photosynthetic autotrophs, and parasites. The main morphological feature that distinguishes protists in this clade is the presence of a rod with either a spiral or a crystalline structure inside each of their flagella (Figure 28.5). The two best-studied groups of euglenozoans are the kinetoplastids and the euglenids.

Kinetoplastids

Protists called **kinetoplastids** have a single, large mitochondrion that contains an organized mass of DNA called a *kinetoplast*. These protists include species that feed on prokaryotes in freshwater, marine, and moist terrestrial ecosystems, as well as species that parasitize animals, plants, and other protists. For example, kinetoplastids in the genus *Trypanosoma* infect humans and cause sleeping sickness, a neurological disease that is invariably fatal if not treated. The infection occurs via the bite of a vector (carrier) organism, the African tsetse fly (Figure 28.6). Trypanosomes also cause Chagas' disease, which

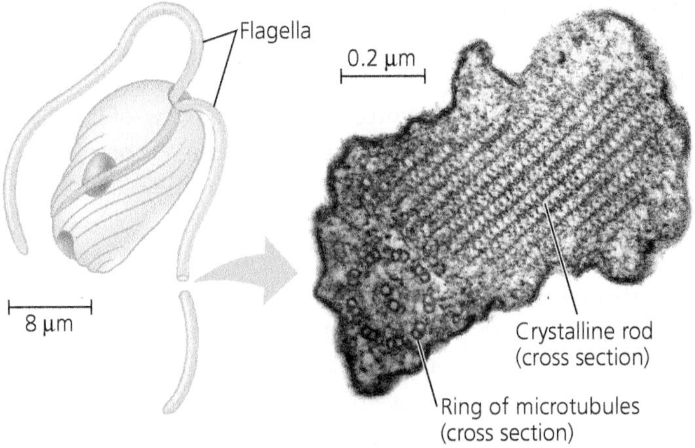

▲ **Figure 28.5 Euglenozoan flagellum.** Most euglenozoans have a crystalline rod inside one of their flagella (the TEM is a flagellum shown in cross section). The rod lies alongside the 9 + 2 ring of microtubules found in all eukaryotic flagella (compare with Figure 6.24).

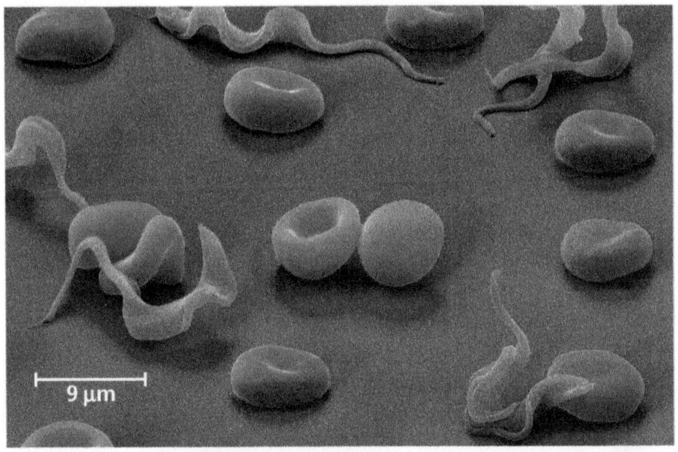

▲ **Figure 28.6 *Trypanosoma*, the kinetoplastid that causes sleeping sickness.** The purple, ribbon-shaped cells among these red blood cells are the trypanosomes (colorized SEM).

is transmitted by bloodsucking insects and can lead to congestive heart failure.

Trypanosomes evade immune responses with an effective "bait-and-switch" defense. The surface of a trypanosome is coated with millions of copies of a single protein. However, before the host's immune system can recognize the protein and mount an attack, new generations of the parasite switch to another surface protein with a different molecular structure. Frequent changes in the surface protein prevent the host from developing immunity (see Figure 43.24). About a third of *Trypanosoma*'s genome is dedicated to producing these surface proteins.

Euglenids

A **euglenid** has a pocket at one end of the cell from which one or two flagella emerge (**Figure 28.7**). Many species of the euglenid *Euglena* are mixotrophs: In sunlight they are autotrophic, but when sunlight is unavailable, they can become heterotrophic, absorbing organic nutrients from their environment. Many other euglenids engulf prey by phagocytosis.

CONCEPT CHECK 28.2

1. Why do some biologists describe the mitochondria of diplomonads and parabasalids as "highly reduced"?
2. **WHAT IF?** DNA sequence data for a diplomonad, a euglenid, a plant, and an unidentified protist suggest that the unidentified species is most closely related to the diplomonad. Further studies reveal that the unknown species has fully functional mitochondria. Based on these data, at what point on the phylogenetic tree in Figure 28.3 did the mystery protist's lineage probably diverge from other eukaryote lineages? Explain.

For suggested answers, see Appendix A.

▼ **Figure 28.7 *Euglena*, a euglenid commonly found in pond water.**

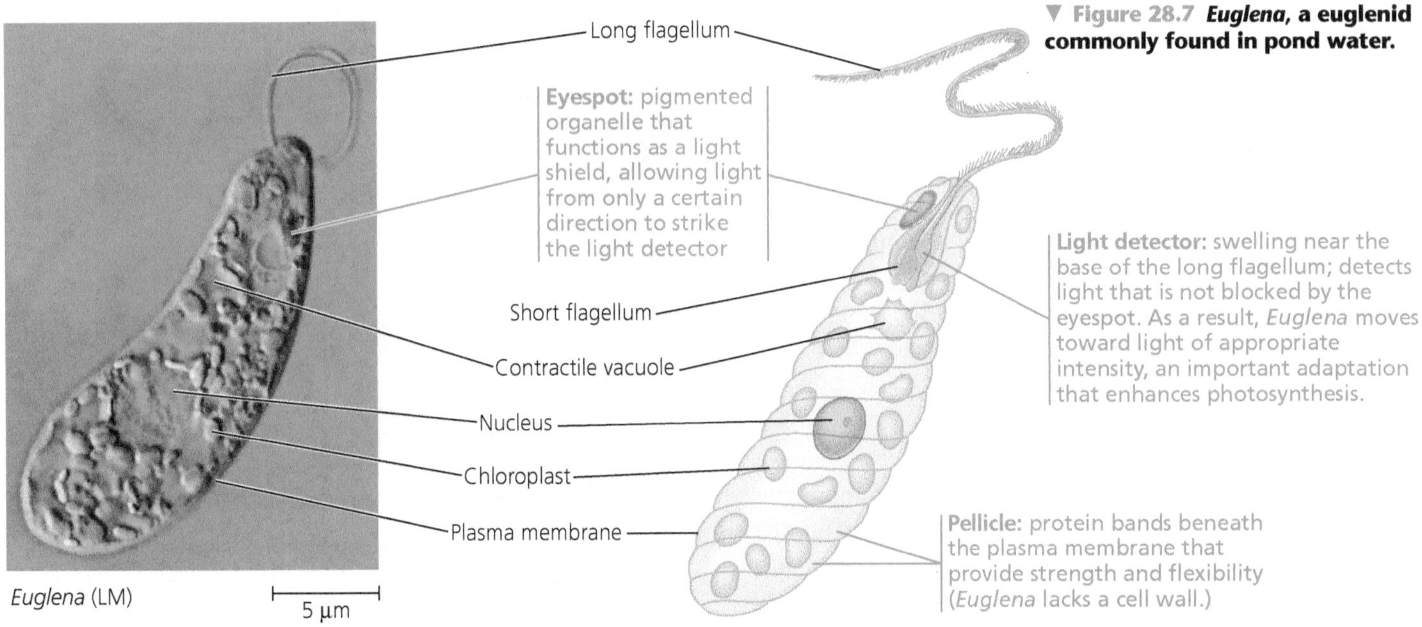

CONCEPT 28.3

Chromalveolates may have originated by secondary endosymbiosis

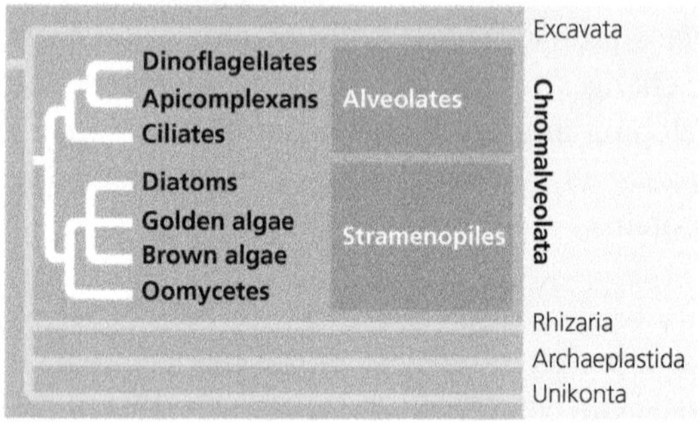

The supergroup **Chromalveolata** (the chromalveolates), a large, extremely diverse clade of protists, has recently been proposed based on two lines of evidence. First, some (though not all) DNA sequence data suggest that the chromalveolates form a monophyletic group. Second, some data support the hypothesis that the chromalveolates originated more than a billion years ago, when a common ancestor of the group engulfed a single-celled, photosynthetic red alga. Because red algae are thought to have originated by primary endosymbiosis (see Figure 28.2), such an origin for the chromalveolates is referred to as secondary endosymbiosis.

How strong is the evidence that the chromalveolates originated by secondary endosymbiosis? Many species in the clade have plastids whose structure and DNA indicate that they are of red algal origin. Others have reduced plastids that seem to be derived from a red algal endosymbiont. Still other species lack plastids altogether, yet some of these species have plastid genes in their nuclear DNA. Such data have led researchers to suggest that the common ancestor of the chromalveolates had plastids of red algal origin, but that later, some evolutionary lineages within the group lost the plastids. Others question this idea, based on the absence of plastid genes in the genomes of several chromalveolates that lack plastids. Overall, the endosymbiotic origin of the chromalveolates is an interesting idea, but like any scientific hypothesis, new data may show it to be incorrect.

The chromalveolates are perhaps the most controversial of the five supergroups we describe in this chapter. Even so, for many scientists, this supergroup represents the best current hypothesis for the phylogeny of the two large protist clades to which we now turn: the alveolates and the stramenopiles.

Alveolates

The **alveolates** are a group of protists whose monophyly is well supported by molecular systematics. Structurally, species in this group have membrane-bounded sacs (alveoli) just under the plasma membrane (Figure 28.8). The function of the alveoli is unknown; researchers hypothesize that they may help stabilize the cell surface or regulate the cell's water and ion content.

The alveolates include three subgroups: a group of flagellates (the dinoflagellates), a group of parasites (the apicomplexans), and a group of protists that move using cilia (the ciliates).

Dinoflagellates

The **dinoflagellates** are characterized by cells that are reinforced by cellulose plates. Two flagella located in grooves in this "armor" make dinoflagellates (from the Greek *dinos*, whirling) spin as they move through the water (Figure 28.9). Dinoflagellates are abundant components of both marine and freshwater plankton, communities of mostly microscopic organisms that drift in currents near the water's surface. These dinoflagellates include some of the most important species of *phytoplankton* (photosynthetic plankton, which include photosynthetic bacteria as well as algae). However, many photosynthetic dinoflagellates are mixotrophic, and roughly half of all dinoflagellates are purely heterotrophic.

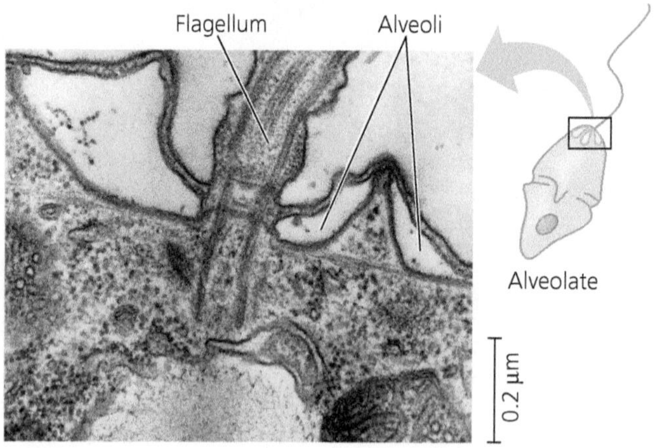

▲ **Figure 28.8 Alveoli.** These sacs under the plasma membrane are a characteristic that distinguishes alveolates from other eukaryotes (TEM).

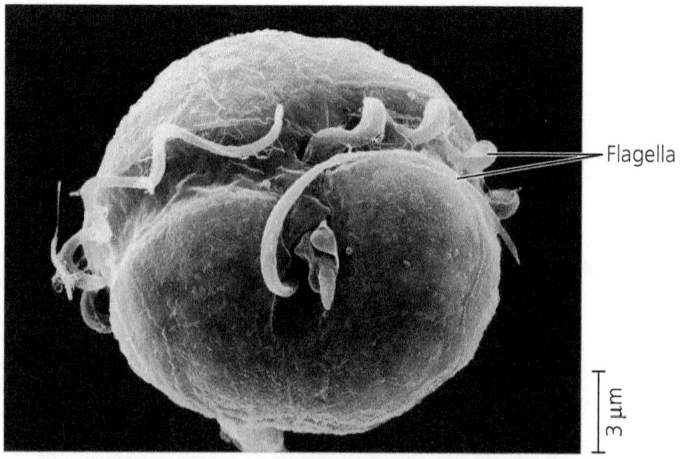

▲ **Figure 28.9 *Pfiesteria shumwayae*, a dinoflagellate.** Beating of the spiral flagellum, which lies in a groove that encircles the cell, makes this alveolate spin (colorized SEM).

Episodes of explosive population growth, or *blooms*, in dinoflagellates sometimes cause a phenomenon called "red tide." The blooms make coastal waters appear brownish red or pink because of the presence of carotenoids, the most common pigments in dinoflagellate plastids. Toxins produced by certain dinoflagellates (such as *Karenia brevis*, which inhabits the Gulf of Mexico) have caused massive kills of invertebrates and fishes. Humans who eat molluscs that have accumulated the toxins are affected as well, sometimes fatally.

Apicomplexans

Nearly all **apicomplexans** are parasites of animals, and some cause serious human diseases. The parasites spread through their host as tiny infectious cells called *sporozoites*. Apicomplexans are so named because one end (the *apex*) of the sporozoite cell contains a *complex* of organelles specialized for penetrating host cells and tissues. Although apicomplexans are not photosynthetic, recent data show that they retain a modified plastid (apicoplast), most likely of red algal origin.

Most apicomplexans have intricate life cycles with both sexual and asexual stages. Those life cycles often require two or more host species for completion. For example, *Plasmodium*, the parasite that causes malaria, lives in both mosquitoes and humans (Figure 28.10).

Historically, malaria has rivaled tuberculosis as the leading cause of human death by infectious disease. The incidence of malaria was greatly diminished in the 1960s by insecticides that reduced carrier populations of *Anopheles* mosquitoes and by drugs that killed *Plasmodium* in humans. But the emergence of resistant varieties of both *Anopheles* and *Plasmodium* has led

▼ Figure 28.10 **The two-host life cycle of *Plasmodium*, the apicomplexan that causes malaria.**

? *Are morphological differences between sporozoites, merozoites, and gametocytes caused by different genomes or by differences in gene expression? Explain.*

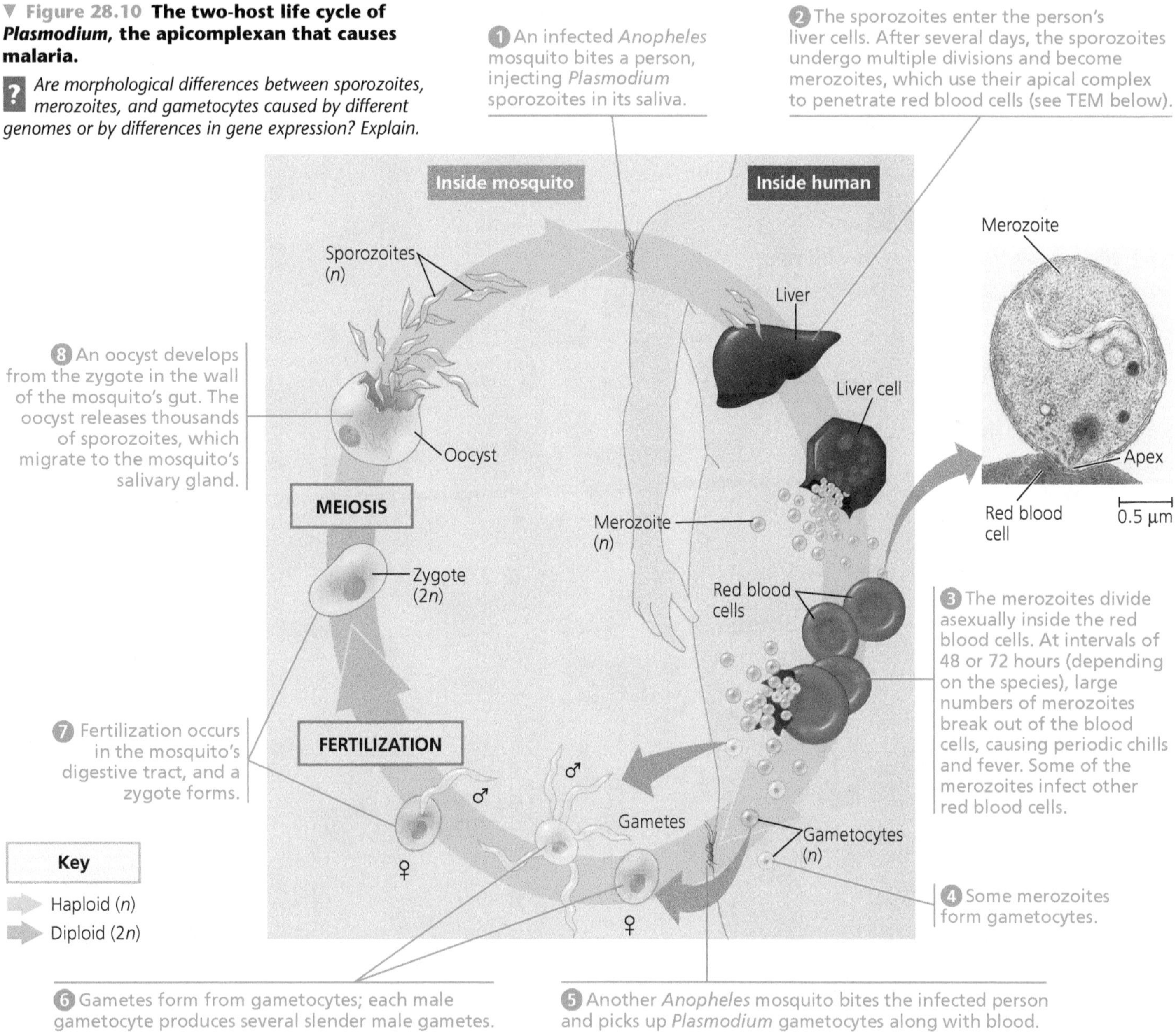

to a resurgence of malaria. About 250 million people in the tropics are currently infected, and 900,000 die each year.

The search for malarial vaccines has been hampered by the fact that *Plasmodium* lives mainly inside cells, hidden from the host's immune system. And, like trypanosomes, *Plasmodium* continually changes its surface proteins. The urgent need for treatments has inspired the sequencing of several *Plasmodium* genomes. Furthermore, researchers have now tracked the expression of most of the parasite's genes at numerous points in its life cycle. This research could help identify vaccine targets. Drugs that target the apicoplast are also in development. This approach may be effective because the apicoplast, derived by secondary endosymbiosis from a prokaryote, has metabolic pathways different from those in humans.

Ciliates

Ciliates are a large, varied group of protists named for their use of cilia to move and feed (Figure 28.11a). The cilia may

▼ Figure 28.11 **Structure and function in the ciliate *Paramecium caudatum*.**

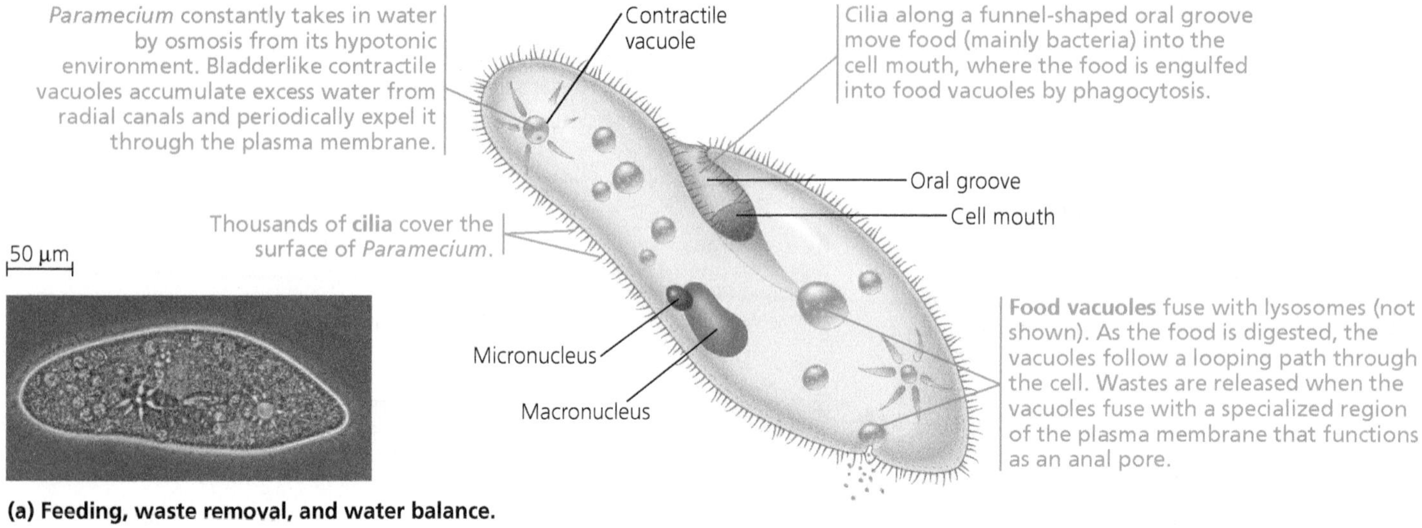

(a) Feeding, waste removal, and water balance.

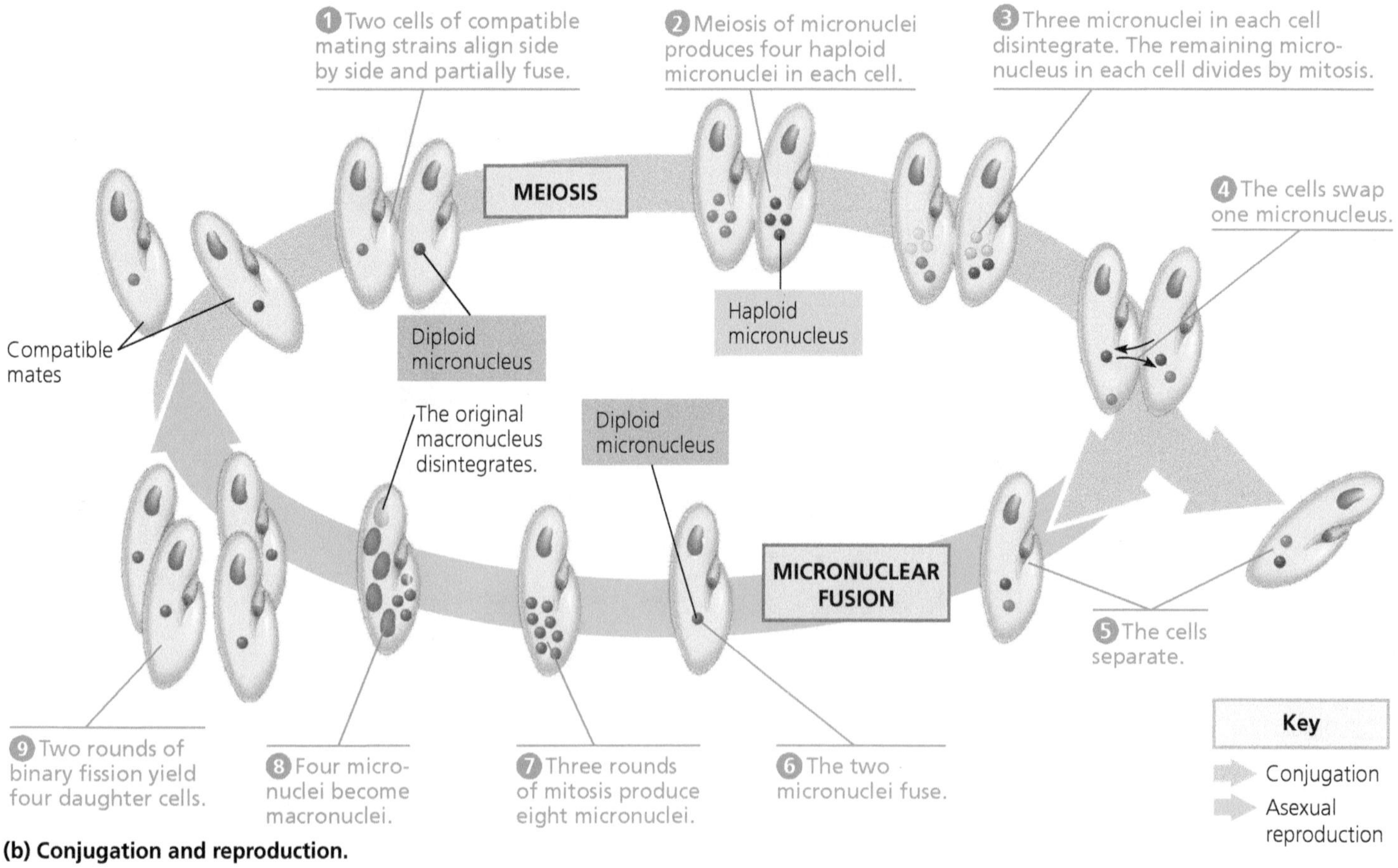

(b) Conjugation and reproduction.

completely cover the cell surface or may be clustered in a few rows or tufts. In certain species, rows of tightly packed cilia function collectively in locomotion. Other ciliates scurry about on leg-like structures constructed from many cilia bonded together.

A distinctive feature of ciliates is the presence of two types of nuclei: tiny micronuclei and large macronuclei. A cell has one or more nuclei of each type. Genetic variation results from **conjugation**, a sexual process in which two individuals exchange haploid micronuclei but do not reproduce (Figure 28.11b). Ciliates generally reproduce asexually by binary fission, during which the existing macronucleus disintegrates and a new one is formed from the cell's micronuclei. Each macronucleus typically contains multiple copies of the ciliate's genome. Genes in the macronucleus control the everyday functions of the cell, such as feeding, waste removal, and maintaining water balance (see Figure 28.11a).

Stramenopiles

Another major subgroup of the chromalveolates is the **stramenopiles**, protists that include some of the most important photosynthetic organisms on the planet, as well as several clades of heterotrophs. Their name (from the Latin *stramen*, straw, and *pilos*, hair) refers to their characteristic flagellum, which has numerous fine, hairlike projections. In most stramenopiles, this "hairy" flagellum is paired with a shorter "smooth" (nonhairy) flagellum (Figure 28.12). Here we'll focus on four groups of stramenopiles: diatoms, golden algae, brown algae, and oomycetes.

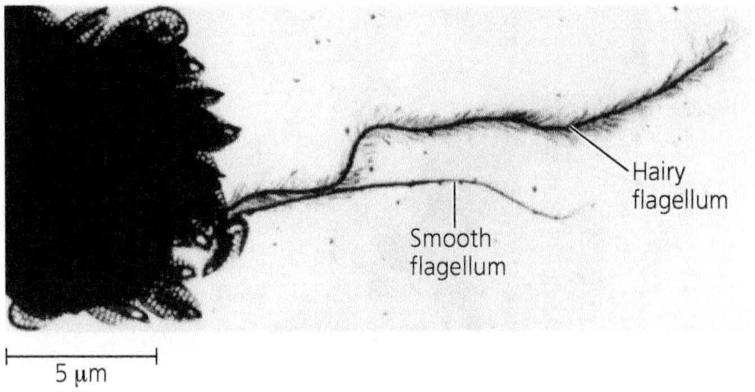

▲ Figure 28.12 **Stramenopile flagella.** Most stramenopiles, such as *Synura petersenii*, have two flagella: one covered with fine, stiff hairs and a shorter one that is smooth.

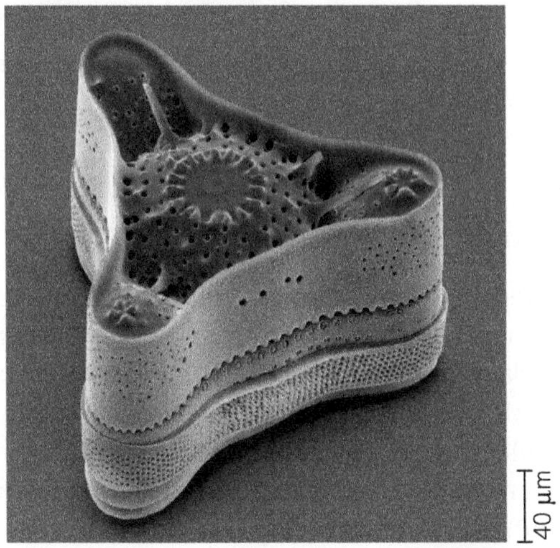

▲ Figure 28.13 **The diatom *Triceratium morlandii*** (colorized SEM).

Diatoms

Diatoms are unicellular algae that have a unique glass-like wall made of hydrated silica (silicon dioxide) embedded in an organic matrix. The wall consists of two parts that overlap like a shoe box and its lid. These walls provide effective protection from the crushing jaws of predators: Live diatoms can withstand pressures as great as 1.4 million kg/m^2, equal to the pressure under each leg of a table supporting an elephant! Much of the diatoms' strength comes from the delicate lacework of holes and grooves in their walls (Figure 28.13); if the walls were smooth, it would take 60% less force to crush them.

With an estimated 100,000 living species, diatoms are a highly diverse group of protists (see Figure 28.3). They are a major component of phytoplankton both in the ocean and in lakes: One bucket of water scooped from the surface of the sea may contain millions of these microscopic algae. The abundance of diatoms in the past is also evident in the fossil record, where massive accumulations of fossilized diatom walls are major constituents of sediments known as *diatomaceous earth*. These sediments are mined for their quality as a filtering medium and for many other uses.

You might expect that since diatoms are so widespread and abundant, their photosynthetic activity would affect global carbon dioxide levels, and this is indeed the case. Diatoms have this effect in part because of the chain of events that follows their rapid population growth (a bloom) when ample nutrients are available. Typically, diatoms are eaten by a variety of protists and invertebrates, but during a bloom, many escape this fate. When these uneaten diatoms die, their bodies sink to the ocean floor. Diatoms that sink to the ocean floor are not very likely to be broken down by bacteria and other decomposers. Hence, the carbon in their bodies remains there, rather than being released as carbon dioxide as the decomposers respire. The overall effect of these events is that carbon dioxide absorbed by diatoms during photosynthesis is transported, or "pumped," to the ocean floor. With an eye toward reducing global warming by lowering atmospheric carbon dioxide levels, some scientists advocate promoting diatom blooms by fertilizing the ocean with essential nutrients such as iron. Other scientists question this strategy, noting that small-scale tests of this idea have yielded mixed results and that it is difficult to predict the effects of large-scale manipulations of ecological communities.

▲ **Figure 28.14** ***Dinobryon*, a colonial golden alga found in fresh water** (LM).

▲ **Figure 28.15 Seaweeds: adapted to life at the ocean's margins.** The sea palm (*Postelsia*) lives on rocks along the coast of the northwestern United States and western Canada. The thallus of this brown alga is well adapted to maintaining a firm foothold despite the crashing surf.

Golden Algae

The characteristic color of **golden algae** results from their yellow and brown carotenoids. The cells of golden algae are typically biflagellated, with both flagella attached near one end of the cell.

Many golden algae are components of freshwater and marine plankton. While all golden algae are photosynthetic, some species are mixotrophic. These mixotrophs can absorb dissolved organic compounds or ingest food particles, including living cells, by phagocytosis. Most species are unicellular, but some, such as those in the freshwater genus *Dinobryon*, are colonial (Figure 28.14). If environmental conditions deteriorate, many species form protective cysts that can survive for decades.

Brown Algae

The largest and most complex algae are **brown algae**. All are multicellular, and most are marine. Brown algae are especially common along temperate coasts, where the water is cool. They owe their characteristic brown or olive color to the carotenoids in their plastids.

Many of the species commonly called "seaweeds" are brown algae. (Some large, multicellular species of red and green algae are also referred to as seaweeds. We will examine them later in this chapter.) Brown algae include species that have the most complex multicellular anatomy of all algae; some even have specialized tissues and organs that resemble those in plants. But morphological and DNA evidence indicates that the similarities evolved independently in the algal and plant lineages and are thus analogous, not homologous.

The term **thallus** (plural, *thalli*; from the Greek *thallos*, sprout) refers to an algal body that is plantlike. Unlike the body of a plant, however, a thallus lacks true roots, stems, and leaves. A typical thallus consists of a rootlike **holdfast**, which anchors the alga, and a stemlike **stipe**, which supports leaflike **blades** (Figure 28.15). The blades provide most of the alga's photosynthetic surface. Some brown algae are equipped with gas-filled, bubble-shaped floats, which help keep the blades up near the water surface. Beyond the intertidal zone in deeper waters live giant seaweeds known as kelps. The stipes of these brown algae may be as long as 60 m, more than half the length of a football field.

Brown algae that inhabit the intertidal zone must cope with water churned by waves and wind, along with low tides that expose the algae to the drying atmosphere and intense rays of the sun. Unique adaptations enable these seaweeds to survive. For example, their cell walls are composed of cellulose and gel-forming polysaccharides that help cushion the thalli from waves and reduce drying when the algae are exposed.

Brown algae are important commodities for humans. Some species are eaten, such as *Laminaria* (Japanese "kombu"), which is used in soups. In addition, the gel-forming substance in the cell walls of brown algae, called algin, is used to thicken many processed foods, including pudding and salad dressing.

Alternation of Generations

A variety of life cycles have evolved among the multicellular algae. The most complex life cycles include an **alternation of generations**, the alternation of multicellular haploid and diploid forms. Although haploid and diploid conditions alternate in *all* sexual life cycles—human gametes, for example, are haploid—the term *alternation of generations* applies only to life cycles in which both haploid and diploid stages are multicellular. As you will read in Chapter 29, alternation of generations also evolved in plants.

The complex life cycle of the brown alga *Laminaria* provides an example of alternation of generations (Figure 28.16). The diploid individual is called the *sporophyte* because it produces spores. The spores are haploid and move by means of flagella; they are called zoospores. The zoospores develop into haploid, multicellular male and female *gametophytes*, which produce gametes. The union of two gametes (fertilization, or syngamy) results in a diploid zygote, which matures and gives rise to a new multicellular sporophyte.

In *Laminaria*, the two generations are **heteromorphic**, meaning that the sporophytes and gametophytes are structurally different. Other algal life cycles have an alternation of **isomorphic** generations, in which the sporophytes and gametophytes look similar to each other, although they differ in chromosome number.

Oomycetes (Water Molds and Their Relatives)

Oomycetes include the water molds, the white rusts, and the downy mildews. Based on their morphology, these organisms were previously classified as fungi (in fact, *oomycete* means

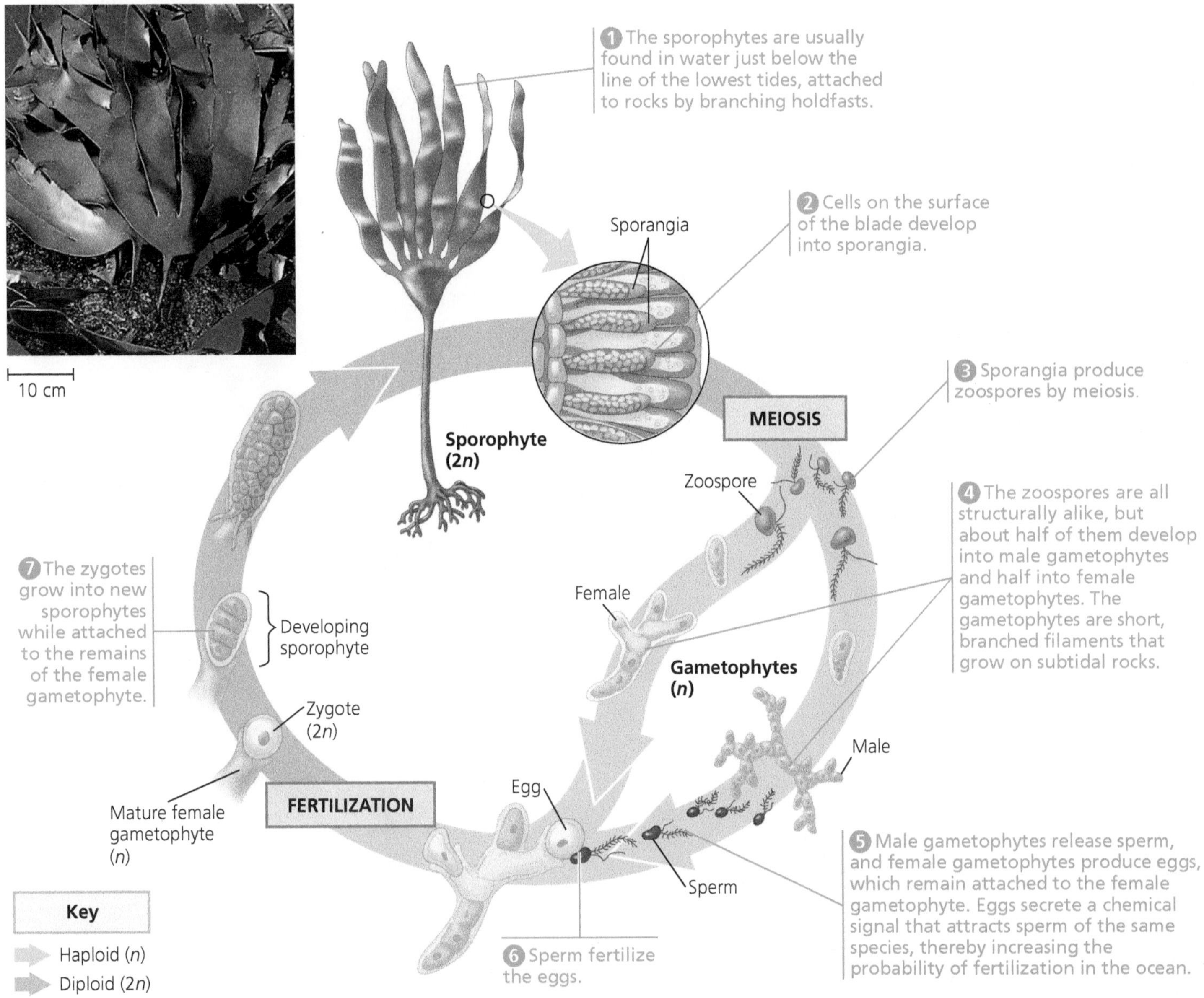

▲ **Figure 28.16 The life cycle of the brown alga *Laminaria*: an example of alternation of generations.**

? *Are the sperm shown in 5 genetically identical to one another? Are they genetically identical to the egg in 6? Explain.*

"egg fungus"). For example, many oomycetes have multinucleate filaments (hyphae) that resemble fungal hyphae (**Figure 28.17**). However, there are key differences between oomycetes and fungi. Among the differences, oomycetes typically have cell walls made of cellulose, whereas the walls of fungi consist mainly of another polysaccharide, chitin. Data from molecular systematics have confirmed that oomycetes are not closely related to fungi. Their superficial similarity is a case of convergent evolution. In both oomycetes and fungi, the high surface-to-volume ratio of filamentous structures enhances the uptake of nutrients from the environment.

Although oomycetes descended from plastid-bearing ancestors, they no longer have plastids and do not perform photosynthesis. Instead, they typically acquire nutrients as decomposers or parasites. Most water molds are decomposers that grow as cottony masses on dead algae and animals, mainly in freshwater habitats (see Figure 28.17). White rusts and downy mildews generally live on land as plant parasites.

The ecological impact of oomycetes can be significant. For example, the oomycete *Phytophthora infestans* causes potato late blight, which turns the stalk and stem of potato plants to black slime. Late blight contributed to the devastating Irish famine of the 19th century, in which a million people died and at least that many were forced to leave Ireland. The disease remains a major problem today, causing crop losses of typically 15% in North America and as high as 70% in some parts of Russia where farmers cannot afford pesticides.

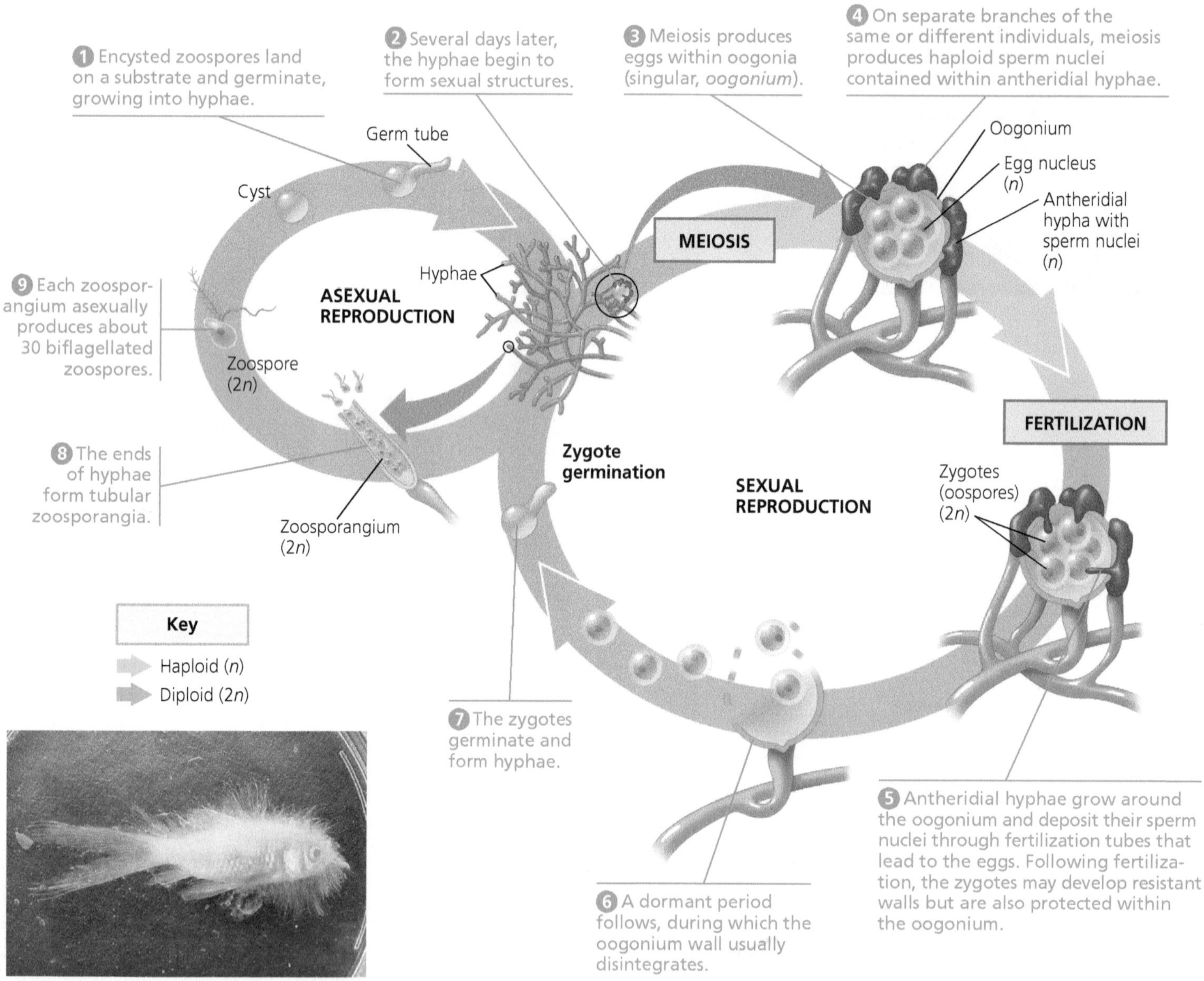

▲ **Figure 28.17 The life cycle of a water mold.** Water molds help decompose dead insects, fishes, and other animals in fresh water. (Note the hyphal mass growing on the goldfish in the photograph.)

To understand this pathogen better, molecular biologists have isolated DNA from a specimen of *P. infestans* preserved from the Irish potato blight of the 1840s. Genetic studies show that in recent decades, this oomycete has acquired genes that make it more aggressive and more resistant to pesticides. Scientists are looking within the genomes of both *Phytophthora* and potatoes to identify new weapons against the disease. Already, researchers have transferred genes from a blight-resistant strain of wild potato into domestic potatoes to produce a resistant crop strain.

CONCEPT CHECK 28.3

1. Summarize the evidence for and against the hypothesis that the species currently classified as chromalveolates are members of a single clade.
2. **WHAT IF?** Would you expect the plastid DNA of photosynthetic dinoflagellates, diatoms, and golden algae to be more similar to the nuclear DNA of plants (domain Eukarya) or to the chromosomal DNA of cyanobacteria (domain Bacteria)? Explain.
3. **MAKE CONNECTIONS** Which of the three life cycles in Figure 13.6 (p. 252) exhibits alternation of generations? How does it differ from the other two?

For suggested answers, see Appendix A.

CONCEPT 28.4

Rhizarians are a diverse group of protists defined by DNA similarities

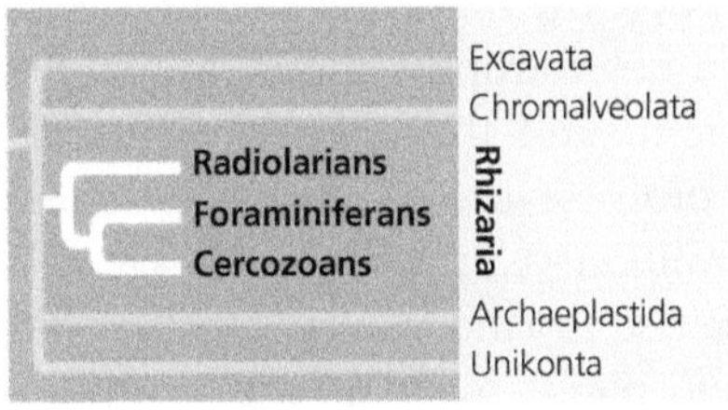

The clade **Rhizaria** has recently been proposed based on results from molecular systematics. Although its members vary greatly in morphology, DNA evidence suggests that rhizarians are a monophyletic group. According to some recent phylogenetic studies, Rhizaria should be nested within Chromalveolata, as discussed in Figure 28.3.

Many species in Rhizaria are among the organisms referred to as amoebas. **Amoebas** were formerly defined as protists that move and feed by means of **pseudopodia**, extensions that may bulge from almost anywhere on the cell surface. An amoeba moves by extending a pseudopodium and anchoring the tip; more cytoplasm then streams into the pseudopodium. However, based on molecular systematics, it is now clear that amoebas do not constitute a monophyletic group but are dispersed across many distantly related eukaryotic

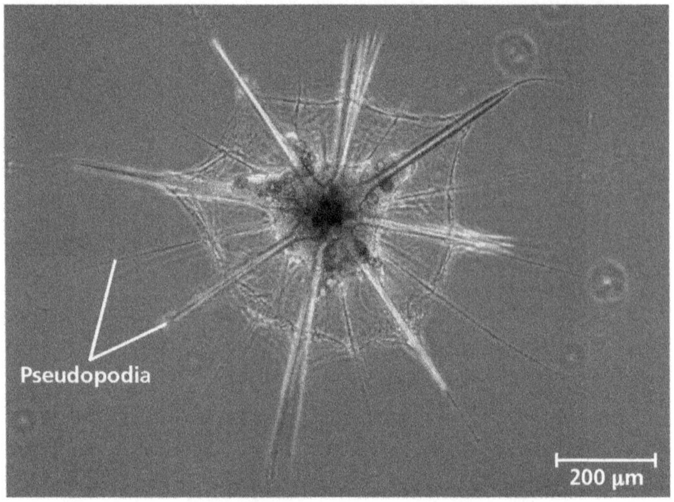

▲ **Figure 28.18 A radiolarian.** Numerous threadlike pseudopodia radiate from the central body of this radiolarian, which is found in the Red Sea (LM).

taxa. Most of those that belong to the clade Rhizaria are distinguished morphologically from other amoebas by having threadlike pseudopodia.

Rhizarians include three groups that we'll examine here: radiolarians, forams, and cercozoans.

Radiolarians

The protists called **radiolarians** have delicate, intricately symmetrical internal skeletons that are generally made of silica. The pseudopodia of these mostly marine protists radiate from the central body (Figure 28.18) and are reinforced by bundles of microtubules. The microtubules are covered by a thin layer of cytoplasm, which engulfs smaller microorganisms that become attached to the pseudopodia. Cytoplasmic streaming then carries the captured prey into the main part of the cell. After radiolarians die, their skeletons settle to the seafloor, where they have accumulated as an ooze that is hundreds of meters thick in some locations.

Forams

The protists called **foraminiferans** (from the Latin *foramen*, little hole, and *ferre*, to bear), or **forams**, are named for their porous shells, called **tests** (see Figure 28.3). Foram tests consist of a single piece of organic material hardened with calcium carbonate. The pseudopodia that extend through the pores function in swimming, test formation, and feeding. Many forams also derive nourishment from the photosynthesis of symbiotic algae that live within the tests.

Forams are found in both the ocean and fresh water. Most species live in sand or attach themselves to rocks or algae, but some are abundant in plankton. The largest forams, though single-celled, grow to a diameter of several centimeters.

Ninety percent of all identified species of forams are known from fossils. Along with the calcium-containing remains of other protists, the fossilized tests of forams are part of marine sediments, including sedimentary rocks that are now land formations. Foram fossils are excellent markers for correlating the ages of sedimentary rocks in different parts of the world.

Cercozoans

First identified in molecular phylogenies, the **cercozoans** form a large group that contains most of the amoeboid and flagellated protists that feed with threadlike pseudopodia. Cercozoan protists are common in marine, freshwater, and soil ecosystems.

Most cercozoans are heterotrophs. Many are parasites of plants, animals, or other protists; many others are predators. The predators include the most important consumers of bacteria in aquatic and soil ecosystems, along with species that eat other protists, fungi, and even small animals. One small group of cercozoans, the chlorarachniophytes (mentioned earlier in the discussion of secondary endosymbiosis), are mixotrophic: These organisms ingest smaller protists and bacteria as well as perform photosynthesis. At least one other cercozoan, *Paulinella chromatophora*, is an autotroph, deriving its energy from light and its carbon from carbon dioxide. This species has a distinctive sausage-shaped internal structure where photosynthesis is performed (Figure 28.19). Genetic and morphological analyses indicate that these structures were derived from a cyanobacterium, although not the same cyanobacterium from which all other plastids were derived. As such, *Paulinella* appears to represent an intriguing additional evolutionary example of a eukaryotic lineage that obtained its photosynthetic apparatus directly from a cyanobacterium.

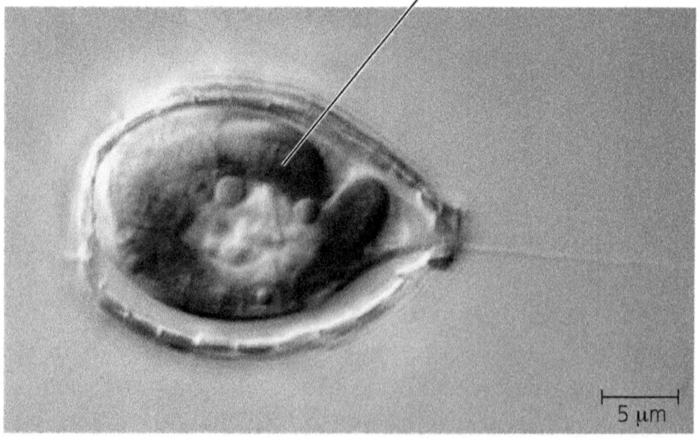

▲ **Figure 28.19 A second case of primary endosymbiosis?** The cercozoan *Paulinella* conducts photosynthesis in a unique structure called a chromatophore (LM). Chromatophores are surrounded by a membrane with a peptidoglycan layer, suggesting that they are derived from a bacterium. DNA evidence indicates that chromatophores are derived from a different cyanobacterium than that from which other plastids are derived.

CONCEPT CHECK 28.4

1. Explain why forams have such a well-preserved fossil record.
2. WHAT IF? Suppose DNA evidence suggests that a newly discovered amoeba is in the clade Rhizaria, yet its morphology is more similar to amoebas in other eukaryotic groups. Suggest an explanation that could account for these conflicting observations.
3. MAKE CONNECTIONS Review Figures 9.2 (p. 163) and 10.6 (p. 188), and then summarize how CO_2 and O_2 are both used and produced by chlorarachniophytes and other aerobic algae.

For suggested answers, see Appendix A.

CONCEPT 28.5

Red algae and green algae are the closest relatives of land plants

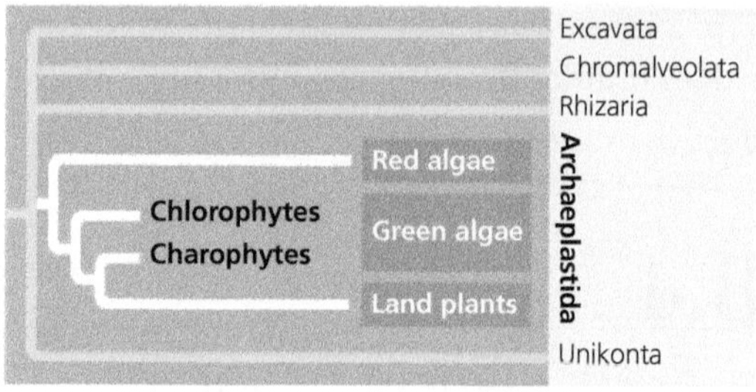

As we described in Chapter 25, molecular systematics and studies of cell structure support the following scenario: More than a billion years ago, a heterotrophic protist acquired a cyanobacterial endosymbiont, and the photosynthetic descendants of this ancient protist evolved into red algae and green algae. At least 475 million years ago, the lineage that produced green algae gave rise to land plants. Together, red algae, green algae, and land plants make up the fourth eukaryotic supergroup, which is called **Archaeplastida**. Archaeplastida is a monophyletic group that descended from the ancient protist that engulfed a cyanobacterium. We will examine land plants in Chapters 29 and 30; here we will look at the diversity of their closest algal relatives, red algae and green algae.

Red Algae

Many of the 6,000 known species of **red algae** (rhodophytes, from the Greek *rhodos*, red) are reddish, owing to a photosynthetic accessory pigment called phycoerythrin, which masks the green of chlorophyll (Figure 28.20). However, species adapted to more shallow water have less phycoerythrin. As a result, red algal species may be greenish red in very shallow

▲ **Figure 28.20 Red algae.**

water, bright red at moderate depths, and almost black in deep water. Some species lack pigmentation altogether and function heterotrophically as parasites on other red algae.

Red algae are the most abundant large algae in the warm coastal waters of tropical oceans. Their accessory pigments, including phycoerythrin, allow them to absorb blue and green light, which penetrate relatively far into the water. A species of red alga has been discovered near the Bahamas at a depth of more than 260 m. There are also a small number of freshwater and terrestrial species.

Most red algae are multicellular. Although none are as big as the giant brown kelps, the largest multicellular red algae are included in the informal designation "seaweeds." You may have eaten one of these multicellular red algae, *Porphyra* (Japanese "nori"), as crispy sheets or as a wrap for sushi (see Figure 28.20). Red algae have especially diverse life cycles, and alternation of generations is common. But unlike other algae, they have no flagellated stages in their life cycle and depend on water currents to bring gametes together for fertilization.

Green Algae

The grass-green chloroplasts of **green algae** have a structure and pigment composition much like the chloroplasts of land plants. Molecular systematics and cellular morphology leave little doubt that green algae and land plants are closely related. In fact, some systematists now advocate including green algae in an expanded "plant" kingdom, Viridiplantae (from the Latin *viridis*, green). Phylogenetically, this change makes sense, since otherwise the green algae are a paraphyletic group.

Green algae are divided into two main groups, the charophytes and the chlorophytes. The charophytes are the algae most closely related to land plants, and so we will discuss them along with plants in Chapter 29.

The second group, the chlorophytes (from the Greek *chloros*, green), includes more than 7,000 species. Most live in fresh water, but there are also many marine and some terrestrial species. The simplest chlorophytes are unicellular organisms such as *Chlamydomonas*, which resemble gametes or zoospores of more complex chlorophytes. Various species of unicellular chlorophytes live in aquatic habitats as phytoplankton or inhabit damp soil. Some live symbiotically within other eukaryotes, contributing part of their photosynthetic output to the food supply of their hosts. Some chlorophytes have even adapted to one of the last habitats you might expect to find them: snow. These chlorophytes carry out photosynthesis despite subfreezing temperatures and intense visible and ultraviolet radiation. They are protected by the snow itself, which acts as a shield, and by radiation-blocking compounds in their cytoplasm. Other chlorophytes contain similar protective compounds in their cell wall or in a durable coat that surrounds the zygote.

Larger size and greater complexity evolved in chlorophytes by three different mechanisms:

1. The formation of colonies of individual cells, as seen in *Volvox* (see Figure 28.3) and in filamentous forms that contribute to the stringy masses known as pond scum

2. The formation of true multicellular bodies by cell division and differentiation, as in *Ulva* (**Figure 28.21a**)
3. The repeated division of nuclei with no cytoplasmic division, as in *Caulerpa* (**Figure 28.21b**)

Most chlorophytes have complex life cycles, with both sexual and asexual reproductive stages. Nearly all species of chlorophytes reproduce sexually by means of biflagellated gametes that have cup-shaped chloroplasts (**Figure 28.22**). Alternation of generations has evolved in some chlorophytes, including *Ulva*.

(a) *Ulva*, or sea lettuce. This edible chlorophyte has a multicellular thallus differentiated into leaflike blades. Its rootlike holdfast anchors the alga.

(b) *Caulerpa*, an intertidal chlorophyte. The branched filaments lack cross-walls and thus are multinucleate. In effect, the thallus is one huge "supercell."

▲ **Figure 28.21 Multicellular chlorophytes.**

CONCEPT CHECK 28.5

1. Contrast red algae and brown algae.
2. Why is it accurate to say that *Ulva* is truly multicellular but *Caulerpa* is not?
3. **WHAT IF?** Suggest a possible reason why species in the green algal lineage may have been more likely to colonize land than species in the red algal lineage.

For suggested answers, see Appendix A.

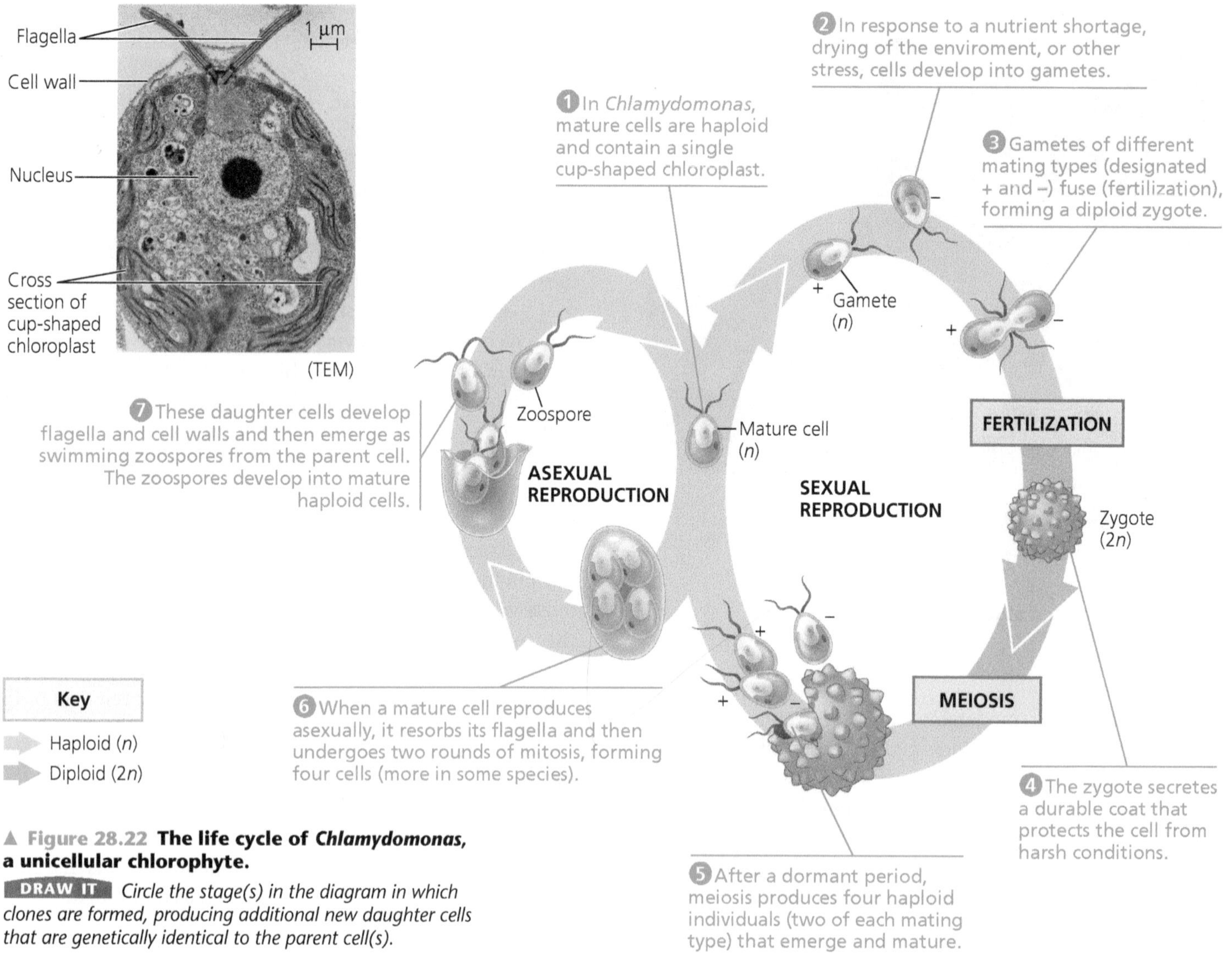

▲ **Figure 28.22 The life cycle of *Chlamydomonas*, a unicellular chlorophyte.**

DRAW IT *Circle the stage(s) in the diagram in which clones are formed, producing additional new daughter cells that are genetically identical to the parent cell(s).*

CONCEPT 28.6

Unikonts include protists that are closely related to fungi and animals

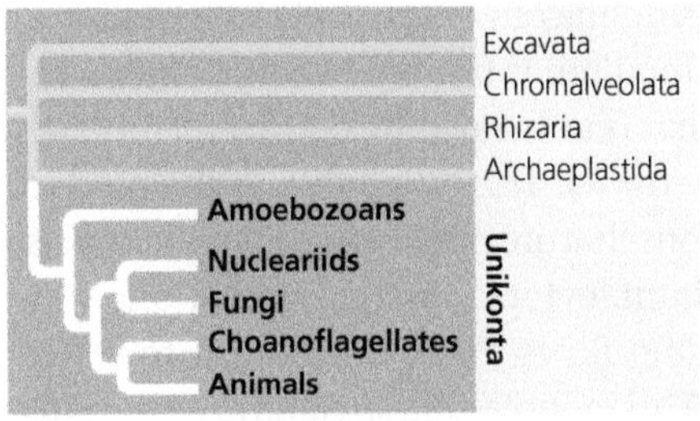

Unikonta is a recently proposed, extremely diverse supergroup of eukaryotes that includes animals, fungi, and some protists. There are two major clades of unikonts, the amoebozoans and the opisthokonts (animals, fungi, and closely related protist groups). Each of these two major clades is strongly supported by molecular systematics. The close relationship between amoebozoans and opisthokonts is more controversial. Support for this close relationship is provided by comparisons of myosin proteins and by several studies based on hundreds of genes, but not by other studies based on single genes.

Another controversy involving the unikonts concerns the root of the eukaryotic tree. Recall that the root of a phylogenetic tree anchors the tree in time: Branch points close to the root are the oldest. At present, the root of the eukaryotic tree is uncertain; thus, we do not know which group of eukaryotes was the first to diverge from other eukaryotes. Some hypotheses, such as the amitochondriate hypothesis described earlier, have been abandoned, but researchers have yet to agree on an alternative. If the root of the eukaryotic tree were known, scientists could infer characteristics of the common ancestor of all eukaryotes. Such information could help resolve some of the current debates about the five supergroups of eukaryotes.

In trying to determine the root of the eukaryotic tree, researchers have based their phylogenies on different sets of genes, producing conflicting results. Researchers at Oxford University have described a different approach, results from which support a radical new hypothesis about the root of the eukaryotic tree (Figure 28.23). According to their hypothesis, the unikonts were the first eukaryotes to diverge from other eukaryotes. This hypothesis proposes that animals and fungi belong to an early-diverging group of eukaryotes, while protists that lack typical mitochondria (such as the diplomonads and parabasalids) diverged much later in the history of life. This idea remains controversial and will require more supporting evidence to be widely accepted.

Amoebozoans

As already mentioned, **amoebozoans** form a clade that is well supported by molecular data. This clade includes many species

▼ Figure 28.23 **INQUIRY**

What is the root of the eukaryotic tree?

EXPERIMENT Responding to the difficulty in determining the root of the eukaryotic phylogenetic tree, Alexandra Stechmann and Thomas Cavalier-Smith, of Oxford University, proposed a new approach. They studied two genes, one for the enzyme dihydrofolate reductase (DHFR), the other for the enzyme thymidylate synthase (TS). Their approach took advantage of a rare evolutionary event: In some organisms, the DHFR and TS genes have fused, leading to the production of a single protein with both enzyme activities. Stechmann and Cavalier-Smith amplified (using PCR; see Figure 20.8) and sequenced DHFR and TS genes in nine species (one choanoflagellate; two amoebozoans; one euglenozoan; two chromalveolates; and three rhizarians). They combined their data with previously published data for species of bacteria, animals, plants, and fungi.

RESULTS The bacteria studied all have separate DHFR and TS genes, suggesting that this is the ancestral condition (red dot on the tree below). Other taxa with separate genes are denoted by red type. Fused genes are a derived character, found in certain members (blue type) of the supergroups Excavata, Chromalveolata, Rhizaria, and Archaeplastida:

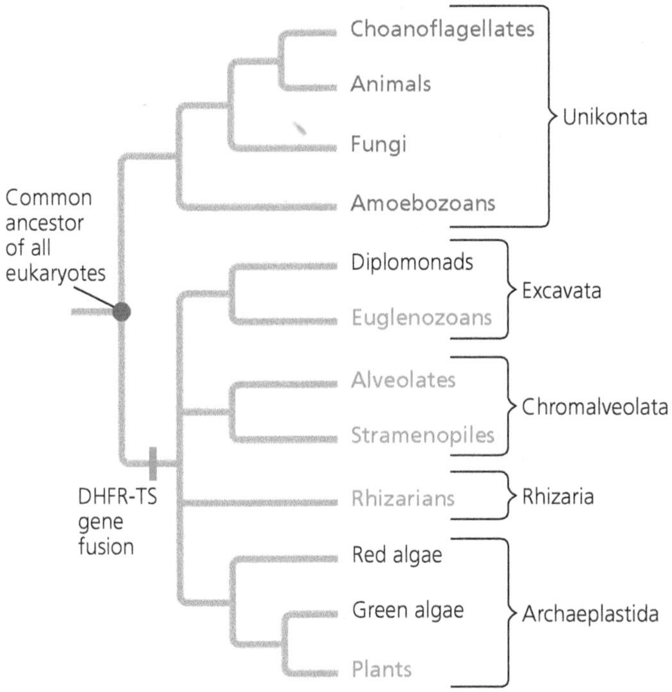

CONCLUSION These results support the hypothesis that the root of the tree is located between the unikonts and all other eukaryotes, suggesting that the unikonts were the first group of eukaryotes to diverge. Because support for this hypothesis is based on only one trait—the fusion of the DHFR and TS genes—more data are needed to evaluate its validity.

SOURCE A. Stechmann and T. Cavalier-Smith, Rooting the eukaryote tree by using a derived gene fusion, *Science* 297:89–91 (2002).

WHAT IF? Stechmann and Cavalier-Smith wrote that their conclusions are "valid only if the genes fused just once and were never secondarily split." Why is this assumption critical to their approach?

of amoebas that have lobe- or tube-shaped, rather than thread-like, pseudopodia. Amoebozoans include slime molds, gymnamoebas, and entamoebas.

Slime Molds

Slime molds, or mycetozoans (from the Latin, meaning "fungus animals"), were once thought to be fungi because, like fungi, they produce fruiting bodies that aid in spore dispersal. However, the resemblance between slime molds and fungi appears to be another example of evolutionary convergence. Molecular systematics places slime molds in Amoebozoa and suggests that they descended from unicellular ancestors. Slime molds have diverged into two main branches, plasmodial slime molds and cellular slime molds, distinguished in part by their unique life cycles.

Plasmodial Slime Molds Many **plasmodial slime molds** are brightly colored, often yellow or orange (Figure 28.24). At one stage in their life cycle, they form a mass called a **plasmodium**, which may grow to a diameter of many centimeters. (Don't confuse a slime mold's plasmodium with the genus *Plasmodium*, which includes the parasitic apicomplexan that causes malaria.) Despite its size, the plasmodium is not multicellular; it is a single mass of cytoplasm that is undivided by plasma membranes and that contains many nuclei. This "supercell" is the product of mitotic nuclear divisions that are not followed by cytokinesis.

Within the plasmodium, cytoplasm streams first one way, then the other, in pulsing flows that are beautiful to watch through a microscope. This cytoplasmic streaming apparently helps distribute nutrients and oxygen. The plasmodium extends pseudopodia through moist soil, leaf mulch, or rotting

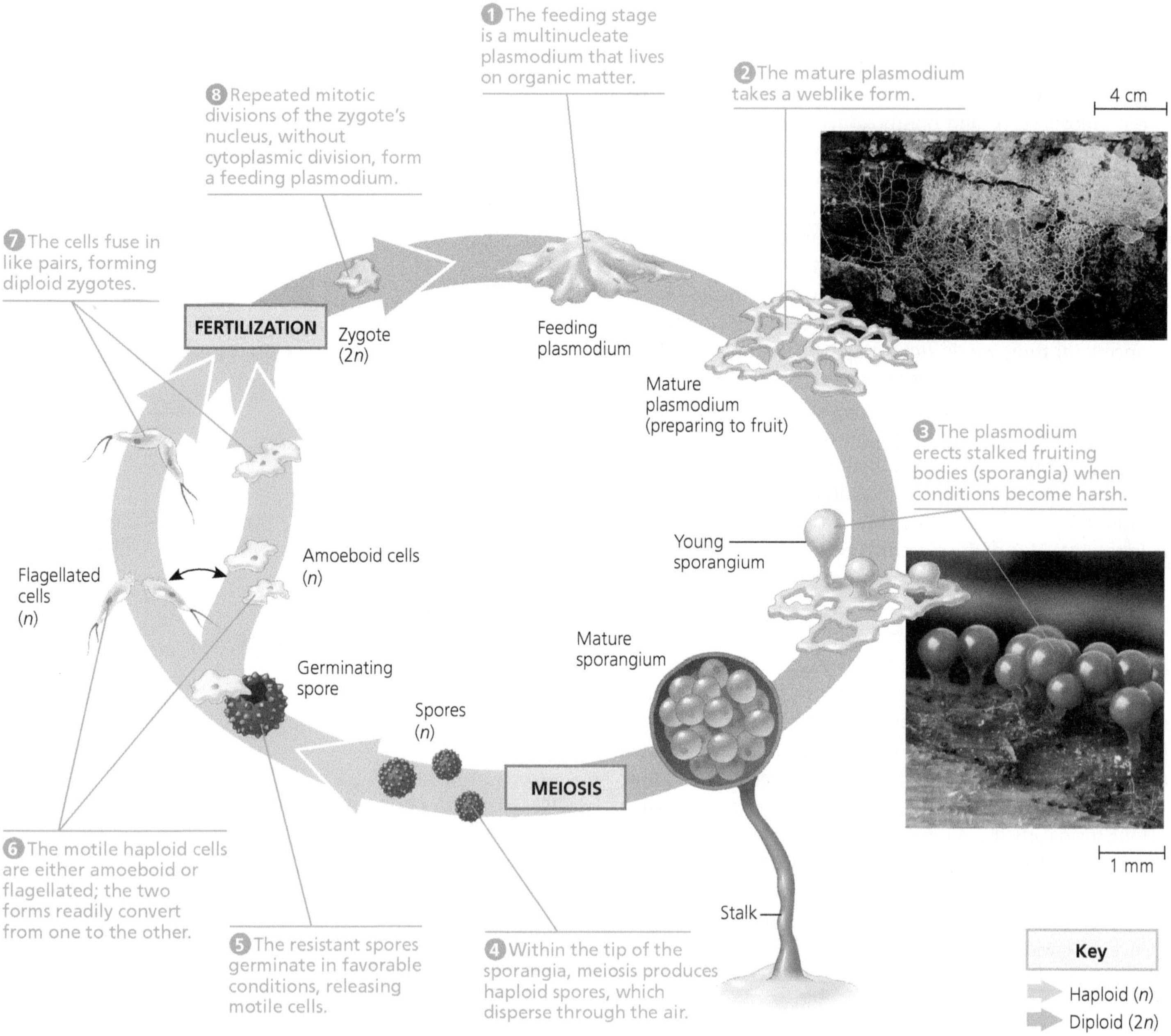

▲ Figure 28.24 **The life cycle of a plasmodial slime mold.**

logs, engulfing food particles by phagocytosis as it grows. If the habitat begins to dry up or there is no food left, the plasmodium stops growing and differentiates into fruiting bodies, which function in sexual reproduction.

Cellular Slime Molds The life cycle of the protists called **cellular slime molds** can prompt us to question what it means to be an individual organism. The feeding stage of these organisms consists of solitary cells that function individually, but when food is depleted, the cells form an aggregate that functions as a unit (**Figure 28.25**). Although this mass of cells superficially resembles a plasmodial slime mold, the cells remain separated by their individual plasma membranes. Cellular slime molds also differ from plasmodial slime molds in being haploid organisms (only the zygote is diploid) and in having fruiting bodies that function in asexual rather than sexual reproduction.

Dictyostelium discoideum, a cellular slime mold commonly found on forest floors, has become a model organism for studying the evolution of multicellularity. One line of research has focused on the slime mold's fruiting body stage. During this stage, the cells that form the stalk die as they dry out, while the spore cells at the top survive and have the potential to reproduce. Scientists have found that mutations in a single gene can turn individual *Dictyostelium* cells into "cheaters" that never become part of the stalk. Because these mutants gain a strong reproductive advantage over noncheaters, why don't all *Dictyostelium* cells cheat?

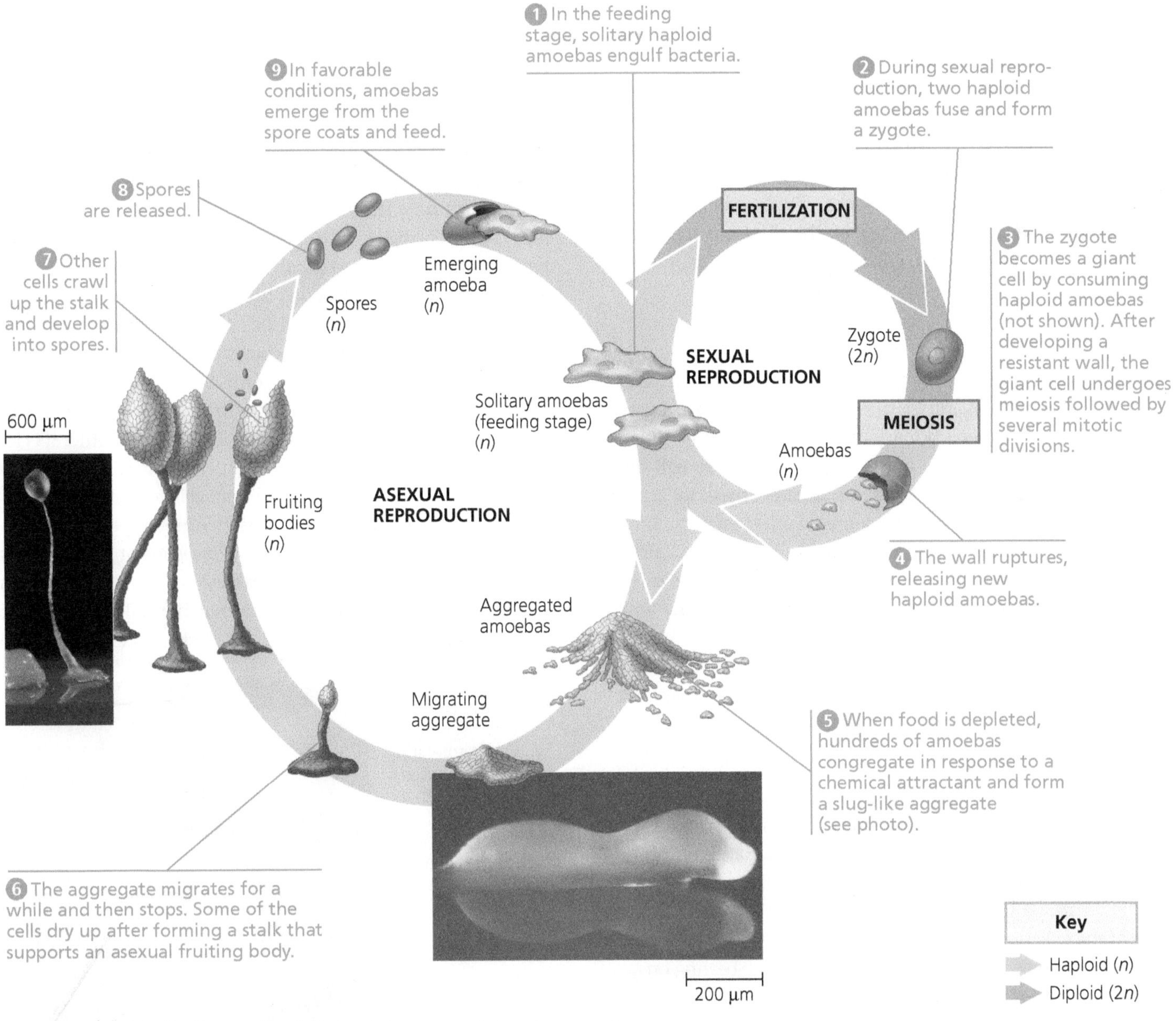

▲ **Figure 28.25 The life cycle of *Dictyostelium*, a cellular slime mold.**

Recent discoveries suggest an answer to this question. Cheating mutants lack a protein on their cell surface, and noncheating cells can recognize this difference. Noncheaters preferentially aggregate with other noncheaters, thus depriving cheaters of the opportunity to exploit them. Such a recognition system may have been important in the evolution of multicellular eukaryotes such as animals and plants.

Gymnamoebas

Gymnamoebas constitute a large and varied group of amoebozoans. These unicellular protists are ubiquitous in soil as well as freshwater and marine environments. Most are heterotrophs that actively seek and consume bacteria and other protists (see Figure 28.3). Some gymnamoebas also feed on detritus (nonliving organic matter).

Entamoebas

Whereas most amoebozoans are free-living, those that belong to the genus *Entamoeba* are parasites. They infect all classes of vertebrate animals as well as some invertebrates. Humans are host to at least six species of *Entamoeba*, but only one, *E. histolytica*, is known to be pathogenic. *E. histolytica* causes amebic dysentery and is spread via contaminated drinking water, food, or eating utensils. Responsible for up to 100,000 deaths worldwide every year, the disease is the third-leading cause of death due to eukaryotic parasites, after malaria (see Figure 28.10) and schistosomiasis (see Figure 33.11).

Opisthokonts

Opisthokonts are an extremely diverse group of eukaryotes that includes animals, fungi, and several groups of protists. We will discuss the evolutionary history of fungi and animals in Chapters 31–34. Of the opisthokont protists, we will discuss the nucleariids in Chapter 31 because they are more closely related to fungi than they are to other protists. Similarly, we will discuss choanoflagellates in Chapter 32, since they are more closely related to animals than they are to other protists. The nucleariids and choanoflagellates illustrate why scientists have abandoned the former kingdom Protista: A monophyletic group that included these single-celled eukaryotes would also have to include the multicellular animals and fungi that are closely related to them.

CONCEPT CHECK 28.6

1. Contrast the pseudopodia of amoebozoans and forams.
2. In what sense is "fungus animal" a fitting description of a slime mold? In what sense is it not fitting?
3. WHAT IF? If further evidence indicates that the root of the eukaryotic tree is as shown in Figure 28.23, would this evidence support, contradict, or have no bearing on the hypothesis that Excavata is monophyletic?

For suggested answers, see Appendix A.

CONCEPT 28.7

Protists play key roles in ecological communities

Most protists are aquatic, and they are found almost anywhere there is water, including moist terrestrial habitats such as damp soil and leaf litter. In oceans, ponds, and lakes, many protists are bottom-dwellers that attach to rocks and other substrates or creep through the sand and silt. Other protists are important constituents of plankton. We'll focus here on two key roles that protists play in the varied habitats in which they live: that of symbiont and that of producer.

Symbiotic Protists

Many protists form symbiotic associations with other species. For example, photosynthetic dinoflagellates are food-providing symbiotic partners of the coral polyps that build coral reefs. Coral reefs are highly diverse ecological communities. That diversity ultimately depends on corals—and on the mutualistic protist symbionts that nourish them. Corals support reef diversity by providing food to some species and habitat to many others.

Another example is the wood-digesting protists that inhabit the gut of many termite species (Figure 28.26). Unaided, termites cannot digest wood, and they rely on protistan or prokaryotic symbionts to do so. Termites cause over $3.5 billion in damage annually to wooden homes in the United States.

Symbiotic protists also include parasites that have compromised the economies of entire countries. Consider the malaria-causing protist *Plasmodium*: Income levels in countries hard hit by malaria are 33% lower than in similar countries free of the disease. Protists can have devastating effects on other species too. Massive fish kills have been attributed to *Pfiesteria shumwayae* (see Figure 28.9), a dinoflagellate parasite that attaches to its victims and eats their skin. Among species that parasitize plants, the oomycete protist *Phytophthora ramorum* has emerged as a major new forest pathogen. This species causes sudden oak death (SOD), a disease that has killed millions of oaks and other trees in California and Oregon (see Chapter 54).

▶ **Figure 28.26 A symbiotic protist.** This organism is a hypermastigote, a member of a group of parabasalids that live in the gut of termites and certain cockroaches and enable the hosts to digest wood (SEM).

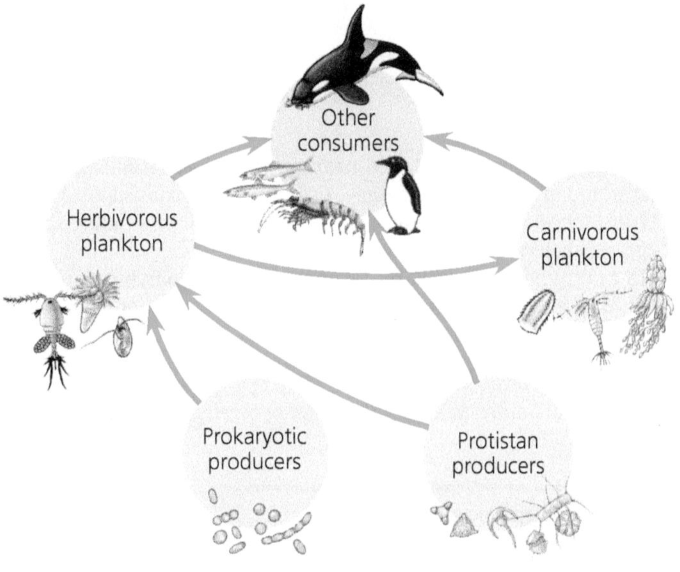

▲ **Figure 28.27 Protists: key producers in aquatic communities.** Arrows in this simplified food web lead from food sources to the organisms that eat them.

Photosynthetic Protists

Many protists are important **producers**, organisms that use energy from light (or inorganic chemicals) to convert carbon dioxide to organic compounds. Producers form the base of ecological food webs. In aquatic communities, the main producers are photosynthetic protists and prokaryotes. All other organisms in the community depend on them for food, either directly (by eating them) or indirectly (by eating an organism that ate a producer; Figure 28.27). Scientists estimate that roughly 30% of the world's photosynthesis is performed by diatoms, dinoflagellates, multicellular algae, and other aquatic protists. Photosynthetic prokaryotes contribute another 20%, and land plants are responsible for the remaining 50%.

Because producers form the foundation of food webs, factors that affect producers can dramatically affect their entire community. In aquatic environments, photosynthetic protists are often held in check by low concentrations of nitrogen, phosphorus, or iron. Various human actions can increase the concentrations of these elements in aquatic communities. For example, when fertilizer is applied to a field, some of the fertilizer may be washed by rainfall into a river that drains into a lake or ocean. When people add nutrients to aquatic communities in this or other ways, the abundance of photosynthetic protists can increase spectacularly. Such increases can alter the abundance of other species in the community, as we'll see in Chapter 55.

A pressing question is how global warming will affect protists and other producers. Satellite data indicate that the growth and biomass of photosynthetic protists and prokaryotes have declined in many regions as sea surface temperatures have increased (Figure 28.28). If sustained, these changes would likely have far-reaching effects on marine ecosystems, fishery yields, and the global carbon cycle (see Chapter 55). Global warming can also affect producers on land, but there the base of food webs is occupied not by protists but by land plants, which we will discuss in Chapters 29 and 30.

▼ **Figure 28.28**

IMPACT

Marine Protists in a Warmer World

Photosynthetic protists are important components of marine food webs, each day converting millions of tons of carbon in CO_2 to organic molecules on which other organisms depend. How has global warming affected these key marine producers? Satellite data indicate that the growth and biomass of marine producers are negatively correlated to sea surface temperature (SST) across much of the tropical and midlatitude oceans (between the heavy black lines on the map below). In regions where SSTs have risen and growth has declined, the available nutrient supply may have been reduced by the formation of a light, warm layer of water that acts as a barrier preventing the rise, or upwelling, of cold, nutrient-rich waters from below.

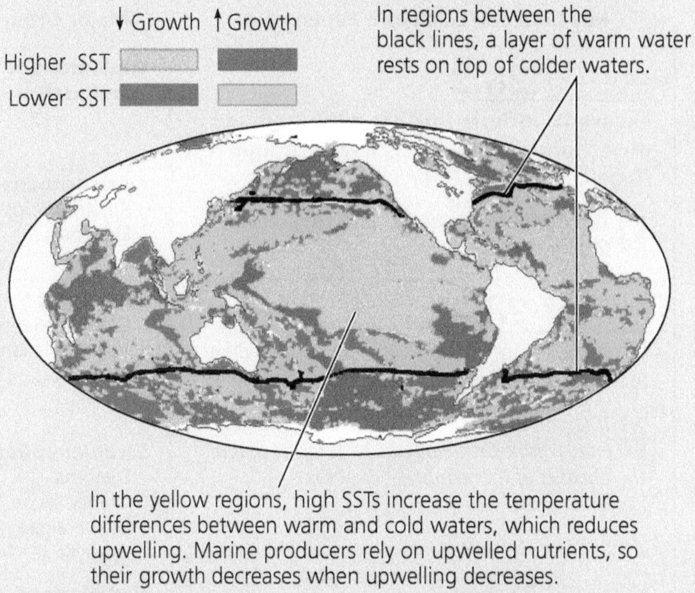

WHY IT MATTERS Major changes to marine ecosystems are expected if the growth and biomass of producers decrease as SSTs increase due to global warming. A decrease in diatom biomass, for example, would likely reduce both the amount of carbon pumped to the ocean floor and the catch of economically important fishes such as salmon and anchovies that feed on phytoplankton.

FURTHER READING M. J. Behrenfeld et al., Climate-driven trends in contemporary ocean productivity, *Nature* 444:752–755 (2006).

WHAT IF? If diatom populations continue to drop as the oceans warm, how might climate be affected in the future?

CONCEPT CHECK 28.7

1. Justify the claim that photosynthetic protists are among the biopshere's most important organisms.
2. Describe three symbioses that include protists.
3. **WHAT IF?** High water temperatures and pollution can cause corals to expel their dinoflagellate symbionts. Predict how such "coral bleaching" would affect corals and other species in the community.

For suggested answers, see Appendix A.

28 CHAPTER REVIEW

SUMMARY OF KEY CONCEPTS

CONCEPT 28.1

Most eukaryotes are single-celled organisms (pp. 575–579)

- Protists are more diverse than all other eukaryotes and are no longer classified in a single kingdom. Most are unicellular. Protists include photoautotrophs, heterotrophs, and mixotrophs. Protists are characterized by a wide diversity of life cycles.
- Mitochondria and plastids are thought to be descendants of bacteria that were engulfed by other cells and became endosymbionts. The plastid-bearing lineage eventually evolved into red algae and green algae. Other protist groups evolved from secondary endosymbiosis events in which red algae or green algae were themselves engulfed.
- In one hypothesis, eukaryotes are grouped into five supergroups, each a monophyletic clade: Excavata, Chromalveolata, Rhizaria, Archaeplastida, and Unikonta.

? *Describe similarities and differences between protists and other eukaryotes.*

Key Concept/Eukaryote Supergroup	Major Groups	Key Morphological Characteristics	Specific Examples
CONCEPT 28.2 Excavates include protists with modified mitochondria and protists with unique flagella (pp. 580–581) **?** *What evidence indicates that the excavates form a clade?*	**Diplomonads and parabasalids**	Modified mitochondria	*Giardia, Trichomonas* 
	Euglenozoans Kinetoplastids Euglenids	Spiral or crystalline rod inside flagella	*Trypanosoma, Euglena* 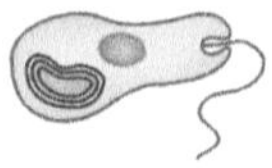
CONCEPT 28.3 Chromalveolates may have originated by secondary endosymbiosis (pp. 582–589) **?** *If Chromalveolata originated by secondary endosymbiosis, what can be inferred about the plastids of its members? Explain.*	**Alveolates** Dinoflagellates Apicomplexans Ciliates	Membrane-bounded sacs (alveoli) beneath plasma membrane	*Pfiesteria, Plasmodium, Paramecium* 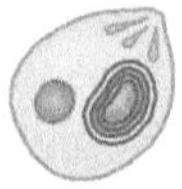
	Stramenopiles Diatoms Golden algae Brown algae Oomycetes	Hairy and smooth flagella	*Phytophthora, Laminaria* 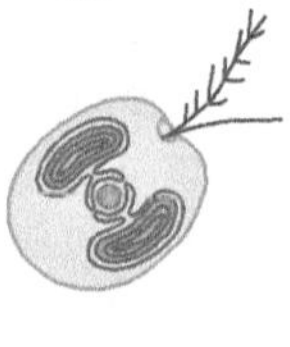
CONCEPT 28.4 Rhizarians are a diverse group of protists defined by DNA similarities (pp. 589–590) **?** *What are the main subgroups of rhizarians, and what unites these subgroups as a clade?*	**Radiolarians**	Amoebas with threadlike pseudopodia radiating from central body	*Hexacontium* 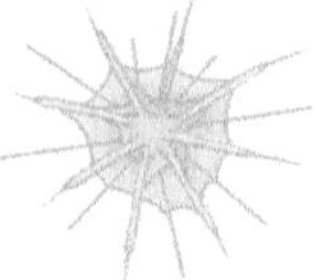
	Forams	Amoebas with threadlike pseudopodia and a porous shell	*Globigerina* 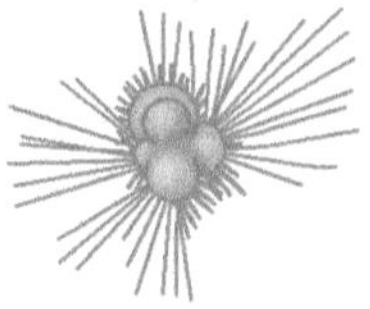
	Cercozoans	Amoebas and flagellated protists with threadlike pseudopodia	*Paulinella*
CONCEPT 28.5 Red algae and green algae are the closest relatives of land plants (pp. 590–592) (Archaeplastida) **?** *On what basis do some systematists place land plants in the same supergroup (Archaeplastida) as red and green algae?*	**Red algae**	Phycoerythrin (accessory pigment)	*Porphyra* 
	Green algae	Plant-type chloroplasts	*Chlamydomonas, Ulva* 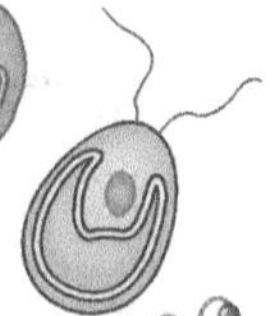
	Land plants	(See Chapters 29 and 30.)	Mosses, ferns, conifers, flowering plants 
CONCEPT 28.6 Unikonts include protists that are closely related to fungi and animals (pp. 593–596) **?** *Describe a key feature for each of the main protist subgroups of Unikonta.*	**Amoebozoans** Slime molds Gymnamoebas Entamoebas	Amoebas with lobe-shaped pseudopodia	*Amoeba, Entamoeba, Dictyostelium* 
	Opisthokonts	(Highly variable; see Chapters 31–34.)	Nucleariids, choanoflagellates, animals, fungi 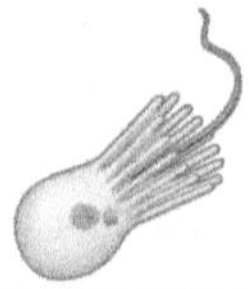

CONCEPT 28.7

Protists play key roles in ecological communities (pp. 596–597)

- Protists form a wide range of mutualistic and parasitic relationships that affect their symbiotic partners and many other members of the community.
- Photosynthetic protists are among the most important producers in aquatic communities. Because they are at the base of the food web, factors that affect photosynthetic protists affect many other species in the community.

? *Describe several protists that are ecologically important.*

TEST YOUR UNDERSTANDING

LEVEL 1: KNOWLEDGE/COMPREHENSION

1. Plastids that are surrounded by more than two membranes are evidence of
   a. evolution from mitochondria.
   b. fusion of plastids.
   c. origin of the plastids from archaea.
   d. secondary endosymbiosis.
   e. budding of the plastids from the nuclear envelope.

2. Biologists suspect that endosymbiosis gave rise to mitochondria before plastids partly because
   a. the products of photosynthesis could not be metabolized without mitochondrial enzymes.
   b. all eukaryotes have mitochondria (or their remnants), whereas many eukaryotes do not have plastids.
   c. mitochondrial DNA is less similar to prokaryotic DNA than is plastid DNA.
   d. without mitochondrial CO_2 production, photosynthesis could not occur.
   e. mitochondrial proteins are synthesized on cytosolic ribosomes, whereas plastids utilize their own ribosomes.

3. Which group is *incorrectly* paired with its description?
   a. rhizarians—morphologically diverse group defined by DNA similarities
   b. diatoms—important producers in aquatic communities
   c. red algae—acquired plastids by secondary endosymbiosis
   d. apicomplexans—parasites with intricate life cycles
   e. diplomonads—protists with modified mitochondria

4. Which protists are in the same eukaryotic supergroup as land plants?
   a. green algae
   b. dinoflagellates
   c. red algae
   d. brown algae
   e. both a and c

5. In life cycles with an alternation of generations, multicellular haploid forms alternate with
   a. unicellular haploid forms.
   b. unicellular diploid forms.
   c. multicellular haploid forms.
   d. multicellular diploid forms.
   e. multicellular polyploid forms.

LEVEL 2: APPLICATION/ANALYSIS

6. Based on the phylogenetic tree in Figure 28.3, which of the following statements is correct?
   a. The most recent common ancestor of Excavata is older than that of Chromalveolata.
   b. The most recent common ancestor of Chromalveolata is older than that of Rhizaria.
   c. The most recent common ancestor of red algae and land plants is older than that of nucleariids and fungi.
   d. The most basal (first to diverge) eukaryotic supergroup cannot be determined.
   e. Excavata is the most basal eukaryotic supergroup.

7. **EVOLUTION CONNECTION**
   DRAW IT Medical researchers seek to develop drugs that can kill or restrict the growth of human pathogens yet have few harmful effects on patients. These drugs often work by disrupting the metabolism of the pathogen or by targeting its structural features.
   Draw and label a phylogenetic tree that includes an ancestral prokaryote and the following groups of organisms: Excavata, Chromalveolata, Rhizaria, Archaeplastida, Unikonta, and, within Unikonta, amoebozoans, animals, choanoflagellates, fungi, and nucleariids. Based on this tree, hypothesize whether it would be most difficult to develop drugs to combat human pathogens that are prokaryotes, protists, animals, or fungi. (You do not need to consider the evolution of drug resistance by the pathogen.)

LEVEL 3: SYNTHESIS/EVALUATION

8. **SCIENTIFIC INQUIRY**
   Applying the "If . . . then" logic of science (see Chapter 1), what are a few of the predictions that arise from the hypothesis that plants evolved from green algae? Put another way, how could you test this hypothesis?

9. **WRITE ABOUT A THEME**
   Ecological Interactions Organisms interact with each other and the physical environment. In a short essay (100–150 words), explain how the response of diatom populations to a drop in nutrient availability can affect both other organisms and aspects of the physical environment (such as carbon dioxide concentrations).

For selected answers, see Appendix A.

29

Plant Diversity I: How Plants Colonized Land

▲ Figure 29.1 **How did plants change the world?**

EVOLUTION

KEY CONCEPTS

29.1 Land plants evolved from green algae
29.2 Mosses and other nonvascular plants have life cycles dominated by gametophytes
29.3 Ferns and other seedless vascular plants were the first plants to grow tall

OVERVIEW

The Greening of Earth

Looking at a lush landscape, such as the forest scene in Figure 29.1, it is difficult to imagine the terrestrial environment without any plants or other organisms. Yet for more than 3 billion years of Earth's history, the land surface was largely lifeless. Geochemical evidence suggests that thin coatings of cyanobacteria existed on land about 1.2 billion years ago. But it was only within the last 500 million years that small plants as well as fungi and animals joined them ashore. Finally, by about 385 million years ago, some plants appeared that could grow much taller, leading to the formation of the first forests (though with a very different set of species than those in Figure 29.1).

Since colonizing land, plants have diversified widely; today, there are more than 290,000 known plant species. Plants inhabit all but the harshest environments, such as some mountaintops, a few desert areas, and the polar regions. A few plant species, such as seagrasses, returned to aquatic habitats during their evolution, but most present-day plants live in terrestrial environments. In this chapter, we'll refer to all plants as *land* plants, even those that are now aquatic, to distinguish them from algae, which are photosynthetic protists.

The presence of land plants has enabled other life-forms—including animals—to survive on land. Plants supply oxygen and ultimately most of the food eaten by terrestrial animals. Also, plant roots create habitats for other organisms by stabilizing the soil in sand dunes and many other environments.

This chapter traces the first 100 million years of plant evolution, including the emergence of seedless plants such as mosses and ferns. Chapter 30 examines the later evolution of seed plants.

CONCEPT **29.1**

Land plants evolved from green algae

As you read in Chapter 28, researchers have identified green algae called charophytes as the closest relatives of land plants. What is the evidence for this relationship, and what does it suggest about the algal ancestors of land plants?

Morphological and Molecular Evidence

Many key traits of land plants also appear in some protists, primarily algae. For example, plants are multicellular, eukaryotic, photosynthetic autotrophs, as are brown, red, and certain green algae. Plants have cell walls made of cellulose, and so do green algae, dinoflagellates, and brown algae. And chloroplasts with chlorophylls *a* and *b* are present in green algae, euglenids, and a few dinoflagellates, as well as in plants.

However, the charophytes are the only algae that share the following four distinctive traits with land plants, strongly suggesting that they are the closest relatives of plants:

- **Rings of cellulose-synthesizing proteins.** The cells of both land plants and charophytes have distinctive circular rings of proteins in the plasma membrane (Figure 29.2). These protein rings synthesize the cellulose microfibrils of the cell wall. In contrast, noncharophyte algae have linear sets of proteins that synthesize cellulose.
- **Peroxisome enzymes.** The peroxisomes (see Figure 6.19) of both land plants and charophytes contain enzymes that help minimize the loss of organic products resulting from photorespiration (see Chapter 10).

▶ **Figure 29.2 Rings of cellulose-synthesizing proteins.** These circular sets of proteins embedded in the plasma membrane are found only in land plants and charophyte algae (SEM).

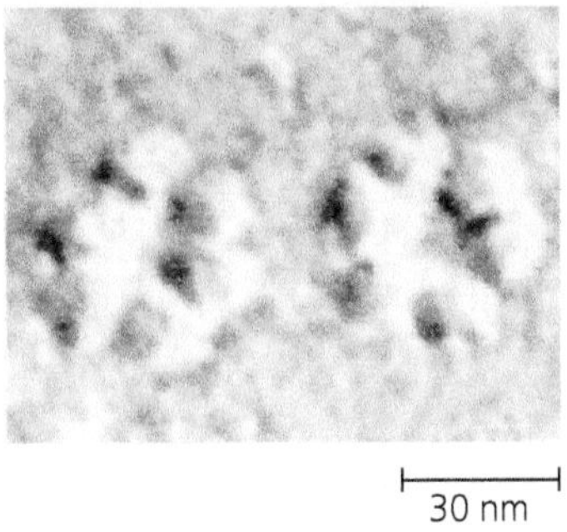

- **Structure of flagellated sperm.** In species of land plants that have flagellated sperm, the structure of the sperm closely resembles that of charophyte sperm.
- **Formation of a phragmoplast.** Particular details of cell division occur only in land plants and certain charophytes, including the genera *Chara* and *Coleochaete*. For example, in land plants and certain charophytes, a group of microtubules known as the **phragmoplast** forms between the daughter nuclei of a dividing cell. A cell plate then develops in the middle of the phragmoplast, across the midline of the dividing cell (see Figure 12.10). The cell plate, in turn, gives rise to a new cross wall that separates the daughter cells.

Genetic evidence also supports the conclusion drawn from these four morphological and biochemical traits. Analyses of nuclear and chloroplast genes from a wide range of plants and algae indicate that charophytes—particularly *Chara* and *Coleochaete*—are the closest living relatives of land plants (Figure 29.3). Note that this does not mean that plants are descended from these living algae; however, present-day charophytes may tell us something about what the algal ancestors of plants were like.

Adaptations Enabling the Move to Land

Many species of charophyte algae inhabit shallow waters around the edges of ponds and lakes, where they are subject to occasional drying. In such environments, natural selection favors individual algae that can survive periods when they are not submerged in water. In charophytes, a layer of a durable polymer called **sporopollenin** prevents exposed zygotes from drying out. A similar chemical adaptation is found in the tough sporopollenin walls that encase the spores of plants.

The accumulation of such traits by at least one population of charophyte ancestors probably enabled their descendants—the first land plants—to live permanently above the waterline. These evolutionary novelties opened a new frontier: a terrestrial habitat that offered enormous benefits. The bright sunlight was unfiltered by water and plankton; the atmosphere offered more plentiful carbon dioxide than did water; the soil by the water's edge was rich in some mineral nutrients; and initially there were relatively few herbivores and pathogens. But these benefits were accompanied by challenges: a relative scarcity of water and a lack of structural support against gravity. (To appreciate why such support is important, picture how the soft body of a jellyfish sags when taken out of water.) Land plants diversified as adaptations evolved that enabled plants to thrive despite these challenges.

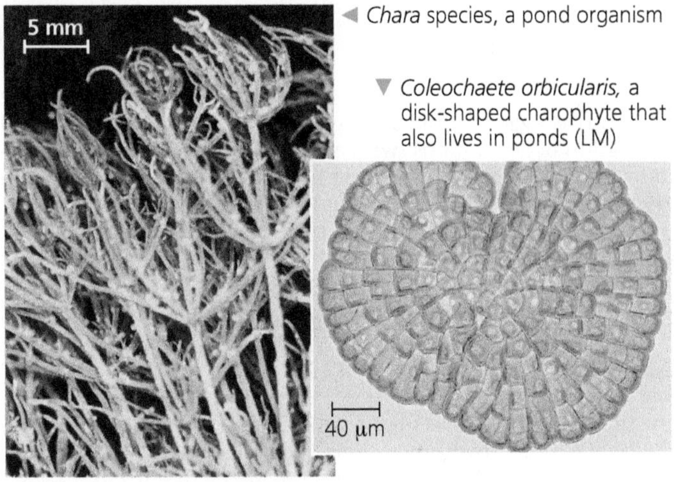

◀ *Chara* species, a pond organism

▼ *Coleochaete orbicularis*, a disk-shaped charophyte that also lives in ponds (LM)

▲ **Figure 29.3 Examples of charophytes, the closest algal relatives of land plants.**

Today, what adaptations are unique to plants? The answer to this question depends on where you draw the boundary dividing land plants from algae (Figure 29.4). Many biologists equate the kingdom Plantae with embryophytes (plants with embryos). Others propose that the boundaries of the plant kingdom should be expanded to include some or all of the green algae (kingdoms Streptophyta and Viridiplantae). Since the debate is ongoing, this text retains the embryophyte definition of the plant kingdom and uses Plantae as the formal name for the taxon. In this context, let's now identify the derived traits that separate land plants from their closest algal relatives.

Derived Traits of Plants

Many of the adaptations that appear to have emerged after land plants diverged from their algal relatives facilitated survival and reproduction on dry land. Figure 29.5, on the next two pages, depicts four key traits that appear in land plants but not in the charophyte algae.

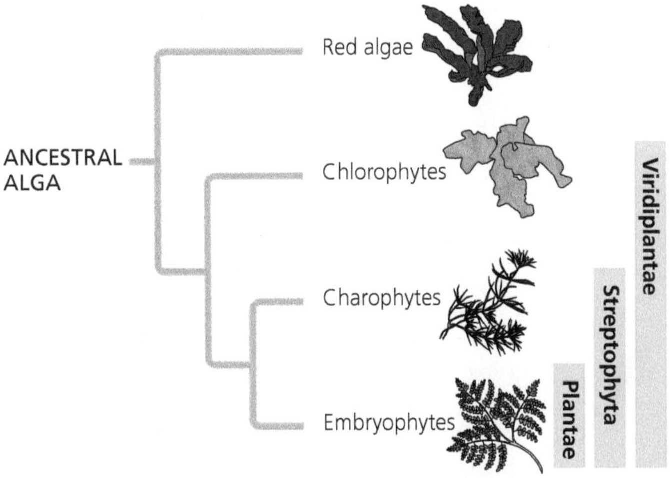

▲ **Figure 29.4 Three possible "plant" kingdoms.**

▼ Figure 29.5

Exploring Derived Traits of Land Plants

Charophyte algae lack the four key traits of land plants described in this figure: alternation of generations (with an associated trait of multicellular, dependent embryos), walled spores produced in sporangia, multicellular gametangia, and apical meristems. This suggests that these four traits were absent in the ancestor common to land plants and charophytes but instead evolved as derived traits of land plants. Note that some of these traits are not unique to plants, having evolved independently in other lineages. And not every land plant exhibits all four of these traits; certain lineages of plants have lost some traits over time.

Alternation of Generations and Multicellular, Dependent Embryos

Alternation of generations: five generalized steps

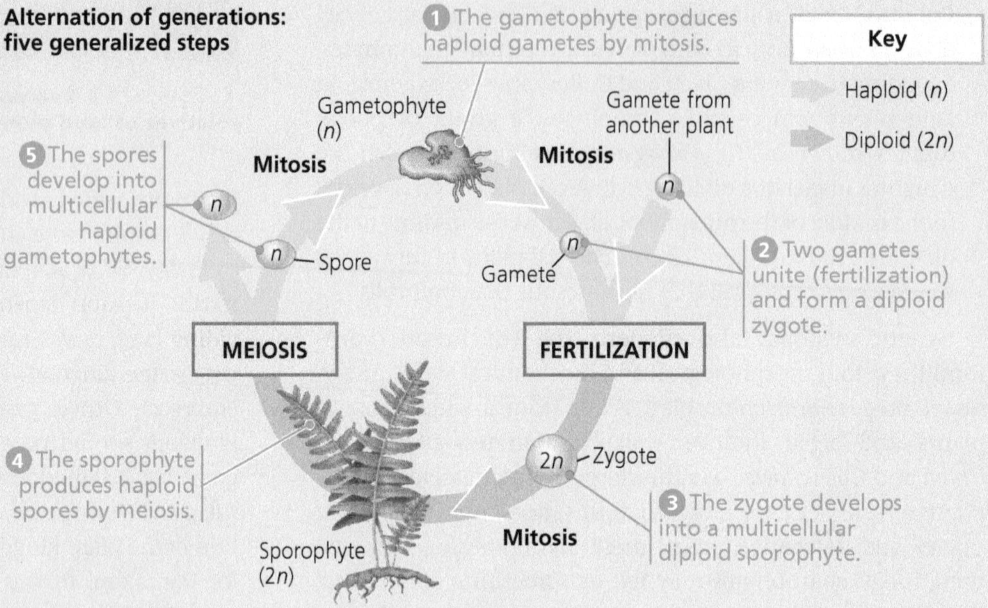

The life cycles of all land plants alternate between two generations of multicellular organisms: gametophytes and sporophytes. As shown in the diagram (using a fern as an example), each generation gives rise to the other, a process that is called **alternation of generations**. This type of reproductive cycle evolved in various groups of algae but does not occur in the charophytes, the algae most closely related to land plants.

Take care not to confuse the alternation of generations in plants with the haploid and diploid stages in the life cycles of other sexually reproducing organisms (see Figure 13.6). In humans, for example, meiosis produces haploid gametes that unite, forming diploid zygotes that divide and become multicellular. The haploid stage is represented only by single-celled gametes. In contrast, alternation of generations is distinguished by the fact that the life cycle includes both multicellular haploid organisms and multicellular diploid organisms. The multicellular haploid **gametophyte** ("gamete-producing plant") is named for its production by mitosis of haploid gametes—eggs and sperm—that fuse during fertilization, forming diploid zygotes. Mitotic division of the zygote produces a multicellular diploid **sporophyte** ("spore-producing plant"). Meiosis in a mature sporophyte produces haploid **spores**, reproductive cells that can develop into a new haploid organism without fusing with another cell. Mitotic division of the spore cell produces a new multicellular gametophyte, and the cycle begins again. In many seedless plants, such as the fern in the diagram, the gametophyte and sporophyte look like different types of plants, even though they are forms of the same species. In seed plants, the gametophytes are microscopic; the familiar plants we see are the sporophytes.

Embryo (LM) and placental transfer cell (TEM) of *Marchantia* (a liverwort)

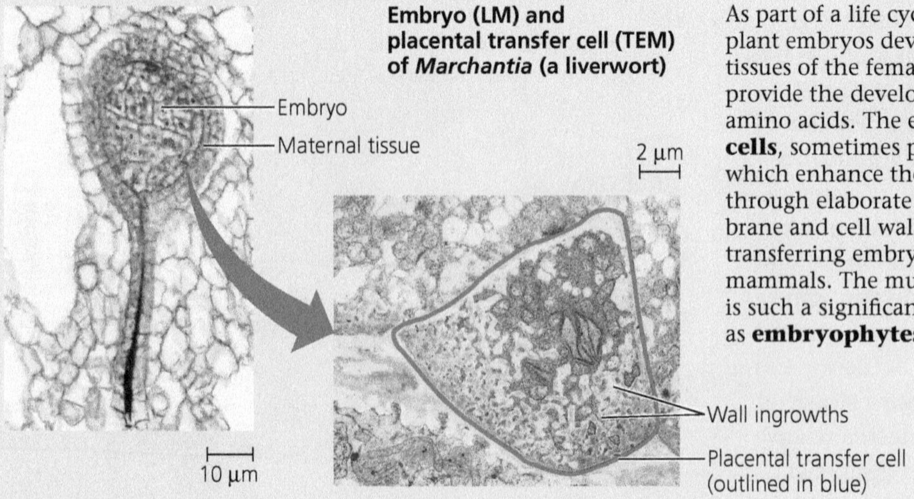

As part of a life cycle with alternation of generations, multicellular plant embryos develop from zygotes that are retained within the tissues of the female parent (a gametophyte). The parental tissues provide the developing embryo with nutrients, such as sugars and amino acids. The embryo has specialized **placental transfer cells**, sometimes present in the adjacent maternal tissue as well, which enhance the transfer of nutrients from parent to embryo through elaborate ingrowths of the wall surface (plasma membrane and cell wall). This interface is analogous to the nutrient-transferring embryo-mother interface of eutherian (placental) mammals. The multicellular, dependent embryo of land plants is such a significant derived trait that land plants are also known as **embryophytes**.

MAKE CONNECTIONS *Review sexual life cycles in Figure 13.6 on p. 252. Identify which life cycle has alternation of generations, and summarize how it differs from other life cycles.*

Walled Spores Produced in Sporangia

Plant spores are haploid reproductive cells that can grow into multicellular haploid gametophytes by mitosis. The polymer sporopollenin makes the walls of plant spores tough and resistant to harsh environments. This chemical adaptation enables spores to be dispersed through dry air without harm.

The sporophyte has multicellular organs called **sporangia** (singular, *sporangium*) that produce the spores. Within a sporangium, diploid cells called **sporocytes**, or spore mother cells, undergo meiosis and generate the haploid spores. The outer tissues of the sporangium protect the developing spores until they are released into the air. Multicellular sporangia that produce spores with sporopollenin-enriched walls are key terrestrial adaptations of land plants. Although charophytes also produce spores, these algae lack multicellular sporangia, and their flagellated, water-dispersed spores lack sporopollenin.

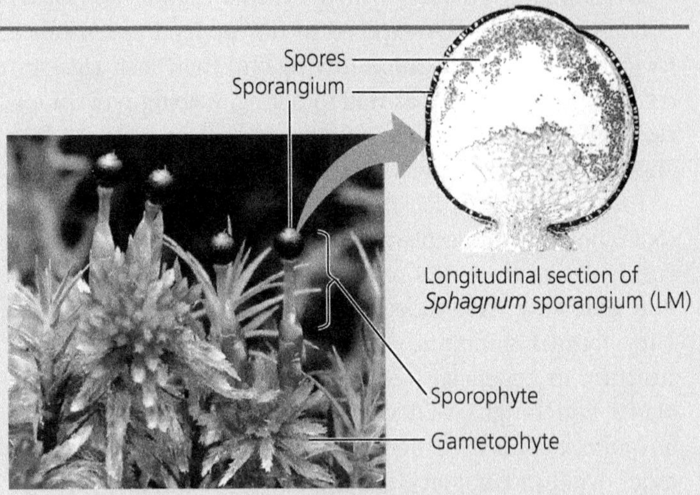

Sporophytes and sporangia of *Sphagnum* (a moss)

Multicellular Gametangia

Another feature distinguishing early land plants from their algal ancestors was the production of gametes within multicellular organs called **gametangia**. The female gametangia are called **archegonia** (singular, *archegonium*). Each archegonium is a pear-shaped organ that produces a single nonmotile egg retained within the bulbous part of the organ (the top for the species shown here). The male gametangia, called **antheridia** (singular, *antheridium*), produce sperm and release them into the environment. In many groups of present-day plants, the sperm have flagella and swim to the eggs through water droplets or a film of water. Each egg is fertilized within an archegonium, where the zygote develops into an embryo. As you will see in Chapter 30, the gametophytes of seed plants are so reduced in size that the archegonia and antheridia have been lost in many lineages.

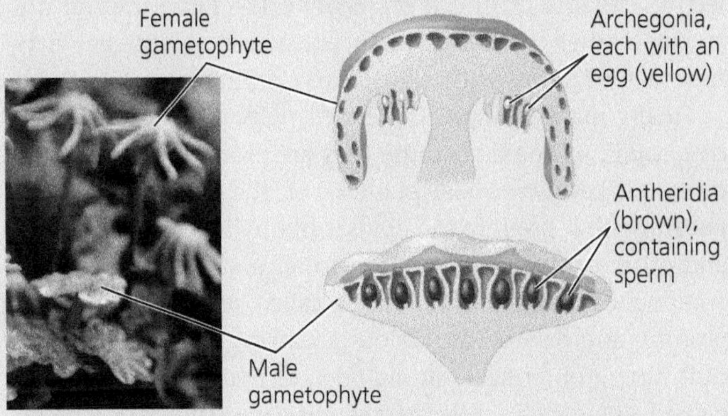

Archegonia and antheridia of *Marchantia* (a liverwort)

Apical Meristems

In terrestrial habitats, a photosynthetic organism finds essential resources in two very different places. Light and CO_2 are mainly available above ground; water and mineral nutrients are found mainly in the soil. Though plants cannot move from place to place, their roots and shoots can elongate, increasing exposure to environmental resources. This growth in length is sustained throughout the plant's life by the activity of **apical meristems**, localized regions of cell division at the tips of roots and shoots. Cells produced by apical meristems differentiate into the outer epidermis, which protects the body, and various types of internal tissues. Shoot apical meristems also generate leaves in most plants. Thus, the complex bodies of plants have specialized below- and aboveground organs.

Apical meristems of plant roots and shoots. The LMs are longitudinal sections at the tips of a root and shoot.

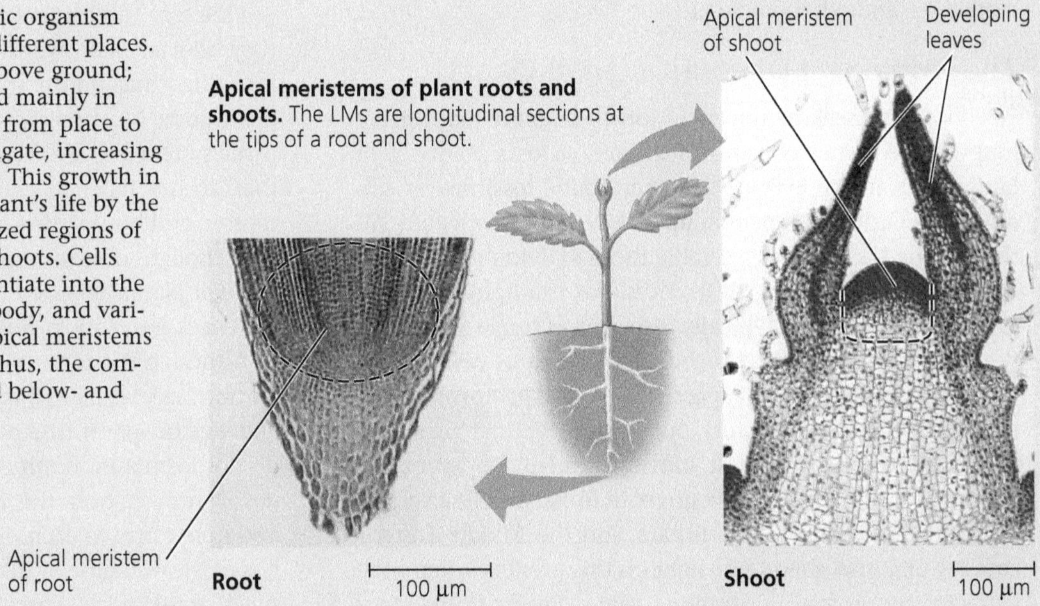

In addition to the four traits shown in Figure 29.5, other derived traits that relate to terrestrial life have evolved in many plant species. For example, the epidermis in many species has a covering, the **cuticle**, which consists of wax and other polymers. Permanently exposed to the air, land plants run a far greater risk of desiccation (drying out) than their algal ancestors. The cuticle acts as waterproofing, helping prevent excessive water loss from the aboveground plant organs, while also providing some protection from microbial attack.

Early land plants lacked true roots and leaves. Without roots, how did these plants absorb nutrients from the soil? Fossils dating from 420 million years ago reveal an adaptation that may have aided early plants in nutrient uptake: They formed symbiotic associations with fungi similar in structure to beneficial associations observed today between plants and fungi. We'll describe these associations, called *mycorrhizae*, and their benefits to both plants and fungi in more detail in Chapter 31. For now, the main point is that mycorrhizal fungi form extensive networks of filaments through the soil, enabling them to absorb nutrients more effectively than a plant can on its own. The fungi transfer nutrients to their symbiotic plant partner, a benefit that may have helped plants without roots to colonize land.

Finally, many land plants produce molecules called *secondary compounds*, so named because they are products of secondary metabolic pathways—side branches off the primary metabolic pathways that produce the lipids, carbohydrates, amino acids, and other compounds common to all organisms. Secondary compounds include compounds called alkaloids, terpenes, tannins, and flavonoids. Various alkaloids, terpenes, and tannins have a bitter taste, strong odor, or toxic effect that helps defend a plant against herbivores and parasites. Flavonoids absorb harmful UV radiation, and some related compounds deter attack by pathogens. Humans also benefit from secondary compounds in plants, many of which are used in spices, medicines, and other products.

The Origin and Diversification of Plants

Paleobotanists seeking the evolutionary origin of plants have long debated what constitutes the oldest fossil evidence of land plants. In the 1970s, researchers found fossil spores dating to the Ordovician period, up to 475 million years old. Although the fossil spores resemble those of living plants, they also have some striking differences. For example, spores of present-day plants are typically dispersed as single grains, but the fossil spores are fused together in groups of two or four. This difference raises the possibility that the fossil spores were not produced by plants, but by some extinct algal relative. Furthermore, the oldest known fragments of plant body tissues are 50 million years younger than the puzzling spores.

In 2003, scientists from Britain and the Middle Eastern country of Oman shed some light on this mystery when they extracted spores from 475-million-year-old rocks from Oman

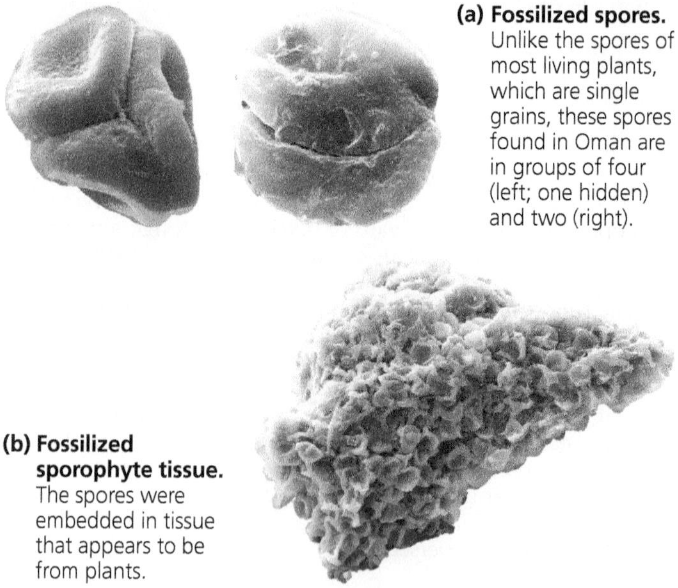

(a) Fossilized spores. Unlike the spores of most living plants, which are single grains, these spores found in Oman are in groups of four (left; one hidden) and two (right).

(b) Fossilized sporophyte tissue. The spores were embedded in tissue that appears to be from plants.

▲ **Figure 29.6 Ancient plant spores and tissue** (colorized SEMs).

(Figure 29.6a). Unlike previously discovered spores of this age, these were embedded in plant cuticle material that is similar to spore-bearing tissue in living plants (Figure 29.6b). After uncovering other small fragments of tissue that clearly belonged to plants, the scientists concluded that the spores from Oman represent fossil plants rather than algae.

Whatever the precise age of the first land plants, those ancestral species gave rise to the vast diversity of living plants. Table 29.1 summarizes the ten extant phyla in the taxonomic scheme used in this text. (Extant lineages are those that have surviving members, not only extinct ones.) As you read the rest of this section, look at Table 29.1 together with Figure 29.7, which reflects a view of plant phylogeny based on plant morphology, biochemistry, and genetics.

One way to distinguish groups of plants is whether or not they have an extensive system of **vascular tissue**, cells joined into tubes that transport water and nutrients throughout the plant body. Most present-day plants have a complex vascular tissue system and are therefore called **vascular plants**. Plants that do not have an extensive transport system—liverworts, mosses, and hornworts—are described as "nonvascular" plants, even though some mosses do have simple vascular tissue. Nonvascular plants are often informally called **bryophytes** (from the Greek *bryon*, moss, and *phyton*, plant).

Although the term *bryophyte* is commonly used to refer to all nonvascular plants, molecular studies and morphological analyses of sperm structure have concluded that bryophytes do not form a monophyletic group (a clade). Debate continues, however, over the relationships of liverworts, mosses, and hornworts to each other and to vascular plants. Regardless of the outcome of this debate, bryophytes share some derived traits with vascular plants, such as multicellular

Table 29.1 Ten Phyla of Extant Plants

	Common Name	Number of Known Species
Nonvascular Plants (Bryophytes)		
Phylum Hepatophyta	Liverworts	9,000
Phylum Bryophyta	Mosses	15,000
Phylum Anthocerophyta	Hornworts	100
Vascular Plants		
Seedless Vascular Plants		
Phylum Lycophyta	Lycophytes	1,200
Phylum Pterophyta	Pterophytes	12,000
Seed Plants		
Gymnosperms		
Phylum Ginkgophyta	Ginkgo	1
Phylum Cycadophyta	Cycads	130
Phylum Gnetophyta	Gnetophytes	75
Phylum Coniferophyta	Conifers	600
Angiosperms		
Phylum Anthophyta	Flowering plants	250,000

embryos and apical meristems, while lacking many innovations of vascular plants, such as roots and true leaves.

Vascular plants, which form a clade that comprises about 93% of all extant plant species, can be categorized further into smaller clades. Two of these clades are the **lycophytes** (club mosses and their relatives) and the **pterophytes** (ferns and their relatives). The plants in each of these clades lack seeds, which is why collectively the two clades are often informally called **seedless vascular plants**. However, notice in Figure 29.7 that seedless vascular plants are paraphyletic, not monophyletic. Groups such as the seedless vascular plants are sometimes referred to as a **grade**, a collection of organisms that share a key biological feature. Grades can be informative by grouping organisms according to features, such as lack of seeds. But members of a grade, unlike members of a clade, do not necessarily share the same ancestry. For example, even though pterophytes and lycophytes are all seedless plants, pterophytes share a more recent common ancestor with seed plants. As a result, we would expect pterophytes and seed plants to share key traits not found in lycophytes—and they do, as you'll read.

A third clade of vascular plants consists of seed plants, which represent the vast majority of living plant species. A **seed** is an embryo packaged with a supply of nutrients inside a protective coat. Seed plants can be divided into two groups, gymnosperms and angiosperms, based on the absence or

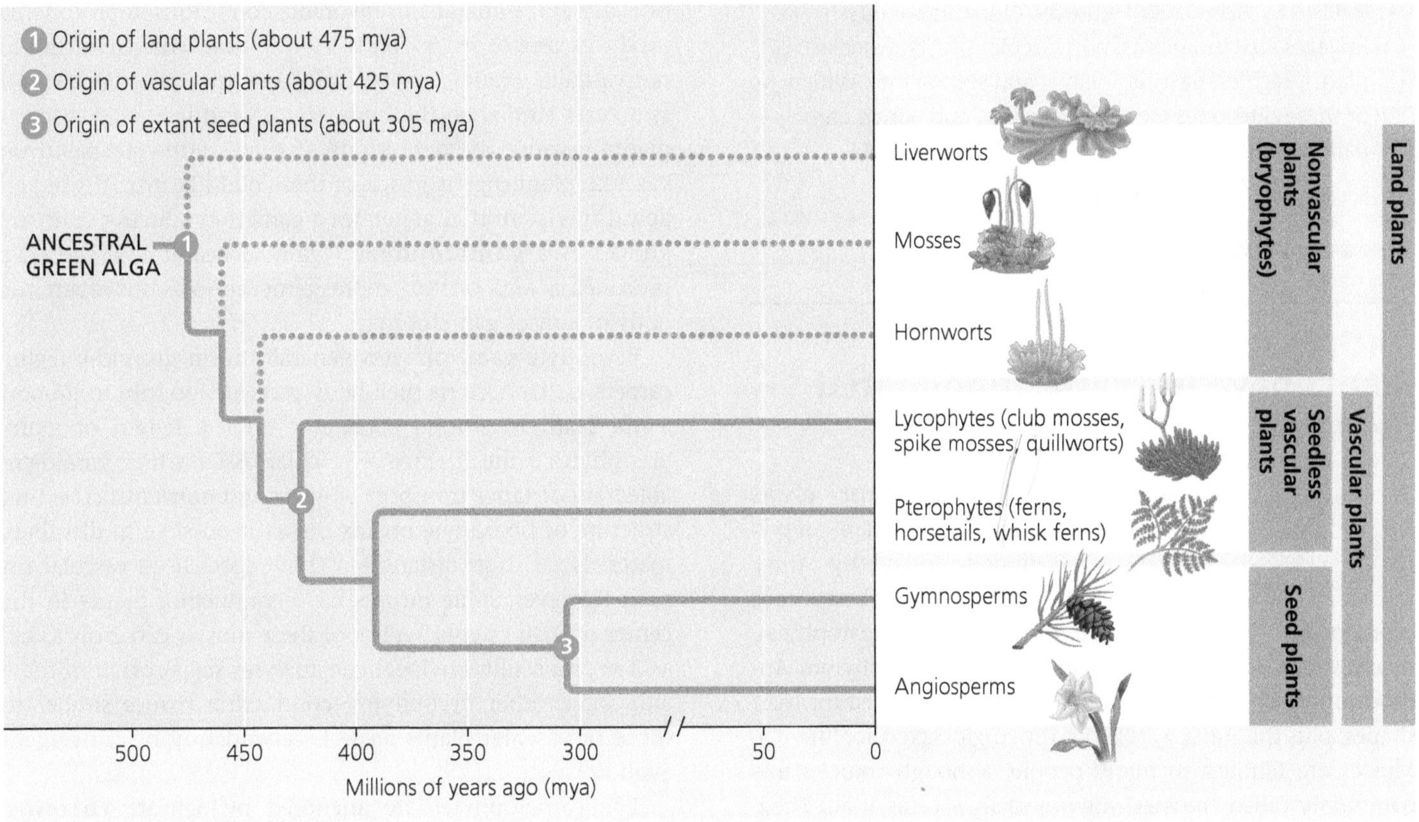

▲ **Figure 29.7 Highlights of plant evolution.** The phylogeny shown here illustrates a leading hypothesis about the relationships between plant groups. The dotted lines indicate groups whose evolutionary relationships continue to be debated.

presence of enclosed chambers in which seeds mature. **Gymnosperms** (from the Greek *gymnos*, naked, and *sperm*, seed) are grouped together as "naked seed" plants because their seeds are not enclosed in chambers. Living gymnosperm species, the most familiar of which are the conifers, probably form a clade. **Angiosperms** (from the Greek *angion*, container) are a huge clade consisting of all flowering plants. Angiosperm seeds develop inside chambers called ovaries, which originate within flowers and mature into fruits. Nearly 90% of living plant species are angiosperms.

Note that the phylogeny depicted in Figure 29.7 focuses only on the relationships between extant plant lineages. Paleobotanists have also discovered fossils belonging to extinct plant lineages. As you'll read later in the chapter, many of these fossils reveal intermediate steps in the emergence of the distinctive plant groups found on Earth today.

CONCEPT CHECK 29.1

1. Why do researchers identify charophytes rather than another group as the closest relatives of land plants?
2. Identify three derived traits that distinguish plants from charophytes *and* facilitate life on land. Explain.
3. **WHAT IF?** What would the human life cycle be like if we had alternation of generations? Assume that the multicellular diploid stage is similar in form to an adult human.
4. **MAKE CONNECTIONS** Figure 29.7 identifies which lineages are land plants, nonvascular plants, vascular plants, seedless vascular plants, and seed plants. Which of these categories are monophyletic, and which are paraphyletic? Explain. See Figure 26.10 on p. 542.

For suggested answers, see Appendix A.

CONCEPT 29.2

Mosses and other nonvascular plants have life cycles dominated by gametophytes

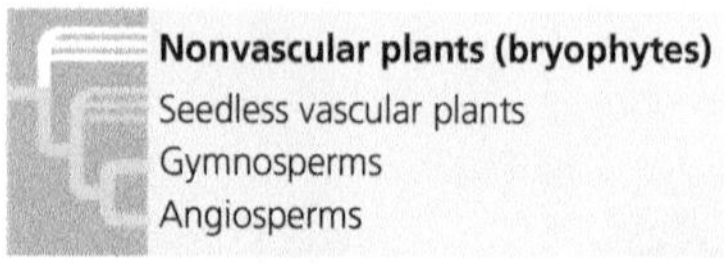

The nonvascular plants (bryophytes) are represented today by three phyla of small herbaceous (nonwoody) plants: **liverworts** (phylum Hepatophyta), **mosses** (phylum Bryophyta), and **hornworts** (phylum Anthocerophyta). Liverworts and hornworts are named for their shapes, plus the suffix *wort* (from the Anglo-Saxon for "herb"). Mosses are familiar to many people, although some plants commonly called "mosses" are not really mosses at all. These include Irish moss (a red seaweed), reindeer moss (a lichen), club mosses (seedless vascular plants), and Spanish mosses (lichens in some regions and flowering plants in others).

Note that the terms *Bryophyta* and *bryophyte* are not synonymous. Bryophyta is the formal taxonomic name for the phylum that consists solely of mosses. As mentioned earlier, the term *bryophyte* is used informally to refer to *all* nonvascular plants—liverworts, mosses, and hornworts.

Liverworts, mosses, and hornworts have acquired many unique adaptations over the long course of their evolution. Nevertheless, living bryophytes likely reflect some traits of the earliest plants. The oldest known fossils of plant fragments, for example, include tissues very similar to those inside liverworts. Researchers hope to discover more parts of these ancient plants to see if this resemblance is reflected more broadly.

Bryophyte Gametophytes

Unlike vascular plants, in all three bryophyte phyla the haploid gametophytes are the dominant stage of the life cycle: That is, they are usually larger and longer-living than the sporophytes, as shown in the moss life cycle in **Figure 29.8**. Sporophytes are typically present only part of the time.

When bryophyte spores are dispersed to a favorable habitat, such as moist soil or tree bark, they may germinate and grow into gametophytes. Germinating moss spores, for example, characteristically produce a mass of green, branched, one-cell-thick filaments known as a **protonema** (plural, *protonemata*; from the Greek *proto*, first, and *nema*, threads). A protonema has a large surface area that enhances absorption of water and minerals. In favorable conditions, a protonema produces one or more "buds." (Note that when referring to nonvascular plants, we typically use quotation marks for structures similar to the buds, stems, and leaves of vascular plants because the definitions of these terms are based on vascular plant organs.) Each of these bud-like growths has an apical meristem that generates a gamete-producing structure known as a **gametophore** ("gamete bearer"). Together, a protonema and one or more gametophores make up the body of a moss gametophyte.

Bryophyte gametophytes generally form ground-hugging carpets, partly because their body parts are too thin to support a tall plant. A second constraint on the height of many bryophytes is the absence of vascular tissue, which would enable long-distance transport of water and nutrients. (The thin structure of bryophyte organs makes it possible to distribute materials for short distances without specialized vascular tissue.) However, some mosses have conducting tissues in the center of their "stems." A few of these mosses can grow as tall as 2 m as a result. Phylogenetic analyses suggest that in these and some other bryophytes, conducting tissues similar to those of vascular plants arose independently by convergent evolution.

The gametophytes are anchored by delicate **rhizoids**, which are long, tubular single cells (in liverworts and hornworts) or filaments of cells (in mosses). Unlike roots, which are found in vascular plant sporophytes, rhizoids are not

▼ **Figure 29.8 The life cycle of a moss.**

? *In this diagram, does the sperm cell that fertilizes the egg cell differ genetically from the egg? Explain.*

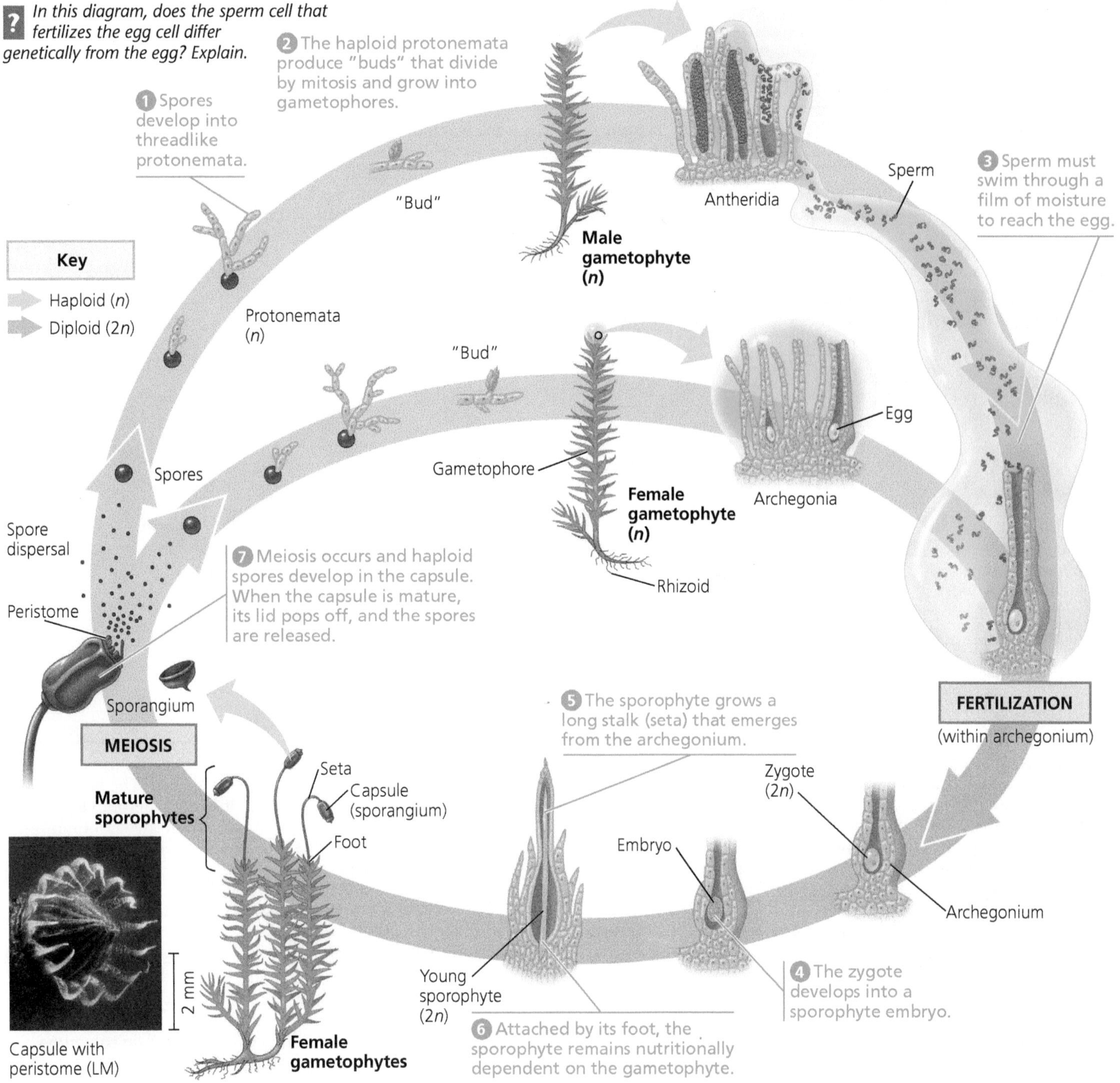

composed of tissues. Bryophyte rhizoids also lack specialized conducting cells and do not play a primary role in water and mineral absorption.

Gametophytes can form multiple gametangia, each of which produces gametes and is covered by protective tissue. Each archegonium produces one egg, whereas each antheridium produces many sperm. Some bryophyte gametophytes are bisexual, but in mosses the archegonia and antheridia are typically carried on separate female and male gametophytes. Flagellated sperm swim through a film of water toward eggs, entering the archegonia in response to chemical attractants. Eggs are not released but instead remain within the bases of archegonia. After fertilization, embryos are retained within the archegonia. Layers of placental transfer cells help transport nutrients to the embryos as they develop into sporophytes.

Bryophyte sperm typically require a film of water to reach the eggs. Given this requirement, it is not surprising that many bryophyte species are found in moist habitats. The fact that sperm swim through water to reach the egg also means that in species with separate male and female gametophytes (most mosses), sexual reproduction is likely to be more successful when individuals are located close to one another.

▼ Figure 29.9

Exploring Bryophyte Diversity

Liverworts (Phylum Hepatophyta)

This phylum's common and scientific names (from the Latin *hepaticus*, liver) refer to the liver-shaped gametophytes of its members, such as *Marchantia*, shown below. In medieval times, their shape was thought to be a sign that the plants could help treat liver diseases. Some liverworts, including *Marchantia*, are described as "thalloid" because of the flattened shape of their gametophytes. (Recall from Chapter 28 that the body of a multicellular alga is called a thallus.) *Marchantia* gametangia are elevated on gametophores that look like miniature trees. You would need a magnifying glass to see the sporophytes, which have a short seta (stalk) with an oval or round capsule. Other liverworts, such as *Plagiochila*, below, are called "leafy" because their stemlike gametophytes have many leaflike appendages. There are many more species of leafy liverworts than thalloid liverworts.

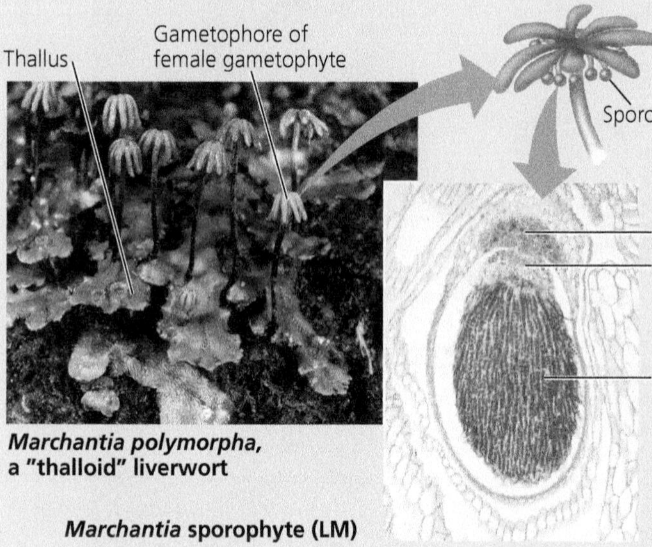

***Marchantia polymorpha*, a "thalloid" liverwort**

***Marchantia* sporophyte (LM)**

***Plagiochila deltoidea*, a "leafy" liverwort**

Hornworts (Phylum Anthocerophyta)

This phylum's common and scientific names (from the Greek *keras*, horn) refer to the long, tapered shape of the sporophyte. A typical sporophyte can grow to about 5 cm high. Unlike a liverwort or moss sporophyte, a hornwort sporophyte lacks a seta and consists only of a sporangium. The sporangium releases mature spores by splitting open, starting at the tip of the horn. The gametophytes, which are usually 1–2 cm in diameter, grow mostly horizontally and often have multiple sporophytes attached. Hornworts are frequently among the first species to colonize open areas with moist soils; a symbiotic relationship with nitrogen-fixing cyanobacteria contributes to their ability to do this (nitrogen is often in short supply in such areas).

An *Anthoceros* hornwort species

Mosses (Phylum Bryophyta)

Moss gametophytes, which range in height from less than 1 mm to up to 2 m, are less than 15 cm tall in most species. The familiar carpet of moss you observe consists mainly of gametophytes. The blades of their "leaves" are usually only one cell thick, but more complex "leaves" that have ridges coated with cuticle can be found on the common hairy-cap moss (*Polytrichum*, below) and its close relatives. Moss sporophytes are typically elongated and visible to the naked eye, with heights ranging up to about 20 cm. Though green and photosynthetic when young, they turn tan or brownish red when ready to release spores.

***Polytrichum commune*, hairy-cap moss**

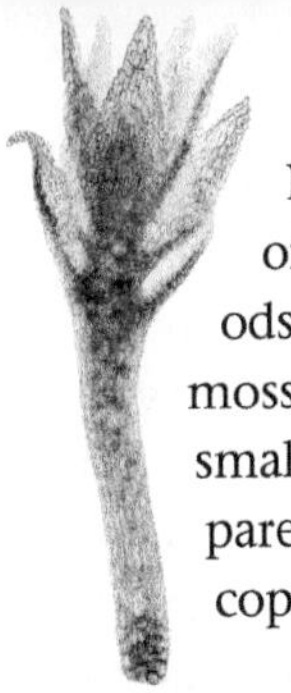

Many bryophyte species can increase the number of individuals in a local area through various methods of asexual reproduction. For example, some mosses reproduce asexually by forming *brood bodies,* small plantlets (as shown at left) that detach from the parent plant and grow into new, genetically identical copies of their parent.

Bryophyte Sporophytes

Although bryophyte sporophytes are usually green and photosynthetic when young, they cannot live independently. They remain attached to their parental gametophytes, from which they absorb sugars, amino acids, minerals, and water.

Bryophytes have the smallest sporophytes of all extant plant groups, consistent with the hypothesis that larger sporophytes evolved only later, in the vascular plants. A typical bryophyte sporophyte consists of a foot, a seta, and a sporangium. Embedded in the archegonium, the **foot** absorbs nutrients from the gametophyte. The **seta** (plural, *setae*), or stalk, conducts these materials to the sporangium, also called a **capsule**, which uses them to produce spores by meiosis. One capsule can generate up to 50 million spores.

In most mosses, the seta becomes elongated, enhancing spore dispersal by elevating the capsule. Typically, the upper part of the capsule features a ring of interlocking, tooth-like structures known as the **peristome** (see Figure 29.8). These "teeth" open under dry conditions and close again when it is moist. This allows spores to be discharged gradually, via periodic gusts of wind that can carry them long distances.

Moss and hornwort sporophytes are often larger and more complex than those of liverworts. Both moss and hornwort sporophytes also have specialized pores called **stomata** (singular, *stoma*), which are also found in all vascular plants. These pores support photosynthesis by allowing the exchange of CO_2 and O_2 between the outside air and the sporophyte interior (see Figure 10.3). Stomata are also the main avenues by which water evaporates from the sporophyte. In hot, dry conditions, the stomata close, minimizing water loss.

The fact that stomata are present in mosses and hornworts but absent in liverworts suggests three possible hypotheses for their evolution. If liverworts are the deepest-branching lineage of land plants, as in Figure 29.7, then stomata may have evolved once in the ancestor of mosses, hornworts, and vascular plants. If hornworts are the deepest-branching lineage, stomata may have evolved once and then been lost in the liverwort lineage. Finally, if hornworts are the deepest-branching lineage and mosses are the closest relatives of vascular plants, it is also possible that hornworts acquired stomata independently of mosses and vascular plants. This question is important to understanding plant evolution because stomata play a crucial role in the success of vascular plants, as you will learn in Chapter 36.

Figure 29.9, on the facing page, shows some examples of gametophytes and sporophytes in the bryophyte phyla.

The Ecological and Economic Importance of Mosses

Wind dispersal of lightweight spores has distributed mosses throughout the world. These plants are particularly common and diverse in moist forests and wetlands. Some mosses colonize bare, sandy soil, where researchers have found they help retain nitrogen in the soil (Figure 29.10). In northern coniferous forests, species such as the feather moss *Pleurozium* harbor nitrogen-fixing cyanobacteria that increase the availability of nitrogen in the ecosystem. Other mosses inhabit such extreme environments as mountaintops, tundra, and deserts. Many mosses are able to live in very cold or dry habitats because they can survive the loss of most of their body water, then rehydrate when moisture is available. Few vascular plants can survive the same degree of desiccation.

▼ Figure 29.10 **INQUIRY**

Can bryophytes reduce the rate at which key nutrients are lost from soils?

EXPERIMENT Soils in terrestrial ecosystems are often low in nitrogen, a nutrient required for normal plant growth. Richard Bowden, of Allegheny College, measured annual inputs (gains) and outputs (losses) of nitrogen in a sandy-soil ecosystem dominated by the moss *Polytrichum*. Nitrogen inputs were measured from rainfall (dissolved ions, such as nitrate, NO_3^-), biological N_2 fixation, and wind deposition. Nitrogen losses were measured in leached water (dissolved ions, such as NO_3^-) and gaseous emissions (such as NO_2 emitted by bacteria). Bowden measured losses for soils with *Polytrichum* and for soils where the moss was removed two months before the experiment began.

RESULTS A total of 10.5 kg of nitrogen per hectare (kg/ha) entered the ecosystem each year. Little nitrogen was lost by gaseous emissions (0.10 kg/ha · yr). The results of comparing nitrogen losses by leaching are shown below.

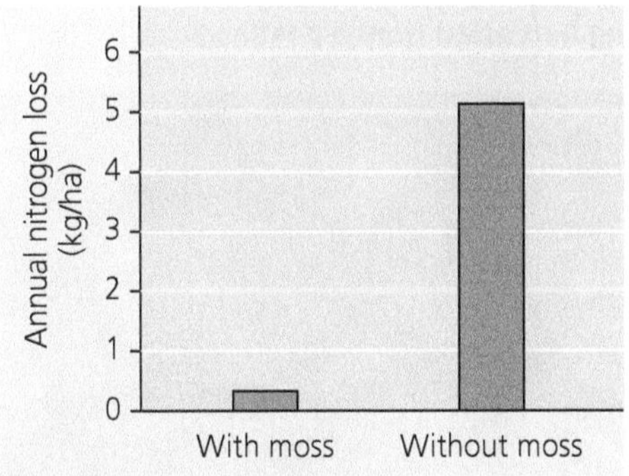

CONCLUSION The moss *Polytrichum* greatly reduced the loss of nitrogen by leaching in this ecosystem. Each year, the moss ecosystem retained over 95% of the 10.5 kg/ha of total nitrogen inputs (only 0.1 kg/ha and 0.3 kg/ha were lost to gaseous emissions and leaching, respectively).

SOURCE R. D. Bowden, Inputs, outputs, and accumulation of nitrogen in an early successional moss (*Polytrichum*) ecosystem, *Ecological Monographs* 61:207–223 (1991).

WHAT IF? How might the presence of *Polytrichum* affect plant species that typically colonize the sandy soils *after* the moss?

One wetland moss genus, *Sphagnum*, or "peat moss," is often a major component of deposits of partially decayed organic material known as **peat** (Figure 29.11a). Boggy regions with thick layers of peat are called peatlands. *Sphagnum* does not decay readily, in part because of phenolic compounds embedded in its cell walls. The low temperature, pH, and oxygen level of peatlands also inhibit decay of moss and other organisms in these boggy wetlands. As a result, some peatlands have preserved corpses for thousands of years (Figure 29.11b).

Peat has long been a fuel source in Europe and Asia, and it is still harvested for fuel today, notably in Ireland and Canada. Peat moss is also useful as a soil conditioner and for packing plant roots during shipment because it has large dead cells that can absorb roughly 20 times the moss's weight in water.

Peatlands cover 3% of Earth's land surface and contain roughly 30% of the world's soil carbon: Globally, an estimated 450 billion tons of organic carbon is stored as peat. These carbon reservoirs have helped to stabilize atmospheric CO_2 concentrations (see Chapter 55). Current overharvesting of *Sphagnum* may reduce peat's beneficial ecological effects and contribute to global warming by releasing stored CO_2. In addition, if global temperatures continue to rise, the water levels of some peatlands are expected to drop. Such a change would expose peat to air and cause it to decompose, thereby releasing additional stored CO_2 and contributing further to global warming. The historical and expected future effects of *Sphagnum* on the global climate underscore the importance of preserving and managing peatlands.

(a) Peat being harvested from a peatland

(b) "Tollund Man," a bog mummy dating from 405–100 B.C.E. The acidic, oxygen-poor conditions produced by *Sphagnum* can preserve human or other animal bodies for thousands of years.

▲ Figure 29.11 ***Sphagnum*, or peat moss: a bryophyte with economic, ecological, and archaeological significance.**

CONCEPT CHECK 29.2

1. How do bryophytes differ from other plants?
2. Give three examples of how structure fits function in bryophytes.
3. WHAT IF? For each hypothesis of stomatal evolution, label each gain and loss of stomata on an appropriately modified version of the tree in Figure 29.7.

For suggested answers, see Appendix A.

CONCEPT 29.3

Ferns and other seedless vascular plants were the first plants to grow tall

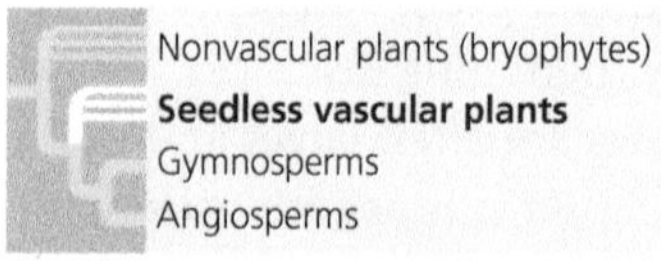

During the first 100 million years of plant evolution, bryophytes or bryophyte-like plants were the prevalent vegetation. But it is vascular plants that dominate most landscapes today. Fossils and living seedless vascular plants can provide insights into plant evolution during the Devonian and Carboniferous periods, when vascular plants began to diversify but most groups of seed plants had not yet evolved. Fossils show that lycophytes, ferns, and other seedless vascular plants had well-developed vascular systems by the Devonian. As we'll see, this evolutionary innovation set the stage for vascular plants to grow taller than their bryophyte counterparts. As in nonvascular plants, however, the sperm of ferns and all other seedless vascular plants are flagellated and swim through a film of water to reach eggs. In part because of these swimming sperm, seedless vascular plants today are most common in damp environments.

Origins and Traits of Vascular Plants

Fossils of the forerunners of present-day vascular plants date back about 425 million years. Unlike the nonvascular plants, these species had branched sporophytes that were not dependent on gametophytes for nutrition (Figure 29.12). Although these ancestors of vascular plants were only about

▶ **Figure 29.12 Sporophytes of *Aglaophyton major*, an ancient relative of present-day vascular plants.** This reconstruction from 405-million-year-old fossils exhibits dichotomous (Y-shaped) branching with sporangia at the ends of the branches. Sporophyte branching characterizes living vascular plants but is lacking in living nonvascular plants (bryophytes).

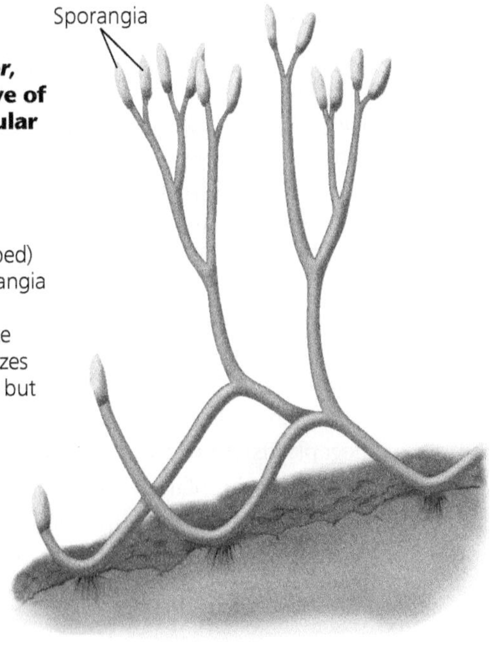

15 cm tall, their branching made possible more complex bodies with multiple sporangia. As plant bodies became increasingly complex, competition for space and sunlight probably increased. As we'll see, that competition may have stimulated still more evolution in vascular plants.

The ancestors of vascular plants already had some derived traits of today's vascular plants, but they lacked roots and some other adaptations that evolved later. This section describes the main traits that characterize living vascular plants: life cycles with dominant sporophytes, transport in vascular tissues called xylem and phloem, and well-developed roots and leaves, including spore-bearing leaves called sporophylls.

Life Cycles with Dominant Sporophytes

Fossils suggest that the ancestors of vascular plants had gametophytes and sporophytes that were about equal in size. Among living vascular plants, however, the sporophyte (diploid) generation is the larger and more complex plant in the alternation of generations (**Figure 29.13**). In ferns, for example, the familiar leafy plants are the sporophytes. You

▼ **Figure 29.13 The life cycle of a fern.**

WHAT IF? *If the ability to disperse sperm by wind evolved in a fern, how might its life cycle be affected?*

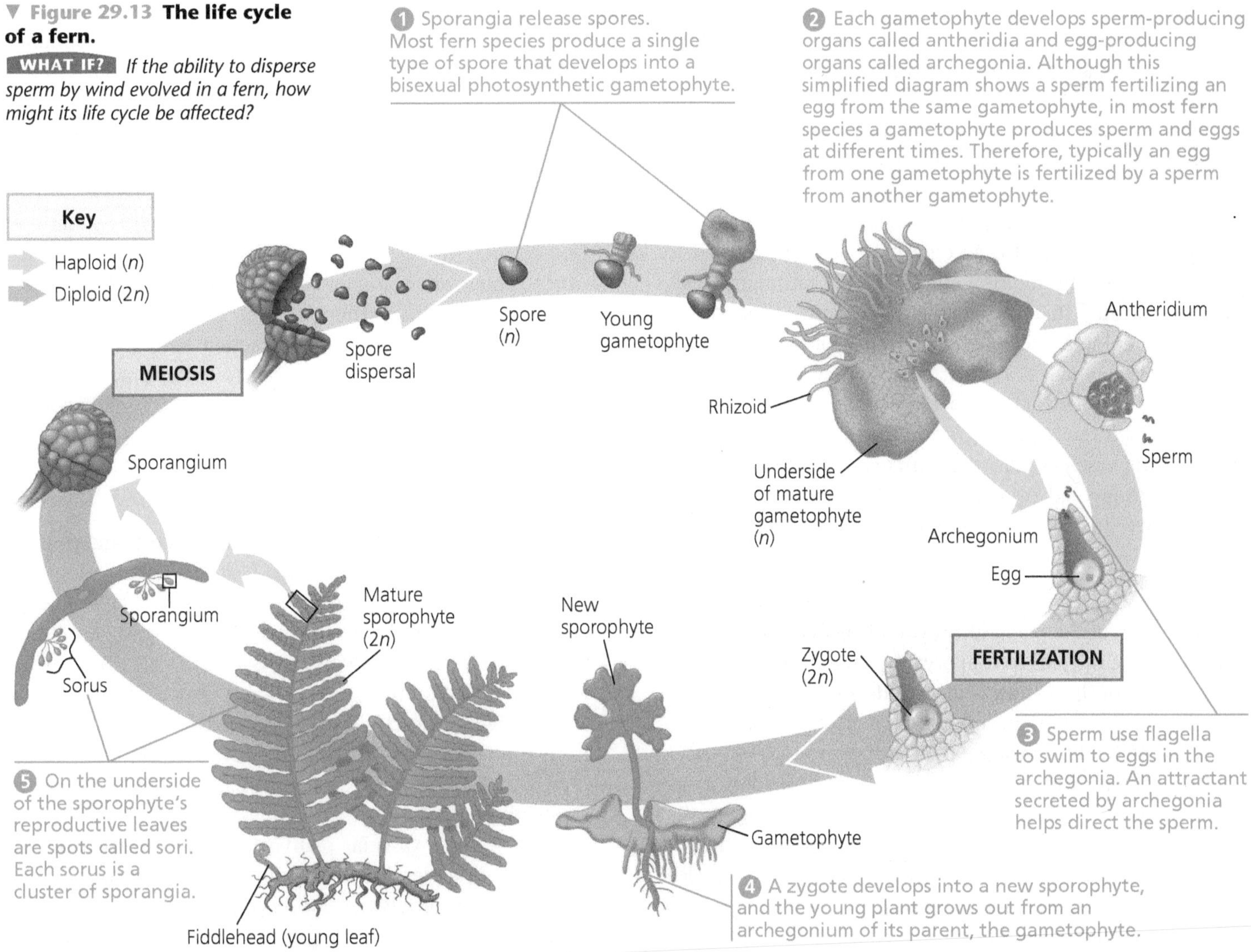

would have to get down on your hands and knees and search the ground carefully to find fern gametophytes, which are tiny structures that often grow on or just below the soil surface. Until you have a chance to do that, you can study the sporophyte-dominant life cycle of seedless vascular plants in Figure 29.13, which uses a fern as an example. Then, for review, compare this life cycle with Figure 29.8, which represents a gametophyte-dominated life cycle typical of mosses and other nonvascular plants. In Chapter 30, you will see that gametophytes became even more reduced during the evolution of seed plants.

Transport in Xylem and Phloem

Vascular plants have two types of vascular tissue: xylem and phloem. **Xylem** conducts most of the water and minerals. The xylem of most vascular plants includes **tracheids**, tube-shaped cells that carry water and minerals up from roots (see Figure 35.10). (Tracheids have been lost in some highly specialized species, such as *Wolffia*, a tiny aquatic angiosperm.) Because nonvascular plants lack tracheids, vascular plants are sometimes referred to as tracheophytes. The water-conducting cells in vascular plants are *lignified*; that is, their cell walls are strengthened by the polymer **lignin**. The tissue called **phloem** has cells arranged into tubes that distribute sugars, amino acids, and other organic products (see Figure 35.10).

Lignified vascular tissue permitted vascular plants to grow tall. Their stems became strong enough to provide support against gravity, and they could transport water and mineral nutrients high above the ground. Tall plants could also outcompete short plants for access to the sunlight needed for photosynthesis. In addition, the spores of tall plants could disperse farther than those of short plants, enabling tall species to colonize new environments rapidly. Overall, the ability to grow tall was a major evolutionary innovation that gave vascular plants a competitive edge over nonvascular plants, which rarely grow above 20 cm in height. Competition among vascular plants also increased, and taller growth forms were favored by natural selection—such as the trees that formed the first forests about 385 million years ago.

Evolution of Roots

Lignified vascular tissue also provides benefits below ground. Instead of the rhizoids seen in bryophytes, roots evolved in the sporophytes of almost all vascular plants. **Roots** are organs that absorb water and nutrients from the soil. Roots also anchor vascular plants, hence allowing the shoot system to grow taller.

Root tissues of living plants closely resemble stem tissues of early vascular plants preserved in fossils. This suggests that roots may have evolved from the lowest belowground portions of stems in ancient vascular plants. It is unclear whether roots evolved only once in the common ancestor of all vascular plants or independently in different lineages. Although the roots of living members of these lineages of vascular plants share many similarities, fossil evidence hints at convergent evolution. The oldest lycophyte fossils, for example, already displayed simple roots 400 million years ago, when the ancestors of ferns and seed plants still had none. Studying genes that control root development in different vascular plant species may help resolve this question.

Evolution of Leaves

Leaves increase the surface area of the plant body and serve as the primary photosynthetic organ of vascular plants. In terms of size and complexity, leaves can be classified as either microphylls or megaphylls. All of the lycophytes (the oldest lineage of present-day vascular plants)—and only the lycophytes—have **microphylls**, small, usually spine-shaped leaves supported by a single strand of vascular tissue. Almost all other vascular plants have **megaphylls**, leaves with a highly branched vascular system; a few species have reduced leaves that appear to have evolved from megaphylls. So named because they are typically larger than microphylls, megaphylls support greater photosynthetic productivity than microphylls as a result of the greater surface area served by their network of veins. Microphylls first appear in the fossil record 410 million years ago, but megaphylls do not emerge until about 370 million years ago, toward the end of the Devonian period.

According to one model of leaf evolution, microphylls originated from sporangia located on the side of the stem (Figure 29.14a). Megaphylls, by contrast, may have evolved from a series of branches lying close together on a stem. As one of these branches came to grow above, or *overtop*, the others, the lower branches became flattened and developed webbing that joined them to one another. These joined branches thus became a leaf attached to the branch that overtopped them (Figure 29.14b). To better understand the origin of leaves, scientists are exploring the genetic control of leaf development.

Sporophylls and Spore Variations

One milestone in the evolution of plants was the emergence of **sporophylls**, modified leaves that bear sporangia. Sporophylls vary greatly in structure. For example, fern sporophylls produce clusters of sporangia known as **sori** (singular, *sorus*), usually on the undersides of the sporophylls (see Figure 29.13). In many lycophytes and in most gymnosperms, groups of sporophylls form cone-like structures called **strobili** (singular, *strobilus*; from the Greek *strobilos*, cone). In Chapter 30, you will see how sporophylls form gymnosperm strobili and parts of angiosperm flowers.

Most seedless vascular plant species are **homosporous**: They have one type of sporangium that produces one type of spore, which typically develops into a bisexual gametophyte, as in most ferns. In contrast, a **heterosporous** species has

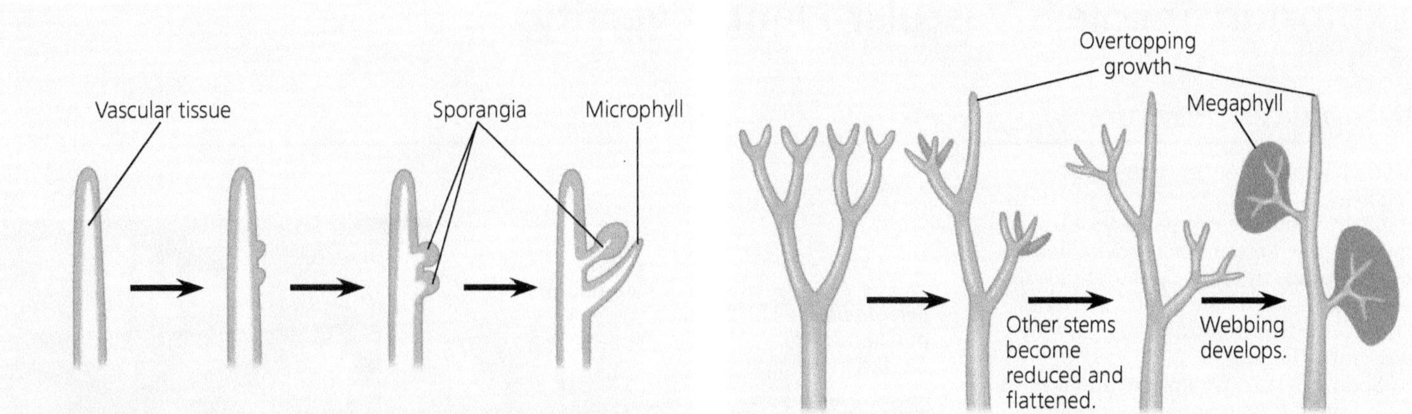

(a) Microphylls, such as those of lycophytes, may have originated from sporangia supported by single, unbranched strands of vascular tissue (shown in cross sections).

(b) Megaphylls, which have branched vascular systems, may have evolved by the fusion of branched stems.

▲ **Figure 29.14 Hypotheses for the evolution of leaves.**

two types of sporangia and produces two kinds of spores: Megasporangia on megasporophylls produce **megaspores**, which develop into female gametophytes; microsporangia on microsporophylls produce the comparatively smaller **microspores**, which develop into male gametophytes. All seed plants and a few seedless vascular plants are heterosporous. The following diagram compares the two conditions:

Homosporous spore production

Sporangium on sporophyll → Single type of spore → Typically a bisexual gametophyte → Eggs / Sperm

Heterosporous spore production

Megasporangium on megasporophyll → Megaspore → Female gametophyte → Eggs

Microsporangium on microsporophyll → Microspore → Male gametophyte → Sperm

Classification of Seedless Vascular Plants

As we noted earlier, biologists recognize two clades of living seedless vascular plants: the lycophytes (phylum Lycophyta) and the pterophytes (phylum Pterophyta). The lycophytes include the club mosses, the spike mosses, and the quillworts. The pterophytes include the ferns, the horsetails, and the whisk ferns and their relatives. Because they differ greatly in appearance, the ferns, horsetails, and whisk ferns have long been considered separate phyla: phylum Pterophyta (ferns), phylum Sphenophyta (horsetails), and phylum Psilophyta (whisk ferns and a related genus). However, recent molecular comparisons provide convincing evidence that all three groups make up a clade. Accordingly, many systematists now classify them together as the phylum Pterophyta, as we do in this chapter. Others refer to these groups as three separate phyla within a clade.

Figure 29.15, on the next page, describes the two main groups of seedless vascular plants.

Phylum Lycophyta: Club Mosses, Spike Mosses, and Quillworts

Present-day species of lycophytes, the most ancient group of vascular plants, are relicts of a far more impressive past. By the Carboniferous period (359–299 million years ago), the lycophyte evolutionary lineage included small herbaceous plants and giant trees with diameters of more than 2 m and heights of more than 40 m. The giant lycophyte trees thrived for millions of years in moist swamps, but they became extinct when Earth's climate became drier at the end of the Carboniferous period. The small lycophytes survived, represented today by about 1,200 species. Though some are commonly called club mosses and spike mosses, they are not true mosses (which, as discussed earlier, are nonvascular plants).

Phylum Pterophyta: Ferns, Horsetails, and Whisk Ferns and Relatives

Ferns radiated extensively from their Devonian origins and grew alongside lycophyte trees and horsetails in the great Carboniferous swamp forests. Today, ferns are by far the most widespread seedless vascular plants, numbering more than 12,000 species. Though most diverse in the tropics, many ferns thrive in temperate forests, and some species are even adapted to arid habitats.

As mentioned earlier, ferns and other pterophytes are more closely related to seed plants than to lycophytes. As a result, pterophytes and seed plants share traits that are not found in lycophytes, including overtopping growth (see Figure 29.14b), megaphyll leaves, and roots that can branch at various points along the length of an existing root. In lycophytes,

▼ Figure 29.15

Exploring Seedless Vascular Plant Diversity

Lycophytes (Phylum Lycophyta)

Many lycophytes grow on tropical trees as *epiphytes*, plants that use other plants as a substrate but are not parasites. Other species grow on temperate forest floors. In some species, the tiny gametophytes live above ground and are photosynthetic. Others live below ground, nurtured by symbiotic fungi.

Sporophytes have upright stems with many small leaves, as well as ground-hugging stems that produce dichotomously branching roots. Spike mosses are usually relatively small and often grow horizontally. In many club mosses and spike mosses, sporophylls are clustered into club-shaped cones (strobili). Quillworts, named for their leaf shape, form a single genus whose members live in marshy areas or as submerged aquatic plants. Club mosses are all homosporous, whereas spike mosses and quillworts are all heterosporous. The spores of club mosses are released in clouds and are so rich in oil that magicians and photographers once ignited them to create smoke or flashes of light.

***Selaginella moellendorffii*, a spike moss**

***Isoetes gunnii*, a quillwort**

***Diphasiastrum tristachyum*, a club moss**

Pterophytes (Phylum Pterophyta)

***Athyrium filix-femina*, lady fern**

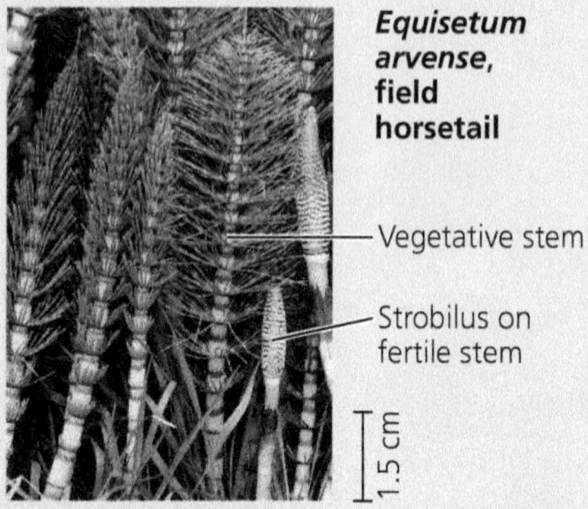

***Equisetum arvense*, field horsetail**

***Psilotum nudum*, a whisk fern**

Ferns

Unlike the lycophytes, ferns have megaphylls (see Figure 29.14b). The sporophytes typically have horizontal stems that give rise to large leaves called fronds, often divided into leaflets. A frond grows as its coiled tip, the fiddlehead, unfurls.

Almost all species are homosporous. The gametophyte in some species shrivels and dies after the young sporophyte detaches itself. In most species, sporophytes have stalked sporangia with springlike devices that catapult spores several meters. Airborne spores can be carried far from their origin. Some species produce more than a trillion spores in a plant's lifetime.

Horsetails

The group's name refers to the brushy appearance of the stems, which have a gritty texture that made them historically useful as "scouring rushes" for pots and pans. Some species have separate fertile (cone-bearing) and vegetative stems. Horsetails are homosporous, with cones releasing spores that typically give rise to bisexual gametophytes.

Horsetails are also called arthrophytes ("jointed plants") because their stems have joints. Rings of small leaves or branches emerge from each joint, but the stem is the main photosynthetic organ. Large air canals carry oxygen to the roots, which often grow in waterlogged soil.

Whisk Ferns and Relatives

Like primitive vascular plant fossils, the sporophytes of whisk ferns (genus *Psilotum*) have dichotomously branching stems but no roots. Stems have scalelike outgrowths that lack vascular tissue and may have resulted from the evolutionary reduction of leaves. Each yellow knob on a stem consists of three fused sporangia. Species of the genus *Tmesipteris*, closely related to whisk ferns and found only in the South Pacific, also lack roots but have small, leaflike outgrowths in their stems, giving them a vine-like appearance. Both genera are homosporous, with spores giving rise to bisexual gametophytes that grow underground and are only about a centimeter long.

by contrast, roots branch only at the growing tip of the root, forming a Y-shaped structure.

The pterophytes called horsetails were very diverse during the Carboniferous period, some growing as tall as 15 m. Today, only 15 species survive as a single, widely distributed genus, *Equisetum*, found in marshy places and along streams.

Psilotum (whisk ferns) and a closely related genus, *Tmesipteris*, form a clade consisting mainly of tropical epiphytes. Plants in these two genera, the only vascular plants lacking true roots, are called "living fossils" because of their resemblance to fossils of ancient relatives of living vascular plants (see Figures 29.12 and 29.15). However, much evidence, including analyses of DNA sequences and sperm structure, indicates that the genera *Psilotum* and *Tmesipteris* are closely related to ferns. This hypothesis suggests that their ancestor's true roots were lost during evolution. Today, plants in these two genera absorb water and nutrients through numerous absorptive rhizoids.

▲ **Figure 29.16 Artist's conception of a Carboniferous forest based on fossil evidence.** In addition to plants, animals, including giant dragonflies like the one in the foreground, also thrived in the "coal forests" of the Carboniferous.

WHAT IF? *What would this forest look like if few lycophyte trees were reproducing (as would often have been the case)?*

The Significance of Seedless Vascular Plants

The ancestors of living lycophytes, horsetails, and ferns, along with their extinct seedless vascular relatives, grew to great heights during the Devonian and early Carboniferous, forming the first forests (Figure 29.16). How did their dramatic growth affect Earth and its other life? With the evolution of vascular tissue, roots, and leaves, these plants accelerated their rate of photosynthesis, dramatically increasing the removal of CO_2 from the atmosphere. Scientists estimate that CO_2 levels dropped by as much as a factor of five during the Carboniferous, causing global cooling that resulted in widespread glacier formation. Ancient CO_2 levels can be estimated in several ways. These include counting the number of stomata in fossil leaves (data from living species show that this number increases as CO_2 levels drop) and measuring carbon isotope levels in fossils of plankton. Different methods yield similar results, suggesting that reconstructions of past climates are accurate.

The seedless vascular plants that formed the first forests eventually became coal. In the stagnant waters of Carboniferous swamps, dead plants did not completely decay. This organic material turned to thick layers of peat, later covered by the sea. Marine sediments piled on top, and over millions of years, heat and pressure converted the peat to coal. In fact, Carboniferous coal deposits are the most extensive ever formed. Coal was crucial to the Industrial Revolution, and people worldwide still burn 6 billion tons a year. It is ironic that coal, formed from plants that contributed to a global cooling, now contributes to global warming by returning carbon to the atmosphere (see Chapter 55).

Growing along with the seedless plants in Carboniferous swamps were primitive seed plants. Though seed plants were not dominant at that time, they rose to prominence after the swamps began to dry up at the end of the Carboniferous period. The next chapter traces the origin and diversification of seed plants, continuing our story of adaptation to life on land.

CONCEPT CHECK 29.3

1. List the key derived traits found in pterophytes and seed plants, but not in lycophytes.
2. How do the main similarities and differences between seedless vascular plants and nonvascular plants influence function in these plants?
3. WHAT IF? If (contrary to the evidence) lycophytes and pterophytes formed a clade, what could you conclude about how members of this clade gained (or lost) traits shared by pterophytes and seed plants?
4. MAKE CONNECTIONS In Figure 29.13, if fertilization occurred between gametes from one gametophyte, how would this affect the production of genetic variation from sexual reproduction? See page 258 of Concept 13.4.

For suggested answers, see Appendix A.

29 CHAPTER REVIEW

SUMMARY OF KEY CONCEPTS

CONCEPT 29.1

Land plants evolved from green algae (pp. 600–606)

- Morphological and biochemical traits, as well as similarities in nuclear and chloroplast genes, suggest that charophytes are the closest living relatives of land plants.
- A protective layer of **sporopollenin** and other traits allow charophytes to tolerate occasional drying along the edges of ponds and lakes. Such traits may have enabled the algal ancestors of plants to survive in terrestrial conditions, opening the way to the colonization of dry land.
- Derived traits that distinguish the clade of land plants from charophytes, their closest algal relatives, include the four shown here:

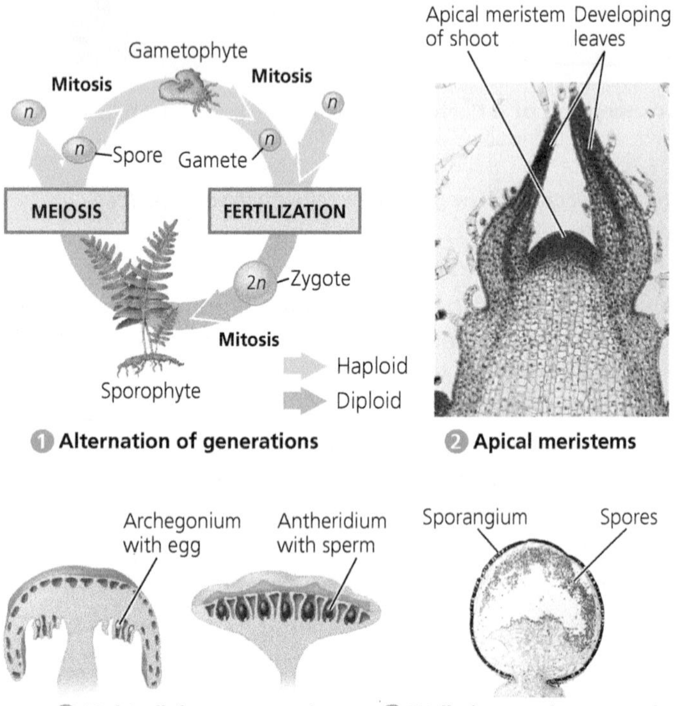

1. Alternation of generations
2. Apical meristems
3. Multicellular gametangia
4. Walled spores in sporangia

- Fossil evidence indicates that plants were on land at least 475 million years ago. Subsequently, plants diverged into several major groups, including nonvascular plants (bryophytes); seedless vascular plants, such as lycophytes and ferns; and the two groups of seed plants: gymnosperms and angiosperms.

? *Draw a phylogenetic tree illustrating our current understanding of land plant phylogeny; label the common ancestor of land plants and the origins of multicellular gametangia, vascular tissue, and seeds.*

CONCEPT 29.2

Mosses and other nonvascular plants have life cycles dominated by gametophytes (pp. 606–610)

- Current evidence indicates that the three phyla of **bryophytes**—liverworts, mosses, and hornworts—do not form a clade.
- In bryophytes, the dominant and typically most visible generation consists of haploid **gametophytes**, such as those that make up a carpet of moss. **Rhizoids** anchor gametophytes to the substrate on which they grow. The flagellated sperm produced by **antheridia** require a film of water to travel to the eggs in the **archegonia**.
- The diploid stage of the bryophyte life cycle—the **sporophytes**—grow out of archegonia and are attached to the gametophytes and dependent on them for nourishment. Smaller and simpler than vascular plant sporophytes, they typically consist of a **foot**, **seta** (stalk), and **sporangium**.
- *Sphagnum*, or peat moss, is common in large regions known as peatlands and has many practical uses, including as a fuel.

? *Summarize the ecological importance of mosses.*

CONCEPT 29.3

Ferns and other seedless vascular plants were the first plants to grow tall (pp. 610–615)

- Fossils of the forerunners of today's vascular plants date back about 425 million years and show that these small plants had independent, branching sporophytes. However, these ancestral species lacked other derived traits of living vascular plants, such as a life cycle with dominant sporophytes; lignified vascular tissue; well-developed roots and leaves; and sporophylls.
- Seedless vascular plants include the **lycophytes** (phylum Lycophyta: club mosses, spike mosses, and quillworts) and the **pterophytes** (phylum Pterophyta: ferns, horsetails, and whisk ferns and relatives). Ancient lycophytes included both small herbaceous plants and large trees. Present-day lycophytes are small herbaceous plants.
- Seedless vascular plants dominated the earliest forests. Their growth may have helped produce the major global cooling that characterized the end of the Carboniferous period. The decaying remnants of the first forests eventually became coal.

? *What trait(s) allowed vascular plants to grow tall, and why might increased height have been advantageous?*

TEST YOUR UNDERSTANDING

LEVEL 1: KNOWLEDGE/COMPREHENSION

1. Which of the following is *not* evidence that charophytes are the closest algal relatives of plants?
   a. similar sperm structure
   b. the presence of chloroplasts
   c. similarities in cell wall formation during cell division
   d. genetic similarities in chloroplasts
   e. similarities in proteins that synthesize cellulose
2. Which of the following characteristics of plants is absent in their closest relatives, the charophyte algae?
   a. chlorophyll *b*
   b. cellulose in cell walls
   c. formation of a cell plate during cytokinesis
   d. sexual reproduction
   e. alternation of multicellular generations

3. In plants, which of the following are produced by meiosis?
   a. haploid sporophytes
   b. haploid gametes
   c. diploid gametes
   d. haploid spores
   e. diploid spores

4. Microphylls are found in which plant group?
   a. mosses
   b. liverworts
   c. lycophytes
   d. ferns
   e. hornworts

5. Which of the following is a land plant that has flagellated sperm and a sporophyte-dominated life cycle?
   a. fern
   b. moss
   c. liverwort
   d. charophyte
   e. hornwort

6. Identify each of the following structures as haploid or diploid.
   a. sporophyte
   b. spore
   c. gametophyte
   d. zygote
   e. sperm

LEVEL 2: APPLICATION/ANALYSIS

7. Suppose an efficient conducting system evolved in a moss that could transport water and other materials as high as a tall tree. Which of the following statements about "trees" of such a species would *not* be true?
   a. Fertilization would probably be more difficult.
   b. Spore dispersal distances would probably increase.
   c. Females could produce only one archegonium.
   d. Unless its body parts were strengthened, such a "tree" would probably flop over.
   e. Individuals would probably compete more effectively for access to light.

8. **EVOLUTION CONNECTION**

   DRAW IT Draw a phylogenetic tree that represents our current understanding of evolutionary relationships between a moss, a gymnosperm, a lycophyte, and a fern. Use a charophyte alga as the outgroup. (See Chapter 26 to review phylogenetic trees.) Label each branch point of the phylogeny with at least one derived character unique to the clade descended from the common ancestor represented by the branch point.

LEVEL 3: SYNTHESIS/EVALUATION

9. **SCIENTIFIC INQUIRY**

   DRAW IT The feather moss *Pleurozium schreberi* harbors species of symbiotic nitrogen-fixing bacteria. Scientists studying this moss in northern forests found that the percentage of the ground surface "covered" by the moss increased from about 5% in forests that had burned 35 to 41 years ago to about 70% in forests that had burned 170 or more years ago. From mosses growing in these forests, they also obtained the following data on nitrogen fixation:

Age (years after fire)	N fixation rate (kg N per ha per yr)
35	0.001
41	0.005
78	0.08
101	0.3
124	0.9
170	2.0
220	1.3
244	2.1
270	1.6
300	3.0
355	2.3

Source: Data from O. Zackrisson et al., Nitrogen fixation increases with successional age in boreal forests, *Ecology* 85: 3327–3334 (2006).

   a. Use the data to draw a line graph, with age on the *x*-axis and the nitrogen fixation rate on the *y*-axis.
   b. Along with the nitrogen added by nitrogen fixation, about 1 kg of nitrogen per hectare per year is deposited into northern forests from the atmosphere as rain and small particles. Evaluate the extent to which *Pleurozium* affects nitrogen availability in northern forests of different ages.

10. **WRITE ABOUT A THEME**

   ENVIRONMENTAL INTERACTIONS Giant lycophyte trees had microphylls, whereas ferns and seed plants have megaphylls. Write a short essay (100–150 words) describing how a forest of lycophyte trees may have differed from a forest of large ferns or seed plants. In your answer, consider how the type of forest in which they grew may have affected interactions among small plants growing beneath the tall ones.

For selected answers, see Appendix A.

30

Plant Diversity II: The Evolution of Seed Plants

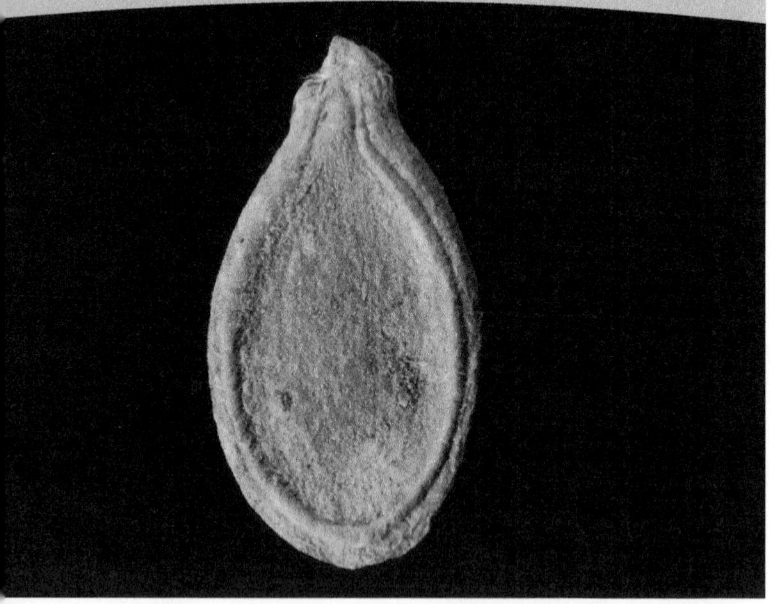

▲ **Figure 30.1 What human reproductive organ is functionally similar to this seed?**

EVOLUTION

KEY CONCEPTS

30.1 Seeds and pollen grains are key adaptations for life on land
30.2 Gymnosperms bear "naked" seeds, typically on cones
30.3 The reproductive adaptations of angiosperms include flowers and fruits
30.4 Human welfare depends greatly on seed plants

OVERVIEW

Transforming the World

Continuing the saga of how plants have transformed Earth, this chapter follows the emergence and diversification of seed plants. Fossils and comparative studies of living plants offer clues about the origin of seed plants some 360 million years ago. As this new group of plants became established, they dramatically altered the course of plant evolution. We'll begin our exploration of how this occurred by looking at the innovation for which seed plants are named: seeds (Figure 30.1).

A **seed** consists of an embryo and its food supply, surrounded by a protective coat. When mature, seeds are dispersed from their parent by wind or other means. Because it nourishes and protects the embryo, yet can move away from the mother plant, a seed is analogous to a detachable and mobile version of a pregnant woman's uterus. As we'll see, seeds are a key adaptation that helped seed plants to become the dominant producers on land and to make up the vast majority of plant biodiversity today.

Seed plants have also had an enormous impact on human society. Starting about 12,000 years ago, humans began to cultivate wheat, figs, maize (commonly called corn in the United States), rice, and other wild seed plants. This practice emerged independently in various parts of the world, including the Near East, East Asia, Africa, and the Americas. One piece of evidence, the well-preserved squash seed in Figure 30.1, was found in a cave in Mexico and dates from between 8,000 and 10,000 years ago. This seed differs from wild squash seeds, suggesting that squash was being domesticated by that time. The domestication of seed plants, particularly angiosperms, produced the most important cultural change in human history, transforming most human societies from roving bands of hunter-gatherers to permanent settlements anchored by agriculture.

In this chapter, we will first examine the general characteristics of seed plants. Then we will look at the distinguishing features and evolution of gymnosperms and angiosperms.

CONCEPT **30.1**

Seeds and pollen grains are key adaptations for life on land

We begin with an overview of terrestrial adaptations that seed plants added to those already present in nonvascular plants (bryophytes) and seedless vascular plants (see Chapter 29). In addition to seeds, the following are common to all seed plants: reduced gametophytes, heterospory, ovules, and pollen. As you'll read, these adaptations provided new ways for seed plants to cope with terrestrial conditions such as drought and exposure to the ultraviolet (UV) radiation in sunlight. Novel adaptations also freed seed plants from requiring water for fertilization, enabling reproduction to occur under a broader range of conditions than in seedless plants.

Advantages of Reduced Gametophytes

Mosses and other bryophytes have life cycles dominated by gametophytes, whereas ferns and other seedless vascular plants have sporophyte-dominated life cycles. The evolutionary trend of gametophyte reduction continued further in the vascular plant lineage that led to seed plants. While the gametophytes

	PLANT GROUP		
	Mosses and other nonvascular plants	**Ferns and other seedless vascular plants**	**Seed plants (gymnosperms and angiosperms)**
Gametophyte	Dominant	Reduced, independent (photosynthetic and free-living)	Reduced (usually microscopic), dependent on surrounding sporophyte tissue for nutrition
Sporophyte	Reduced, dependent on gametophyte for nutrition	Dominant	Dominant
Example			

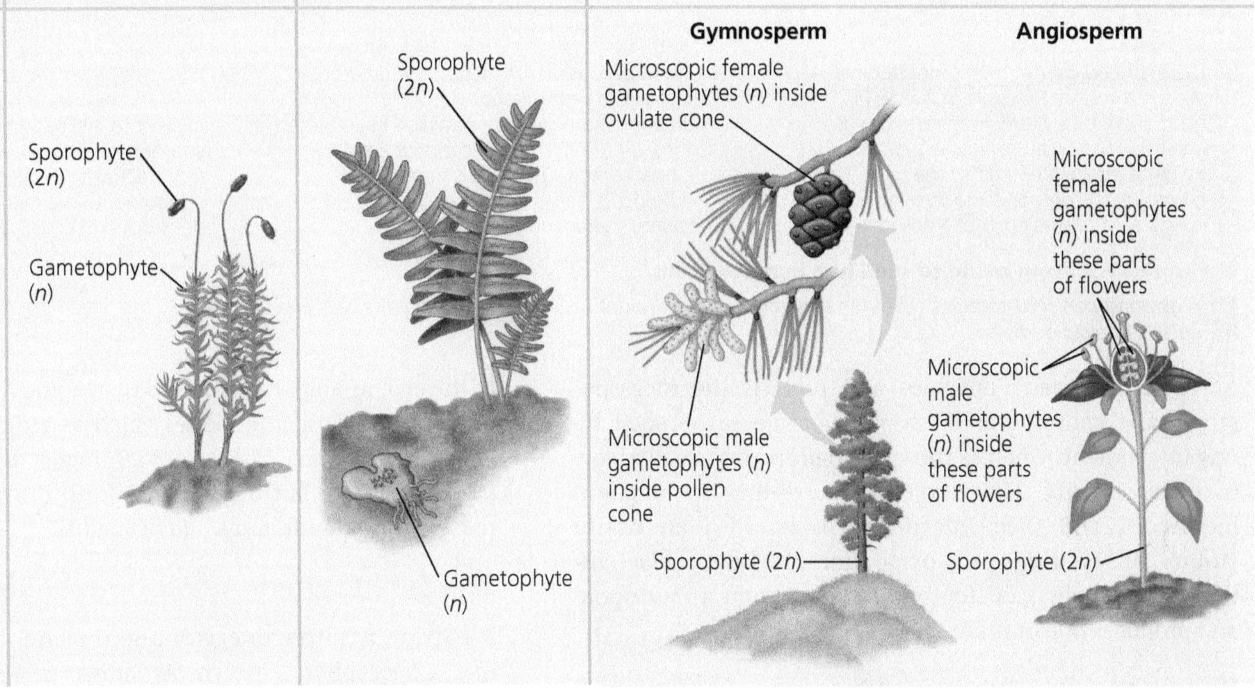

▲ Figure 30.2 **Gametophyte-sporophyte relationships in different plant groups.**

MAKE CONNECTIONS *In seed plants, how does retaining the gametophyte within the sporophyte likely affect embryo fitness? (See pp. 346, 472, and 480 in Chapters 17 and 23 to review mutagens, mutations, and fitness.)*

of seedless vascular plants are visible to the naked eye, the gametophytes of seed plants are mostly microscopic.

This miniaturization allowed for an important evolutionary innovation in seed plants: Their tiny gametophytes can develop from spores retained within the sporangia of the parental sporophyte. This arrangement protects the gametophytes from environmental stresses. The moist reproductive tissues of the sporophyte shield the gametophytes from UV radiation and protect them from drying out. This relationship also enables the dependent gametophytes to obtain nutrients from the sporophyte. In contrast, the free-living gametophytes of seedless plants must fend for themselves. Figure 30.2 contrasts the gametophyte-sporophyte relationships in nonvascular plants, seedless vascular plants, and seed plants.

Heterospory: The Rule Among Seed Plants

You read in Chapter 29 that most seedless plants are *homosporous*—they produce one kind of spore, which usually gives rise to a bisexual gametophyte. Ferns and other close relatives of seed plants are homosporous, suggesting that seed plants had homosporous ancestors. At some point, seed plants or their ancestors became *heterosporous*, producing two kinds of spores: Megasporangia produce *megaspores* that give rise to female gametophytes, and microsporangia produce *microspores* that give rise to male gametophytes. Each megasporangium has a single functional megaspore, whereas each microsporangium contains vast numbers of microspores.

As we noted previously, the miniaturization of seed plant gametophytes likely contributed to the great success of this clade. Next we will look at the development of the female gametophyte within an ovule and the development of the male gametophyte in a pollen grain. Then we will follow the transformation of a fertilized ovule into a seed.

Ovules and Production of Eggs

Although a few species of seedless plants are heterosporous, seed plants are unique in retaining the megasporangium within the parent sporophyte. A layer of sporophyte tissue

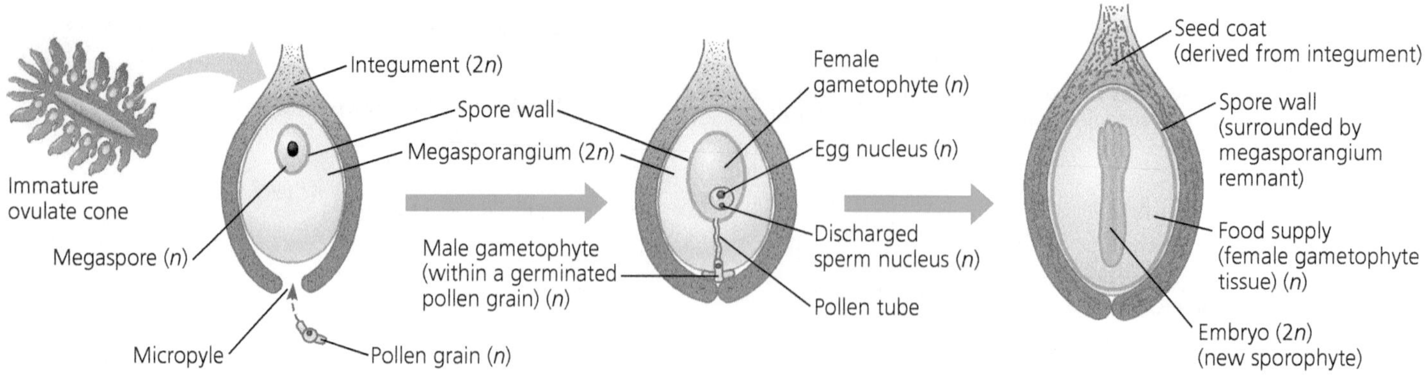

(a) Unfertilized ovule. In this longitudinal section through the ovule of a pine (a gymnosperm), a fleshy megasporangium is surrounded by a protective layer of tissue called an integument. The micropyle, the only opening through the integument, allows entry of a pollen grain.

(b) Fertilized ovule. A megaspore develops into a female gametophyte, which produces an egg. The pollen grain, which had entered through the micropyle, contains a male gametophyte. The male gametophyte develops a pollen tube that discharges sperm, thereby fertilizing the egg.

(c) Gymnosperm seed. Fertilization initiates the transformation of the ovule into a seed, which consists of a sporophyte embryo, a food supply, and a protective seed coat derived from the integument. The megasporangium dries out and collapses.

▲ Figure 30.3 **From ovule to seed in a gymnosperm.**

? *A gymnosperm seed contains cells from how many different plant generations? Identify the cells and whether each is haploid or diploid.*

called **integument** envelops and protects the megasporangium. Gymnosperm megasporangia are surrounded by one integument, whereas those in angiosperms usually have two integuments. The whole structure—megasporangium, megaspore, and their integument(s)—is called an **ovule** (Figure 30.3a). Inside each ovule (from the Latin *ovulum*, little egg), a female gametophyte develops from a megaspore and produces one or more eggs.

Pollen and Production of Sperm

A microspore develops into a **pollen grain** that consists of a male gametophyte enclosed within the pollen wall. (The outer layer of the pollen wall is composed of molecules secreted by sporophyte cells; hence, we refer to the male gametophyte as being *in* the pollen grain, not *equivalent to* the pollen grain.) The tough pollen wall, which contains the polymer sporopollenin, protects a pollen grain as it is transported from the parent plant by wind, for example, or by hitchhiking on the body of an animal. The transfer of pollen to the part of a seed plant that contains the ovules is called **pollination**. If a pollen grain germinates (begins growing), it gives rise to a pollen tube that discharges sperm into the female gametophyte within the ovule, as shown in Figure 30.3b.

Recall that in nonvascular plants and seedless vascular plants such as ferns, free-living gametophytes release flagellated sperm that swim through a film of water to reach eggs. The distance for this sperm transport rarely exceeds a few centimeters. By contrast, in seed plants a sperm-producing male gametophyte inside a pollen grain can be carried long distances by wind or by animals, eliminating the dependence on water for sperm transport. The sperm of seed plants also do not require motility because sperm are carried directly to the eggs by pollen tubes. Living gymnosperms provide evidence of the evolutionary transition to nonmotile sperm. The sperm of some gymnosperm species (such as ginkgos and cycads, shown a little later in Figure 30.5) retain the ancient flagellated condition, but flagella have been lost in the sperm of most gymnosperms and all angiosperms.

The Evolutionary Advantage of Seeds

If a sperm fertilizes an egg of a seed plant, the zygote grows into a sporophyte embryo. As shown in Figure 30.3c, the whole ovule develops into a seed: the embryo, along with a food supply, packaged within a protective coat derived from the integument(s).

Until the advent of seeds, the spore was the only protective stage in any plant life cycle. Moss spores, for example, may survive even if the local environment becomes too cold, too hot, or too dry for the mosses themselves to live. Their tiny size enables the spores to be dispersed in a dormant state to a new area, where they can germinate and give rise to new moss gametophytes if and when conditions are favorable enough for them to break dormancy. Spores were the main way that mosses, ferns, and other seedless plants spread over Earth for the first 100 million years of plant life on land.

Although mosses and other seedless plants continue to be very successful today, seeds represent a major evolutionary innovation that contributed to the opening of new ways of life for seed plants. What advantages do seeds provide over spores? Spores are usually single-celled, whereas seeds are multicellular, consisting of an embryo protected by a layer of tissue, the seed coat. A seed can remain dormant for days, months, or even years after being released from the parent plant, whereas most spores have shorter lifetimes. Also, unlike spores, seeds have a supply of stored food. Under favorable conditions, the seed can emerge from dormancy and germinate, with its stored food providing critical support for growth as the sporophyte embryo emerges as a seedling. Most seeds land close to their parent sporophyte plant, but some are carried long distances (up to hundreds of kilometers) by wind or animals.

CONCEPT CHECK 30.1

1. Contrast sperm delivery in seedless plants with sperm delivery in seed plants.
2. What features not present in seedless plants have contributed to the enormous success of seed plants on land?
3. **WHAT IF?** If a seed could not enter dormancy, how might that affect the embryo's transport or survival?

For suggested answers, see Appendix A.

◀ **Figure 30.4 A progymnosperm.** *Archaeopteris,* which lived 380 million years ago, produced wood and was heterosporous, but it did not produce seeds. Growing up to 20 m tall, it had fernlike leaves.

CONCEPT 30.2

Gymnosperms bear "naked" seeds, typically on cones

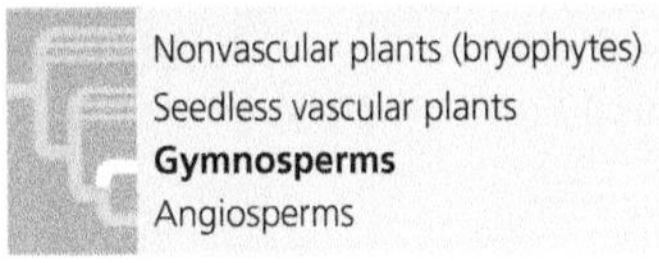

As shown in this phylogeny, extant seed plants form two sister clades: gymnosperms and angiosperms. Recall from Chapter 29 that gymnosperms have "naked" seeds that are not enclosed in ovaries. Their seeds are exposed on modified leaves (sporophylls) that usually form cones (strobili). (Angiosperm seeds are enclosed in fruits, which are mature ovaries.) We turn now to the origin of gymnosperms and other early seed plants.

Gymnosperm Evolution

Fossils reveal that by the late Devonian period (about 380 million years ago), some plants had acquired adaptations characteristic of seed plants. For example, *Archaeopteris* was a heterosporous tree with a woody stem (Figure 30.4). But it did not bear seeds. Such transitional species of seedless vascular plants are sometimes called **progymnosperms**.

The first seed plants to appear in the fossil record date from around 360 million years ago, 55 million years before the first gymnosperm fossils and more than 200 million years before the first angiosperm fossils. These early seed plants became extinct, as did several later lineages. It remains uncertain which of these extinct seed plant lineages ultimately gave rise to the gymnosperms.

The earliest fossils of gymnosperms are about 305 million years old. These early gymnosperms lived in Carboniferous ecosystems still dominated by lycophytes, horsetails, ferns, and other seedless vascular plants. As the Carboniferous period gave way to the Permian, markedly drier climatic conditions favored the spread of gymnosperms. The flora and fauna changed dramatically, as many groups of organisms disappeared and others became prominent (see Chapter 25). Though most pronounced in the seas, the changeover also affected terrestrial life. For example, in the animal kingdom, amphibians decreased in diversity and were replaced by reptiles, which were especially well adapted to the arid conditions. Similarly, the lycophytes, horsetails, and ferns that dominated the Carboniferous swamps were largely replaced by gymnosperms, which were more suited to the drier climate. Gymnosperms have the key terrestrial adaptations found in all seed plants, such as seeds and pollen. In addition, some gymnosperms were particularly well suited to arid conditions because of the thick cuticles and relatively small surface areas of their needle-shaped leaves.

Geologists consider the end of the Permian period, about 251 million years ago, to be the boundary between the Paleozoic ("old life") and Mesozoic ("middle life") eras. Life changed profoundly as gymnosperms dominated terrestrial ecosystems throughout much of the Mesozoic, serving as the food supply for giant herbivorous dinosaurs. Toward the end of the Mesozoic, angiosperms began to replace gymnosperms in some ecosystems. The Mesozoic era ended 65 million years ago with mass extinctions of dinosaurs and many other animal groups, and further increases in the biodiversity and importance of angiosperms. Although angiosperms now dominate most terrestrial ecosystems, many gymnosperms remain an important part of Earth's flora. For example, vast regions in northern latitudes are covered by forests of cone-bearing gymnosperms called **conifers**, which include spruce, pine, fir, and redwood (see Figure 52.12, p. 1155).

Of the ten plant phyla in the taxonomic scheme adopted by this textbook (see Table 29.1), four are gymnosperms: Cycadophyta, Ginkgophyta, Gnetophyta, and Coniferophyta. The relationships of these four phyla to each other are uncertain. Figure 30.5, on the next two pages, surveys the diversity of extant gymnosperms.

▼ Figure 30.5

Exploring Gymnosperm Diversity

Phylum Cycadophyta

Cycads are the next largest group of gymnosperms after the conifers. They have large cones and palmlike leaves (true palm species are angiosperms). Only about 130 species survive today, but cycads thrived during the Mesozoic era, known as the age of cycads as well as the age of dinosaurs.

Cycas revoluta

Phylum Ginkgophyta

Ginkgo biloba is the only surviving species of this phylum. Also known as the maidenhair tree, it has deciduous fanlike leaves that turn gold in autumn. It is a popular ornamental tree in cities because it tolerates air pollution well. Landscapers often plant only pollen-producing trees because the fleshy seeds smell rancid as they decay.

Phylum Gnetophyta

Plants in the phylum Gnetophyta, called gnetophytes, consist of three genera: *Gnetum*, *Ephedra*, and *Welwitschia*. Some species are tropical, whereas others live in deserts. Although very different in appearance, the genera are grouped together based on molecular data.

◄ ***Gnetum.*** This genus includes about 35 species of tropical trees, shrubs, and vines, mainly native to Africa and Asia. Their leaves look similar to those of flowering plants, and their seeds look somewhat like fruits.

► ***Welwitschia.*** This genus consists of one species, *Welwitschia mirabilis*, a plant that lives only in the deserts of southwestern Africa. Its straplike leaves are among the largest leaves known.

► ***Ephedra.*** This genus includes about 40 species that inhabit arid regions worldwide. These desert shrubs, commonly called "Mormon tea," produce the compound ephedrine, which is used medicinally as a decongestant.

Phylum Coniferophyta

Phylum Coniferophyta is by far the largest of the gymnosperm phyla, consisting of about 600 species of conifers (from the Latin *conus*, cone, and *ferre*, to carry). Many are large trees, such as cypresses and redwoods. A few conifer species dominate vast forested regions of the Northern Hemisphere, where the growing season is relatively short because of latitude or altitude.

Most conifers are evergreens; they retain their leaves throughout the year. Even during winter, a limited amount of photosynthesis occurs on sunny days. When spring comes, conifers already have fully developed leaves that can take advantage of the sunnier, warmer days. Some conifers, such as the dawn redwood, tamarack, and larch, are deciduous trees that lose leaves each autumn.

▶ **Douglas fir.** This evergreen tree (*Pseudotsuga menziesii*) provides more timber than any other North American tree species. Some uses include house framing, plywood, pulpwood for paper, railroad ties, and boxes and crates.

▶ **Common juniper.** The "berries" of the common juniper (*Juniperus communis*) are actually ovule-producing cones consisting of fleshy sporophylls.

◀ **European larch.** The needle-like leaves of this deciduous conifer (*Larix decidua*) turn yellow before they are shed in autumn. Native to the mountains of central Europe, including Switzerland's Matterhorn, depicted here, this species is extremely cold-tolerant, able to survive winter temperatures that plunge to –50°C.

◀ **Wollemi pine.** Survivors of a conifer group once known only from fossils, living Wollemi pines (*Wollemia nobilis*) were discovered in 1994 in a national park only 150 km from Sydney, Australia. The species consists of just 40 known individuals in two small groves. The inset photo compares the leaves of this "living fossil" with actual fossils.

▶ **Sequoia.** This giant sequoia (*Sequoiadendron giganteum*) in California's Sequoia National Park weighs about 2,500 metric tons, equivalent to about 24 blue whales (the largest animals) or 40,000 people. The giant sequoia is one of the largest living organisms and also among the most ancient, with some individuals estimated to be between 1,800 and 2,700 years old. Their cousins, the coast redwoods (*Sequoia sempervirens*), grow to heights of more than 110 m (taller than the Statue of Liberty) and are found only in a narrow coastal strip of northern California and southern Oregon.

▶ **Bristlecone pine.** This species (*Pinus longaeva*), which is found in the White Mountains of California, includes some of the oldest living organisms, reaching ages of more than 4,600 years. One tree (not shown here) is called Methuselah because it may be the world's oldest living tree. To protect the tree, scientists keep its location a secret.

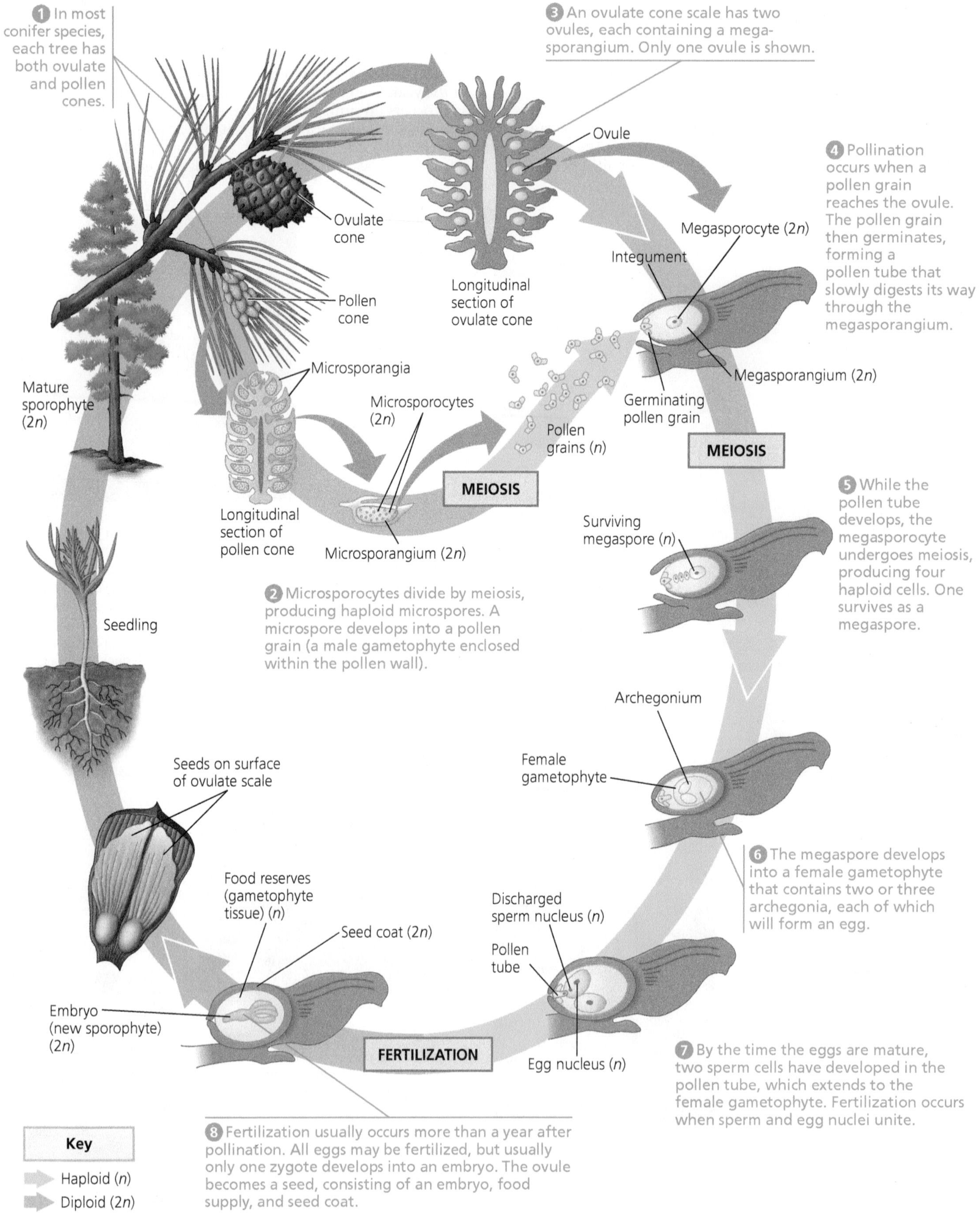

▼ **Figure 30.6 The life cycle of a pine.**

MAKE CONNECTIONS *What type of cell division occurs as a megaspore becomes a female gametophyte? (See Figure 13.9, p. 256.)*

The Life Cycle of a Pine: *A Closer Look*

As you read earlier, seed plant evolution has included three key reproductive adaptations: the increasing dominance of the sporophyte; the advent of the seed as a resistant, dispersible stage in the life cycle; and the appearance of pollen as an airborne agent that brings gametes together. Figure 30.6, on the facing page, shows how these adaptations come into play during the life cycle of a pine, a familiar conifer.

The pine tree is the sporophyte; its sporangia are located on scalelike structures packed densely in cones. Like all seed plants, conifers are heterosporous. In conifers, the two types of spores are produced by separate cones: small pollen cones and large ovulate cones. In most pine species, each tree has both types of cones. In pollen cones, microsporocytes (microspore mother cells) undergo meiosis, producing haploid microspores. Each microspore develops into a pollen grain containing a male gametophyte. In pines and other conifers, the yellow pollen is released in large amounts and carried by the wind, dusting everything in its path. Meanwhile, in ovulate cones, megasporocytes (megaspore mother cells) undergo meiosis and produce haploid megaspores inside the ovule. Surviving megaspores develop into multicellular female gametophytes, which are retained within the sporangia.

From the time young pollen and ovulate cones appear on the tree, it takes nearly three years for the male and female gametophytes to be produced and brought together and for mature seeds to form from the fertilized ovules. The scales of each ovulate cone then separate, and the seeds are dispersed by the wind. A seed that lands in a suitable environment then germinates, its embryo emerging as a pine seedling.

CONCEPT CHECK 30.2

1. Use examples from Figure 30.5 to describe how various gymnosperms are similar yet distinctive.
2. Explain how the pine life cycle in Figure 30.6 reflects the five adaptations common to all seed plants (see p. 618).
3. **MAKE CONNECTIONS** Does the hypothesis that gymnosperms and angiosperms are sister clades imply that they originated at the same time? (See pp. 538–539.)

For suggested answers, see Appendix A.

CONCEPT 30.3

The reproductive adaptations of angiosperms include flowers and fruits

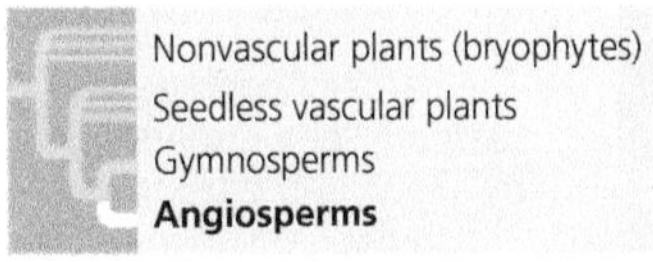

Commonly known as flowering plants, angiosperms are seed plants that produce the reproductive structures called flowers and fruits. The name *angiosperm* (from the Greek *angion*, container) refers to seeds contained in fruits, the mature ovaries. Today, angiosperms are the most diverse and widespread of all plants, with more than 250,000 species (about 90% of all plant species).

Characteristics of Angiosperms

All angiosperms are classified in a single phylum, Anthophyta (from the Greek *anthos*, flower). Before considering the evolution of angiosperms, we will examine their key adaptations—flowers and fruits—and the roles of these structures in the angiosperm life cycle.

Flowers

The **flower** is an angiosperm structure specialized for sexual reproduction. In many angiosperm species, insects or other animals transfer pollen from one flower to the sex organs on another flower, which makes pollination more directed than the wind-dependent pollination of most gymnosperms. However, some angiosperms *are* wind-pollinated, particularly those species that occur in dense populations, such as grasses and tree species in temperate forests.

A flower is a specialized shoot that can have up to four rings of modified leaves (sporophylls) called floral organs: sepals, petals, stamens, and carpels (Figure 30.7). Starting at the base of the flower are the **sepals**, which are usually green and enclose the flower before it opens (think of a rosebud). Interior to the sepals are the **petals**, which are brightly colored in most flowers and aid in attracting pollinators. Flowers that are wind-pollinated, however, generally lack brightly colored parts. In all angiosperms, the sepals and petals are sterile floral organs, meaning that they do not produce sperm or eggs. Within the petals are two whorls of fertile floral organs that produce spores,

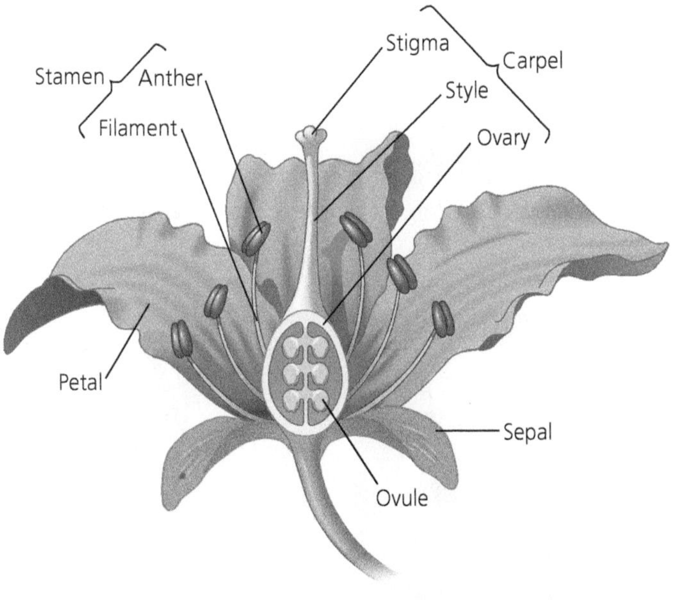

▲ Figure 30.7 **The structure of an idealized flower.**

the stamens and carpels. **Stamens** produce microspores that develop into pollen grains containing male gametophytes. A stamen consists of a stalk called the **filament** and a terminal sac, the **anther**, where pollen is produced. **Carpels** make megaspores and their products, female gametophytes. Some flowers have a single carpel, whereas others have multiple carpels, which are either separate or fused together. At the tip of the carpel is a sticky **stigma** that receives pollen. A **style** leads from the stigma to the **ovary** at the base of the carpel; the ovary contains one or more ovules. If fertilized, an ovule develops into a seed.

Fruits

A **fruit** typically consists of a mature ovary but can also include other flower parts. As seeds develop from ovules after fertilization, the ovary wall thickens. A pea pod is an example of a fruit, with seeds (mature ovules, the peas) encased in the ripened ovary (the pod). (We'll examine the developmental origin of fruits in Figure 38.10.)

Fruits protect dormant seeds and aid in their dispersal. Mature fruits can be either fleshy or dry **(Figure 30.8)**. Tomatoes, plums, and grapes are examples of fleshy fruits, in which the wall (pericarp) of the ovary becomes soft during ripening. Dry fruits include beans, nuts, and grains. Some dry fruits split open at maturity to release seeds, whereas others remain closed. The dry, wind-dispersed fruits of grasses, harvested while on the plant, are major staple foods for humans. The cereal grains of maize, rice, wheat, and other grasses, though easily mistaken for seeds, are each actually a fruit with a dry outer covering (the former wall of the ovary) that adheres to the seed coat of the seed within.

As shown in **Figure 30.9**, various adaptations of fruits and seeds help to disperse seeds. The seeds of some flowering plants, such as dandelions and maples, are contained within fruits that function like parachutes or propellers, adaptations that enhance dispersal by wind. Some fruits, such as coconuts, are adapted to dispersal by water (see Figure 38.11). And many angiosperms rely on animals to carry seeds. Some of these plants have fruits modified as burrs that cling to animal fur (or the clothes of humans). Other angiosperms produce edible fruits, which are usually nutritious, sweet tasting, and vividly colored, advertising their ripeness. When an animal eats the fruit, it digests the fruit's fleshy part, but the tough seeds usually pass unharmed through the animal's digestive tract. Animals may deposit the seeds, along with a supply of natural fertilizer, many kilometers from where the fruit was eaten.

▼ **Figure 30.8 Some variations in fruit structure.**

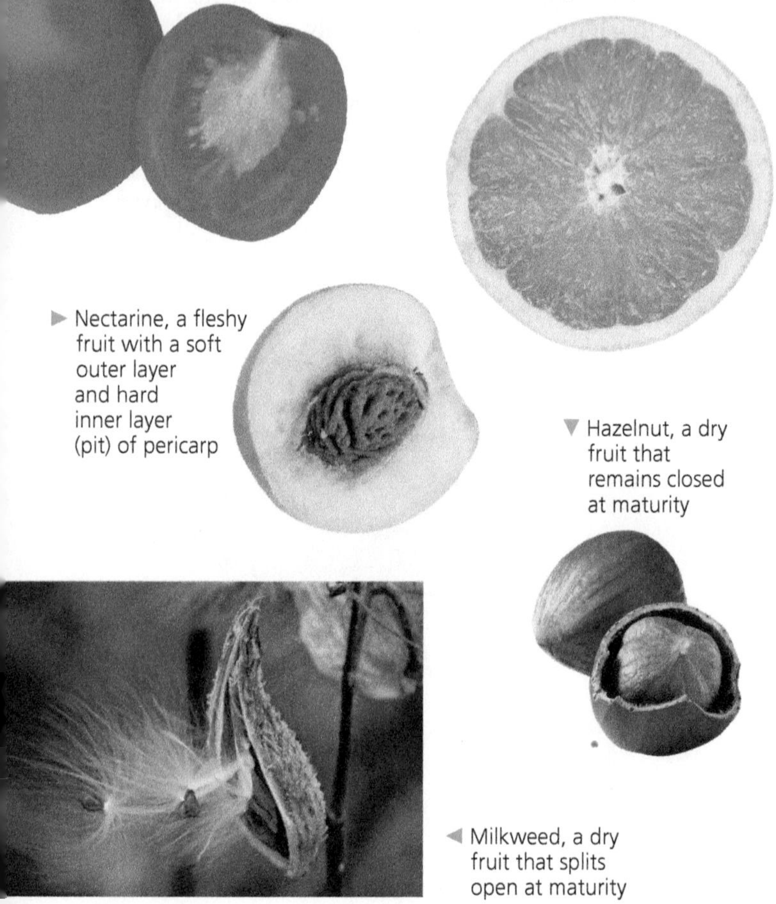

▼ Tomato, a fleshy fruit with soft outer and inner layers of pericarp (fruit wall)

▼ Ruby grapefruit, a fleshy fruit with a firm outer layer and soft inner layer of pericarp

► Nectarine, a fleshy fruit with a soft outer layer and hard inner layer (pit) of pericarp

▼ Hazelnut, a dry fruit that remains closed at maturity

◄ Milkweed, a dry fruit that splits open at maturity

▼ **Figure 30.9 Fruit adaptations that enhance seed dispersal.**

► Wings enable maple fruits to be carried by the wind.

◄ Seeds within berries and other edible fruits are often dispersed in animal feces.

◄ The barbs of cockleburs facilitate seed dispersal by allowing the fruits to "hitchhike" on animals.

The Angiosperm Life Cycle

You can follow a typical angiosperm life cycle in Figure 30.10. The flower of the sporophyte produces microspores that form male gametophytes and megaspores that form female gametophytes. The male gametophytes are in the pollen grains, which develop within microsporangia in the anthers. Each male gametophyte has two haploid cells: a *generative cell* that divides, forming two sperm, and a *tube cell* that produces a pollen tube. Each ovule, which develops in the ovary, contains a female gametophyte, also known as an **embryo sac**. The embryo sac consists of only a few cells, one of which is the egg. (We will discuss gametophyte development in more detail in Chapter 38.)

After its release from the anther, the pollen is carried to the sticky stigma at the tip of a carpel. Although some flowers self-pollinate, most have mechanisms that ensure **cross-pollination**, which in angiosperms is the transfer of pollen from an anther of a flower on one plant to the stigma of a flower on another plant of the same species. Cross-pollination enhances genetic

▼ Figure 30.10 **The life cycle of an angiosperm.**

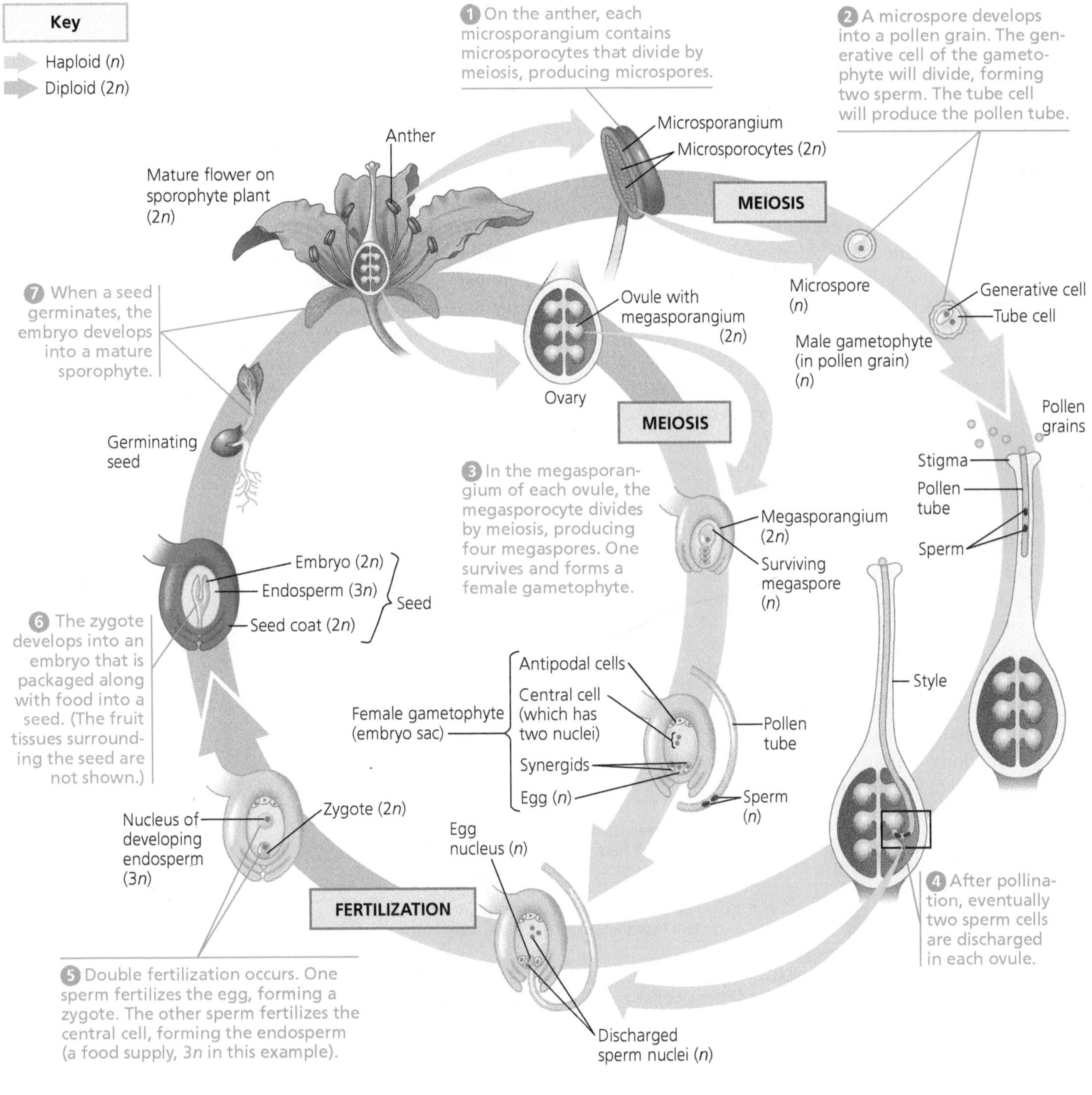

variability. In some species, stamens and carpels of a single flower may mature at different times, or they may be so arranged that self-pollination is unlikely.

The pollen grain absorbs water and germinates after it adheres to the stigma of a carpel. The tube cell produces a pollen tube that grows down within the style of the carpel. After reaching the ovary, the pollen tube penetrates through the **micropyle**, a pore in the integuments of the ovule, and discharges two sperm cells into the female gametophyte (embryo sac). One sperm fertilizes the egg, forming a diploid zygote. The other sperm fuses with the two nuclei in the large central cell of the female gametophyte, producing a triploid cell. This type of **double fertilization**, in which one fertilization event produces a zygote and the other produces a triploid cell, is unique to angiosperms.

After double fertilization, the ovule matures into a seed. The zygote develops into a sporophyte embryo with a rudimentary root and one or two seed leaves called **cotyledons**. The triploid central cell of the female gametophyte develops into **endosperm**, tissue rich in starch and other food reserves that nourish the developing embryo.

What is the function of double fertilization in angiosperms? One hypothesis is that double fertilization synchronizes the development of food storage in the seed with the development of the embryo. If a particular flower is not pollinated or sperm cells are not discharged into the embryo sac, fertilization does not occur, and neither endosperm nor embryo forms. So perhaps double fertilization is an adaptation that prevents flowering plants from squandering nutrients on infertile ovules.

Another type of double fertilization occurs in some gymnosperm species belonging to the phylum Gnetophyta. However, double fertilization in these species gives rise to two embryos rather than to an embryo and endosperm.

As you read earlier, the seed consists of the embryo, the endosperm, and a seed coat derived from the integuments. An ovary develops into a fruit as its ovules become seeds. After being dispersed, a seed may germinate if environmental conditions are favorable. The coat ruptures and the embryo emerges as a seedling, using food stored in the endosperm and cotyledons until it can produce its own food by photosynthesis.

Angiosperm Evolution

Clarifying the origin of angiosperms—what Charles Darwin once called an "abominable mystery"—poses fascinating challenges to evolutionary biologists. Angiosperms originated at least 140 million years ago, and during the late Mesozoic, the major branches of the clade diverged from their common ancestor. By the mid-Cretaceous period (100 million years ago), angiosperms began to dominate many terrestrial ecosystems. Landscapes changed dramatically as conifers, cycads, and other gymnosperms gave way to flowering plants in many parts of the world.

The flowers and fruits of angiosperms distinguish them markedly from living gymnosperms, which makes the origins of angiosperms puzzling. To understand how the angiosperm body plan emerged, scientists are studying fossils, refining angiosperm phylogeny, and elucidating developmental patterns that underlie flowers and other angiosperm innovations. As we'll see, much progress has been made toward solving Darwin's mystery—but we still do not fully understand how angiosperms originated from earlier seed plants.

Fossil Angiosperms

In the late 1990s, scientists in China discovered several intriguing fossils of 125-million-year-old angiosperms. These fossils, now named *Archaefructus liaoningensis* and *Archaefructus sinensis* (Figure 30.11), share some traits with living angiosperms but lack others. *Archaefructus sinensis*, for example, has anthers and also has seeds inside closed carpels but lacks petals and sepals. In 2002, scientists completed a phylogenetic comparison of *Archaefructus* with 173 living plant species. The researchers concluded that *Archaefructus* may belong to the earliest-diverging group of angiosperms known.

(a) *Archaefructus sinensis*, a 125-million-year-old fossil. This species may represent the sister group to all other angiosperms, or it may belong to the water lily group (see Figure 30.12). Researchers are testing these two hypotheses with phylogenetic analyses.

(b) Artist's reconstruction of *Archaefructus sinensis*

▲ Figure 30.11 **An early flowering plant.**

Based on *Archaefructus* fossils, can we infer traits of the common ancestor of *Archaefructus* and living angiosperms? The fossils indicate that *Archaefructus* had simple flowers and was herbaceous with bulbous structures that may have served as floats, suggesting it was aquatic. But investigating whether the angiosperm common ancestor had simple flowers and was herbaceous and aquatic also requires examining fossils of other seed plants thought to have been closely related to angiosperms. All of those plants were woody, indicating that the common ancestor was probably woody. Furthermore, paleobotanists have found angiosperm fossils from later-diverging lineages that became aquatic and have flowers resembling those of *Archaefructus*. This suggests that simple flowers and an aquatic growth form may have been derived traits of *Archaefructus* rather than traits of the common ancestor. Overall, while most researchers agree that the angiosperm common ancestor was woody, debate continues about many of its other features.

Angiosperm Phylogeny

To shed light on the body plan of early angiosperms, scientists have long sought to identify which seed plants, including fossil species, are most closely related to angiosperms. Molecular and morphological evidence suggests that living gymnosperms are a monophyletic group whose earliest lineages diverged from the ancestors of angiosperms about 305 million years ago. Note that this does not necessarily imply that angiosperms originated 305 million years ago, but that the most recent common ancestor of gymnosperms and angiosperms lived at that time. Angiosperms may in fact be most closely related to extinct seed plants such as the Bennettitales, a group with flowerlike structures that may have been pollinated by insects (**Figure 30.12a**). Systematists hope to resolve this issue through phylogenetic studies that combine data from fossil and living species of a wide range of seed plants.

Making sense of the origin of angiosperms also depends on working out the order in which angiosperm clades diverged from one another. Here, dramatic progress has been made in recent years. Molecular and morphological evidence suggests that a small South Pacific shrub called *Amborella trichopoda* and water lilies are living representatives of two of the most ancient angiosperm lineages (**Figure 30.12b**).

Developmental Patterns in Angiosperms

Additional clues about the origin of flowering plants are emerging from studies of plant development. For example, a 2006 study demonstrated that in *Amborella*, eggs form from precursor cells that differ from the egg precursor cells of most other living angiosperms. Intriguingly, the way in which eggs form in *Amborella* has similarities to how eggs

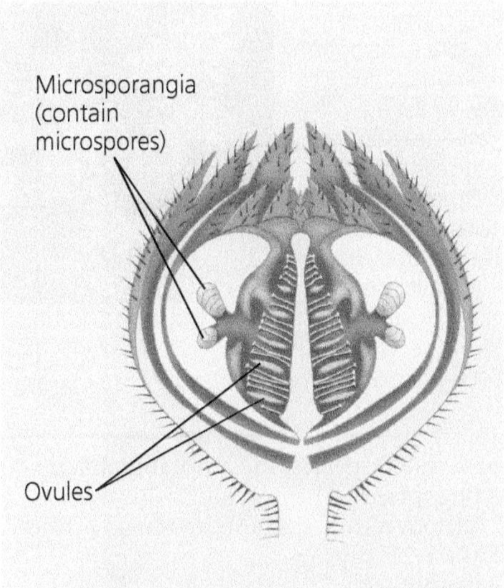

(a) A possible ancestor of the angiosperms? This reconstruction shows a cross section through the flowerlike structures found in the Bennettitales, an extinct group of seed plants hypothesized to be more closely related to angiosperms than to gymnosperms.

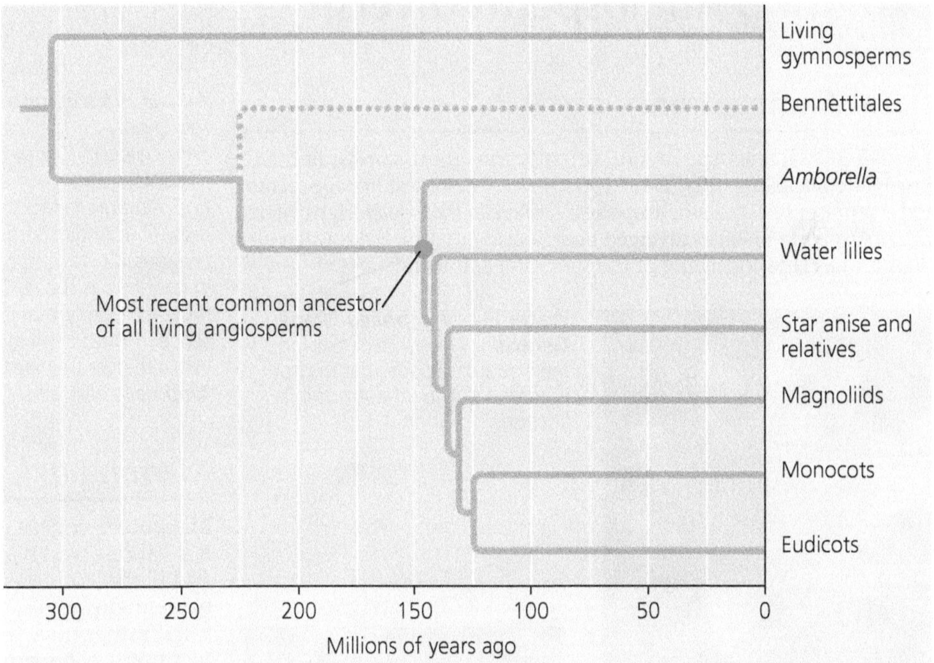

(b) Angiosperm phylogeny. This tree represents one current hypothesis of angiosperm evolutionary relationships, based on morphological and molecular evidence. Angiosperms originated at least 140 million years ago. The dotted line indicates the uncertain position of the Bennettitales, a possible sister group to the angiosperms.

▲ **Figure 30.12 Angiosperm evolutionary history.**

? *Would the branching order of the phylogeny in (b) necessarily have to be redrawn if a 150-million-year-old fossil monocot were discovered? Explain.*

form in gymnosperms—a possible link to the ancient common ancestor of gymnosperms and angiosperms. Other studies suggest that in a variety of early angiosperms (as well as in *Amborella*), the outer of the two protective integuments appears to be a modified leaf that originates separately from the inner integument. Because gymnosperms have only one integument, scientists are curious about exactly how the second integument originated in angiosperms. Researchers are also studying key developmental genes in gymnosperms and angiosperms, including genes that control flower development in angiosperms. Early results have uncovered developmental pathways shared by gymnosperms and angiosperms. These shared pathways may reveal clues about steps leading to the origin of flowering plants.

Angiosperm Diversity

From their humble beginnings in the Mesozoic, angiosperms have diversified into more than 250,000 living species. Until the late 1990s, most systematists divided flowering plants into two groups, based partly on the number of cotyledons, or seed leaves, in the embryo. Species with one cotyledon were called **monocots**, and those with two were called **dicots**. Other features, such as flower and leaf structure, were also used to define the two groups. For example, monocots typically have parallel leaf veins (think of a grass blade), whereas the veins of most dicots have a netlike pattern (think of an oak leaf). Some examples of monocots are orchids, palms, and grain crops such as maize, wheat, and rice. Some examples of dicots are roses, peas, sunflowers, and maples.

Recent DNA studies, however, indicate that the monocot-dicot distinction does not completely reflect evolutionary relationships. Current research supports the hypothesis that monocots form a clade but reveals that the species traditionally called dicots are polyphyletic. The vast majority of species once categorized as dicots form a large clade, now known as **eudicots** ("true" dicots). The rest of the former dicots are now grouped into several small lineages. Three of these lineages are informally called **basal angiosperms** because they appear to include the flowering plants belonging to the oldest lineages. A fourth lineage, called the **magnoliids**, evolved later. Figure 30.13 provides an overview of angiosperm diversity.

▼ Figure 30.13

Exploring Angiosperm Diversity

Basal Angiosperms

Surviving basal angiosperms are currently thought to consist of three lineages comprising only about 100 species. The oldest lineage seems to be represented by a single species, *Amborella trichopoda* (right). The other surviving lineages diverged later: a clade that includes water lilies and a clade consisting of the star anise and its relatives.

Water lily (*Nymphaea "Rene Gerard"*). Water lilies are living members of a clade that may be predated only by the *Amborella* lineage.

Star anise (*Illicium*). This genus belongs to a third surviving lineage of basal angiosperms.

***Amborella trichopoda*.** This small shrub, found only on the South Pacific island of New Caledonia, may be the sole survivor of a branch at the base of the angiosperm tree. *Amborella* lacks vessels, which are present in angiosperms in later-developing lineages. Consisting of xylem cells arranged in continuous tubes, vessels transport water more efficiently than tracheids. Their absence in *Amborella* indicates they may have evolved after the lineage that gave rise to *Amborella* diverged.

Magnoliids

Magnoliids consist of about 8,000 species, most notably magnolias, laurels, and black pepper plants. They include both woody and herbaceous species. Although they share some traits with basal angiosperms, such as a typically spiral rather than whorled arrangement of floral organs, magnoliids are more closely related to eudicots and monocots.

Southern magnolia (*Magnolia grandiflora*). This member of the magnolia family is a woody magnoliid. The variety of southern magnolia shown here, called "Goliath," has flowers that measure up to about a foot across.

Monocots

About one-quarter of angiosperm species are monocots—about 70,000 species. These examples represent some of the largest families.

Orchid (*Lemboglossum rossii*)

Pygmy date palm (*Phoenix roebelenii*)

Lily (*Lilium* "Enchantment")

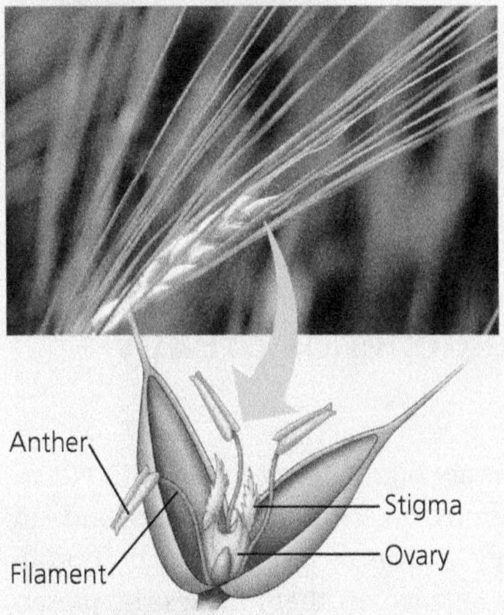

Barley (*Hordeum vulgare*), a grass

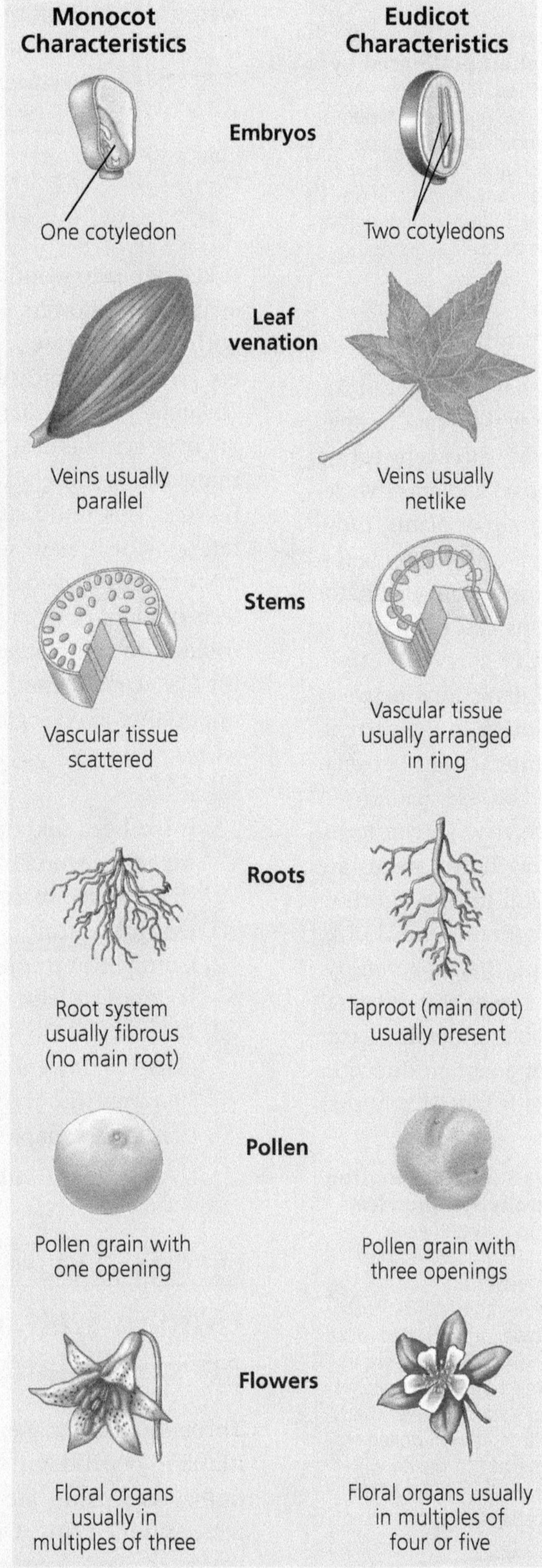

Eudicots

More than two-thirds of angiosperm species are eudicots—roughly 170,000 species. Below is a sampling of eudicot floral diversity.

California poppy (*Eschscholzia californica*)

Pyrenean oak (*Quercus pyrenaica*)

Dog rose (*Rosa canina*), a wild rose

Snow pea (*Pisum sativum*), a legume

Zucchini (*Cucurbita pepo*) flowers

◀ **Figure 30.14 A plant pollinated by flies.** *Rafflesia arnoldii*, the "monster flower" of Indonesia, is the size of an automobile tire. It attracts fly pollinators with an odor like that of a decaying corpse.

Evolutionary Links Between Angiosperms and Animals

Ever since they colonized land, animals have influenced the evolution of terrestrial plants, and vice versa. For example, herbivores can reduce a plant's reproductive success by eating its roots, leaves, or seeds. As a result, if a novel and effective defense against herbivores originates in a group of plants, those plants may be favored by natural selection—as will any herbivores that can overcome this new defense. Plant-pollinator and other mutually beneficial interactions can have similar evolutionary effects, as seen in Figure 30.14.

In the examples we just discussed, interactions between plants and animals led to reciprocal evolution in the particular pairs of species involved. However, interactions between plants and animals also may have affected broader patterns in the history of life, such as rates at which new species form. Consider the evolutionary impact of how flower petals are arranged. Flower petals can be symmetrical in one direction only (*bilateral symmetry*, as in the pea blossom in Figure 30.13), or they can be symmetrical in all directions (*radial symmetry*, as in the dog rose in Figure 30.13). On a flower with bilateral symmetry, an insect pollinator may be able to obtain nectar only when it approaches the flower from a certain direction (Figure 30.15). This constraint can make it more likely that as an insect moves from flower to flower, pollen is placed on a part of the insect's body that will come into contact with the stigma of a flower of the same species. Such specificity of pollen transfer tends to reduce gene flow between diverging populations and hence could lead to increased rates of plant speciation.

◀ **Figure 30.15 Pollinating a bilaterally symmetrical flower.** To harvest nectar (a sugary solution secreted by flower glands) from this bilaterally symmetrical Scottish broom flower, a honeybee must land as shown. This releases a tripping mechanism that arches the flower's stamens over the bee and dusts it with pollen. Later, some of this pollen will rub off onto the stigma of the next flower of this species that the bee visits.

How can this hypothesis be tested? One approach is illustrated in this diagram:

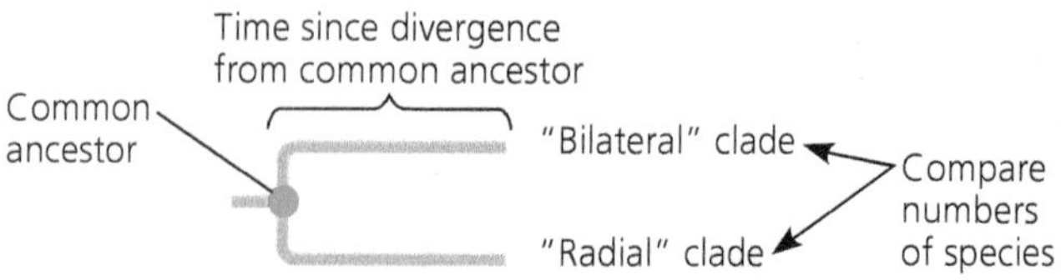

A key step is to identify cases in which a clade with bilaterally symmetrical flowers shares an immediate common ancestor with a clade whose members have radially symmetrical flowers. One recent study identified 19 such pairs of closely related "bilateral" and "radial" clades. On average, the clade with bilaterally symmetrical flowers had nearly 2,400 more species than did its closely related clade with radially symmetrical flowers. This result suggests that flower shape can affect the rate at which new species form, with speciation occurring more rapidly in clades with bilateral symmetry. Overall, the effects of plant-pollinator interactions are thought to have contributed to the increasing dominance of flowering plants in the Cretaceous period, helping to make angiosperms of central importance in ecological communites.

CONCEPT CHECK 30.3

1. It has been said that an oak is an acorn's way of making more acorns. Write an explanation that includes these terms: sporophyte, gametophyte, ovule, seed, ovary, and fruit.
2. Compare and contrast a pine cone and a flower in terms of structure and function.
3. **WHAT IF?** Do speciation rates in closely related clades of flowering plants show that flower shape is *correlated with* the rate at which new species form, or that flower shape is *responsible for* this rate? Explain.

For suggested answers, see Appendix A.

CONCEPT 30.4

Human welfare depends greatly on seed plants

Throughout Unit Five, we are highlighting the ways in which humans depend on various organisms. In forests and on farms, seed plants are key sources of food, fuel, wood products, and medicine. Our reliance on them makes the preservation of plant diversity critical.

Products from Seed Plants

Most of our food comes from angiosperms. Just six crops—maize, rice, wheat, potatoes, cassava, and sweet potatoes—yield 80% of all the calories consumed by humans. We also depend on angiosperms to feed livestock: It takes 5–7 kg of grain to produce 1 kg of grain-fed beef.

Today's crops are the products of artificial selection—the result of plant domestication that began about 12,000 years ago. To appreciate the scale of this transformation, note how the number and size of seeds in domesticated plants are greater than those of their wild relatives, as in the case of maize and the grass teosinte (see Figure 38.16). Scientists can glean information about domestication by comparing the genes of crops with those of wild relatives. With maize, dramatic changes such as increased cob size and loss of the hard coating around teosinte kernels may have been initiated by as few as five mutations.

Flowering plants also provide other edible products. Two popular beverages come from tea leaves and coffee beans, and you can thank the tropical cacao tree for cocoa and chocolate. Spices are derived from various plant parts, such as flowers (cloves, saffron), fruits and seeds (vanilla, black pepper, mustard), leaves (basil, mint, sage), and even bark (cinnamon).

Many seed plants are sources of wood, which is absent in all living seedless plants. Wood consists of tough-walled xylem cells (see Figure 35.22). It is the primary source of fuel for much of the world, and wood pulp, typically derived from conifers such as fir and pine, is used to make paper. Wood also remains the most widely used construction material.

For centuries, humans have also depended on seed plants for medicines. Many cultures use herbal remedies, and scientists have extracted and identified the relevant secondary compounds (see p. 604) from many of these plants, and later synthesized them. Willow leaves and bark, for instance, have long been used in pain-relieving remedies, including prescriptions by the Greek physician Hippocrates. In the 1800s, scientists traced the willow's medicinal property to the chemical salicin. A synthesized derivative, acetylsalicylic acid, is what we call aspirin. Plants also remain a direct source of medicinal compounds. In the United States, about 25% of prescription drugs contain an active ingredient from plants, typically seed plants. Other ingredients were discovered in seed plants and then synthesized artificially. Table 30.1 lists some medicinal uses of secondary compounds found in seed plants.

Table 30.1 Examples of Plant-Derived Medicines

Compound	Source	Use
Atropine	Belladonna plant	Eye pupil dilator
Digitalin	Foxglove	Heart medication
Menthol	Eucalyptus tree	Throat soother
Quinine	Cinchona tree	Malaria preventive
Taxol	Pacific yew	Ovarian cancer drug
Tubocurarine	Curare tree	Muscle relaxant
Vinblastine	Periwinkle	Leukemia drug

Threats to Plant Diversity

Although plants may be a renewable resource, plant diversity is not. The exploding human population and its demand for space and resources are extinguishing plant species at a high rate. The problem is especially severe in the tropics, where more than two-thirds of the human population live and where population growth is fastest. About 55,000 km^2 (14 million acres) of tropical rain forest are cleared each year (Figure 30.16), a rate that would completely eliminate the remaining 11 million km^2

▼ Figure 30.16

IMPACT

Clear-Cutting of Tropical Forests

Over the past several hundred years, nearly half of Earth's tropical forests have been cut down and converted to farmland and other uses. Satellite images, such as those below, show that together these regions cover an area roughly the size of Canada. Living trees release large quantities of water to the atmosphere, cooling the local environment (much as evaporation of sweat cools your body) and putting moisture into the air that is recycled as rain. When trees are cut down, less moisture is released to the atmosphere, causing increased temperatures and decreased rainfall. Tree removal also reduces the absorption of atmospheric carbon dioxide (CO_2) that occurs during photosynthesis.

A satellite image from 2000 shows clear-cut areas in Brazil surrounded by dense tropical forest.

By 2009, much more of this same tropical forest had been cut down.

WHY IT MATTERS Higher temperatures and increased atmospheric CO_2 resulting from destruction of tropical forests contribute to global warming, making preservation of these forests a high priority. Moreover, changes in rainfall patterns are expected to reduce agricultural production in some of the poorest countries. Finally, tropical forests harbor 50% or more of all species on Earth. Hence, higher temperatures, reduced rainfall, and habitat loss caused by clear-cutting tropical forests may lead to extinction of many species.

FURTHER READING G. P. Asner, T. K. Rudel, T. M. Aide, R. Defries, and R. Emerson, A contemporary assessment of change in humid tropical forests, *Conservation Biology* 23:1386–1395 (2009).

WHAT IF? How would clear-cutting affect the temperature and moisture along the edges of a remaining forest fragment?

of tropical forests in 200 years. The most common cause of this destruction is slash-and-burn clearing of forests for agricultural use (see Chapter 56). As forests disappear, so do large numbers of plant species. Of course, once a species becomes extinct, it can never return.

The loss of plant species is often accompanied by the loss of insects and other rain forest animals. Researchers estimate that habitat destruction in rain forests and other ecosystems is pushing hundreds of species toward extinction each year. If current rates of loss in the tropics and elsewhere continue, scientists estimate that within the next few centuries, 50% or more of Earth's species will become extinct. Such losses would constitute a global mass extinction, rivaling the Permian and Cretaceous mass extinctions and forever changing the evolutionary history of land plants (and many other organisms).

Many people have ethical concerns about contributing to the extinction of living forms. In addition, there are practical reasons to be concerned about the loss of plant diversity. So far, we have explored the potential uses of only a tiny fraction of the more than 290,000 known plant species. For example, almost all our food is based on the cultivation of only about two dozen species of seed plants. And fewer than 5,000 plant species have been studied as potential sources of medicines. The tropical rain forest may be a medicine chest of healing plants that could be extinct before we even know they exist. If we begin to view rain forests and other ecosystems as living treasures that can regenerate only slowly, we may learn to harvest their products at sustainable rates. What else can we do to preserve plant diversity? Few questions are as important, as we'll explore more fully in Unit Eight (Ecology).

CONCEPT CHECK 30.4

1. Explain why plant diversity can be considered a nonrenewable resource.
2. **WHAT IF?** How could phylogenies be used to help researchers search more efficiently for novel medicines derived from seed plants?

For suggested answers, see Appendix A.

30 CHAPTER REVIEW

SUMMARY OF KEY CONCEPTS

CONCEPT 30.1

Seeds and pollen grains are key adaptations for life on land (pp. 618–621)

Five Derived Traits of Seed Plants		
Reduced gametophytes	Microscopic male and female gametophytes (*n*) are nourished and protected by the sporophyte (2*n*)	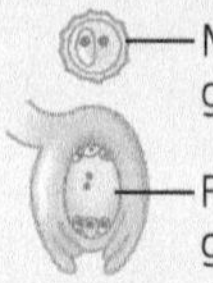
Heterospory	Microspore (gives rise to a male gametophyte) Megaspore (gives rise to a female gametophyte)	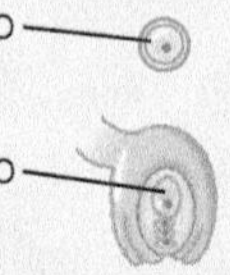
Ovules	Ovule (gymnosperm): Integument (2*n*), Megaspore (*n*), Megasporangium (2*n*)	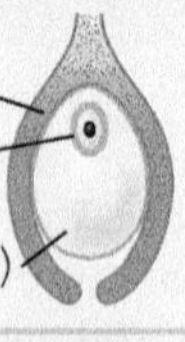
Pollen	Pollen grains make water unnecessary for fertilization	
Seeds	Seeds: survive better than unprotected spores, can be transported long distances; Seed coat, Food supply, Embryo	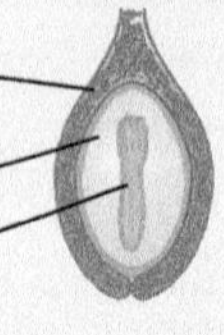

? *Describe how the parts of an ovule (integument, megaspore, megasporangium) correspond to the parts of a seed.*

CONCEPT 30.2

Gymnosperms bear "naked" seeds, typically on cones (pp. 621–625)

- Gymnosperms appear early in the plant fossil record and dominated many Mesozoic terrestrial ecosystems. Living seed plants can be divided into two monophyletic groups: gymnosperms and angiosperms. Extant gymnosperms include cycads, *Ginkgo biloba*, gnetophytes, and conifers.
- Dominance of the sporophyte generation, the development of seeds from fertilized ovules, and the role of pollen in transferring sperm to ovules are key features of a typical gymnosperm life cycle.

? *Although there are fewer than 1,000 species of gymnosperms, the group is still very successful in terms of its evolutionary longevity, adaptations, and geographic distribution. Explain.*

CONCEPT 30.3

The reproductive adaptations of angiosperms include flowers and fruits (pp. 625–632)

- Flowers generally consist of four whorls of modified leaves: sepals, petals, stamens (which produce pollen), and carpels (which produce ovules). Ovaries ripen into fruits, which often carry seeds by wind, water, or animals to new locations.
- An adaptive radiation of angiosperms occurred during the Cretaceous period. Fossils, phylogenetic analyses, and developmental studies offer insights into the origin of flowers.
- Several groups of basal angiosperms have been identified. Other major clades of angiosperms include magnoliids, monocots, and eudicots.

- Pollination and other interactions between angiosperms and animals may have contributed to the success of flowering plants during the last 100 million years.

? *What makes the origin of angiosperms puzzling? Has Darwin's "abominable mystery" been solved? Explain.*

CONCEPT 30.4

Human welfare depends greatly on seed plants (pp. 632–634)

- Humans depend on seed plants for products such as food, wood, and many medicines.
- Destruction of habitat threatens the extinction of many plant species and the animal species they support.

? *Explain why destroying the remaining tropical forests might harm humans and lead to a mass extinction.*

TEST YOUR UNDERSTANDING

LEVEL 1: KNOWLEDGE/COMPREHENSION

1. Where in an angiosperm would you find a megasporangium?
   a. in the style of a flower
   b. inside the tip of a pollen tube
   c. enclosed in the stigma of a flower
   d. within an ovule contained within an ovary of a flower
   e. packed into pollen sacs within the anthers found on a stamen

2. A fruit is most commonly
   a. a mature ovary.
   b. a thickened style.
   c. an enlarged ovule.
   d. a modified root.
   e. a mature female gametophyte.

3. With respect to angiosperms, which of the following is *incorrectly* paired with its chromosome count?
   a. egg—n
   b. megaspore—$2n$
   c. microspore—n
   d. zygote—$2n$
   e. sperm—n

4. Which of the following is *not* a characteristic that distinguishes gymnosperms and angiosperms from other plants?
   a. alternation of generations
   b. ovules
   c. integuments
   d. pollen
   e. dependent gametophytes

5. Gymnosperms and angiosperms have the following in common *except*
   a. seeds.
   b. pollen.
   c. vascular tissue.
   d. ovaries.
   e. ovules.

LEVEL 2: APPLICATION/ANALYSIS

6. **DRAW IT** Use the letters a–d to label where on the phylogenetic tree each of the following derived characters appear.
   a. flowers
   b. embryos
   c. seeds
   d. vascular tissue

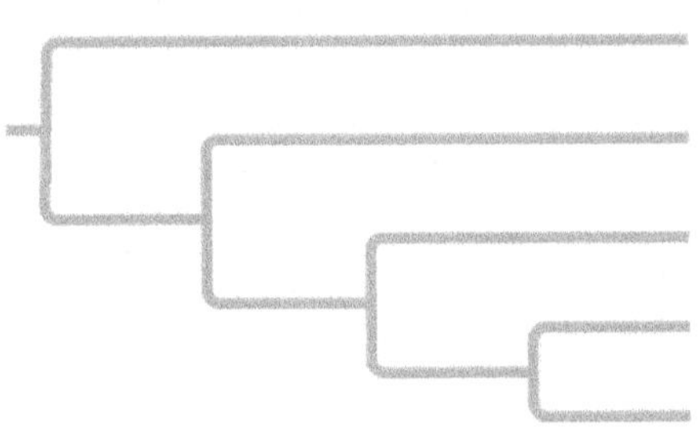

7. **EVOLUTION CONNECTION**
The history of life has been punctuated by several mass extinctions. For example, the impact of a meteorite may have wiped out most of the dinosaurs and many forms of marine life at the end of the Cretaceous period (see Chapter 25). Fossils indicate that plants were less severely affected by this and other mass extinctions. What adaptations may have enabled plants to withstand these disasters better than animals?

LEVEL 3: SYNTHESIS/EVALUATION

8. **SCIENTIFIC INQUIRY**
DRAW IT As will be described in detail in Chapter 38, the female gametophyte of angiosperms typically has seven cells, one of which, the central cell, contains two haploid nuclei. After double fertilization, the central cell develops into endosperm, which is triploid. Because magnoliids, monocots, and eudicots typically have female gametophytes with seven cells and triploid endosperm, scientists assumed that this was the ancestral state for angiosperms. Consider, however, the following recent discoveries:
   - Our understanding of angiosperm phylogeny has changed to that shown in Figure 30.12b.
   - *Amborella trichopoda* has eight-celled female gametophytes and triploid endosperm.
   - Water lilies and star anise have four-celled female gametophytes and diploid endosperm.

   a. Draw a phylogeny of the angiosperms (see Figure 30.12b), incorporating the data given above about the number of cells in female gametophytes and the ploidy of the endosperm. Assume that all of the star anise relatives have four-celled female gametophytes and diploid endosperm.
   b. What does your labeled phylogeny suggest about the evolution of the female gametophyte and endosperm in angiosperms?

9. **WRITE ABOUT A THEME**
The Cellular Basis of Life Cells are the basic units of structure and function in all organisms. A key feature in the life cycle of plants is the alternation of multicellular haploid and diploid generations. Imagine a lineage of flowering plants in which mitotic cell division did not occur between the events of meiosis and fertilization (see Figure 30.10). In a short essay (100–150 words), describe how this change in the timing of cell division would affect the structure and life cycle of plants in this lineage.

For selected answers, see Appendix A.

31

Fungi

▲ **Figure 31.1 Can you spot the largest organism in this forest?**

EVOLUTION

KEY CONCEPTS

31.1 Fungi are heterotrophs that feed by absorption
31.2 Fungi produce spores through sexual or asexual life cycles
31.3 The ancestor of fungi was an aquatic, single-celled, flagellated protist
31.4 Fungi have radiated into a diverse set of lineages
31.5 Fungi play key roles in nutrient cycling, ecological interactions, and human welfare

OVERVIEW

Mighty Mushrooms

Hiking through the Malheur National Forest in eastern Oregon, you might notice a few clusters of honey mushrooms (*Armillaria ostoyae*) scattered here and there beneath the towering trees (Figure 31.1). The trees appear to dwarf the mushrooms, but as strange as it sounds, the reverse is actually true. All these mushrooms are just the aboveground portion of a single enormous fungus. Its subterranean network of filaments spreads through 965 hectares of the forest—more than the area of 1,800 football fields. Based on its current growth rate, scientists estimate that this fungus, which weighs hundreds of tons, has been growing for more than 1,900 years.

The inconspicuous honey mushrooms on the forest floor are a fitting symbol of the neglected grandeur of the kingdom Fungi. Most of us are barely aware of these eukaryotes beyond the mushrooms we eat or the occasional brush with athlete's foot. Yet fungi are a huge and important component of the biosphere. While about 100,000 species have been described, it is estimated that there are actually as many as 1.5 million species of fungi. Some fungi are exclusively single-celled, though most have complex multicellular bodies, which in many cases include the structures we know as mushrooms. These diverse organisms are found in just about every imaginable terrestrial and aquatic habitat; airborne spores have even been found 160 km above ground.

Fungi are not only diverse and widespread; they are also essential for the well-being of most ecosystems. They break down organic material and recycle nutrients, allowing other organisms to assimilate essential chemical elements. Humans make use of fungi as a food source, for applications in agriculture and forestry, and in manufacturing products ranging from bread to antibiotics. But it is also true that some fungi cause disease in plants and animals.

In this chapter, we will investigate the structure and evolutionary history of fungi, survey the major groups of fungi, and discuss their ecological and commercial significance.

CONCEPT **31.1**

Fungi are heterotrophs that feed by absorption

Despite their vast diversity, all fungi share some key traits, most importantly the way they derive nutrition. In addition, many fungi grow by forming multicellular filaments, a body structure that plays an important role in how they obtain food.

Nutrition and Ecology

Like animals, fungi are heterotrophs: They cannot make their own food as plants and algae can. But unlike animals, fungi do not ingest (eat) their food. Instead, a fungus absorbs nutrients from the environment outside of its body. Many fungi accomplish this task by secreting powerful hydrolytic enzymes into their surroundings. These enzymes break down complex molecules to smaller organic compounds that the fungi can absorb into their bodies and use. Other fungi use enzymes to penetrate the walls of cells, enabling the fungi to absorb nutrients from the cells. Collectively, the different enzymes found in various fungal species can digest compounds from a wide range of sources, living or dead.

This diversity of food sources corresponds to the varied roles of fungi in ecological communitities, with different species living as decomposers, parasites, or mutualists. Decomposer fungi break down and absorb nutrients from nonliving organic material, such as fallen logs, animal corpses, and the wastes of living organisms. Parasitic fungi absorb nutrients from the cells of living hosts. Some parasitic fungi are pathogenic, including many species that cause diseases in plants. Mutualistic fungi also absorb nutrients from a host organism, but they reciprocate with actions that benefit the host. For example, mutualistic fungi that live inside certain termite species use their enzymes to break down wood, as do mutualistic protists in other termite species (see Figure 28.26).

The versatile enzymes that enable fungi to digest a wide range of food sources are not the only reason for their ecological success. Another important factor is how their body structure increases the efficiency of nutrient absorption.

Body Structure

The most common fungal body structures are multicellular filaments and single cells (**yeasts**). Many species can grow as both filaments and yeasts, but even more grow only as filaments; relatively few species grow only as yeasts. Yeasts often inhabit moist environments, including plant sap and animal tissues, where there is a ready supply of soluble nutrients, such as sugars and amino acids. We'll discuss yeasts again later in the chapter.

The morphology of multicellular fungi enhances their ability to grow into and absorb nutrients from their surroundings (Figure 31.2). The bodies of these fungi typically form a network of tiny filaments called **hyphae** (singular, *hypha*). Hyphae consist of tubular cell walls surrounding the plasma membrane and cytoplasm of the cells. Unlike plant cell walls, which contain cellulose, fungal cell walls are strengthened by **chitin**. This strong but flexible nitrogen-containing polysaccharide is also found in the external skeletons of insects and other arthropods.

Fungal hyphae form an interwoven mass called a **mycelium** (plural, *mycelia*) that infiltrates the material on which the fungus feeds. A mycelium's structure maximizes its surface-to-volume ratio, making feeding very efficient. Just 1 cm^3 of rich soil may contain as much as 1 km of hyphae with a total surface area of 300 cm^2 in contact with the soil. A fungal mycelium grows rapidly, as proteins and other materials synthesized by the fungus are channeled through cytoplasmic streaming to the tips of the extending hyphae. The fungus concentrates its energy and resources on adding hyphal length and thus overall absorptive surface area, rather than on increasing hyphal girth. Fungi are not motile in the typical sense—they cannot run, swim, or fly in search of food or mates. However, as they grow, fungi can move into new territory, swiftly extending the tips of their hyphae.

In most fungi, the hyphae are divided into cells by crosswalls, or **septa** (singular, *septum*) (Figure 31.3a). Septa generally have pores large enough to allow ribosomes, mitochondria, and even nuclei to flow from cell to cell. Some fungi lack septa (Figure 31.3b). Known as **coenocytic fungi**, these organisms consist of a continuous cytoplasmic mass having hundreds or thousands of nuclei. The coenocytic condition results from the repeated division of nuclei without cytokinesis. This description

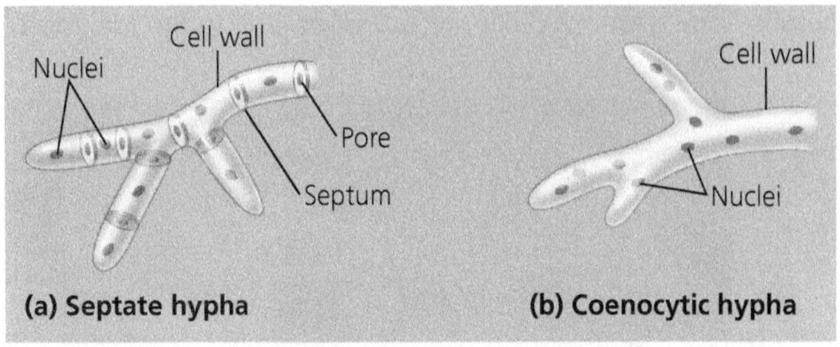

▲ Figure 31.3 **Two forms of hyphae.**

▲ Figure 31.2 **Structure of a multicellular fungus.** The top photograph shows the sexual structures, in this case called mushrooms, of the penny bun fungus (*Boletus edulis*). The bottom photograph shows a mycelium growing on fallen conifer needles. The inset SEM shows hyphae.

? *Although the mushrooms in the top photograph appear to be different individuals, could their DNA be identical? Explain.*

may remind you of the plasmodial slime molds you read about in Chapter 28, which also consist of cytoplasmic masses containing many nuclei. This similarity is one reason that slime molds were once classified as fungi; molecular data have since shown that slime molds and fungi belong to distinct clades.

Specialized Hyphae in Mycorrhizal Fungi

Some fungi have specialized hyphae that allow them to feed on living animals (Figure 31.4a). Other fungal species have specialized hyphae called **haustoria**, which the fungi use to extract nutrients from, or exchange nutrients with, their plant hosts (Figure 31.4b). Mutually beneficial relationships between such fungi and plant roots are called **mycorrhizae** (the term means "fungus roots").

Mycorrhizal fungi (fungi that form mycorrhizae) can improve delivery of phosphate ions and other minerals to plants because the vast mycelial networks of the fungi are more efficient than the plants' roots at acquiring these minerals from the soil. In exchange, the plants supply the fungi with organic nutrients such as carbohydrates. There are two main types of mycorrhizal fungi. **Ectomycorrhizal fungi** (from the Greek *ektos*, out) form sheaths of hyphae over the surface of a root and typically grow into the extracellular spaces of the root cortex (see Figure 37.13a). **Arbuscular mycorrhizal fungi** (from the Latin *arbor*, tree) extend branching hyphae through the root cell wall and into tubes formed by invagination (pushing inward) of the root cell plasma membrane (see Figure 37.13b).

Mycorrhizae are enormously important in natural ecosystems and agriculture. Almost all vascular plants have mycorrhizae and rely on their fungal partners for essential nutrients. Many studies have demonstrated the significance of mycorrhizae by comparing the growth of plants with and without them (see Figure 37.14). Foresters commonly inoculate pine seedlings with mycorrhizal fungi to promote growth. In the absence of human intervention, mycorrhizal fungi colonize soils by dispersing haploid cells called **spores** that form new mycelia after germinating. Spore dispersal is a key component of how fungi reproduce and spread to new areas, as we discuss next.

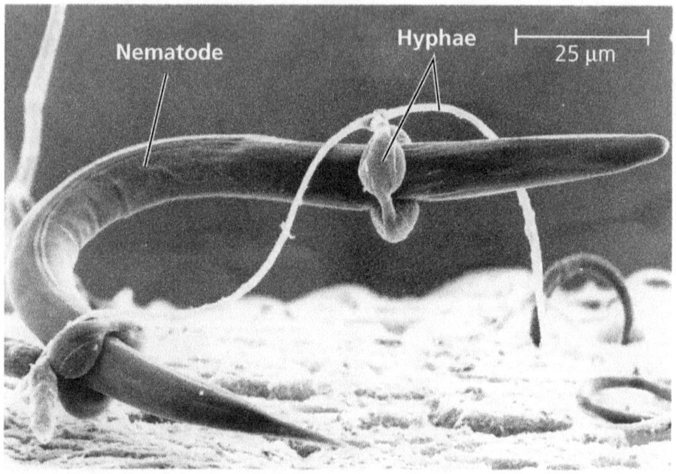

(a) Hyphae adapted for trapping and killing prey. In *Arthrobotrys*, a soil fungus, portions of the hyphae are modified as hoops that can constrict around a nematode (roundworm) in less than a second. The fungus then penetrates its prey with hyphae and digests the prey's inner tissues (SEM).

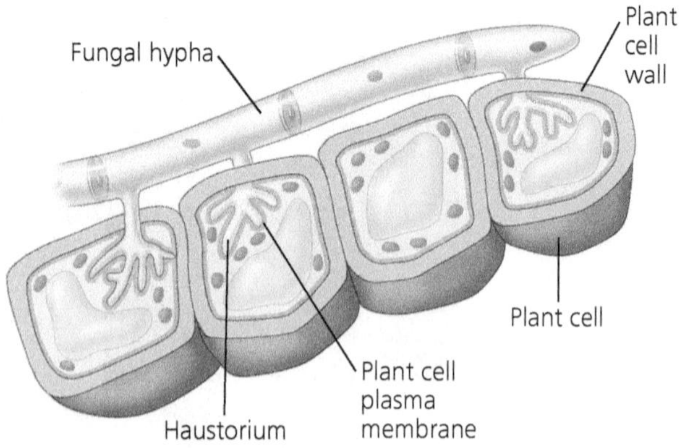

(b) Haustoria. Some mutualistic and parasitic fungi grow specialized hyphae called haustoria that can extract nutrients from living plant cells. Haustoria remain separated from a plant cell's cytoplasm by the plasma membrane of the plant cell (orange).

▲ Figure 31.4 **Specialized hyphae.**

CONCEPT CHECK 31.1

1. Compare and contrast the nutritional mode of a fungus with your own nutritional mode.
2. WHAT IF? Suppose a certain fungus is a mutualist that lives within an insect host, yet its ancestors were parasites that grew in and on the insect's body. What derived traits might you find in this mutualistic fungus?
3. MAKE CONNECTIONS Review Figure 10.4 (p. 186) and Figure 10.6 (p. 188). If a plant has mycorrhizae, where might carbon that enters the plant's stomata as CO_2 eventually be deposited: in the plant, in the mycorrhizal fungus, or in both? Explain.

For suggested answers, see Appendix A.

CONCEPT 31.2

Fungi produce spores through sexual or asexual life cycles

Most fungi propagate themselves by producing vast numbers of spores, either sexually or asexually. For example, puffballs, the reproductive structures of certain fungal species, may release trillions of spores in cloud-like bursts (see Figure 31.18). Spores can be carried long distances by wind or water. If they land in a moist place where there is food, they germinate, producing new mycelia. To appreciate how effective spores are at dispersing, leave a slice of melon exposed to the air. Even without a visible source of spores nearby, within a week or so, you will likely observe fuzzy mycelia growing from the microscopic spores that have fallen onto the melon.

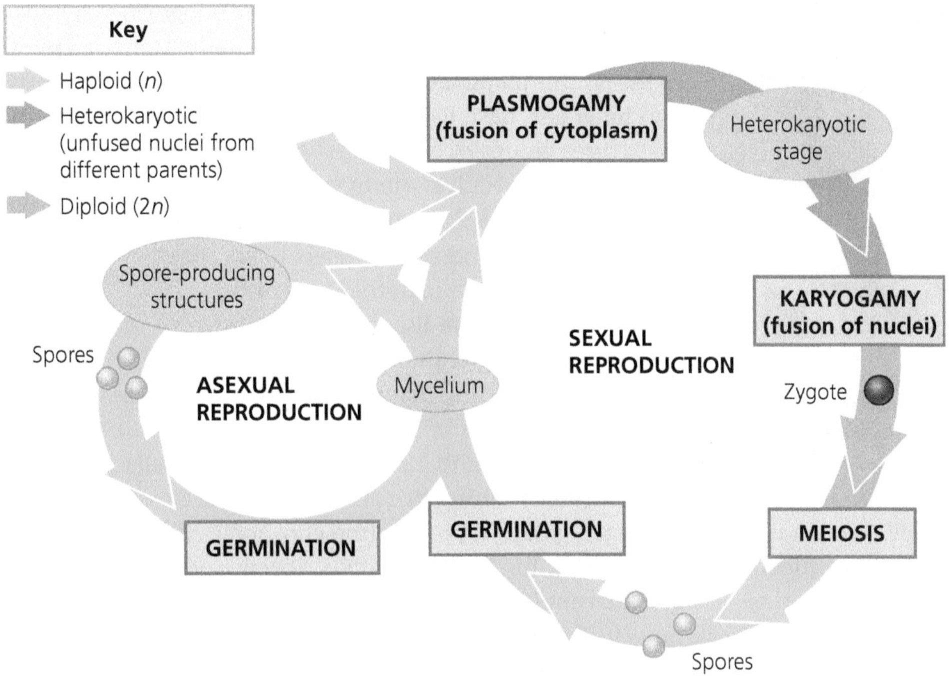

▲ **Figure 31.5 Generalized life cycle of fungi.** Many—but not all—fungi reproduce both sexually and asexually. Some reproduce only sexually, others only asexually.

Figure 31.5 generalizes the many different life cycles that can produce fungal spores. In this section, we will survey general aspects of the sexual and asexual life cycles of fungi. Later, we'll examine more closely the life cycles of specific fungi.

Sexual Reproduction

The nuclei of fungal hyphae and the spores of most fungal species are haploid, although many fungi have transient diploid stages that form during sexual life cycles. In fungi, sexual reproduction often begins when hyphae from two mycelia release sexual signaling molecules called **pheromones**. If the mycelia are of different mating types, the pheromones from each partner bind to receptors on the other, and the hyphae extend toward the source of the pheromones. When the hyphae meet, they fuse. In species with such a "compatibility test," this process contributes to genetic variation by preventing hyphae from fusing with other hyphae from the same mycelium or another genetically identical mycelium.

The union of the cytoplasms of two parent mycelia is known as **plasmogamy**. In most fungi, the haploid nuclei contributed by each parent do not fuse right away. Instead, parts of the fused mycelium contain coexisting, genetically different nuclei. Such a mycelium is said to be a **heterokaryon** (meaning "different nuclei"). In some species, the different nuclei may even exchange chromosomes and genes in a process similar to crossing over (see Chapter 13). In other species, the haploid nuclei pair off two to a cell, one from each parent. Such a mycelium is **dikaryotic** (meaning "two nuclei"). As a dikaryotic mycelium grows, the two nuclei in each cell divide in tandem without fusing. Because these cells retain two separate haploid nuclei, they differ from diploid cells, which have pairs of homologous chromosomes within a single nucleus.

Hours, days, or (in some fungi) even centuries may pass between plasmogamy and the next stage in the sexual cycle, **karyogamy**. During karyogamy, the haploid nuclei contributed by the two parents fuse, producing diploid cells. Zygotes and other transient structures form during karyogamy, the only diploid stage in most fungi. Meiosis then restores the haploid condition, leading to the formation of spores that enable the fungus to disperse.

The sexual processes of karyogamy and meiosis generate extensive genetic variation, a prerequisite for natural selection. (See Chapters 13 and 23 to review how sex can increase genetic diversity in a population.) The heterokaryotic condition also offers some of the advantages of diploidy in that one haploid genome may compensate for harmful mutations in the other.

Asexual Reproduction

Many fungi can reproduce both sexually and asexually. Some 20,000 fungal species are only known to reproduce asexually. As with sexual reproduction, the processes of asexual reproduction vary widely among fungi.

Many fungi reproduce asexually by growing as filamentous fungi that produce (haploid) spores by mitosis; such species are known informally as **molds** if they form visible mycelia. Depending on your housekeeping habits, you may have observed molds in your kitchen, forming furry carpets on fruit, bread, and other foods (Figure 31.6). Molds typically grow rapidly and produce many spores asexually, enabling the fungi to colonize new sources of food. Many species that produce such spores can also reproduce sexually if they happen to contact a member of their species of a different mating type.

▲ **Figure 31.6 *Penicillium*, a mold commonly encountered as a decomposer of food.** The bead-like clusters in the colorized SEM are conidia, structures involved in asexual reproduction.

Other fungi reproduce asexually by growing as single-celled yeasts. Instead of producing spores, asexual reproduction in yeasts occurs by ordinary cell division or by the pinching of small "bud cells" off a parent cell (Figure 31.7). As already mentioned, some fungi that grow as yeasts can also grow as filamentous mycelia, depending on the availability of nutrients.

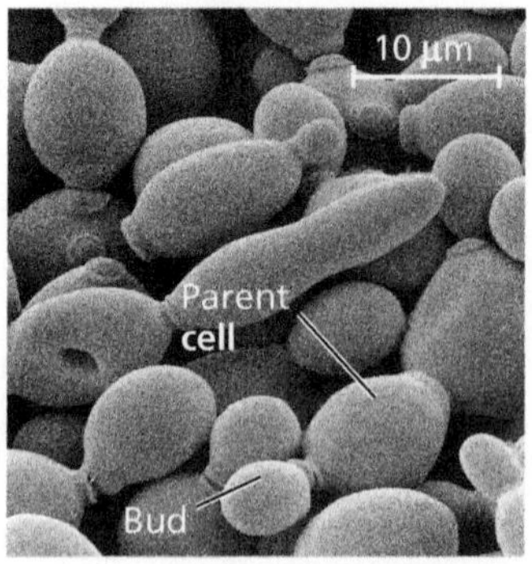

▲ **Figure 31.7 The yeast *Saccharomyces cerevisiae* in several stages of budding** (SEM).

Many yeasts and filamentous fungi have no known sexual stage in their life cycle. Since early mycologists (biologists who study fungi) classified fungi based mainly on their type of sexual structure, this posed a problem. Mycologists have traditionally lumped all fungi lacking sexual reproduction into a group called **deuteromycetes** (from the Greek *deutero*, second, and *mycete*, fungus). Whenever a sexual stage is discovered for a so-called deuteromycete, the species is reclassified in a particular phylum, depending on the type of sexual structures it forms. In addition to searching for sexual stages of such unassigned fungi, mycologists can now use genetic techniques to classify them.

CONCEPT CHECK 31.2

1. **MAKE CONNECTIONS** Compare Figure 31.5 with Figure 13.6 (p. 252). In terms of haploidy versus diploidy, how do the life cycles of fungi and humans differ?
2. **WHAT IF?** Suppose that you sample the DNA of two mushrooms on opposite sides of your yard and find that they are identical. Propose two hypotheses that could reasonably account for this result.

For suggested answers, see Appendix A.

CONCEPT 31.3

The ancestor of fungi was an aquatic, single-celled, flagellated protist

Data from both paleontology and molecular systematics offer insights into the early evolution of fungi. As a result, systematists now recognize that fungi and animals are more closely related to each other than either group is to plants or most other eukaryotes.

The Origin of Fungi

Phylogenetic systematics suggests that fungi evolved from a flagellated ancestor. While the majority of fungi lack flagella, some of the earliest-diverging lineages of fungi (the chytrids, discussed later in this chapter) do have flagella. Moreover, most of the protists that share a close common ancestor with animals and fungi also have flagella. DNA sequence data indicate that these three groups of eukaryotes—the fungi, the animals, and their protistan relatives—form a clade (Figure 31.8). As discussed in Chapter 28, members of this clade are called **opisthokonts**, a name that refers to the posterior (*opistho-*) location of the flagellum in these organisms.

DNA sequence data also indicate that fungi are more closely related to several groups of single-celled protists than they are to animals, suggesting that the ancestor of fungi was unicellular. One such group of unicellular protists, the **nucleariids**, consists of amoebas that feed on algae and bacteria. DNA evidence further indicates that animals are more closely related to a *different* group of protists (the choanoflagellates) than they are to either fungi or nucleariids. Together, these results suggest that multicellularity must have evolved in animals and fungi independently, from different single-celled ancestors.

Based on molecular clock analysis (see Chapter 26), scientists have estimated that the ancestors of animals and fungi diverged into separate lineages about 1 billion years ago. However, the oldest undisputed fossils of fungi are only about 460 million years old (Figure 31.9). One possible explanation for this discrepancy is that the microscopic ancestors of today's terrestrial fungi fossilized poorly.

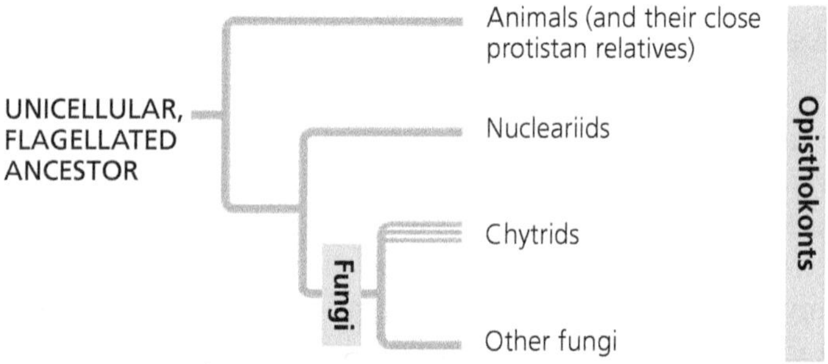

▲ **Figure 31.8 Fungi and their close relatives.** Molecular evidence indicates that the nucleariids, a group of single-celled protists, are the closest living relatives of fungi. The three parallel lines leading to the chytrids indicate that this group may be paraphyletic.

▶ **Figure 31.9 Fossil fungal hyphae and spores from the Ordovician period (about 460 million years ago)** (LM).

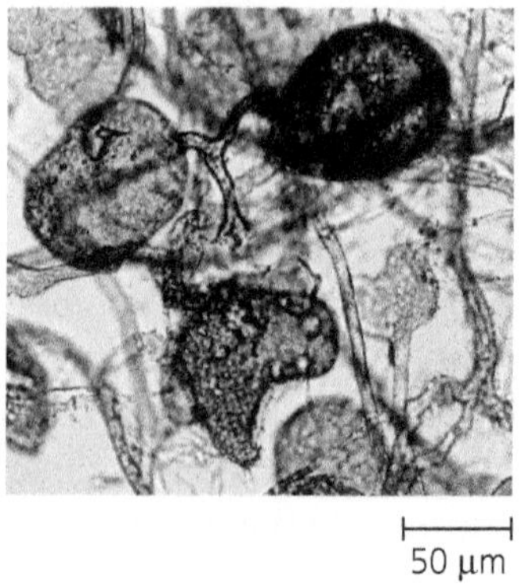

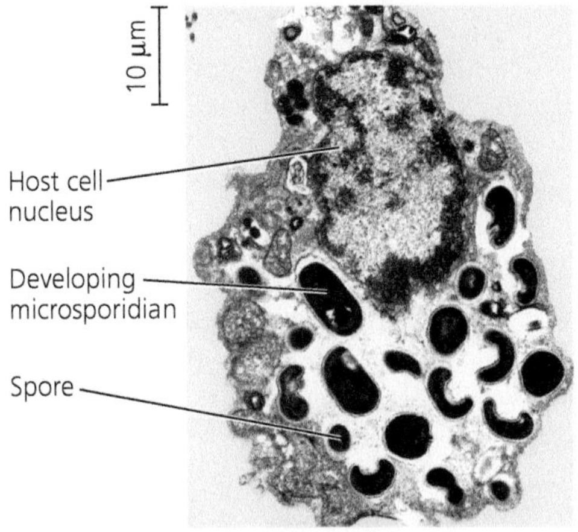

▲ **Figure 31.10 A eukaryotic cell infected by microsporidia.** A large vacuole inside this host eukaryotic cell contains spores and developing forms of the parasite *Encephalitozoon intestinalis* (TEM).

Are Microsporidia Fungi?

In addition to animals and protists such as the nucleariids, another group of organisms, the microsporidia, are closely related to fungi—and may in fact be fungi. Microsporidia are unicellular parasites of animals and protists (Figure 31.10). They are often used to control insect pests. While microsporidia do not normally cause illness in humans, they do pose a risk to people with AIDS and other immune-compromised conditions.

In many ways, microsporidia are unlike most other eukaryotes. They do not have conventional mitochondria, for example. As a result, microsporidia have been something of a taxonomic mystery, thought by some researchers to be a basal lineage of eukaryotes. In recent years, however, researchers have discovered that microsporidia actually have tiny organelles derived from mitochondria. In addition, most molecular comparisons indicate that microsporidia are fungi, suggesting that they are highly derived parasites. One such study, a 2006 analysis of DNA sequence data from six genes in nearly 200 fungal species, concluded that microsporidia are members of an early-diverging lineage of fungi. Additional genetic data from species belonging to early-diverging lineages of fungi are needed to fully resolve whether microsporidia are fungi or are a closely related but distinct group of organisms.

The Move to Land

Much of the fungal diversity we observe today may have originated during an adaptive radiation that began when multicellular plants and animals colonized land. For example, fossils of the earliest known vascular plants from the late Silurian period (420 million years ago) contain evidence of mycorrhizal relationships between plants and fungi. This evidence includes fossils of hyphae that have penetrated within plant cells and formed structures that closely resemble the haustoria of arbuscular mycorrhizae. Indeed, plants probably existed in beneficial relationships with fungi from the earliest periods of colonization of land.

CONCEPT CHECK 31.3

1. Why are fungi classified as opisthokonts despite the fact that most fungi lack flagella?
2. Explain the evolutionary significance of the presence of mycorrhizae in the earliest vascular plants.
3. **WHAT IF?** If fungi had colonized land before plants, where might the fungi have lived? What might they have used for food?

For suggested answers, see Appendix A.

CONCEPT 31.4

Fungi have radiated into a diverse set of lineages

The phylogeny of fungi is currently the subject of much research. In the past decade, molecular analyses have helped clarify the evolutionary relationships between fungal groups, although there are still areas of uncertainty. Figure 31.11, on the next page, presents a simplified version of one current hypothesis. In this section, we will survey each of the major fungal groups identified in this phylogenetic tree.

Chytrids

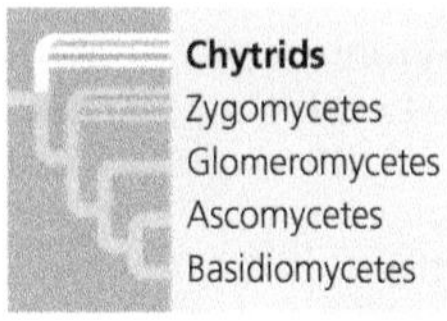

The fungi classified in the phylum Chytridiomycota, called **chytrids**, are ubiquitous in lakes and soil. Some of the approximately 1,000 chytrid species are decomposers, while others are parasites of protists, other fungi, plants, or animals; as we'll see later in the chapter, one such chytrid parasite has likely contributed to the global decline of amphibian populations. Still other chytrids are important mutualists. For example, anaerobic chytrids that live in the digestive tracts of sheep and cattle help to break down plant matter, thereby contributing significantly to the animal's growth.

Molecular evidence supports the hypothesis that chytrids diverged early in fungal evolution. Like other fungi, chytrids have cell walls made of chitin, and they also share certain key enzymes and metabolic pathways with other fungal groups. Some chytrids form colonies with hyphae, while others exist as single spherical cells. But chytrids are unique among fungi in having flagellated spores, called **zoospores** (Figure 31.12).

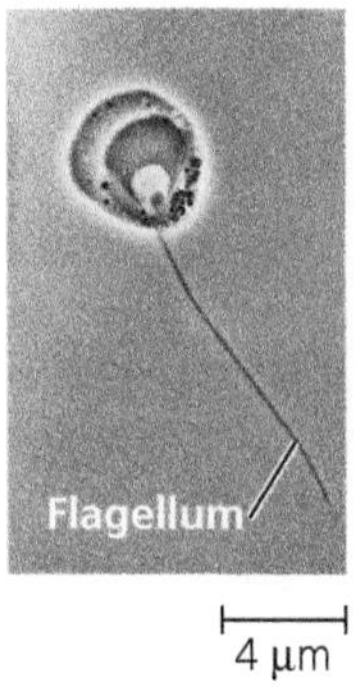

▲ **Figure 31.12 Flagellated chytrid zoospore** (TEM).

▼ Figure 31.11

Exploring Fungal Diversity

Most mycologists currently recognize five major groups of fungi, although the chytrids and zygomycetes are probably paraphyletic (as indicated by the parallel lines).

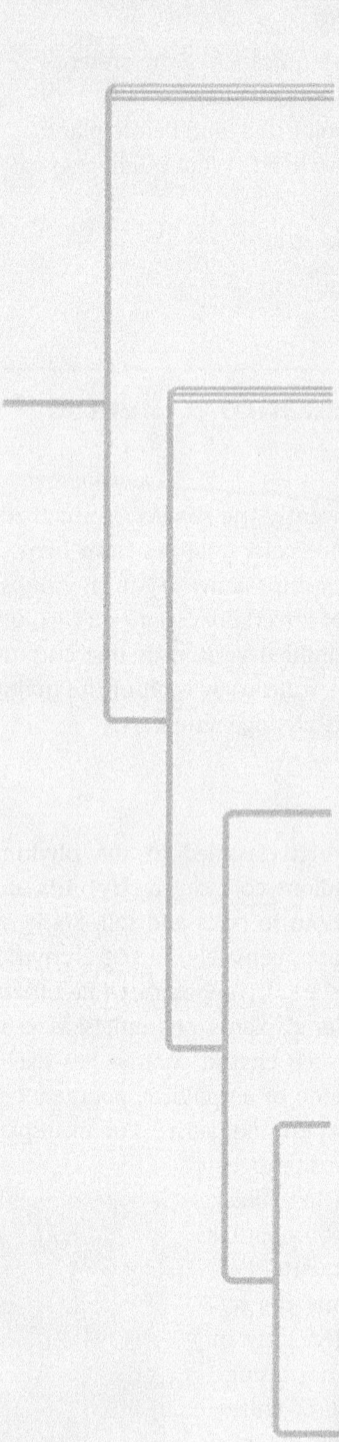

Chytrids (1,000 species)

In chytrids such as *Chytridium*, the globular fruiting body forms multicellular, branched hyphae (LM); other species are single-celled. Chytrids have flagellated spores and are thought to include some of the earliest fungal groups to diverge from other fungi.

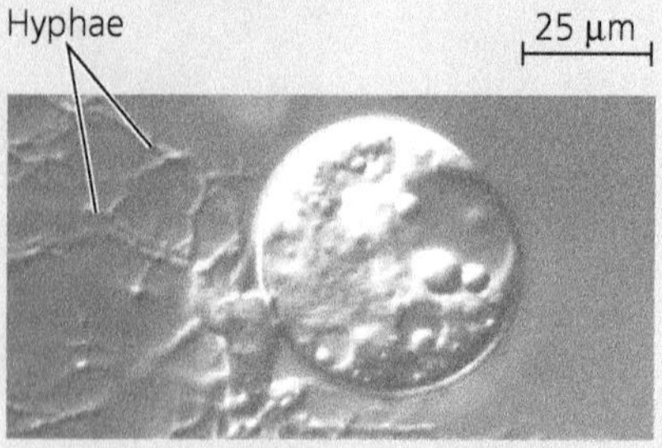

Zygomycetes (1,000 species)

The hyphae of some zygomycetes, including this mold in the genus *Mucor* (LM), grow rapidly into foods such as fruits and bread. As such, the fungi may act as decomposers (if the food is not alive) or parasites; other species live as neutral (commensal) symbionts. According to some recent analyses, the zygomycetes include the enigmatic group known as microsporidia; other studies have classified microsporidia as chytrids.

Glomeromycetes (160 species)

The glomeromycetes (arbuscular mycorrhizal fungi) are of great ecological importance. Many plants form mycorrhizal associations with these fungi. This LM shows glomeromycete hyphae (stained dark blue) within a plant root.

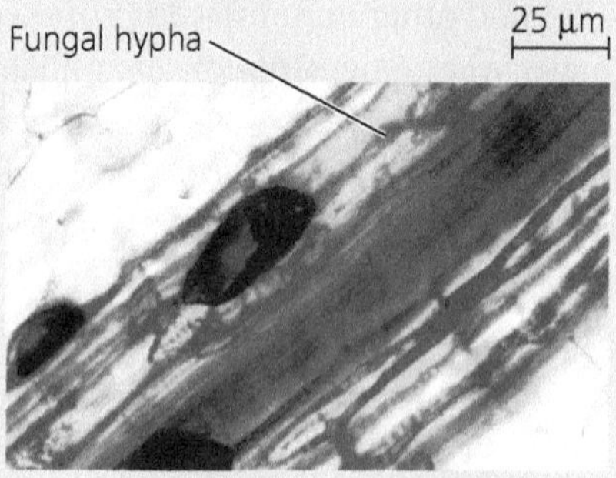

Ascomycetes (65,000 species)

Also called sac fungi, members of this diverse group are common to many marine, freshwater, and terrestrial habitats. The cup-shaped ascocarp (fruiting body) of the ascomycete shown here (*Aleuria aurantia*) gives this species its common name: orange peel fungus.

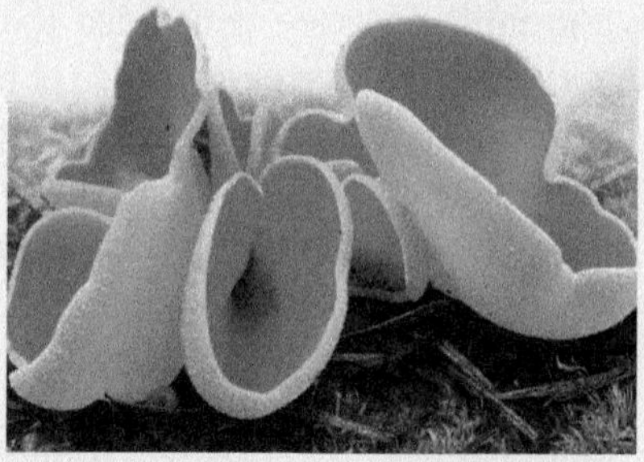

Basidiomycetes (30,000 species)

Often important as decomposers and ectomycorrhizal fungi, basidiomycetes, or club fungi, are unusual in having a long-lived, dikaryotic mycelium. The fruiting bodies—commonly called mushrooms—of this fly agaric (*Amanita muscaria*) are a familiar sight in coniferous forests of the Northern Hemisphere.

Zygomycetes

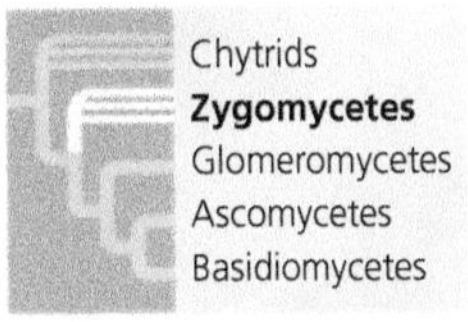

There are approximately 1,000 known species of **zygomycetes**, fungi in the phylum Zygomycota. This diverse phylum includes species of fast-growing molds responsible for causing foods such as bread, peaches, strawberries, and sweet potatoes to rot during storage. Other zygomycetes live as parasites or as commensal (neutral) symbionts of animals.

The life cycle of *Rhizopus stolonifer* (black bread mold) is fairly typical of zygomycete species (**Figure 31.13**). Its hyphae spread out over the food surface, penetrate it, and absorb nutrients. The hyphae are coenocytic, with septa found only where reproductive cells are formed. In the asexual phase, bulbous black sporangia develop at the tips of upright hyphae. Within each sporangium, hundreds of haploid spores develop and are dispersed through the air. Spores that happen to land on moist food germinate, growing into new mycelia.

If environmental conditions deteriorate—for instance, if the mold consumes all its food—*Rhizopus* may reproduce sexually. The parents in a sexual union are mycelia of different mating types, which possess different chemical markers but may appear identical. Plasmogamy produces a sturdy

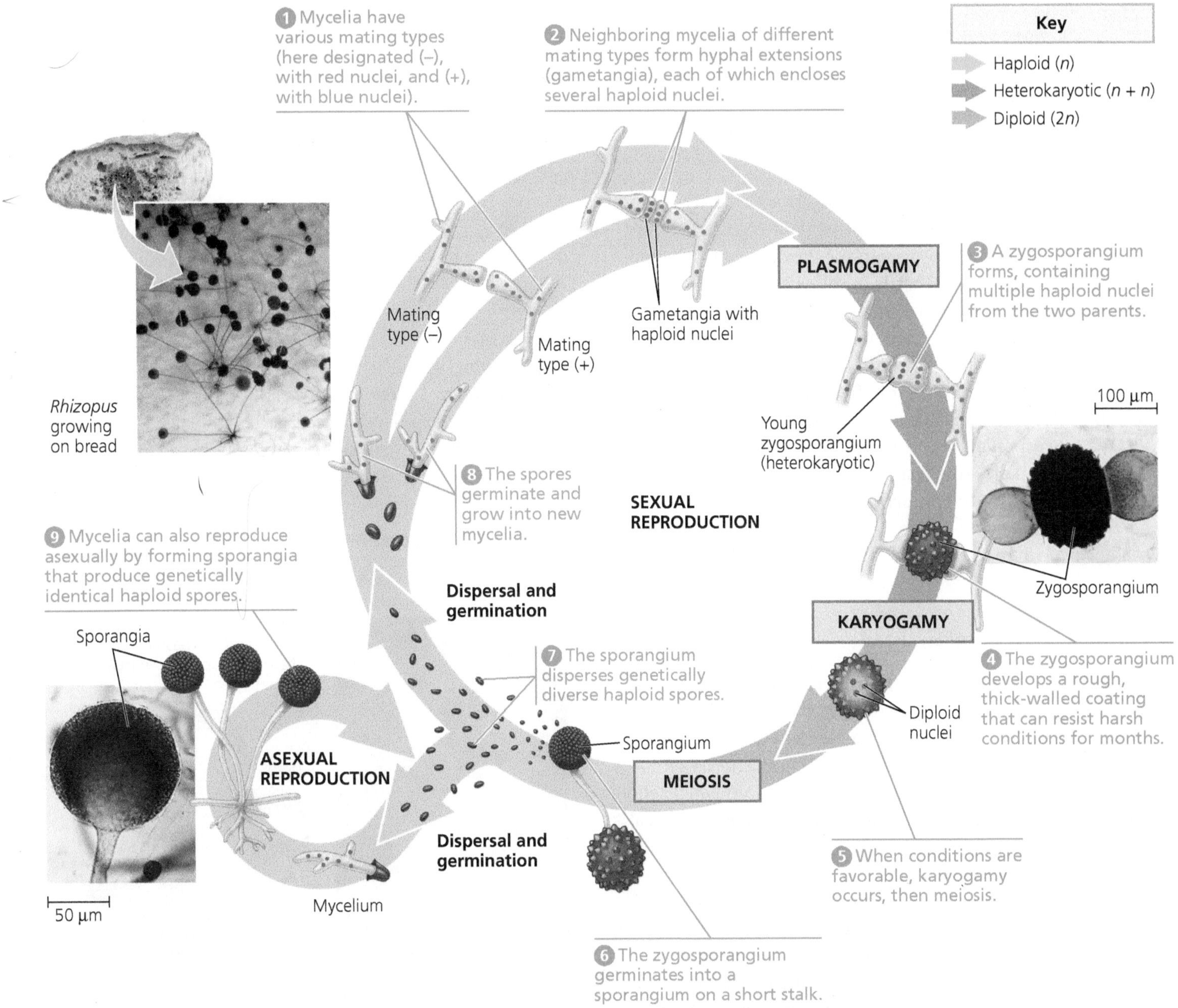

▲ **Figure 31.13 The life cycle of the zygomycete *Rhizopus stolonifer* (black bread mold).**

▲ **Figure 31.14** ***Pilobolus* aiming its sporangia.** This zygomycete decomposes animal dung. Its spore-bearing hyphae bend toward light, where there are likely to be openings in the vegetation through which spores may reach fresh grass. The fungus then launches its sporangia in a jet of water that can travel up to 2.5 m. Grazing animals ingest the fungi with the grass and then scatter the spores in feces, thereby enabling the next generation of fungi to grow.

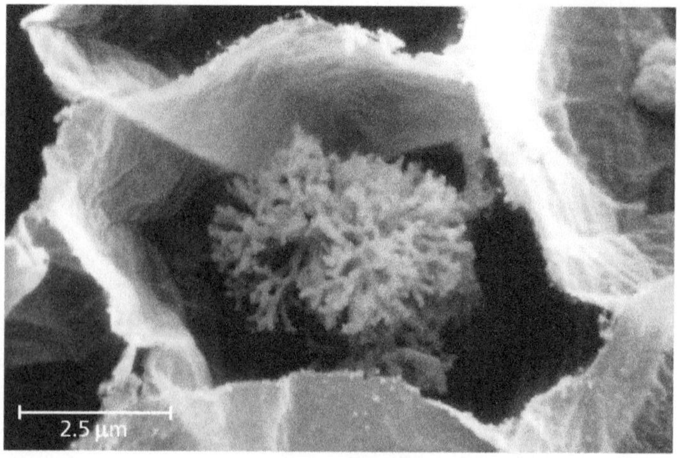

▲ **Figure 31.15** **Arbuscular mycorrhizae.** Most glomeromycetes form arbuscular mycorrhizae with plant roots, supplying minerals and other nutrients to the roots. This SEM depicts the branched hyphae—an arbuscule—of *Glomus mosseae* bulging into a root cell by pushing in the membrane (the root has been treated to remove the cytoplasm).

structure called a **zygosporangium**, in which karyogamy and then meiosis occur. Note that while a zygosporangium represents the zygote ($2n$) stage in the life cycle, it is not a zygote in the usual sense (that is, a cell with one diploid nucleus). Rather, a zygosporangium is a multinucleate structure, first heterokaryotic with many haploid nuclei from the two parents, then with many diploid nuclei after karyogamy.

Zygosporangia are resistant to freezing and drying and are metabolically inactive. When conditions improve, the nuclei of the zygosporangium undergo meiosis, the zygosporangium germinates into a sporangium, and the sporangium releases genetically diverse haploid spores that may colonize a new substrate. Some zygomycetes, such as *Pilobolus*, can actually "aim" and then shoot their sporangia toward bright light (**Figure 31.14**).

Glomeromycetes

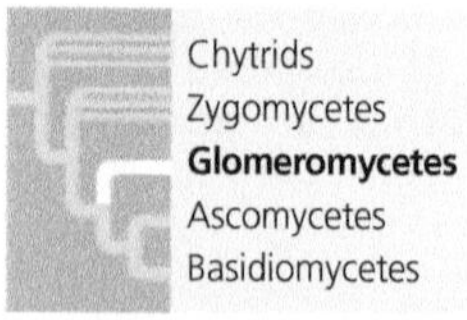

The **glomeromycetes**, fungi assigned to the phylum Glomeromycota, were formerly thought to be zygomycetes. But recent molecular studies, including a phylogenetic analysis of DNA sequence data from hundreds of fungal species, indicate that glomeromycetes form a separate clade (monophyletic group). Although only 160 species have been identified to date, the glomeromycetes are an ecologically significant group in that nearly all of them form arbuscular mycorrhizae (**Figure 31.15**). The tips of the hyphae that push into plant root cells branch into tiny treelike arbuscules. About 90% of all plant species have such mutualistic partnerships with glomeromycetes.

Ascomycetes

Mycologists have described 65,000 species of **ascomycetes**, fungi in the phylum Ascomycota, from a wide variety of marine, freshwater, and terrestrial habitats. The defining feature of ascomycetes is the production of spores in saclike **asci** (singular, *ascus*) during sexual reproduction; thus, they are commonly called *sac fungi*. Unlike zygomycetes, during their sexual stage most ascomycetes develop fruiting bodies, called **ascocarps**, which range in size from microscopic to macroscopic (**Figure 31.16**). The ascocarps contain the spore-forming asci.

▼ The edible ascocarp of *Morchella esculenta*, the tasty morel, is often found under trees in orchards.

▼ *Tuber melanosporum* is a truffle species that forms ectomycorrhizae with trees. The ascocarp grows underground and emits a strong odor. These ascocarps have been dug up and the middle one sliced open.

▲ **Figure 31.16** **Ascomycetes (sac fungi).**

? *Ascomycetes vary greatly in morphology (see also Figure 31.11). How could you confirm that a fungus is an ascomycete?*

Ascomycetes vary in size and complexity from unicellular yeasts to elaborate cup fungi and morels (see Figure 31.16). They include some of the most devastating plant pathogens, which we will discuss later. However, many ascomycetes are important decomposers, particularly of plant material. More than 25% of all ascomycete species live with green algae or cyanobacteria in beneficial symbiotic associations called lichens. Some ascomycetes form mycorrhizae with plants. Many others live between mesophyll cells in leaves; some of these species release toxic compounds that help protect the plant from insects.

Although the life cycles of various ascomycete groups differ in the details of their reproductive structures and processes, we'll illustrate some common elements using the bread mold *Neurospora crassa* (**Figure 31.17**). Ascomycetes reproduce asexually by producing enormous numbers of asexual spores called **conidia** (singular, *conidium*). Conidia are not formed inside sporangia, as are the asexual spores of most zygomycetes. Rather, they are produced externally at the tips of specialized hyphae called conidiophores, often in clusters or long chains, from which they may be dispersed by the wind.

Conidia may also be involved in sexual reproduction, fusing with hyphae from a mycelium of a different mating type, as occurs in *Neurospora*. Fusion of two different mating types is followed by plasmogamy, resulting in the formation of dikaryotic cells, each with two haploid nuclei representing

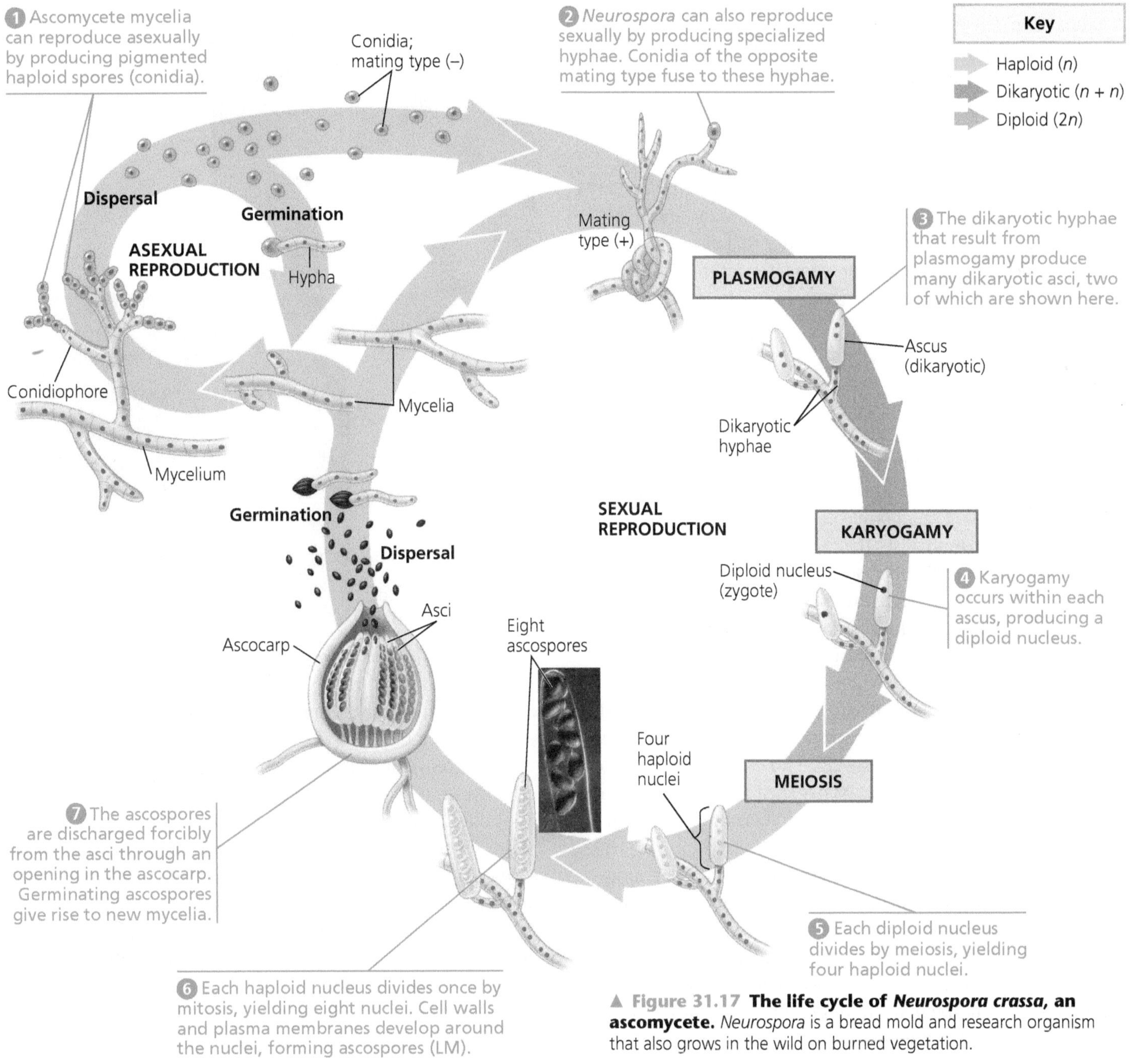

▲ **Figure 31.17 The life cycle of *Neurospora crassa*, an ascomycete.** *Neurospora* is a bread mold and research organism that also grows in the wild on burned vegetation.

the two parents. The cells at the tips of these dikaryotic hyphae develop into many asci. Within each ascus, karyogamy combines the two parental genomes, and then meiosis forms four genetically different nuclei. This is usually followed by a mitotic division, forming eight ascospores. The ascospores develop in and are eventually discharged from the ascocarp.

In contrast to the life cycle of zygomycetes, the extended dikaryotic stage of ascomycetes (and also basidiomycetes) provides increased opportunity for genetic recombination. In *Neurospora*, for example, many dikaryotic cells can develop into asci, recombining genomes during meiosis and resulting in a multitude of genetically different offspring from one mating event (see steps 2 and 3 in Figure 31.17).

Neurospora has a significant history in biological research. As we discussed in Chapter 17, biologists in the 1930s used *Neurospora* in research that led to the one gene–one enzyme hypothesis. Today, this ascomycete continues to serve as a model research organism. In 2003, its entire genome was published. With 10,000 genes, this tiny fungus has about three-fourths as many genes as the fruit fly *Drosophila* and about half as many as a human. The *Neurospora* genome is relatively compact, having few of the stretches of noncoding DNA that occupy so much space in the genomes of humans and many other eukaryotes. In fact, there is evidence that *Neurospora* has a genomic defense system that prevents noncoding DNA such as transposons from accumulating.

Basidiomycetes

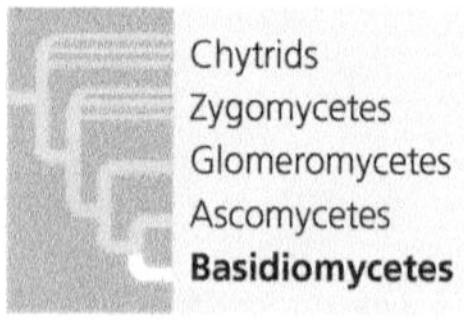

Approximately 30,000 species, including mushrooms, puffballs, and shelf fungi, are called **basidiomycetes** and are classified in the phylum Basidiomycota (**Figure 31.18**). This phylum also includes mutualists that form mycorrhizae and two groups of destructive plant parasites: rusts and smuts. The name of the phylum derives from the **basidium** (Latin for "little pedestal"), a cell in which karyogamy occurs, followed immediately by meiosis. The club-like shape of the basidium also gives rise to the common name *club fungus*.

Basidiomycetes are important decomposers of wood and other plant material. Of all the fungi, certain basidiomycetes are the best at decomposing the complex polymer lignin, an abundant component of wood. Many shelf fungi break down the wood of weak or damaged trees and continue to decompose the wood after the tree dies.

The life cycle of a basidiomycete usually includes a long-lived dikaryotic mycelium (**Figure 31.19**). As in ascomycetes, this extended dikaryotic stage provides opportunities for many genetic recombination events, in effect multiplying the result of a single mating. Periodically, in response to environmental stimuli, the mycelium reproduces sexually by producing elaborate fruiting bodies called **basidiocarps**. The common white mushrooms in the supermarket are familiar examples of a basidiocarp.

▲ **Figure 31.18 Basidiomycetes (club fungi).**

By concentrating growth in the hyphae of mushrooms, a basidiomycete mycelium can erect its fruiting structures in just a few hours; a mushroom pops up as it absorbs water and as cytoplasm streams in from the dikaryotic mycelium. By this process, a ring of mushrooms, popularly called a "fairy ring," may appear literally overnight (**Figure 31.20**). The mycelium below the fairy ring expands outward at a rate of about 30 cm per year, decomposing organic matter in the soil as it grows. Some giant fairy rings are produced by mycelia that are centuries old.

The numerous basidia in a basidiocarp are the sources of sexual spores called basidiospores. After a mushroom forms,

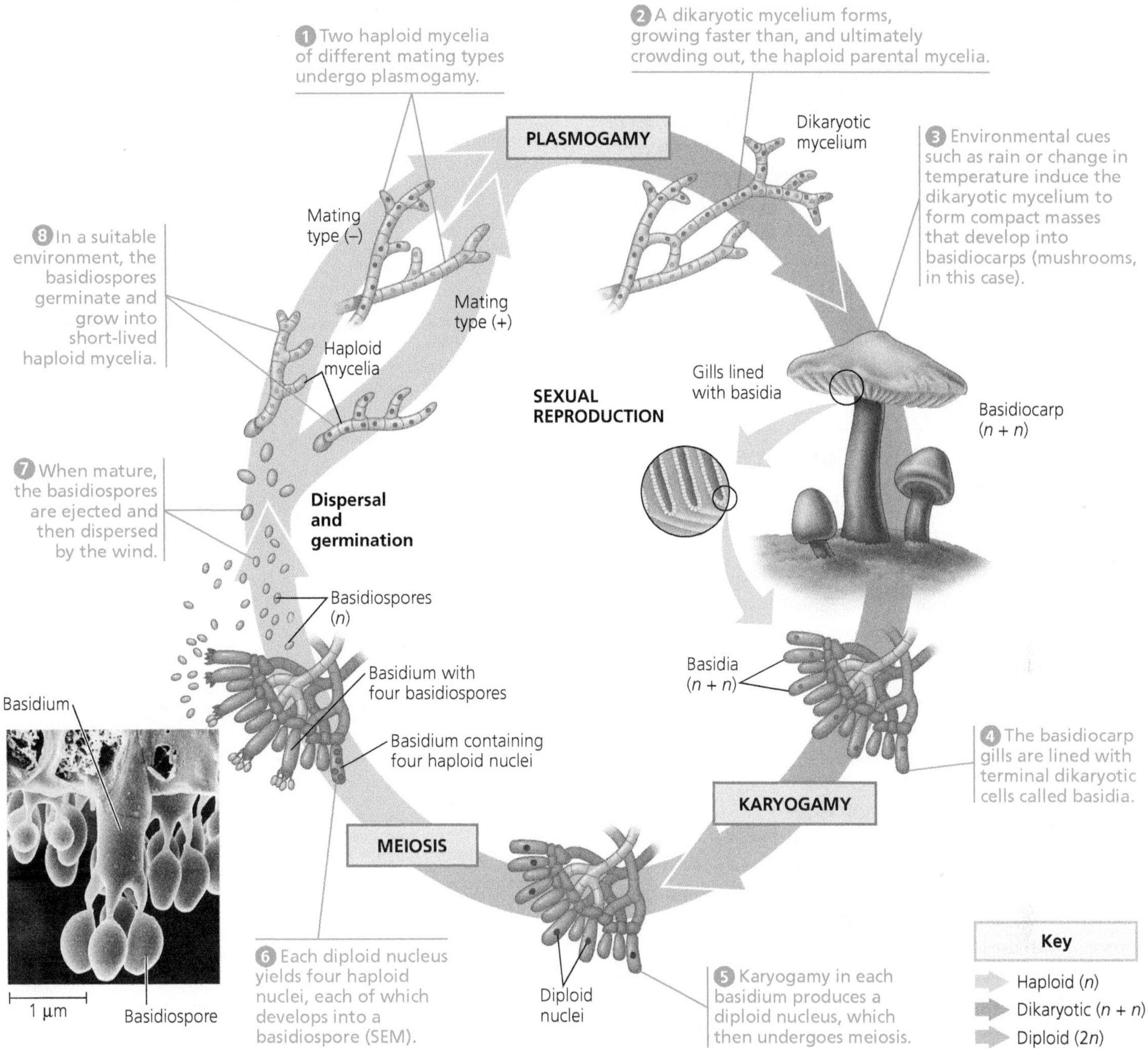

▲ **Figure 31.19 The life cycle of a mushroom-forming basidiomycete.**

its cap supports and protects a large surface area of dikaryotic basidia on gills. During karyogamy, the two nuclei in each basidium fuse, producing a diploid nucleus (see Figure 31.19). This nucleus then undergoes meiosis, yielding four haploid nuclei. The basidium then grows four appendages, and one haploid nucleus enters each appendage and develops into a basidiospore. Large numbers of basidiospores are produced: The gills of a common white mushroom have a surface area of about 200 cm^2 and may release a billion basidiospores, which drop from the bottom of the cap and are blown away.

▲ **Figure 31.20 A fairy ring.** According to legend, these mushrooms spring up where fairies have danced in a ring on a moonlit night. (The text provides a biological explanation of how fairy rings form.)

CONCEPT CHECK 31.4

1. What feature of chytrids supports the hypothesis that they represent an early-diverging fungal lineage?
2. Give examples of how form fits function in zygomycetes, glomeromycetes, ascomycetes, and basidiomycetes.
3. **WHAT IF?** Suppose that the mutation of an ascomycete changed its life cycle so that plasmogamy, karyogamy, and meiosis occurred in quick succession. How might this affect the ascospores and ascocarp?

For suggested answers, see Appendix A.

CONCEPT 31.5

Fungi play key roles in nutrient cycling, ecological interactions, and human welfare

In our survey of fungal classification, we've touched on some of the ways fungi influence other organisms. We will now look more closely at these impacts, focusing on how fungi act as decomposers, mutualists, and pathogens.

Fungi as Decomposers

Fungi are well adapted as decomposers of organic material, including the cellulose and lignin of plant cell walls. In fact, almost any carbon-containing substrate—even jet fuel and house paint—can be consumed by at least some fungi. As you might expect, researchers are developing ways to use a variety of fungal species in bioremediation projects. In addition, fungi and bacteria are primarily responsible for keeping ecosystems stocked with the inorganic nutrients essential for plant growth. Without these decomposers, carbon, nitrogen, and other elements would remain tied up in organic matter. Plants and the animals that eat them could not exist because elements taken from the soil would not be returned (see Chapter 55). Without decomposers, life as we know it would cease.

Fungi as Mutualists

Fungi may form mutualistic relationships with plants, algae, cyanobacteria, and animals. All of these relationships have profound ecological effects, often affecting the growth, survival, or reproduction of many species in a community.

Fungus-Plant Mutualisms

We've already considered the enormous importance of the mutualistic associations that most vascular plants form with mycorrhizal fungi. In addition, all plant species studied to date appear to harbor symbiotic **endophytes**, fungi that live inside leaves or other plant parts without causing harm. Most endophytes identified to date are ascomycetes. Endophytes have been shown to benefit certain grasses and other nonwoody plants by making toxins that deter herbivores or by increasing host plant tolerance of heat, drought, or heavy metals. Seeking to discover how endophytes affect a woody plant, researchers tested whether leaf endophytes benefit seedlings of the cacao tree, *Theobroma cacao* (Figure 31.21). Their findings show that the endophytes of woody flowering plants can play an important role in defending against pathogens.

▼ **Figure 31.21** INQUIRY

Do endophytes benefit a woody plant?

EXPERIMENT Endophytes are symbiotic fungi found within the bodies of all plants examined to date. A. Elizabeth Arnold, at the University of Arizona, Tucson, and colleagues tested whether endophytes benefit the cacao tree (*Theobroma cacao*). This tree, whose name means "food of the gods" in Greek, is the source of the beans used to make chocolate, and it is cultivated throughout the tropics. Endophytes were added to the leaves of some cacao seedlings, but not others. (In cacao, endophytes colonize leaves after the seedling germinates.) The seedlings were then inoculated with a virulent pathogen, the protist *Phytophthora* (see Chapter 28).

RESULTS Fewer leaves were killed by the pathogen in seedlings with endophytes than in seedlings without endophytes. Among leaves that survived, pathogens damaged less of the leaf surface area in seedlings with endophytes than in seedlings without endophytes.

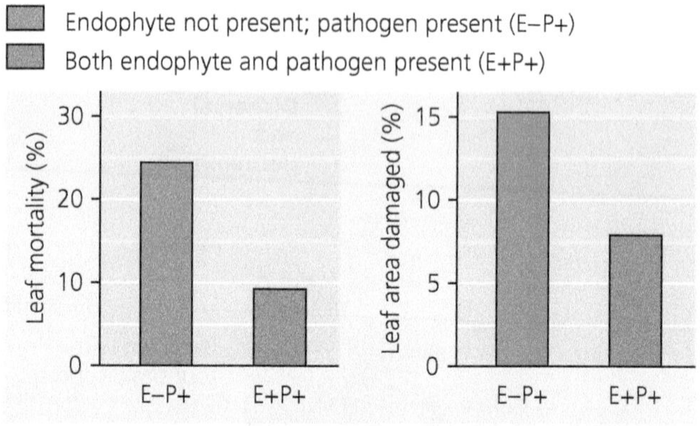

CONCLUSION The presence of endophytes appears to benefit cacao trees by reducing the leaf mortality and damage caused by *Phytophthora*.

SOURCE A. E. Arnold et al., Fungal endophytes limit pathogen damage in a tropical tree, *Proceedings of the National Academy of Sciences* 100:15649–15654 (2003).

WHAT IF? Arnold and colleagues also performed control treatments. Suggest two controls they might have used, and explain how each would be helpful in interpreting the results described here.

Fungus-Animal Mutualisms

As mentioned earlier, some fungi share their digestive services with animals, helping break down plant material in the guts of cattle and other grazing mammals. Many species of ants take advantage of the digestive power of fungi by raising them in "farms." Leaf-cutter ants, for example, scour tropical forests in search of leaves, which they cannot digest on their own but

▲ **Figure 31.22 Fungus-gardening insects.** These leaf-cutting ants depend on fungi to convert plant material to a form the insects can digest. The fungi, in turn, depend on the nutrients from the leaves the ants feed them.

carry back to their nests and feed to the fungi (Figure 31.22). As the fungi grow, their hyphae develop specialized swollen tips that are rich in proteins and carbohydrates. The ants feed primarily on these nutrient-rich tips. The fungi break down plant leaves into substances the insects can digest, and they also detoxify plant defensive compounds that would otherwise kill or harm the ants. In some tropical forests, the fungi have helped these insects become the major consumers of leaves.

The evolution of such farmer ants and that of their fungal "crops" have been tightly linked for over 50 million years. The fungi have become so dependent on their caretakers that in many cases they can no longer survive without the ants, and vice versa.

Lichens

A **lichen** is a symbiotic association between a photosynthetic microorganism and a fungus in which millions of photosynthetic cells are held in a mass of fungal hyphae. Lichens grow on the surfaces of rocks, rotting logs, trees, and roofs in various forms (Figure 31.23). The photosynthetic partners are unicellular or filamentous green algae or cyanobacteria. The fungal component is most often an ascomycete, but one glomeromycete and 75 basidiomycete lichens are known. The fungus usually gives a lichen its overall shape and structure, and tissues formed by hyphae account for most of the lichen's mass. The algae or cyanobacteria generally occupy an inner layer below the lichen surface (Figure 31.24).

The merger of fungus and alga or cyanobacterium is so complete that lichens are given scientific names as though they were single organisms; to date, 17,000 lichen species have been described. As might be expected of such "dual organisms," asexual reproduction as a symbiotic unit is common. This can occur either by fragmentation of the parental lichen or by the formation of **soredia**, small clusters of hyphae with embedded algae (see Figure 31.24). The fungi of many lichens also reproduce sexually, and lichen algae can reproduce independently of the fungus by asexual cell division.

In most lichens, each partner provides something the other could not obtain on its own. The algae provide carbon compounds; the cyanobacteria also fix nitrogen (see Chapter 27) and provide organic nitrogen compounds. The fungi provide their photosynthetic partners with a suitable environment for growth. The physical arrangement of hyphae allows for gas

▼ **Figure 31.23 Variation in lichen growth forms.**

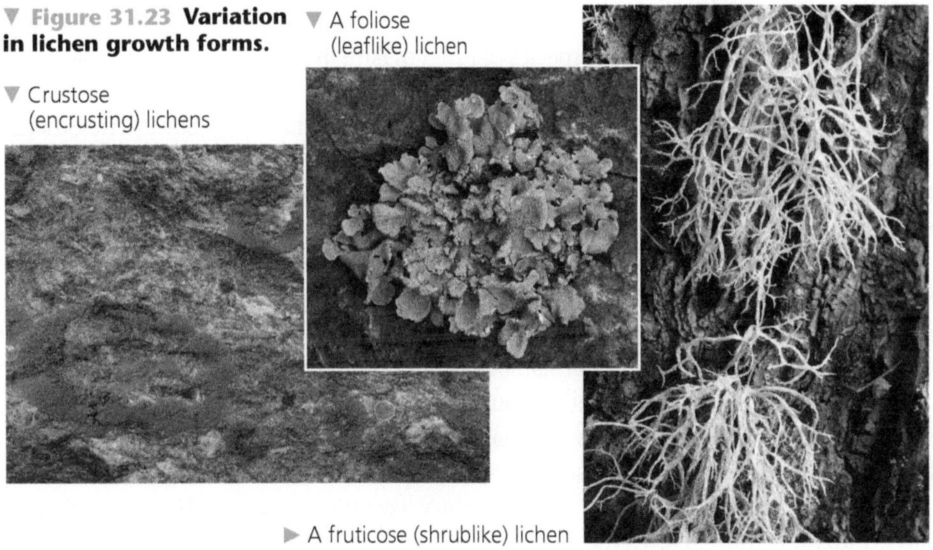

▼ Crustose (encrusting) lichens

▼ A foliose (leaflike) lichen

▶ A fruticose (shrublike) lichen

▼ **Figure 31.24 Anatomy of an ascomycete lichen** (colorized SEM).

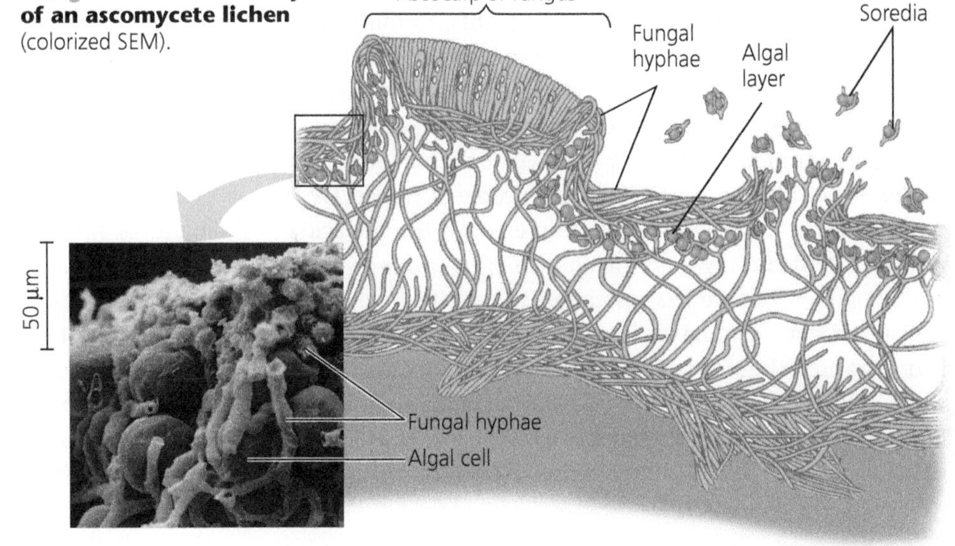

exchange, protects the photosynthetic partner, and retains water and minerals, most of which are absorbed either from airborne dust or from rain. The fungi also secrete acids, which aid in the uptake of minerals.

Lichens are important pioneers on cleared rock and soil surfaces, such as volcanic flows and burned forests. They break down the surface by physically penetrating and chemically attacking it, and they trap windblown soil. Nitrogen-fixing lichens also add organic nitrogen to some ecosystems. These processes make it possible for a succession of plants to grow (see Chapter 54). Lichens may also have aided the colonization of land by plants. Fossils of lichens or lichen-like organisms date to 550–600 million years ago, long before plants grew on land. Early lichens may have modified rocks and soil much as they do today, helping pave the way for plants.

As tough as lichens are, however, many do not stand up well to air pollution. Their passive mode of mineral uptake from rain and moist air makes them particularly sensitive to sulfur dioxide and other airborne poisons.

(a) Corn smut on corn

(b) Tar spot fungus on maple leaves

(c) Ergots on rye

▲ Figure 31.25 **Examples of fungal diseases of plants.**

Fungi as Pathogens

About 30% of the 100,000 known species of fungi make a living as parasites or pathogens, mostly of plants (Figure 31.25). For example, *Cryphonectria parasitica*, the ascomycete fungus that causes chestnut blight, dramatically changed the landscape of the northeastern United States. Accidentally introduced on trees imported from Asia in the early 1900s, spores of the fungus enter cracks in the bark of American chestnut trees and produce hyphae, killing the tree. The once-common chestnuts now survive mainly as sprouts from the stumps of former trees. Another ascomycete, *Fusarium circinatum*, causes pine pitch canker, a disease that threatens pines throughout the world. Between 10% and 50% of the world's fruit harvest is lost annually due to fungi, and grain crops also suffer major losses each year.

Some fungi that attack food crops produce compounds that are toxic to humans. Certain species of the ascomycete *Aspergillus* contaminate grain and peanuts by secreting compounds called aflatoxins. Another example is the ascomycete *Claviceps purpurea*, which grows on rye plants, forming purple structures called ergots. If infected rye is milled into flour, toxins from the ergots can cause ergotism, characterized by gangrene, nervous spasms, burning sensations, hallucinations, and temporary insanity. An epidemic of ergotism around 944 CE killed more than 40,000 people in France. One compound that has been isolated from ergots is lysergic acid, the raw material from which the hallucinogen LSD is made.

Although animals are less susceptible to parasitic fungi than are plants, about 500 fungi are known to parasitize animals. One such parasite, the chytrid *Batrachochytrium dendrobatidis*, has been implicated in the recent decline or extinction of about 200 species of frogs and other amphibians (Figure 31.26). This chytrid can cause severe skin infections, leading to massive die-offs. Field observations and studies of museum specimens indicate that *B. dendrobatidis* first appeared in frog populations shortly before their declines in Australia, Costa Rica, the United States, and other countries. In addition, in regions where it infects frogs, this chytrid has very low levels of genetic diversity. These findings are consistent with the hypothesis that *B. dendrobatidis* has emerged recently and spread rapidly across the globe, decimating many amphibian populations.

The general term for an infection caused by a fungal parasite is **mycosis**. In humans, skin mycoses include the disease ringworm, so named because it appears as circular red areas on the skin. The ascomycetes that cause ringworm can infect almost any skin surface. Most commonly, they grow on the feet, causing the intense itching and blisters known as athlete's foot. Though highly contagious, athlete's foot and other ringworm infections can be treated with fungicidal lotions and powders.

Systemic mycoses, by contrast, spread through the body and usually cause very serious illnesses. They are typically caused by inhaled spores. For example, coccidioidomycosis is a systemic mycosis that produces tuberculosis-like symptoms in the lungs. Each year, hundreds of cases in North America require treatment with antifungal drugs, without which the disease would be fatal.

Some mycoses are opportunistic, occurring only when a change in the body's microorganisms, chemical environment, or immune system allows fungi to grow unchecked. *Candida albicans*, for example, is one of the normal inhabitants of moist epithelia, such as the vaginal lining. Under certain circumstances, *Candida* can grow too rapidly and become pathogenic, leading to so-called "yeast infections." Many other opportunistic mycoses in humans have become more common in recent decades, due in part to AIDS, which compromises the immune system.

▼ Figure 31.26
IMPACT

Amphibians Under Attack

Could a fungal parasite have caused the hundreds of amphibian population declines and extinctions during the last three decades? While habitat losses resulting from human activities have often been the culprit, the underlying causes have been unknown for nearly half the declining species. However, recent studies have implicated the global spread of a parasitic fungus, the chytrid *Batrachochytrium dendrobatidis*. For example, Vance Vredenburg, at San Francisco State University, and colleagues showed that the number of yellow-legged frogs (*Rana muscosa*) plummeted after the chytrid reached the Sixty Lake Basin area of California. Prior to the chytrid's 2004 arrival, on average there were 2,325 frogs in these lakes. By 2009, only 38 frogs remained. All the surviving frogs were in two lakes (yellow) where researchers had applied a fungicide to reduce the chytrid's impact.

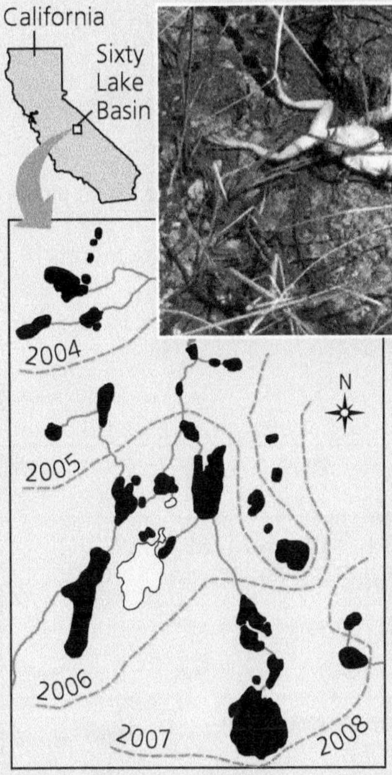

▲ Yellow-legged frogs killed by *B. dendrobatidis* infection

WHY IT MATTERS Worldwide, over one-third of amphibian species are suffering serious population declines. Information about the causes of these declines is essential if we are to protect these animals from extinction. Furthermore, because about 60% of human diseases originate from diseases in other animals, it is in our best interest to understand emerging diseases in amphibians.

FURTHER READING V. T. Vredenburg, et al., Large-scale amphibian die-offs driven by the dynamics of an emerging infectious disease, *Proceedings of the National Academy of Sciences* 107:9689-9694 (2010).

WHAT IF? Do the data depicted indicate that the chytrid *caused* or *is correlated to* the drop in frog numbers? Explain.

Practical Uses of Fungi

The dangers posed by fungi should not overshadow their immense benefits. We depend on their ecological services as decomposers and recyclers of organic matter. And without mycorrhizae, farming would be far less productive.

Mushrooms are not the only fungi of interest for human consumption. Fungi are used to ripen Roquefort and other blue cheeses. A species of *Aspergillus* produces citric acid used in colas. Morels and truffles, the edible fruiting bodies of various ascomycetes, are highly prized for their complex flavors (see Figure 31.16). These fungi can sell for hundreds to thousands of dollars a pound. Truffles release strong odors that attract mammals and insects, which in nature feed on them and disperse their spores. In some cases, the odors mimic the pheromones (sex attractants) of certain mammals. For example, the odors of several European truffles mimic the pheromones released by male pigs, which explains why *female* pigs are used to help find these delicacies.

Humans have used yeasts to produce alcoholic beverages and bread for thousands of years. Under anaerobic conditions, yeasts ferment sugars to alcohol and CO_2, which causes dough to rise. Only relatively recently have the yeasts involved been separated into pure cultures for more controlled use. The yeast *Saccharomyces cerevisiae* is the most important of all cultured fungi (see Figure 31.7). It is available as many strains of baker's yeast and brewer's yeast.

Many fungi have great medical value as well. For example, a compound extracted from ergots is used to reduce high blood pressure and to stop maternal bleeding after childbirth. Some fungi produce antibiotics that are effective in treating bacterial infections. In fact, the first antibiotic discovered was penicillin, made by the ascomycete mold *Penicillium* (**Figure 31.27**). Other examples of pharmaceuticals derived from fungi include cholesterol-lowering drugs and cyclosporine, a drug used to suppress the immune system after organ transplants.

Fungi also figure prominently in research. For example, the yeast *Saccharomyces cerevisiae* is used to study the molecular genetics of eukaryotes because its cells are easy to culture and manipulate. Scientists are gaining insight into the genes involved in Parkinson's disease and other human diseases by examining the functions of homologous genes in *S. cerevisiae*.

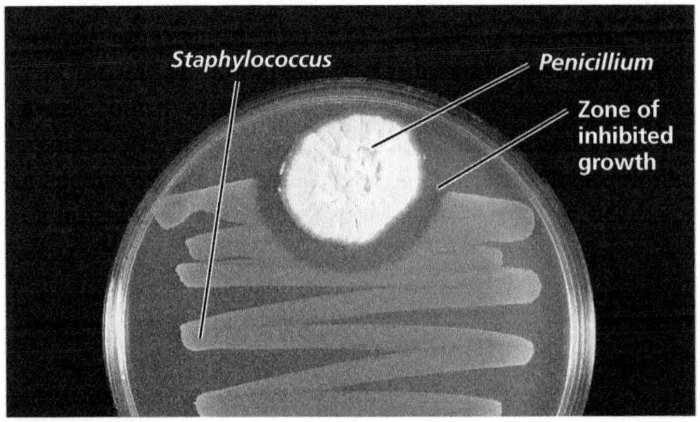

▲ **Figure 31.27 Fungal production of an antibiotic.** The mold *Penicillium* produces an antibiotic (penicillin) that inhibits the growth of *Staphylococcus* bacteria, resulting in the clear area between the mold and the bacteria.

Genetically modified fungi hold much promise. Although bacteria such as *Escherichia coli* can produce some useful proteins, they cannot synthesize glycoproteins because they lack enzymes that can attach carbohydrates to proteins. Fungi, on the other hand, do produce such enzymes. In 2003, scientists succeeded in engineering a strain of *S. cerevisiae* that produces human glycoproteins, including insulin-like growth factor. Such fungus-produced glycoproteins have the potential to treat people with medical conditions that prevent them from producing these compounds. Meanwhile, other researchers are sequencing the genome of the wood-digesting basidiomycete *Phanerochaete chrysosporium*, one of many "white rot" fungi. They hope to decipher the metabolic pathways by which white rot breaks down wood, with the goal of harnessing these pathways to produce paper pulp.

Having now completed our survey of the kingdom Fungi, we will turn in the remaining chapters of this unit to the closely related kingdom Animalia, to which we humans belong.

CONCEPT CHECK 31.5

1. What are some of the benefits that lichen algae can derive from their relationship with fungi?
2. What characteristics of pathogenic fungi result in their being efficiently transmitted?
3. **WHAT IF?** How might life on Earth differ from what we know today if no mutualistic relationships between fungi and other organisms had ever evolved?

For suggested answers, see Appendix A.

31 CHAPTER REVIEW

SUMMARY OF KEY CONCEPTS

CONCEPT 31.1

Fungi are heterotrophs that feed by absorption (pp. 636–638)

- All **fungi** (including decomposers and symbionts) are heterotrophs that acquire nutrients by absorption. Many fungi secrete enzymes that break down complex molecules to smaller molecules that can be absorbed.
- Most fungi grow as thin, multicellular filaments called **hyphae**; relatively few species grow only as single-celled **yeasts**. In their multicellular form, fungi consist of **mycelia**, networks of branched hyphae adapted for absorption. Mycorrhizal fungi have specialized hyphae that enable them to form a mutually beneficial relationship with plants.

? *How does the morphology of multicellular fungi affect the efficiency of nutrient absorption?*

CONCEPT 31.2

Fungi produce spores through sexual or asexual life cycles (pp. 638–640)

- The sexual cycle involves cytoplasmic fusion (**plasmogamy**) and nuclear fusion (**karyogamy**), with an intervening heterokaryotic stage in which cells have haploid nuclei from two parents. The diploid cells resulting from karyogamy are short-lived and undergo meiosis, producing haploid **spores**.
- Many fungi can reproduce asexually as filamentous fungi or yeasts. DNA sequence data now allow mycologists to classify all fungi, even those lacking a known sexual cycle.

DRAW IT *Draw a fungal life cycle, labeling asexual and sexual reproduction, meiosis, plasmogamy, karyogamy, and the points in the cycle when spores and the zygote are produced.*

CONCEPT 31.3

The ancestor of fungi was an aquatic, single-celled, flagellated protist (pp. 640–641)

- Molecular evidence supports the hypothesis that fungi and animals diverged from a common ancestor that was unicellular and had a flagellum.
- Unicellular parasites called microsporidia appear to be an early-diverging fungal lineage.
- Fungi were among the earliest colonizers of land, including species that were symbionts with early land plants.

? *Did multicellularity originate independently in fungi and animals? Explain.*

CONCEPT 31.4

Fungi have radiated into a diverse set of lineages (pp. 641–648)

Fungal Phylum	Distinguishing Features of Morphology and Life Cycles	
Chytridiomycota **(chytrids)**	Flagellated spores	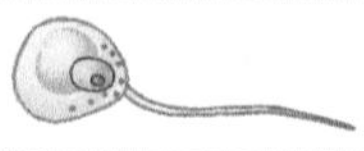
Zygomycota **(zygote fungi)**	Resistant zygosporangium as sexual stage	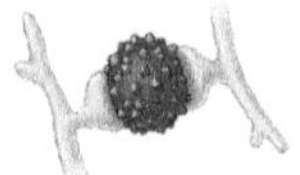
Glomeromycota **(arbuscular mycorrhizal fungi)**	Arbuscular mycorrhizae formed with plants	
Ascomycota (**ascomycetes**, or **sac fungi**)	Sexual spores (ascospores) borne internally in sacs called asci; vast numbers of asexual spores (conidia) produced	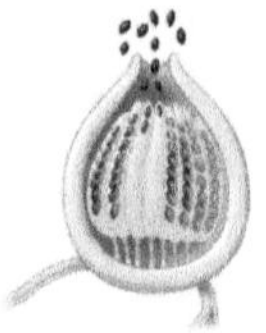
Basidiomycota (**basidiomycetes**, or **club fungi**)	Elaborate fruiting body (basidiocarp) containing many basidia that produce sexual spores (basidiospores)	

DRAW IT *Draw a phylogenetic tree showing relationships among the five major groups of fungi.*

CONCEPT 31.5

Fungi play key roles in nutrient cycling, ecological interactions, and human welfare (pp. 648–652)

- Fungi perform essential recycling of chemical elements between the living and nonliving world.
- Some **endophytes** help protect plants from herbivores and pathogens, while other fungi help certain animals digest plant tissue. **Lichens** are highly integrated symbiotic associations of fungi and algae or cyanobacteria.
- About 30% of all known fungal species are parasites, mostly of plants. Some fungi also cause disease in animals.
- Humans eat many fungi and use others to make cheeses, alcoholic beverages, and bread. Antibiotics produced by fungi treat bacterial infections. Genetic research on fungi is leading to applications in biotechnology.

? *Summarize how fungi are important as decomposers, mutualists, and pathogens.*

TEST YOUR UNDERSTANDING

LEVEL 1: KNOWLEDGE/COMPREHENSION

1. *All* fungi share which of the following characteristics?
   a. symbiotic
   b. heterotrophic
   c. flagellated
   d. pathogenic
   e. act as decomposers
2. Which feature seen in chytrids supports the hypothesis that they diverged earliest in fungal evolution?
   a. the absence of chitin within the cell wall
   b. coenocytic hyphae
   c. flagellated spores
   d. formation of resistant zygosporangia
   e. parasitic lifestyle
3. Which of the following cells or structures are associated with *asexual* reproduction in fungi?
   a. ascospores
   b. basidiospores
   c. zygosporangia
   d. conidiophores
   e. ascocarps
4. The photosynthetic symbiont of a lichen is often
   a. a moss.
   b. a green alga.
   c. a brown alga.
   d. an ascomycete.
   e. a small vascular plant.
5. Among the organisms listed here, which are thought to be the closest relatives of fungi?
   a. animals
   b. vascular plants
   c. mosses
   d. brown algae
   e. slime molds

LEVEL 2: APPLICATION/ANALYSIS

6. The adaptive advantage associated with the filamentous nature of fungal mycelia is primarily related to
   a. the ability to form haustoria and parasitize other organisms.
   b. avoiding sexual reproduction until the environment changes.
   c. the potential to inhabit almost all terrestrial habitats.
   d. the increased probability of contact between different mating types.
   e. an extensive surface area well suited for invasive growth and absorptive nutrition.
7. **SCIENTIFIC INQUIRY**
   DRAW IT The grass *Dichanthelium languinosum* lives in hot soils and houses fungi of the genus *Curvularia* as endophytes. Regina Redman, of Montana State University, and colleagues performed field experiments to test the impact of *Curvularia* on the heat tolerance of this grass. They grew plants without (E−) and with (E+) *Curvularia* endophytes in soils of different temperatures and measured plant mass and the number of new shoots the plants produced. Draw a bar graph of the results for plant mass versus temperature and interpret it.

Soil Temp.	*Curvularia* Presence	Plant Mass (g)	Number of New Shoots
30°C	E−	16.2	32
	E+	22.8	60
35°C	E−	21.7	43
	E+	28.4	60
40°C	E−	8.8	10
	E+	22.2	37
45°C	E−	0	0
	E+	15.1	24

Source: R. S. Redman et al., Thermotolerance generated by plant/fungal symbiosis, *Science* 298:1581 (2002).

LEVEL 3: SYNTHESIS/EVALUATION

8. **EVOLUTION CONNECTION**
   The fungus-alga symbiosis that makes up a lichen is thought to have evolved multiple times independently in different fungal groups. However, lichens fall into three well-defined growth forms (see Figure 31.23). What research could you perform to test the following hypotheses?

   Hypothesis 1: Crustose, foliose, and fruticose lichens each represent a monophyletic group.

   Hypothesis 2: Each lichen growth form represents convergent evolution by taxonomically diverse fungi.
9. **WRITE ABOUT A THEME**
   Emergent Properties As you read in this chapter, fungi have long formed symbiotic associations with plants and with algae. In a short essay (100–150 words), describe how these two types of associations may lead to emergent properties in biological communities.

For selected answers, see Appendix A.

32

An Overview of Animal Diversity

▲ **Figure 32.1 Which of these organisms are animals?**

EVOLUTION

KEY CONCEPTS

32.1 Animals are multicellular, heterotrophic eukaryotes with tissues that develop from embryonic layers

32.2 The history of animals spans more than half a billion years

32.3 Animals can be characterized by "body plans"

32.4 New views of animal phylogeny are emerging from molecular data

OVERVIEW

Welcome to Your Kingdom

Reading the last few chapters, you may have felt like a [redacted] among some unfamiliar organisms, such as slime [redacted] whisk ferns, and sac fungi. You probably are more at [redacted] ith the topic introduced in this chapter—the animal kingdom, which of course includes yourself. But animal diversity extends far beyond humans and the dogs, cats, birds, and other animals we humans regularly encounter. For example, the diverse organisms in Figure 32.1 are all animals, including those that appear to resemble lacy branches, thick stems, and curly leaves. To date, biologists have identified 1.3 million extant (living) species of animals. Estimates of the actual number of animal species run far higher. This vast diversity encompasses a spectacular range of morphological variation, from corals to cockroaches to crocodiles.

In this chapter, we embark on a tour of the animal kingdom that will continue in the next two chapters. We will consider the characteristics that all animals share, as well as those that distinguish various taxonomic groups. This information is central to understanding animal phylogeny, a topic that is a lively arena of biological research and debate, as you will read.

CONCEPT 32.1

Animals are multicellular, heterotrophic eukaryotes with tissues that develop from embryonic layers

Listing features shared by all animals is challenging, as there are exceptions to nearly every criterion for distinguishing animals from other life-forms. When taken together, however, several characteristics of animals sufficiently describe the group for our discussion.

Nutritional Mode

Animals differ from both plants and fungi in their mode of nutrition. Plants are autotrophic eukaryotes capable of generating organic molecules through photosynthesis. Fungi are heterotrophs that grow on or near their food and that feed by absorption (often after they have released enzymes that digest the food outside their bodies). Unlike plants, animals cannot construct all of their own organic molecules and so, in most cases, they ingest them—either by eating other living organisms or by eating nonliving organic material. But unlike fungi, most animals do not feed by absorption; instead, animals ingest their food and then use enzymes to digest it within their bodies.

Cell Structure and Specialization

Animals are eukaryotes, and like plants and most fungi, animals are multicellular. In contrast to plants and fungi, however, animals lack the structural support of cell walls. Instead, a variety of proteins external to the cell membrane provide structural support to animal cells and connect them to one another (see Figure 6.30). The most abundant of these proteins is collagen, which is found only in animals.

Many animals have two types of specialized cells not found in other multicellular organisms: muscle cells and nerve cells. In most animals, these cells are organized into **tissues**, groups of cells that have a common structure, function, or both. Muscle tissue and nervous tissue are responsible for moving the body and conducting nerve impulses, respectively. The ability to move and conduct nerve impulses underlies many of the adaptations that differentiate animals from plants and fungi. For this reason, muscle and nerve cells are central to the animal lifestyle.

Reproduction and Development

Most animals reproduce sexually, and the diploid stage usually dominates the life cycle. In the haploid stage, sperm and egg cells are produced directly by meiotic division, unlike what occurs in plants and fungi (see Figure 13.6). In most animal species, a small, flagellated sperm fertilizes a larger, nonmotile egg, forming a diploid zygote. The zygote then undergoes **cleavage**, a succession of mitotic cell divisions without cell growth between the divisions. During the development of most animals, cleavage leads to the formation of a multicellular stage called a **blastula**, which in many animals takes the form of a hollow ball (Figure 32.2). Following the blastula stage is the process of **gastrulation**, during which the layers of embryonic tissues that will develop into adult body parts are produced. The resulting developmental stage is called a **gastrula**.

Although some animals, including humans, develop directly into adults, the life cycles of most animals include at least one larval stage. A **larva** is a sexually immature form of an animal that is morphologically distinct from the adult, usually eats different food, and may even have a different habitat than the adult, as in the case of the aquatic larva of a mosquito or dragonfly. Animal larvae eventually undergo **metamorphosis**, a developmental transformation that turns the animal into a juvenile that resembles an adult but is not yet sexually mature.

Although adult animals vary widely in morphology, the genes that control animal development are similar across a broad range of taxa. All animals have developmental genes that regulate the expression of other genes, and many of these regulatory genes contain sets of DNA sequences called *homeoboxes* (see Chapter 21). Most animals share a unique homeobox-containing family of genes, known as *Hox* genes. *Hox* genes play important roles in the development of animal embryos, controlling the expression of dozens or even hundreds of other genes that influence animal morphology (see Chapter 25).

Sponges, which are among the simplest extant animals, lack *Hox* genes. However, they have other homeobox genes that influence their shape, such as those that regulate the formation of water channels in the body wall, a key feature of sponge morphology (see Figure 33.4). In the ancestors of more complex animals, the *Hox* gene family arose via the duplication of earlier homeobox genes. Over time, the *Hox* gene family underwent a series of duplications, yielding a versatile "toolkit" for regulating development. In vertebrates, insects, and most other animals, *Hox* genes regulate the formation of the anterior-posterior (front-to-back) axis, as well as other aspects of development. Similar sets of conserved genes govern the development of both flies and humans, despite their obvious differences and hundreds of millions of years of divergent evolution.

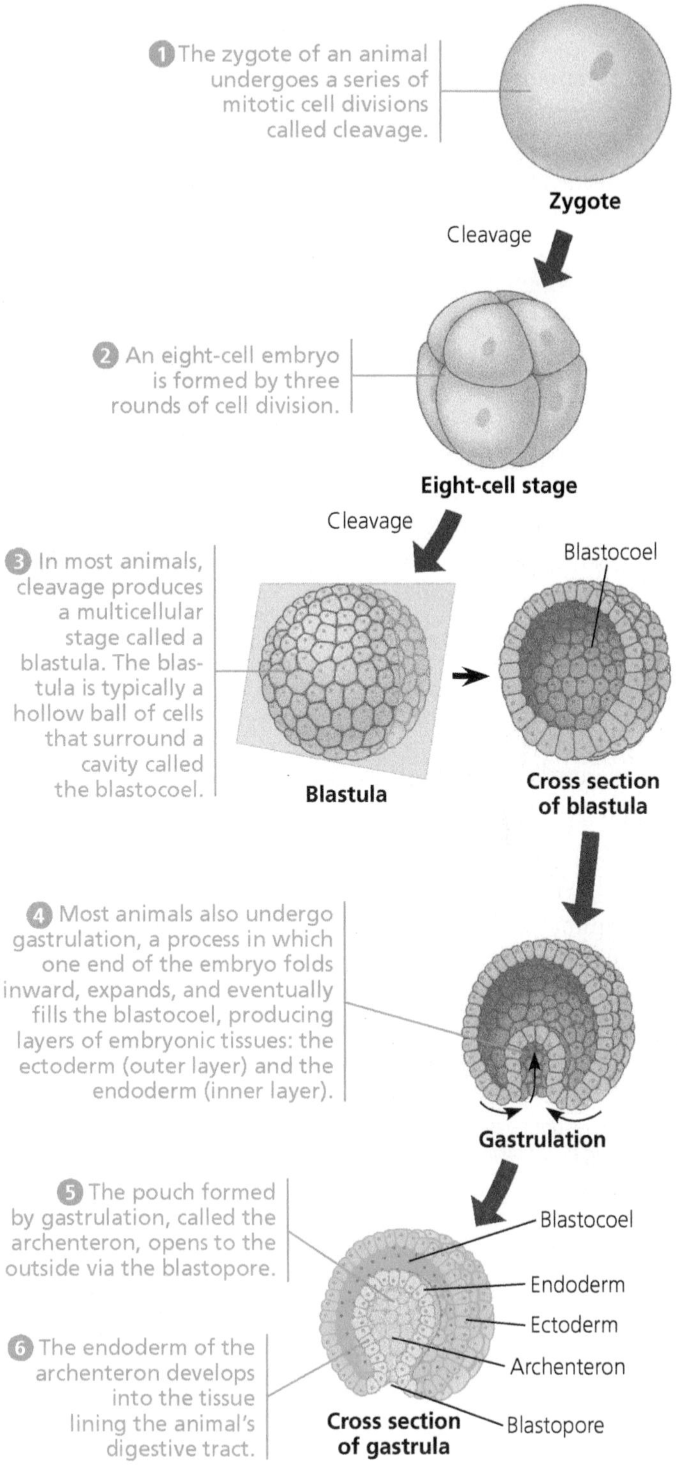

▲ Figure 32.2 **Early embryonic development in animals.**

CONCEPT CHECK 32.1

1. Summarize the main stages of animal development. What family of control genes plays a major role?
2. **WHAT IF?** What animal characteristics would be needed by an imaginary plant that could chase, capture, and digest its prey—yet could also extract nutrients from soil and conduct photosynthesis?
3. **MAKE CONNECTIONS** Humans have about the same number of protein-coding genes as do animals such as tunicates (see photograph) that have very simple body forms and few neurons. In contrast, humans have many more microRNA molecules (miRNAs) than these animals. Review Concept 18.3 (pp. 365–366); then suggest a possible reason for this observation.

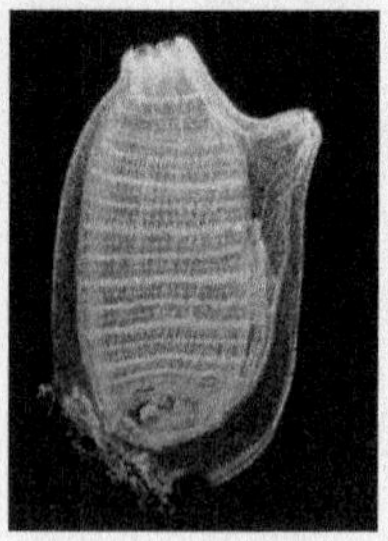

For suggested answers, see Appendix A.

CONCEPT 32.2

The history of animals spans more than half a billion years

The animal kingdom includes not only a great diversity of living species, but an even greater diversity of extinct ones. (Some paleontologists have estimated that over 99% of all animal species are extinct.) Various studies suggest that this great diversity originated during the last billion years. For example, some estimates based on molecular clocks suggest that the ancestors of animals diverged from the ancestors of fungi about a billion years ago. Other such studies have estimated that the common ancestor of living animals lived sometime between 800 and 675 million years ago.

To learn what this common ancestor may have been like, scientists have sought to identify protist groups that are closely related to animals. As shown in Figure 32.3, a combination of morphological and molecular evidence indicates that choanoflagellates are among the closest living relatives of animals. Based on such evidence, researchers hypothesize that the common ancestor of living animals may have been a suspension feeder similar to present-day choanoflagellates. We will next survey the fossil evidence for how animals evolved from their distant common ancestor over four geologic eras (see Table 25.1 to review the geologic time scale).

Neoproterozoic Era (1 Billion–542 Million Years Ago)

Despite the molecular data indicating an earlier origin of animals, the first generally accepted macroscopic fossils of animals date from 565 to 550 million years ago. These fossils are members of an early group of soft-bodied multicellular eukaryotes, known collectively as the **Ediacaran biota**. The name comes from the Ediacara Hills of Australia, where these animals were first discovered (Figure 32.4). Similar fossils have since been found on other continents.

▼ **Figure 32.3 Three lines of evidence that choanoflagellates are closely related to animals.**

? *Are the data described in ③ consistent with predictions that could be made from the evidence in ① and ②? Explain.*

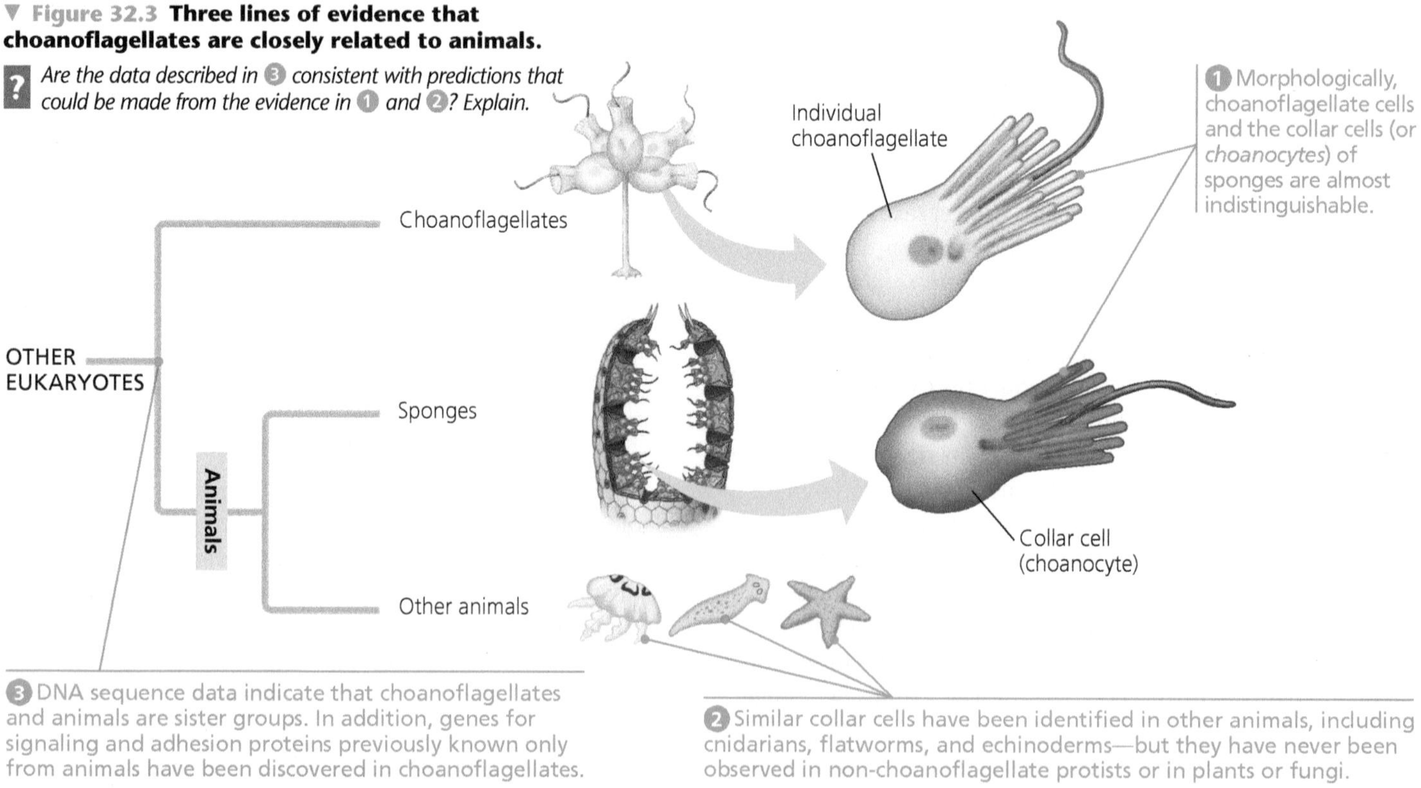

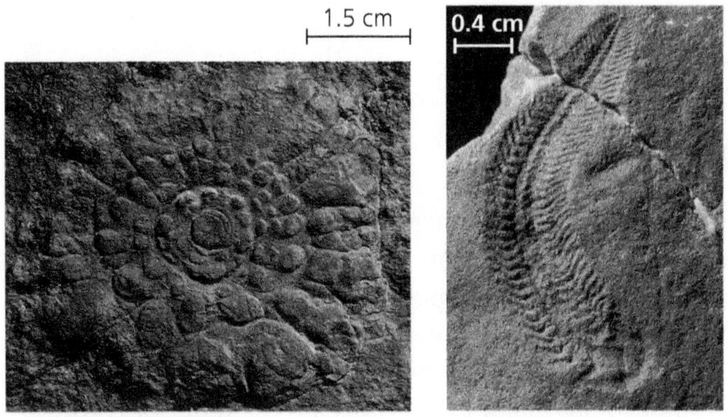

(a) ***Mawsonites spriggi*** (b) ***Spriggina floundersi***

▲ **Figure 32.4 Ediacaran fossils.** Fossils dating to 565–550 million years ago include animals **(a)** with simple, radial forms and **(b)** with many body segments.

▲ **Figure 32.5 A Cambrian seascape.** This artist's reconstruction depicts a diverse array of organisms found in fossils from the Burgess Shale site in British Columbia, Canada. The animals include *Pikaia* (eel-like chordate at top left), *Marella* (arthropod swimming at left), *Anomalocaris* (large animal with anterior grasping limbs and a circular mouth), and *Hallucigenia* (animals with toothpick-like spikes on the seafloor).

Some are sponges, while others may be related to living cnidarians. Still others of these fossil organisms have proved difficult to classify, as they do not seem to be closely related to any living animal or algal groups.

In addition to these macroscopic fossils, Neoproterozoic rocks have also yielded what may be microscopic signs of early animals. As you read in Chapter 25, 575-million-year-old microfossils discovered in China appear to exhibit the basic structural organization of present-day animal embryos. However, debate continues about whether the fossil embryos are animals or are members of extinct groups that are closely related to animals (but are not actually animals). Though older fossils of animals may be discovered in the future, the fossil record as it is known today shows that the late Neoproterozoic era was a time of increasing animal diversity.

Paleozoic Era (542–251 Million Years Ago)

Another wave of animal diversification occurred 535–525 million years ago, during the Cambrian period of the Paleozoic era—a phenomenon referred to as the **Cambrian explosion** (see Chapter 25). In strata formed before the Cambrian explosion, only a few animal phyla have been observed. But in strata that are 535–525 million years old, paleontologists have found the oldest fossils of about half of all extant animal phyla, including the first arthropods, chordates, and echinoderms. Many of these distinctive fossils, which include the first animals with hard, mineralized skeletons, look very different from most living animals (Figure 32.5). But for the most part, paleontologists have established that these Cambrian fossils are members of extant animal phyla, or at least are close relatives.

The increase in the diversity of animal phyla during the Cambrian was accompanied by a decline in the diversity of Ediacaran life-forms. What caused these trends? There are several current hypotheses. Some evidence suggests that during the Cambrian period, predators acquired novel adaptations, such as forms of locomotion that helped them catch prey, while prey species acquired new defenses, such as protective shells. As new predator-prey relationships emerged, natural selection may have led to the decline of some groups and the rise of others. Another hypothesis focuses on an increase in atmospheric oxygen that preceded the Cambrian explosion. More plentiful oxygen would have enabled animals with higher metabolic rates and larger body sizes to thrive, while potentially harming other species. A third hypothesis proposes that the origin of *Hox* genes and other genetic changes affecting the regulation of developmental genes facilitated the evolution of new body forms. These hypotheses are not mutually exclusive, however; predator-prey relationships, atmospheric changes, and changes in the regulation of development may each have played a role.

The Cambrian period was followed by the Ordovician, Silurian, and Devonian periods, when animal diversity continued to increase, although punctuated by episodes of mass extinction (see Figure 25.15). Vertebrates (fishes) emerged as the top predators of the marine food web. By 460 million years ago, groups that diversified during the Cambrian period were making an impact on land. Arthropods began to adapt to terrestrial habitats, as indicated by the appearance of millipedes and centipedes. Another clue is seen in fossilized fern galls—enlarged cavities that fern plants form in response to stimulation by resident insects, which then use the galls for protection. Fossils indicate that fern galls date back at least

302 million years, suggesting that insects and plants were influencing each other's evolution by that time.

Vertebrates made the transition to land around 365 million years ago and diversified into numerous terrestrial groups. Two of these survive today: the amphibians (such as frogs and salamanders) and the amniotes (reptiles, including birds, and mammals). We will explore these groups, known collectively as the tetrapods, in more detail in Chapter 34.

Mesozoic Era (251–65.5 Million Years Ago)

The animal phyla that had evolved during the Paleozoic now began to spread into new habitats. In the oceans, the first coral reefs formed, providing other marine animals with new habitats. Some reptiles returned to the water, leaving plesiosaurs (see Figure 25.4) and other large aquatic predators as their descendants. On land, descent with modification in some tetrapods led to the origin of wings and other flight equipment in pterosaurs and birds. Large and small dinosaurs emerged, both as predators and herbivores. At the same time, the first mammals—tiny nocturnal insect-eaters—appeared on the scene. In addition, as you read in Chapter 30, flowering plants (angiosperms) and insects both underwent dramatic diversifications during the late Mesozoic.

Cenozoic Era (65.5 Million Years Ago to the Present)

Mass extinctions of both terrestrial and marine animals ushered in a new era, the Cenozoic. Among the groups of species that disappeared were the large, nonflying dinosaurs and the marine reptiles. The fossil record of the early Cenozoic documents the rise of large mammalian herbivores and predators as mammals began to exploit the vacated ecological niches. The global climate gradually cooled throughout the Cenozoic, triggering significant shifts in many animal lineages. Among primates, for example, some species in Africa adapted to the open woodlands and savannas that replaced many of the former dense forests. The ancestors of our own species were among those grassland apes.

CONCEPT CHECK 32.2

1. Put the following milestones in animal evolution in chronological order from oldest to most recent: (a) origin of mammals, (b) earliest evidence of terrestrial arthropods, (c) Ediacaran fauna, (d) extinction of large, nonflying dinosaurs.
2. **WHAT IF?** Suppose the most recent common ancestor of fungi and animals lived 1 billion years ago. If the first fungi lived 990 million years ago, would animals also have been alive at that time? Explain.

For suggested answers, see Appendix A.

CONCEPT 32.3

Animals can be characterized by "body plans"

Animal species vary tremendously in morphology, but their great diversity in form can be described by a relatively small number of major "body plans." A **body plan** is a particular set of morphological and developmental traits, integrated into a functional whole—the living animal. The term *plan* here does not imply that animal forms are the result of conscious planning or invention. But body plans do provide a succinct way to compare and contrast key animal features. They also are of interest in the study of *evo-devo*, the interface between evolution and development (see Chapters 21 and 25).

Like all features of organisms, animal body plans have evolved over time. Some of the evolutionary changes appear to have occurred early in the history of animal life. For example, recent research suggests that a key step in the molecular control of gastrulation has remained unchanged for more than 500 million years (Figure 32.6). This early evolutionary innovation was of fundamental importance: Gastrulation helps to explain why most animals are not a hollow ball of cells. As we'll discuss, however, other aspects of animal body plans have changed multiple times over the course of evolution. Thus, as we explore the major features of animal body plans, bear in mind that similar body forms may have evolved independently in different lineages. In addition, body features can be lost over the course of evolution, causing some closely related species to look very different from one another.

Symmetry

A basic feature of animal bodies is their type of symmetry—or absence of symmetry. (Many sponges, for example, lack symmetry altogether.) Some animals exhibit **radial symmetry**, the type of symmetry found in a flowerpot (Figure 32.7a). Sea anemones, for example, have a top side (where the mouth is located) and a bottom side. But they have no front and back ends and no left and right sides.

The two-sided symmetry seen in a shovel is an example of **bilateral symmetry** (Figure 32.7b). A bilateral animal has two axes of orientation: front to back and top to bottom. Such animals have a **dorsal** (top) side and a **ventral** (bottom) side, a left side and a right side, and an **anterior** (front) end and a **posterior** (back) end. Many animals with a bilaterally symmetrical body plan (such as arthropods and mammals) have sensory equipment concentrated at their anterior end, including a central nervous system ("brain") in the head—an evolutionary trend called **cephalization** (from the Greek *kephale*, head).

The symmetry of an animal generally fits its lifestyle. Many radial animals are sessile (living attached to a substrate) or planktonic (drifting or weakly swimming, such as jellies,

▼ Figure 32.6 **INQUIRY**

Did β-catenin play an ancient role in the molecular control of gastrulation?

EXPERIMENT In most animals, gastrulation leads to the formation of three layers of embryonic cells. In some of these species, such as worms, sea urchins, and vertebrates, the protein β-catenin marks the site of gastrulation and activates the transcription of genes necessary for the process. Athula Wikramanayake and Mark Martindale, of the University of Hawaii, and colleagues tested whether β-catenin also helps to control gastrulation in the sea anemone *Nematostella vectensis*. This species is a member of the phylum Cnidaria, a group that predates the origin of animals whose embryos form three layers of cells.

RESULTS

1. In early stages of development, β-catenin (here labeled with green fluorescent protein) is found throughout the *N. vectensis* embryo.
2. By the 32-cell stage, β-catenin is concentrated on the side of the embryo where gastrulation will occur.
3. In the early gastrula stage, β-catenin activity (here stained a darker red) occurs in the inner layer of cells.
4. In embryos in which β-catenin activity is blocked (by a protein that binds to β-catenin), gastrulation does not occur.

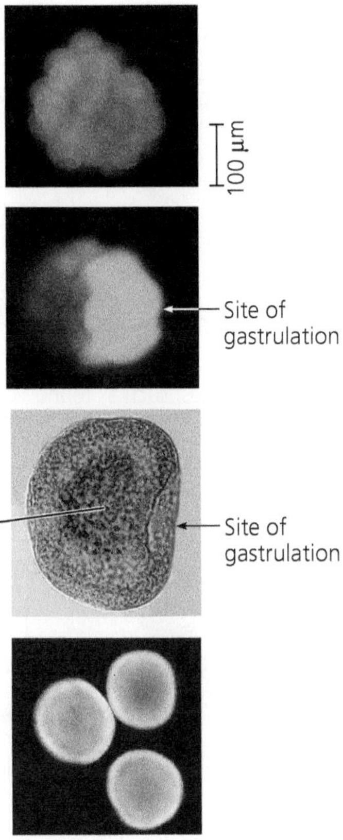

CONCLUSION In *N. vectensis*, β-catenin is required for gastrulation to occur and may help to determine the site of gastrulation. Since the fossil record indicates that cnidarians diverged more than 500 million years ago from species in which β-catenin is known to influence gastrulation, it seems likely that β-catenin played an ancient role in the molecular control of gastrulation.

SOURCE A. H. Wikramanayake et al., An ancient role for nuclear β-catenin in the evolution of axial polarity and germ layer segregation, *Nature* 426:446–450 (2003).

WHAT IF? β-catenin binds to DNA, thereby stimulating the transcription of genes necessary for gastrulation. Based on this information, suggest a different experiment that could be used to confirm the results in step 4. What would be the purpose of performing such an experiment?

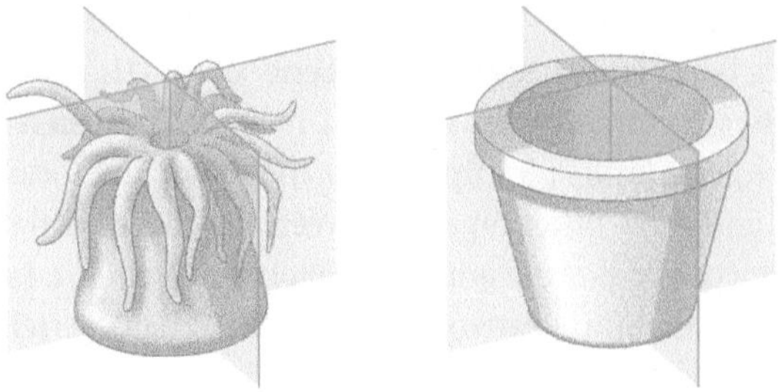

(a) Radial symmetry. A radial animal, such as a sea anemone (phylum Cnidaria), does not have a left side and a right side. Any imaginary slice through the central axis divides the animal into mirror images.

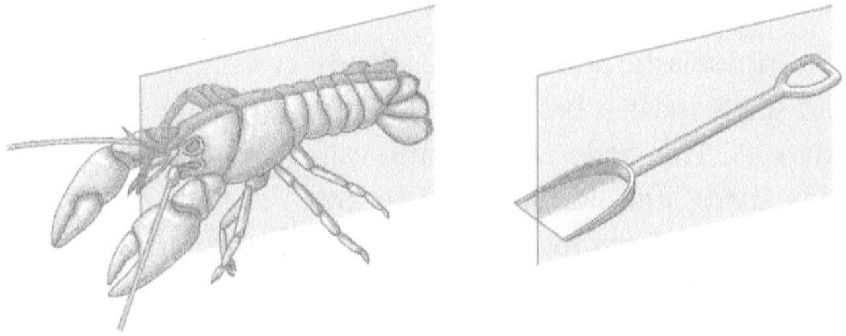

(b) Bilateral symmetry. A bilateral animal, such as a lobster (phylum Arthropoda), has a left side and a right side. Only one imaginary cut divides the animal into mirror-image halves.

▲ Figure 32.7 **Body symmetry.** The flowerpot and shovel are included to help you remember the radial-bilateral distinction.

commonly called jellyfishes). Their symmetry equips them to meet the environment equally well from all sides. In contrast, bilateral animals typically move actively from place to place. Most bilateral animals have a central nervous system that enables them to coordinate the complex movements involved in crawling, burrowing, flying, or swimming. Fossil evidence indicates that these two fundamentally different kinds of symmetry have been present for at least 550 million years.

Tissues

Animal body plans also vary with regard to tissue organization. In animals, true tissues are collections of specialized cells isolated from other tissues by membranous layers. While sponges and a few other groups lack true tissues, in all other animals, the embryo becomes layered through the process of gastrulation (see Figure 32.2). As development progresses, these concentric layers, called *germ layers*, form the various tissues and organs of the body. **Ectoderm**, the germ layer covering the surface of the embryo, gives rise to the outer covering of the animal and, in some phyla, to the central nervous system. **Endoderm**, the innermost germ layer, lines the pouch that forms during gastrulation (the archenteron) and gives rise to the lining of the digestive tract (or cavity) and organs such as the liver and lungs of vertebrates.

Animals that have only these two germ layers are said to be **diploblastic**. Diploblasts include the animals called cnidarians (jellies and corals, for example) as well as the comb jellies (see Chapter 33). All bilaterally symmetrical animals have a third germ layer, called the **mesoderm**, which fills much of the space between the ectoderm and endoderm. Thus, animals with bilateral symmetry are also said to be **triploblastic** (having three germ layers). In triploblasts, the mesoderm forms the muscles and most other organs between the digestive tract and the outer covering of the animal. Triploblasts include a broad range of animals, from flatworms to arthropods to vertebrates. (Although some diploblasts actually do have a third germ layer, it is not nearly as well developed as the mesoderm of animals considered to be triploblastic.)

Body Cavities

Most triploblastic animals have a **body cavity**, a fluid- or air-filled space located between the digestive tract and the outer body wall. This body cavity is also called a **coelom** (from the Greek *koilos*, hollow). A so-called "true" coelom forms from tissue derived from mesoderm. The inner and outer layers of tissue that surround the cavity connect and form structures that suspend the internal organs. Animals with a true coelom are known as **coelomates** (Figure 32.8a).

Some triploblastic animals have a body cavity that is formed from mesoderm and endoderm (Figure 32.8b). Such a cavity is called a "pseudocoelom" (from the Greek *pseudo*, false), and the animals that have one are called **pseudocoelomates**. Despite its name, however, a pseudocoelom is not false; it is a fully functional body cavity. Finally, some triplobastic animals lack a body cavity altogether (Figure 32.8c). They are known collectively as **acoelomates** (from the Greek *a-*, without).

A body cavity has many functions. Its fluid cushions the suspended organs, helping to prevent internal injury. In soft-bodied coelomates, such as earthworms, the coelom contains noncompressible fluid that acts like a skeleton against which muscles can work. The cavity also enables the internal organs to grow and move independently of the outer body wall. If it were not for your coelom, for example, every beat of your heart or ripple of your intestine would warp your body's surface.

Terms such as *coelomates* and *pseudocoelomates* refer to organisms that have a similar body plan and hence belong to the same *grade* (a group whose members share key biological features). However, phylogenetic studies show that true coeloms and pseudocoeloms have been independently gained or lost multiple times in the course of animal evolution. As illustrated by this example, a grade is not necessarily equivalent to a *clade* (a group that includes an ancestral species and all of its descendants). Thus, while describing an organism as a coelomate or pseudocoelomate can be helpful in describing certain of its features, these terms must be interpreted with caution when seeking to understand evolutionary history.

Protostome and Deuterostome Development

Based on certain aspects of early development, many animals can be described as having one of two developmental modes: **protostome development** or **deuterostome development**. These modes can generally be distinguished by differences in cleavage, coelom formation, and fate of the blastopore.

▼ Figure 32.8 **Body cavities of triploblastic animals.** The various organ systems of a triploblastic animal develop from the three germ layers that form in the embryo. Blue represents tissue derived from ectoderm, red from mesoderm, and yellow from endoderm.

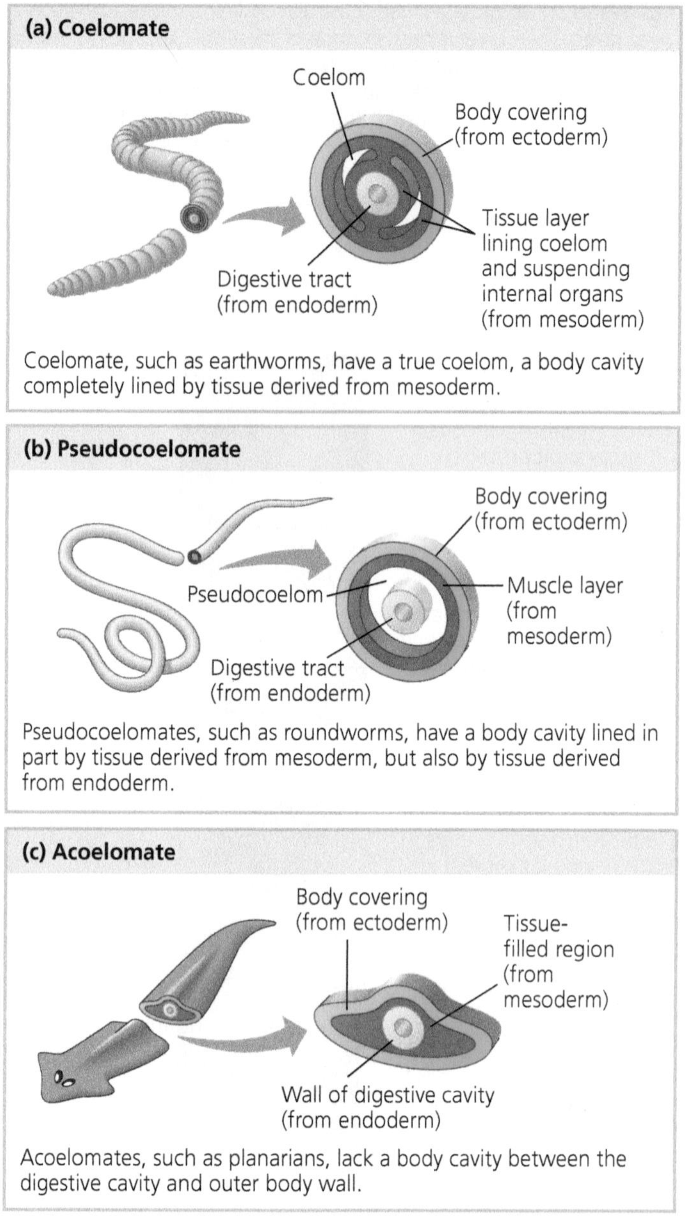

Cleavage

Many animals with protostome development undergo **spiral cleavage**, in which the planes of cell division are diagonal to the vertical axis of the embryo; as seen in the eight-cell stage of the embryo, smaller cells are centered over the grooves between larger, underlying cells (Figure 32.9a, left). Furthermore, the so-called **determinate cleavage** of some animals with protostome development rigidly casts ("determines") the developmental fate of each embryonic cell very early. A cell

▶ **Figure 32.9 A comparison of protostome and deuterostome development.** These are useful general distinctions, though there are many variations and exceptions to these patterns.

MAKE CONNECTIONS *Review Figure 20.21 (p. 415). As an early embryo, which would more likely have stem cells capable of giving rise to cells of any type: an animal with protostome development or with deuterostome development? Explain.*

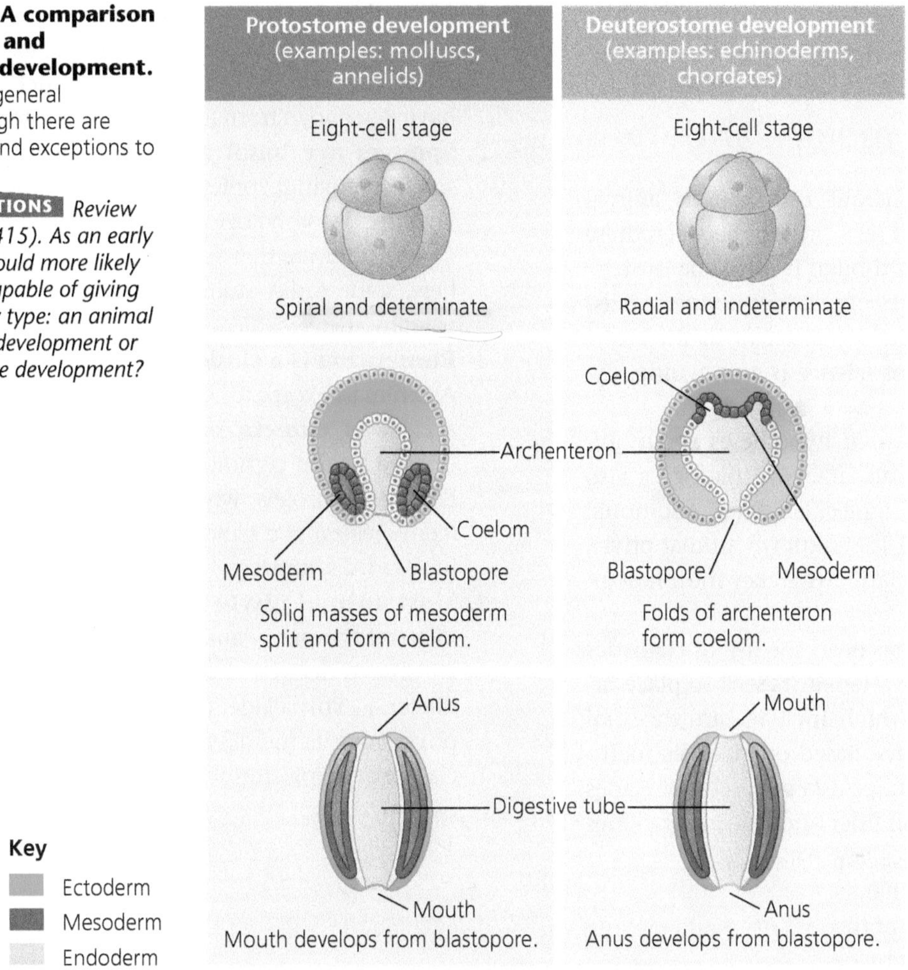

(a) Cleavage. In general, protostome development begins with spiral, determinate cleavage. Deuterostome development is characterized by radial, indeterminate cleavage.

(b) Coelom formation. Coelom formation begins in the gastrula stage. In protostome development, the coelom forms from splits in the mesoderm. In deuterostome development, the coelom forms from mesodermal outpocketings of the archenteron.

(c) Fate of the blastopore. In protostome development, the mouth forms from the blastopore. In deuterostome development, the mouth forms from a secondary opening.

isolated from a snail at the four-cell stage, for example, cannot develop into a whole animal. Instead, after repeated divisions, such a cell will form an inviable embryo that lacks many parts.

In contrast to the spiral cleavage pattern, deuterostome development is predominantly characterized by **radial cleavage**. The cleavage planes are either parallel or perpendicular to the vertical axis of the embryo; as seen at the eight-cell stage, the tiers of cells are aligned, one directly above the other (see Figure 32.9a, right). Most animals with deuterostome development also have **indeterminate cleavage**, meaning that each cell produced by early cleavage divisions retains the capacity to develop into a complete embryo. For example, if the cells of a sea urchin embryo are separated at the four-cell stage, each can form a complete larva. Similarly, it is the indeterminate cleavage of the human zygote that makes identical twins possible.

Coelom Formation

During gastrulation, an embryo's developing digestive tube initially forms as a blind pouch, the **archenteron**, which becomes the gut (Figure 32.9b). As the archenteron forms in protostome development, initially solid masses of mesoderm split and form the coelom. In contrast, in deuterostome development, the mesoderm buds from the wall of the archenteron, and its cavity becomes the coelom.

Fate of the Blastopore

Protostome and deuterostome development often differ in the fate of the **blastopore**, the indentation that during gastrulation leads to the formation of the archenteron (Figure 32.9c). After the archenteron develops, in most animals a second opening forms at the opposite end of the gastrula. In many species, the blastopore and this second opening become the two openings of the digestive tube: the mouth and the anus. In protostome development, the mouth generally develops from the first opening, the blastopore, and it is for this characteristic that the term *protostome* derives (from the Greek *protos*, first, and *stoma*, mouth). In deuterostome development (from the Greek *deuteros*, second), the mouth is derived from the secondary opening, and the blastopore usually forms the anus.

CONCEPT CHECK 32.3

1. Distinguish the terms *grade* and *clade*.
2. Compare three aspects of the early development of a snail (a mollusc) and a human (a chordate).
3. **WHAT IF?** Evaluate this claim: Ignoring the details of their specific anatomy, worms, humans, and most other triploblasts have a shape analogous to that of a doughnut.

For suggested answers, see Appendix A.

CONCEPT 32.4

New views of animal phylogeny are emerging from molecular data

Zoologists currently recognize about three dozen animal phyla. But the boundaries of and relationships between these phyla continue to be debated. Although it might be frustrating that the phylogenies in textbooks cannot be memorized as set-in-stone truths, the uncertainty inherent in these diagrams is a healthy reminder that science is an ongoing, dynamic process of inquiry.

Researchers have long based their hypotheses about animal phylogeny on morphological data. Now biologists also reconstruct phylogenies using molecular data. Additional clues have come from studies of lesser-known animal phyla, along with fossil data that help clarify when key morphological traits arose in various groups.

Another important change has been the use of cladistics (see Chapter 26). Phylogenetic systematists seek to place organisms into clades, each of which includes an ancestral species and all of its descendants. Based on cladistic methods, a phylogenetic tree takes shape as a hierarchy of clades nested within larger clades—the finer and thicker branches of the tree, respectively. Clades are inferred from shared derived characters that are unique to members of the clade. For example, a clade might be inferred from key anatomical and embryological similarities that researchers conclude are homologous. Molecular data such as DNA sequences are another source of information for inferring common ancestry. But whether the data used are "traditional" morphological characters or "new" molecular sequences or a combination, the goal is the same: to reconstruct evolutionary history.

To get a sense of the debates in animal systematics, we'll compare a traditional view of animal phylogeny, based primarily on morphological data (Figure 32.10), with a more current view, based mainly on molecular data (Figure 32.11).

Points of Agreement

These two views agree on several significant aspects of animal phylogeny. Notice how the following points are reflected in Figures 32.10 and 32.11.

1. **All animals share a common ancestor.** Both trees indicate that animals are monophyletic, forming a clade called Metazoa. All extant and extinct animal lineages have descended from a common ancestor.
2. **Sponges are basal animals.** Among the extant taxa, sponges (phylum Porifera) branch from the base of both animal trees. Morphological and molecular analyses published in 2009 indicate that sponges are monophyletic, as shown here; some earlier studies had suggested that sponges are paraphyletic.
3. **Eumetazoa is a clade of animals with true tissues.** All animals except for sponges and a few others belong to a clade of **eumetazoans** ("true animals"). True tissues evolved in the common ancestor of living eumetazoans. Basal eumetazoans, which include the phyla Ctenophora (comb jellies) and Cnidaria, are diploblastic and generally have radial symmetry.
4. **Most animal phyla belong to the clade Bilateria.** Bilateral symmetry and the presence of three germ layers are shared derived characters that help define the clade Bilateria. This clade contains the majority of animal phyla, and its members are known as **bilaterians**. The Cambrian explosion was primarily a rapid diversification of bilaterians.

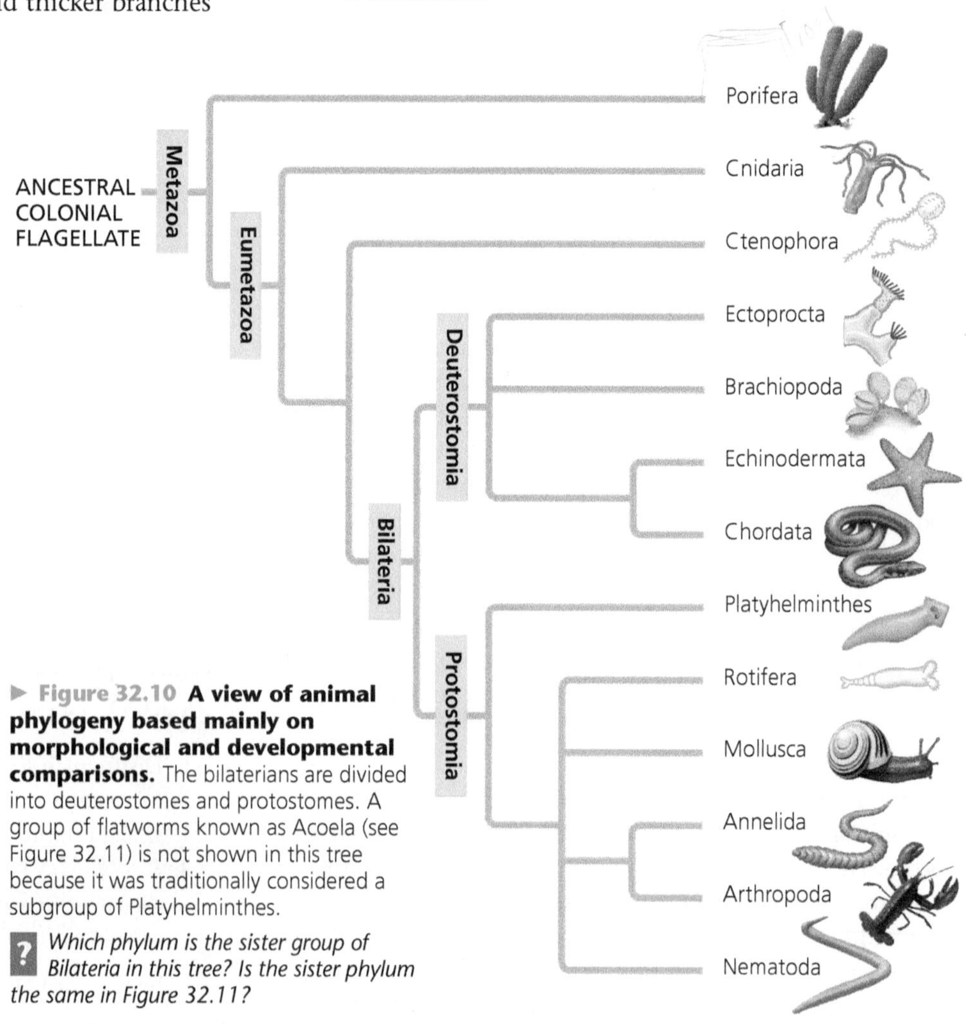

▶ Figure 32.10 **A view of animal phylogeny based mainly on morphological and developmental comparisons.** The bilaterians are divided into deuterostomes and protostomes. A group of flatworms known as Acoela (see Figure 32.11) is not shown in this tree because it was traditionally considered a subgroup of Platyhelminthes.

? *Which phylum is the sister group of Bilateria in this tree? Is the sister phylum the same in Figure 32.11?*

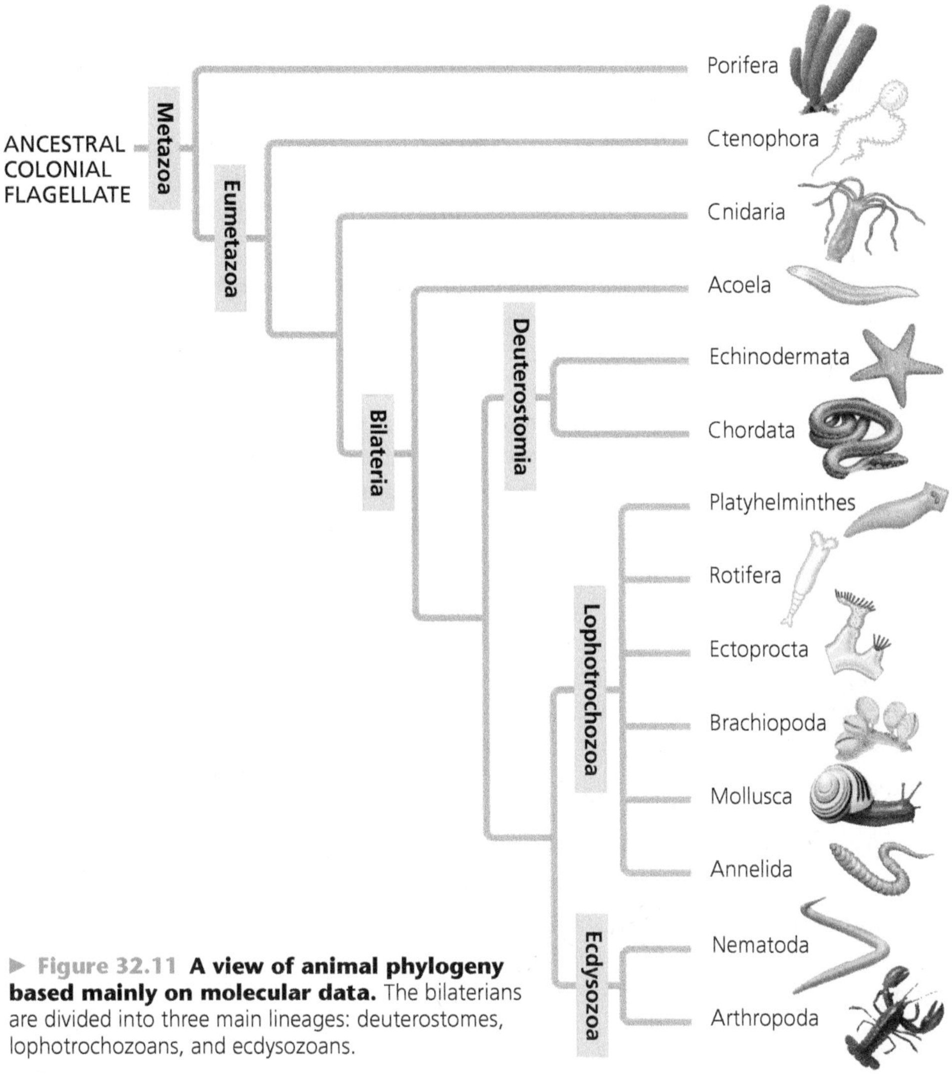

▶ **Figure 32.11 A view of animal phylogeny based mainly on molecular data.** The bilaterians are divided into three main lineages: deuterostomes, lophotrochozoans, and ecdysozoans.

5. **Chordates and some other phyla belong to the clade Deuterostomia.** The term *deuterostome* refers not only to a mode of animal development, but also to the members of a clade that includes vertebrates and other chordates. (Note, however, that the traditional and molecular views of animal phylogeny disagree as to which other phyla are also deuterostomes.)

Progress in Resolving Bilaterian Relationships

While evolutionary relationships inferred from morphological data and molecular data are similar in many respects, there are some differences. For example, the morphology-based tree in Figure 32.10 divides the bilaterians into deuterostomes and protostomes. This view assumes that these two modes of development reflect a phylogenetic pattern. Within the protostomes, arthropods (such as insects and crustaceans) are grouped with annelids. Both groups have segmented bodies (think of the tail of a lobster, which is an arthropod, and an earthworm, which is an annelid).

A different view has emerged from molecular phylogenies based on ribosomal genes, *Hox* genes, and dozens of other protein-coding nuclear genes, as well as mitochondrial genes. Collectively, these studies indicate that there are three major clades of bilaterally symmetrical animals: the Deuterostomia, Lophotrochozoa, and Ecdysozoa (see Figure 32.11). In contrast to the traditional morphological view, the molecular phylogeny holds that the arthropods and annelids are not closely related to one another. Note also that Figure 32.11 includes a group of acoelomate flatworms (Acoela) not shown in Figure 32.10. Traditionally, acoelomate flatworms were classified with other flatworms in the phylum Platyhelminthes. However, recent research indicates that acoelomate flatworms are basal bilaterians, and not members of the phylum Platyhelminthes. Acoela's basal position suggests that the bilaterians may have descended from a common ancestor that resembled living acoelomate flatworms—that is, from an ancestor that had a simple nervous system, a saclike gut with a single opening (the "mouth"), and no excretory system.

As seen in Figure 32.11, the molecular phylogeny assigns the animal phyla that are not in Deuterostomia to two taxa rather than one: the **ecdysozoans** and the **lophotrochozoans.** The clade name Ecdysozoa refers to a characteristic shared by nematodes, arthropods, and some of the other ecdysozoan phyla that are not included in our survey. These animals secrete external skeletons (exoskeletons); the stiff covering of a cicada or cricket is an example. As the animal grows, it molts, squirming out of its old exoskeleton and secreting a larger one. The process of shedding the old exoskeleton is called *ecdysis* (Figure 32.12). Though named for this characteristic, the

◀ **Figure 32.12 Ecdysis.** This molting cicada is in the process of emerging from its old exoskeleton. The animal will now secrete a new, larger exoskeleton.

clade was proposed mainly on the basis of molecular data that support the common ancestry of its members. Furthermore, some taxa excluded from this clade by their molecular data, such as certain species of leeches, do in fact molt.

The name Lophotrochozoa refers to two different features observed in some animals belonging to this clade. Some lophotrochozoans, such as ectoprocts, develop a structure called a **lophophore** (from the Greek *lophos*, crest, and *pherein*, to carry), a crown of ciliated tentacles that function in feeding (Figure 32.13a). Individuals in other phyla, including molluscs and annelids, go through a distinctive developmental stage called the **trochophore larva** (Figure 32.13b)—hence the name lophotrochozoan.

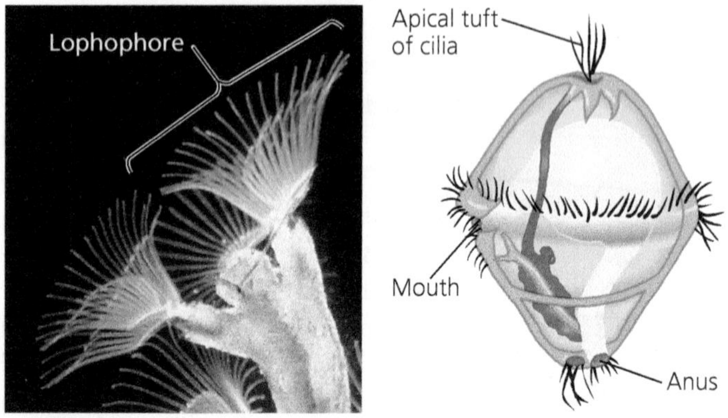

(a) Lophophore feeding structures of an ectoproct

(b) Structure of a trochophore larva

▲ Figure 32.13 **Morphological characteristics of lophotrochozoans.**

Future Directions in Animal Systematics

Like any area of scientific inquiry, animal systematics is a work in progress. At present, most systematists think that the tree shown in Figure 32.11 is more strongly supported than is the tree shown in Figure 32.10. Of course, as new information emerges, our understanding of the evolutionary relationships shown in these trees may change. Researchers continue to conduct large-scale analyses of multiple genes and morphological traits across a wide sample of animal phyla. A better understanding of the relationships between these phyla will give scientists a clearer picture of how the diversity of animal body plans arose. In Chapters 33 and 34, we will take a closer look at the diverse phyla of extant animals and their evolutionary history.

CONCEPT CHECK 32.4

1. Describe the evidence that cnidarians share a more recent common ancestor with other animals than with sponges.
2. How do the phylogenetic hypotheses presented in Figures 32.10 and 32.11 differ in structuring the major branches within the clade Bilateria?
3. **MAKE CONNECTIONS** Based on the phylogeny in Figure 32.11 and the information in Figure 25.10 (p. 518), evaluate this statement: "The Cambrian explosion actually consists of three explosions, not one."

For suggested answers, see Appendix A.

32 CHAPTER REVIEW

SUMMARY OF KEY CONCEPTS

CONCEPT 32.1

Animals are multicellular, heterotrophic eukaryotes with tissues that develop from embryonic layers (pp. 654–656)

- Animals are heterotrophs that ingest their food.
- Animals are multicellular eukaryotes. Their cells are supported and connected to one another by collagen and other structural proteins located outside the cell membrane. Nervous tissue and muscle tissue are key animal features.
- In most animals, **gastrulation** follows the formation of the **blastula** and leads to the formation of embryonic tissue layers. All animals have *Hox* genes that regulate the development of body form. Although *Hox* genes have been highly conserved over the course of evolution, they can produce a wide diversity of animal morphology.

? *Describe key ways that animals differ from plants and fungi.*

CONCEPT 32.2

The history of animals spans more than half a billion years (pp. 656–658)

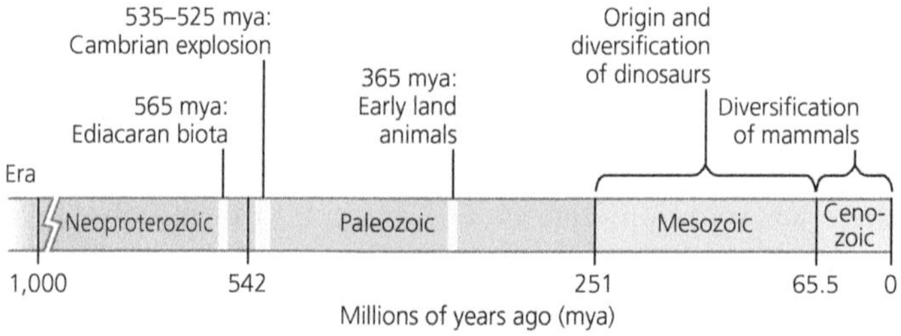

? *What caused the Cambrian explosion? Describe current hypotheses.*

CONCEPT 32.3

Animals can be characterized by "body plans" (pp. 658–661)

- Animals may lack symmetry or may have radial or bilateral symmetry. Bilaterally symmetrical animals have dorsal and ventral sides, as well as anterior and posterior ends.

- Among eumetazoans (animals with true tissues), embryos may be **diploblastic** (having two germ layers) or **triploblastic** (having three germ layers).
- In triploblastic animals, a body cavity may be present or absent. A body cavity can be a **pseudocoelom** (derived from both mesoderm and endoderm) or a true **coelom** (derived only from mesoderm).
- **Protostome** and **deuterostome** development often differ in patterns of cleavage, coelom formation, and blastopore fate.

? *Describe how body plans provide useful information yet should be interpreted cautiously when scientists are trying to understand evolutionary relationships.*

CONCEPT 32.4

New views of animal phylogeny are emerging from molecular data (pp. 662–664)

This phylogenetic tree shows key steps in animal evolution:

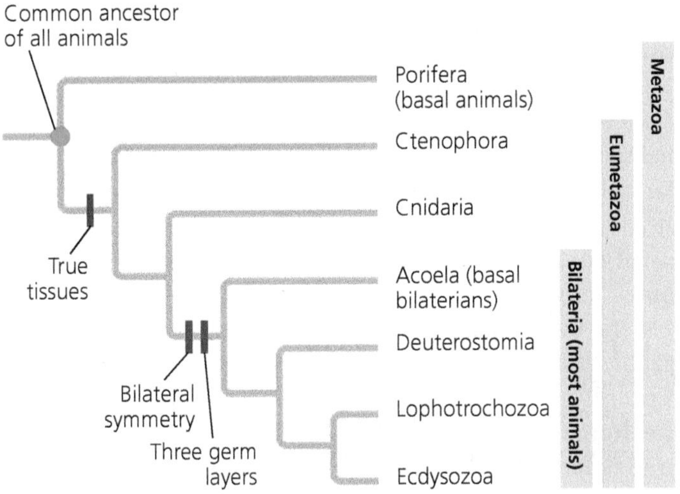

? *Describe the data and methods used today to reconstruct animal phylogeny.*

TEST YOUR UNDERSTANDING

LEVEL 1: KNOWLEDGE/COMPREHENSION

1. Among the characteristics unique to animals is
   a. gastrulation.
   b. multicellularity.
   c. sexual reproduction.
   d. flagellated sperm.
   e. heterotrophic nutrition.

2. The distinction between sponges and other animal phyla is based mainly on the absence versus the presence of
   a. a body cavity.
   b. a complete digestive tract.
   c. a circulatory system.
   d. true tissues.
   e. mesoderm.

3. Acoelomates are characterized by
   a. the absence of a brain.
   b. the absence of mesoderm.
   c. deuterostome development.
   d. a coelom that is not completely lined with mesoderm.
   e. a solid body without a cavity surrounding internal organs.

4. Which of the following was probably the *least* important factor in bringing about the Cambrian explosion?
   a. the emergence of predator-prey relationships among animals
   b. the accumulation of diverse adaptations, such as shells and different modes of locomotion
   c. the movement of animals onto land
   d. the origin of *Hox* genes and other genetic changes affecting the regulation of developmental genes
   e. the accumulation of sufficient atmospheric oxygen to support the more active metabolism of mobile animals

LEVEL 2: APPLICATION/ANALYSIS

5. Which of these is a point of conflict between the phylogenetic analyses presented in Figures 32.10 and 32.11?
   a. the monophyly of the animal kingdom
   b. the relationship of taxa of segmented animals to taxa of nonsegmented animals
   c. that sponges are basal animals
   d. that chordates are deuterostomes
   e. the monophyly of the bilaterians

LEVEL 3: SYNTHESIS/EVALUATION

6. **EVOLUTION CONNECTION**
   A professor begins a lecture on animal phylogeny by saying, "We are all worms." In this context, what did she mean?

7. **SCIENTIFIC INQUIRY**
   DRAW IT Redraw the bilaterian portion of Figure 32.11 for the nine phyla in the table below. Consider these blastopore fates: protostomy (mouth develops from the blastopore), deuterostomy (anus develops from the blastopore), or neither (the blastopore closes and the mouth develops elsewhere). Depending on the blastopore fate of its members, label each branch that leads to a phylum with P, D, N, or a combination of these letters. What is the ancestral blastopore fate? How many times has blastopore fate changed over the course of evolution? Explain.

Blastopore Fate	Phyla
Protostomy (P)	Platyhelminthes, Rotifera, Nematoda; most Mollusca, most Annelida; few Arthropoda
Deuterostomy (D)	Echinodermata, Chordata; most Arthropoda; few Mollusca, few Annelida
Neither (N)	Acoela

Source: A. Hejnol and M. Martindale, The mouth, the anus, and the blastopore—open questions about questionable openings. In *Animal Evolution: Genomes, Fossils and Trees*, eds. D. T. J. Littlewood and M. J. Telford, Oxford University Press, pp. 33–40 (2009).

8. **WRITE ABOUT A THEME**
   Feedback Regulation Animal life changed greatly during the Cambrian explosion, with some groups expanding in diversity and others declining. Write a short essay (100–150 words) interpreting these events as feedback regulation at the level of the biological community.

For selected answers, see Appendix A.

MasteringBIOLOGY www.masteringbiology.com

1. MasteringBiology® Assignments
Tutorial Animal Body Plans
Activities Protostome Diversity • Animal Phylogenetic Tree
Questions Student Misconceptions • Reading Quiz • Multiple Choice • End-of-Chapter

2. eText
Read your book online, search, take notes, highlight text, and more.

3. The Study Area
Practice Tests • Cumulative Test • *BioFlix* 3-D Animations • MP3 Tutor Sessions • Videos • Activities • Investigations • Lab Media • Audio Glossary • Word Study Tools • Art

33

An Introduction to Invertebrates

▲ Figure 33.1 **What function do the red whorls of this organism have?**

EVOLUTION

KEY CONCEPTS

33.1 Sponges are basal animals that lack true tissues

33.2 Cnidarians are an ancient phylum of eumetazoans

33.3 Lophotrochozoans, a clade identified by molecular data, have the widest range of animal body forms

33.4 Ecdysozoans are the most species-rich animal group

33.5 Echinoderms and chordates are deuterostomes

OVERVIEW

Life Without a Backbone

At first glance, you might mistake the organism shown in Figure 33.1 for a type of seaweed. But this colorful inhabitant of coral reefs is actually an animal, not an alga. Specifically, it is a species of segmented worm known as a Christmas tree worm (*Spirobranchus giganteus*). The two tree-shaped whorls are tentacles, which the worm uses for gas exchange and for removing small food particles from the surrounding water. The tentacles emerge from a tube of calcium carbonate secreted by the worm that protects and supports its soft body. Light-sensitive structures on the tentacles can detect the shadow cast by a predator, triggering the worm to contract muscles that rapidly withdraw the tentacles into the tube.

Christmas tree worms are **invertebrates**—animals that lack a backbone. Invertebrates account for 95% of known animal species. They occupy almost every habitat on Earth, from the scalding water released by deep-sea hydrothermal vents to the rocky, frozen ground of Antarctica. Adaptation to these varied environments has produced an immense diversity of forms, ranging from a species consisting of a flat bilayer of cells to other species with features such as silk-spinning glands, pivoting spines, and tentacles covered with suction cups. Invertebrate species also show enormous variation in size, from microscopic organisms to organisms that can grow to 18 m long (1.5 times the length of a school bus).

In this chapter, we'll take a tour of the invertebrate world, using the phylogenetic tree in Figure 33.2 as a guide. Figure 33.3, on the next three pages, surveys 23 invertebrate phyla. Serving as representatives of invertebrate diversity, many of those phyla are explored in more detail in the rest of this chapter.

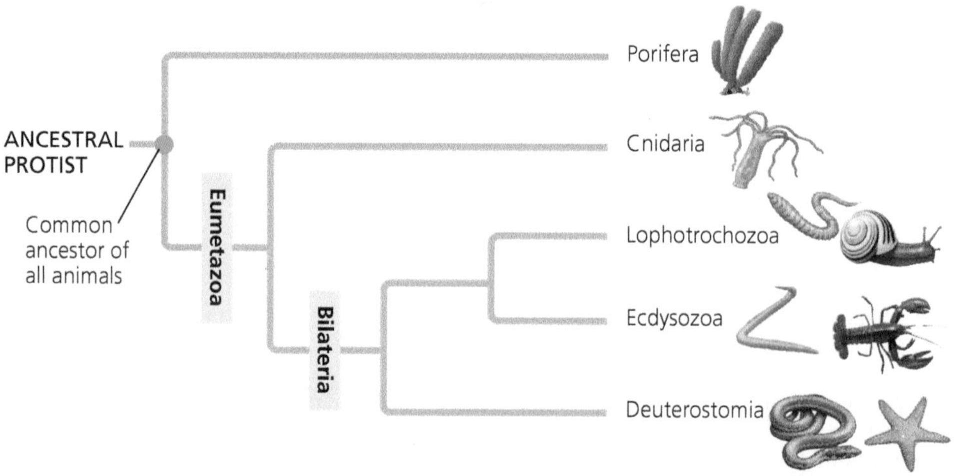

▲ Figure 33.2 **Review of animal phylogeny.** Except for sponges (basal animals in phylum Porifera) and a few other groups, all animals have tissues and are in the clade Eumetazoa. Most animals are in the diverse clade Bilateria. The evolutionary tree shown here provides an overview of material covered in Chapter 32 but omits many groups; for a more complete view of animal relationships, see Figure 32.11.

▼ Figure 33.3

Exploring Invertebrate Diversity

Kingdom Animalia encompasses 1.3 million known species, and estimates of total species range as high as 10–20 million species. Of the 23 phyla surveyed here, 12 are discussed more fully in this chapter, Chapter 32, or Chapter 34; cross-references are given at the end of their descriptions.

Porifera (5,500 species)

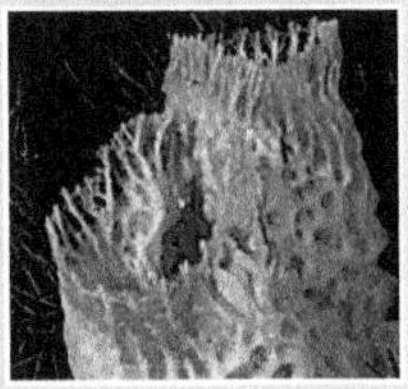

A sponge

Animals in this phylum are informally called sponges. Sponges are sessile animals that lack true tissues. They live as suspension feeders, trapping particles that pass through the internal channels of their body (see Concept 33.1).

Cnidaria (10,000 species)

Cnidarians include corals, jellies, and hydras. These animals have a diploblastic, radially symmetrical body plan that includes a gastrovascular cavity with a single opening that serves as both mouth and anus (see Concept 33.2).

A jelly

Acoela (400 species)

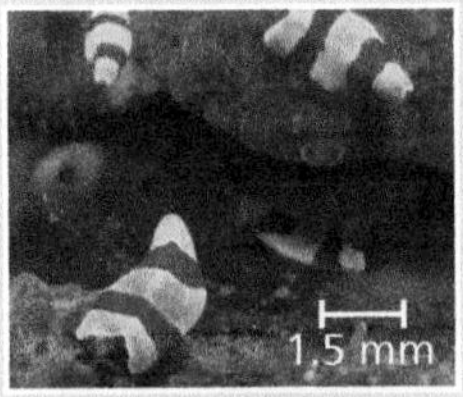

Acoel flatworms (LM)

Acoel flatworms have a simple nervous system and a saclike gut, and thus were once placed in phylum Platyhelminthes. Molecular analyses, however, indicate that Acoela is a separate lineage that diverged before the three main bilaterian clades (see Concept 32.4).

Placozoa (1 species)

The single known species in this phylum, *Trichoplax adhaerens*, doesn't even look like an animal. It consists of a simple bilayer of a few thousand cells. Placozoans are thought to be basal animals, but it is not yet known how they are related to other early-diverging animal groups such as Porifera and Cnidaria. *Trichoplax* can reproduce by dividing into two individuals or by budding off many multicellular individuals.

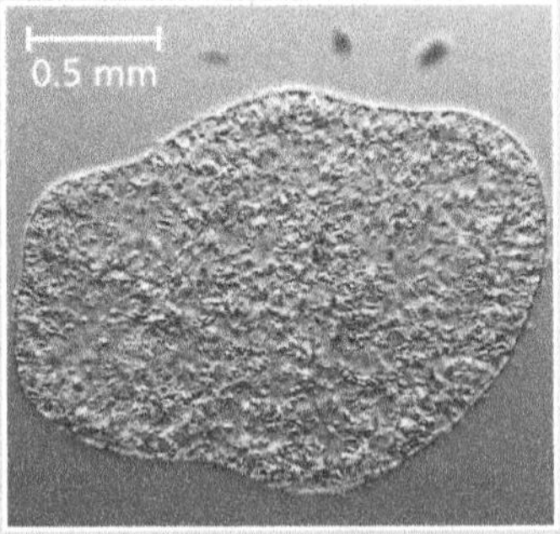

A placozoan (LM)

Ctenophora (100 species)

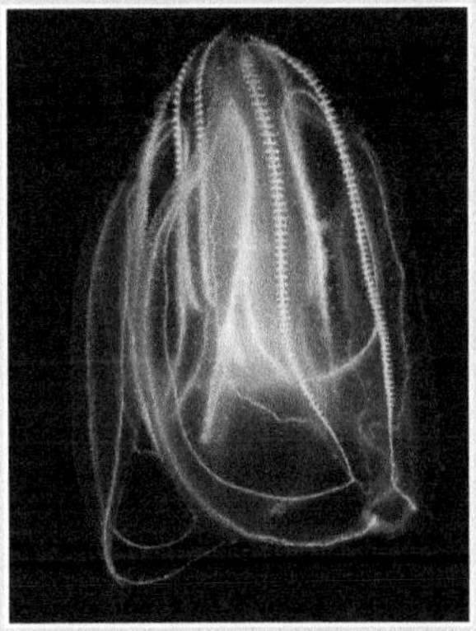

A ctenophore, or comb jelly

Ctenophores (comb jellies) are diploblastic and radially symmetrical like cnidarians, suggesting that both phyla diverged from other animals very early (see Figure 32.11). Comb jellies make up much of the ocean's plankton. They have many distinctive traits, including eight "combs" of cilia that propel the animals through the water. When a small animal contacts the tentacles of some comb jellies, specialized cells burst open, covering the prey with sticky threads.

Lophotrochozoa

Platyhelminthes (20,000 species)

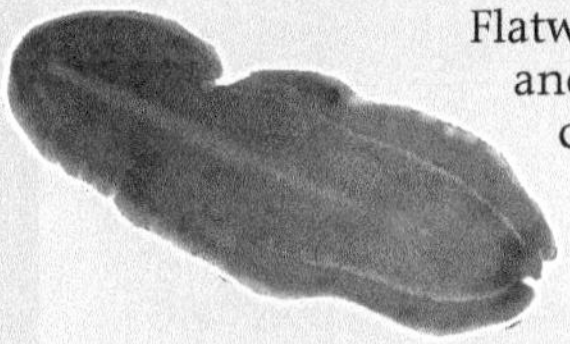

A marine flatworm

Flatworms (including tapeworms, planarians, and flukes) have bilateral symmetry and a central nervous system that processes information from sensory structures. They have no body cavity or organs for circulation (see Concept 33.3).

Rotifera (1,800 species)

Despite their microscopic size, rotifers have specialized organ systems, including an *alimentary canal* (a digestive tract with both a mouth and an anus). They feed on microorganisms suspended in water (see Concept 33.3).

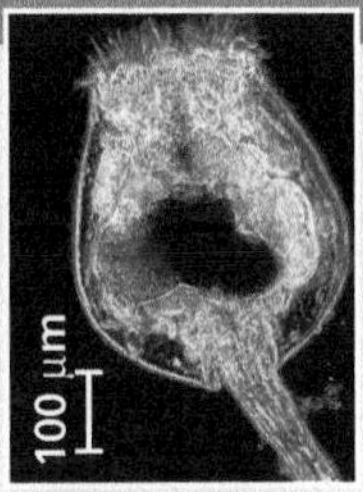

A rotifer (LM)

Ectoprocta (4,500 species)

Ectoprocts (also known as bryozoans) live as sessile colonies and are covered by a tough exoskeleton (see Concept 33.3).

Ectoprocts

Brachiopoda (335 species)

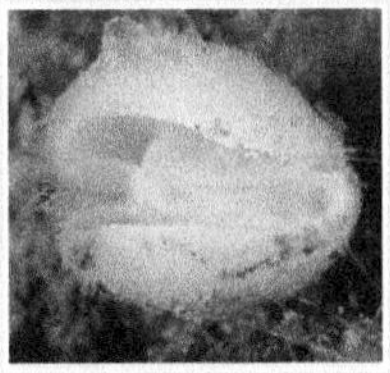

A brachiopod

Brachiopods, or lamp shells, may be easily mistaken for clams or other molluscs. However, most brachiopods have a unique stalk that anchors them to their substrate, as well as a crown of cilia called a lophophore (see Concept 33.3).

Continued on next page

Exploring Invertebrate Diversity

Lophotrochozoa (continued)

Acanthocephala (1,100 species)

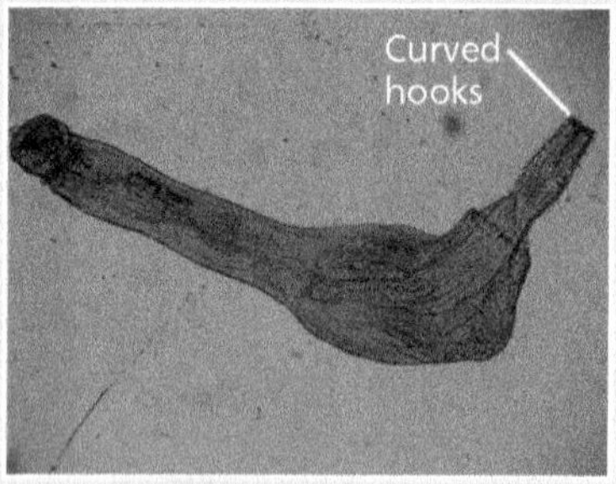

An acanthocephalan (LM)

Acanthocephalans are called spiny-headed worms because of the curved hooks on the proboscis at the anterior end of their body. All species are parasites. Some acanthocephalans manipulate the behavior of their intermediate hosts (generally arthropods) in ways that increase their chances of reaching their final hosts (generally vertebrates). For example, acanthocephalans that infect New Zealand mud crabs force their hosts to move to more visible areas on the beach, where the crabs are more likely to be eaten by birds, the worms' final hosts. Some phylogenetic analyses place the acanthocephalans within Rotifera.

Cycliophora (1 species)

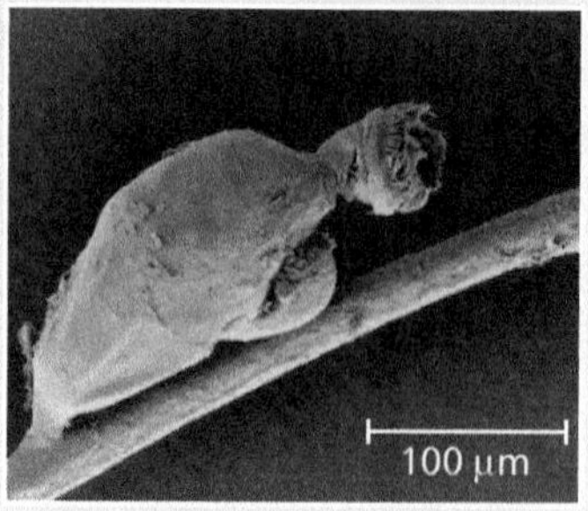

A cycliophoran (colorized SEM)

The only known cycliophoran species, *Symbion pandora*, was discovered in 1995 on the mouthparts of a lobster. This tiny, vase-shaped creature has a unique body plan and a particularly bizarre life cycle. Males impregnate females that are still developing in their mothers' bodies. The fertilized females then escape, settle elsewhere on the lobster, and release their offspring. The offspring apparently leave that lobster and search for another one to which they attach.

Nemertea (900 species)

A ribbon worm

Also called proboscis worms or ribbon worms, nemerteans swim through water or burrow in sand, extending a unique proboscis to capture prey. Like flatworms, they lack a true coelom. However, unlike flatworms, nemerteans have an alimentary canal and a closed circulatory system in which the blood is contained in vessels and hence is distinct from fluid in the body cavity.

Annelida (16,500 species)

Annelids, or segmented worms, are distinguished from other worms by their body segmentation. Earthworms are the most familiar annelids, but the phylum consists primarily of marine and freshwater species (see Concept 33.3).

A marine annelid

Mollusca (93,000 species)

Molluscs (including snails, clams, squids, and octopuses) have a soft body that in many species is protected by a hard shell (see Concept 33.3).

An octopus

Ecdysozoa

Loricifera (10 species)

Loriciferans (from the Latin *lorica*, corset, and *ferre*, to bear) are tiny animals that inhabit the deep-sea bottom. A loriciferan can telescope its head, neck, and thorax in and out of the lorica, a pocket formed by six plates surrounding the abdomen. Though the natural history of loriciferans is mostly a mystery, at least some species likely eat bacteria.

A loriciferan (LM)

Priapula (16 species)

A priapulan

Priapulans are worms with a large, rounded proboscis at the anterior end. (They are named after Priapos, the Greek god of fertility, who was symbolized by a giant penis.) Ranging from 0.5 mm to 20 cm in length, most species burrow through seafloor sediments. Fossil evidence suggests that priapulans were among the major predators during the Cambrian period.

Ecdysozoa (continued)

Onychophora (110 species)

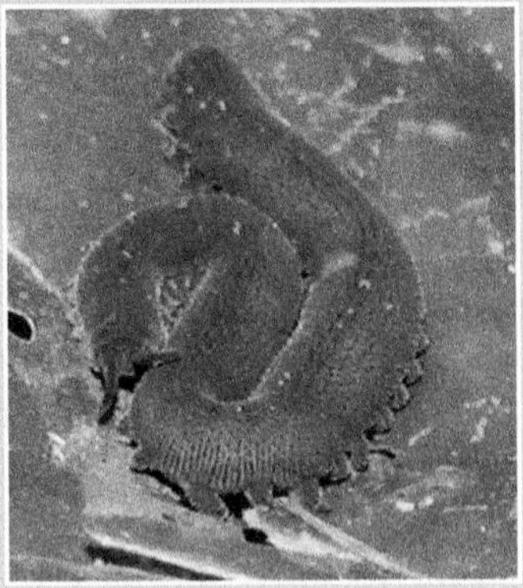

An onychophoran

Onychophorans, also called velvet worms, originated during the Cambrian explosion (see Chapter 32). Originally, they thrived in the ocean, but at some point they succeeded in colonizing land. Today they live only in humid forests. Onychophorans have fleshy antennae and several dozen pairs of saclike legs.

Tardigrada (800 species)

Tardigrades (from the Latin *tardus*, slow, and *gradus*, step) are sometimes called water bears for their rounded shape, stubby appendages, and lumbering, bearlike gait. Most tardigrades are less than 0.5 mm in length. Some live in oceans or fresh water, while others live on plants or animals. As many as 2 million tardigrades can be found on a square meter of moss. Harsh conditions may cause tardigrades to enter a state of dormancy; while dormant, they can survive temperatures as low as −272°C, close to absolute zero!

Tardigrades (colorized SEM)

Nematoda (25,000 species)

A roundworm (colored SEM)

Also called roundworms, nematodes are enormously abundant and diverse in the soil and in aquatic habitats; many species parasitize plants and animals. Their most distinctive feature is a tough cuticle that coats the body (see Concept 33.4).

Arthropoda (1,000,000 species)

The vast majority of known animal species, including insects, crustaceans, and arachnids, are arthropods. All arthropods have a segmented exoskeleton and jointed appendages (see Concept 33.4).

A scorpion (an arachnid)

Deuterostomia

Hemichordata (85 species)

An acorn worm

Like echinoderms and chordates, hemichordates are members of the deuterostome clade (see Chapter 32). Hemichordates share some traits with chordates, such as gill slits and a dorsal nerve cord. The largest group of hemichordates is the enteropneusts, or acorn worms. Acorn worms are marine and generally live buried in mud or under rocks; they may grow to more than 2 m in length.

Chordata (52,000 species)

More than 90% of all known chordate species have backbones (and thus are vertebrates). However, the phylum Chordata also includes three groups of invertebrates: lancelets, tunicates, and hagfishes. See Chapter 34 for a full discussion of this phylum.

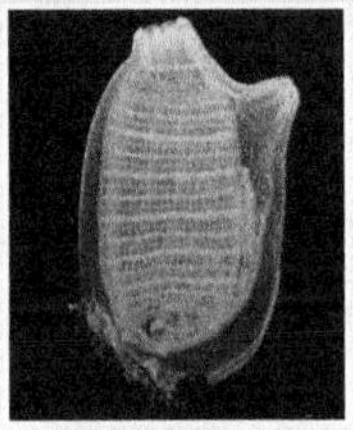

A tunicate

Echinodermata (7,000 species)

Echinoderms, such as sand dollars, sea stars, and sea urchins, are marine animals in the deuterostome clade that are bilaterally symmetrical as larvae but not as adults. They move and feed by using a network of internal canals to pump water to different parts of their body (see Concept 33.5).

A sea urchin

CONCEPT 33.1

Sponges are basal animals that lack true tissues

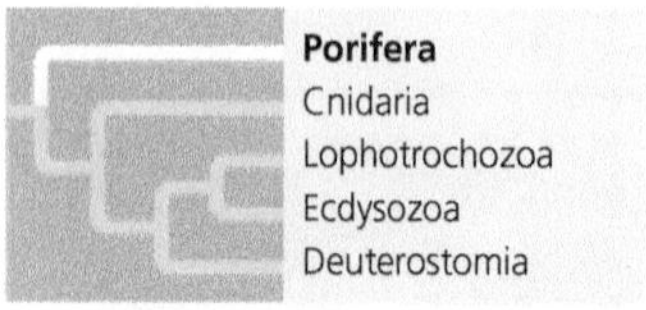

Animals in the phylum Porifera are known informally as sponges. (Recent molecular studies indicate that sponges are monophyletic, and that is the phylogeny we follow here; this remains under debate, however, as some studies suggest that sponges are paraphyletic.) Among the simplest of animals, sponges are sedentary and were mistaken for plants by the ancient Greeks. They range in size from a few millimeters to a few meters, and most species are marine, though a few live in fresh water. Sponges are **suspension feeders**: They capture food particles suspended in the water that passes through their body, which in some species resembles a sac perforated with pores. Water is drawn through the pores into a central cavity, the **spongocoel**, and then flows out of the sponge through a larger opening called the **osculum** (Figure 33.4). More complex sponges have folded body walls, and many contain branched water canals and several oscula.

Sponges are basal animals; that is, they represent a lineage that originates near the root of the phylogenetic tree of animals. Unlike nearly all other animals, sponges lack true tissues, groups of similar cells that act as a functional unit and are isolated from other tissues by membranous layers. However, the sponge body does contain several different cell types. For example, lining the interior of the spongocoel are flagellated **choanocytes**, or collar cells (named for the finger-like projections that form a "collar" around the flagellum). These cells engulf bacteria and other food particles by phagocytosis. The similarity between choanocytes and the cells of choanoflagellates supports molecular evidence suggesting that animals evolved from a choanoflagellate-like ancestor (see Figure 32.3).

The body of a sponge consists of two layers of cells separated by a gelatinous region called the **mesohyl**. Because both cell layers are in contact with water, processes such as gas exchange and waste removal can occur by diffusion across the membranes of these cells. Other tasks are performed by cells called **amoebocytes**, named for their use of pseudopodia. These cells move through the mesohyl and have many functions. For example, they take up food from the surrounding water and from choanocytes, digest it, and carry nutrients to other cells. Amoebocytes also manufacture tough skeletal fibers within the mesohyl. In some sponges, these fibers are sharp spicules made from calcium carbonate or silica. Other sponges produce more flexible fibers composed of a protein called spongin; you may have seen these pliant skeletons

▼ **Figure 33.4 Anatomy of a sponge.**

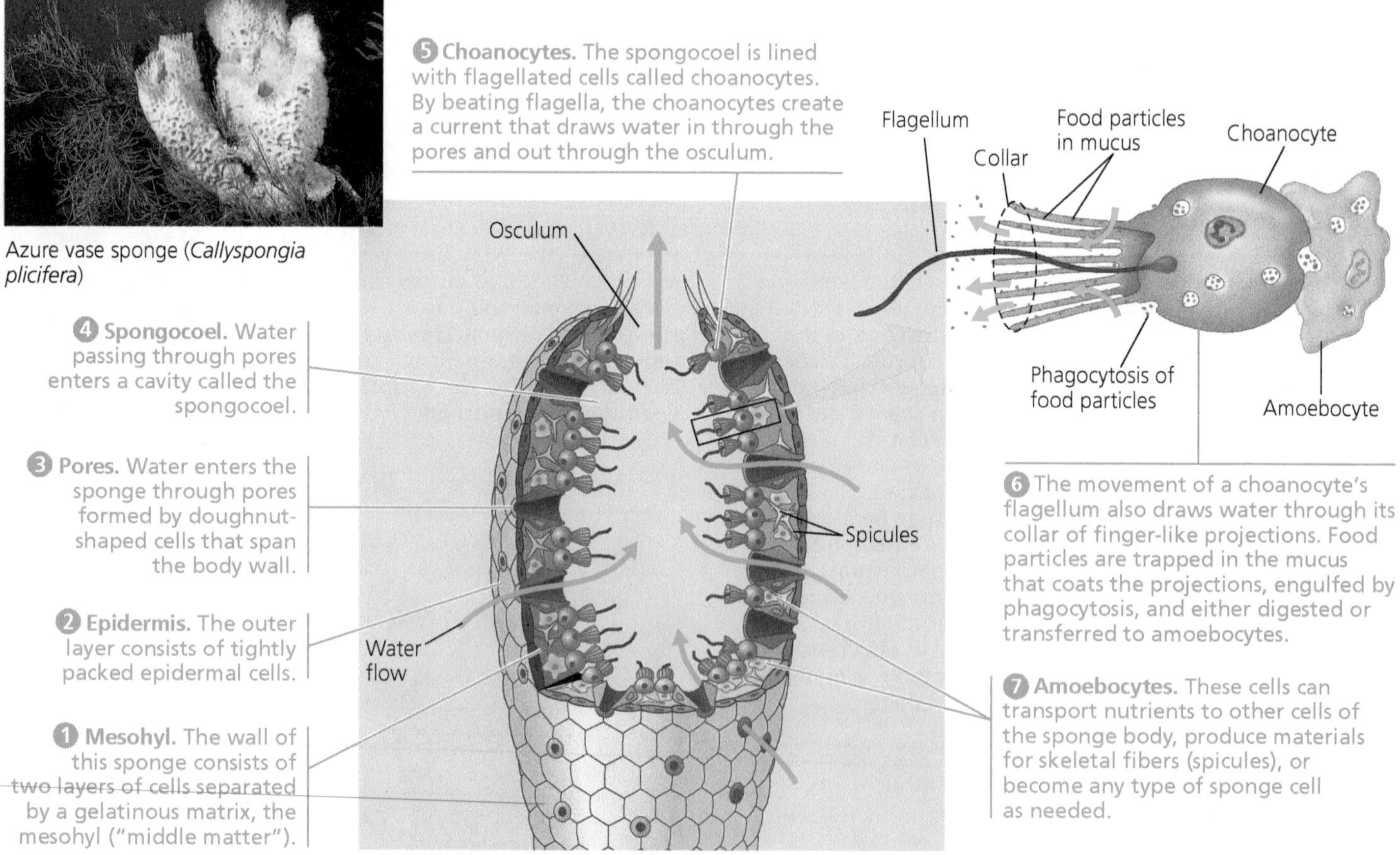

being sold as brown bath sponges. Finally, and perhaps most importantly, amoebocytes are capable of becoming other types of sponge cells. This gives the sponge body remarkable flexibility, enabling it to adjust its shape in response to changes in its physical environment (such as the direction of water currents).

Most sponges are **hermaphrodites**, meaning that each individual functions as both male and female in sexual reproduction by producing sperm *and* eggs. Almost all sponges exhibit sequential hermaphroditism: They function first as one sex and then as the other.

Sponge gametes arise from choanocytes or amoebocytes. Eggs reside in the mesohyl, but sperm are carried out of the sponge by the water current. Cross-fertilization results from some of the sperm being drawn into neighboring individuals. Fertilization occurs in the mesohyl, where the zygotes develop into flagellated, swimming larvae that disperse from the parent sponge. After settling on a suitable substrate, a larva develops into a sessile adult.

Sponges produce a variety of antibiotics and other defensive compounds. Researchers are now isolating these compounds, which hold promise for fighting human diseases. For example, a compound called cribrostatin isolated from marine sponges can kill penicillin-resistant strains of the bacterium *Streptococcus*. Other sponge-derived compounds are being tested as possible anticancer agents.

CONCEPT CHECK 33.1

1. Describe how sponges feed.
2. **WHAT IF?** Some molecular evidence suggests that the sister group of animals is not the choanoflagellates, but rather a group of parasitic protists, Mesomycetozoa. Given that these parasites lack collar cells, can this hypothesis be correct? Explain.

For suggested answers, see Appendix A.

CONCEPT 33.2

Cnidarians are an ancient phylum of eumetazoans

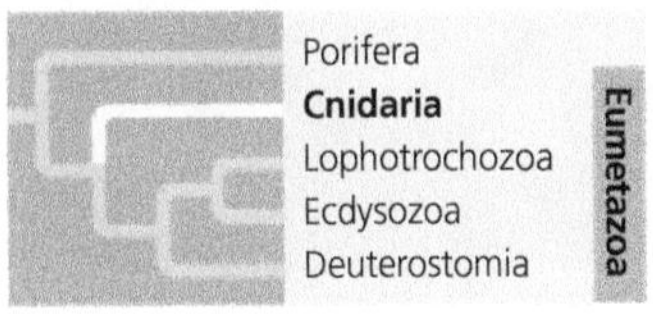

All animals except sponges and a few other groups belong to the clade Eumetazoa, animals with true tissues (see Chapter 32). One of the oldest lineages in this clade is the phylum Cnidaria. Cnidarians have diversified into a wide range of sessile and motile forms, including hydras, corals, and jellies (commonly called "jellyfish"). Yet most cnidarians still exhibit the relatively simple, diploblastic, radial body plan that existed in early members of the group some 560 million years ago.

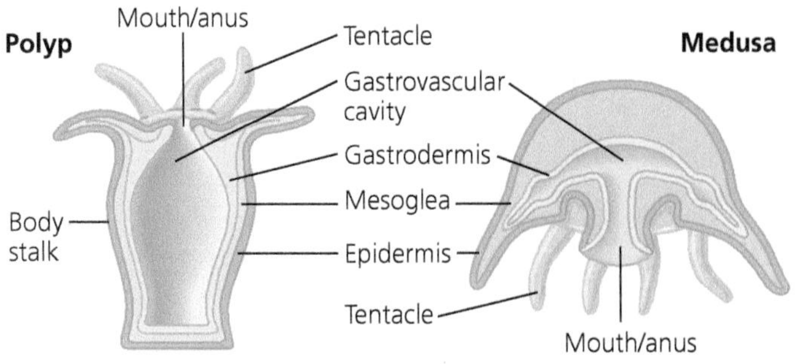

▲ **Figure 33.5 Polyp and medusa forms of cnidarians.** The body wall of a cnidarian has two layers of cells: an outer layer of epidermis (darker blue; derived from ectoderm) and an inner layer of gastrodermis (yellow; derived from endoderm). Digestion begins in the gastrovascular cavity and is completed inside food vacuoles in the gastrodermal cells. Flagella on the gastrodermal cells keep the contents of the gastrovascular cavity agitated and help distribute nutrients. Sandwiched between the epidermis and gastrodermis is a gelatinous layer, the mesoglea.

The basic body plan of a cnidarian is a sac with a central digestive compartment, the **gastrovascular cavity**. A single opening to this cavity functions as both mouth and anus. There are two variations on this body plan: the sessile polyp and the motile medusa (Figure 33.5). **Polyps** are cylindrical forms that adhere to the substrate by the aboral end of their body (the end opposite the mouth) and extend their tentacles, waiting for prey. Examples of the polyp form include hydras and sea anemones. A **medusa** (plural, *medusae*) resembles a flattened, mouth-down version of the polyp. It moves freely in the water by a combination of passive drifting and contractions of its bell-shaped body. Medusae include free-swimming jellies. The tentacles of a jelly dangle from the oral surface, which points downward. Some cnidarians exist only as polyps or only as medusae; others have both a polyp stage and a medusa stage in their life cycle.

Cnidarians are carnivores that often use tentacles arranged in a ring around their mouth to capture prey and push the food into their gastrovascular cavity, where digestion begins. Enzymes are secreted into the cavity, thus breaking down the prey into a nutrient-rich broth. Cells lining the cavity then absorb these nutrients and complete the digestive process; any undigested remains are expelled through the mouth/anus. The tentacles are armed with batteries of **cnidocytes**, cells unique to cnidarians that function in defense and prey capture (Figure 33.6). Cnidocytes contain *cnidae* (from the Greek *cnide*, nettle), capsule-like organelles that are capable of exploding outward and that give phylum Cnidaria its name. Specialized cnidae called **nematocysts** contain a stinging thread that can penetrate the body wall of the cnidarian's prey. Other kinds of cnidae have long threads that stick to or entangle small prey that bump into the cnidarian's tentacles.

Contractile tissues and nerves occur in their simplest forms in cnidarians. Cells of the epidermis (outer layer) and gastrodermis (inner layer) have bundles of microfilaments arranged into contractile fibers (see Chapter 6). The gastrovascular

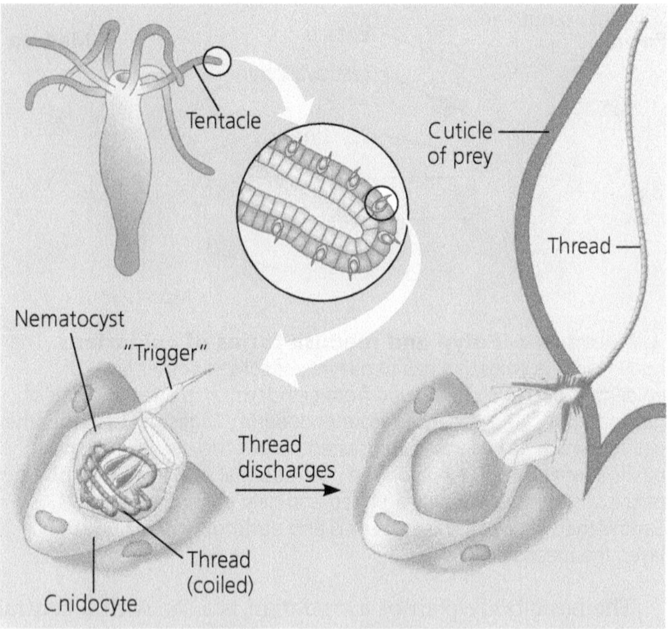

▲ **Figure 33.6 A cnidocyte of a hydra.** This type of cnidocyte contains a stinging capsule, the nematocyst, which contains a coiled thread. When a "trigger" is stimulated by touch or by certain chemicals, the thread shoots out, puncturing and injecting poison into prey.

cavity acts as a hydrostatic skeleton (see Concept 50.6) against which the contractile cells can work. When a cnidarian closes its mouth, the volume of the cavity is fixed, and contraction of selected cells causes the animal to change shape. Movements are coordinated by a nerve net. Cnidarians have no brain, and the noncentralized nerve net is associated with sensory structures that are distributed around the body. Thus, the animal can detect and respond to stimuli from all directions.

The phylum Cnidaria is divided into four major clades: Hydrozoa, Scyphozoa, Cubozoa, and Anthozoa (Figure 33.7).

Hydrozoans

Most hydrozoans alternate between the polyp and medusa forms, as seen in the life cycle of *Obelia* (Figure 33.8). The polyp stage, a colony of interconnected polyps in the case of *Obelia*, is more conspicuous than the medusa. Hydras, among the few cnidarians found in fresh water, are unusual hydrozoans in that they exist only in polyp form. When environmental conditions are favorable, a hydra reproduces asexually by budding, forming outgrowths that pinch off from the parent and live independently (see Figure 13.2). When conditions deteriorate, hydras can reproduce sexually, forming resistant zygotes that remain dormant until conditions improve.

Scyphozoans

The medusa is the predominant stage in the life cycle of most scyphozoans. The medusae of most species live among the plankton as jellies. Most coastal scyphozoans go through a stage as small polyps during their life cycle, whereas those that live in the open ocean generally lack the polyp stage altogether.

Cubozoans

As their name (which means "cube animals") suggests, cubozoans have a box-shaped medusa stage. Cubozoans can be distinguished from scyphozoans in other ways, such as having complex eyes embedded in the fringe of their medusae. They also are comparatively strong swimmers and as a result are less likely to be stranded on shore. Most cubozoans live in tropical oceans and are equipped with highly toxic cnidocytes. The sea wasp (*Chironex fleckeri*), a cubozoan that lives off the coast of northern Australia, is one of the deadliest organisms known: Its sting causes intense pain and can lead to respiratory failure, cardiac arrest, and death within minutes. The poison of sea wasps isn't universally fatal, however; sea turtles have defenses against it, allowing them to eat the cubozoan in great quantities.

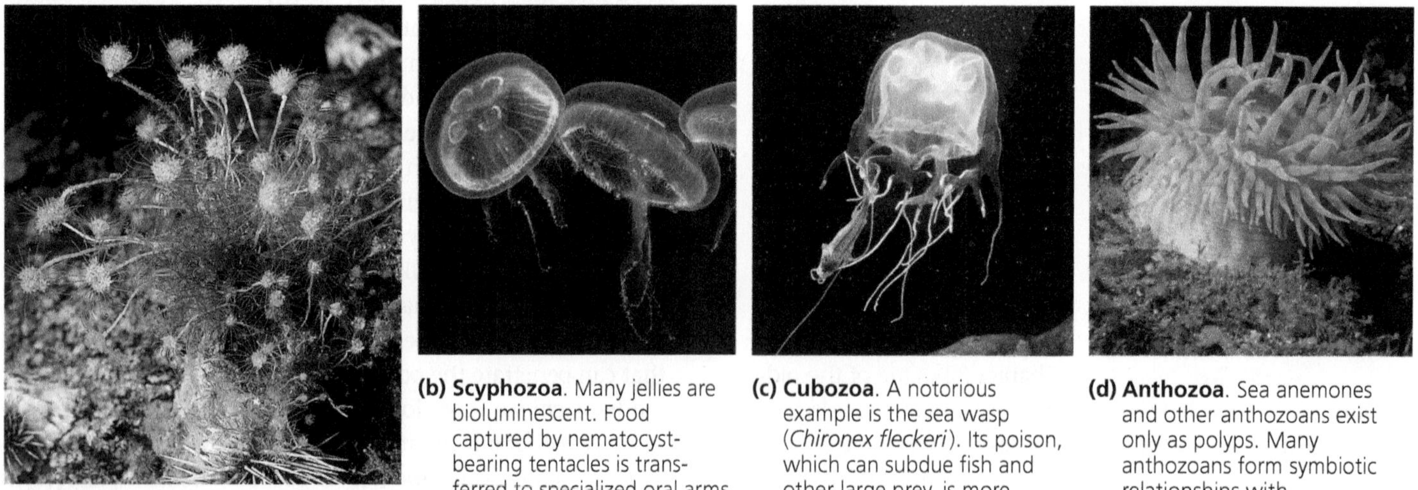

(a) Hydrozoa. Some species, such as this one, live as colonial polyps.

(b) Scyphozoa. Many jellies are bioluminescent. Food captured by nematocyst-bearing tentacles is transferred to specialized oral arms (that lack nematocysts) for transport to the mouth.

(c) Cubozoa. A notorious example is the sea wasp (*Chironex fleckeri*). Its poison, which can subdue fish and other large prey, is more potent than cobra venom.

(d) Anthozoa. Sea anemones and other anthozoans exist only as polyps. Many anthozoans form symbiotic relationships with photosynthetic algae.

▲ **Figure 33.7 Cnidarians.**

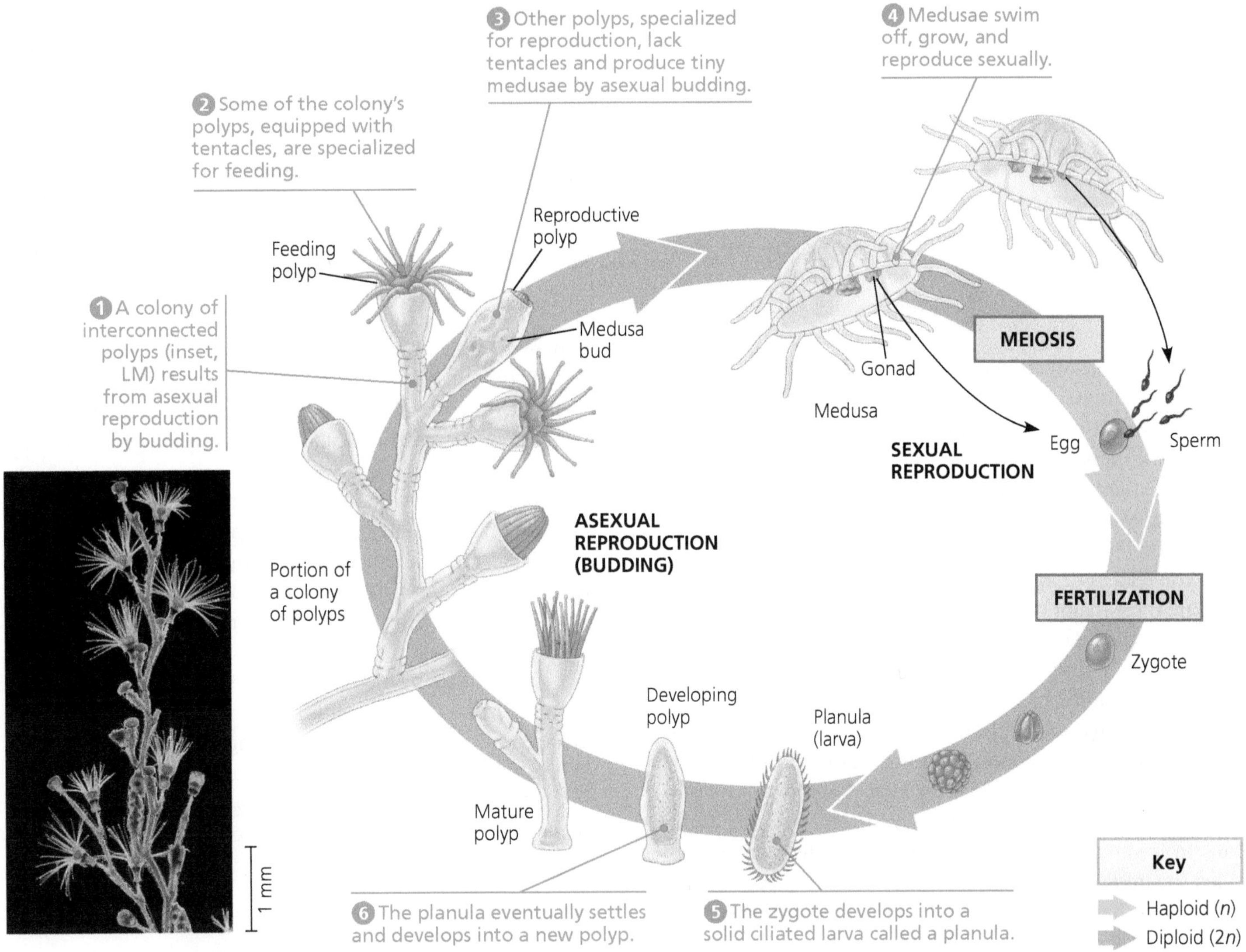

▲ **Figure 33.8 The life cycle of the hydrozoan *Obelia*.** The polyp is asexual, and the medusa is sexual, releasing eggs and sperm. These two stages alternate, one producing the other. Do not confuse this with the alternation of generations that occurs in plants and some algae: In *Obelia,* both the polyp and the medusa are diploid organisms. Typical of animals, only the single-celled gametes are haploid. By contrast, plants have a multicellular haploid generation and a multicellular diploid generation.

WHAT IF? *Suppose that* Obelia *medusae and gametes were haploid, but all other stages were diploid. What aspects of its actual life cycle would have to change for this to occur?*

Anthozoans

Sea anemones (see Figure 33.7d) and corals belong to the clade Anthozoa (meaning "flower animals"). These cnidarians occur only as polyps. Corals live as solitary or colonial forms, often forming symbioses with algae (see Chapter 28). Many species secrete a hard external skeleton of calcium carbonate. Each polyp generation builds on the skeletal remains of earlier generations, constructing "rocks" with shapes characteristic of their species. These skeletons are what we usually think of as coral.

Coral reefs are to tropical seas what rain forests are to tropical land areas: They provide habitat for many other species. Unfortunately, these reefs are being destroyed at an alarming rate. Pollution and overfishing are major threats, and global warming may also be contributing to their demise by raising seawater temperatures above the narrow range in which corals thrive.

CONCEPT CHECK 33.2

1. Compare and contrast the polyp and medusa forms of cnidarians.
2. Describe the structure and function of the stinging cells for which cnidarians are named.
3. **MAKE CONNECTIONS** As you read in Concept 25.3 (pp. 518–519), many new animal body plans emerged during and after the Cambrian explosion. In contrast, cnidarians today retain the same diploblastic, radial body plan found in cnidarians 560 million years ago. Are cnidarians therefore less successful or less "highly evolved" than other animal groups? Explain. (See also Concept 25.6, pp. 529–530.)

For suggested answers, see Appendix A.

CONCEPT 33.3

Lophotrochozoans, a clade identified by molecular data, have the widest range of animal body forms

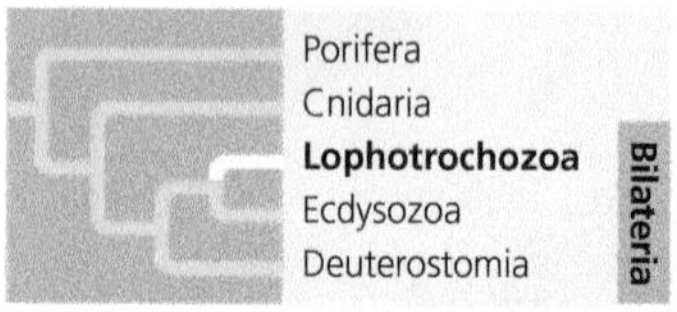

The vast majority of animal species belong to the clade Bilateria, whose members exhibit bilateral symmetry and triploblastic development (see Chapter 32). Most bilaterians also have a digestive tract with two openings (a mouth and an anus) and a coelom. While the sequence of bilaterian evolution is a subject of active investigation, the most recent common ancestor of living bilaterians probably existed in the late Proterozoic eon (about 575 million years ago). Many of the major groups of bilaterians first appeared in the fossil record during the Cambrian explosion.

As you read in Chapter 32, molecular evidence suggests that there are three major clades of bilaterally symmetrical animals: Lophotrochozoa, Ecdysozoa, and Deuterostomia. This section will focus on the first of these clades, the lophotrochozoans. Concepts 33.4 and 33.5 will explore the other two clades.

Although the clade Lophotrochozoa was identified by molecular data, its name comes from features found in some of its members. Some lophotrochozoans develop a structure called a *lophophore*, a crown of ciliated tentacles that functions in feeding, while others go through a distinctive stage called the *trochophore larva* (see Figure 32.13). Other members of the group have neither of these features. Few other unique morphological features are widely shared within the group—in fact, the lophotrochozoans are the most diverse bilaterian clade in terms of body plan. This diversity in form is reflected in the number of phyla classified in the group: Lophotrochozoa includes about 18 phyla, more than twice the number in any other clade of bilaterians.

We'll now introduce six diverse lophotrochozoan phyla: the flatworms, rotifers, ectoprocts, brachiopods, molluscs, and annelids.

Flatworms

Flatworms (phylum Platyhelminthes) live in marine, freshwater, and damp terrestrial habitats. In addition to free-living species, flatworms include many parasitic species, such as flukes and tapeworms. Flatworms are so named because they have thin bodies that are flattened dorsoventrally (between the dorsal and ventral surfaces); the word *platyhelminth* means "flat worm." (Note that *worm* is not a formal taxonomic name but rather refers to a grade of animals with long, thin bodies.) The smallest flatworms are nearly microscopic free-living species, while some tapeworms are more than 20 m long.

Although flatworms undergo triploblastic development, they are acoelomates (animals that lack a body cavity). Their flat shape places all their cells close to water in the surrounding environment or in their gut. Because of this proximity to water, gas exchange and the elimination of nitrogenous waste (ammonia) can occur by diffusion across the body surface. Flatworms have no organs specialized for gas exchange, and their relatively simple excretory apparatus functions mainly to maintain osmotic balance with their surroundings. This apparatus consists of **protonephridia**, networks of tubules with ciliated structures called *flame bulbs* that pull fluid through branched ducts opening to the outside (see Figure 44.11). Most flatworms have a gastrovascular cavity with only one opening. Though flatworms lack a circulatory system, the fine branches of the gastrovascular cavity distribute food directly to the animal's cells.

Early in their evolutionary history, flatworms separated into two lineages, Catenulida and Rhabditophora. Catenulida is a small clade of about 100 flatworm species, most of which live in freshwater habitats. Catenulids typically reproduce asexually by budding at their posterior end. The offspring often produce their own buds before detaching from the parent, thereby forming a chain of two to four genetically identical individuals—hence their informal name, "chain worms."

The other ancient flatworm lineage, Rhabditophora, is a diverse clade of about 20,000 freshwater and marine species, one example of which is shown in Figure 33.9. We'll explore this group in more detail, focusing on free-living and parasitic members of this clade.

Free-Living Species

Free-living rhabditophorans are important as predators and scavengers in a wide range of freshwater and marine habitats. The best-known members of this group are freshwater species in the genus *Dugesia*, commonly called **planarians**. Abundant in unpolluted ponds and streams, planarians prey on

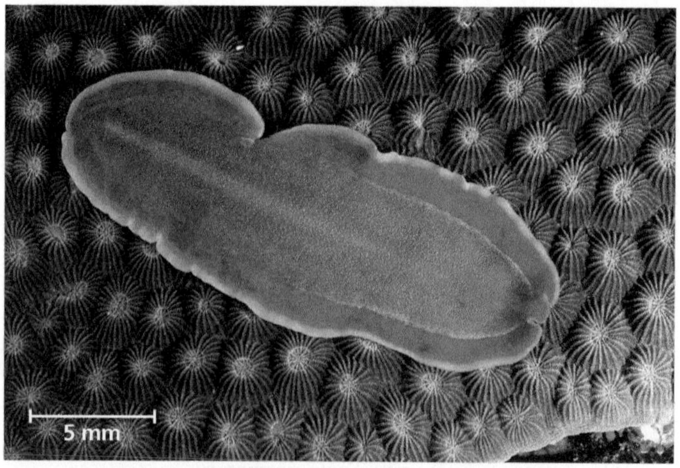

▲ **Figure 33.9 A free-living marine flatworm.**

smaller animals or feed on dead animals. They move by using cilia on their ventral surface, gliding along a film of mucus they secrete. Some other rhabditophorans also use their muscles to swim through water with an undulating motion.

A planarian's head is equipped with a pair of light-sensitive eyespots and lateral flaps that function mainly to detect specific chemicals. The planarian nervous system is more complex and centralized than the nerve nets of cnidarians (Figure 33.10). Experiments have shown that planarians can learn to modify their responses to stimuli.

Some planarians can reproduce asexually through fission. The parent constricts roughly in the middle of its body, separating into a head end and a tail end; each end then regenerates the missing parts. Sexual reproduction also occurs. Planarians are hermaphrodites, and copulating mates typically cross-fertilize each other.

▼ **Figure 33.10 Anatomy of a planarian.**

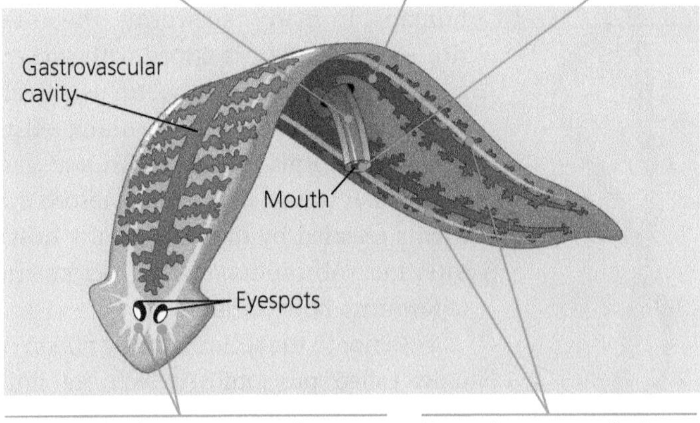

Parasitic Species

More than half of the known species of rhabditophorans live as parasites in or on other animals. Many have suckers that attach to the internal organs or outer surfaces of the host animal. In most species, a tough covering helps protect the parasites within their hosts. Reproductive organs occupy nearly the entire interior of these worms. We'll discuss two ecologically and economically important subgroups of parasitic rhabditophorans, the trematodes and the tapeworms.

Trematodes As a group, trematodes parasitize a wide range of hosts, and most species have complex life cycles with alternating sexual and asexual stages. Many trematodes require an intermediate host in which larvae develop before infecting the final host (usually a vertebrate), where the adult worms live. For example, trematodes that parasitize humans spend part of their lives in snail hosts (Figure 33.11). Around the world, some 200 million people are infected with trematodes called blood flukes (*Schistosoma*) and suffer from schistosomiasis, a disease whose symptoms include pain, anemia, and diarrhea.

Living within different hosts puts demands on trematodes that free-living animals don't face. A blood fluke, for instance, must evade the immune systems of both snails and humans. By mimicking the surface proteins of its hosts, the blood fluke creates a partial immunological camouflage for itself. It

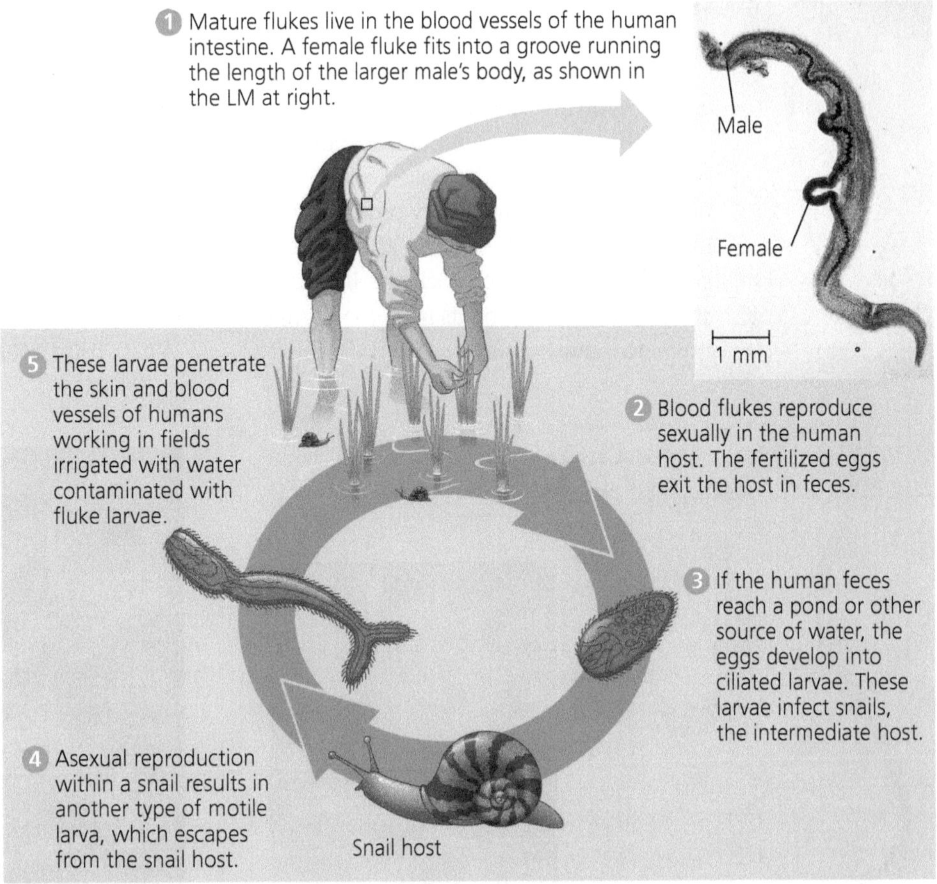

▲ **Figure 33.11 The life cycle of a blood fluke (*Schistosoma mansoni*), a trematode.**

WHAT IF? *Snails eat algae, whose growth is stimulated by nutrients found in fertilizer. How would the contamination of irrigation water with fertilizer likely affect the occurrence of schistosomiasis? Explain.*

also releases molecules that manipulate the hosts' immune systems into tolerating the parasite's existence. These defenses are so effective that individual blood flukes can survive in humans for more than 40 years.

Tapeworms The tapeworms are a second large and diverse group of parasitic rhabditophorans (Figure 33.12). The adults live mostly inside vertebrates, including humans. In many tapeworms, the anterior end, or scolex, is armed with suckers and often hooks that the worm uses to attach itself to the intestinal lining of its host. Tapeworms lack a mouth and gastrovascular cavity; they simply absorb nutrients released by digestion in the host's intestine. Absorption occurs across the tapeworm's body surface.

Posterior to the scolex is a long ribbon of units called proglottids, which are little more than sacs of sex organs. After sexual reproduction, proglottids loaded with thousands of fertilized eggs are released from the posterior end of a tapeworm and leave the host's body in feces. In one type of life cycle, feces carrying the eggs contaminate the food or water of intermediate hosts, such as pigs or cattle, and the tapeworm eggs develop into larvae that encyst in muscles of these animals. A human acquires the larvae by eating undercooked meat containing the cysts, and the worms develop into mature adults within the human. Large tapeworms can block the intestines and rob enough nutrients from the human host to cause nutritional deficiencies. Doctors have patients take the drug niclosamide by mouth to kill the adult worms.

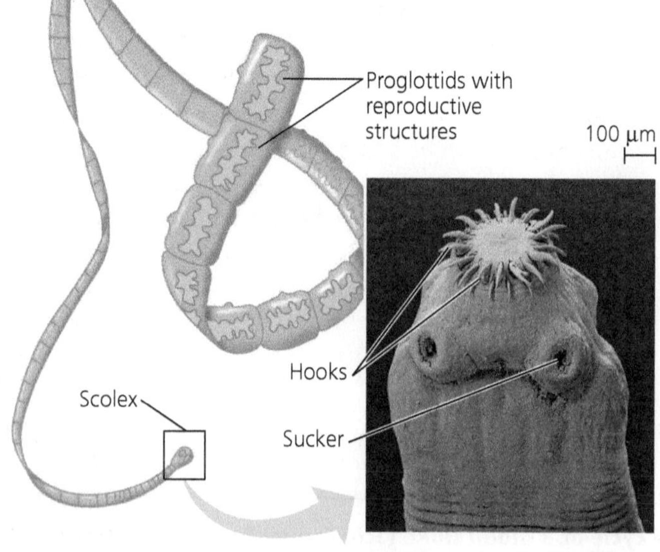

▲ **Figure 33.12 Anatomy of a tapeworm.** The inset shows a close-up of the scolex (colorized SEM).

Rotifers

Rotifers (phylum Rotifera) are tiny animals that inhabit freshwater, marine, and damp soil habitats. Ranging in size from about 50 μm to 2 mm, rotifers are smaller than many protists but nevertheless are multicellular and have specialized organ systems (Figure 33.13). In contrast to cnidarians and flatworms, which have a gastrovascular cavity, rotifers have an **alimentary canal**, a digestive tube with two openings, a mouth and an anus. Internal organs lie within the pseudocoelom, a body cavity that is not completely lined by mesoderm (see Figure 32.8b). Fluid in the pseudocoelom serves as a hydrostatic skeleton. Movement of a rotifer's body distributes the fluid throughout the body, circulating nutrients.

The word *rotifer* is derived from the Latin meaning "wheel-bearer," a reference to the crown of cilia that draws a vortex of water into the mouth. Posterior to the mouth, a region of the digestive tract called the pharynx bears jaws called trophi that grind up food, mostly microorganisms suspended in the water. Digestion is then completed farther along the alimentary canal. Most other bilaterians also have an alimentary canal, which enables the stepwise digestion of a wide range of food particles.

Rotifers exhibit some unusual forms of reproduction. Some species consist only of females that produce more females from unfertilized eggs, a type of asexual reproduction called **parthenogenesis**. Some other invertebrates (for example, aphids and some bees) and even some vertebrates (for example, some lizards and some fishes) can also reproduce in this way. In addition to being able to produce females by parthenogeneis, some rotifers can also reproduce sexually under certain conditions, such as high levels of crowding. When this occurs, a female produces two types of eggs. Eggs

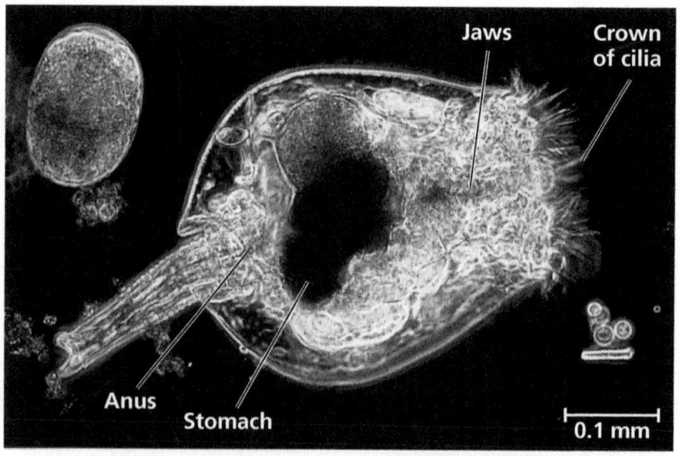

▲ **Figure 33.13 A rotifer.** These pseudocoelomates, smaller than many protists, are generally more anatomically complex than flatworms (LM).

of one type develop into females, and eggs of the other type develop into males. In some cases, the males do not feed and survive only long enough to fertilize eggs. The fertilized eggs develop into resistant embryos capable of remaining dormant for years. Once the embryos break dormancy, they develop into a new female generation that reproduces by parthenogenesis until conditions once again favor sexual reproduction.

It is puzzling that many rotifer species survive without males. The vast majority of animals and plants reproduce sexually at least some of the time, and sexual reproduction has certain advantages over asexual reproduction (see Concept 46.1). For example, species that reproduce asexually tend to accumulate harmful mutations in their genomes faster than sexually reproducing species. As a result, asexual species should experience higher rates of extinction and lower rates of speciation.

Seeking to understand this unusual group, researchers have been studying a clade of asexual rotifers named Bdelloidea. Some 360 species of bdelloid rotifers are known, and all of them reproduce by parthenogenesis without any males. Paleontologists have discovered bdelloid rotifers preserved in 35-million-year-old amber, and the morphology of these fossils resembles only the female form, with no evidence of males. By comparing the DNA of bdelloids with that of their closest sexually reproducing rotifer relatives, scientists have concluded that bdelloids have likely been asexual for 100 million years. How these animals manage to flout the general rule against long-lasting asexuality remains a puzzle.

Lophophorates: Ectoprocts and Brachiopods

Bilaterians in the phyla Ectoprocta and Brachiopoda are among those known as lophophorates. These animals have a *lophophore*, a crown of ciliated tentacles around their mouth (see Figure 32.13a). As the cilia draw water toward the mouth, the tentacles trap suspended food particles. Other similarities, such as a U-shaped alimentary canal and the absence of a distinct head, reflect these organisms' sessile existence. In contrast to flatworms, which lack a body cavity, and rotifers, which have a pseudocoelom, lophophorates have a true coelom that is completely lined by mesoderm (see Figure 32.8a).

Ectoprocts (from the Greek *ecto*, outside, and *procta*, anus) are colonial animals that superficially resemble clumps of moss. (In fact, their common name, bryozoans, means "moss animals.") In most species, the colony is encased in a hard **exoskeleton** (external skeleton) studded with pores through which the lophophores extend (Figure 33.14a). Most ectoproct species live in the sea, where they are among the most widespread and numerous sessile animals. Several species are important reef builders. Ectoprocts also live in lakes and rivers. Colonies of the freshwater ectoproct *Pectinatella magnifica* grow on submerged sticks or rocks and can grow into a gelatinous, ball-shaped mass more than 10 cm across.

(a) Ectoprocts, such as this creeping bryozoan (*Plumatella repens*), are colonial lophophorates.

(b) Brachiopods, such as this lampshell (*Terebratulina retusa*), have a hinged shell. The two parts of the shell are dorsal and ventral.

▲ **Figure 33.14 Lophophorates.**

Brachiopods, or lamp shells, superficially resemble clams and other hinge-shelled molluscs, but the two halves of the brachiopod shell are dorsal and ventral rather than lateral, as in clams (Figure 33.14b). All brachiopods are marine. Most live attached to the seafloor by a stalk, opening their shell slightly to allow water to flow through the lophophore. The living brachiopods are remnants of a much richer past that included 30,000 species in the Paleozoic and Mesozoic eras. Some living brachiopods, such as those in the genus *Lingula*, appear nearly identical to fossils of species that lived 400 million years ago.

Molluscs

Snails and slugs, oysters and clams, and octopuses and squids are all molluscs (phylum Mollusca). There are 93,000 known species, making them the second most diverse phylum of animals (after the arthropods, discussed later). Although the majority of molluscs are marine, roughly 8,000 species inhabit fresh water, and 28,000 species of snails and slugs live on land. All molluscs are soft-bodied (from the Latin *molluscus*, soft), and most secrete a hard protective shell made of calcium carbonate. Slugs, squids, and octopuses have a reduced internal shell or have lost their shell completely during their evolution.

Despite their apparent differences, all molluscs have a similar body plan (Figure 33.15, on the next page). Molluscs are coelomates, and their bodies have three main parts: a muscular **foot**, usually used for movement; a **visceral mass** containing most of the internal organs; and a **mantle**, a fold of tissue that drapes over the visceral mass and secretes a shell (if one is present). In many molluscs, the mantle extends beyond the visceral mass, producing a water-filled chamber, the **mantle cavity**, which houses the gills, anus, and excretory pores. Many molluscs feed by using a straplike organ called a **radula** to scrape up food.

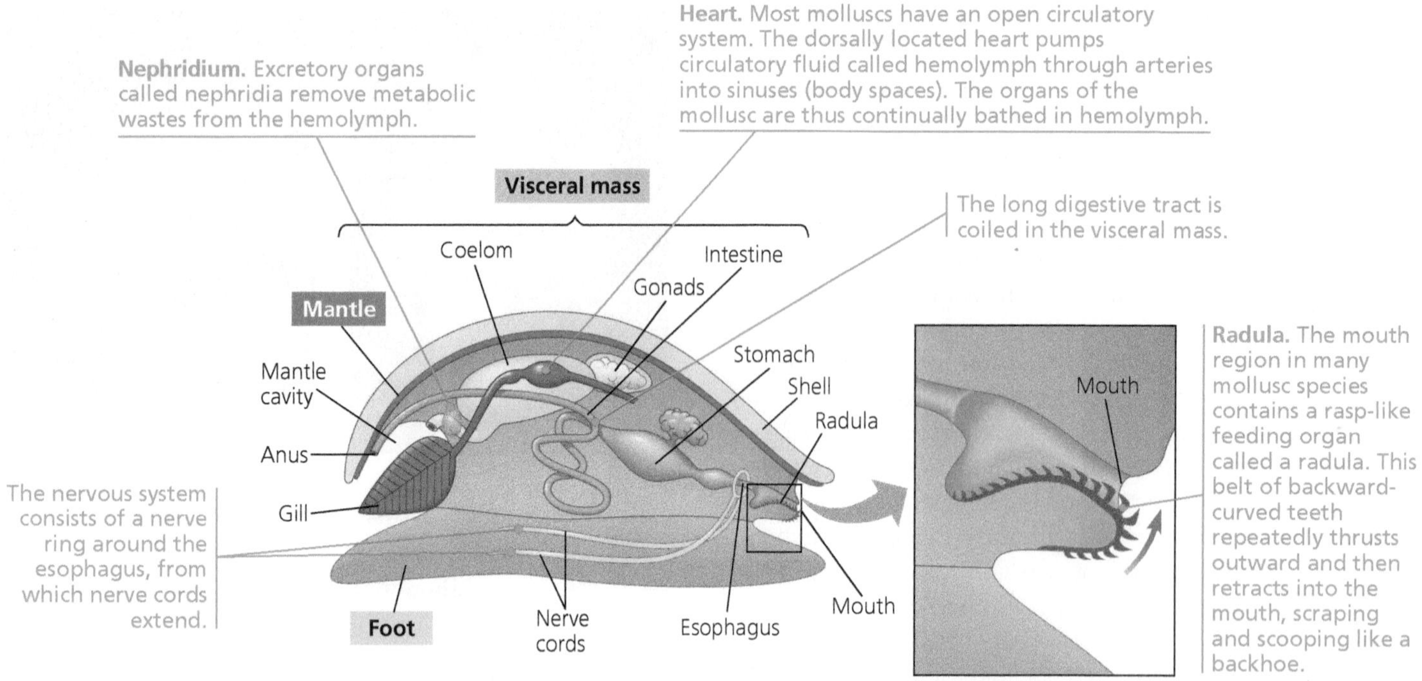

▲ **Figure 33.15 The basic body plan of a mollusc.**

Most molluscs have separate sexes, and their gonads (ovaries or testes) are located in the visceral mass. Many snails, however, are hermaphrodites. The life cycle of many marine molluscs includes a ciliated larval stage, the trochophore (see Figure 32.13b), which is also characteristic of marine annelids (segmented worms) and some other lophotrochozoans.

The basic body plan of molluscs has evolved in various ways in the phylum's seven or eight clades (experts disagree on the number). We'll examine four of those clades here: Polyplacophora (chitons), Gastropoda (snails and slugs), Bivalvia (clams, oysters, and other bivalves), and Cephalopoda (squids, octopuses, cuttlefishes, and chambered nautiluses). We will then focus on threats facing some groups of molluscs.

▲ **Figure 33.16 A chiton.** Note the eight-plate shell characteristic of molluscs in the clade Polyplacophora.

Chitons

Chitons have an oval-shaped body and a shell composed of eight dorsal plates (**Figure 33.16**). The chiton's body itself, however, is unsegmented. You can find these marine animals clinging to rocks along the shore during low tide. If you try to dislodge a chiton by hand, you will be surprised at how well its foot, acting as a suction cup, grips the rock. A chiton can also use its foot to creep slowly over the rock surface. Chitons use their radula to scrape algae off the rock surface.

Gastropods

About three-quarters of all living species of molluscs are gastropods (**Figure 33.17**). Most gastropods are marine, but there are also freshwater species. Still other gastropods have adapted to life on land, where snails and slugs thrive in habitats ranging from deserts to rain forests.

(a) A land snail

(b) A sea slug. Nudibranchs, or sea slugs, lost their shell during their evolution.

▲ **Figure 33.17 Gastropods.**

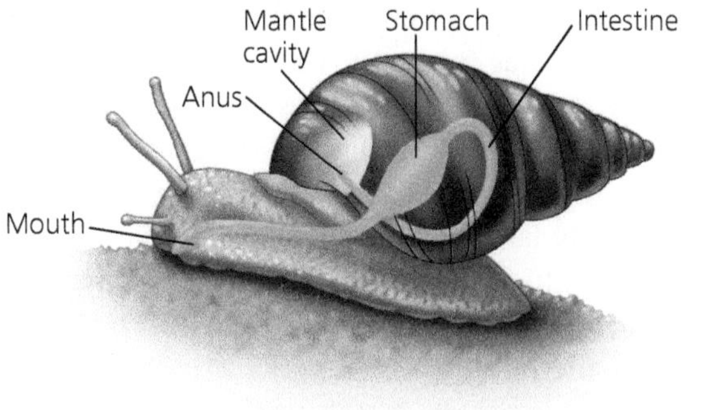

▲ **Figure 33.18 The results of torsion in a gastropod.** Because of torsion (twisting of the visceral mass) during embryonic development, the digestive tract is coiled and the anus is near the anterior end of the animal.

Gastropods undergo a distinctive developmental process known as **torsion**. As a gastropod embryo develops, its visceral mass rotates up to 180°, causing the animal's anus and mantle cavity to wind up above its head (Figure 33.18). After torsion, some organs that were bilateral may be reduced in size, while others may be lost on one side of the body. Torsion should not be confused with the formation of a coiled shell, which is a separate developmental process.

Most gastropods have a single, spiraled shell into which the animal can retreat when threatened. The shell is often conical but is somewhat flattened in abalones and limpets. Many gastropods have a distinct head with eyes at the tips of tentacles. Gastropods move literally at a snail's pace by a rippling motion of their foot or by means of cilia, often leaving a trail of slime in their wake. Most gastropods use their radula to graze on algae or plants. Several groups, however, are predators, and their radula has become modified for boring holes in the shells of other molluscs or for tearing apart prey. In the cone snails, the teeth of the radula act as poison darts that are used to subdue prey (see the Unit 7 interview with Baldomero Olivera on pp. 850–851 to learn more about cone snails and their venom).

Terrestrial snails lack the gills typical of most aquatic gastropods. Instead, the lining of their mantle cavity functions as a lung, exchanging respiratory gases with the air.

Bivalves

The molluscs of the clade Bivalvia are all aquatic and include many species of clams, oysters, mussels, and scallops. Bivalves have a shell divided into two halves (Figure 33.19). The halves are hinged, and powerful adductor muscles draw them tightly together to protect the animal's soft body. Bivalves have no distinct head, and the radula has been lost. Some bivalves have eyes and sensory tentacles along the outer edge of their mantle.

The mantle cavity of a bivalve contains gills that are used for gas exchange as well as feeding in most species (Figure 33.20). Most bivalves are suspension feeders. They trap small food particles in mucus that coats their gills, and cilia then convey those particles to the mouth. Water enters the mantle cavity through an incurrent siphon, passes over the gills, and then exits the mantle cavity through an excurrent siphon.

▲ **Figure 33.19 A bivalve.** This scallop has many eyes (dark blue spots) lining each half of its hinged shell.

Most bivalves lead sedentary lives, a characteristic suited to suspension feeding. Mussels secrete strong threads that tether them to rocks, docks, boats, and the shells of other animals. However, clams can pull themselves into the sand or mud, using their muscular foot for an anchor, and scallops can skitter along the seafloor by flapping their shells, rather like the mechanical false teeth sold in novelty shops.

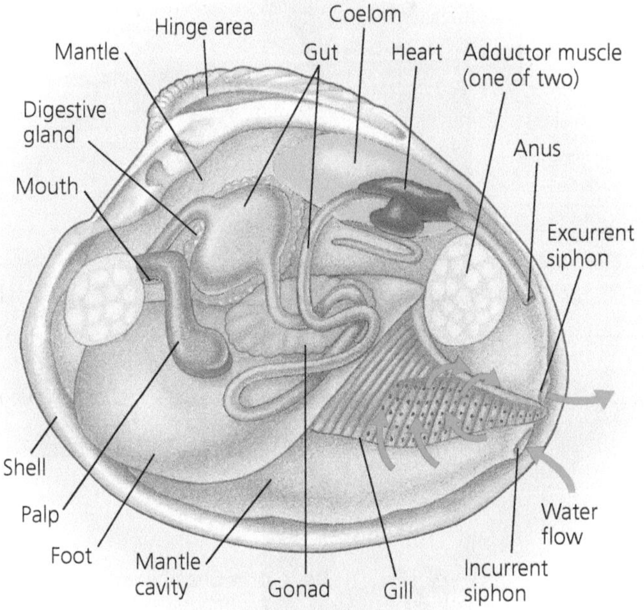

▲ **Figure 33.20 Anatomy of a clam.** Food particles suspended in water that enters through the incurrent siphon are collected by the gills and passed via cilia and the palps to the mouth.

Cephalopods

Cephalopods are active marine predators (Figure 33.21). They use their tentacles to grasp prey, which they then bite with beak-like jaws and immobilize with a poison present in their saliva. The foot of a cephalopod has become modified into a muscular excurrent siphon and part of the tentacles. Squids dart about by drawing water into their mantle cavity and then firing a jet of water through the excurrent siphon; they steer by pointing the siphon in different directions. Octopuses use a similar mechanism to escape predators.

The mantle covers the visceral mass of cephalopods, but the shell is generally reduced and internal (in most species) or missing altogether (in some cuttlefishes and some octopuses). One small group of cephalopods with external shells, the chambered nautiluses, survives today.

Cephalopods are the only molluscs with a *closed circulatory system*, in which the blood remains separate from fluid in the body cavity. They also have well-developed sense organs and a complex brain. The ability to learn and behave in a complex manner is probably more critical to fast-moving predators than to sedentary animals such as clams.

The ancestors of octopuses and squids were probably shelled molluscs that took up a predatory lifestyle; the shell was lost in later evolution. Shelled cephalopods called **ammonites**, some of them as large as truck tires, were the dominant invertebrate predators of the seas for hundreds of millions of years until their disappearance during the mass extinction at the end of the Cretaceous period, 65.5 million years ago (see Table 25.1).

Most species of squid are less than 75 cm long, but some are considerably larger. The giant squid *Architeuthis dux* was for a long time the largest squid known, with a mantle up to 2.25 m long and a total length of 18 m. In 2003, however, a specimen of the rare species *Mesonychoteuthis hamiltoni* was caught near Antarctica; its mantle was 2.5 m long. Some biologists think that this specimen was a juvenile and estimate that adults of its species could be twice as large! Unlike *A. dux*, which has large suckers and small teeth on its tentacles, *M. hamiltoni* has two rows of sharp hooks at the ends of its tentacles that can inflict deadly lacerations.

It is likely that *A. dux* and *M. hamiltoni* spend most of their time in the deep ocean, where they may feed on large fishes. Remains of both giant squid species have been found in the stomachs of sperm whales, which are probably their only natural predator. In 2005, scientists reported the first observations of *A. dux* in the wild, photographed while attacking baited hooks at a depth of 900 m. *M. hamiltoni* has yet to be observed in nature. Overall, these marine giants remain among the great mysteries of invertebrate life.

◀ Squids are speedy carnivores with beak-like jaws and well-developed eyes.

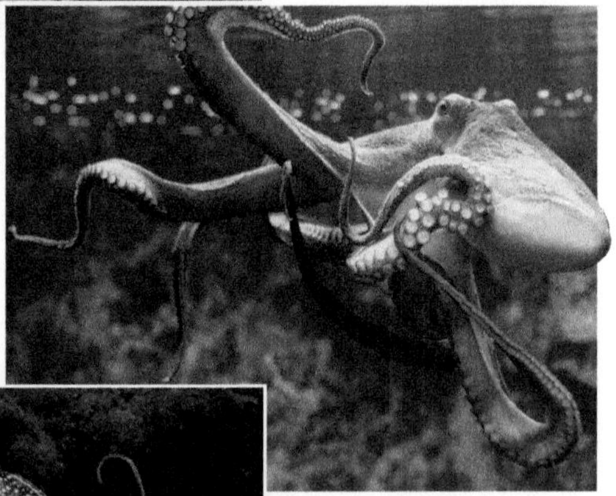

▶ Octopuses are considered among the most intelligent invertebrates.

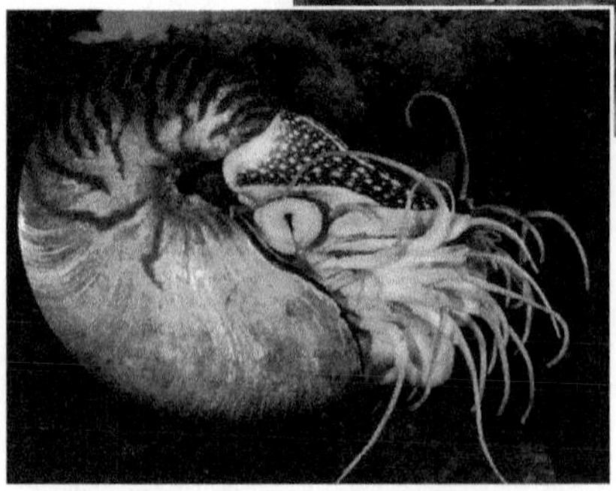

◀ Chambered nautiluses are the only living cephalopods with an external shell.

▲ **Figure 33.21 Cephalopods.**

Protecting Freshwater and Terrestrial Molluscs

Species extinction rates have increased dramatically in the last 400 years, raising concern that a sixth, human-caused mass extinction may be under way (see Chapter 25). Among the many taxa under threat, molluscs have the dubious distinction of being the animal group with the largest number of documented extinctions (Figure 33.22).

Threats to molluscs are especially severe in two groups, freshwater bivalves and terrestrial gastropods. The pearl mussels, a group of freshwater bivalves that can make natural pearls (gems that form when a mussel or oyster secretes layers of a lustrous coating around a grain of sand or other small irritant), are among the world's most endangered animals. Roughly 10% of the 300 pearl mussel species that once lived in North America have become extinct in the last 100 years, and over two-thirds of those that remain are threatened by extinction. Terrestrial gastropods, such as the snail in Figure 33.22, fare no better. Hundreds of Pacific island land snails have disappeared since 1800. Overall, more than 50% of the Pacific island land snails are extinct or under imminent threat of extinction.

Threats faced by freshwater and terrestrial molluscs include habitat loss, pollution, and competition or predation by non-native species introduced by people. Is it too late to protect these molluscs? In some locations, reducing water pollution and changing how water is released from dams have led to dramatic rebounds in pearl mussel populations. Such results provide hope that with corrective measures, other endangered mollusc species can be revived.

▼ Figure 33.22
IMPACT

Molluscs: The Silent Extinction

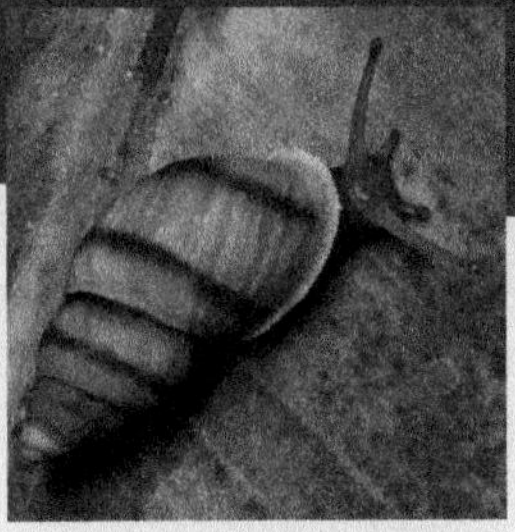

▲ An endangered Pacific island land snail, *Partula suturalis*

Molluscs account for a largely unheralded but sobering 40% of all documented extinctions of animal species. These extinctions have resulted from habitat loss, pollution, introduced species, overharvesting, and other human actions. Many pearl mussel populations, for example, were driven to extinction by overharvesting for their shells, which were used to make buttons and other goods. Today, remaining populations of these and other freshwater bivalves face threats from pollution and introduced species. Terrestrial gastropods such as the species pictured above are highly vulnerable to the same threats and are among the world's most imperiled animal groups.

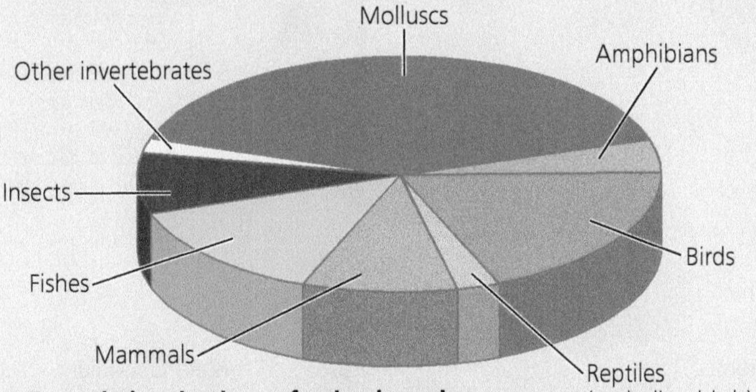

▲ **Recorded extinctions of animal species.**
(Data: International Union for Conservation of Nature, 2008)

▲ Workers on a mound of pearl mussels killed to make buttons (ca. 1919)

WHY IT MATTERS The extinctions of molluscs represent an irreversible loss of biological diversity and greatly threaten other organisms, too. Land snails, for example, play a key role in nutrient cycling, while the filtering activities of freshwater bivalves purify the waters of streams, rivers, and lakes.

FURTHER READING C. Lydeard et al., The global decline of nonmarine mollusks, *BioScience* 54:321–330 (2004).

MAKE CONNECTIONS Freshwater bivalves feed on and can reduce the abundance of photosynthetic protists and bacteria. As such, would the extinction of freshwater bivalves likely have weak or strong effects on aquatic communities (see Concept 28.7, p. 597)? Explain.

◀ **Figure 33.23 A polychaete.** *Hesiolyra bergi* lives on the seafloor around deep-sea hydrothermal vents.

Annelids

Annelida means "little rings," referring to the annelid body's resemblance to a series of fused rings. Annelids are segmented worms that live in the sea, in most freshwater habitats, and in damp soil. Annelids are coelomates, and they range in length from less than 1 mm to more than 3 m, the length of a giant Australian earthworm.

The phylum Annelida can be divided into two main groups: Polychaeta (the polychaetes) and Oligochaeta (the earthworms and their relatives, and the leeches). Some recent phylogenetic analyses have suggested that the oligochaetes are actually a subgroup of the polychaetes. However, since this idea continues to be debated, we discuss polychaetes and oligochaetes separately.

Polychaetes

Each segment of a polychaete (from the Greek *poly*, many, and *chaitē*, long hair) has a pair of paddle-like or ridge-like structures called parapodia ("beside feet") that function in locomotion (**Figure 33.23**). Each parapodium has numerous chaetae, bristles made of chitin. In many polychaetes, the parapodia are richly supplied with blood vessels and also function as gills.

Polychaetes make up a large and diverse group, most of whose members are marine. A few species drift and swim among the plankton, many crawl on or burrow in the seafloor, and many others live in tubes. Some tube-dwellers, such as the fan worms, build their tubes by mixing mucus with bits of sand and broken shells. Others, such as Christmas tree worms (see Figure 33.1), construct tubes using only their own secretions.

Oligochaetes

Oligochaetes (*oligos*, few, and *chaitē*, long hair) are named for their relatively sparse chaetae (far fewer per segment than in polychaetes). Molecular data indicate that these segmented worms form a diverse clade that includes the earthworms and their aquatic relatives, along with the leeches.

Earthworms Earthworms eat their way through the soil, extracting nutrients as the soil passes through the alimentary canal.

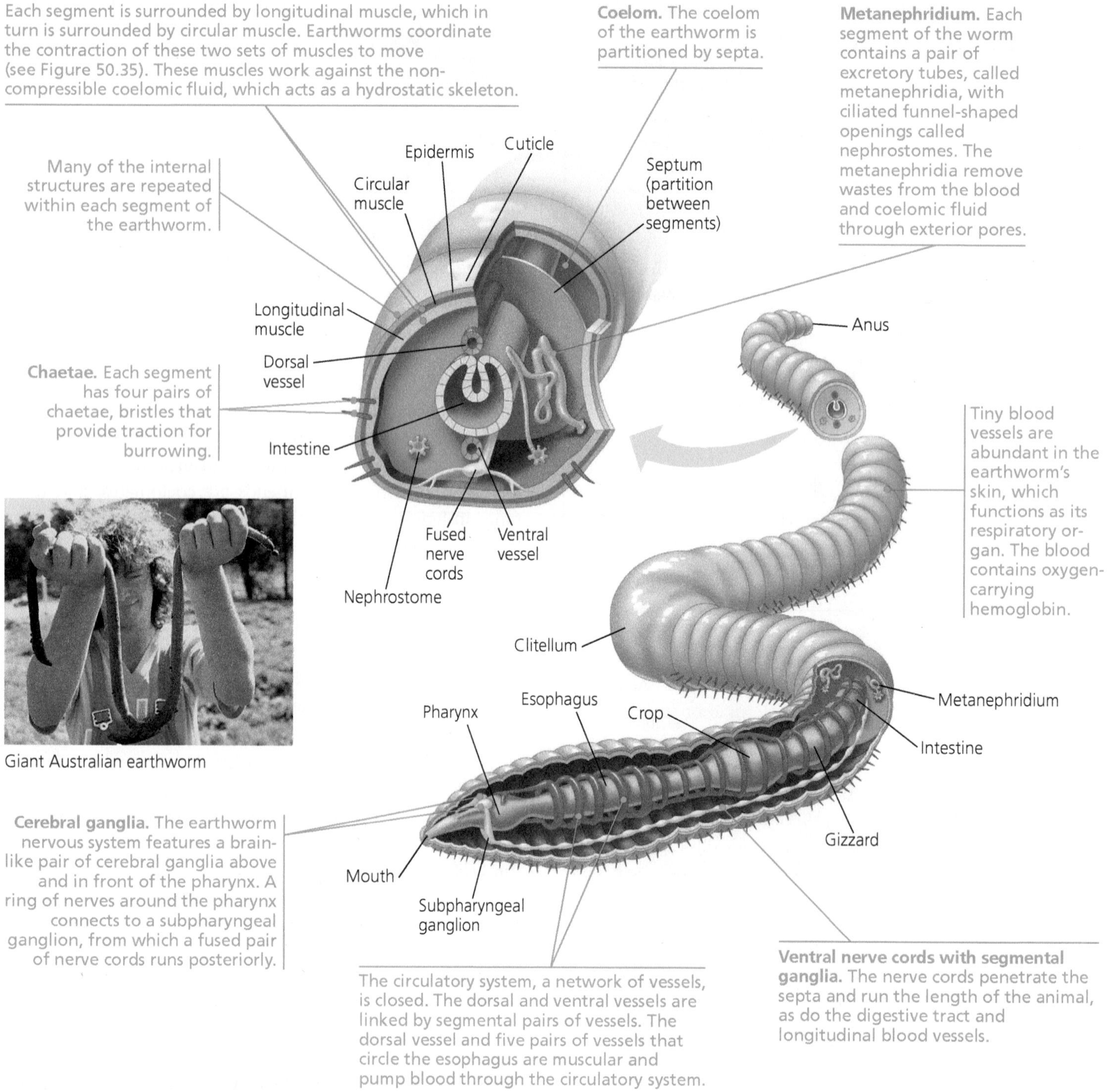

▲ **Figure 33.24 Anatomy of an earthworm, an oligochaete.**

Undigested material, mixed with mucus secreted into the canal, is eliminated as fecal castings through the anus. Farmers value earthworms because the animals till and aerate the earth, and their castings improve the texture of the soil. (Charles Darwin estimated that a single acre of British farmland contains about 50,000 earthworms, producing 18 tons of castings per year.)

A guided tour of the anatomy of an earthworm, which is representative of annelids, is shown in **Figure 33.24**. Earthworms are hermaphrodites, but they do cross-fertilize. Two earthworms mate by aligning themselves in opposite directions in such a way that they exchange sperm, and then they separate. The received sperm are stored temporarily while an organ called the clitellum secretes a cocoon of mucus. The cocoon slides along the worm, picking up the eggs and then the stored sperm. The cocoon then slips off the worm's head and remains in the soil while the embryos develop. Some earthworms can also reproduce asexually by fragmentation followed by regeneration.

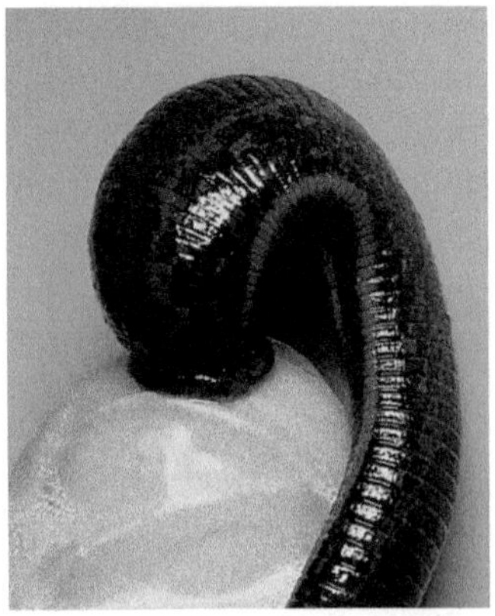

▶ **Figure 33.25 A leech.** A nurse applied this medicinal leech (*Hirudo medicinalis*) to a patient's sore thumb to drain blood from a hematoma (an abnormal accumulation of blood around an internal injury).

Leeches Most leeches inhabit fresh water, but there are also marine species and terrestrial leeches, which live in moist vegetation. Leeches range in length from 1 to 30 cm. Many are predators that feed on other invertebrates, but some are parasites that suck blood by attaching temporarily to other animals, including humans (Figure 33.25). Some parasitic species use bladelike jaws to slit the skin of their host, whereas others secrete enzymes that digest a hole through the skin. The host is usually oblivious to this attack because the leech secretes an anesthetic. After making the incision, the leech secretes another chemical, hirudin, which keeps the blood of the host from coagulating near the incision. The parasite then sucks as much blood as it can hold, often more than ten times its own weight. After this gorging, a leech can last for months without another meal.

Until the 20th century, leeches were frequently used for bloodletting. Today they are used to drain blood that accumulates in tissues following certain injuries or surgeries. Researchers have also investigated the potential use of purified hirudin to dissolve unwanted blood clots that form during surgery or as a result of heart disease. Several forms of hirudin have been developed using recombinant DNA techniques; two of these were recently approved for clinical use.

As a group, Lophotrochozoa encompasses a remarkable range of body plans, as illustrated by members of such phyla as Rotifera, Ectoprocta, Mollusca, and Annelida. Next we'll explore the diversity of Ecdysozoa, a dominant presence on Earth in terms of sheer number of species.

CONCEPT CHECK 33.3

1. Explain how tapeworms can survive without a coelom, a mouth, a digestive system, or an excretory system.
2. Annelid anatomy can be described as "a tube within a tube." Explain.
3. **MAKE CONNECTIONS** Explain how the molluscan foot in gastropods and the excurrent siphon in cephalopods represent an example of descent with modification (see Concept 22.2, pp. 457–460).

For suggested answers, see Appendix A.

CONCEPT 33.4

Ecdysozoans are the most species-rich animal group

Although defined primarily by molecular evidence, the clade Ecdysozoa includes animals that shed a tough external coat (**cuticle**) as they grow; in fact, the group derives its name from this process, which is called *ecdysis*, or **molting**. Ecdysozoa consists of about eight animal phyla and contains more known species than all other animal, protist, fungus, and plant groups combined. Here we'll focus on the two largest ecdysozoan phyla, the nematodes and arthropods, which are among the most successful and abundant of all animal groups.

Nematodes

Among the most ubiquitous of animals, nematodes (phylum Nematoda), or roundworms, are found in most aquatic habitats, in the soil, in the moist tissues of plants, and in the body fluids and tissues of animals. In contrast to annelids, nematodes do not have segmented bodies. The cylindrical bodies of nematodes range from less than 1 mm to more than 1 m long, often tapering to a fine tip at the posterior end and to a blunter tip at the anterior end (Figure 33.26). A nematode's body is covered by a tough cuticle (a type of exoskeleton); as the worm grows, it periodically sheds its old cuticle and secretes a new, larger one. Nematodes have an alimentary canal, though they lack a circulatory system. Nutrients are transported throughout the body via fluid in the pseudocoelom. The body wall muscles are all longitudinal, and their contraction produces a thrashing motion.

Nematodes usually reproduce sexually, by internal fertilization. In most species, the sexes are separate and females are larger than males. A female may deposit 100,000 or more fertilized eggs (zygotes) per day. The zygotes of most species are resistant cells that can survive harsh conditions.

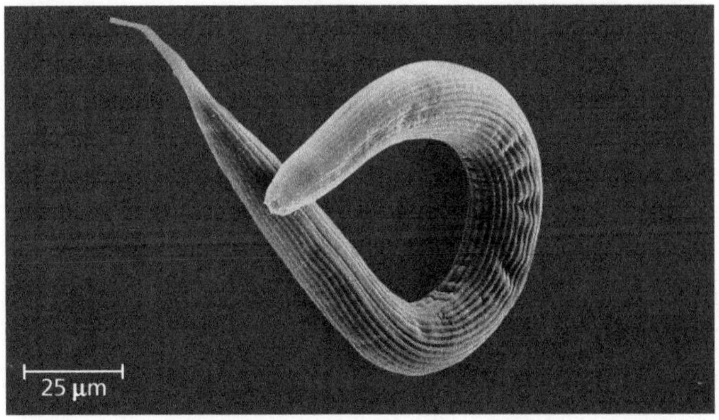

▲ **Figure 33.26 A free-living nematode** (colorized SEM).

Multitudes of nematodes live in moist soil and in decomposing organic matter on the bottoms of lakes and oceans. While 25,000 species are known, perhaps 20 times that number actually exist. It has been said that if nothing of Earth or its organisms remained but nematodes, they would still preserve the outline of the planet and many of its features. These free-living worms play an important role in decomposition and nutrient cycling, but little is known about most species. One species of soil nematode, *Caenorhabditis elegans*, however, is very well studied and has become a model research organism in biology (see Chapter 47). Ongoing studies of *C. elegans* are revealing some of the mechanisms involved in aging in humans, among other findings.

Phylum Nematoda includes many species that parasitize plants, and some are major agricultural pests that attack the roots of crops. Other nematodes parasitize animals. Some of these species benefit humans by attacking insects such as cutworms that feed on the roots of crop plants. On the other hand, humans are hosts to at least 50 nematode species, including various pinworms and hookworms. One notorious nematode is *Trichinella spiralis*, the worm that causes trichinosis (Figure 33.27). Humans acquire this nematode by eating raw or undercooked pork or other meat (including wild game such as bear or walrus) that has juvenile worms encysted in the muscle tissue. Within the human intestines, the juveniles develop into sexually mature adults. Females burrow into the intestinal muscles and produce more juveniles, which bore through the body or travel in lymphatic vessels to other organs, including skeletal muscles, where they encyst.

Parasitic nematodes have an extraordinary molecular toolkit that enables them to redirect some of the cellular functions of their hosts and thus evade their immune systems. Some species inject their plant hosts with molecules that induce the development of root cells, which then supply nutrients to the parasites. *Trichinella*, which parasitizes animals, controls the expression of specific muscle cell genes that code for proteins that make the cell elastic enough to house the nematode. Additionally, the infected muscle cell releases signals that promote the growth of new blood vessels, which then supply the nematode with nutrients.

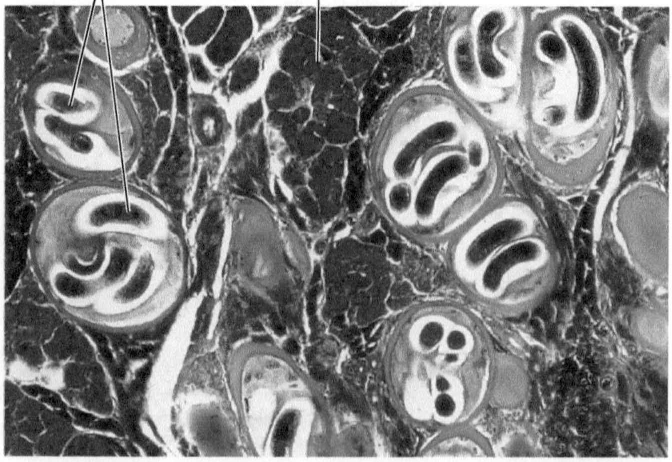

▲ **Figure 33.27 Juveniles of the parasitic nematode *Trichinella spiralis* encysted in human muscle tissue** (LM).

Arthropods

Zoologists estimate that there are about a billion billion (10^{18}) arthropods living on Earth. More than 1 million arthropod species have been described, most of which are insects. In fact, two out of every three known species are arthropods, and members of the phylum Arthropoda can be found in nearly all habitats of the biosphere. By the criteria of species diversity, distribution, and sheer numbers, arthropods must be regarded as the most successful of all animal phyla.

Arthropod Origins

Biologists hypothesize that the diversity and success of **arthropods** are related to their body plan—their segmented body, hard exoskeleton, and jointed appendages (*arthropod* means "jointed feet"). The earliest fossils with this body plan are from the Cambrian explosion (535–525 million years ago), indicating that the arthropods are at least that old.

Along with arthropods, the fossil record of the Cambrian explosion contains many species of *lobopods*, an extinct group from which arthropods may have evolved. Lobopods such as *Hallucigenia* (see Figure 25.4) had segmented bodies, but most of their body segments were identical to one another. Early arthropods, such as the trilobites, also showed little variation from segment to segment (Figure 33.28). As arthropods continued to evolve, the segments tended to fuse and become fewer, and the appendages became specialized for a variety of functions. These evolutionary changes resulted not only in great diversification but also in an efficient body plan that permits the division of labor among different body regions.

► **Figure 33.28 A trilobite fossil.** Trilobites were common denizens of the shallow seas throughout the Paleozoic era but disappeared with the great Permian extinctions about 250 million years ago. Paleontologists have described about 4,000 trilobite species.

▼ **Figure 33.29** **INQUIRY**

Did the arthropod body plan result from new *Hox* genes?

EXPERIMENT How did the highly successful arthropod body plan arise? One hypothesis suggests that it resulted from the origin (by a gene duplication event) of two unusual *Hox* genes found in arthropods: *Ultrabithorax* (*Ubx*) and *abdominal-A* (*abd-A*). To test this hypothesis, Sean Carroll, of the University of Wisconsin, Madison, and colleagues turned to the onychophorans, a group of invertebrates closely related to arthropods. Unlike many living arthropods, onychophorans have a body plan in which most body segments are identical to one another. Thus, Carroll and colleagues reasoned that if the origin of the *Ubx* and *abd-A Hox* genes drove the evolution of body segment diversity in arthropods, these genes probably arose on the arthropod branch of the evolutionary tree:

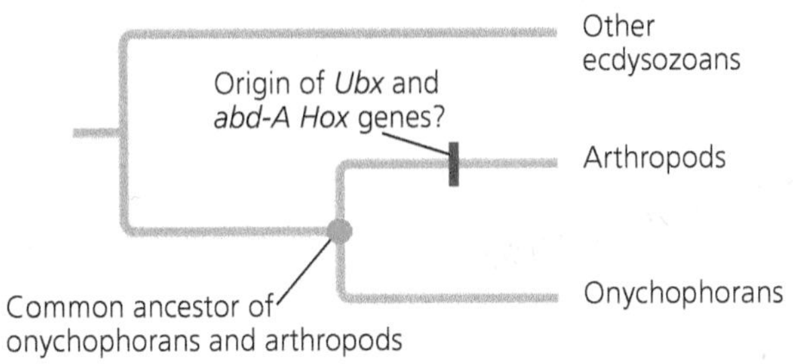

According to this hypothesis, *Ubx* and *abd-A* would not have been present in the common ancestor of arthropods and onychophorans; hence, onychophorans should not have these genes. To find out whether this was the case, Carroll and colleagues examined the *Hox* genes of the onychophoran *Acanthokara kaputensis.*

RESULTS The onychophoran *A. kaputensis* has all arthropod *Hox* genes, including *Ubx* and *abd-A*.

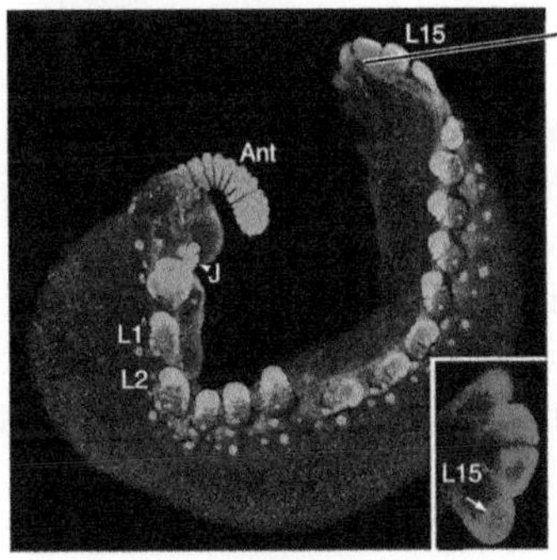

Red indicates the body regions of this onychophoran embryo in which *Ubx* or *abd-A* genes were expressed. (The inset shows this area enlarged.)

Ant = antenna
J = jaws
L1–L15 = body segments

CONCLUSION Since *A. kaputensis*, an onychophoran, has the arthropod *Hox* genes, the evolution of increased body segment diversity in arthropods must not have been related to the origin of new *Hox* genes.

SOURCE J. K. Grenier, S. Carroll, et al., Evolution of the entire arthropod *Hox* gene set predated the origin and radiation of the onychophoran/arthropod clade, *Current Biology* 7:547–553 (1997).

WHAT IF? If Carroll and colleagues had found that *A. kaputensis* did *not* have the *Ubx* and *abd-A Hox* genes, how would their conclusion have been affected? Explain.

What genetic changes led to the increasing complexity of the arthropod body plan? Arthropods today have two unusual *Hox* genes, both of which influence segmentation. To test whether these genes could have driven the evolution of increased body segment diversity in arthropods, researchers studied *Hox* genes in onychophorans (see Figure 33.3), close relatives of arthropods (**Figure 33.29**). Their results indicate that arthropod body plan diversity did *not* arise from the acquisition of new *Hox* genes. Instead, the evolution of body segment diversity in arthropods may have been driven by changes in the sequence or regulation of existing *Hox* genes. (See Chapter 25 for a discussion of how changes in form can result from changes in the sequence or regulation of developmental genes such as *Hox* genes.)

General Characteristics of Arthropods

Over the course of evolution, the appendages of some arthropods have become modified, specializing in functions such as walking, feeding, sensory reception, reproduction, and defense. Like the appendages from which they were derived, these modified structures are jointed and come in pairs. **Figure 33.30** illustrates the diverse appendages and other arthropod characteristics of a lobster.

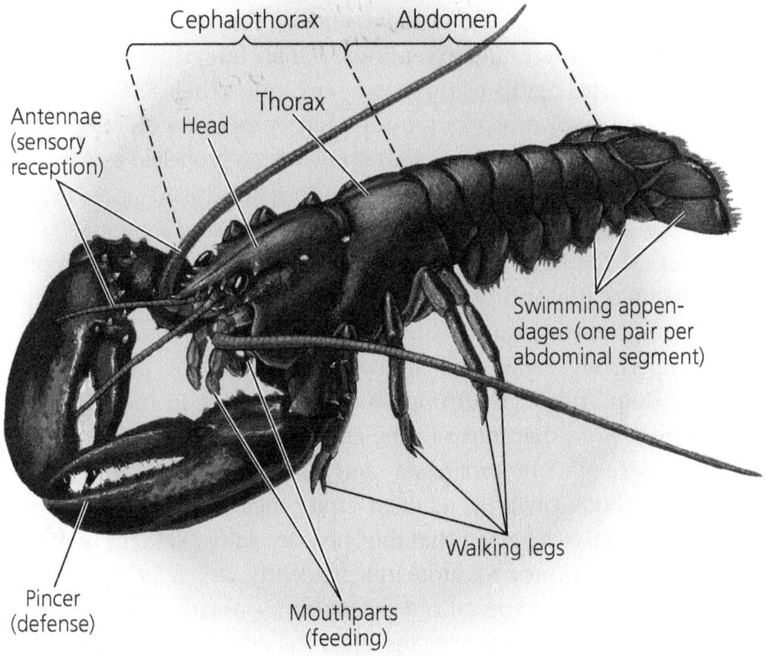

▲ **Figure 33.30** **External anatomy of an arthropod.** Many of the distinctive features of arthropods are apparent in this dorsal view of a lobster, along with some uniquely crustacean characteristics. The body is segmented, but this characteristic is obvious only in the abdomen. The appendages (including antennae, pincers, mouthparts, walking legs, and swimming appendages) are jointed. The head bears a pair of compound (multilens) eyes, each situated on a movable stalk. The whole body, including appendages, is covered by an exoskeleton.

The body of an arthropod is completely covered by the cuticle, an exoskeleton constructed from layers of protein and the polysaccharide chitin. The cuticle can be thick and hard over some parts of the body and paper-thin and flexible over others, such as the joints. The rigid exoskeleton protects the animal and provides points of attachment for the muscles that move the appendages. But it also means that an arthropod cannot grow without occasionally shedding its exoskeleton and producing a larger one. This molting process is energetically expensive. A molting or recently molted arthropod is also vulnerable to predation and other dangers until its new, soft exoskeleton hardens.

When the arthropod exoskeleton first evolved in the sea, its main functions were probably protection and anchorage for muscles, but it later enabled certain arthropods to live on land. The exoskeleton's relative impermeability to water helped prevent desiccation, and its strength solved the problem of support when arthropods left the buoyancy of water. Arthropods began to diversify on land following the colonization of land by plants in the early Paleozoic. Evidence includes a 428-million-year-old fossil of a millipede found in 2004 by an amateur fossil hunter in Scotland. Fossilized tracks of other terrestrial arthropods date from about 450 million years ago.

Arthropods have well-developed sensory organs, including eyes, olfactory (smell) receptors, and antennae that function in both touch and smell. Most sensory organs are concentrated at the anterior end of the animal, although there are interesting exceptions. Female butterflies, for example, "taste" plants using sensory organs on their feet.

Like many molluscs, arthropods have an **open circulatory system**, in which fluid called *hemolymph* is propelled by a heart through short arteries and then into spaces called sinuses surrounding the tissues and organs. (The term *blood* is generally reserved for fluid in a closed circulatory system.) Hemolymph reenters the arthropod heart through pores that are usually equipped with valves. The hemolymph-filled body sinuses are collectively called the *hemocoel*, which is not part of the coelom. Although arthropods are coelomates, in most species the coelom that forms in the embryo becomes much reduced as development progresses, and the hemocoel becomes the main body cavity in adults. Despite their similarity, phylogenetic analyses suggest that the open circulatory systems of molluscs and arthropods arose independently.

A variety of specialized gas exchange organs have evolved in arthropods. These organs allow the diffusion of respiratory gases in spite of the exoskeleton. Most aquatic species have gills with thin, feathery extensions that place an extensive surface area in contact with the surrounding water. Terrestrial arthropods generally have internal surfaces specialized for gas exchange. Most insects, for instance, have tracheal systems, branched air ducts leading into the interior from pores in the cuticle.

▲ Figure 33.31 **Horseshoe crabs (*Limulus polyphemus*).** Common on the Atlantic and Gulf coasts of the United States, these "living fossils" have changed little in hundreds of millions of years. They are surviving members of a rich diversity of chelicerates that once filled the seas.

Morphological and molecular evidence suggests that living arthropods consist of four major lineages that diverged early in the evolution of the phylum: **chelicerates** (sea spiders, horseshoe crabs, scorpions, ticks, mites, and spiders); **myriapods** (centipedes and millipedes); **hexapods** (insects and their wingless, six-legged relatives); and **crustaceans** (crabs, lobsters, shrimps, barnacles, and many others).

Chelicerates

Chelicerates (subphylum Chelicerata; from the Greek *cheilos*, lips, and *cheir*, arm) are named for clawlike feeding appendages called **chelicerae**, which serve as pincers or fangs. Chelicerates have an anterior cephalothorax and a posterior abdomen. They lack antennae, and most have simple eyes (eyes with a single lens).

The earliest chelicerates were **eurypterids**, or water scorpions. These marine and freshwater predators grew up to 3 m long; it is thought that some species could have walked on land, much as land crabs do today. Most of the marine chelicerates, including all of the eurypterids, are extinct. Among the marine chelicerates that survive today are the sea spiders (pycnogonids) and horseshoe crabs (Figure 33.31).

The bulk of modern chelicerates are **arachnids**, a group that includes scorpions, spiders, ticks, and mites (Figure 33.32). Ticks and many mites are among a large group of parasitic arthropods. Nearly all ticks are bloodsucking parasites that live on the body surfaces of reptiles or mammals. Parasitic mites live on or in a wide variety of vertebrates, invertebrates, and plants.

Arachnids have a cephalothorax that has six pairs of appendages: the chelicerae; a pair of appendages called *pedipalps* that function in sensing, feeding, or reproduction; and four pairs of walking legs (Figure 33.33). Spiders use their fang-like chelicerae, which are equipped with poison glands, to attack

▲ Scorpions have pedipalps that are pincers specialized for defense and the capture of food. The tip of the tail bears a poisonous stinger.

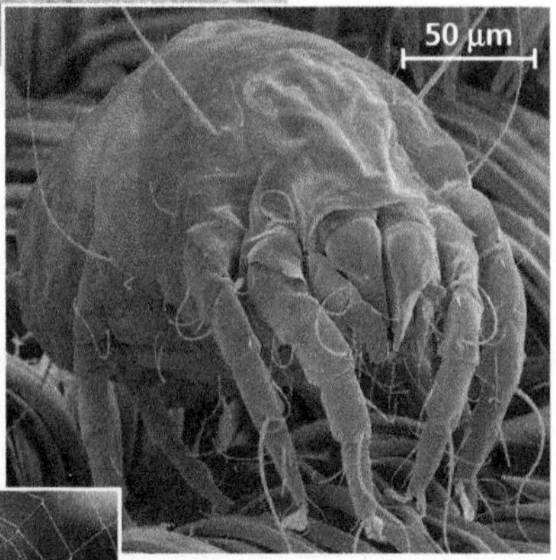

▲ Dust mites are ubiquitous scavengers in human dwellings but are harmless except to those people who are allergic to them (colorized SEM).

◄ Web-building spiders are generally most active during the daytime.

▲ **Figure 33.32 Arachnids.**

(a) Millipede

(b) Centipede

▲ **Figure 33.34 Myriapods.**

prey. As the chelicerae pierce the prey, the spider secretes digestive juices onto the prey's torn tissues. The food softens, and the spider sucks up the liquid meal.

In most spiders, gas exchange is carried out by **book lungs**, stacked platelike structures contained in an internal chamber (see Figure 33.33). The extensive surface area of these respiratory organs is a structural adaptation that enhances the exchange of O_2 and CO_2 between the hemolymph and air.

A unique adaptation of many spiders is the ability to catch insects by constructing webs of silk, a liquid protein produced by specialized abdominal glands. The silk is spun by organs called spinnerets into fibers that then solidify. Each spider engineers a web characteristic of its species and builds it perfectly on the first try, indicating that this complex behavior is inherited. Various spiders also use silk in other ways: as droplines for rapid escape, as a cover for eggs, and even as "gift wrap" for food that males offer females during courtship. Many small spiders also extrude silk into the air and let themselves be transported by wind, a behavior known as "ballooning."

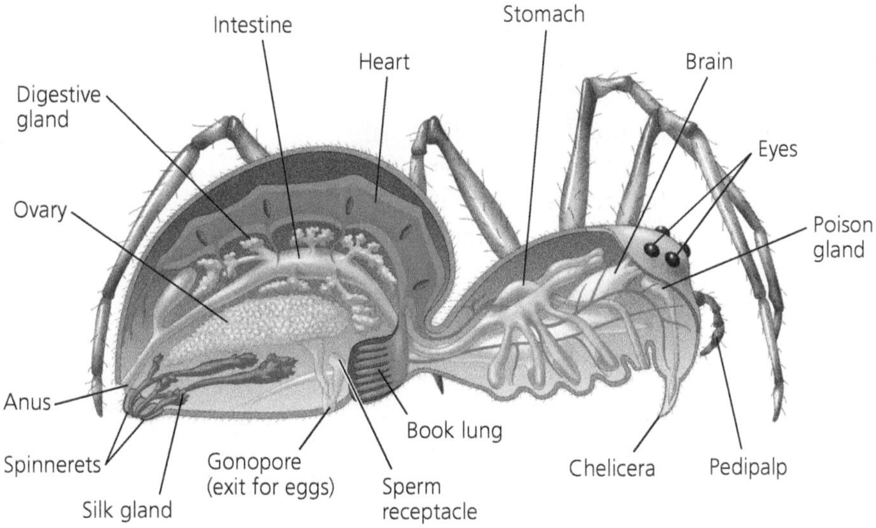

▲ **Figure 33.33 Anatomy of a spider.**

Myriapods

Millipedes and centipedes belong to the subphylum Myriapoda (Figure 33.34). All living myriapods are terrestrial. The myriapod head has a pair of antennae and three pairs of appendages modified as mouthparts, including the jaw-like **mandibles**.

Millipedes have a large number of legs, though fewer than the thousand their name implies. Each trunk segment is formed from two fused segments and bears two pairs of legs (see Figure 33.34a). Millipedes eat decaying leaves and other plant matter. They may have been among the earliest animals on land, living on mosses and early vascular plants.

Unlike millipedes, centipedes are carnivores. Each segment of a centipede's trunk region has one pair of legs (see Figure 33.34b). Centipedes have poison claws on their foremost trunk segment that paralyze prey and aid in defense.

Insects

Insects and their relatives (subphylum Hexapoda) are more species-rich than all other forms of life combined. They live in almost every terrestrial habitat and in fresh water, and flying insects fill the air. Insects are rare, though not absent, in marine habitats, where crustaceans are the dominant arthropods. The internal anatomy of an insect includes several complex organ systems, which are highlighted in **Figure 33.35**.

The oldest insect fossils date from the Devonian period, which began about 416 million years ago. However, when insect flight evolved during the Carboniferous and Permian periods, it spurred an explosion in insect diversity. A fossil record of diverse insect mouthparts indicates that specialized feeding on gymnosperms and other Carboniferous plants also contributed to early adaptive radiations of insects. Later, a major increase in insect diversity appears to have been stimulated by the evolutionary expansion of flowering plants during the mid-Cretaceous period (about 90 million years ago). Although insect and plant diversity decreased during the Cretaceous mass extinction, both groups rebounded over the next 65 million years. Studies indicate that increases in the diversity of particular insect groups often were associated with radiations of the flowering plants on which they fed.

Flight is obviously one key to the great success of insects. An animal that can fly can escape many predators, find food and mates, and disperse to new habitats much faster than an animal that must crawl about on the ground. Many insects have one or two pairs of wings that emerge from the dorsal side of the thorax (**Figure 33.36**). Because the wings are extensions of the cuticle and not true appendages, insects can fly without sacrificing any walking legs. By contrast, the flying vertebrates—birds and bats—have one of their two pairs of walking legs modified into wings, making some of these species clumsy on the ground.

Insect wings may have first evolved as extensions of the cuticle that helped the insect body absorb heat, only later becoming organs for flight. Other hypotheses suggest that wings allowed terrestrial insects to glide from vegetation to the ground or that they served as gills in aquatic insects. Still another hypothesis is that insect wings functioned for swimming before they functioned for flight.

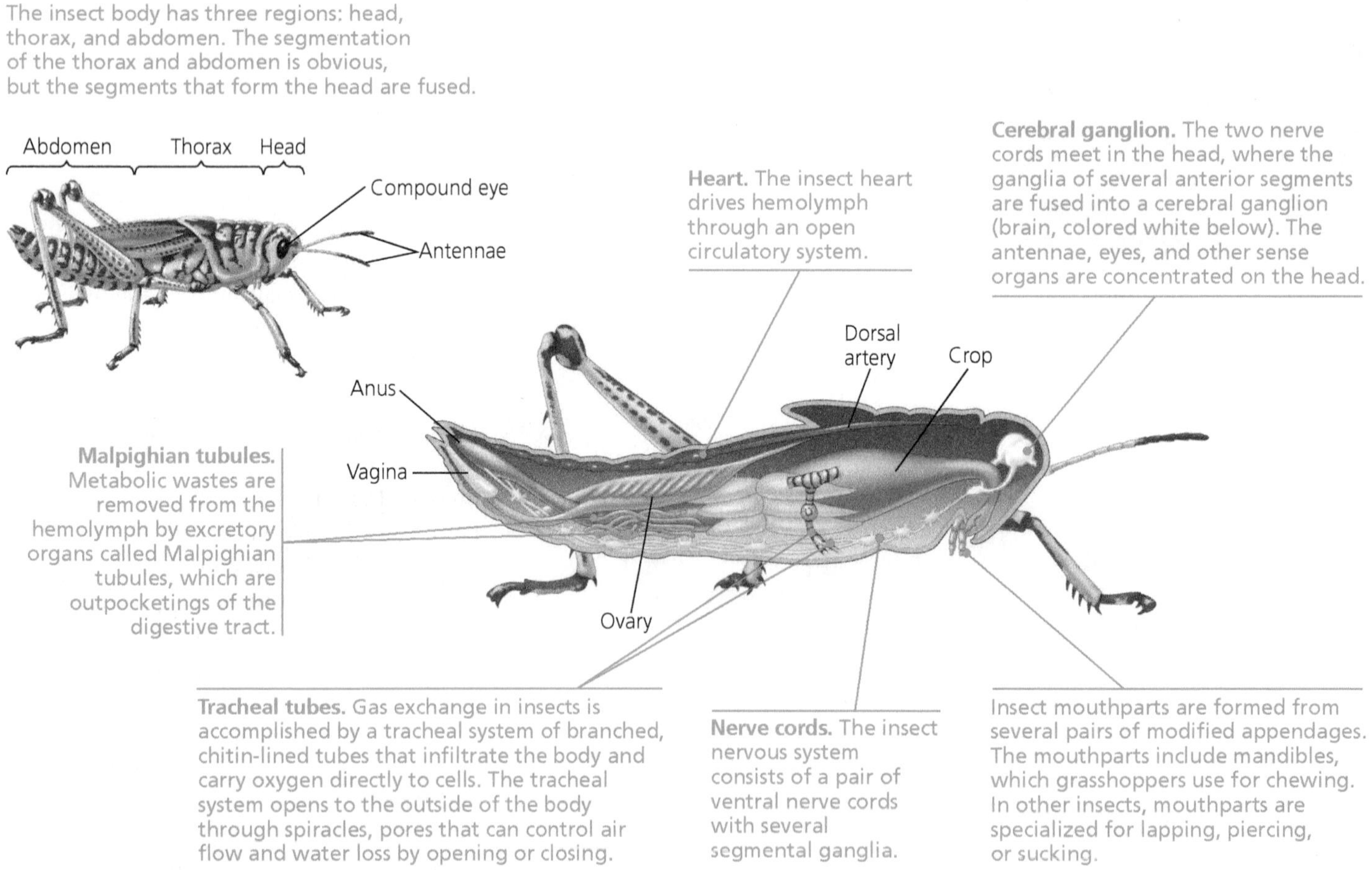

▲ **Figure 33.35 Anatomy of a grasshopper, an insect.**

▶ **Figure 33.36 Ladybird beetle in flight.**

Morphological and molecular data indicate that wings evolved only once in insects. Dragonflies, which have two similar pairs of wings, were among the first insects to fly. Several insect orders that evolved later than dragonflies have modified flight equipment. The wings of bees and wasps, for instance, are hooked together and move as a single pair. Butterfly wings operate in a similar fashion because the anterior pair overlaps the posterior wings. In beetles, the posterior wings function in flight, while the anterior ones are modified as covers that protect the flight wings when the beetle is walking on the ground or burrowing.

Many insects undergo metamorphosis during their development. In the **incomplete metamorphosis** of grasshoppers and some other insect groups, the young (called nymphs) resemble adults but are smaller, have different body proportions, and lack wings. The nymph undergoes a series of molts, each time looking more like an adult. With the final molt, the insect reaches full size, acquires wings, and becomes sexually mature. Insects with **complete metamorphosis** have larval stages specialized for eating and growing that are known by such names as caterpillar, maggot, or grub. The larval stage looks entirely different from the adult stage, which is specialized for dispersal and reproduction. Metamorphosis from the larval stage to the adult occurs during a pupal stage (Figure 33.37).

Reproduction in insects is usually sexual, with separate male and female individuals. Adults come together and recognize each other as members of the same species by advertising with bright colors (as in butterflies), sounds (as in crickets), or odors (as in moths). Fertilization is generally internal. In most species, sperm are deposited directly into the female's vagina at the time of copulation, though in some species the male deposits a sperm packet outside the female, and the female picks it up. An internal structure in the female called the spermatheca stores the sperm, usually enough to fertilize more than one batch of eggs. Many insects mate only once in a lifetime. After mating, a female often lays her eggs on an appropriate food source where the next generation can begin eating as soon as it hatches.

Insects are classified in more than 30 orders, 8 of which are introduced in Figure 33.38.

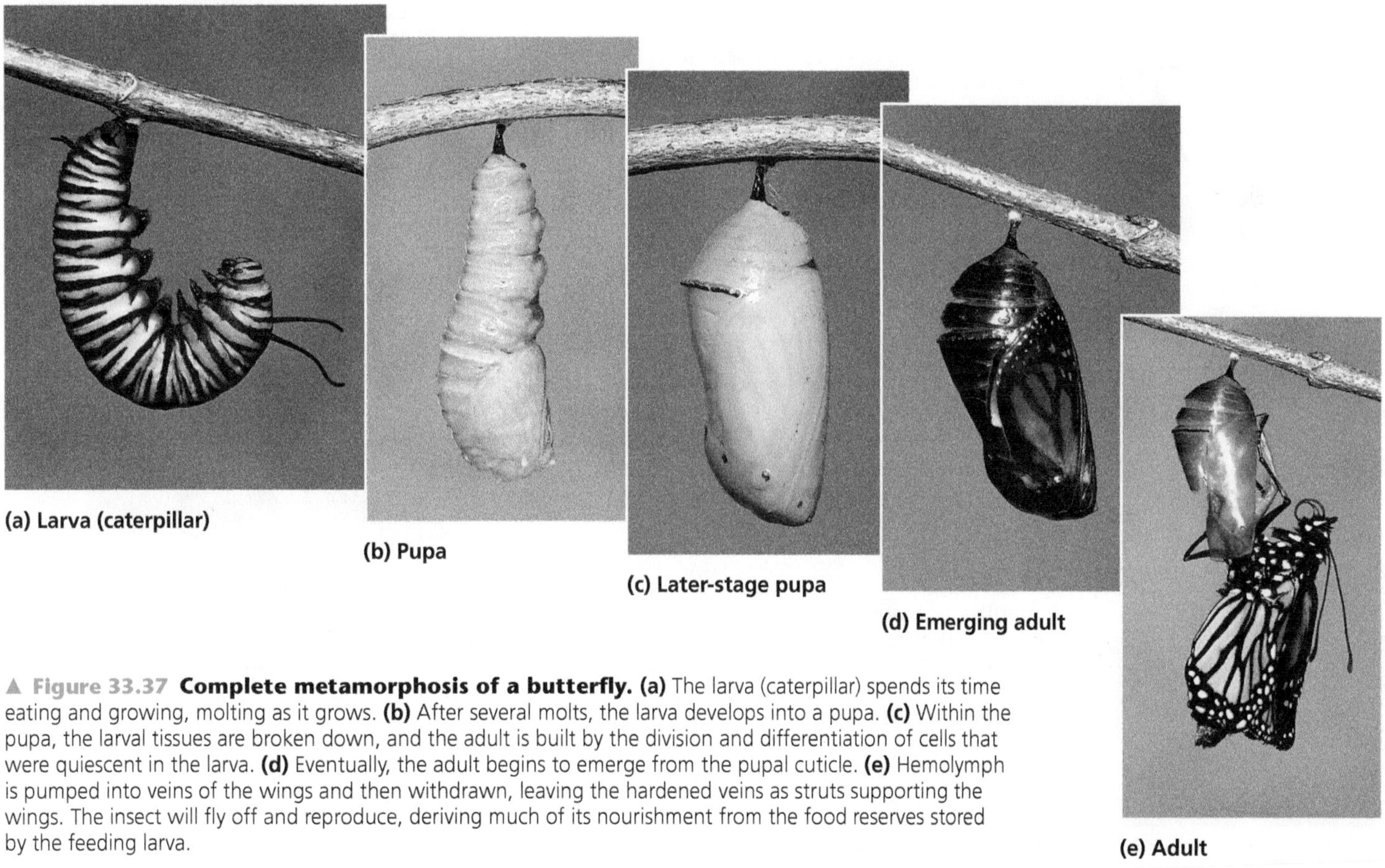

▲ **Figure 33.37 Complete metamorphosis of a butterfly. (a)** The larva (caterpillar) spends its time eating and growing, molting as it grows. **(b)** After several molts, the larva develops into a pupa. **(c)** Within the pupa, the larval tissues are broken down, and the adult is built by the division and differentiation of cells that were quiescent in the larva. **(d)** Eventually, the adult begins to emerge from the pupal cuticle. **(e)** Hemolymph is pumped into veins of the wings and then withdrawn, leaving the hardened veins as struts supporting the wings. The insect will fly off and reproduce, deriving much of its nourishment from the food reserves stored by the feeding larva.

▼ Figure 33.38

Exploring Insect Diversity

Although there are more than 30 orders of insects, we'll focus on just 8 here. Two early-diverging groups of wingless insects are the bristletails (Archaeognatha) and silverfish (Thysanura). Evolutionary relationships among the other groups discussed here are under debate and so are not depicted on the tree.

Archaeognatha (bristletails; 350 species)

These wingless insects are found under bark and in other moist, dark habitats such as leaf litter, compost piles, and rock crevices. They feed on algae, plant debris, and lichens.

Thysanura (silverfish; 450 species)

These small, wingless insects have a flattened body and reduced eyes. They live in leaf litter or under bark. They can also infest buildings, where they can become pests.

Winged insects (many orders; six are shown below)

Complete metamorphosis

Coleoptera (beetles; 350,000 species)

Beetles, such as this male snout weevil (*Rhiastus lasternus*), constitute the most species-rich order of insects. They have two pairs of wings, one of which is thick and stiff, the other membranous. They have an armored exoskeleton and mouthparts adapted for biting and chewing.

Diptera (151,000 species)

Dipterans have one pair of wings; the second pair has become modified into balancing organs called halteres. Their mouthparts are adapted for sucking, piercing, or lapping. Flies and mosquitoes are among the best-known dipterans, which live as scavengers, predators, and parasites. Like many other insects, flies such as this red tachinid (*Adejeania vexatrix*) have well-developed compound eyes that provide a wide-angle view and excel at detecting fast movements.

Hymenoptera (125,000 species)

Most hymenopterans, which include ants, bees, and wasps, are highly social insects. They have two pairs of membranous wings, a mobile head, and chewing or sucking mouthparts. The females of many species have a posterior stinging organ. Many species, such as this European paper wasp (*Polistes dominulus*), build elaborate nests.

Lepidoptera (120,000 species)

Butterflies and moths have two pairs of wings covered with tiny scales. To feed, they uncoil a long proboscis, visible in this photograph of a hummingbird hawkmoth (*Macroglossum stellatarum*). This moth's name refers to its ability to hover in the air while feeding from a flower. Most lepidopterans feed on nectar, but some species feed on other substances, including animal blood or tears.

Incomplete metamorphosis

Hemiptera (85,000 species)

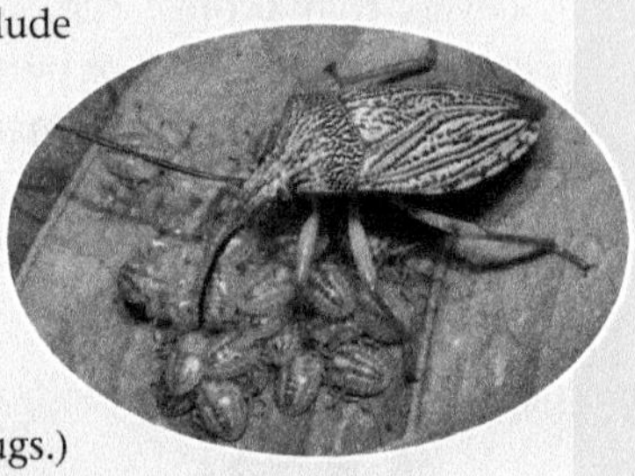

Hemipterans include so-called "true bugs," such as stink bugs, bed bugs, and assassin bugs. (Insects in other orders are sometimes erroneously called bugs.) Hemipterans have two pairs of wings, one pair partly leathery, the other pair membranous. They have piercing or sucking mouthparts and undergo incomplete metamorphosis, as shown in this image of an adult stink bug guarding its offspring (nymphs).

Orthoptera (13,000 species)

Grasshoppers, crickets, and their relatives are mostly herbivorous. They have large hind legs adapted for jumping, two pairs of wings (one leathery, one membranous), and biting or chewing mouthparts. This aptly named spear-bearer katydid (*Cophiphora* sp.) has a face and legs well adapted to making a threatening display. Male orthopterans commonly make courtship sounds by rubbing together body parts, such as ridges on their hind legs.

Animals as numerous, diverse, and widespread as insects are bound to affect the lives of most other terrestrial organisms, including humans. Insects consume enormous quantities of plant matter; play key roles as predators, parasites, and decomposers; and are an essential source of food for larger animals such as lizards, rodents, and birds. Humans depend on bees, flies, and many other insects to pollinate crops and orchards. In addition, people in many parts of the world eat insects as an important source of protein. On the other hand, insects are carriers for many diseases, including African sleeping sickness (spread by tsetse flies that carry the protist *Trypanosoma*; see Figure 28.6) and malaria (spread by mosquitoes that carry the protist *Plasmodium*; see Figure 28.10).

Insects also compete with humans for food. In parts of Africa, for instance, insects claim about 75% of the crops. In the United States, billions of dollars are spent each year on pesticides, spraying crops with massive doses of some of the deadliest poisons ever invented. Try as they may, not even humans have challenged the preeminence of insects and their arthropod kin. As Cornell University entomologist Thomas Eisner puts it: "Bugs are not going to inherit the Earth. They own it now. So we might as well make peace with the landlord."

(a) Ghost crabs live on sandy ocean beaches worldwide. Primarily nocturnal, they take shelter in burrows during the day.

(b) Planktonic crustaceans known as krill are consumed in vast quantities by some whales.

(c) The jointed appendages projecting from the shells of these barnacles capture organisms and organic particles suspended in the water.

▲ **Figure 33.39 Crustaceans.**

Crustaceans

While arachnids and insects thrive on land, crustaceans, for the most part, have remained in marine and freshwater environments. Crustaceans (subphylum Crustacea) typically have highly specialized appendages. Lobsters and crayfishes, for instance, have a toolkit of 19 pairs of appendages (see Figure 33.30). The anterior-most appendages are antennae; crustaceans are the only arthropods with two pairs. Three or more pairs of appendages are modified as mouthparts, including the hard mandibles. Walking legs are present on the thorax, and, unlike insects, crustaceans also have appendages on their abdomen. A lost appendage can be regenerated at the next molt.

Small crustaceans exchange gases across thin areas of the cuticle; larger species have gills. Nitrogenous wastes also diffuse through thin areas of the cuticle, but a pair of glands regulates the salt balance of the hemolymph.

Sexes are separate in most crustaceans. In the case of lobsters and crayfishes, the male uses a specialized pair of abdominal appendages to transfer sperm to the reproductive pore of the female during copulation. Most aquatic crustaceans go through one or more swimming larval stages.

One of the largest groups of crustaceans (numbering over 11,000 species) is the **isopods**, which include terrestrial, freshwater, and marine species. Some isopod species are abundant in habitats at the bottom of the deep ocean. Among the terrestrial isopods are the pill bugs, or wood lice, common on the undersides of moist logs and leaves.

Lobsters, crayfishes, crabs, and shrimps are all relatively large crustaceans called **decapods** (Figure 33.39a). The cuticle of decapods is hardened by calcium carbonate; the portion that covers the dorsal side of the cephalothorax forms a shield called the carapace. Most decapod species are marine. Crayfishes, however, live in fresh water, and some tropical crabs live on land.

Many small crustaceans are important members of marine and freshwater plankton communities. Planktonic crustaceans include many species of **copepods**, which are among the most numerous of all animals. Some copepods are grazers that feed upon algae, while others are predators that eat small animals (including smaller copepods!). Copepods are rivaled in abundance by the shrimplike krill, which grow to about 5 cm long (Figure 33.39b). A major food source for baleen whales (including blue whales, humpbacks, and right whales), krill are now being harvested in great numbers by humans for food and agricultural fertilizer. The larvae of many larger-bodied crustaceans are also planktonic.

With the exception of a few parasitic species, barnacles are a group of sessile crustaceans whose cuticle is hardened into a shell containing calcium carbonate (Figure 33.39c). Most barnacles anchor themselves to rocks, boat hulls, pilings, and other submerged surfaces. Their natural adhesive is as strong as synthetic glues. These barnacles feed by extending appendages from their shell to strain food from the water. Barnacles were not recognized as crustaceans until the 1800s, when naturalists discovered that barnacle larvae resemble the larvae of other crustaceans. The remarkable mix of unique traits and crustacean homologies found in barnacles was a major inspiration to Charles Darwin as he developed his theory of evolution.

CONCEPT CHECK 33.4

1. How do nematode and annelid body plans differ?
2. Describe two adaptations that have enabled insects to thrive on land.
3. In contrast to mammalian jaws, which move up and down, the mouthparts of arthropods move side to side. Explain this feature of arthropods in terms of the origin of their mouthparts.
4. **MAKE CONNECTIONS** Traditionally, annelids and arthropods were viewed as closely related because both have body segmentation. Yet DNA sequence data indicate that annelids belong to one clade (Lophotrochozoa) and arthropods to another (Ecdysozoa). Could traditional and molecular hypotheses be tested by studying the expression of *Hox* genes that control body segmentation (see Concept 21.6, pp. 442–447)? Explain.

For suggested answers, see Appendix A.

CONCEPT 33.5

Echinoderms and chordates are deuterostomes

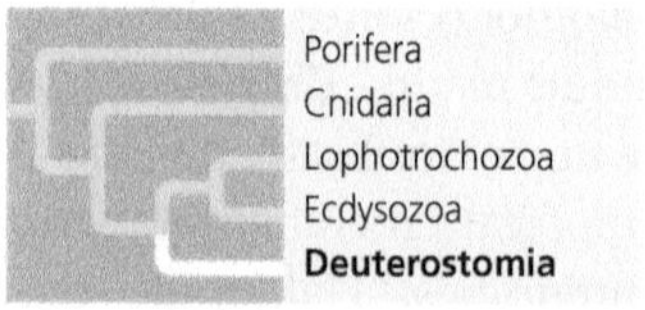

Sea stars, sea urchins, and other echinoderms (phylum Echinodermata) may seem to have little in common with vertebrates (animals that have a backbone) and other members of phylum Chordata. Nevertheless, DNA evidence indicates that echinoderms and chordates are closely related, with both phyla belonging to the Deuterostomia clade of bilaterian animals. Echinoderms and chordates also share features characteristic of a deuterostome mode of development, such as radial cleavage and formation of the anus from the blastopore (see Figure 32.9). As discussed in Chapter 32, however, some animal phyla with members that have deuterostome developmental features, including ectoprocts and brachiopods, are not in the deuterostome clade. Hence, despite its name, the clade Deuterostomia is defined primarily by DNA similarities—not developmental similarities.

Echinoderms

Sea stars (commonly called starfish) and most other **echinoderms** (from the Greek *echin*, spiny, and *derma*, skin) are slow-moving or sessile marine animals. A thin epidermis covers an endoskeleton of hard calcareous plates. Most echinoderms are prickly from skeletal bumps and spines. Unique to echinoderms is the **water vascular system**, a network of hydraulic canals branching into extensions called **tube feet** that function in locomotion and feeding (Figure 33.40). Sexual reproduction of echinoderms usually involves separate male and female individuals that release their gametes into the water.

The internal and external parts of most adult echinoderms radiate from the center, often as five spokes. However, echinoderm larvae have bilateral symmetry. Furthermore, the symmetry of adult echinoderms is not truly radial. For example, the opening (madreporite) of a sea star's water vascular system is not central but shifted to one side.

Living echinoderms are divided into five clades.

Asteroidea: Sea Stars and Sea Daisies

Sea stars have arms radiating from a central disk; the undersurfaces of the arms bear tube feet. By a combination of muscular and chemical actions, the tube feet can attach to or detach from a substrate. The sea star adheres firmly to rocks or creeps along slowly as its tube feet extend, grip, release, extend, and grip again. Although the base of the tube foot has a flattened disk that resembles a suction cup, the gripping action results from adhesive chemicals, not suction (see Figure 33.40).

Sea stars also use their tube feet to grasp prey, such as clams and oysters. The arms of the sea star embrace the closed bivalve, clinging tightly with their tube feet. The sea star then turns part of its stomach inside out, everting it through its mouth and into the narrow opening between the halves of the bivalve's shell. Next, the digestive system of the sea star secretes juices that begin digesting the mollusc within its own shell. The stomach is then brought back inside the seastar's body, where digestion of the mollusc's (now liquefied) body is completed. The ability to begin the digestive process outside of its body allows a sea star to consume bivalves and other prey species that are much larger than its mouth.

Sea stars and some other echinoderms have considerable powers of regeneration. Sea stars can regrow lost arms, and members of one genus can even regrow an entire body from a single arm if part of the central disk remains attached.

The clade Asteroidea, to which sea stars belong, also includes a small group of armless species, the *sea daisies*. Discovered in 1986, only three species of sea daisies are known, all of which live on submerged wood. A sea daisy's body is typically disk-shaped; it has a five-sided organization and measures less than a centimeter in diameter (Figure 33.41). The edge of the body is ringed with small spines. Sea daisies absorb nutrients through a membrane that surrounds their body.

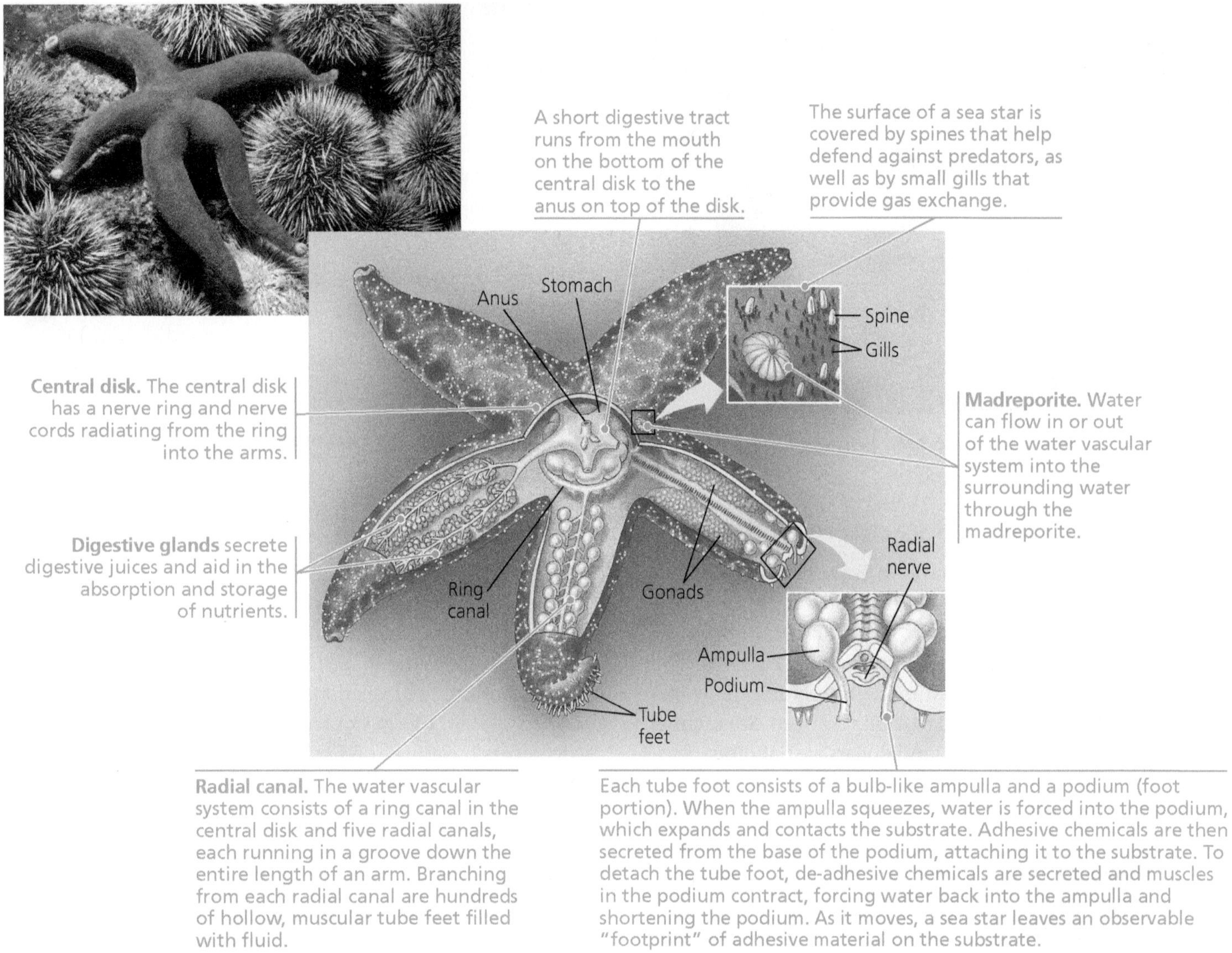

▲ **Figure 33.40 Anatomy of a sea star, an echinoderm.**

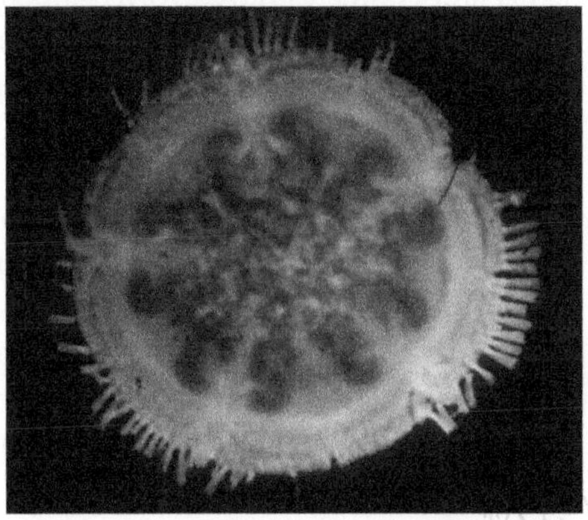

► **Figure 33.41 A sea daisy (clade Asteroidea).**

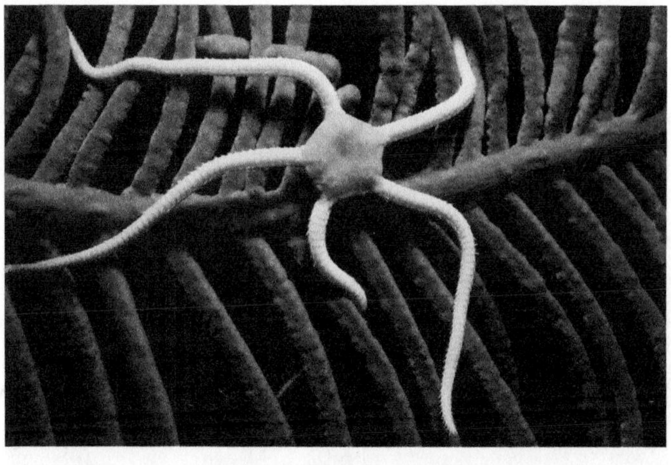

▲ **Figure 33.42 A brittle star (clade Ophiuroidea).**

Ophiuroidea: Brittle Stars

Brittle stars have a distinct central disk and long, flexible arms (Figure 33.42). They move primarily by lashing their arms in serpentine movements. The base of a brittle star tube foot lacks the flattened disk found in sea stars but does secrete adhesive chemicals. Hence, like sea stars and other echinoderms, brittle stars can use their tube feet to grip substrates. Some species are suspension feeders; others are predators or scavengers.

▲ **Figure 33.43 A sea urchin (clade Echinoidea).**

▲ **Figure 33.45 A sea cucumber (clade Holothuroidea).**

Echinoidea: Sea Urchins and Sand Dollars

Sea urchins and sand dollars have no arms, but they do have five rows of tube feet that function in slow movement. Sea urchins also have muscles that pivot their long spines, which aid in locomotion as well as protection (Figure 33.43). The mouth of a sea urchin is ringed by highly complex, jaw-like structures that are well adapted to eating seaweed. Sea urchins are roughly spherical, whereas sand dollars are flat disks.

Crinoidea: Sea Lilies and Feather Stars

Sea lilies live attached to the substrate by a stalk; feather stars crawl about by using their long, flexible arms. Both use their arms in suspension feeding. The arms encircle the mouth, which is directed upward, away from the substrate (Figure 33.44). Crinoidea is an ancient group whose morphology has changed little over the course of evolution; fossilized sea lilies some 500 million years old are extremely similar to present-day members of the clade.

▲ **Figure 33.44 A feather star (clade Crinoidea).**

Holothuroidea: Sea Cucumbers

On casual inspection, sea cucumbers do not look much like other echinoderms. They lack spines, and their endoskeleton is much reduced. They are also elongated in their oral-aboral axis, giving them the shape for which they are named and further disguising their relationship to sea stars and sea urchins (Figure 33.45). Closer examination, however, reveals that sea cucumbers have five rows of tube feet. Some of the tube feet around the mouth are developed as feeding tentacles.

Chordates

Phylum Chordata consists of two subphyla of invertebrates, as well as the hagfishes and the vertebrates. Chordates are bilaterally symmetrical coelomates with segmented bodies. The close relationship between echinoderms and chordates does not mean that one phylum evolved from the other. In fact, echinoderms and chordates have evolved independently of one another for over 500 million years. We will trace the phylogeny of chordates in Chapter 34, focusing on the history of vertebrates.

CONCEPT CHECK 33.5

1. How do sea star tube feet attach to substrates?
2. **WHAT IF?** The insect *Drosophila melanogaster* and the nematode *Caenorhabditis elegans* are prominent model organisms. Are these species the most appropriate invertebrates for making inferences about humans and other vertebrates? Explain.
3. **MAKE CONNECTIONS** Describe how the features and diversity of echinoderms illustrate the unity of life, the diversity of life, and the match between organisms and their environments (see Concept 22.2, pp. 455–460).

For suggested answers, see Appendix A.

33 CHAPTER REVIEW

SUMMARY OF KEY CONCEPTS

The table below summarizes the groups of animals surveyed in this chapter.

Selected Animal Phyla

Key Concept	Clades	Phylum	Description
Concept 33.1 Sponges are basal animals that lack true tissues (pp. 670–671) **?** *Lacking tissues and organs, how do sponges accomplish tasks such as gas exchange, nutrient transport, and waste removal?*	Metazoa	Porifera (sponges)	 Lack true tissues; have choanocytes (collar cells—flagellated cells that ingest bacteria and tiny food particles)
Concept 33.2 Cnidarians are an ancient phylum of eumetazoans (pp. 671–673) **?** *Describe the cnidarian body plan and its two major variations.*	Metazoa, Eumetazoa	Cnidaria (hydras, jellies, sea anemones, corals)	 Unique stinging structures (nematocysts) housed in specialized cells (cnidocytes); diploblastic; radially symmetrical; gastrovascular cavity (digestive compartment with a single opening)
Concept 33.3 Lophotrochozoans, a clade identified by molecular data, have the widest range of animal body forms (pp. 674–683) **?** *Is the lophotrochozoan clade united by unique morphological features shared by all of its members? Explain.*	Metazoa, Eumetazoa, Bilateria, Lophotrochozoa	Platyhelminthes (flatworms)	 Dorsoventrally flattened, unsegmented acoelomates; gastrovascular cavity or no digestive tract
	Metazoa, Eumetazoa, Bilateria, Lophotrochozoa	Rotifera (rotifers)	 Pseudocoelomates with alimentary canal (digestive tube with mouth and anus); jaws (trophi) in pharynx; head with ciliated crown
	Metazoa, Eumetazoa, Bilateria, Lophotrochozoa	Lophophorates: Ectoprocta, Brachiopoda	 Coelomates with lophophores (feeding structures bearing ciliated tentacles)
	Metazoa, Eumetazoa, Bilateria, Lophotrochozoa	Mollusca (clams, snails, squids)	 Coelomates with three main body parts (muscular foot, visceral mass, mantle); coelom reduced; most have hard shell made of calcium carbonate
	Metazoa, Eumetazoa, Bilateria, Lophotrochozoa	Annelida (segmented worms)	 Coelomates with segmented body wall and internal organs (except digestive tract, which is unsegmented)
Concept 33.4 Ecdysozoans are the most species-rich animal group (pp. 683–692) **?** *Describe ecological roles of nematodes and arthropods.*	Metazoa, Eumetazoa, Bilateria, Ecdysozoa	Nematoda (roundworms)	 Cylindrical, unsegmented pseudocoelomates with tapered ends; no circulatory system; undergo ecdysis
	Metazoa, Eumetazoa, Bilateria, Ecdysozoa	Arthropoda (crustaceans, insects, spiders)	 Coelomates with segmented body, jointed appendages, and exoskeleton made of protein and chitin
Concept 33.5 Echinoderms and chordates are deuterostomes (pp. 692–694) **?** *You've read that echinoderms and chordates are closely related and have evolved independently for over 500 million years. Explain how both of these statements can be correct.*	Metazoa, Eumetazoa, Bilateria, Deuterostomia	Echinodermata (sea stars, sea urchins)	 Coelomates with bilaterally symmetrical larvae and five-part body organization as adults; unique water vascular system; endoskeleton
	Metazoa, Eumetazoa, Bilateria, Deuterostomia	Chordata (lancelets, tunicates, vertebrates)	 Coelomates with notochord; dorsal, hollow nerve cord; pharyngeal slits; post-anal tail (see Chapter 34)

TEST YOUR UNDERSTANDING

LEVEL 1: KNOWLEDGE/COMPREHENSION

1. A land snail, a clam, and an octopus all share
   a. a mantle.
   b. a radula.
   c. gills.
   d. embryonic torsion.
   e. distinct cephalization.

2. Which phylum is characterized by animals that have a segmented body?
   a. Cnidaria
   b. Platyhelminthes
   c. Porifera
   d. Arthropoda
   e. Mollusca

3. The water vascular system of echinoderms
   a. functions as a circulatory system that distributes nutrients to body cells.
   b. functions in locomotion and feeding.
   c. is bilateral in organization, even though the adult animal is not bilaterally symmetrical.
   d. moves water through the animal's body during suspension feeding.
   e. is analogous to the gastrovascular cavity of flatworms.

4. Which of the following combinations of phylum and description is *incorrect?*
   a. Echinodermata—bilateral symmetry as a larva, coelom present
   b. Nematoda—roundworms, pseudocoelomate
   c. Cnidaria—radial symmetry, polyp and medusa body forms
   d. Platyhelminthes—flatworms, gastrovascular cavity, acoelomate
   e. Porifera—gastrovascular cavity, coelom present

LEVEL 2: APPLICATION/ANALYSIS

5. In Figure 33.2, which two main clades branch from the most recent common ancestor of the eumetazoans?
   a. Porifera and Cnidaria
   b. Lophotrochozoa and Ecdysozoa
   c. Cnidaria and Bilateria
   d. Rotifera and Deuterostomia
   e. Deuterostomia and Bilateria

6. **MAKE CONNECTIONS** In Figure 33.8, assume that the two medusae shown at step 4 were produced by one polyp colony. Review Concept 12.1 (pp. 229–230) and Concept 13.4 (pp. 257–260), and then use your understanding of mitosis and meiosis to evaluate whether the following sentence is true or false. If false, select the answer that provides the correct reason.

   Although the two medusae are genetically identical, a sperm produced by one will differ genetically from an egg produced by the other.

   a. F (the medusae are genetically identical, but so are the gametes)
   b. F (neither the medusae or the gametes are genetically identical)
   c. F (the medusae are not identical but the gametes are)
   d. T

LEVEL 3: SYNTHESIS/EVALUATION

7. **EVOLUTION CONNECTION**
   DRAW IT Draw a phylogenetic tree of Bilateria that includes the ten phyla of bilaterians discussed in detail in this chapter. Label each branch that leads to a phylum with a C, P, or A, depending on whether members of the phylum are coelomates (C), pseudocoelomates (P), or acoelomates (A). Use your labeled tree to answer the following questions:
   a. For each of the three major clades of bilaterians, what (if anything) can be inferred about whether the common ancestor of the clade had a true coelom?
   b. To what extent has the presence of a true coelom in animals changed over the course of evolution?

8. **SCIENTIFIC INQUIRY**
   Bats emit ultrasonic sounds and then use the returning echoes of those sounds to locate and capture flying insects, such as moths, in the dark. In response to bat attacks, some tiger moths make ultrasonic clicks of their own. Researchers hypothesize that tiger moth clicks likely either (1) jam the bat's sonar or (2) warn the bat about the moth's toxic chemical defenses. The graph below shows two patterns observed in studies of moth capture rates over time.

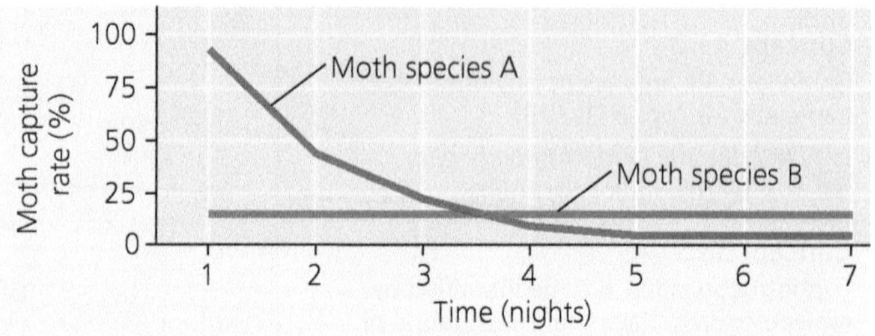

   Bats in these experiments were "naive," meaning that prior to the study the bats had not previously hunted tiger moths. Do the results support hypothesis (1), hypothesis (2), or both? Why did the researchers use naive bats? Explain.

9. **WRITE ABOUT A THEME**
   Structure and Function Write a short essay (100–150 words) that explains how the structure of the digestive tract in different invertebrate groups affects the size of the organisms that they can eat.

For selected answers, see Appendix A.

34

The Origin and Evolution of Vertebrates

▲ Figure 34.1 **What is the relationship of this ancient organism to humans?**

KEY CONCEPTS

34.1 Chordates have a notochord and a dorsal, hollow nerve cord
34.2 Craniates are chordates that have a head
34.3 Vertebrates are craniates that have a backbone
34.4 Gnathostomes are vertebrates that have jaws
34.5 Tetrapods are gnathostomes that have limbs
34.6 Amniotes are tetrapods that have a terrestrially adapted egg
34.7 Mammals are amniotes that have hair and produce milk
34.8 Humans are mammals that have a large brain and bipedal locomotion

OVERVIEW

Half a Billion Years of Backbones

Early in the Cambrian period, some 530 million years ago, an immense variety of invertebrate animals inhabited Earth's oceans. Predators used sharp claws and mandibles to skewer their prey. Many animals had protective spikes or armor as well as modified mouthparts that enabled their bearers to filter food from the water. Worms slithered in the bottom muck, feeding on organic matter. Amidst this bustle, it would have been easy to overlook certain slender, 3-cm-long creatures gliding through the water: *Myllokunmingia fengjiaoa* (Figure 34.1). Although lacking armor and appendages, this ancient species was closely related to one of the most successful groups of animals ever to swim, walk, slither, or fly: the **vertebrates**, which derive their name from vertebrae, the series of bones that make up the vertebral column, or backbone.

For more than 150 million years, vertebrates were restricted to the oceans, but about 365 million years ago, the evolution of limbs in one lineage of vertebrates set the stage for these vertebrates to colonize land. There they diversified into amphibians, reptiles (including birds), and mammals.

There are approximately 52,000 species of vertebrates, a relatively small number compared to, say, the 1 million insect species on Earth. But what vertebrates lack in species diversity they make up for in *disparity*, varying enormously in characteristics such as body mass. Vertebrates include the heaviest animals ever to walk on land, plant-eating dinosaurs as massive as 40,000 kg (more than 13 pickup trucks). They also include the biggest animal ever to exist on Earth, the blue whale, which can exceed a mass of 100,000 kg. On the other end of the spectrum, a fish discovered in 2004 is just 8.4 mm long and has a mass roughly 100 billion times smaller than that of a blue whale.

In this chapter, you will learn about current hypotheses regarding the origins of vertebrates from invertebrate ancestors. We will track the evolution of the vertebrate body plan, from a notochord to a head to a mineralized skeleton. We'll also explore the major groups of vertebrates (both living and extinct), as well as the evolutionary history of our own species.

CONCEPT 34.1

Chordates have a notochord and a dorsal, hollow nerve cord

Vertebrates are members of the phylum Chordata, the chordates. **Chordates** are bilaterian (bilaterally symmetrical) animals, and within Bilateria, they belong to the clade of animals known as Deuterostomia (see Chapter 32). The best-known deuterostomes, aside from vertebrates, are the echinoderms, the group that includes sea stars and sea urchins.

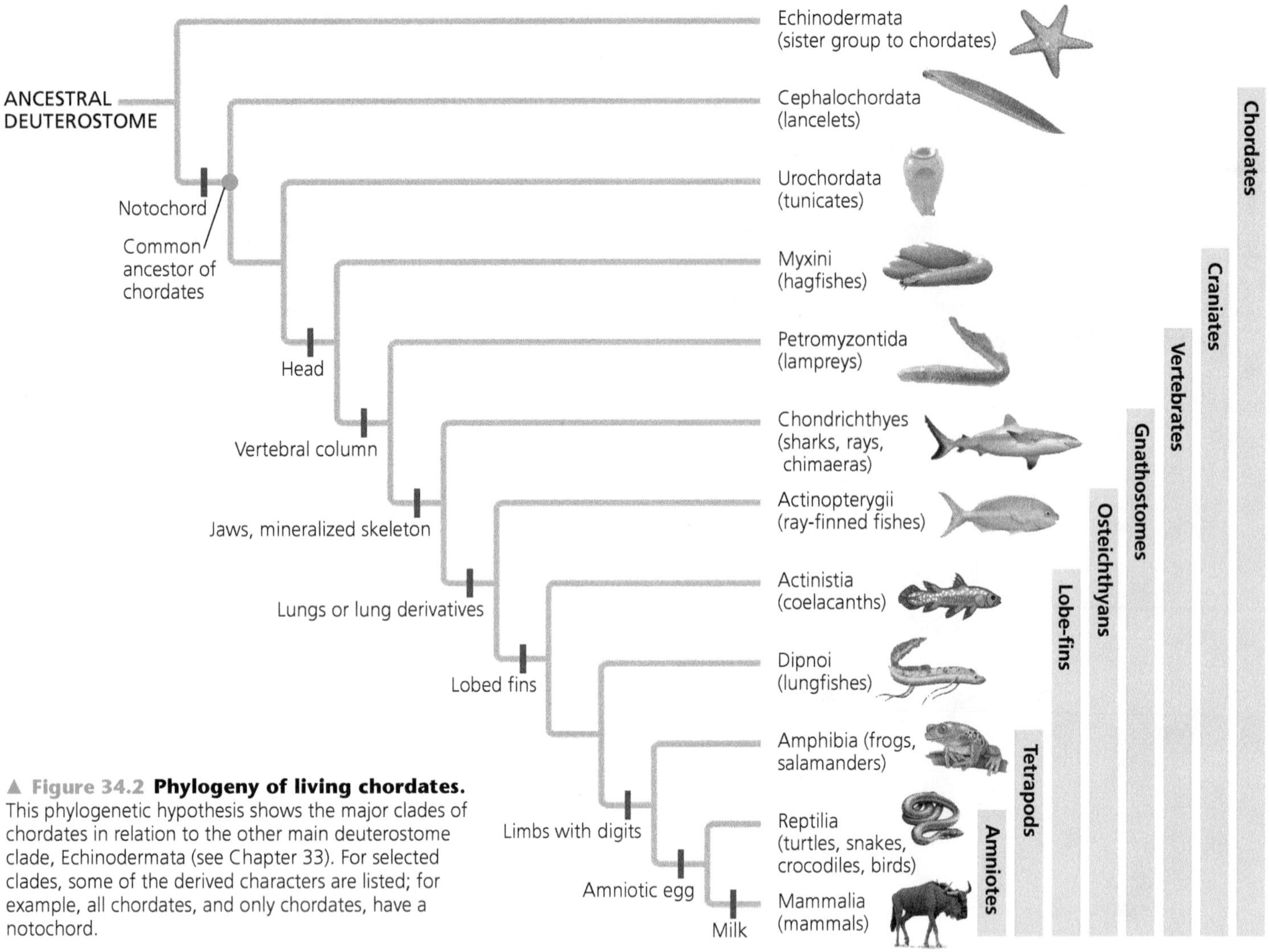

▲ **Figure 34.2 Phylogeny of living chordates.** This phylogenetic hypothesis shows the major clades of chordates in relation to the other main deuterostome clade, Echinodermata (see Chapter 33). For selected clades, some of the derived characters are listed; for example, all chordates, and only chordates, have a notochord.

However, as shown in Figure 34.2, the cephalochordates and the urochordates are two groups of invertebrate deuterostomes that are more closely related to vertebrates than to other invertebrates. Along with the hagfishes and the vertebrates, they make up the chordates.

Derived Characters of Chordates

All chordates share a set of derived characters, though many species possess some of these traits only during embryonic development. Figure 34.3 illustrates four key characters of chordates: a notochord; a dorsal, hollow nerve cord; pharyngeal slits or clefts; and a muscular, post-anal tail.

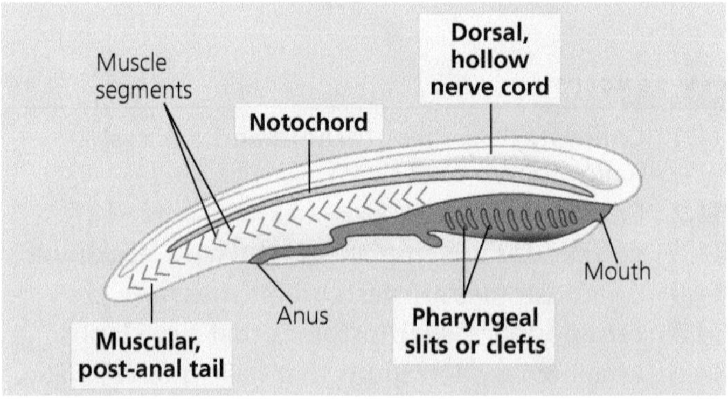

▲ **Figure 34.3 Chordate characteristics.** All chordates possess the four highlighted structural trademarks at some point during their development.

Notochord

Chordates are named for a skeletal structure, the notochord, present in all chordate embryos as well as in some adult chordates. The **notochord** is a longitudinal, flexible rod located between the digestive tube and the nerve cord. It is composed of large, fluid-filled cells encased in fairly stiff, fibrous tissue. The notochord provides skeletal support throughout most of the length of a chordate, and in larvae or adults that retain it, it also provides a firm but flexible structure against which muscles can work during swimming. In most vertebrates, a more complex, jointed skeleton develops around the ancestral notochord, and the adult retains only remnants of the embryonic notochord. In humans, the notochord is reduced and forms part of the gelatinous disks sandwiched between the vertebrae.

Dorsal, Hollow Nerve Cord

The nerve cord of a chordate embryo develops from a plate of ectoderm that rolls into a tube located dorsal to the notochord. The resulting dorsal, hollow nerve cord is unique to chordates. Other animal phyla have solid nerve cords, and in most cases they are ventrally located. The nerve cord of a chordate embryo develops into the central nervous system: the brain and spinal cord.

Pharyngeal Slits or Clefts

The digestive tube of chordates extends from the mouth to the anus. The region just posterior to the mouth is the pharynx. In all chordate embryos, a series of pouches separated by grooves forms along the sides of the pharynx. In most chordates, these grooves (known as **pharyngeal clefts**) develop into slits that open to the outside of the body. These **pharyngeal slits** allow water entering the mouth to exit the body without passing through the entire digestive tract. Pharyngeal slits function as suspension-feeding devices in many invertebrate chordates. In vertebrates (with the exception of vertebrates with limbs, the tetrapods), these slits and the structures that support them have been modified for gas exchange and are known as gill slits. In tetrapods, the pharyngeal clefts do not develop into slits. Instead, they play an important role in the development of parts of the ear and other structures in the head and neck.

Muscular, Post-Anal Tail

Chordates have a tail that extends posterior to the anus, although in many species it is greatly reduced during embryonic development. In contrast, most nonchordates have a digestive tract that extends nearly the whole length of the body. The chordate tail contains skeletal elements and muscles, and it helps propel many aquatic species in the water.

Lancelets

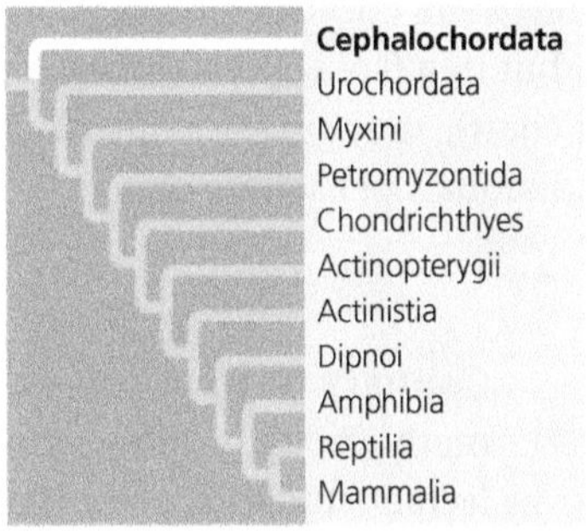

The most basal (earliest-diverging) group of living chordates are animals called **lancelets** (Cephalochordata), which get their name from their bladelike shape (**Figure 34.4**). As larvae, lancelets develop a notochord, a dorsal, hollow nerve cord, numerous pharyngeal slits, and a post-anal tail. The larvae feed on plankton in the water column, alternating between upward swimming and passive sinking. As the larvae sink, they trap plankton and other suspended particles in their pharynx.

Adult lancelets can reach 6 cm in length. They retain key chordate traits, closely resembling the idealized chordate shown in Figure 34.3. Following metamorphosis, an adult lancelet swims down to the seafloor and wriggles backward into the sand, leaving only its anterior end exposed. Cilia draw seawater into the lancelet's mouth. A net of mucus secreted across the pharyngeal slits removes tiny food particles as the water passes through the slits, and the trapped food enters the intestine. The pharynx and pharyngeal slits play a minor role in gas exchange, which occurs mainly across the external body surface.

A lancelet frequently leaves its burrow to swim to a new location. Though feeble swimmers, these invertebrate chordates display, in a simple form, the swimming mechanism of fishes.

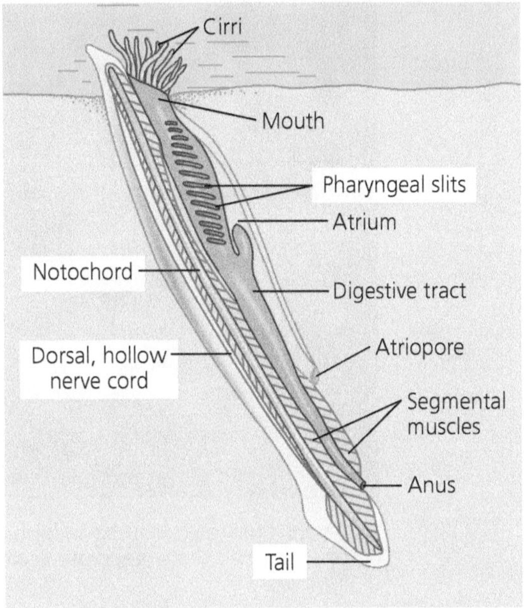

◀ **Figure 34.4 The lancelet *Branchiostoma*, a cephalochordate.** This small invertebrate displays all four main chordate characters. Water enters the mouth and passes through the pharyngeal slits into the atrium, a chamber that vents to the outside via the atriopore; large particles are blocked from entering the mouth by tentacle-like cirri. The serially arranged segmental muscles produce the lancelet's wavelike swimming movements.

Coordinated contraction of muscles arranged like rows of chevrons (<<<<) along the sides of the notochord flexes the notochord, producing side-to-side undulations that thrust the body forward. This serial arrangement of muscles is evidence of the lancelet's segmentation. The muscle segments develop from blocks of mesoderm called *somites*, which are found along each side of the notochord in all chordate embryos.

Globally, lancelets are rare, but in a few regions (including Tampa Bay, along the Florida coast), they occasionally reach densities in excess of 5,000 individuals per square meter.

Tunicates

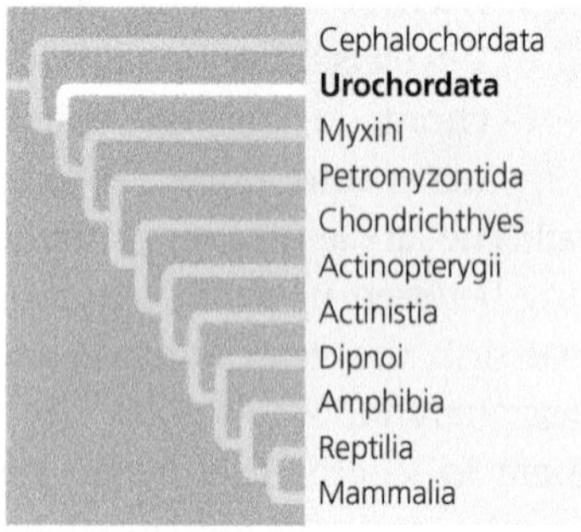

Contrary to what was formerly thought, recent molecular studies suggest that the **tunicates** (Urochordata) are more closely related to other chordates than are lancelets. The chordate characters of tunicates are most apparent during their larval stage, which may be as brief as a few minutes (Figure 34.5a). In many species, the larva uses its tail muscles and notochord to swim through water in search of a suitable substrate on which it can settle, guided by cues it receives from light- and gravity-sensitive cells.

Once a tunicate has settled on a substrate, it undergoes a radical metamorphosis in which many of its chordate characters disappear. Its tail and notochord are resorbed; its nervous system degenerates; and its remaining organs rotate 90°. As an adult, a tunicate draws in water through an incurrent siphon; the water then passes through the pharyngeal slits into a chamber called the atrium and exits through an excurrent siphon (Figure 34.5b and c). Food particles are filtered from the water by a mucous net and transported by cilia to the esophagus. The anus empties into the excurrent siphon. Some tunicate species shoot a jet of water through their excurrent siphon when attacked, earning them the informal name of "sea squirts."

The loss of chordate characters in the adult stage of tunicates appears to have occurred after the tunicate lineage branched off from other chordates. Even the tunicate larva appears to be highly derived. For example, tunicates have 9 *Hox* genes, whereas all other chordates studied to date—including the early-diverging lancelets—share a set of 13 *Hox* genes. The apparent loss of 4 *Hox* genes indicates that the chordate body plan of a tunicate larva is built using a different set of genetic controls than other chordates.

Early Chordate Evolution

Although lancelets and tunicates are relatively obscure animals, they occupy key positions in the history of life and can provide clues about the evolutionary origin of vertebrates. As you have read, for example, lancelets display key chordate characters as adults, and their lineage branches from the base of the chordate phylogenetic tree. These findings suggest that the ancestral chordate may have looked something like a lancelet—that is, it had an anterior end with a mouth; a notochord; a dorsal, hollow nerved cord; pharyngeal slits; and a post-anal tail.

Research on lancelets has also revealed important clues about the evolution of the chordate brain. Rather than a full-fledged brain, lancelets have only a slightly swollen tip on the anterior end of their dorsal nerve cord. But the same *Hox* genes that organize major regions of the forebrain, midbrain,

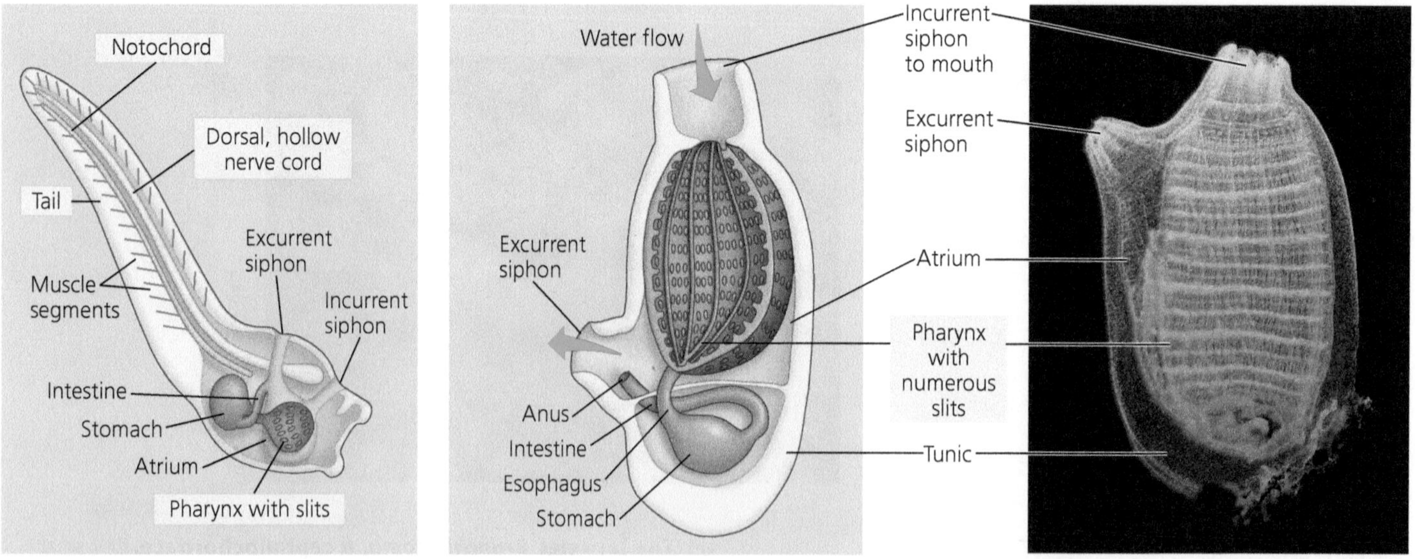

(a) A tunicate larva is a free-swimming but nonfeeding "tadpole" in which all four main characters of chordates are evident.

(b) In the adult, prominent pharyngeal slits function in suspension feeding, but other chordate characters are not obvious.

(c) An adult tunicate, or sea squirt, is a sessile animal (photo is approximately life-sized).

▲ Figure 34.5 **A tunicate, a urochordate.**

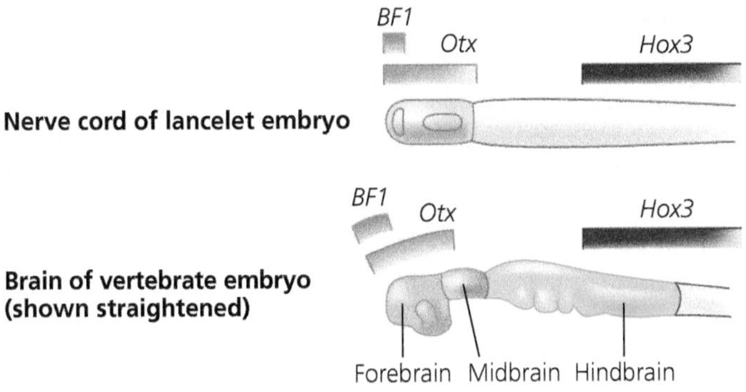

▲ **Figure 34.6 Expression of developmental genes in lancelets and vertebrates.** *Hox* genes (including *BF1*, *Otx*, and *Hox3*) control the development of major regions of the vertebrate brain. These genes are expressed in the same anterior-to-posterior order in lancelets and vertebrates. Each colored bar is positioned above the portion of the brain whose development that gene controls.

MAKE CONNECTIONS *What do these results and those in Figure 21.18 indicate about* Hox *genes and their evolution?*

and hindbrain of vertebrates express themselves in a corresponding pattern in this small cluster of cells in the lancelet's nerve cord (Figure 34.6). This suggests that the vertebrate brain is an elaboration of an ancestral structure similar to the lancelet's simple nerve cord tip.

As for tunicates, their genome has been completely sequenced and can be used to identify genes likely to have been present in early chordates. Researchers taking this approach have suggested that ancestral chordates had genes associated with vertebrate organs such as the heart and thyroid gland. These genes are found in tunicates and vertebrates but are absent from nonchordate invertebrates. In contrast, tunicates lack many genes that in vertebrates are associated with the long-range transmission of nerve impulses. This result suggests that such genes arose in an early vertebrate and are unique to the vertebrate evolutionary lineage.

CONCEPT CHECK 34.1

1. Identify four derived characters that all chordates have at some point during their life.
2. You are a chordate, yet you lack most of the main derived characters of chordates. Explain.
3. **WHAT IF?** Suppose lancelets lacked a gene found in tunicates and vertebrates. Would this imply that the chordates' most recent common ancestor also lacked this gene? Explain.

For suggested answers, see Appendix A.

CONCEPT 34.2

Craniates are chordates that have a head

After the evolution of the basic chordate body plan, that seen in lancelets and tunicate larvae, the next major transition in chordate evolution was the appearance of a head. Chordates with a head are known as **craniates** (from the word *cranium*, skull). The origin of a head—consisting of a brain at the anterior end of the dorsal nerve cord, eyes and other sensory organs, and a skull—enabled chordates to coordinate more complex movement and feeding behaviors. (Note that heads evolved independently in other animal lineages as well; see Chapter 33.)

Derived Characters of Craniates

Living craniates share a set of derived characters that distinguish them from other chordates. As a result of gene duplication, craniates possess two or more sets of *Hox* genes (lancelets and tunicates have only one). Other important families of genes that produce signaling molecules and transcription factors are also duplicated in craniates. Divergence of sequences in the duplicate genes led to additional genetic complexity. This may have made it possible for craniates to develop more complex morphologies than those of lancelets and tunicates.

One feature unique to craniates is the **neural crest**, a collection of cells that appears near the dorsal margins of the closing neural tube in an embryo (Figure 34.7). Neural crest cells disperse throughout the body, where they give rise to a variety of structures, including teeth, some of the bones and cartilage of the skull, the inner layer of skin (dermis) of the facial region, several types of neurons, and the sensory capsules in which eyes and other sense organs develop.

In aquatic craniates, the pharyngeal clefts evolved into gill slits. Unlike the pharyngeal slits of lancelets, which are used primarily for suspension feeding, gill slits are associated with muscles and nerves that allow water to be pumped through

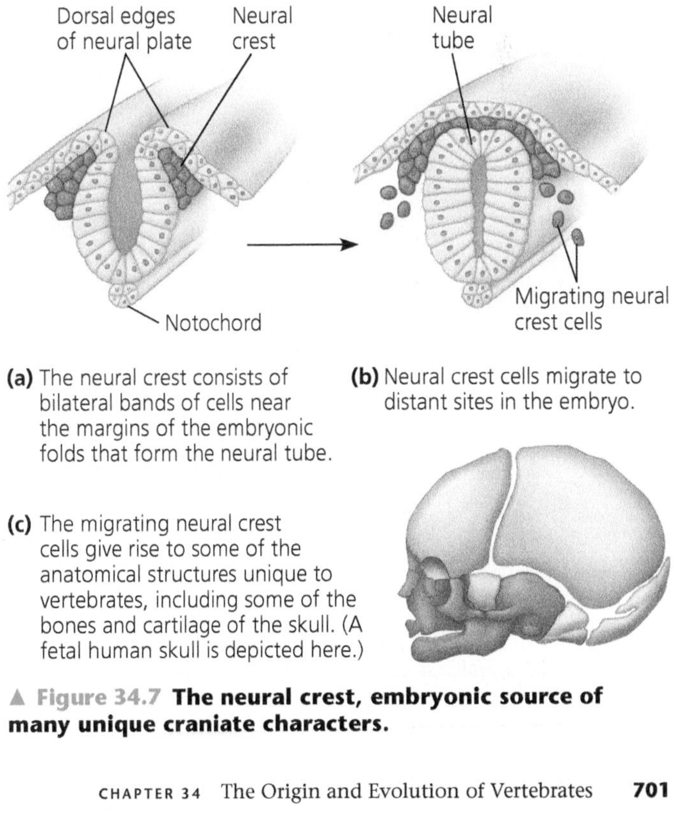

(a) The neural crest consists of bilateral bands of cells near the margins of the embryonic folds that form the neural tube.

(b) Neural crest cells migrate to distant sites in the embryo.

(c) The migrating neural crest cells give rise to some of the anatomical structures unique to vertebrates, including some of the bones and cartilage of the skull. (A fetal human skull is depicted here.)

▲ **Figure 34.7 The neural crest, embryonic source of many unique craniate characters.**

the slits. This pumping can assist in sucking in food, and it facilitates gas exchange. (In terrestrial craniates, the pharyngeal clefts develop into other structures, as we'll explain later.)

Craniates, which are more active than lancelets and tunicates, also have a higher metabolic rate and a much more extensive muscular system. Muscles lining their digestive tract aid digestion by moving food through the tract. Craniates also have a heart with at least two chambers, red blood cells with hemoglobin, and kidneys that remove waste products from the blood.

The Origin of Craniates

In the late 1990s, paleontologists working in China discovered a vast supply of fossils of early chordates that appear to straddle the transition to craniates. The fossils were formed during the Cambrian explosion 530 million years ago, when many groups of animals were diversifying (see Chapter 32).

The most primitive of the fossils are the 3-cm-long *Haikouella* (**Figure 34.8**). In many ways, *Haikouella* resembled a lancelet. Its mouth structure indicates that, like lancelets, it probably was a suspension feeder. However, *Haikouella* also had some of the characters of craniates. For example, it had a well-formed brain, small eyes, and muscle segments along the body, as do the vertebrate fishes. It also had respiratory gills in its pharynx, which all the more basal chordates lack. However, *Haikouella* did not have a skull or ear organs, suggesting that these characters emerged with further innovations to the chordate nervous system. (The earliest "ears" were organs for maintaining balance, a function still performed by the ears of humans and other living vertebrates.)

▲ **Figure 34.8 Fossil of an early chordate.** Discovered in 1999 in southern China, *Haikouella* had eyes and a brain but lacked a skull, a derived trait of craniates. The colors in the illustration are fanciful.

In other Cambrian rocks, paleontologists have found fossils of more advanced chordates, such as *Myllokunmingia* (see Figure 34.1). About the same size as *Haikouella*, *Myllokunmingia* had ear capsules and eye capsules, parts of the skull that surround these organs. Based on these and other characters, paleontologists have identified *Myllokunmingia* as a true craniate.

Hagfishes

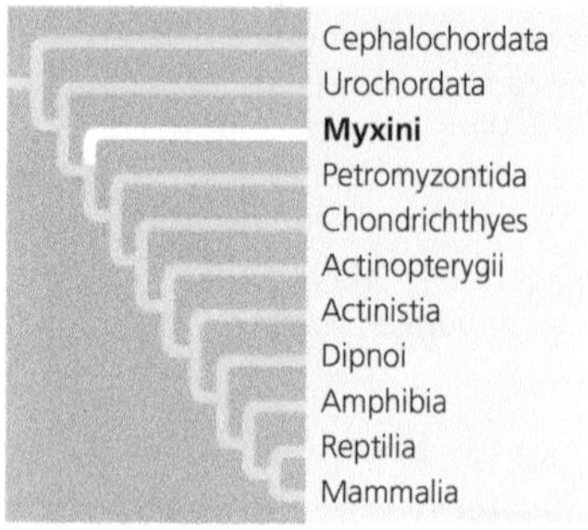

The most basal group of craniates is Myxini, the hagfishes (**Figure 34.9**). Hagfishes have a skull made of cartilage, but they lack jaws and vertebrae. They swim in a snakelike fashion by using their segmental muscles to exert force against their notochord, which they retain in adulthood as a strong, flexible rod of cartilage. Hagfishes have a small brain, eyes, ears, and a nasal opening that connects with the pharynx. Their mouths contain toothlike formations made of the protein keratin.

All of the 30 living species of hagfishes are marine. Measuring up to 60 cm in length, most are bottom-dwelling scavengers that feed on worms and sick or dead fish. Rows of slime glands on a hagfish's flanks secrete a substance that absorbs water, forming a slime that may repulse other scavengers when a hagfish is feeding (see Figure 34.9). When attacked by a predator, a hagfish can produce several liters of slime in less than a minute. The slime coats the gills of the attacking fish, sending it into retreat or even suffocating it. Several teams of biologists and engineers are investigating the properties of hagfish slime in hopes of producing an artificial slime that could act as a space-filling gel. Such a gel might be used, for instance, to curtail bleeding during surgery.

▲ **Figure 34.9 A hagfish.**

CONCEPT CHECK 34.2

1. What characteristics do hagfishes have that lancelets and tunicates lack?
2. Which extinct chordate is more closely related to humans, *Myllokunmingia* or *Haikouella*? Explain.
3. **WHAT IF?** In several different animal lineages, organisms with a head first appeared roughly 530 million years ago. Does this finding constitute proof that having a head is favored by natural selection? Explain.

For suggested answers, see Appendix A.

CONCEPT 34.3

Vertebrates are craniates that have a backbone

During the Cambrian period, a lineage of craniates gave rise to vertebrates. With a more complex nervous system and a more elaborate skeleton than those of their ancestors, vertebrates became more efficient at two essential tasks: capturing food and avoiding being eaten.

Derived Characters of Vertebrates

After vertebrates branched off from other craniates, they underwent another gene duplication, this one involving a group of transcription factor genes called the *Dlx* family. The resulting additional genetic complexity may be associated with innovations in the vertebrate nervous system and skeleton, including a more extensive skull and a backbone composed of vertebrae. In some vertebrates, the vertebrae are little more than small prongs of cartilage arrayed dorsally along the notochord. In the majority of vertebrates, however, the vertebrae enclose the spinal cord and have taken over the mechanical roles of the notochord. Aquatic vertebrates also acquired dorsal, ventral, and anal fins stiffened by bony structures called fin rays, which provide thrust and steering control when swimming after prey or away from predators. Faster swimming was supported by other adaptations, including a more efficient gas exchange system in the gills.

Lampreys

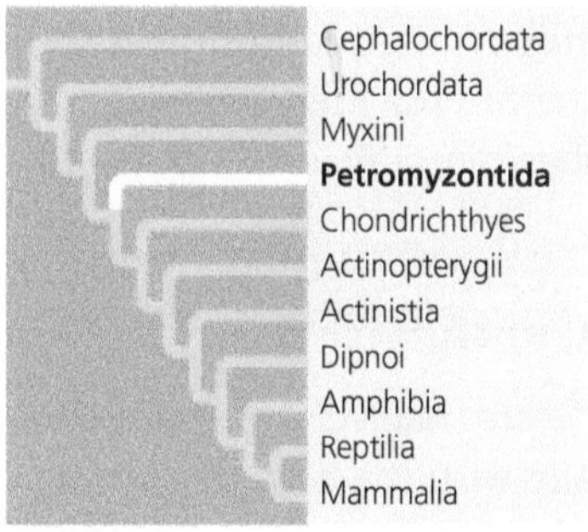

Lampreys (Petromyzontida) are the most basal lineage of living vertebrates. Like hagfishes, lampreys may offer clues to early chordate evolution, but they have also acquired unique characters.

There are about 35 species of lampreys inhabiting various marine and freshwater environments (Figure 34.10). Most are parasites that feed by clamping their round, jawless mouth onto the flank of a live fish. They then use their rasping tongue to penetrate the skin of the fish and ingest the fish's blood.

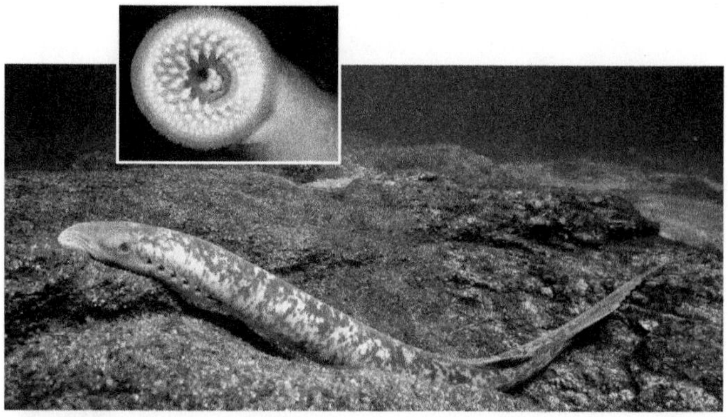

▲ **Figure 34.10 A sea lamprey.** Most lampreys use their mouth (inset) and tongue to bore a hole in the side of a fish. The lamprey then ingests the blood and other tissues of its host.

As larvae, lampreys live in freshwater streams. The larva is a suspension feeder that resembles a lancelet and spends much of its time partially buried in sediment. Some species of lampreys feed only as larvae; following several years in streams, they mature sexually, reproduce, and die within a few days. Most lampreys, however, migrate to the sea or lakes as they mature into adults. Sea lampreys (*Petromyzon marinus*) have invaded the Great Lakes over the past 170 years and have devastated a number of fisheries there.

The skeleton of lampreys is made of cartilage. Unlike the cartilage found in most vertebrates, lamprey cartilage contains no collagen. Instead, it is a stiff matrix of other proteins. The notochord of lampreys persists as the main axial skeleton in the adult, as it does in hagfishes. However, lampreys also have a flexible sheath around their rodlike notochord. Along the length of this sheath, pairs of cartilaginous projections related to vertebrae extend dorsally, partially enclosing the nerve cord.

Fossils of Early Vertebrates

After the ancestors of lampreys branched off from other vertebrates during the Cambrian period, many other lineages of vertebrates emerged. Like lampreys, the early members of these lineages lacked jaws, but the resemblance stopped there.

Conodonts were slender, soft-bodied vertebrates with prominent eyes controlled by numerous muscles. Most conodonts were 3–10 cm in length, although some may have been as long as 30 cm. They probably hunted with the help of their large eyes, impaling prey on a set of barbed hooks at the anterior end of their mouth. These hooks were made of dental tissues that were *mineralized*—composed of minerals such as calcium that provide rigidity (Figure 34.11). The food was then passed back to the pharynx, where a different set of dental elements sliced and crushed the food.

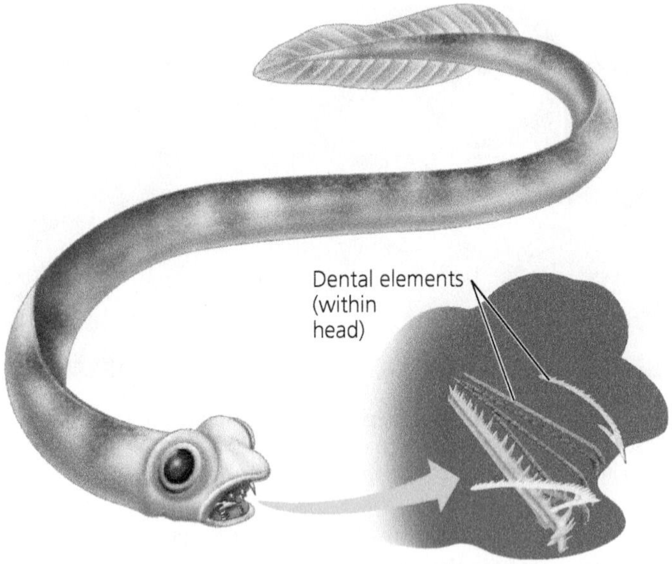

▲ **Figure 34.11 A conodont.** Conodonts were early vertebrates that lived from the late Cambrian until the late Triassic. Unlike lampreys, conodonts had mineralized mouthparts, which they used for either predation or scavenging.

Conodonts were extremely abundant for over 300 million years. Their fossilized dental elements are so plentiful that they have been used for decades by petroleum geologists as guides to the age of rock layers in which they search for oil. (These elements also gave conodonts their name, which means "cone teeth.")

Vertebrates with additional innovations emerged during the Ordovician, Silurian, and Devonian periods. These vertebrates had paired fins and, as in lampreys, an inner ear with two semicircular canals that provided a sense of balance. Although they, too, lacked jaws, they had a muscular pharynx, which they may have used to suck in bottom-dwelling organisms or detritus. They were also armored with mineralized bone, which covered varying amounts of their body (**Figure 34.12**). The armor, which in some species included spines, may have offered protection from predators. There were many species of these jawless, armored swimming vertebrates, but they all became extinct by the end of the Devonian period.

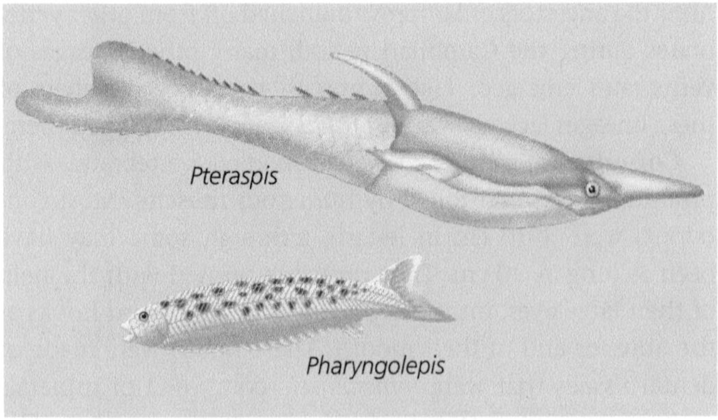

▲ **Figure 34.12 Jawless armored vertebrates.** *Pteraspis* and *Pharyngolepis* were two of many genera of jawless vertebrates that emerged during the Ordovician, Silurian, and Devonian periods.

Origins of Bone and Teeth

The human skeleton is heavily mineralized bone, whereas cartilage plays a fairly minor role. But a bony skeleton was a relatively late development in the history of vertebrates. As we've seen, the vertebrate skeleton evolved initially as a structure made of unmineralized cartilage.

What initiated the process of mineralization in vertebrates? One hypothesis is that mineralization was associated with a transition in feeding mechanisms. Early chordates probably were suspension feeders, like lancelets, but over time they became larger and were able to ingest larger particles, including some small animals. The earliest known mineralized structures in vertebrates—conodont dental elements—were an adaptation that may have allowed these animals to become scavengers and predators. In addition, when the bony armor of later jawless vertebrates was examined under the microscope, scientists found that it was composed of small tooth-like structures. These findings suggest that mineralization of the vertebrate body may have begun in the mouth and later was incorporated into protective armor. Only in more derived vertebrates did the endoskeleton begin to mineralize, starting with the skull. As you'll read in the next section, more recent lineages of vertebrates underwent even further mineralization.

CONCEPT CHECK 34.3

1. How are differences in the anatomy of lampreys and conodonts reflected in each animal's feeding method?
2. **WHAT IF?** Suggest key roles that mineralized bone might have played in early vertebrates.

For suggested answers, see Appendix A.

CONCEPT 34.4

Gnathostomes are vertebrates that have jaws

Hagfishes and lampreys are survivors from the early Paleozoic era, when jawless craniates were common. Since then, jawless vertebrates have been far outnumbered by jawed vertebrates, known as **gnathostomes**. Living gnathostomes are a diverse group that includes sharks and their relatives, ray-finned fishes, lobe-finned fishes, amphibians, reptiles (including birds), and mammals.

Derived Characters of Gnathostomes

Gnathostomes ("jaw mouth") are named for their jaws, hinged structures that, especially with the help of teeth, enable gnathostomes to grip food items firmly and slice them.

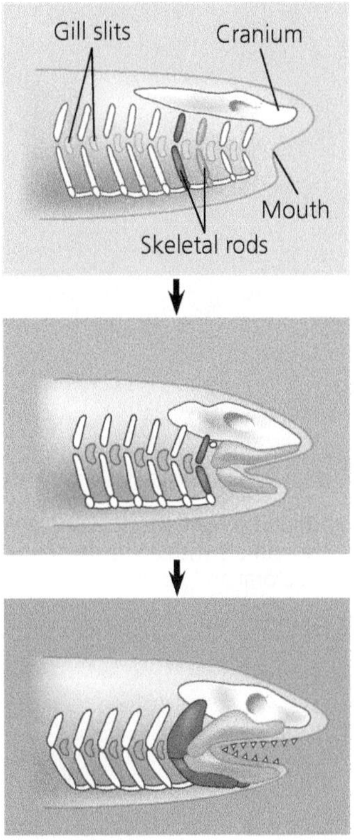

▶ Figure 34.13 **Hypothesis for the evolution of vertebrate jaws.** The skeleton of the jaws and their supports may have evolved from two pairs of skeletal rods (red and green) located between gill slits near the mouth. According to this hypothesis, pairs of rods anterior to those that formed the jaws were either lost or incorporated into the cranium or jaws.

▲ Figure 34.14 **Fossil of an early gnathostome.** The placoderm *Dunkleosteus* grew up to 10 m in length. A 2006 analysis of its jaw structure concluded that *Dunkleosteus* could exert a force of 560 kg/cm^2 (8,000 pounds per square inch) at the tip of its jaws.

According to one hypothesis, gnathostome jaws evolved by modification of the skeletal rods that had previously supported the anterior pharyngeal (gill) slits (Figure 34.13). The remaining gill slits, no longer required for suspension feeding, remained as the major sites of respiratory gas exchange with the external environment.

Gnathostomes share other derived characters besides jaws. The common ancestors of all gnathostomes underwent an additional duplication of *Hox* genes, such that the single set present in early chordates became four. In fact, the entire genome appears to have duplicated, and together these genetic changes likely enabled the origin of jaws and other novel features in gnathostomes. The gnathostome forebrain is enlarged compared to that of other craniates, mainly in association with enhanced senses of smell and vision. Another characteristic of aquatic gnathostomes is the **lateral line system**, organs that form a row along each side of the body and are sensitive to vibrations in the surrounding water. Precursors of these organs were present in the head shields of some jawless vertebrates.

Fossil Gnathostomes

Gnathostomes appeared in the fossil record in the late Ordovician period, about 450 million years ago, and steadily became more diverse. Their success probably resulted from a combination of anatomical features: Their paired fins and tail (which were also found in jawless vertebrates) allowed them to swim efficiently after prey, and their jaws enabled them to grab prey or simply bite off chunks of flesh.

The earliest gnathostomes in the fossil record include extinct lineages of armored vertebrates known as **placoderms**, which means "plate-skinned." Most placoderms were less than a meter long, though some giants measured more than 10 m (Figure 34.14). Other groups of jawed vertebrates, collectively called **acanthodians**, emerged at roughly the same time and radiated during the Silurian and Devonian periods (444–359 million years ago). Placoderms had disappeared by 359 million years ago, and acanthodians became extinct about 70 million years later.

In the past several years, new fossil discoveries have revealed that 450–420 million years ago was a period of tumultuous evolutionary change. Gnathostomes that lived during this period had highly variable forms, and by 420 million years ago, they had diverged into the three lineages of jawed vertebrates that survive today: chondrichthyans, ray-finned fishes, and lobe-fins.

Chondrichthyans (Sharks, Rays, and Their Relatives)

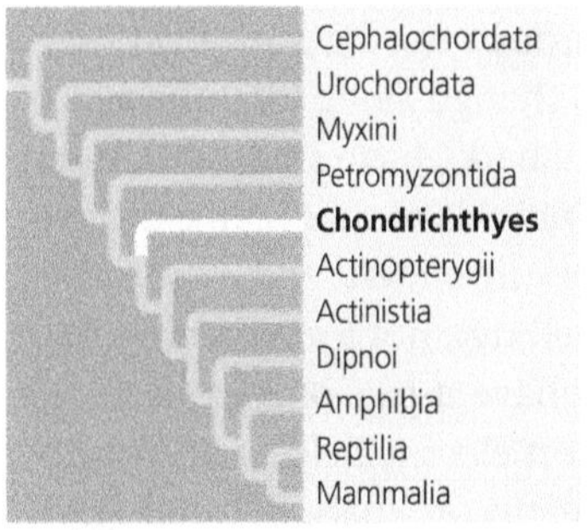

Sharks, rays, and their relatives include some of the biggest and most successful vertebrate predators in the oceans. They belong to the clade Chondrichthyes, which means "cartilage fish." As their name indicates, the **chondrichthyans** have a skeleton composed predominantly of cartilage, though often impregnated with calcium.

When the name Chondrichthyes was first coined in the 1800s, scientists thought that chondrichthyans represented an early stage in the evolution of the vertebrate skeleton and that mineralization had evolved only in more derived lineages (such as "bony fishes"). However, as conodonts and armored jawless vertebrates demonstrate, the mineralization of the vertebrate skeleton had already begun before the chondrichthyan lineage branched off from other vertebrates. Moreover, bone-like tissues have been found in early chondrichthyans, such as the fin skeleton of a shark that lived in the Carboniferous period. Traces of bone can also be found in living chondrichthyans—in their scales, at the base of their teeth, and, in some sharks, in a thin layer on the surface of their vertebrae. Such findings strongly suggest that the restricted distribution of bone in the chondrichthyan body is a derived condition, emerging after chondrichthyans diverged from other gnathostomes.

There are about 1,000 species of living chondrichthyans. The largest and most diverse group consists of the sharks, rays, and skates (**Figure 34.15a** and **b**). A second group is composed of a few dozen species of ratfishes, or chimaeras (**Figure 34.15c**).

Most sharks have a streamlined body and are swift swimmers, but they do not maneuver very well. Powerful movements of the trunk and the tail fin propel them forward. The dorsal fins function mainly as stabilizers, and the paired pectoral (fore) and pelvic (hind) fins are important for maneuvering. Although a shark gains buoyancy by storing a large amount of oil in its huge liver, the animal is still more dense than water, and if it stops swimming it sinks. Continual swimming also ensures that water flows into the shark's mouth and out through the gills, where gas exchange occurs. However, some sharks and many skates and rays spend a good deal of time resting on the seafloor. When resting, they use muscles of their jaws and pharynx to pump water over the gills.

The largest sharks and rays are suspension feeders that consume plankton. Most sharks, however, are carnivores that swallow their prey whole or use their powerful jaws and sharp teeth to tear flesh from animals too large to swallow in one piece. Sharks have several rows of teeth that gradually move to the front of the mouth as old teeth are lost. The digestive tract of many sharks is proportionately shorter than that of many other vertebrates. Within the shark intestine is a *spiral valve*, a corkscrew-shaped ridge that increases surface area and prolongs the passage of food through the digestive tract.

Acute senses are adaptations that go along with the active, carnivorous lifestyle of sharks. Sharks have sharp vision but cannot distinguish colors. The nostrils of sharks, like those of most aquatic vertebrates, open into dead-end cups. They function only for olfaction (smelling), not for breathing. Like some other vertebrates, sharks have a pair of regions in the skin of their head that can detect electric fields generated by the muscle contractions of nearby animals. Like all (nonmammalian) aquatic vertebrates, sharks have no eardrums, structures that terrestrial vertebrates use to transmit sound waves in air to the auditory organs. Sound reaches a shark through water, and the animal's entire body transmits the sound to the hearing organs of the inner ear.

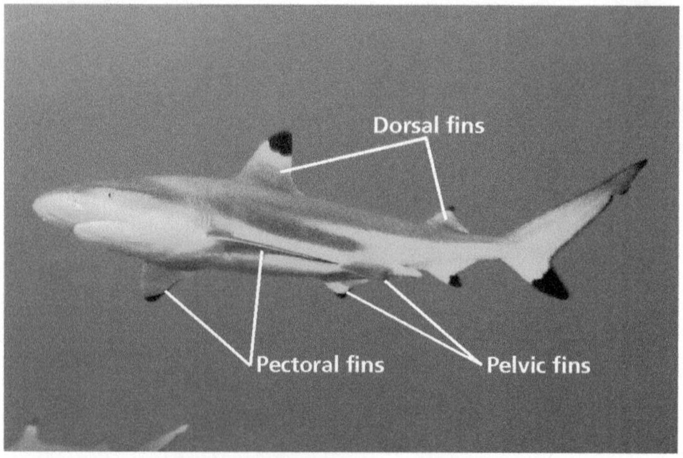

(a) Blacktip reef shark (*Carcharhinus melanopterus*). Sharks are fast swimmers with acute senses. Like all gnathosomes, they have paired pectoral and pelvic fins.

(b) Southern stingray (*Dasyatis americana*). Most rays are bottom-dwellers that feed on molluscs and crustaceans. Some rays cruise in open water and scoop food into their gaping mouth.

(c) Spotted ratfish (*Hydrolagus colliei*). Ratfishes, or chimaeras, typically live at depths greater than 80 m and feed on shrimp, molluscs, and sea urchins. Some species have a venomous spine at the front of their first dorsal fin.

▲ **Figure 34.15 Chondrichthyans.**

Shark eggs are fertilized internally. The male has a pair of claspers on its pelvic fins that transfer sperm into the reproductive tract of the female. Some species of sharks are **oviparous**; they lay eggs that hatch outside the mother's body. These sharks release their eggs after encasing them in protective coats. Other species are **ovoviviparous**; they retain the fertilized eggs in the oviduct. Nourished by the egg yolk, the embryos develop into young that are born after hatching within the uterus. A few species are **viviparous**; the young develop within the uterus and obtain nourishment prior to birth by receiving nutrients from the mother's blood through a yolk sac placenta, by absorbing a nutritious fluid produced by the uterus, or by eating other eggs. The reproductive tract of the shark empties along with the excretory system and digestive tract into the **cloaca**, a common chamber that has a single opening to the outside.

Although rays are closely related to sharks, they have adopted a very different lifestyle. Most rays are bottom-dwellers that feed by using their jaws to crush molluscs and crustaceans. They have a flattened shape and use their greatly enlarged pectoral fins like water wings to propel themselves through the water. The tail of many rays is whiplike and, in some species, bears venomous barbs that function in defense.

Chondrichthyans have thrived for over 400 million years. Today, however, they are severely threatened with overfishing. A recent report indicated that shark stocks in the northwest Atlantic had declined 75% over a 15-year period.

Ray-Finned Fishes and Lobe-Fins

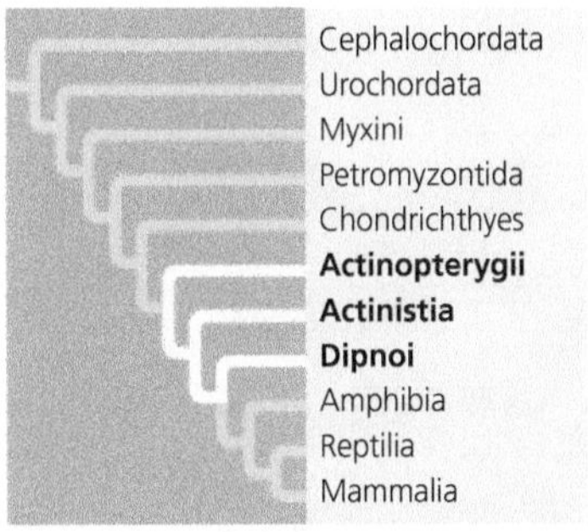

The vast majority of vertebrates belong to the clade of gnathostomes called Osteichthyes. Unlike chondrichthyans, nearly all living **osteichthyans** have an ossified (bony) endoskeleton with a hard matrix of calcium phosphate. Like many other taxonomic names, the name Osteichthyes ("bony fish") was coined long before the advent of phylogenetic systematics. When it was originally defined, the group excluded tetrapods, but we now know that such a taxon would be paraphyletic (see Figure 34.2). Therefore, systematists today include tetrapods along with bony fishes in the clade Osteichthyes. Clearly, the name of the group does not accurately describe all of its members.

In this section, we'll discuss the aquatic osteichthyans known informally as fishes. Most fishes breathe by drawing water over four or five pairs of gills located in chambers covered by a protective bony flap called the **operculum** (Figure 34.16). Water is drawn into the mouth, through the pharynx, and out between the gills by movement of the operculum and contraction of muscles surrounding the gill chambers.

Most fishes can control their buoyancy with an air sac known as a **swim bladder**. Movement of gases from the blood to the swim bladder increases buoyancy, making the animal rise; transfer of gas back to the blood causes the animal to sink. Charles Darwin proposed that the lungs of tetrapods evolved from swim bladders, but strange as it may sound, the opposite seems to be true. Osteichthyans in many early-branching lineages have lungs, which they use to breathe air as a supplement to gas exchange in their gills. The weight of evidence indicates that lungs arose in early osteichthyans; later, swim bladders evolved from lungs in some lineages.

In nearly all fishes, the skin is covered by flattened, bony scales that differ in structure from the tooth-like scales of sharks. Glands in the skin secrete a slimy mucus over the skin, an adaptation that reduces drag during swimming. Like the ancient aquatic gnathostomes mentioned earlier, fishes have a lateral line system, which is evident as a row of tiny pits in the skin on either side of the body.

The details of fish reproduction vary extensively. Most species are oviparous, reproducing by external fertilization after the female sheds large numbers of small eggs. However, internal fertilization and birthing characterize other species.

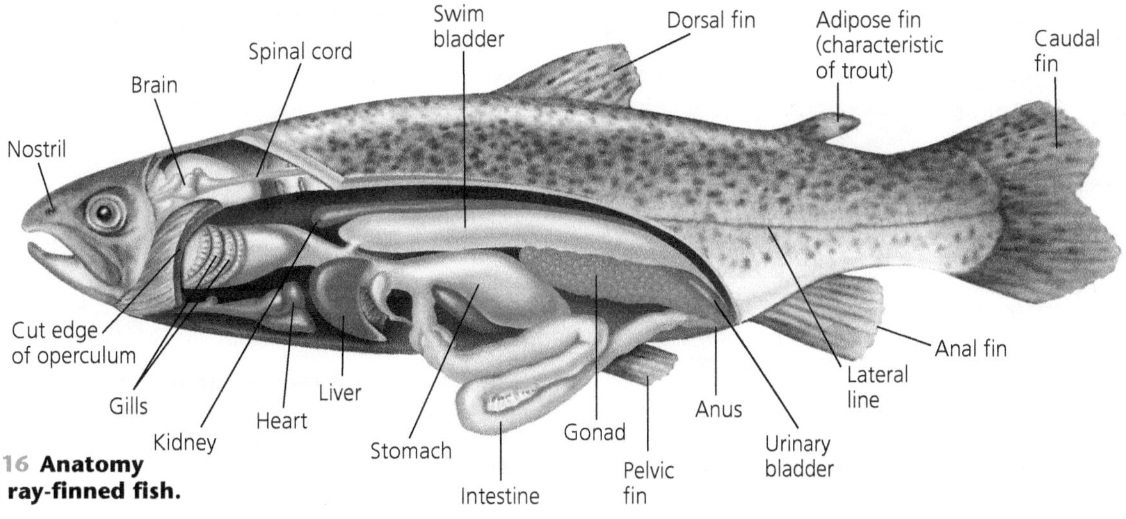

▲ Figure 34.16 **Anatomy of a trout, a ray-finned fish.**

Ray-Finned Fishes

Nearly all the aquatic osteichthyans familiar to us are among the over 27,000 species of **ray-finned fishes** (Actinopterygii) (**Figure 34.17**). Named for the bony rays that support their fins, the ray-finned fishes originated during the Silurian period (444–416 million years ago). The group has diversified greatly since that time, as suggested by modifications in body form and fin structure that affect maneuvering, defense, and other functions (see Figure 34.17).

▲ Yellowfin tuna (*Thunnus albacares*) is a fast-swimming, schooling fish that is commercially important worldwide.

► Native to coral reefs of the Pacific Ocean, the brightly colored red lionfish (*Pterois volitans*) can inject venom through its spines, causing a severe and painful reaction in humans.

▲ The sea horse has a highly modified body form, as exemplified by *Hippocampus ramulosus*, shown above. Sea horses are unusual among animals in that the male carries the young during their embryonic development.

▲ The fine-spotted moray eel (*Gymnothorax dovii*) is a predator that ambushes prey from crevices in its coral reef habitat.

▲ **Figure 34.17 Ray-finned fishes (Actinopterygii).**

Ray-finned fishes serve as a major source of protein for humans, who have harvested them for thousands of years. However, industrial-scale fishing operations appear to have driven some of the world's biggest fisheries to collapse. For example, after decades of abundant harvests, in the 1990s the catch of cod (*Gadus morhua*) in the northwest Atlantic plummeted to just 5% of its historic maximum, bringing codfishing there to a near halt. Despite ongoing restrictions on the fishery, cod populations have yet to recover to sustainable levels. Ray-finned fishes also face other pressures from humans, such as the diversion of rivers by dams. Changing water flow patterns can hamper the fishes' ability to obtain food and interferes with migratory pathways and spawning grounds.

Lobe-Fins

Like the ray-finned fishes, the other major lineage of osteichthyans, the **lobe-fins** (Sarcopterygii), also originated during the Silurian period (**Figure 34.18**). The key derived character of lobe-fins is the presence of rod-shaped bones surrounded by a thick layer of muscle in their pectoral and pelvic fins. During the Devonian (416–359 million years ago), many lobe-fins lived in brackish waters, such as in coastal wetlands. There they may have used their lobed fins to swim and "walk" underwater across the substrate (as do some living lobe-fins). Some Devonian lobe-fins were gigantic predators. It is not uncommon to find spike-shaped fossils of Devonian lobe-fin teeth as big as your thumb.

By the end of the Devonian period, lobe-fin diversity was dwindling, and today only three lineages survive. One lineage,

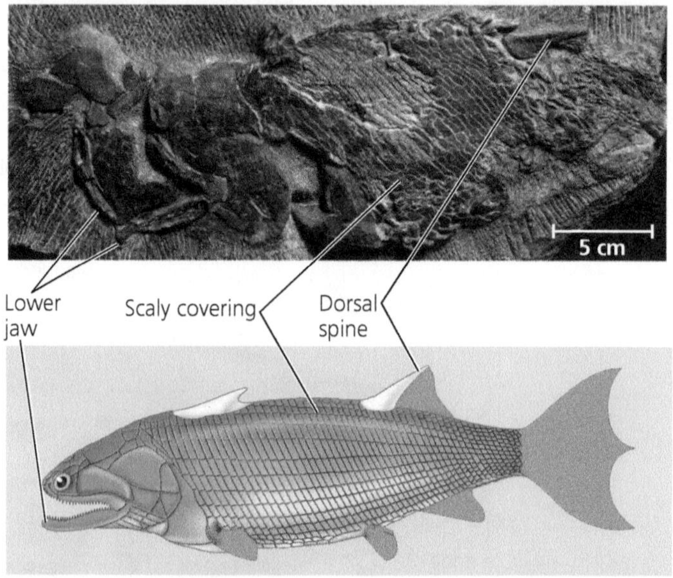

▲ **Figure 34.18 A reconstruction of an ancient lobe-fin.** Discovered in 2009, *Guiyu oneiros* is the earliest known lobe-fin, dating to 420 million years ago. The fossil of this species was nearly complete, allowing for an accurate reconstruction.

▲ **Figure 34.19 A coelacanth (*Latimeria*).** These lobe-fins were found living off the coasts of southern Africa and Indonesia.

the coelacanths (Actinistia), was thought to have become extinct 75 million years ago. However, in 1938, fishermen caught a living coelacanth off the east coast of South Africa (Figure 34.19). Until the 1990s, all subsequent discoveries were near the Comoros Islands in the western Indian Ocean. Since 1999, coelacanths have also been found at various places along the eastern coast of Africa and in the eastern Indian Ocean, near Indonesia. The Indonesian population may represent a second species.

The second lineage of living lobe-fins, the lungfishes (Dipnoi), is represented today by six species in three genera, all of which are found in the Southern Hemisphere. Lungfishes arose in the ocean but today are found only in fresh water, generally in stagnant ponds and swamps. They surface to gulp air into lungs connected to their pharynx. Lungfishes also have gills, which are the main organs for gas exchange in Australian lungfishes. When ponds shrink during the dry season, some lungfishes can burrow into the mud and estivate (wait in a state of torpor; see Chapter 40).

The third lineage of lobe-fins that survives today is far more diverse than the coelacanths or the lungfishes. During the mid-Devonian, these organisms adapted to life on land and gave rise to vertebrates with limbs and feet, called tetrapods—a lineage that includes humans. The tetrapod clade is the topic of the next section.

CONCEPT CHECK 34.4

1. What derived characters do sharks and tuna share? What are some characteristics that distinguish tuna from sharks?
2. Describe key adaptations of aquatic gnathostomes.
3. **WHAT IF?** Imagine that we could replay the history of life. Is it possible that a group of vertebrates that colonized land could have arisen from aquatic gnathostomes other than the lobe-fins? Explain.

For suggested answers, see Appendix A.

CONCEPT 34.5

Tetrapods are gnathostomes that have limbs

One of the most significant events in vertebrate history took place about 365 million years ago, when the fins of some lobe-fins evolved into the limbs and feet of tetrapods. Until then, all vertebrates had shared the same basic fishlike anatomy. After tetrapods moved onto land, they took on many new forms, from leaping frogs to flying eagles to bipedal humans.

Derived Characters of Tetrapods

The most significant character of **tetrapods** gives the group its name, which means "four feet" in Greek. In place of pectoral and pelvic fins, tetrapods have limbs with digits. Limbs support a tetrapod's weight on land, while feet with digits efficiently transmit muscle-generated forces to the ground when it walks.

Life on land brought numerous other changes to the tetrapod body plan. In tetrapods, the head is separated from the body by a neck that originally had one vertebra on which the skull could move up and down. Later, with the origin of a second vertebra in the neck, the head could also swing from side to side. The bones of the pelvic girdle, to which the hind legs are attached, are fused to the backbone, permitting forces generated by the hind legs against the ground to be transferred to the rest of the body. Except for some fully aquatic species (such as the axolotl discussed below), the adults of living tetrapods do not have gills; during embryonic development, the pharyngeal clefts instead give rise to parts of the ears, certain glands, and other structures.

As you will see, some of these characters were dramatically altered or lost in various lineages of tetrapods. In birds, for example, the pectoral limbs became wings, and in whales, the entire body converged toward a fishlike shape.

The Origin of Tetrapods

As you have read, the Devonian coastal wetlands were home to a wide range of lobe-fins. Those that entered particularly shallow, oxygen-poor water could use their lungs to breathe air. Some species probably used their stout fins to help them move across logs or the muddy bottom. Thus, the tetrapod body plan did not evolve "out of nowhere" but was simply a modification of a preexisting body plan.

The recent discovery of a fossil called *Tiktaalik* has provided new details on how this process occurred. Like a fish, this species had fins, gills, and lungs, and its body was covered in scales. But unlike a fish, *Tiktaalik* had a full set of ribs

▼ Figure 34.20
IMPACT

Discovery of a "Fishapod": *Tiktaalik*

Paleontologists were on the hunt for fossils that could shed light on the evolutionary origin of tetrapods. Based on the ages of previously discovered fossils, researchers were looking for a dig site with rocks about 365–385 million years old. Ellesmere Island, in the Canadian Arctic, was one of the few such sites likely to contain fossils, because it was once a river. The search at this site was rewarded by the discovery of fossils of a 375-million-year-old lobe-fin, named *Tiktaalik*. As shown in the chart and photographs below, *Tiktaalik* exhibits both fish and tetrapod characters. (Figure 34.21, on the facing page, includes an artist's conception of what *Tiktaalik* might have looked like.)

WHY IT MATTERS As the most tetrapod-like fish known, *Tiktaalik* documents key steps in the vertebrate transition from water to land. Since *Tiktaalik* predates the oldest known tetrapod by 10 million years, its features suggest that key "tetrapod" traits, such as a wrist, ribs, and a neck, were in fact ancestral to the tetrapod lineage. The discovery also shows the predictive capacity of paleontology in identifying likely locations of fossils of interest.

FURTHER READING E. B. Daeschler, N. H. Shubin, and F. A. Jenkins, A Devonian tetrapod-like fish and the evolution of the tetrapod body plan, *Nature* 440:757–763 (2006).

MAKE CONNECTIONS Describe how *Tiktaalik*'s features illustrate Darwin's concept of descent with modification (see Concept 22.2, pp. 457–460).

Fish Characters	Tetrapod Characters
Scales	Neck
Fins	Ribs
Gills and lungs	Fin skeleton
	Flat skull
	Eyes on top of skull

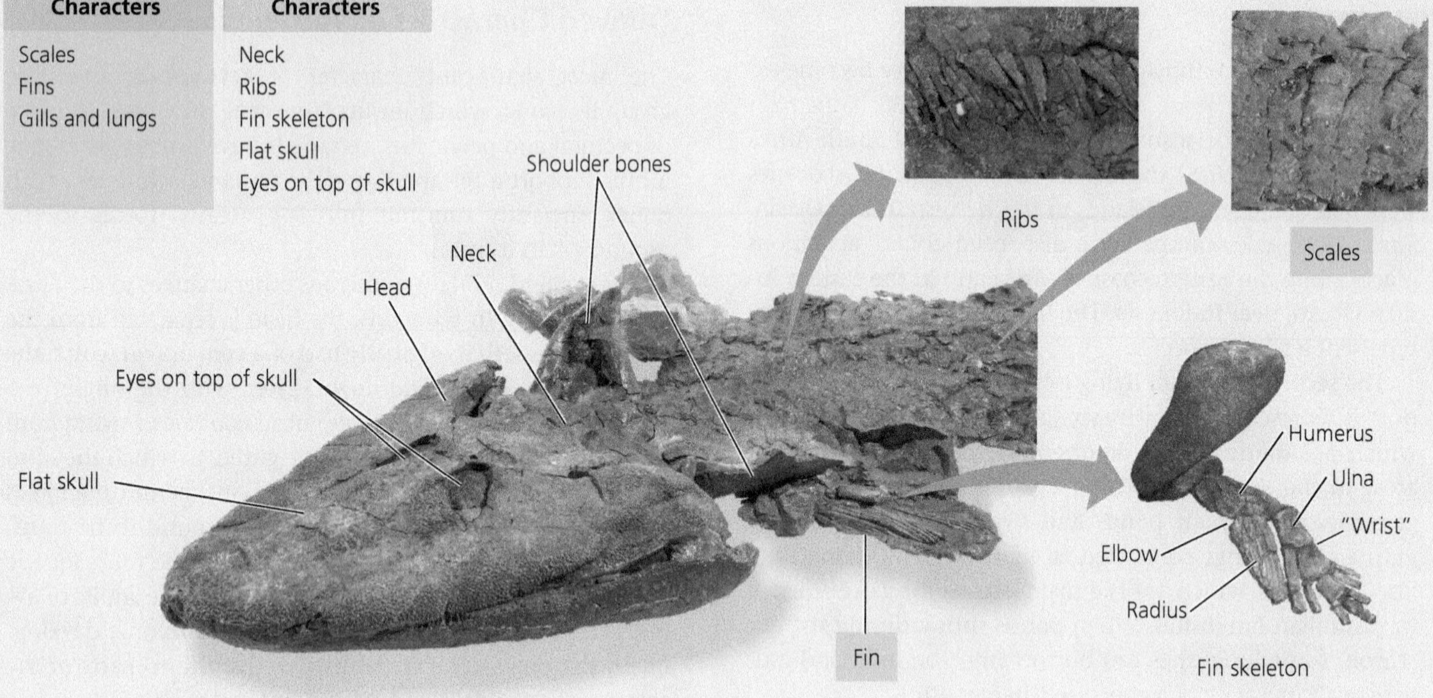

that would have helped it breathe air and support its body (**Figure 34.20**). Also unlike a fish, *Tiktaalik* had a neck and shoulders, allowing it to move its head about. Finally, the bones of *Tiktaalik*'s front fin have the same basic pattern found in all limbed animals: one bone (the humerus), followed by two bones (the radius and ulna), followed by a group of small bones that comprise the wrist. Although it is unlikely that *Tiktaalik* could walk on land, its front fin skeleton suggests that it could prop itself up in water on its fins.

Tiktaalik and other extraordinary fossil discoveries have allowed paleontologists to reconstruct how fins became progressively more limb-like over time, culminating in the appearance of the first tetrapods 365 million years ago (**Figure 34.21**). Over the next 60 million years, a great diversity of tetrapods arose. Judging from the morphology and locations of their fossils, most of these early tetrapods probably remained tied to water, a characteristic they share with some members of a group of living tetrapods called amphibians.

Amphibians

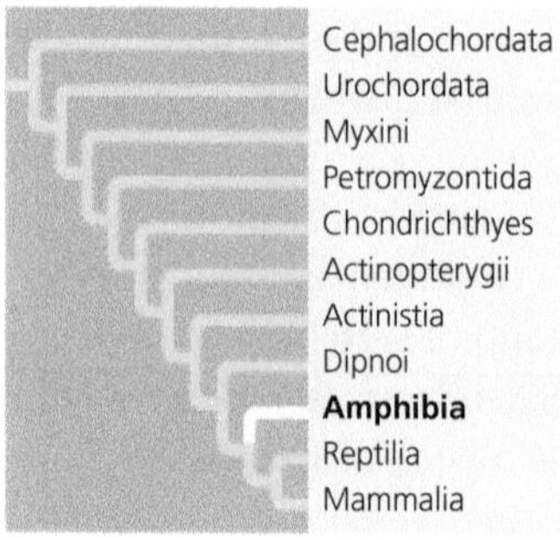

The **amphibians** (class Amphibia) are represented today by about 6,150 species of salamanders (order Urodela, "tailed ones"), frogs (order Anura, "tail-less ones"), and caecilians (order Apoda, "legless ones").

About 550 species of urodeles are known. Some are entirely aquatic, but others live on land as adults or

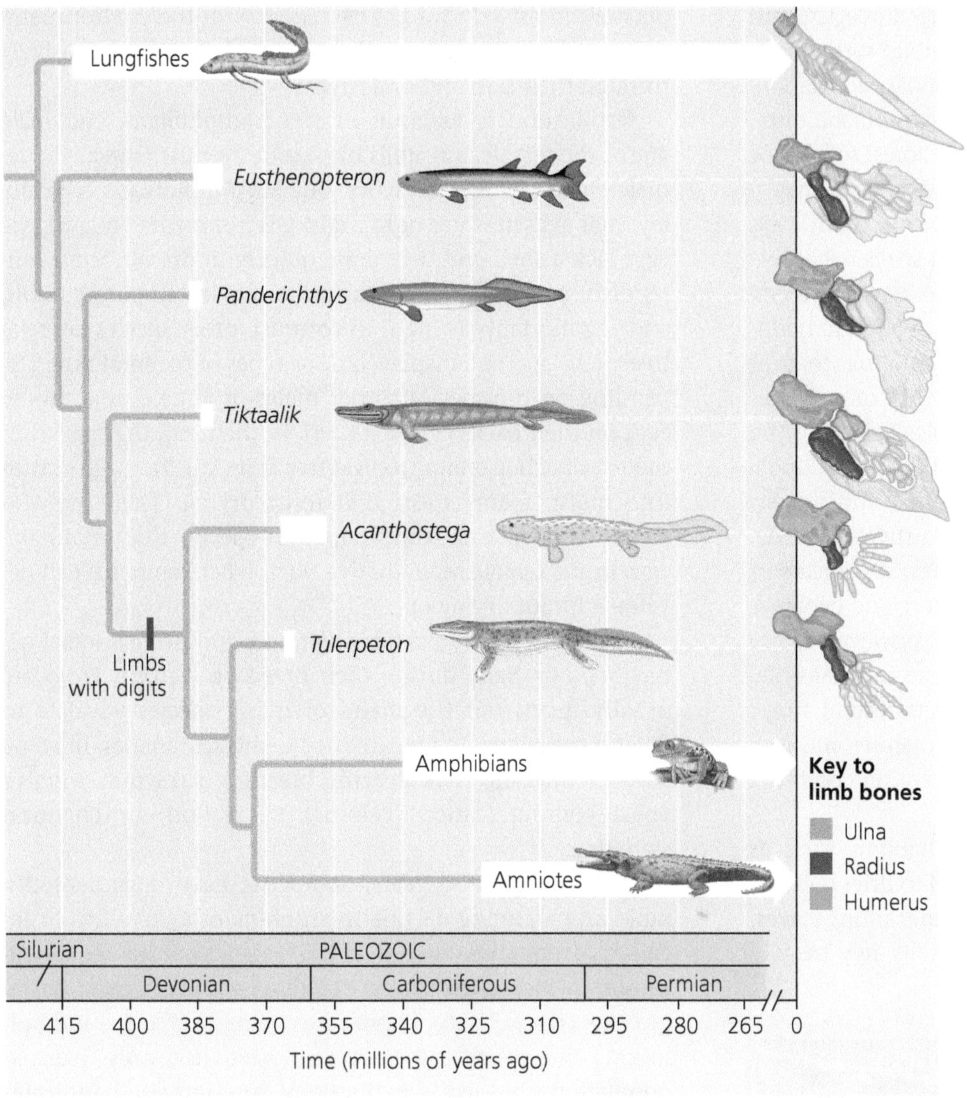

◄ **Figure 34.21 Steps in the origin of limbs with digits.** The white bars on the branches of this diagram place known fossils in time; arrowheads indicate lineages that extend to today. The drawings of extinct organisms are based on fossilized skeletons, but the colors are fanciful.

WHAT IF? *If the most recent common ancestor of* Tulerpeton *and living tetrapods originated 380 million years ago, what range of dates would include the origin of amphibians?*

throughout life. Most salamanders that live on land walk with a side-to-side bending of the body, a trait also found in early terrestrial tetrapods (Figure 34.22a). Paedomorphosis is common among aquatic salamanders; the axolotl, for instance, retains larval features even when it is sexually mature (see Figure 25.22).

Anurans, numbering about 5,420 species, are more specialized than urodeles for moving on land (Figure 34.22b). Adult frogs use their powerful hind legs to hop along the terrain. Although often distinctive in appearance, the animals known as "toads" are simply frogs that have leathery skin or other adaptations for life on land. A frog nabs insects and other prey by flicking out its long, sticky tongue, which is attached to the front of the mouth. Frogs display a great variety of adaptations that help them avoid being eaten by larger predators. Their skin glands secrete distasteful or even poisonous mucus. Many poisonous species have bright coloration, which predators apparently associate with danger (see Figure 54.5b). Other frogs have color patterns that camouflage them (see Figure 54.5a).

(a) Order Urodela. Urodeles (salamanders) retain their tail as adults.

(b) Order Anura. Anurans, such as this poison dart frog, lack a tail as adults.

(c) Order Apoda. Apodans, or caecilians, are legless, mainly burrowing amphibians.

► **Figure 34.22 Amphibians.**

Apodans, the caecilians (about 170 species), are legless and nearly blind, and superficially they resemble earthworms (Figure 34.22c). Their absence of legs is a secondary adaptation, as they evolved from a legged ancestor. Caecilians inhabit tropical areas, where most species burrow in moist forest soil. A few South American species live in freshwater ponds and streams.

Amphibian (derived from *amphibious*, meaning "both ways of life") refers to the life stages of many frog species that live first in water and then on land (Figure 34.23). The larval stage of a frog, called a tadpole, is usually an aquatic herbivore with gills, a lateral line system resembling that of aquatic vertebrates, and a long, finned tail. The tadpole initially lacks legs; it swims by undulating its tail. During the metamorphosis that leads to the "second life," the tadpole develops legs, lungs, a pair of external eardrums, and a digestive system adapted to a carnivorous diet. At the same time, the gills disappear; the lateral line system also disappears in most species. The young frog crawls onto shore and becomes a terrestrial hunter. In spite of their name, however, many amphibians do not live a dual—aquatic and terrestrial—life. There are some strictly aquatic or strictly terrestrial frogs, salamanders, and caecilians. Moreover, salamander and caecilian larvae look much like the adults, and typically both the larvae and the adults are carnivorous.

Most amphibians are found in damp habitats such as swamps and rain forests. Even those adapted to drier habitats spend much of their time in burrows or under moist leaves, where humidity is high. Amphibians generally rely heavily on their moist skin for gas exchange with the environment. Some terrestrial species lack lungs and breathe exclusively through their skin and oral cavity.

Fertilization is external in most amphibians; the male grasps the female and spills his sperm over the eggs as the female sheds them (see Figure 34.23c). Amphibians typically lay their eggs in water or in moist environments on land; the eggs lack a shell and dehydrate quickly in dry air. Some amphibian species lay vast numbers of eggs in temporary pools, and egg mortality is high. In contrast, other species lay relatively few eggs and display various types of parental care. Depending on the species, either males or females may house eggs on their back (Figure 34.24), in their mouth, or even in their stomach. Certain tropical tree frogs stir their egg masses into moist, foamy nests that resist drying. There are also some ovoviviparous and viviparous species that retain the eggs in the female reproductive tract, where embryos can develop without drying out.

Many amphibians exhibit complex and diverse social behaviors, especially during their breeding seasons. Frogs are usually quiet, but the males of many species vocalize to defend their breeding territory or to attract females. In some species, migrations to specific breeding sites may involve vocal communication, celestial navigation, or chemical signaling.

Over the past 30 years, zoologists have documented a rapid and alarming decline in amphibian populations in locations throughout the world. There appear to be several causes, including the spread of a disease-causing chytrid fungus (see Figure 31.26), habitat loss, climate change, and pollution. These and other factors have not only reduced populations, but led to extinctions. A recent study indicates that at least 9 amphibian species have become extinct since 1980; more than 100 other species have not been seen since that time and are considered possibly extinct.

(a) The tadpole is an aquatic herbivore with a fishlike tail and internal gills.

(b) During metamorphosis, the gills and tail are resorbed, and walking legs develop. The adult frog will live on land.

(c) The adults return to water to mate. The male grasps the female, stimulating her to release eggs. The eggs are laid and fertilized in water. They have a jelly coat but lack a shell and would desiccate in air.

▲ Figure 34.23 **The "dual life" of a frog (*Rana temporaria*).**

▲ Figure 34.24 **A mobile nursery.** A female pygmy marsupial frog, *Flectonotus pygmaeus,* incubates her eggs in a pouch of skin on her back, helping to protect the eggs from predators. When the eggs hatch, the female deposits the tadpoles in water where they begin life on their own.

CONCEPT CHECK 34.5

1. Describe the origin of tetrapods and identify some of their key derived traits.
2. Some amphibians never leave the water, whereas others can survive in relatively dry terrestrial environments. Contrast the adaptations that facilitate these two lifestyles.
3. **WHAT IF?** Scientists think that amphibian populations may provide an early warning system of environmental problems. What features of amphibians might make them particularly sensitive to environmental problems?

For suggested answers, see Appendix A.

CONCEPT 34.6

Amniotes are tetrapods that have a terrestrially adapted egg

The **amniotes** are a group of tetrapods whose extant members are the reptiles (including birds) and mammals (Figure 34.25). During their evolution, amniotes acquired a number of new adaptations to life on land.

Derived Characters of Amniotes

Amniotes are named for the major derived character of the clade, the **amniotic egg**, which contains four specialized membranes: the amnion, the chorion, the yolk sac, and the

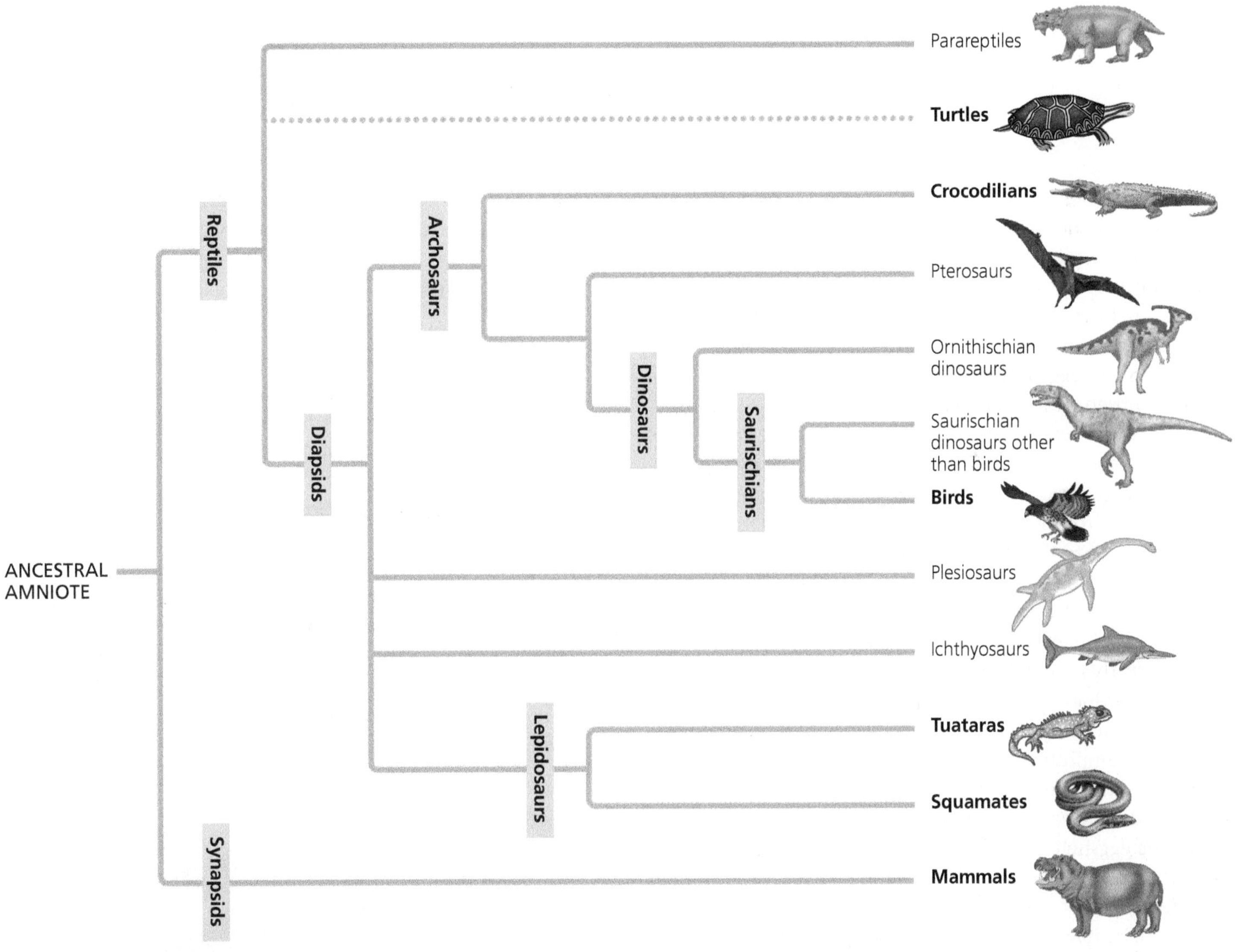

▲ **Figure 34.25 A phylogeny of amniotes.** Extant groups are named at the tips of the branches in boldface type. The dotted line of the turtle branch indicates the uncertain relationship of turtles to other reptiles. Turtles may be a sister group to parareptiles (as indicated by some morphological data), or they may be diapsids more closely related to lepidosaurs (as indicated by other morphological analyses) or to archosaurs (as indicated by many molecular studies).

? *Based on this phylogeny, DNA sequences in birds are likely most similar to DNA sequences in which other extant group of amniotes? Explain.*

▶ **Figure 34.26 The amniotic egg.** The embryos of reptiles and mammals form four extraembryonic membranes: the amnion, chorion, yolk sac, and allantois. This diagram shows these membranes in the shelled egg of a reptile.

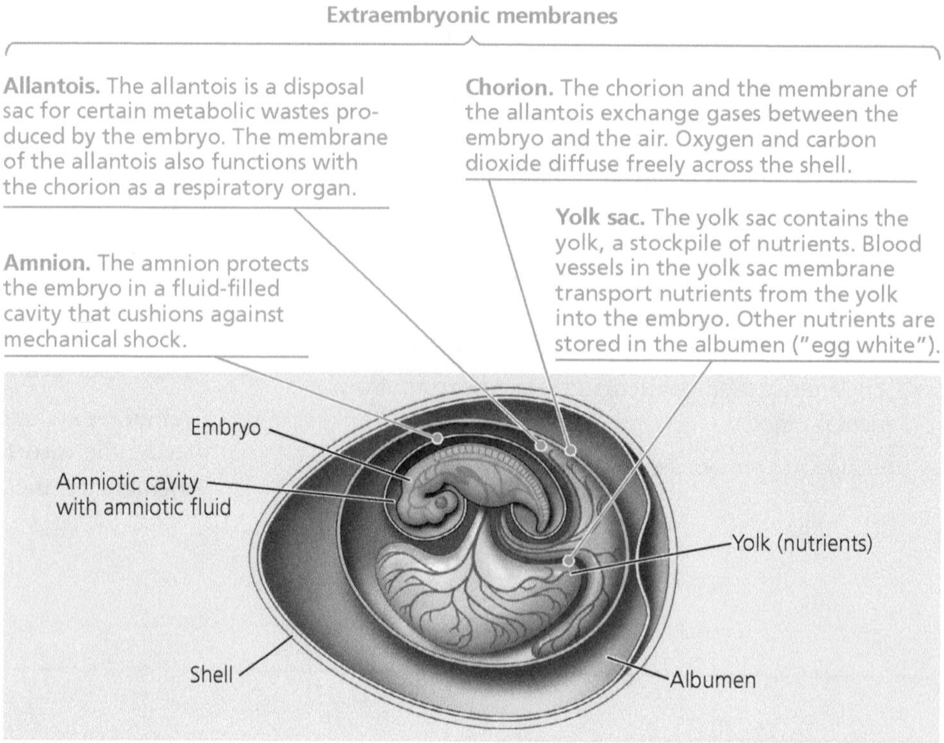

allantois (Figure 34.26). Called *extraembryonic membranes* because they are not part of the body of the embryo itself, these membranes develop from tissue layers that grow out from the embryo. The amniotic egg is named for the amnion, which encloses a compartment of fluid that bathes the embryo and acts as a hydraulic shock absorber. The other membranes in the egg function in gas exchange, the transfer of stored nutrients to the embryo, and waste storage. The amniotic egg was a key evolutionary innovation for terrestrial life: It allowed the embryo to develop on land in its own private "pond," hence reducing the dependence of tetrapods on an aqueous environment for reproduction.

In contrast to the shell-less eggs of amphibians, the amniotic eggs of most reptiles and some mammals have a shell. The shells of bird eggs are calcareous (made of calcium carbonate) and inflexible, while the eggshells of many other reptiles are leathery and flexible. Either kind of shell significantly slows dehydration of the egg in air, an adaptation that helped amniotes to occupy a wider range of terrestrial habitats than amphibians, their closest living relatives. (Seeds played a similar role in the evolution of land plants, as we discussed in Chapter 30.) Most mammals have dispensed with the eggshell over the course of their evolution, and the embryo avoids desiccation by developing within the amnion inside the mother's body.

Amniotes have acquired other key adaptations to life on land. For example, amniotes use their rib cage to ventilate their lungs. This method is more efficient than throat-based ventilation, which amphibians use as a supplement to breathing through their skin. The increased efficiency of rib cage ventilation may have allowed amniotes to abandon breathing through their skin and develop less permeable skin, thereby conserving water.

Early Amniotes

The most recent common ancestor of living amphibians and amniotes likely lived about 350 million years ago. No fossils of amniotic eggs have been found from that time, which is not surprising given how delicate they are. Thus, it is not yet possible to say when the amniotic egg evolved, although it must have existed in the last common ancestor of living amniotes, which all have amniotic eggs.

Based on where their fossils have been found, the earliest amniotes lived in warm, moist environments, as did the first tetrapods. Over time, however, early amniotes expanded into a wide range of new environments, including dry and high-latitude regions. The earliest amniotes were small and had sharp teeth, a sign that they were predators (Figure 34.27). Later groups also included herbivores, as evidenced by their grinding teeth and other features.

▲ **Figure 34.27 Artist's reconstruction of *Hylonomus*, an early amniote.** About 25 cm long, this species lived 310 million years ago and probably ate insects and other small invertebrates.

Reptiles

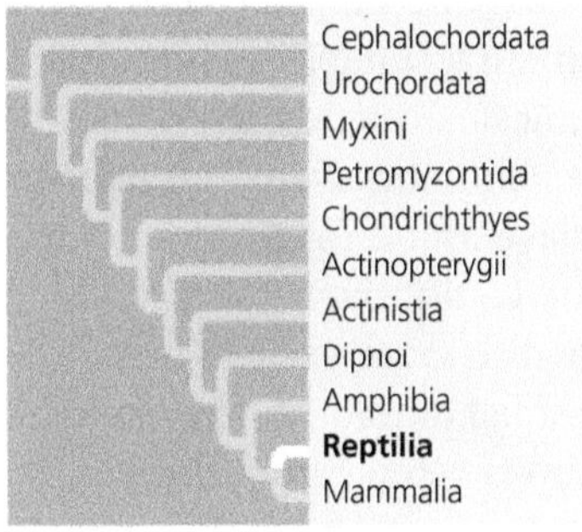

The **reptile** clade includes tuataras, lizards, snakes, turtles, crocodilians, and birds, along with a number of extinct groups, such as plesiosaurs and ichthyosaurs (see Figure 34.25).

Fossil evidence indicates that the earliest reptiles lived about 310 million years ago and resembled lizards. Reptiles have diverged greatly since that time, but as a group they share several derived characters that distinguish them from other tetrapods. For example, unlike amphibians, reptiles have scales that contain the protein keratin (as does a human nail). Scales help protect the animal's skin from desiccation and abrasion. In addition, most reptiles lay their shelled eggs on land (**Figure 34.28**). Fertilization must occur internally, before the eggshell is secreted. Many species of snakes and lizards are viviparous; in such species, the extraembryonic membranes form a kind of placenta that enables the embryo to obtain nutrients from its mother.

Reptiles such as lizards and snakes are sometimes described as "cold-blooded" because they do not use their metabolism extensively to control their body temperature. However, they do regulate their body temperature by using behavioral adaptations. For example, many lizards bask in the sun when the air is cool and seek shade when the air is too warm. A more accurate description of these reptiles is to say that they are **ectothermic**, which means that they absorb external heat as their main source of body heat. (This topic is discussed in more detail in Chapter 40.) By warming themselves directly with solar energy rather than through the metabolic breakdown of food, an ectothermic reptile can survive on less than 10% of the food energy required by a mammal of the same size. But the reptile clade is not entirely ectothermic; birds are **endothermic**, capable of maintaining body temperature through metabolic activity.

▲ **Figure 34.28 Hatching reptiles.** These bushmaster snakes (*Lachesis muta*) are breaking out of their parchment-like shells, a common type of shell among living reptiles other than birds.

The Origin and Evolutionary Radiation of Reptiles

The oldest reptilian fossils, found in rocks from Nova Scotia, date from the late Carboniferous period. As reptiles diverged from their lizard-like ancestors, one of the first major groups to emerge were the **parareptiles**, which were mostly large, stocky, quadrupedal herbivores. Some parareptiles had plates on their skin that may have provided them with defense against predators. Parareptiles died out by about 200 million years ago, at the end of the Triassic period.

As parareptiles were dwindling, another ancient clade of reptiles, the **diapsids**, was diversifying. One of the most obvious derived characters of diapsids is a pair of holes on each side of the skull, behind the eye socket; muscles pass through these holes and attach to the jaw, controlling jaw movement. The diapsids are composed of two main lineages. One lineage gave rise to the **lepidosaurs**, which include tuataras, lizards, and snakes. This lineage also produced a number of marine reptiles, including the giant mososaurs. Some of these marine species rivaled today's whales in length; all of them are extinct. (We'll say more about living lepidosaurs shortly.)

The other diapsid lineage, the **archosaurs**, produced the crocodilians (which we'll discuss later), pterosaurs, and dinosaurs. **Pterosaurs**, which originated in the late Triassic, were the first tetrapods to exhibit flapping flight. The pterosaur wing was completely different from the wings of birds and bats. It consisted of a collagen-strengthened membrane that stretched between the trunk or hind leg and a very long digit on the foreleg. Well-preserved fossils show evidence of muscles, blood vessels, and nerves in the wing membranes, suggesting that pterosaurs could dynamically adjust their membranes to assist their flight.

The smallest pterosaurs were no bigger than a sparrow, and the largest had a wingspan of nearly 11 m. They appear to have converged on many of the ecological roles later played by birds; some were insect-eaters, others grabbed fish out of the ocean, and still others filtered small animals through thousands of fine needlelike teeth. But by the end of the Cretaceous period 65 million years ago, pterosaurs had become extinct.

On land, the **dinosaurs** diversified into a vast range of shapes and sizes, from bipeds the size of a pigeon to 45-m-long quadrupeds with necks long enough to let them browse the tops of trees. One lineage of dinosaurs, the ornithischians, were herbivores; they included many species with elaborate defenses against predators, such as tail clubs and horned crests. The other main lineage of dinosaurs, the saurischians, included the long-necked giants and a group called the **theropods**, which were bipedal carnivores. Theropods included the famous *Tyrannosaurus rex* as well as the ancestors of birds.

There is continuing debate about the metabolism of dinosaurs. Some researchers have pointed out that the Mesozoic climate over much of the dinosaurs' range was relatively warm and unvarying, and they have suggested that the low surface-to-volume ratios of large dinosaurs combined with behavioral adaptations such as basking may have been sufficient for an ectotherm to maintain a suitable body temperature. However, some anatomical evidence supports the hypothesis that at least some dinosaurs were endotherms. Furthermore, paleontologists have found fossils of dinosaurs in both Antarctica and the Arctic; although the climate in these areas was milder when dinosaurs existed than it is today, it was cool enough that small dinosaurs may have had difficulty maintaining a high body temperature through ectothermy. The dinosaur that gave rise to birds was *certainly* endothermic, as are all birds.

▼ Figure 34.29 **Extant reptiles (other than birds).**

(a) Tuatara (*Sphenodon punctatus*)

(b) Australian thorny devil lizard (*Moloch horridus*)

(c) Wagler's pit viper (*Tropidolaemus wagleri*)

(d) Eastern box turtle (*Terrapene carolina carolina*)

(e) American alligator (*Alligator mississippiensis*)

Traditionally, dinosaurs were considered slow, sluggish creatures. Since the early 1970s, however, fossil discoveries and research have led to the conclusion that many dinosaurs were agile and fast moving. Dinosaurs had a limb structure that enabled them to walk and run more efficiently than could earlier tetrapods, which had a sprawling gait. Fossilized footprints and other evidence suggest that some species were social—they lived and traveled in groups, much as many mammals do today. Paleontologists have also discovered evidence that some dinosaurs built nests and brooded their eggs, as birds do today (see Figure 26.17).

All dinosaurs except birds became extinct by the end of the Cretaceous period. Their extinction may have been caused at least in part by the asteroid or comet impact you read about in Chapter 25. Some analyses of the fossil record are consistent with this idea in that they show a sudden decline in dinosaur diversity at the end of the Cretaceous. However, other analyses indicate that the number of dinosaur species had begun to decline several million years before the Cretaceous ended. Further fossil discoveries and new analyses will be needed to resolve this debate.

Lepidosaurs

One surviving lineage of lepidosaurs is represented by two species of lizard-like reptiles called tuataras (Figure 34.29a). Fossil evidence indicates that tuatara ancestors lived at least 220 million years ago. These organisms thrived on many continents well into the Cretaceous period, reaching up to a meter in length. Today, however, tuataras are found only on 30 islands off the coast of New Zealand. When humans arrived in New Zealand 750 years ago, the rats that accompanied them devoured tuatara eggs, eventually eliminating the reptiles on the main islands. The tuataras that remain on the outlying islands are about 50 cm long and feed on insects, small lizards, and bird eggs and chicks. They can live to be over 100 years old. Their future survival depends on whether their remaining habitats are kept rat-free.

The other major living lineage of lepidosaurs consists of the lizards and snakes, or squamates, which number about 7,900 species. Lizards are the most numerous and diverse reptiles (apart from birds) alive today (Figure 34.29b). Many lizards are small; the Jaragua lizard, discovered in the Dominican Republic in 2001, is only 16 mm long—small enough to fit comfortably on a dime. In contrast, the Komodo dragon of Indonesia is a lizard that can reach a length of 3 m. It hunts deer and other large prey, delivering venom with its bite.

Snakes are legless lepidosaurs (Figure 34.29c). As described in Chapter 26, snakes descended from lizards with legs. Today, some species of snakes retain vestigial pelvic and limb bones, providing evidence of their ancestry. Despite their lack of legs, snakes are quite proficient at moving on land, most often by producing waves of lateral bending that pass from head to tail. Force exerted by the bends against solid objects pushes the snake forward. Snakes can also move by gripping the ground with their belly scales at several points along the body while the scales at intervening points are lifted slightly off the ground and pulled forward.

Snakes are carnivorous, and a number of adaptations aid them in hunting and eating prey. They have acute chemical sensors, and though they lack eardrums, they are sensitive to ground vibrations, which helps them detect the movements of prey. Heat-detecting organs between the eyes and nostrils of pit vipers, including rattlesnakes, are sensitive to minute temperature changes, enabling these night hunters to locate warm animals. Venomous snakes inject their toxin through a pair of sharp teeth that may be hollow or grooved. The flicking tongue is not venomous but helps fan odors toward olfactory (smell) organs on the roof of the mouth. Loosely articulated jawbones and elastic skin enable most snakes to swallow prey larger than the diameter of the snake's head (see Figure 23.14).

Turtles

Turtles are one of the most distinctive group of reptiles alive today. All turtles have a boxlike shell made of upper and lower shields that are fused to the vertebrae, clavicles (collarbones), and ribs (Figure 34.29d). Most of the 307 known species of turtles have a hard shell, providing excellent defense against predators. A 2008 study reported the discovery of the oldest known fossil of the turtle lineage, dating to 220 million years ago. This fossil has a complete lower shell but an incomplete upper shell, suggesting that turtles may have acquired full shells in stages. The marine sediments in which this fossil was found also suggest that turtles may have originated in shallow coastal waters. However, as other scientists have argued, it is also possible that turtles originated on land and that the incomplete upper shell of this fossil may have been a specialized adaptation for an aquatic lifestyle. Scientists continue to hunt for fossils that could shed light on the origin of the turtle shell.

The earliest turtles could not retract their head into their shell, but mechanisms for doing so evolved independently in two separate branches of turtles. The side-necked turtles fold their neck horizontally, while the vertical-necked turtles fold their neck vertically.

Some turtles have adapted to deserts, and others live almost entirely in ponds and rivers. Still others have returned to the sea. Sea turtles have a reduced shell and enlarged forelimbs that function as flippers. They include the largest living turtles, the deep-diving leatherbacks, which can exceed a mass of 1,500 kg and feed on jellies. Leatherbacks and other sea turtles are endangered by being caught in fishing nets, as well as by development of the beaches where the turtles lay their eggs.

Alligators and Crocodiles

Alligators and crocodiles (collectively called crocodilians) belong to a lineage that reaches back to the late Triassic (Figure 34.29e). The earliest members of this lineage were small terrestrial quadrupeds with long, slender legs. Later species became larger and adapted to aquatic habitats, breathing air through their upturned nostrils. Some Mesozoic crocodilians grew as long as 12 m and may have attacked dinosaurs and other prey at the water's edge.

The 23 known species of living crocodilians are confined to warm regions of the globe. Alligators in the southeastern United States have made a comeback after spending years on the endangered species list.

Birds

There are about 10,000 species of birds in the world. Like crocodilians, birds are archosaurs, but almost every feature of their anatomy has been modified in their adaptation to flight.

Derived Characters of Birds Many of the characters of birds are adaptations that facilitate flight, including weight-saving modifications that make flying more efficient. For example, birds lack a urinary bladder, and the females of most species have only one ovary. The gonads of both females and males are usually small, except during the breeding season, when they increase in size. Living birds are also toothless, an adaptation that trims the weight of the head.

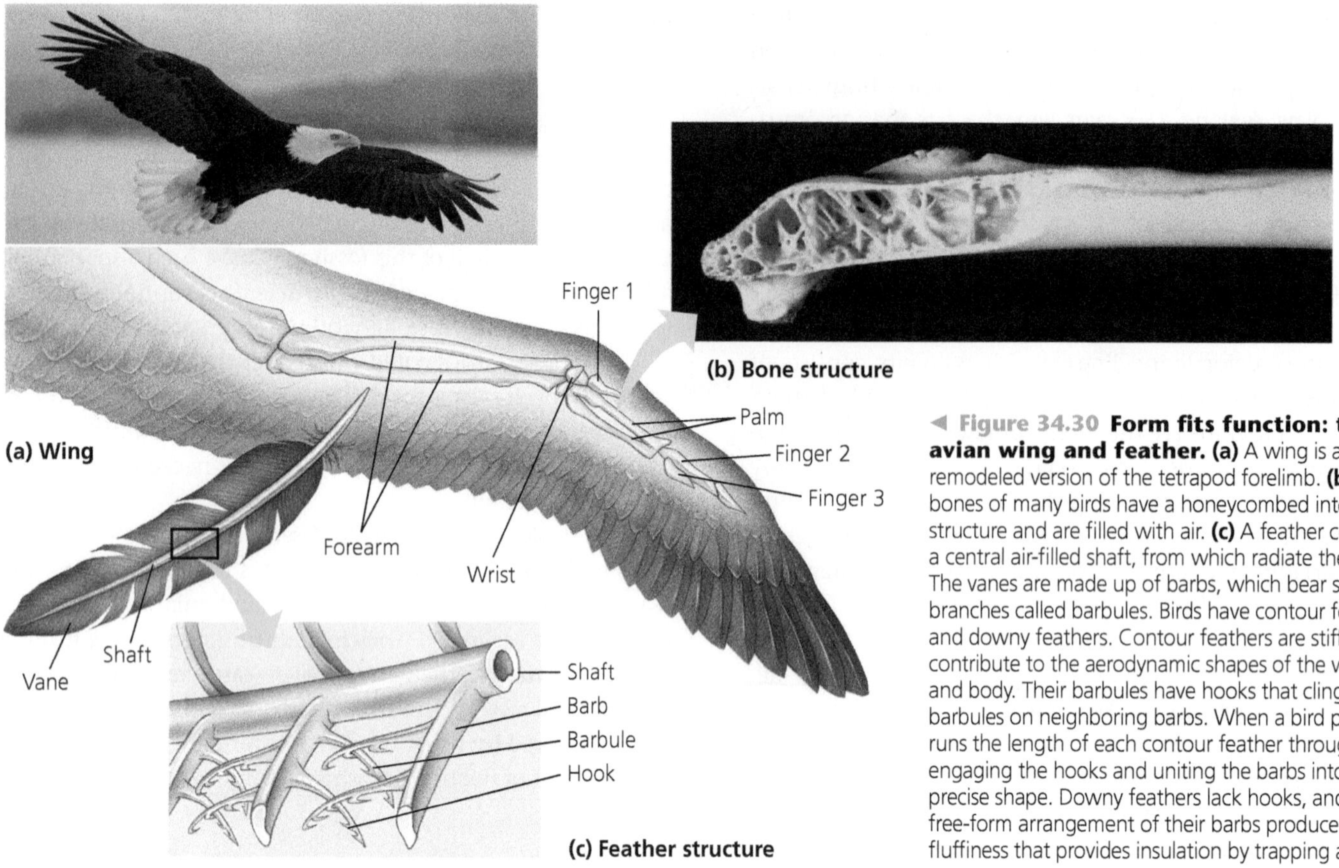

◄ Figure 34.30 **Form fits function: the avian wing and feather.** **(a)** A wing is a remodeled version of the tetrapod forelimb. **(b)** The bones of many birds have a honeycombed internal structure and are filled with air. **(c)** A feather consists of a central air-filled shaft, from which radiate the vanes. The vanes are made up of barbs, which bear small branches called barbules. Birds have contour feathers and downy feathers. Contour feathers are stiff and contribute to the aerodynamic shapes of the wings and body. Their barbules have hooks that cling to barbules on neighboring barbs. When a bird preens, it runs the length of each contour feather through its bill, engaging the hooks and uniting the barbs into a precise shape. Downy feathers lack hooks, and the free-form arrangement of their barbs produces a fluffiness that provides insulation by trapping air.

A bird's most obvious adaptations for flight are its wings and feathers (Figure 34.30). Feathers are made of the protein β-keratin, which is also found in the scales of other reptiles. The shape and arrangement of the feathers form the wings into airfoils, and they illustrate some of the same principles of aerodynamics as the wings of an airplane. Power for flapping the wings comes from contractions of large pectoral (breast) muscles anchored to a keel on the sternum (breastbone). Some birds, such as eagles and hawks, have wings adapted for soaring on air currents and flap their wings only occasionally; other birds, including hummingbirds, must flap continuously to stay aloft (see Figure 34.34). Among the fastest birds are the appropriately named swifts, which can fly up to 170 km/hr.

Flight provides numerous benefits. It enhances hunting and scavenging; many birds consume flying insects, an abundant, highly nutritious food resource. Flight also provides ready escape from earthbound predators and enables some birds to migrate great distances to exploit different food resources and seasonal breeding areas.

Flying requires a great expenditure of energy from an active metabolism. Birds are endothermic; they use their own metabolic heat to maintain a high, constant body temperature. Feathers and in some species a layer of fat provide insulation that enables birds to retain body heat. The lungs have tiny tubes leading to and from elastic air sacs that improve airflow and oxygen uptake. This efficient respiratory system and a circulatory system with a four-chambered heart keep tissues well supplied with oxygen and nutrients, supporting a high rate of metabolism.

Flight also requires both acute vision and fine muscle control. Birds have color vision and excellent eyesight. The visual and motor areas of the brain are well developed, and the brain is proportionately larger than those of amphibians and nonbird reptiles.

Birds generally display very complex behaviors, particularly during breeding season, when they engage in elaborate courtship rituals. Because eggs have shells by the time they are laid, fertilization must be internal. Copulation usually involves contact between the mates' vents, the openings to their cloacas. After eggs are laid, the avian embryo must be kept warm through brooding by the mother, the father, or both, depending on the species.

The Origin of Birds Cladistic analyses of birds and reptilian fossils indicate that birds belong to the group of bipedal saurischian dinosaurs called theropods. Since the late 1990s, Chinese paleontologists have unearthed a spectacular trove of feathered theropod fossils that are shedding light on the origin of birds. Several species of dinosaurs closely related to birds had feathers with vanes, and a wider range of species had filamentous feathers. Such findings imply that feathers evolved long before powered flight. Among the possible functions of these early feathers were insulation, camouflage, and courtship display.

How did flight evolve in the theropods? In one scenario, feathers may have enabled small, running dinosaurs chasing prey or escaping predators to gain extra lift as they jumped into the air. Or small dinosaurs could have gained traction as they ran up hills by flapping their feathered forelimbs—a behavior seen in some birds today. In a third scenario, some dinosaurs could have climbed trees and glided, aided by feathers. Whether birds took to the air from the ground up or the trees down, an essential question being studied by scientists ranging from paleontologists to engineers is how their efficient flight stroke evolved.

By 150 million years ago, feathered theropods had evolved into birds. *Archaeopteryx*, which was discovered in a German limestone quarry in 1861, remains the earliest known bird (Figure 34.31). It had feathered wings but retained ancestral characters such as teeth, clawed digits in its wings, and a long tail. *Archaeopteryx* flew well at high speeds, but unlike a present-day bird, it could not take off from a standing position. Fossils of later birds from the Cretaceous show a gradual loss of certain ancestral dinosaur features, such as teeth and clawed forelimbs, as well as the acquisition of innovations found in extant birds, including a short tail covered by a fan of feathers.

▲ Figure 34.31 **Artist's reconstruction of *Archaeopteryx*, the earliest known bird.** Fossil evidence indicates that *Archaeopteryx* was capable of powered flight but retained many characters of nonbird dinosaurs.

▲ Figure 34.32 **An emu (*Dromaius novaehollandiae*), a flightless bird native to Australia.**

Living Birds Clear evidence of Neornithes, the clade that includes the 28 orders of living birds, can be found before the Cretaceous-Paleogene boundary 65.5 million years ago. Several groups of living and extinct birds include one or more flightless species. The **ratites** (order Struthioniformes), which consist of the ostrich, rhea, kiwi, cassowary, and emu, are all flightless (Figure 34.32). In ratites, the sternal keel is absent, and the pectoral muscles are small relative to those of birds that can fly.

Penguins make up the flightless order Sphenisciformes, but, like flying birds, they have powerful pectoral muscles. They use these muscles to "fly" in the water: As they swim, they flap their flipper-like wings in a manner that resembles the flight stroke of a more typical bird (Figure 34.33). Certain species of rails, ducks, and pigeons are also flightless.

Although the demands of flight have rendered the general body forms of many flying birds similar to one another, experienced bird-watchers can distinguish species by their profile, colors, flying style, behavior, and beak shape. The skeleton of a hummingbird wing is unique, making them the only birds

▲ Figure 34.33 **A king penguin (*Aptenodytes patagonicus*) "flying" underwater.** With their streamlined shape and powerful pectoral muscles, penguins are fast and agile swimmers.

◀ **Figure 34.34 Hummingbird feeding while hovering.** A hummingbird can rotate its wings in all directions, enabling it to hover and fly backwards.

that can hover and fly backwards (Figure 34.34). Adult birds lack teeth, but during the course of avian evolution their beaks have taken on a variety of shapes suited to different diets. Some birds, such as parrots, have crushing beaks with which they can crack open hard nuts and seeds. Other birds, such as flamingoes, are filter feeders. Their beaks have remarkable 'strainers' that enable them to capture food particles from the water (Figure 34.35). Foot structure, too, shows considerable variation. Various birds use their feet for perching on branches (Figure 34.36), grasping food, defense, swimming or walking, and even courtship (see Figure 24.3e).

◀ **Figure 34.35 Specialized beaks.** This greater flamingo (*Phoenicopterus ruber*) dips its beak into the water and strains out the food.

▲ **Figure 34.36 Feet adapted to perching.** This great tit (*Parus major*) is a member of the Passeriformes, the perching birds. The toes of these birds can lock around a branch or wire, enabling the bird to rest for long periods.

CONCEPT CHECK 34.6

1. Describe three key amniote adaptations for life on land.
2. Are snakes tetrapods? Explain.
3. Identify four avian adaptations for flight.
4. **WHAT IF?** Suppose turtles are more closely related to lepidosaurs than to other reptiles. Redraw Figure 34.25 to show this relationship, and mark the node that represents the most recent common ancestor shared by all living reptiles. Defining the reptile clade as consisting of all descendants of that ancestor, list the reptiles.

For suggested answers, see Appendix A.

CONCEPT **34.7**

Mammals are amniotes that have hair and produce milk

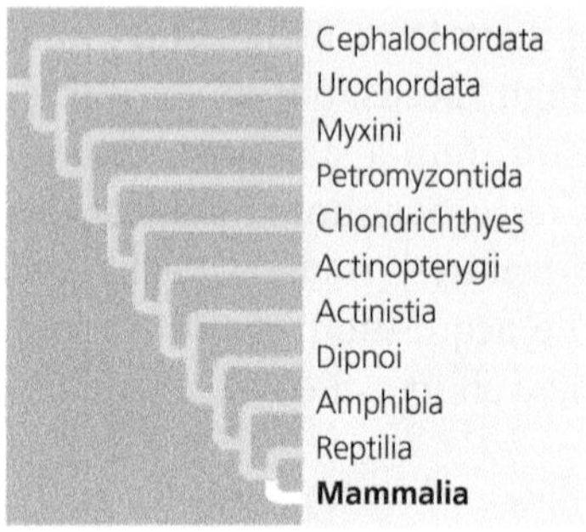

The reptiles we have been discussing represent one of the two living lineages of amniotes. The other amniote lineage is our own, the **mammals** (class Mammalia). Today, there are more than 5,300 known species of mammals on Earth.

Derived Characters of Mammals

The distinctive character from which mammals derive their name is their mammary glands, which produce milk for offspring. All mammalian mothers nourish their young with milk, a balanced diet rich in fats, sugars, proteins, minerals, and vitamins. Hair, another mammalian characteristic, and a fat layer under the skin help the body retain heat. Like birds, mammals are endothermic, and most have a high metabolic rate. Efficient respiratory and circulatory systems (including a four-chambered heart) support a mammal's metabolism. A sheet of muscle called the diaphragm helps ventilate the lungs.

Like birds, mammals generally have a larger brain than other vertebrates of equivalent size, and many species are capable learners. And as in birds, the relatively long duration of parental care extends the time for offspring to learn important survival skills by observing their parents.

Differentiated teeth are another important mammalian trait. Whereas the teeth of reptiles are generally uniform in size and shape, the jaws of mammals bear a variety of teeth with sizes and shapes adapted for chewing many kinds of foods. Humans, like most mammals, have teeth modified for shearing (incisors and canine teeth) and for crushing and grinding (premolars and molars; see Figure 41.16).

Early Evolution of Mammals

Mammals belong to a group of amniotes known as **synapsids**. Early nonmammalian synapsids lacked hair, had a sprawling gait, and laid eggs. A distinctive characteristic of synapsids is the single temporal fenestra, a hole behind the eye socket on each side of the skull. Humans retain this feature; your jaw muscles pass through the temporal fenestra and anchor on your temple. Fossil evidence shows that the jaw was remodeled as mammalian features arose gradually in successive lineages of earlier synapsids (see Figure 25.6); in all, these changes took more than 100 million years. In addition, two of the bones that formerly made up the jaw joint were incorporated into the mammalian middle ear (**Figure 34.37**). This evolutionary change is reflected in changes that occur during development. For example, as a mammalian embryo grows, the posterior region of its jaw—which in a reptile forms the articular bone—can be observed to detach from the jaw and migrate to the ear, where it forms the malleus.

Synapsids evolved into large herbivores and carnivores during the Permian period, and for a time they were the dominant tetrapods. However, the Permian-Triassic extinctions took a heavy toll on them, and their diversity fell during the Triassic (251–200 million years ago). Increasingly mammal-like synapsids emerged by the end of the Triassic. While not true mammals, these synapsids had acquired a number of the derived characters that distinguish mammals from other amniotes. They were small and probably hairy, and they likely fed on insects at night. Their bones show that they grew faster than other synapsids, suggesting that they probably had a relatively high metabolic rate; however, they still laid eggs.

During the Jurassic (200–145 million years ago), the first true mammals arose and diversified into many short-lived lineages. A diverse set of mammal species coexisted with dinosaurs in Jurassic and Cretaceous periods, but these species were not abundant or dominant members of their community, and most measured less than 1 m. One possible explanation for their small size is that dinosaurs already occupied ecological niches of large-bodied animals.

By the early Cretaceous, the three major lineages of mammals had emerged: those leading to monotremes (egg-laying mammals), marsupials (mammals with a pouch), and eutherians (placental mammals). After the extinction of large dinosaurs, pterosaurs, and marine reptiles during the late Cretaceous period, mammals underwent an adaptive radiation, giving rise to large predators and herbivores as well as flying and aquatic species.

Monotremes

Monotremes are found only in Australia and New Guinea and are represented by one species of platypus and four species of echidnas (spiny anteaters). Monotremes lay eggs, a character that is ancestral for amniotes and retained in most

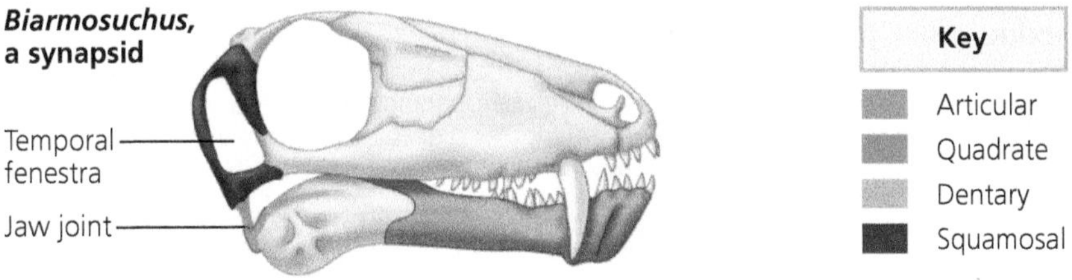

(a) In *Biarmosuchus*, the articular and quadrate bones formed the jaw joint.

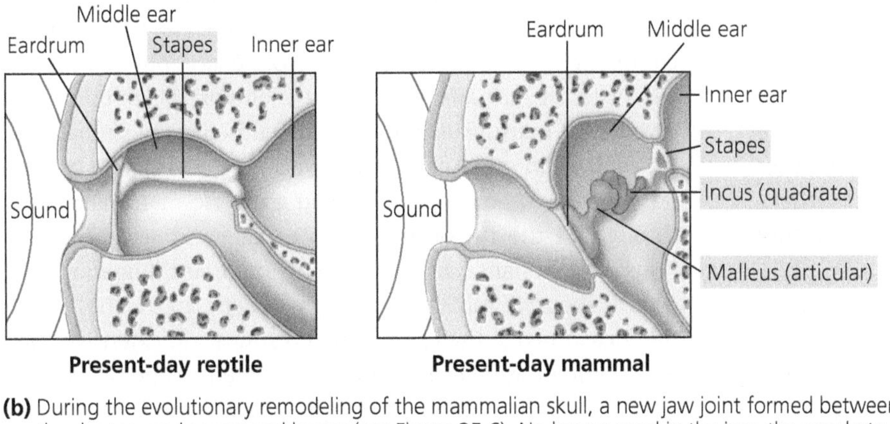

(b) During the evolutionary remodeling of the mammalian skull, a new jaw joint formed between the dentary and squamosal bones (see Figure 25.6). No longer used in the jaw, the quadrate and articular bones became incorporated into the middle ear as two of the three bones that transmit sound from the eardrum to the inner ear.

◄ **Figure 34.37 The evolution of the mammalian ear bones.** *Biarmosuchus* was a synapsid, a lineage that eventually gave rise to the mammals. Bones that transmit sound in the ear of mammals arose from the modification of bones in the jaw of nonmammalian synapsids.

MAKE CONNECTIONS *Review the definition of* exaptation *in Concept 25.6 (p. 530). Summarize the process by which exaptation occurs and explain how the incorporation of the articular and quadrate bones into the mammalian inner ear is an example.*

▲ **Figure 34.38** **Short-beaked echidna (*Tachyglossus aculeatus*), an Australian monotreme.** Monotremes have hair and produce milk, but they lack nipples. Monotremes are the only mammals that lay eggs (inset).

reptiles (Figure 34.38). Like all mammals, monotremes have hair and produce milk, but they lack nipples. Milk is secreted by glands on the belly of the mother. After hatching, the baby sucks the milk from the mother's fur.

Marsupials

Opossums, kangaroos, and koalas are examples of **marsupials**. Both marsupials and eutherians share derived characters not found among monotremes. They have higher metabolic rates and nipples that provide milk, and they give birth to live young. The embryo develops inside the uterus of the female's reproductive tract. The lining of the uterus and the extraembryonic membranes that arise from the embryo form a **placenta**, a structure in which nutrients diffuse into the embryo from the mother's blood.

A marsupial is born very early in its development and completes its embryonic development while nursing. In most species, the nursing young are held within a maternal pouch called a *marsupium* (Figure 34.39a). A red kangaroo, for instance, is about the size of a honeybee at its birth, just 33 days after fertilization. Its back legs are merely buds, but its front legs are strong enough for it to crawl from the exit of its mother's reproductive tract to a pouch that opens to the front of her body, a journey that lasts a few minutes. In other species, the marsupium opens to the rear of the mother's body; in bandicoots, this protects the young as their mother burrows in the dirt (Figure 34.39b).

Marsupials existed worldwide during the Mesozoic era, but today they are found only in the Australian region and in North and South America. The biogeography of marsupials is an example of the interplay between biological and geologic evolution (see Concept 25.4). After the breakup of the supercontinent Pangaea, South America and Australia became island continents, and their marsupials diversified in isolation from the eutherians that began an adaptive radiation on the northern continents. Australia has not been in contact with another continent since early in the Cenozoic era, about 65 million years ago. In Australia, convergent evolution has resulted in a diversity of marsupials that resemble eutherians in similar ecological roles in other parts of the world (Figure 34.40). In contrast, although South America had a diverse marsupial fauna throughout the Paleogene, it has experienced several migrations of eutherians. One of the most important migrations occurred about 3 million years ago, when North and South America joined at the Panamanian isthmus and extensive two-way traffic of animals took place over the land bridge. Today, only three families of marsupials live outside the Australian region, and the only marsupials found in the wild in North America are a few species of opossum.

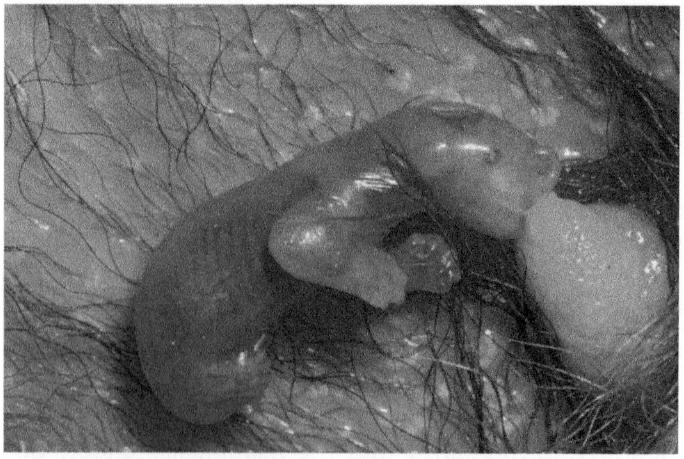

(a) A young brushtail possum. The offspring of marsupials are born very early in their development. They finish their growth while nursing from a nipple (in their mother's pouch in most species).

(b) Long-nosed bandicoot. Most bandicoots are diggers and burrowers that eat mainly insects but also some small vertebrates and plant material. Their rear-opening pouch helps protect the young from dirt as the mother digs. Other marsupials, such as kangaroos, have a pouch that opens to the front.

▲ **Figure 34.39** **Australian marsupials.**

▲ Figure 34.40 **Convergent evolution of marsupials and eutherians (placental mammals).** (Drawings are not to scale.)

Eutherians (Placental Mammals)

Eutherians are commonly called placental mammals because their placentas are more complex than those of marsupials. Eutherians have a longer pregnancy than marsupials. Young eutherians complete their embryonic development within the uterus, joined to their mother by the placenta. The eutherian placenta provides an intimate and long-lasting association between the mother and her developing young.

The major groups of living eutherians are thought to have diverged from one another in a burst of evolutionary change. The timing of this burst is uncertain: It is dated to 100 million years ago by molecular data and 60 million years ago by morphological data. Figure 34.41, on the next two pages, explores the major eutherian orders and their possible phylogenetic relationships with each other as well as with the monotremes and marsupials.

Primates

The mammalian order Primates includes the lemurs, tarsiers, monkeys, and apes. Humans are members of the ape group.

Derived Characters of Primates Most primates have hands and feet adapted for grasping, and their digits have flat nails instead of the narrow claws of other mammals. There are other characteristic features of the hands and feet, too, such as skin ridges on the fingers (which account for human fingerprints). Relative to other mammals, primates have a large brain and short jaws, giving them a flat face. Their forward-looking eyes are close together on the front of the face. Primates also exhibit relatively well-developed parental care and complex social behavior.

The earliest known primates were tree-dwellers, and many of the characteristics of primates are adaptations to the demands of living in the trees. Grasping hands and feet allow primates to hang onto tree branches. All living primates, except humans, have a big toe that is widely separated from the other toes, enabling them to grasp branches with their feet. All primates also have a thumb that is relatively movable and separate from the fingers, but monkeys and apes have a fully **opposable thumb**; that is, they can touch the ventral surface (fingerprint side) of the tip of all four fingers with the ventral surface of the thumb of the same hand. In monkeys and apes other than humans, the opposable thumb functions in a grasping "power grip." In humans, a distinctive bone structure at the base of the thumb allows it to be used for more precise manipulation. The unique dexterity of humans represents descent with modification from our tree-dwelling ancestors. Arboreal maneuvering also requires excellent eye-hand coordination. The overlapping visual fields of the two forward-facing eyes enhance depth perception, an obvious advantage when brachiating (traveling by swinging from branch to branch in trees).

▼ Figure 34.41

Exploring Mammalian Diversity

Phylogenetic Relationships of Mammals

Evidence from numerous fossils and molecular analyses indicates that monotremes diverged from other mammals about 180 million years ago and that marsupials diverged from eutherians (placental mammals) about 140 million years ago. Molecular systematics has helped to clarify the evolutionary relationships between the eutherian orders, though there is still no broad consensus on a phylogenetic tree. One current hypothesis, represented by the tree shown below, clusters the eutherian orders into four main clades.

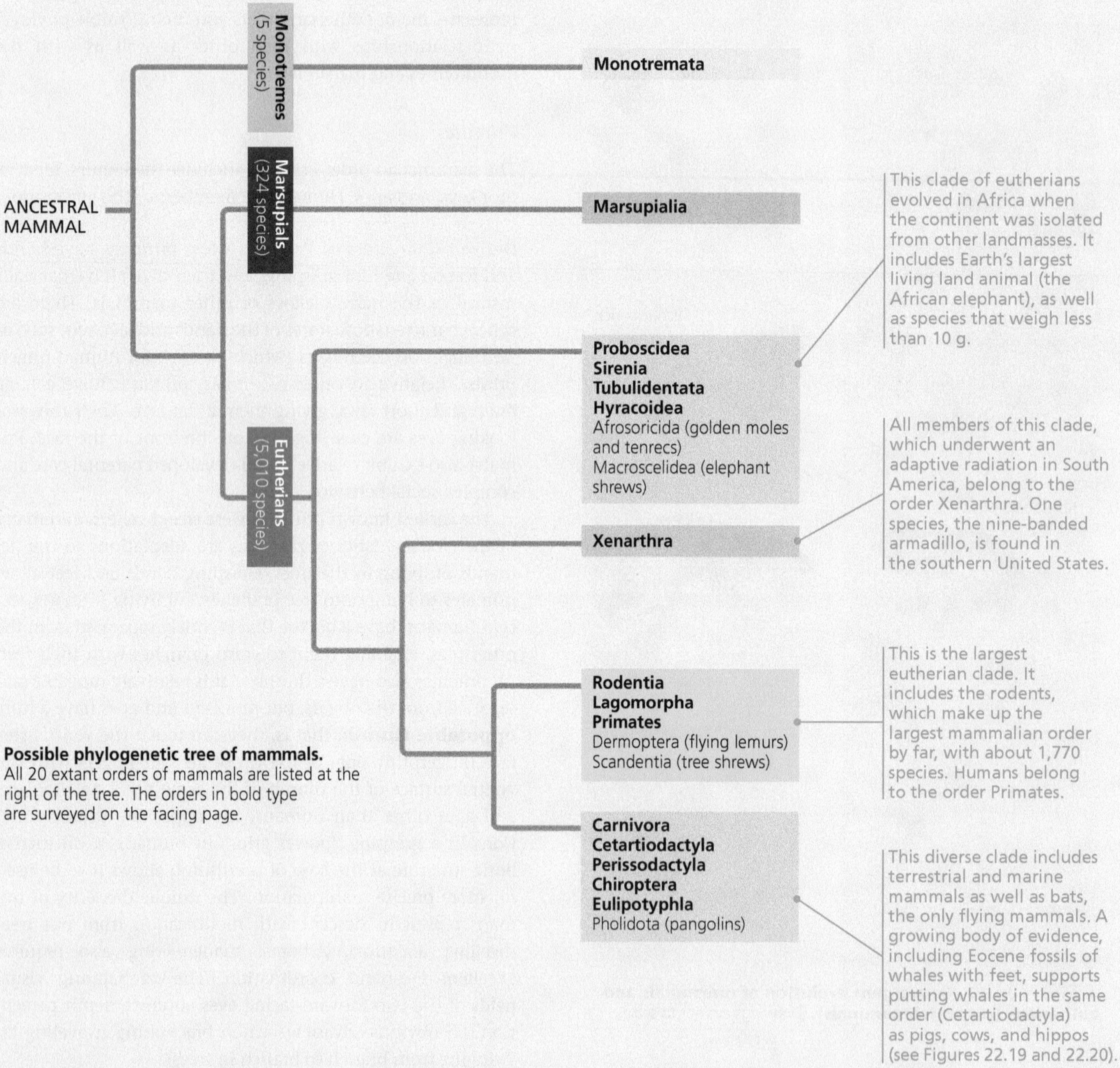

Possible phylogenetic tree of mammals. All 20 extant orders of mammals are listed at the right of the tree. The orders in bold type are surveyed on the facing page.

Orders and Examples	Main Characteristics
Monotremata Platypuses, echidnas  Echidna	Lay eggs; no nipples; young suck milk from fur of mother
Proboscidea Elephants  African elephant	Long, muscular trunk; thick, loose skin; upper incisors elongated as tusks
Sirenia Manatees, dugongs  Manatee	Aquatic; finlike forelimbs and no hind limbs; herbivorous
Xenarthra Sloths, anteaters, armadillos  Tamandua	Reduced teeth or no teeth; herbivorous (sloths) or carnivorous (anteaters, armadillos)
Lagomorpha Rabbits, hares, picas  Jackrabbit	Chisel-like incisors; hind legs longer than forelegs and adapted for running and jumping; herbivorous
Carnivora Dogs, wolves, bears, cats, weasels, otters, seals, walruses  Coyote	Sharp, pointed canine teeth and molars for shearing; carnivorous
Cetartiodactyla Artiodactyls Sheep, pigs, cattle, deer, giraffes  Bighorn sheep	Hooves with an even number of toes on each foot; herbivorous
Cetaceans Whales, dolphins, porpoises  Pacific white-sided porpoise	Aquatic; streamlined body; paddle-like forelimbs and no hind limbs; thick layer of insulating blubber; carnivorous
Marsupialia Kangaroos, opossums, koalas  Koala	Completes embryonic development in pouch on mother's body
Tubulidentata Aardvarks  Aardvark	Teeth consisting of many thin tubes cemented together; eats ants and termites
Hyracoidea Hyraxes  Rock hyrax	Short legs; stumpy tail; herbivorous; complex, multichambered stomach
Rodentia Squirrels, beavers, rats, porcupines, mice  Red squirrel	Chisel-like, continuously growing incisors worn down by gnawing; herbivorous
Primates Lemurs, monkeys, chimpanzees, gorillas, humans  Golden lion tamarin	Opposable thumbs; forward-facing eyes; well-developed cerebral cortex; omnivorous
Perissodactyla Horses, zebras, tapirs, rhinoceroses  Indian rhinoceros	Hooves with an odd number of toes on each foot; herbivorous
Chiroptera Bats  Frog-eating bat	Adapted for flight; broad skinfold that extends from elongated fingers to body and legs; carnivorous or herbivorous
Eulipotyphla "Core insectivores": some moles, some shrews  Star-nosed mole	Eat mainly insects and other small invertebrates

Living Primates There are three main groups of living primates: (1) the lemurs of Madagascar (Figure 34.42) and the lorises and bush babies of tropical Africa and southern Asia; (2) the tarsiers, which live in Southeast Asia; and (3) the **anthropoids**, which include monkeys and apes and are found worldwide. The first group—lemurs, lorises, and bush babies—probably resemble early arboreal primates. The oldest known anthropoid fossils, discovered in China in mid-Eocene strata dating to 45 million years ago, indicate that tarsiers are more closely related to anthropoids than to the lemur group (Figure 34.43).

▶ **Figure 34.42 Coquerel's sifakas (*Propithecus verreauxi coquereli*), a type of lemur.**

You can see in Figure 34.38 that monkeys do not form a clade but rather consist of two groups, the New and Old World monkeys. Both of these groups are thought to have originated in Africa or Asia. The fossil record indicates that New World monkeys first colonized South America roughly 25 million years ago. By that time, South America and Africa had drifted apart, and monkeys may have reached South America from Africa by rafting on logs or other debris. What is certain is that New World monkeys and Old World monkeys underwent separate adaptive radiations during their many millions of years of separation (Figure 34.44). All species of New World monkeys are arboreal, whereas Old World monkeys include ground-dwelling as well as arboreal species. Most monkeys in both groups are diurnal (active during the day) and usually live in bands held together by social behavior.

The other group of anthropoids consists of primates informally called apes (Figure 34.45). The ape group includes the genera *Hylobates* (gibbons), *Pongo* (orangutans), *Gorilla* (gorillas), *Pan* (chimpanzees and bonobos), and *Homo* (humans).

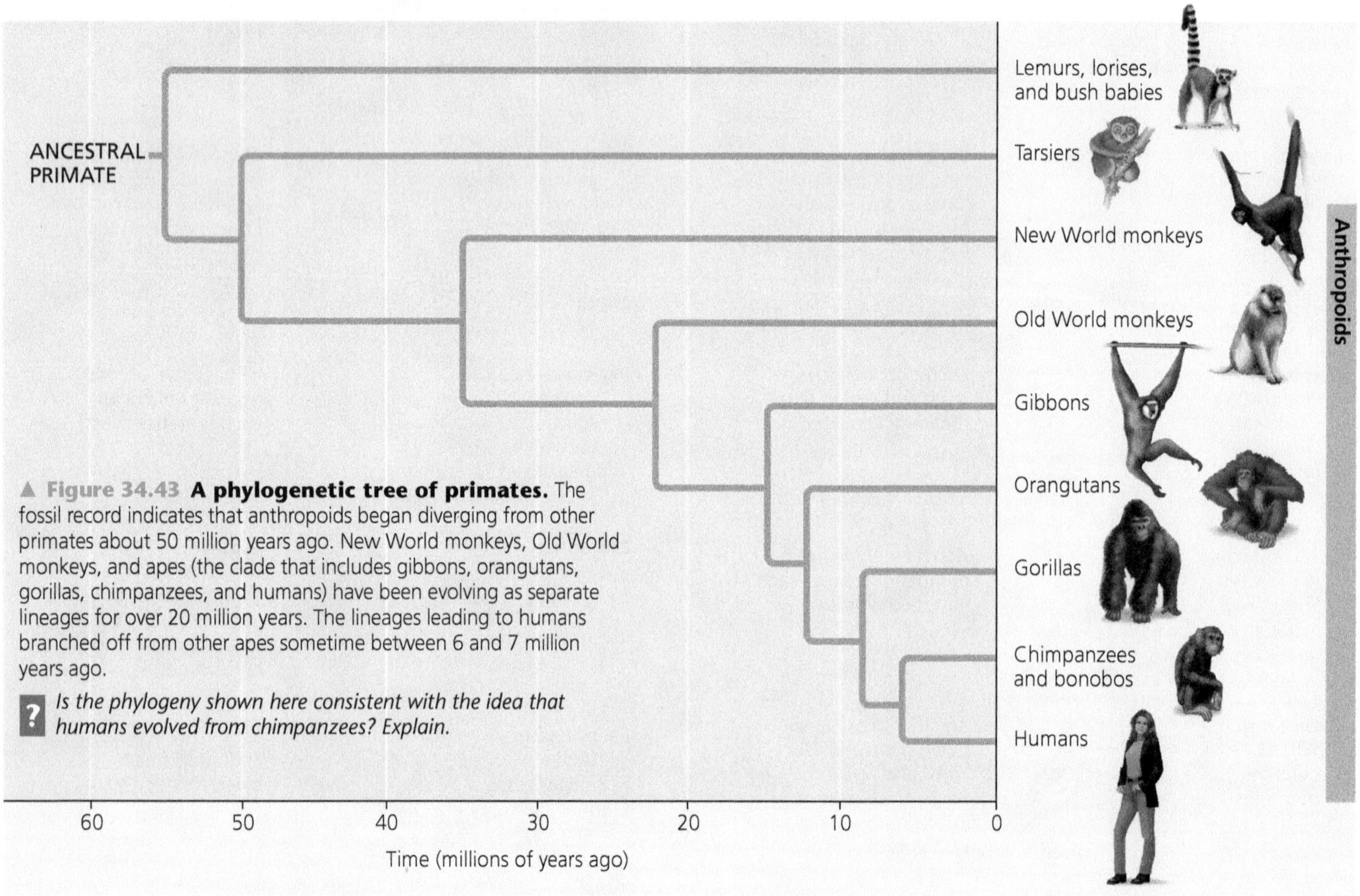

▲ **Figure 34.43 A phylogenetic tree of primates.** The fossil record indicates that anthropoids began diverging from other primates about 50 million years ago. New World monkeys, Old World monkeys, and apes (the clade that includes gibbons, orangutans, gorillas, chimpanzees, and humans) have been evolving as separate lineages for over 20 million years. The lineages leading to humans branched off from other apes sometime between 6 and 7 million years ago.

? *Is the phylogeny shown here consistent with the idea that humans evolved from chimpanzees? Explain.*

▼ **Figure 34.44 New World monkeys and Old World monkeys.**

(a) New World monkeys, such as spider monkeys (shown here), squirrel monkeys, and capuchins, have a prehensile tail and nostrils that open to the sides.

(b) Old World monkeys lack a prehensile tail, and their nostrils open downward. This group includes macaques (shown here), mandrils, baboons, and rhesus monkeys.

The apes diverged from Old World monkeys about 20–25 million years ago. Today, nonhuman apes are found exclusively in tropical regions of the Old World. With the exception of gibbons, living apes are larger than either New or Old World monkeys. All living apes have relatively long arms, short legs, and no tail. Although all nonhuman apes spend time in trees, only gibbons and orangutans are primarily arboreal. Social organization varies among the apes; gorillas and chimpanzees are highly social. Finally, compared to other primates, apes have a larger brain in proportion to their body size, and their behavior is more flexible. These two characteristics are especially prominent in the next group we'll consider, the hominins.

(a) Gibbons, such as this Muller's gibbon, are found only in southeastern Asia. Their very long arms and fingers are adaptations for brachiating (swinging by the arms from branch to branch).

(b) Orangutans are shy apes that live in the rain forests of Sumatra and Borneo. They spend most of their time in trees; note the foot adapted for grasping and the opposable thumb.

(c) Gorillas are the largest apes; some males are almost 2 m tall and weigh about 200 kg. Found only in Africa, these herbivores usually live in groups of up to about 20 individuals.

(d) Chimpanzees live in tropical Africa. They feed and sleep in trees but also spend a great deal of time on the ground. Chimpanzees are intelligent, communicative, and social.

(e) Bonobos are in the same genus (*Pan*) as chimpanzees but are smaller. They survive today only in the African nation of Congo.

▲ **Figure 34.45 Nonhuman apes.**

CONCEPT CHECK 34.7

1. Contrast monotremes, marsupials, and eutherians in terms of how they bear young.
2. Identify at least five derived traits of primates.
3. **MAKE CONNECTIONS** Develop a hypothesis to explain why the diversity of mammals increased in the Cenozoic. Your explanation should consider mammalian adaptations as well as factors such as mass extinctions and continental drift (review these factors in Concept 25.4, pp. 519–524).

For suggested answers, see Appendix A.

CONCEPT 34.8

Humans are mammals that have a large brain and bipedal locomotion

In our tour of Earth's biodiversity, we come at last to our own species, *Homo sapiens*, which is about 200,000 years old. When you consider that life has existed on Earth for at least 3.5 billion years, we are clearly evolutionary newcomers.

Derived Characters of Humans

Many characters distinguish humans from other apes. Most obviously, humans stand upright and are bipedal (walk on two legs). Humans have a much larger brain and are capable of language, symbolic thought, artistic expression, and the manufacture and use of complex tools. Humans also have reduced jawbones and jaw muscles, along with a shorter digestive tract.

At the molecular level, the list of derived characters of humans is growing as scientists compare the genomes of humans and chimpanzees. Although the two genomes are 99% identical, a difference of 1% can translate into a large number of changes in a genome that contains 3 billion base pairs. Furthermore, changes in a small number of genes can have large effects. This point was highlighted by recent results showing that humans and chimpanzees differ in the expression of 19 regulatory genes. These genes turn other genes on and off and hence may account for many differences between humans and chimpanzees.

Bear in mind that such genomic differences—and whatever derived phenotypic traits they code for—separate humans from other *living* apes. But many of these new characters first emerged in our ancestors, long before our own species appeared. We will consider some of these ancestors to see how these characters originated.

The Earliest Hominins

The study of human origins is known as **paleoanthropology**. Paleoanthropologists have unearthed fossils of approximately 20 extinct species that are more closely related to humans than to chimpanzees. These species are known as **hominins** (Figure 34.46, on the facing page). (Although a majority of anthropologists now use the term *hominin*, its older synonym, *hominid*, continues to be used by some). Since 1994, fossils of four hominin species dating to more than 4 million years ago have been discovered. The oldest of these hominins, *Sahelanthropus tchadensis*, lived about 6.5 million years ago.

Sahelanthropus and other early hominins shared some of the derived characters of humans. For example, they had reduced canine teeth, and some fossils suggest that they had relatively flat faces. They also show signs of having been more upright and bipedal than other apes. One clue to their upright stance can be found in the foramen magnum, the hole at the base of the skull through which the spinal cord exits. In chimpanzees, the foramen magnum is relatively far back on the skull, while in early hominins (and in humans), it is located underneath the skull. This position allows us to hold our head directly over our body, as apparently early hominins did as well. The pelvis, leg bones, and feet of the 4.4-million-year-old *Ardipithecus ramidus* also suggest that early hominins were increasingly bipedal (Figure 34.47). (We will return to the subject of bipedalism later.)

Note that the characters that distinguish humans from other living apes did not all evolve in tight unison. While early hominins were showing signs of bipedalism, their brains remained small—about 300–450 cm^3 in volume, compared with an average of 1,300 cm^3 for *Homo sapiens*. The earliest hominins were also small overall. *A. ramidus*, for example, is

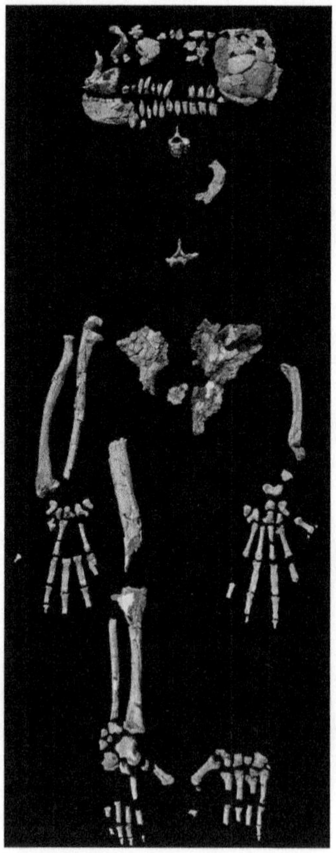

◄ **Figure 34.47 The skeleton of "Ardi," a 4.4-million-year-old hominin, *Ardipithecus ramidus*.**

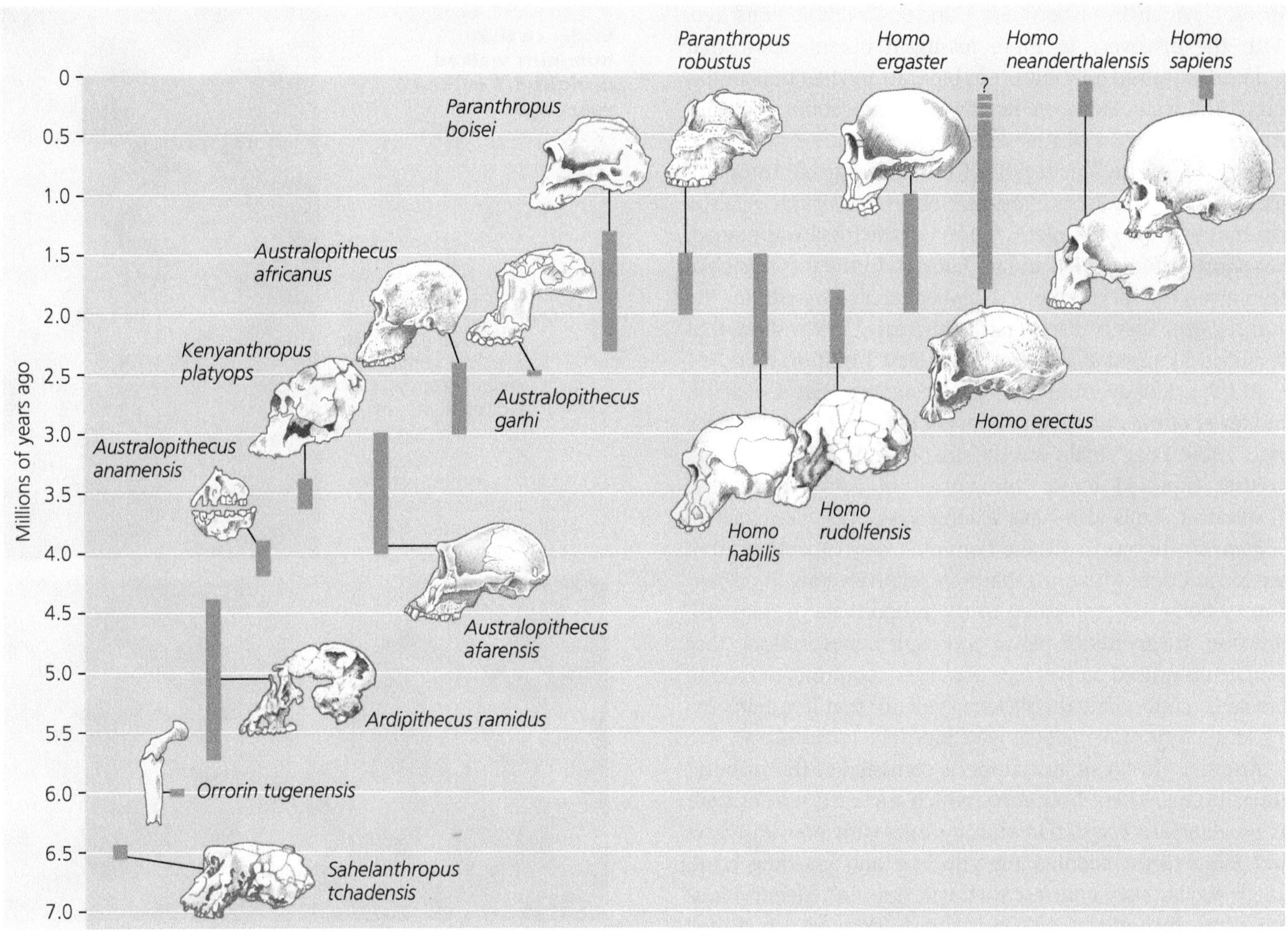

▲ **Figure 34.46 A timeline for some selected hominin species.** Most of these fossils come from sites in eastern and southern Africa. Note that at most times in hominin history, two or more hominin species were contemporaries. Some of the species are controversial, reflecting phylogenetic debates about the interpretation of skeletal details and biogeography.

estimated to have weighed only 50 kg, with relatively large teeth and a jaw that projected beyond the upper part of the face. Humans, in contrast, have a relatively flat face; compare your own face with that of the chimpanzees in Figure 34.45d.

It's important to avoid two common misconceptions when considering early hominins. One is to think of them either as chimpanzees or as having evolved from chimpanzees. Chimpanzees represent the tip of a separate branch of evolution, and they acquired derived characters of their own after they diverged from their common ancestor with humans.

Another misconception is to think of human evolution as a ladder leading directly from an ancestral ape to *Homo sapiens*. This error is often illustrated as a parade of fossil species that become progressively more like ourselves as they march across the page. If human evolution is a parade, it is a very disorderly one, with many groups breaking away to wander other evolutionary paths. At times, several hominin species coexisted. These species often differed in skull shape, body size, and diet (as inferred from their teeth). Ultimately, all but one lineage—the one that gave rise to *Homo sapiens*—ended in extinction. But when the characteristics of all hominins that lived over the past 6 million years are considered, *H. sapiens* appears not as the end result of a straight evolutionary path, but rather as the only surviving member of a highly branched evolutionary tree.

Australopiths

The fossil record indicates that hominin diversity increased dramatically between 4 and 2 million years ago. Many of the hominins from this period are collectively called australopiths. Their phylogeny remains unresolved on many points, but as a group, they are almost certainly paraphyletic. The earliest member of the group, *Australopithecus anamensis*, lived 4.2–3.9 million years ago, close in time to older hominins such as *Ardipithecus ramidus*.

Australopiths got their name from the 1924 discovery in South Africa of *Australopithecus africanus* ("southern ape of

Africa"), which lived between 3 and 2.4 million years ago. With the discovery of more fossils, it became clear that *A. africanus* walked fully erect (was bipedal) and had human-like hands and teeth. However, its brain was only about one-third the size of the brain of a present-day human.

In 1974, in the Afar region of Ethiopia, paleoanthropologists discovered a 3.2-million-year-old *Australopithecus* skeleton that was 40% complete. "Lucy," as the fossil was named, was short—only about 1 m tall. Lucy and similar fossils have been given the species name *Australopithecus afarensis* (for the Afar region). Fossils discovered in the early 1990s show that *A. afarensis* existed as a species for at least 1 million years.

At the risk of oversimplifying, we could say that *A. afarensis* had fewer of the derived characters of humans above the neck than below. Lucy's brain was the size of a softball, a size similar to that expected for a chimpanzee of Lucy's body size. *A. afarensis* skulls also have a long lower jaw. Skeletons of *A. afarensis* suggest that these hominins were capable of arboreal locomotion, with arms that were relatively long in proportion to body size (compared to the proportions in humans). However, fragments of pelvic and skull bones indicate that *A. afarensis* walked on two legs. Fossilized footprints in Laetoli, Tanzania, corroborate the skeletal evidence that hominins living at the time of *A. afarensis* were bipedal (Figure 34.48).

Another lineage of australopiths consisted of the "robust" australopiths. These hominins, which included species such as *Paranthropus boisei*, had sturdy skulls with powerful jaws and large teeth, adapted for grinding and chewing hard, tough foods. They contrast with the "gracile" (slender) australopiths, including *A. afarensis* and *A. africanus*, which had lighter feeding equipment adapted for softer foods.

Combining evidence from the earliest hominins with the much richer fossil record of later australopiths makes it possible to formulate hypotheses about significant trends in hominin evolution. Let's consider two of these trends: the emergence of bipedalism and tool use.

▶ **Figure 34.48 Evidence that hominins walked upright 3.5 million years ago.**

(a) The Laetoli footprints, more than 3.5 million years old, confirm that upright posture evolved quite early in hominin history.

(b) An artist's reconstruction of *A. afarensis*, a hominin alive at the time of the Laetoli footprints.

Bipedalism

Our anthropoid ancestors of 35–30 million years ago were still tree-dwellers. But by about 10 million years ago, the Himalayan mountain range had formed, thrust up in the aftermath of the Indian plate's collision with the Eurasian plate (see Figure 25.13). The climate became drier, and the forests of what are now Africa and Asia contracted. The result was an increased area of savanna (grassland) habitat, with fewer trees. For decades, paleoanthropologists have seen a strong connection between the rise of savannas and the rise of bipedal hominins. According to one hypothesis, tree-dwelling hominins could no longer move through the canopy, so natural selection favored adaptations that made moving over open ground more efficient. Underlying this idea is the fact that while nonhuman apes are superbly adapted for climbing trees, they are less well suited for ground travel. For example, as a chimpanzee walks, it uses four times the amount of energy used by a human.

Although elements of this hypothesis survive, the picture now appears somewhat more complex. Although all recently discovered fossils of early hominins show indications of bipedalism, none of these hominins lived in savannas. Instead, they lived in mixed habitats ranging from forests to open woodlands. Furthermore, whatever the selective pressure that led to bipedalism, hominins did not become more bipedal in a simple, linear fashion. *Ardipithecus* had skeletal elements indicating that it could switch to upright walking but also was well suited for climbing trees. Australopiths seem to have had various locomotor styles, and some species spent more time on the ground than others. Only about 1.9 million years ago did hominins begin to walk long distances on two legs. These hominins lived in more arid environments, where bipedal walking requires less energy than walking on all fours.

Tool Use

As you read earlier, the manufacture and use of complex tools is a derived behavioral character of humans. Determining the origin of tool use in hominin evolution is one of paleoanthropology's great challenges. Other apes are capable of surprisingly sophisticated tool use. Orangutans, for example, can fashion sticks into probes for retrieving insects from their nests. Chimpanzees are even more adept, using rocks to smash open food and putting leaves on their feet to walk over thorns. It's likely that early hominins were capable of this sort of simple tool use, but finding fossils of modified sticks or leaves that were used as shoes is practically impossible.

The oldest generally accepted evidence of tool use by hominins is 2.5-million-year-old cut marks on animal bones found in Ethiopia. These marks suggest that hominins cut flesh from the bones of animals using stone tools. Interestingly, the hominins whose fossils were found near the site where the bones were discovered had a relatively small brain. If these hominins, which have been named *Australopithecus garhi*, were in fact the creators of the stone tools used on the bones, that would suggest that stone tool use originated before the evolution of large brains in hominins.

Early *Homo*

The earliest fossils that paleoanthropologists place in our genus, *Homo*, include those of the species *Homo habilis*. These fossils, ranging in age from about 2.4 to 1.6 million years, show clear signs of certain derived hominin characters above the neck. Compared to the australopiths, *H. habilis* had a shorter jaw and a larger brain volume, about 600–750 cm^3. Sharp stone tools have also been found with some fossils of *H. habilis* (the name means "handy man").

Fossils from 1.9 to 1.5 million years ago mark a new stage in hominin evolution. A number of paleoanthropologists recognize these fossils as those of a distinct species, *Homo ergaster*. *Homo ergaster* had a substantially larger brain than *H. habilis* (over 900 cm^3), as well as long, slender legs with hip joints well adapted for long-distance walking (Figure 34.49). The fingers were relatively short and straight, suggesting that *H. ergaster* did not climb trees like earlier hominins. *Homo ergaster* fossils have been discovered in far more arid environments than earlier hominins and have been associated with more sophisticated stone tools. Its smaller teeth also suggest that *H. ergaster* either ate different foods than australopiths (more meat and less plant material) or prepared some of its food before chewing, perhaps by cooking or mashing the food.

Homo ergaster marks an important shift in the relative sizes of the sexes. In primates, a size difference between males and females is a major component of sexual dimorphism (see Chapter 23). On average, male gorillas and orangutans weigh about twice as much as females of their species. In chimpanzees and bonobos, males are only about 1.35 times as heavy as females, on average. In *Australopithecus afarensis*, males were 1.5 times as heavy as females. But in early *Homo*, sexual dimorphism was significantly reduced, and this trend continues through our own species: Human males average about 1.2 times the weight of females.

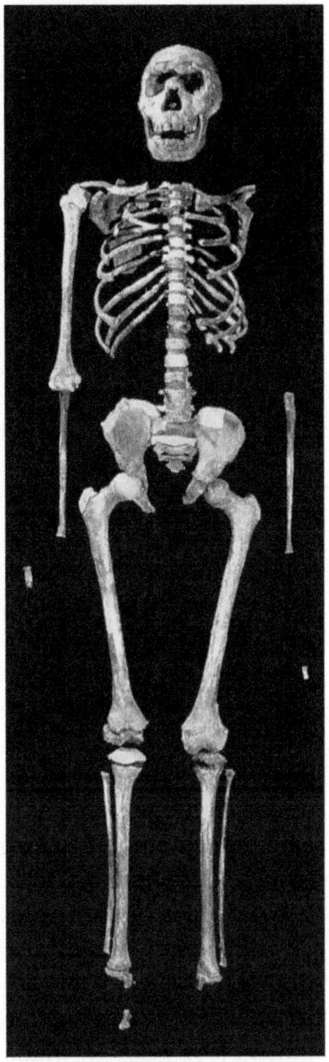

▶ Figure 34.49 **Fossil of *Homo ergaster*.** This 1.7-million-year-old fossil from Kenya belongs to a young *Homo ergaster* male. This individual was tall, slender, and fully bipedal, and he had a relatively large brain.

The reduced sexual dimorphism may offer some clues to the social systems of extinct hominins. In extant primates, extreme sexual dimorphism is associated with intense male-male competition for multiple females. In species that undergo more pair-bonding (including our own), sexual dimorphism is less dramatic. In *H. ergaster*, therefore, males and females may have engaged in more pair-bonding than earlier hominins did. This shift may have been associated with long-term care of the young by both parents. Human babies depend on their parents for food and protection much longer than do the young of other apes.

Fossils now generally recognized as *H. ergaster* were originally considered early members of another species, *Homo erectus*, and some paleoanthropologists still hold this position. *Homo erectus* originated in Africa and was the first hominin to migrate out of Africa. The oldest fossils of hominins outside Africa, dating back 1.8 million years, were discovered in 2000 in the former Soviet Republic of Georgia. *Homo erectus* eventually migrated as far as the Indonesian archipelago. Fossil evidence indicates that *H. erectus* became extinct sometime after 200,000 years ago; one group may have persisted on Java until roughly 50,000 years ago.

Neanderthals

In 1856, miners discovered some mysterious human fossils in a cave in the Neander Valley in Germany. The 40,000-year-old fossils belonged to a thick-boned hominin with a prominent brow. The hominin was named *Homo neanderthalensis* and is commonly called a Neanderthal. Neanderthals were living in Europe by 350,000 years ago and later spread to the Near East, central Asia, and southern Siberia. They had a brain as large as that of present-day humans, buried their dead, and made hunting tools from stone and wood. But despite their adaptations and culture, Neanderthals apparently became extinct about 28,000 years ago.

At one time, many paleoanthropologists considered Neanderthals to be a stage in the evolution of *Homo erectus* into *Homo sapiens*. Now most have abandoned this view, partly due to the analysis of mitochondrial DNA (**Figure 34.50**). These and other genetic results suggest that Neanderthals may have contributed little to the gene pool of *H. sapiens*. However, a 2010 analysis of the DNA sequence of the Neanderthal genome appears to be consistent with limited gene flow between the two species. In addition, some researchers have argued that evidence of gene flow can be found in fossils that show a mixture of *H. sapiens* and Neanderthal characteristics. Further genetic analyses and fossil discoveries will be needed to resolve the ongoing debate over the extent of genetic exchange between the two species.

Homo sapiens

Evidence from fossils, archaeology, and DNA studies has led to a compelling hypothesis about how our own species, *Homo sapiens*, emerged and spread around the world.

Fossil evidence indicates that the ancestors of humans originated in Africa. Older species (perhaps *H. ergaster* or *H. erectus*) gave rise to later species, ultimately including *H. sapiens*. Furthermore, the oldest known fossils of our own species have been found at two different sites in Ethiopia and include specimens that are 195,000 and 160,000 years old (**Figure 34.51**). These early humans had less pronounced browridges than found in *H. erectus* and Neanderthals, and they were more slender than other recent hominins.

The Ethiopian fossils support inferences about the origin of humans from molecular evidence. As shown in Figure 34.50, DNA analyses indicate that all living humans are more closely related to one another than to Neanderthals. Other studies on human DNA show that Europeans and Asians share a relatively recent common ancestor and that many African lineages branched off more basal positions on the human family tree. These findings strongly suggest that all living humans have ancestors that originated as *H. sapiens* in Africa, which is further supported by analysis of mitochondrial DNA and Y chromosomes from members of various human populations.

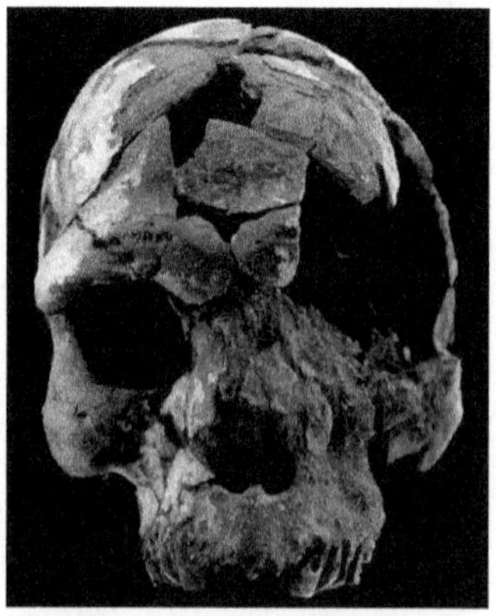

▲ **Figure 34.51 A 160,000-year-old fossil of *Homo sapiens*.** This skull, discovered in Ethiopia in 2003, differs little from the skulls of living humans.

The oldest fossils of *H. sapiens* outside Africa are from the Middle East and date back about 115,000 years.

▼ **Figure 34.50** **INQUIRY**

Did Neanderthals give rise to European humans?

EXPERIMENT People have long been fascinated by Neanderthals and their relationship to *Homo sapiens*. Several fossils discovered in Europe have been interpreted by some researchers as showing a mixture of Neanderthal and human features, leading to the suggestion that European humans bred extensively with or descended from Neanderthals. Igor Ovchinnikov and William Goodwin, then at the University of Glasgow, and their team used genetic methods to assess the relationship between Neanderthals and *H. sapiens*. The team extracted mitochondrial DNA (mtDNA) from a Neanderthal fossil (Neanderthal 1) and compared its sequence to an mtDNA sequence that other researchers had obtained three years earlier from a different Neanderthal fossil (Neanderthal 2). Mitochondrial DNA sequences were also obtained for a number of living humans from Europe, Africa, and Asia. The researchers then used Neanderthal and *H. sapiens* mtDNA sequences to construct a phylogenetic tree for Neanderthals and humans; data from chimpanzees were used to root the tree. This approach permitted the researchers to test the following hypothesis:

Hypothesis: Neanderthals gave rise to European humans.

Expected phylogeny:

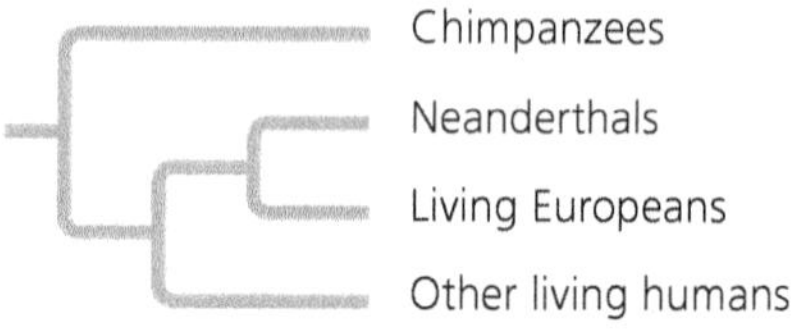

RESULTS The two Neanderthal mtDNA sequences differed at 3.5% of the bases, whereas on average, the Neanderthal and *H. sapiens* mtDNA differed at 24% of the bases. The phylogenetic analysis yielded the following tree:

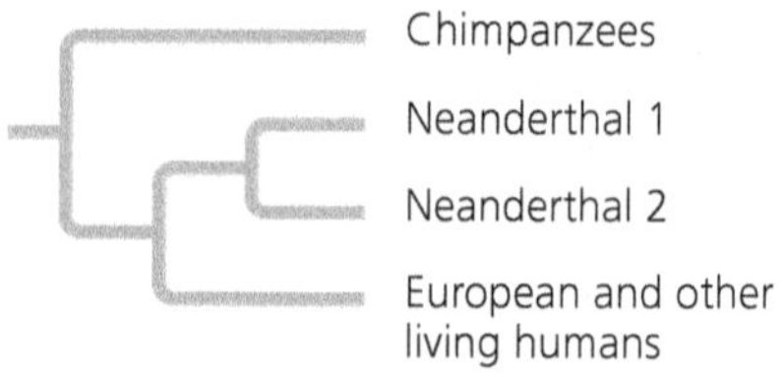

CONCLUSION The Neanderthals form one clade, and living humans form another, separate clade. Thus, it is not likely that Neanderthals gave rise to European humans.

SOURCE I. V. Ovchinnikov et al., Molecular analysis of Neanderthal DNA from the northern Caucasus, *Nature* 404:490–493 (2000).

WHAT IF? The human and chimpanzee lineages diverged about 6 million years ago. Can the phylogeny shown in RESULTS be used to infer when Neanderthal and human lineages diverged? Explain.

Studies of the human Y chromosome suggest that humans spread beyond Africa in one or more waves, first into Asia and then to Europe and Australia. The date of the first arrival of humans in the New World is uncertain, although the oldest generally accepted evidence puts that date at about 15,000 years ago.

New findings continually update our understanding of the evolution of *H. sapiens*. For example, in 2004, researchers reported an astonishing find: skeletal remains of adult hominins dating from just 18,000 years ago and representing a previously unknown species, which they named *Homo floresiensis*. Discovered in a limestone cave on the Indonesian island of Flores, the individuals were much shorter and had a much smaller brain volume than *H. sapiens*—more similar, in fact, to an australopith. The researchers who discovered these fossils argue that the skeletons also display many derived traits, including skull thickness and proportions and teeth shape, suggesting that the species is descended from the larger *H. erectus*. Not convinced, some researchers have argued that the fossils represent small *H. sapiens* individuals with deformed, miniature brains, a condition called microcephaly.

However, a 2007 study found that the wrist bones of the Flores fossils are similar in shape to those of nonhuman apes and early hominins, but different from those of Neanderthals and *H. sapiens*. These researchers concluded that the Flores fossils represent a species whose lineage branched off before the origin of the clade that includes Neanderthals and humans. A later study comparing the foot bones of the Flores fossils with those of other hominins also indicated that *H. floresiensis* arose before *H. sapiens*; in fact, these researchers suggested that *H. floresiensis* may have descended from an as-yet-unidentified hominin that lived even earlier than *H. erectus*.

If further evidence continues to support the designation of *H. floresiensis* as a new hominin, one intriguing explanation for this species' apparent "shrinkage" is that isolation on the island may have resulted in selection for greatly reduced size. Such dramatic size reduction is well studied in other dwarf mammalian species that are endemic to islands, including primitive pygmy elephants found near the Flores fossils. One such study found that on islands, the brains of dwarf fossil hippos were proportionally even smaller than their bodies. One possible explanation for this finding is that smaller brains resulted from selection for reduced energy consumption (the mammalian brain uses large amounts of energy). Applying their results to the Flores fossils, the researchers concluded that the brain size of *H. floresiensis* closely matches that predicted for a dwarf hominin of its body size. Compelling questions that may yet be answered from the cache of anthropological and archaeological finds on Flores include how *H. floresiensis* originated and whether it encountered *H. sapiens*, which also was living in Indonesia 18,000 years ago.

The rapid expansion of our species may have been spurred by changes in human cognition as *H. sapiens* evolved in Africa. Evidence of sophisticated thought in *H. sapiens* includes a 2002 discovery in South Africa of 77,000-year-old art—geometric markings made on pieces of ochre (Figure 34.52). And in 2004, archaeologists working in southern and eastern Africa found 75,000-year-old ostrich eggs and snail shells with holes neatly drilled through them. By 36,000 years ago, humans were producing spectacular cave paintings (see Figure 56.33a). While these developments can help us understand the spread of *H. sapiens*, it is not clear whether they played a role in the extinction of other hominins. Neanderthals, for example, also

▲ **Figure 34.52 Art, a human hallmark.** The engravings on this 77,000-year-old piece of ochre, discovered in South Africa's Blombos Cave, are among the earliest signs of symbolic thought in humans.

made complex tools and showed a capacity for symbolic thought. As a result, the earlier suggestion that Neanderthals were driven to extinction by competition with *H. sapiens* is now being questioned by some scientists.

Our discussion of humans brings this unit on biological diversity to an end. But this organization isn't meant to imply that life consists of a ladder leading from lowly microorganisms to lofty humanity. Biological diversity is the product of branching phylogeny, not ladderlike "progress," however we choose to measure it. The fact that there are more species of ray-finned fishes alive today than all other vertebrates combined is a clear indication that our finned relatives are not outmoded underachievers that failed to leave the water. The tetrapods—amphibians, reptiles, and mammals—are derived from one lineage of lobe-finned vertebrates. As tetrapods diversified on land, fishes continued their branching evolution in the greatest portion of the biosphere's volume. Similarly, the ubiquity of diverse prokaryotes throughout the biosphere today is a reminder of the enduring ability of these relatively simple organisms to keep up with the times through adaptive evolution. Biology exalts life's diversity, past and present.

CONCEPT CHECK 34.8

1. Identify some characters that distinguish hominins from other apes.
2. Provide an example in which different features of organisms in the hominin evolutionary lineage evolved at different rates.
3. **WHAT IF?** Some genetic studies suggest that the most recent common ancestor of *Homo sapiens* that lived outside of Africa spread from Africa about 50,000 years ago. Compare this date with the dates of fossils given in the text. Can both the genetic results and the dates ascribed to the fossils be correct? Explain.

For suggested answers, see Appendix A.

34 CHAPTER REVIEW

SUMMARY OF KEY CONCEPTS

Key Concept	Clade	Description
Concept 34.1 Chordates have a notochord and a dorsal, hollow nerve cord (pp. 697–701) **?** *Describe likely features of the chordate common ancestor and explain your reasoning.*	Cephalochordata (lancelets) 	Basal chordates; marine suspension feeders that exhibit four key derived characters of chordates
	Urochordata (tunicates) 	Marine suspension feeders; larvae display the derived traits of chordates
Concept 34.2 Craniates are chordates that have a head (pp. 701–703) **?** *Compare the typical lifestyle of craniates with that of lancelets and tunicates.*	Myxini (hagfishes and relatives) 	Jawless marine organisms; have head that includes a skull and brain, eyes, and other sensory organs
Concept 34.3 Vertebrates are craniates that have a backbone (pp. 703–704) **?** *Identify the shared features of early fossil vertebrates.*	Petromyzontida (lampreys) 	Jawless vertebrates; typically feed by attaching to a live fish and ingesting its blood
Concept 34.4 Gnathostomes are vertebrates that have jaws (pp. 704–709) **?** *How would the appearance of organisms with jaws have altered ecological interactions? Provide supporting evidence.*	Chondrichthyes (sharks, rays, skates, ratfishes) 	Aquatic gnathostomes; have cartilaginous skeleton, a derived trait formed by the reduction of an ancestral mineralized skeleton
	Actinopterygii (ray-finned fishes) 	Aquatic gnathostomes; have bony skeleton and maneuverable fins supported by rays
	Actinistia (coelacanths) 	Ancient lineage of aquatic lobe-fins still surviving in Indian Ocean
	Dipnoi (lungfishes) 	Freshwater lobe-fins with both lungs and gills; sister group of tetrapods
Concept 34.5 Tetrapods are gnathostomes that have limbs (pp. 709–713) **?** *Which features of amphibians restrict most species to living in aquatic or moist terrestrial habitats?*	Amphibia (salamanders, frogs, caecilians) 	Have four limbs descended from modified fins; most have moist skin that functions in gas exchange; many live both in water (as larvae) and on land (as adults)
Concept 34.6 Amniotes are tetrapods that have a terrestrially adapted egg (pp. 713–720) **?** *Explain why birds are considered reptiles.*	Reptilia (tuataras, lizards and snakes, turtles, crocodilians, birds)  	One of two groups of living amniotes; have amniotic eggs and rib cage ventilation, key adaptations for life on land
Concept 34.7 Mammals are amniotes that have hair and produce milk (pp. 720–728) **?** *Describe the origin and early evolution of mammals.*	Mammalia (monotremes, marsupials, eutherians)  	Evolved from synapsid ancestors; include egg-laying monotremes (echidnas, platypus); pouched marsupials (such as kangaroos, opossums); and eutherians (placental mammals, such as rodents, primates)

Chordates: notochord; dorsal, hollow nerve cord; pharyngeal slits; post-anal tail

Craniates: two sets of *Hox* genes, neural crest

Vertebrates: *Dlx* genes duplication, backbone of vertebrae

Gnathostomes: hinged jaws, four sets of *Hox* genes

Osteichthyans: bony skeleton

Lobe-fins: muscular fins or limbs

Tetrapods: four limbs, neck, fused pelvic girdle

Amniotes: amniotic egg, rib cage ventilation

CONCEPT 34.8

Humans are mammals that have a large brain and bipedal locomotion (pp. 728–733)

- Derived characters of humans include that we are bipedal and have a larger brain and reduced jaw compared with other apes.
- Hominins—humans and species that are more closely related to humans than to chimpanzees—originated in Africa at least 6 million years ago. Early hominins had a small brain but probably walked upright.
- The oldest evidence of tool use is 2.5 million years old.
- *Homo ergaster* was the first fully bipedal, large-brained hominin. *Homo erectus* was the first hominin to leave Africa.
- Neanderthals lived in Europe and the Near East from about 350,000 to 28,000 years ago.
- *Homo sapiens* originated in Africa about 195,000 years ago and began to spread to other continents about 115,000 years ago.

? *Explain why it is misleading to portray human evolution as a "ladder" leading to* Homo sapiens.

TEST YOUR UNDERSTANDING

LEVEL 1: KNOWLEDGE/COMPREHENSION

1. Vertebrates and tunicates share
   a. jaws adapted for feeding.
   b. a high degree of cephalization.
   c. the formation of structures from the neural crest.
   d. an endoskeleton that includes a skull.
   e. a notochord and a dorsal, hollow nerve cord.
2. Some animals that lived 530 million years ago resembled lancelets but had a brain and a skull. These animals may represent
   a. the first chordates.
   b. a "missing link" between urochordates and cephalochordates.
   c. early craniates.
   d. marsupials.
   e. nontetrapod gnathostomes.
3. Which of the following could be considered the most recent common ancestor of living tetrapods?
   a. a sturdy-finned, shallow-water lobe-fin whose appendages had skeletal supports similar to those of terrestrial vertebrates
   b. an armored, jawed placoderm with two pairs of appendages
   c. an early ray-finned fish that developed bony skeletal supports in its paired fins
   d. a salamander that had legs supported by a bony skeleton but moved with the side-to-side bending typical of fishes
   e. an early terrestrial caecilian whose legless condition had evolved secondarily
4. Unlike eutherians, *both* monotremes and marsupials
   a. lack nipples.
   b. have some embryonic development outside the uterus.
   c. lay eggs.
   d. are found in Australia and Africa.
   e. include only insectivores and herbivores.
5. Which clade does *not* include humans?
   a. synapsids
   b. lobe-fins
   c. diapsids
   d. craniates
   e. osteichthyans
6. As hominins diverged from other primates, which of the following appeared first?
   a. reduced jawbones
   b. language
   c. bipedal locomotion
   d. the making of stone tools
   e. an enlarged brain

LEVEL 2: APPLICATION/ANALYSIS

7. **EVOLUTION CONNECTION**
   Living members of a vertebrate lineage can be very different from early members of the lineage, and evolutionary reversals (character losses) are common. Give examples that illustrate these observations, and explain their evolutionary causes.

LEVEL 3: SYNTHESIS/EVALUATION

8. **SCIENTIFIC INQUIRY**
   DRAW IT As a consequence of size alone, organisms that are large tend to have larger brains than organisms that are small. However, some organisms have brains that are considerably larger than expected for an animal of their size. There are high energetic costs associated with the development and maintenance of brains that are large relative to body size.
   (a) The fossil record documents trends in which brains that are large relative to body size evolved in certain lineages, including hominins. In such lineages, what can you infer about the relative magnitude of the costs and benefits of large brains?
   (b) Hypothesize how natural selection might favor the evolution of large brains despite their high maintenance costs.
   (c) Data for 14 bird species are listed below. Graph the data, placing deviation from expected brain size on the *x*-axis and mortality rate on the *y*-axis. What can you conclude about the relationship between brain size and mortality?

Deviation from Expected Brain Size*	−2.4	−2.1	2.0	−1.8	−1.0	0.0	0.3	0.7	1.2	1.3	2.0	2.3	3.0	3.2
Mortality Rate	0.9	0.7	0.5	0.9	0.4	0.7	0.8	0.4	0.8	0.3	0.6	0.6	0.3	0.6

D. Sol et al., Big-brained birds survive better in nature, *Proceedings of the Royal Society B* 274:763–769 (2007).

*Values <0 indicate brain sizes smaller than expected; values >0 indicate sizes larger than expected.

9. **WRITE ABOUT A THEME**
   Emergent Properties Early tetrapods had a sprawling gait (like that of a lizard): As the right front foot moved forward, the body twisted to the left and the left rib cage and lung were compressed; the reverse occurred with the next step. Normal breathing, in which both lungs expand equally with each breath, was hindered during walking and prevented during running. In a short essay (100–150 words), explain how the origin of organisms such as dinosaurs, whose gait allowed them to move without compressing their lungs, could have led to emergent properties in biological communities.

For selected answers, see Appendix A.

APPENDIX A Answers

Chapter 1

Figure Questions

Figure 1.7 The arrangement of fingers and opposable thumb in the human hand, combined with fingernails and a complex system of nerves and muscles, allows the hand to grasp and manipulate objects with great dexterity. **Figure 1.13** Substance B would be made continuously and would accumulate in large amounts. Neither C nor D would be made, so D would not be able to inhibit Enzyme 1 and regulate the pathway. **Figure 1.27** The percentage of brown artificial snakes attacked would probably be higher than the percentage of artificial kingsnakes attacked in all areas (whether or not inhabited by coral snakes).

Concept Check 1.1

1. Examples: A molecule consists of *atoms* bonded together. Each organelle has an orderly arrangement of *molecules*. Photosynthetic plant cells contain *organelles* called chloroplasts. A tissue consists of a group of similar *cells*. Organs such as the heart are constructed from several *tissues*. A complex multicellular organism, such as a plant, has several types of *organs*, such as leaves and roots. A population is a set of *organisms* of the same species. A community consists of *populations* of the various species inhabiting a specific area. An ecosystem consists of a biological *community* along with the nonliving factors important to life, such as air, soil, and water. The biosphere is made up of all of Earth's *ecosystems*. **2.** (a) Structure and function are correlated. (b) Cells are an organism's basic units, *and* the continuity of life is based on heritable information in the form of DNA. (c) Organisms interact with other organisms and with the physical environment, *and* life requires energy transfer and transformation. **3.** Some possible answers: *Emergent properties*: The ability of a human heart to pump blood requires an intact heart; it is not a capability of any of the heart's tissues or cells working alone. *Environmental interactions*: A mouse eats food, such as nuts or grasses, and deposits some of the food material as feces and urine. Construction of a nest rearranges the physical environment and may hasten degradation of some of its components. The mouse may also act as food for a predator. *Energy transfer*: A plant, such as a grass, absorbs energy from the sun and transforms it into molecules that act as stored fuel. Animals can eat parts of the plant and use the food for energy to carry out their activities. *Structure and function*: The strong, sharp teeth of a wolf are well suited to grasping and dismembering its prey. *The cellular basis of life*: The digestion of food is made possible by chemicals (chiefly enzymes) made by cells of the digestive tract. *The genetic basis of life*: Human eye color is determined by the combination of genes inherited from the two parents. *Feedback regulation*: When your stomach is full, it signals your brain to decrease your appetite. *Evolution*: All plants have chloroplasts, indicating their descent from a common ancestor.

Concept Check 1.2

1. An address pinpoints a location by tracking from broader to narrower categories—a state, city, zip, street, and building number. This is analogous to the groups-subordinate-to-groups structure of biological taxonomy. **2.** The naturally occurring heritable variation in a population is "edited" by natural selection because individuals with heritable traits better suited to the environment survive and reproduce more successfully than others. Over time, better-suited individuals persist and their percentage in the population increases, while less suited individuals become less prevalent—a type of population editing.

3.

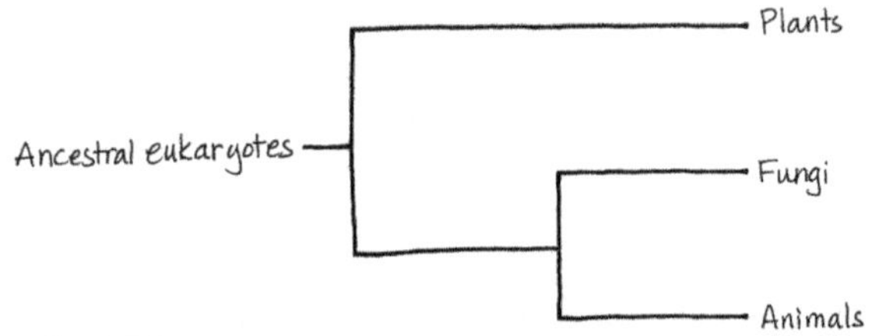

Concept Check 1.3

1. Inductive reasoning derives generalizations from specific cases; deductive reasoning predicts specific outcomes from general premises. **2.** The coloration pattern on the snakes **3.** Compared to a hypothesis, a scientific theory is usually more general and substantiated by a much greater amount of evidence. Natural selection is an explanatory idea that applies to all kinds of organisms and is supported by vast amounts of evidence of various kinds. **4.** Based on the results shown in Figure 1.27, you might predict that the colorful artificial snakes would be attacked more often than the brown ones, simply because they are easier to see. This prediction assumes that the area in Virginia where you are working has predators that attack snakes but no venomous snakes that resemble the colorful artificial snakes.

Concept Check 1.4

1. Science aims to understand natural phenomena and how they work, while technology involves application of scientific discoveries for a particular purpose or to solve a specific problem. **2.** Natural selection could be operating. Malaria is present in sub-Saharan Africa, so there might be an advantage to people with the sickle-cell disease form of the gene that makes them more able to survive and pass on their genes to offspring. Among those of African descent living in the United States, where malaria is absent, there would be no advantage, so they would be selected against more strongly, resulting in fewer individuals with the sickle-cell disease form of the gene.

Summary of Key Concepts Questions

1.1 Evolution explains the most fundamental aspects of all life on earth. It accounts for the common features shared by all forms of life due to descent from a common ancestor, while also providing an explanation for how the great diversity of living organisms on the planet has arisen. **1.2** Ancestors of this plant may have exhibited variation in how well their leaves conserved water. Because not much soil is present in the crevices where these plants are found, the variant plants that could conserve water may have survived better and been able to produce more offspring. Over time, a higher and higher proportion of individuals in the population would have had the adaptation of thick, water-conserving leaves. **1.3** Inductive reasoning is used in forming hypotheses, while deductive reasoning leads to predictions that are used to test hypotheses. **1.4** Different approaches taken by scientists studying natural phenomena at different levels complement each other, so more is learned about each problem being studied. A diversity of backgrounds among scientists may lead to fruitful ideas in the same way that important innovations have often arisen where a mix of cultures coexist.

Test Your Understanding

1. b **2.** d **3.** a **4.** c **5.** c **6.** c **7.** b **8.** c **9.** c **10.** d

11. Your figure should show: (1) For the biosphere, the Earth with an arrow coming out of a tropical ocean; (2) for the ecosystem, a distant view of a coral reef; (3) for the community, a collection of reef animals and algae, with corals, fishes, some seaweed, and any other organisms you can think of; (4) for the population, a group of fish of the same species; (5) for the organism, one fish from your population; (6) for the organ, the fish's stomach, and for the organ system, the whole digestive tract (see Chapter 41 for help); (7) for a tissue, a group of similar cells from the stomach; (8) for a cell, one cell from the tissue, showing its nucleus and a few other organelles; (9) for an organelle, the nucleus, where most of the cell's DNA is located; and (10) for a molecule, a DNA double helix. Your sketches can be very rough!

Chapter 2

Figure Questions

Figure 2.2 The most significant difference in the results would be that the two *Cedrela* saplings inside each garden would show similar amounts of dying leaf tissue because a poisonous chemical released from the *Duroia* trees would presumably reach the saplings via the air or soil and would not be blocked by the insect barrier. The *Cedrela* saplings planted outside the gardens would not show damage unless *Duroia* trees were nearby. Also, any ants present on the unprotected *Cedrela* saplings inside the gardens would probably not be observed making injections into the leaves. However, formic acid would likely still be found in the ants' glands, as it is for most species of ants. **Figure 2.9** Atomic number = 12; 12 protons, 12 electrons; 3 electron shells; 2 valence electrons **Figure 2.16** One possible answer:

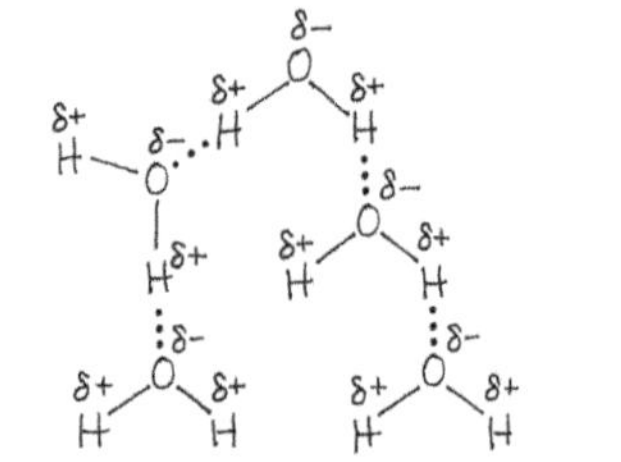

Figure 2.19 The plant is submerged in water (H_2O), in which the CO_2 is dissolved. The sun's energy is used to make sugar, which is found in the plant and can act as food for the plant itself, as well as for animals that eat the plant. The oxygen (O_2) is present in the bubbles.

Concept Check 2.1

1. Table salt (sodium chloride) is made up of sodium and chlorine. We are able to eat the compound, showing that it has different properties from those of a metal (sodium) and a poisonous gas (chlorine). **2.** Yes, because an organism requires trace elements, even though only in small amounts **3.** A person with an iron deficiency will probably show fatigue and other effects of a low oxygen level in the blood. (The condition is called anemia and can also result from too few red blood cells or abnormal hemoglobin.) **4.** Variant ancestral plants that could tolerate the toxic elements could grow and reproduce in serpentine soils. (Plants that were well adapted to nonserpentine soils would not be expected to survive in serpentine areas.) The offspring of the variants would also vary, with those most capable of thriving under serpentine conditions growing best and reproducing most. Over many generations, this probably led to the serpentine-adapted species we see today.

Concept Check 2.2

1. 7 **2.** $^{15}_{7}N$ **3.** 9 electrons; two electron shells; 1*s*, 2*s*, 2*p* (three orbitals); 1 electron is needed to fill the valence shell. **4.** The elements in a row all have the same number of electron shells. In a column, all the elements have the same number of electrons in their valence shells.

Concept Check 2.3

1. Each carbon atom has only three covalent bonds instead of the required four. **2.** The attraction between oppositely charged ions, forming ionic bonds **3.** If you could synthesize molecules that mimic these shapes, you might be able to treat diseases or conditions caused by the inability of affected individuals to synthesize such molecules.

Concept Check 2.4

1.

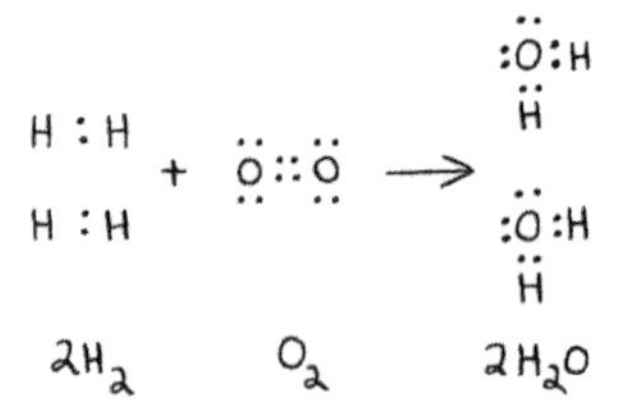

2. At equilibrium, the forward and reverse reactions occur at the same rate. **3.** $C_6H_{12}O_6 + 6\ O_2 \rightarrow 6\ CO_2 + 6\ H_2O$ + Energy. Glucose and oxygen react to form carbon dioxide and water, releasing energy. We breathe in oxygen because we need it for this reaction to occur, and we breathe out carbon dioxide because it is a by-product of this reaction. (This reaction is called cellular respiration, and you will learn more about it in Chapter 9.)

Summary of Key Concepts Questions

2.1 Iodine (part of a thyroid hormone) and iron (part of hemoglobin in blood) are both trace elements, required in minute quantities. Calcium and phosphorus (components of bones and teeth) are needed by the body in much greater quantities.
2.2

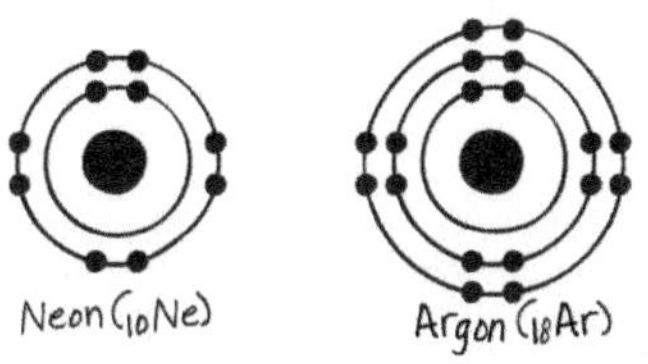

Both neon and argon have completed valence shells, containing 8 electrons. They do not have unpaired electrons that could participate in chemical bonds. **2.3** Electrons are shared equally between the two atoms in a nonpolar covalent bond. In a polar covalent bond, the electrons are drawn closer to the more electronegative atom. In the formation of ions, an electron is completely transferred from one atom to a much more electronegative atom. **2.4** The concentration of products would increase as the added reactants were converted to products. Eventually, an equilibrium would again be reached in which the forward and reverse reactions were proceeding at the same rate and the relative concentrations of reactants and products returned to where they were before the addition of more reactants.

Test Your Understanding

1. a **2.** e **3.** b **4.** a **5.** d **6.** b **7.** c **8.** e

9. a. 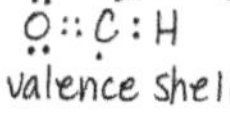 This structure doesn't make sense because the valence shell of carbon is incomplete; carbon can form 4 bonds.

b. 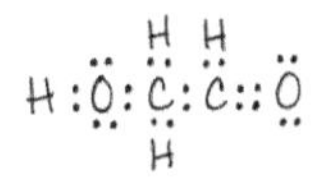 This structure makes sense because all valence shells are complete, and all bonds have the correct number of electrons.

c. 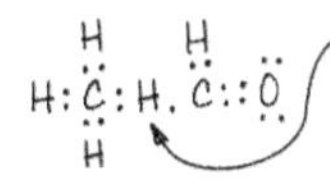 This structure doesn't make sense because H has only 1 electron to share, so it cannot form bonds with 2 atoms.

d. This structure doesn't make sense for several reasons:

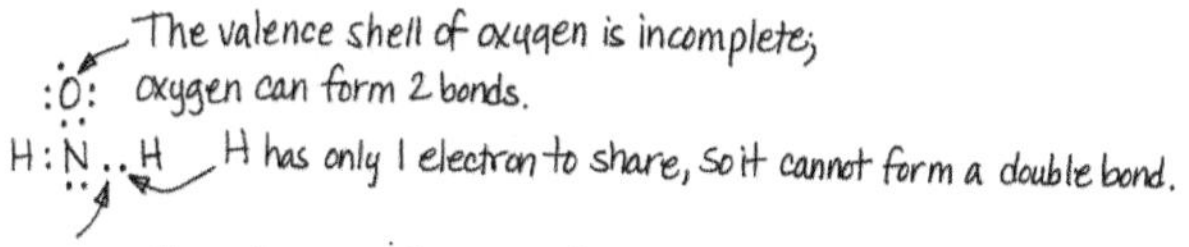

Nitrogen usually makes only 3 bonds. It does not have enough electrons to make 2 single bonds, make a double bond, and complete its valence shell.

Chapter 3

Figure Questions

Figure 3.2 One possible answer:

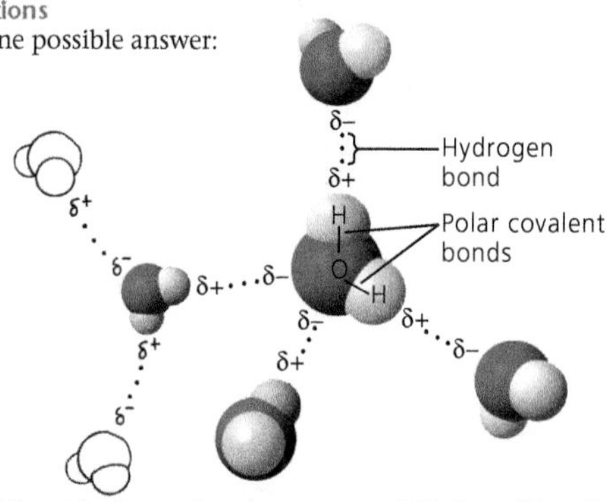

Figure 3.6 Without hydrogen bonds, water would behave like other small molecules, and the solid phase (ice) would be denser than liquid water. The ice would sink to the bottom and would no longer insulate the whole body of water, which would eventually freeze because the average annual temperature at the South Pole is –50°C. The krill could not survive. **Figure 3.7** Heating the solution would cause the water to evaporate faster than it is evaporating at room temperature. At a certain point, there wouldn't be enough water molecules to dissolve the salt ions. The salt would start coming out of solution and re-forming crystals. Eventually, all the water would evaporate, leaving behind a pile of salt like the original pile. **Figure 3.12** By causing the loss of coral reefs, a decrease in the ocean's carbonate concentration would have a ripple effect on noncalcifying organisms. Some of these organisms depend on the reef structure for protection, while others feed on species associated with reefs.

Concept Check 3.1

1. Electronegativity is the attraction of an atom for the electrons of a covalent bond. Because oxygen is more electronegative than hydrogen, the oxygen atom in H_2O pulls electrons toward itself, resulting in a partial negative charge on the oxygen atom and partial positive charges on the hydrogen atoms. Atoms in neighboring water molecules with opposite partial charges are attracted to each other, forming a hydrogen bond. **2.** The hydrogen atoms of one molecule, with their partial positive charges, would repel the hydrogen atoms of the adjacent molecule. **3.** The covalent bonds of water molecules would not be polar, and water molecules would not form hydrogen bonds with each other.

Concept Check 3.2

1. Hydrogen bonds hold neighboring water molecules together. This cohesion helps the chain of water molecules move upward against gravity in water-conducting cells as water evaporates from the leaves. Adhesion between water molecules and the walls of the water-conducting cells also helps counter gravity. **2.** High humidity hampers cooling by suppressing the evaporation of sweat. **3.** As water freezes, it expands because water molecules move farther apart in forming ice crystals. When there is water in a crevice of a boulder, expansion due to freezing may crack the boulder. **4.** A liter of blood would contain 7.8×10^{13} molecules of ghrelin (1.3×10^{-10} moles per liter $\times\ 6.02 \times 10^{23}$ molecules per mole). **5.** The hydrophobic substance repels water, perhaps helping to keep the ends of the legs from becoming coated with water and breaking through the surface. If the legs were coated with a hydrophilic substance, water would be drawn up them, possibly making it more difficult for the water strider to walk on water.

Concept Check 3.3

1. 10^5, or 100,000 **2.** $[H^+] = 0.01\ M = 10^{-2} M$, so pH = 2. **3.** $CH_3COOH \rightarrow CH_3COO^- + H^+$. CH_3COOH is the acid (the H^+ donor), and CH_3COO^- is the base (the H^+ acceptor). **4.** The pH of the water should decrease from 7 to about 2; the pH of the acetic acid solution will decrease only a small amount, because the reaction shown for question 3 will shift to the left, with CH_3COO^- accepting the influx of H^+ and becoming CH_3COOH molecules.

Summary of Key Concepts Questions

3.1

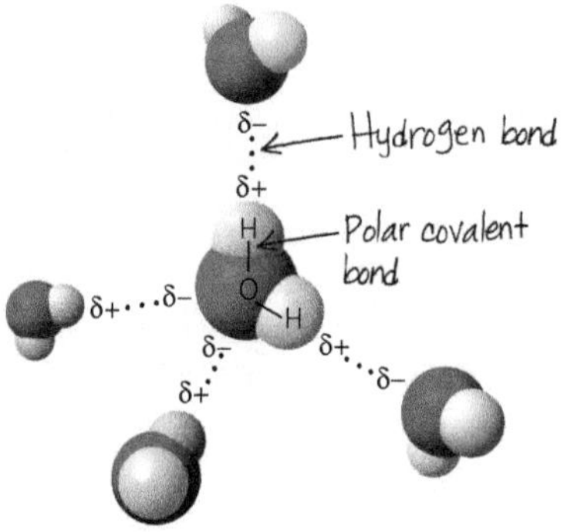

Each water molecule can make four hydrogen bonds with neighboring molecules. **3.2** Ions dissolve in water when polar water molecules form a hydration shell around them. Polar molecules dissolve as water molecules form hydrogen bonds

Appendix A Answers

with them and surround them. Solutions are homogeneous mixtures of solute and solvent. Colloids form when particles that are too large to dissolve remain suspended in a liquid. **3.3** CO_2 reacts with H_2O to form carbonic acid (H_2CO_3), which dissociates into H^+ and bicarbonate (HCO_3^-). Although the carbonic acid–bicarbonate reaction is a buffering system, adding CO_2 drives the reaction to the right, releasing more H^+ and lowering pH. The excess protons combine with CO_3^{2-} to form bicarbonate, lowering the concentration of carbonate available for the formation of calcium carbonate (calcification) by corals.

Test Your Understanding

1. d **2.** b **3.** c **4.** e **5.** c **6.** a **7.** e **8.** d
9.

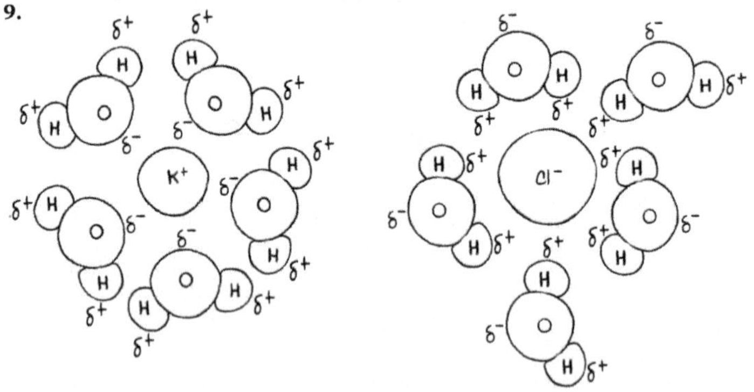

10. Both global warming and ocean acidification are caused by increasing levels of carbon dioxide in the atmosphere, the result of burning fossil fuels. **11.** Due to intermolecular hydrogen bonds, water has a high specific heat (the amount of heat required to increase the temperature of water by 1°C). When water is heated, much of the heat is absorbed in breaking hydrogen bonds before the water molecules increase their motion and the temperature increases. Conversely, when water is cooled, many H bonds are formed, which releases a significant amount of heat. This release of heat can provide some protection against freezing of the plants' leaves, thus protecting the cells from damage.

Chapter 4

Figure Questions

Figure 4.2 Because the concentration of the reactants influences the equilibrium (as discussed in Chapter 2), there might have been more HCN relative to CH_2O, since there would have been a higher concentration of the reactant gas containing nitrogen.
Figure 4.4

Figure 4.6 The tails of fats contain only carbon-hydrogen bonds, which are relatively nonpolar. Because the tails occupy the bulk of a fat molecule, they make the molecule as a whole nonpolar and therefore incapable of forming hydrogen bonds with water.
Figure 4.7

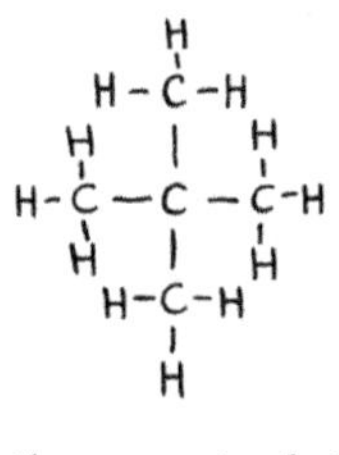

Figure 4.9 Molecule b, because there are not only the two electronegative oxygens of the carboxyl group, but also an oxygen on the next (carbonyl) carbon. All of these oxygens help make the bond between the O and H of the —OH group more polar, thus making the dissociation of H^+ more likely.

Concept Check 4.1

1. Prior to Wöhler's experiment, the prevailing view was that only living organisms could synthesize "organic" compounds. Wöhler made urea, an organic compound, without the involvement of living organisms. **2.** The spark provided energy needed for the inorganic molecules in the atmosphere to react with each other. (You'll learn more about energy and chemical reactions in Chapter 8.)

Concept Check 4.2

1.

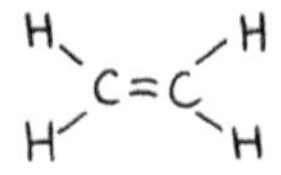

2. The forms of C_4H_{10} in (b) are structural isomers, as are the butenes in (c). **3.** Both consist largely of hydrocarbon chains. **4.** No. There is not enough diversity in the atoms. It can't form structural isomers because there is only one way for three carbons to attach to each other (in a line). There are no double bonds, so *cis-trans* isomers are not possible. Each carbon has at least two hydrogens attached to it, so the molecule is symmetrical and cannot have enantiomers.

Concept Check 4.3

1. It has both an amino group (—NH_2), which makes it an amine, and a carboxyl group (—COOH), which makes it a carboxylic acid. **2.** The ATP molecule loses a phosphate, becoming ADP. **3.** A chemical group that can act as a base has been replaced with a group that can act as an acid, increasing the acidic properties of the molecule. The shape of the molecule would also change, likely changing the molecules with which it can interact. The original cysteine molecule has an asymmetric carbon in the center. After replacement of the amino group with a carboxyl group, this carbon is no longer asymmetric.

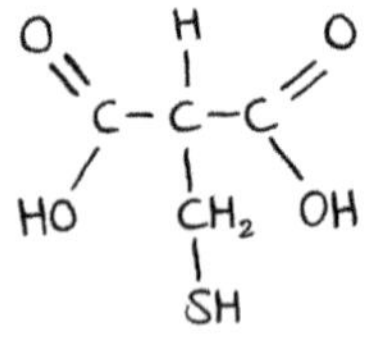

Summary of Key Concepts Questions

4.1 Miller showed that organic molecules could form under the physical and chemical conditions estimated to have been present on early Earth. This abiotic synthesis of organic molecules would have been a first step in the origin of life. **4.2** Acetone and propanal are structural isomers. Acetic acid and glycine have no asymmetric carbons, whereas glycerol phosphate has one. Therefore, glycerol phosphate can exist as forms that are enantiomers, but acetic acid and glycine cannot. **4.3** The methyl group is nonpolar and not reactive. The other six groups are called functional groups. They are each hydrophilic, increasing the solubility of organic compounds in water, and can participate in chemical reactions.

Test Your Understanding

1. b **2.** b **3.** d **4.** d **5.** a **6.** b **7.** a **8.** The molecule on the right; the middle carbon is asymmetric.
9. 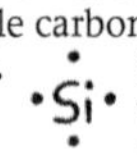 Si has 4 valence electrons, the same number as carbon. Therefore, silicon would be able to form long chains, including branches, that could act as skeletons for large molecules. It would clearly do this much better than neon (with no valence electrons) or aluminum (with 3 valence electrons).

Chapter 5

Figure Questions

Figure 5.3 Glucose and fructose are structural isomers.
Figure 5.4

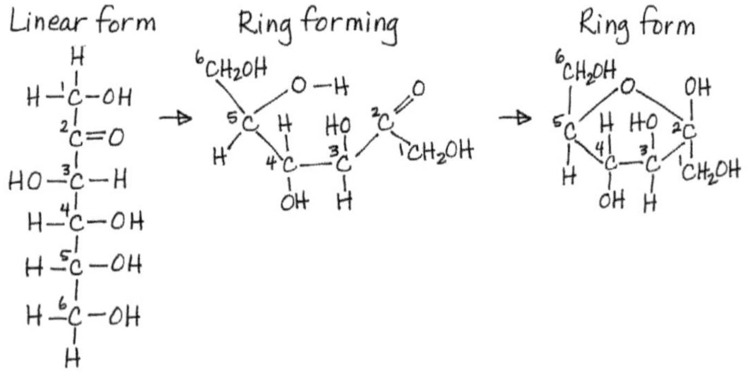

Note that the oxygen on carbon 5 lost its proton and that the oxygen on carbon 2, which used to be the carbonyl oxygen, gained a proton. Four carbons are in the fructose ring, and two are not. (The latter two carbons are attached to carbons 2 and 5, which are in the ring.) The fructose ring differs from the glucose ring, which has five carbons in the ring and one that is not. (Note that the orientation of this fructose molecule is flipped relative to that of the one in Figure 5.5b.)

Figure 5.5

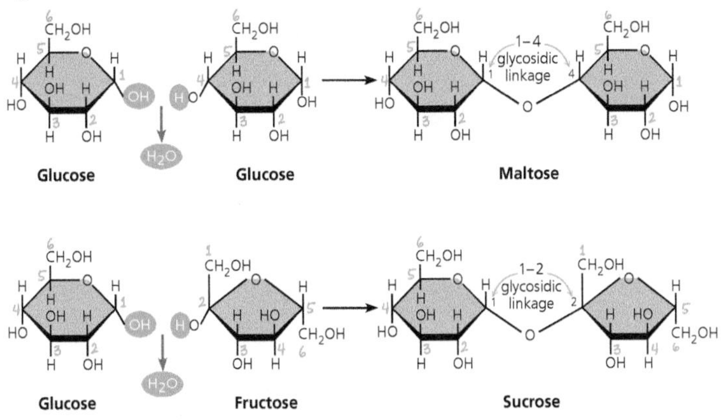

Figure 5.12

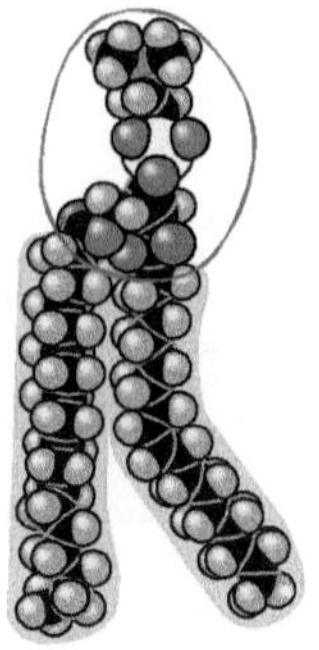

Figure 5.14

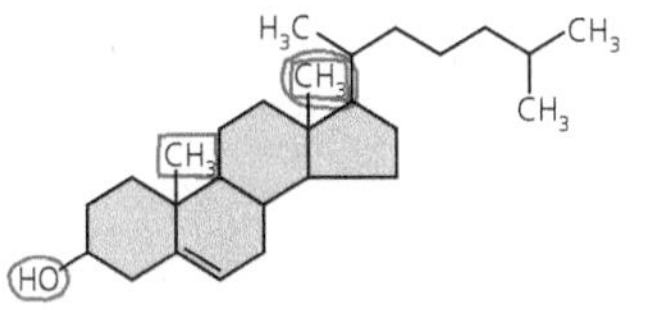

Figure 5.17

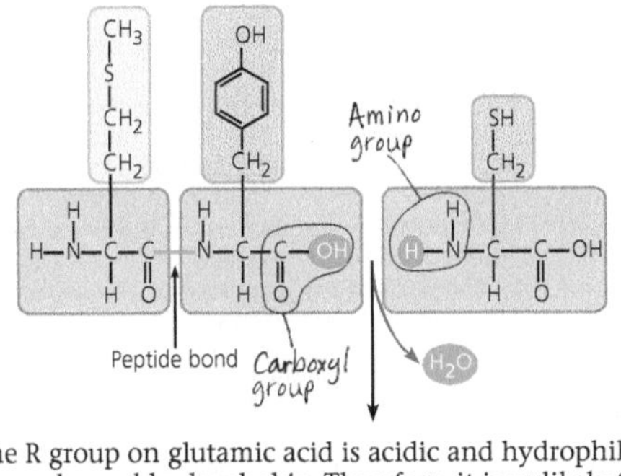

Figure 5.21 The R group on glutamic acid is acidic and hydrophilic, whereas that on valine is nonpolar and hydrophobic. Therefore, it is unlikely that valine can participate in the same intramolecular interactions that glutamic acid can. A change in these interactions causes a disruption of molecular structure.
Figure 5.24 The spirals are α helices.

Concept Check 5.1

1. The four main classes are proteins, carbohydrates, lipids, and nucleic acids. Lipids are not polymers. **2.** Nine, with one water molecule required to hydrolyze each connected pair of monomers **3.** The amino acids in the fish protein must be released in hydrolysis reactions and incorporated into other proteins in dehydration reactions.

Concept Check 5.2

1. $C_3H_6O_3$ **2.** $C_{12}H_{22}O_{11}$ **3.** The antibiotic treatment is likely to have killed the cellulose-digesting prokaryotes in the cow's stomach. The absence of these prokaryotes would hamper the cow's ability to obtain energy from food and could lead to weight loss and possibly death. Thus, prokaryotic species are reintroduced, in appropriate combinations, in the gut culture given to treated cows.

Concept Check 5.3

1. Both have a glycerol molecule attached to fatty acids. The glycerol of a fat has three fatty acids attached, whereas the glycerol of a phospholipid is attached to two fatty acids and one phosphate group. **2.** Human sex hormones are steroids, a type of hydrophobic compound. **3.** The oil droplet membrane could consist of a single layer of phospholipids rather than a bilayer, because an arrangement in which the hydrophobic tails of the membrane phospholipids were in contact with the hydrocarbon regions of the oil molecules would be more stable.

Concept Check 5.4

1. The function of a protein is a consequence of its specific shape, which is lost when a protein becomes denatured. **2.** Secondary structure involves hydrogen bonds between atoms of the polypeptide backbone. Tertiary structure involves interactions between atoms of the side chains of the amino acid subunits. **3.** These are all nonpolar amino acids, so you would expect this region to be located in the interior of the folded polypeptide, where it would not contact the aqueous environment inside the cell.

Concept Check 5.5

1.

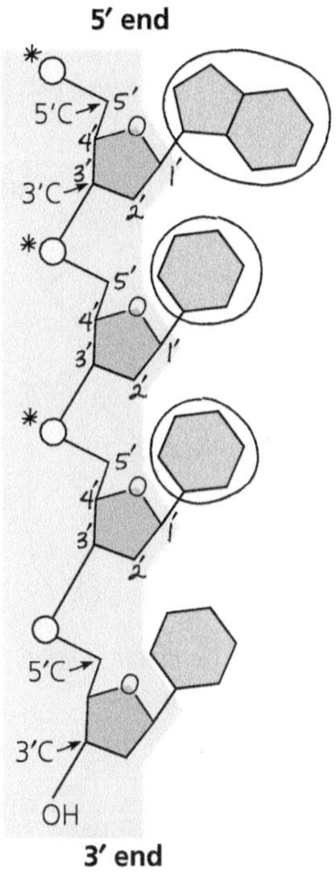

2. 5′–T A G G C C T–3′
3′–A T C C G G A–5′

3. a. Mismatch
5′–T A A G C C T–3′
3′–A T C C G G A–5′

b. 3′–A T T C G G A–5′

Summary of Key Concepts Questions

Concept 5.1 The polymers of carbohydrates, proteins, and nucleic acids are built from three different types of monomers: monosaccharides, amino acids, and nucleotides, respectively. **Concept 5.2** Both starch and cellulose are polymers of glucose, but the glucose monomers are in the α configuration in starch and the β configuration in cellulose. The glycosidic linkages thus have different geometries, giving the polymers different shapes and thus different properties. Starch is an energy-storage compound in plants; cellulose is a structural component of plant cell walls. Humans can hydrolyze starch to provide energy but cannot hydrolyze cellulose. Cellulose aids in the passage of food through the digestive tract. **Concept 5.3** Lipids are not polymers because they do not exist as a chain of linked monomers. They are not considered macromolecules because they do not reach the giant size of many polysaccharides, proteins, and nucleic acids. **Concept 5.4** A polypeptide, which may consist of hundreds of amino acids in a specific sequence (primary structure), has regions of coils and pleats (secondary structure), which are then folded into irregular contortions (tertiary structure) and may be noncovalently associated with other polypeptides (quaternary structure). The linear order of amino acids, with the varying properties of their side chains (R groups), determines what secondary and tertiary structures will form to produce a protein. The resulting unique three-dimensional shapes of proteins are key to their specific and diverse functions. **Concept 5.5** The complementary base pairing of the two strands of DNA makes possible the precise replication of DNA every time a cell divides, ensuring that genetic information is faithfully transmitted. In some types of RNA, complementary base pairing enables

RNA molecules to assume specific three-dimensional shapes that facilitate diverse functions.

Test Your Understanding

1. d **2.** a **3.** b **4.** a **5.** b **6.** c **7.** d

8.

	Monomers or Components	Polymer or larger molecule	Type of linkage
Carbohydrates	Monosaccharides	Polysaccharides	Glycosidic linkages
Lipids	Fatty acids	Triacylglycerols	Ester linkages
Proteins	Amino acids	Polypeptides	Peptide bonds
Nucleic acids	Nucleotides	Polynucleotides	Phosphodiester linkages

9.

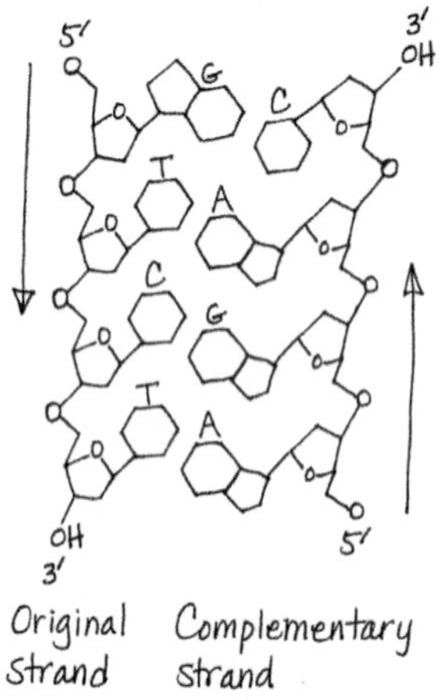

Chapter 6

Figure Questions

Figure 6.6 A phospholipid is a lipid, consisting of a glycerol molecule joined to two fatty acids and one phosphate group. Together, the glycerol and phosphate end of the phospholipid form the "head," which is hydrophilic, while the hydrocarbon chains on the fatty acids form hydrophobic "tails." The presence in a single molecule of both a hydrophilic and a hydrophobic region makes the molecule ideal as the main building block of a membrane. **Figure 6.9** The DNA in a chromosome dictates synthesis of a messenger RNA (mRNA) molecule, which then moves out to the cytoplasm. There, the information is used for the production, on ribosomes, of proteins that carry out cellular functions. **Figure 6.10** Any of the bound ribosomes (attached to the endoplasmic reticulum) could be circled, because any could be making a protein that will be secreted. **Figure 6.22** Each centriole has 9 sets of 3 microtubules, so the entire centrosome (two centrioles) has 54 microtubules. Each microtubule consists of a helical array of tubulin dimers (as shown in Table 6.1).

Figure 6.24

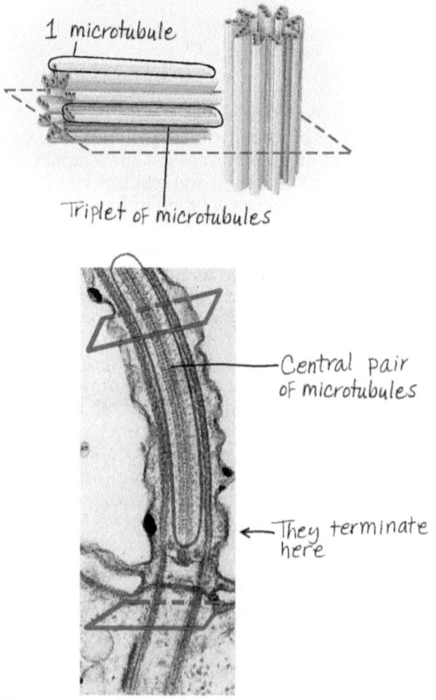

The two central microtubules terminate above the basal body, so they aren't present at the level of the cross section through the basal body, indicated by the lower red rectangle in (a). **Figure 6.29** The microtubules would reorient, and based on the earlier results, the cellulose synthase proteins would also change their path, orienting along the repositioned microtubules. (This is, in fact, what was observed.)

Concept Check 6.1

1. Stains used for light microscopy are colored molecules that bind to cell components, affecting the light passing through, while stains used for electron microscopy involve heavy metals that affect the beams of electrons passing through. **2.** (a) Light microscope, (b) scanning electron microscope

Concept Check 6.2

1. See Figure 6.8.

2.

This cell would have the same volume as the cells in columns 2 and 3 but proportionally more surface area than that in column 2 and less than that in column 3. Thus, the surface-to-volume ratio should be greater than 1.2 but less than 6. To obtain the surface area, you would add the area of the six sides (the top, bottom, sides, and ends): 125 + 125 + 125 + 125 + 1 + 1 = 502. The surface-to-volume ratio equals 502 divided by a volume of 125, or 4.0.

Concept Check 6.3

1. Ribosomes in the cytoplasm translate the genetic message, carried from the DNA in the nucleus by mRNA, into a polypeptide chain. **2.** Nucleoli consist of DNA and the ribosomal RNA (rRNA) made according to its instructions, as well as proteins imported from the cytoplasm. Together, the rRNA and proteins are assembled into large and small ribosomal subunits. (These are exported through nuclear pores to the cytoplasm, where they will participate in polypeptide synthesis.) **3.** No. Each chromosome is present whether its chromatin is relatively diffuse (when the cell is not dividing) or condensed (when the cell is dividing).

Concept Check 6.4

1. The primary distinction between rough and smooth ER is the presence of bound ribosomes on the rough ER. Both types of ER make phospholipids, but membrane proteins and secretory proteins are all produced on the ribosomes of the rough ER. The smooth ER also functions in detoxification, carbohydrate metabolism, and storage of calcium ions. **2.** Transport vesicles move membranes and substances they enclose between other components of the endomembrane system. **3.** The mRNA is synthesized in the nucleus and then passes out through a nuclear pore to be translated on a bound ribosome, attached to the rough ER. The protein is synthesized into the lumen of the ER and perhaps modified there. A transport vesicle carries the protein to the Golgi apparatus. After further modification in the Golgi, another transport vesicle carries it back to the ER, where it will perform its cellular function.

Concept Check 6.5

1. Both organelles are involved in energy transformation, mitochondria in cellular respiration and chloroplasts in photosynthesis. They both have multiple membranes that separate their interiors into compartments. In both organelles, the innermost membranes—cristae, or infoldings of the inner membrane, in mitochondria, and the thylakoid membranes in chloroplasts—have large surface areas with embedded enzymes that carry out their main functions. **2.** Yes. Plant cells are able to make their own sugar by photosynthesis, but mitochondria in these eukaryotic cells are the organelles that are able to generate energy from sugars, a function required in all cells. **3.** Mitochondria and chloroplasts are not derived from the ER, nor are they connected physically or via transport vesicles to organelles of the endomembrane system. Mitochondria and chloroplasts are structurally quite different from vesicles derived from the ER, which are bounded by a single membrane.

Concept Check 6.6

1. Both systems of movement involve long filaments that are moved in relation to each other by motor proteins that grip, release, and grip again adjacent polymers. **2.** Dynein arms, powered by ATP, move neighboring doublets of microtubules relative to each other. Because they are anchored within the organelle and with respect to one another, the doublets bend instead of sliding past each other. Synchronized bending of the nine microtubule doublets brings about bending of both structures. **3.** Such individuals have defects in the microtubule-based movement of cilia and flagella. Thus, the sperm can't move because of malfunctioning or nonexistent flagella, and the airways are compromised because cilia that line the trachea malfunction or don't exist, and so mucus cannot be cleared from the lungs.

Concept Check 6.7

1. The most obvious difference is the presence of direct cytoplasmic connections between cells of plants (plasmodesmata) and animals (gap junctions). These connections result in the cytoplasm being continuous between adjacent cells. **2.** The cell would not be able to function properly and would probably soon die, as the cell wall or ECM must be permeable to allow the exchange of matter between the cell and its external environment. Molecules involved in energy production and use must be allowed entry, as well as those that provide information about the cell's environment. Other molecules, such as products synthesized by the cell for export and the by-products of cellular respiration, must be allowed to exit. **3.** The parts of the protein that face aqueous regions would be expected to have polar or charged (hydrophilic) amino acids, while the parts that go through the membrane would be expected to have nonpolar (hydrophobic) amino acids. You would predict polar or charged amino acids at each end (tail), in the region of the cytoplasmic loop, and in the regions of the two extracellular loops. You would predict nonpolar amino acids in the four regions that go through the membrane between the tails and loops.

Summary of Key Concepts Questions

6.1 Both light and electron microscopy allow cells to be studied visually, thus helping us understand internal cellular structure and the arrangement of cell components. Cell fractionation techniques separate out different groups of cell components, which can then be analyzed biochemically to determine their function. Performing microscopy on the same cell fraction helps to correlate the biochemical function of the cell with the cell component responsible. **6.2** The separation of different functions in different organelles has several advantages. Reactants and enzymes can be concentrated in one area instead of spread throughout the cell. Reactions that require specific conditions, such as a lower pH, can be compartmentalized. And enzymes for specific reactions are often embedded in the membranes that enclose or partition an organelle. **6.3** The nucleus contains the genetic material of the cell in the form of DNA, which codes for messenger RNA, which in turn provides instructions for the synthesis of proteins (including the proteins that make up part of the ribosomes). DNA also codes for ribosomal RNA, which is combined with proteins in the nucleolus into the subunits of ribosomes. Within the cytoplasm, ribosomes join with mRNA to build polypeptides, using the genetic information in the mRNA. **6.4** Transport vesicles move proteins and membranes synthesized by the rough ER to the Golgi for further processing and then to the plasma membrane, lysosomes, or other locations in the cell, including back to the ER. **6.5** According to the endosymbiont theory, mitochondria originated from an oxygen-using prokaryotic cell that was engulfed by an ancestral eukaryotic cell. Over time, the host and endosymbiont evolved into a single organism. Chloroplasts originated when at least one of these eukaryotic cells containing mitochondria engulfed and then retained a photosynthetic prokaryote. **6.6** Inside the cell, motor proteins interact with components of the cytoskeleton to move cellular parts. Motor proteins may "walk" vesicles along microtubules. The movement of cytoplasm within a cell involves interactions of the motor protein myosin and microfilaments (actin filaments). Whole cells can be moved by the rapid bending of flagella or cilia, which is caused by the motor-protein-powered sliding of microtubules within these structures. Cell movement can also occur when pseudopodia form at one end of a cell (caused by actin polymerization into a filamentous network), followed by contraction of the cell toward that end; this is powered by interactions of microfilaments with myosin. Interactions of motor proteins and microfilaments in muscle cells can propel whole organisms. **6.7** A plant cell wall is primarily composed of microfibrils of cellulose embedded in other polysaccharides and proteins. The ECM of animal cells is primarily composed of collagen and other protein fibers, such as the glycoprotein fibronectins. These fibers are embedded in a network of carbohydrate-rich proteoglycans. A plant cell wall provides structural support for the cell and, collectively, for the plant body. In addition to giving support, the ECM of an animal cell allows for communication of environmental changes into the cell.

Test Your Understanding

1. b **2.** d **3.** b **4.** e **5.** a **6.** d **7.** c **8.** See Figure 6.8.

Chapter 7

Figure Questions

Figure 7.2

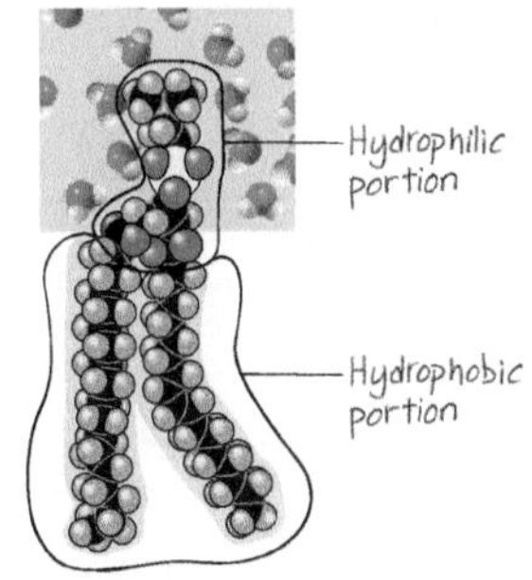

The hydrophilic portion is in contact with an aqueous environment (cytosol or extracellular fluid), and the hydrophobic portion is in contact with the hydrophobic portions of other phospholipids in the interior of the bilayer. **Figure 7.7** You couldn't rule out movement of proteins within membranes of the same species. You might propose that the membrane lipids and proteins from one species weren't able to mingle with those from the other species because of some incompatibility. **Figure 7.10** A transmembrane protein like the dimer in (f) might change its shape upon binding to a particular ECM molecule. The new shape might enable the interior portion of the protein to bind to a second, cytoplasmic protein that would relay the message to the inside of the cell, as shown in (c). **Figure 7.11** The shape of a protein on the HIV surface is likely to be complementary to the shape of the receptor (CD4) and also to that of the co-receptor (CCR5). A molecule that was a similar shape to the HIV surface protein could bind CCR5, blocking HIV binding. (Another alternative would be a molecule that bound to CCR5 and changed the shape of CCR5 so it could no longer bind HIV.)

Figure 7.12

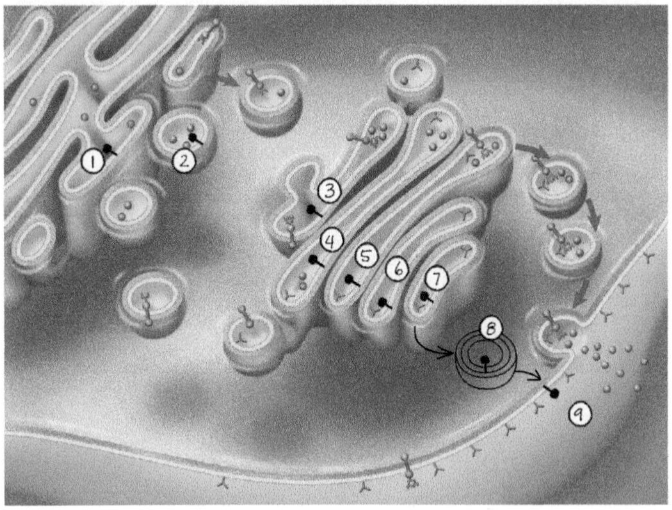

The protein would contact the extracellular fluid. **Figure 7.14** The orange dye would be evenly distributed throughout the solution on both sides of the membrane. The solution levels would not be affected because the orange dye can diffuse through the membrane and equalize its concentration. Thus, no additional osmosis would take place in either direction. **Figure 7.19** The diamond solutes are moving into the cell (down), and the round solutes are moving out of the cell (up); both are moving against their concentration gradient.

Concept Check 7.1

1. They are on the inner side of the transport vesicle membrane. **2.** The grasses living in the cooler region would be expected to have more unsaturated fatty acids in their membranes because those fatty acids remain fluid at lower temperatures. The grasses living immediately adjacent to the hot springs would be expected to have more saturated fatty acids, which would allow the fatty acids to "stack" more closely, making the membranes less fluid and therefore helping them to stay intact at higher temperatures. (Cholesterol could not be used to moderate the effects of temperature on membrane fluidity because it is not found within plant cell membranes.)

Concept Check 7.2

1. O_2 and CO_2 are both nonpolar molecules that can easily pass through the hydrophobic interior of a membrane. **2.** Water is a polar molecule, so it cannot pass very rapidly through the hydrophobic region in the middle of a phospholipid bilayer. **3.** The hydronium ion is charged, while glycerol is not. Charge is probably more significant than size as a basis for exclusion by the aquaporin channel.

Concept Check 7.3

1. CO_2 is a nonpolar molecule that can diffuse through the plasma membrane. As long as it diffuses away so that the concentration remains low outside the cell, it will continue to exit the cell in this way. (This is the opposite of the case for O_2, described in this section.) **2.** The water is hypotonic to the plant cells, so the plant cells take up water. Thus, the cells of the vegetable remain turgid rather than plasmolyzing, and the vegetable (for example, lettuce or spinach) remains crisp and not wilted. **3.** The activity of *Paramecium caudatum*'s contractile vacuole will decrease. The vacuole pumps out excess water that accumulates in the cell; this accumulation occurs only in a hypotonic environment.

Concept Check 7.4

1. The pump uses ATP. To establish a voltage, ions have to be pumped against their gradients, which requires energy. **2.** Each ion is being transported against its electrochemical gradient. If either ion were transported down its electrochemical gradient, this *would* be considered cotransport. **3.** The internal environment of a lysosome is acidic, so it has a higher concentration of H^+ than does the cytoplasm. Therefore, you might expect the membrane of the lysosome to have a proton pump such as that shown in Figure 7.20 to pump H^+ into the lysosome.

Concept Check 7.5

1. Exocytosis. When a transport vesicle fuses with the plasma membrane, the vesicle membrane becomes part of the plasma membrane.

2.

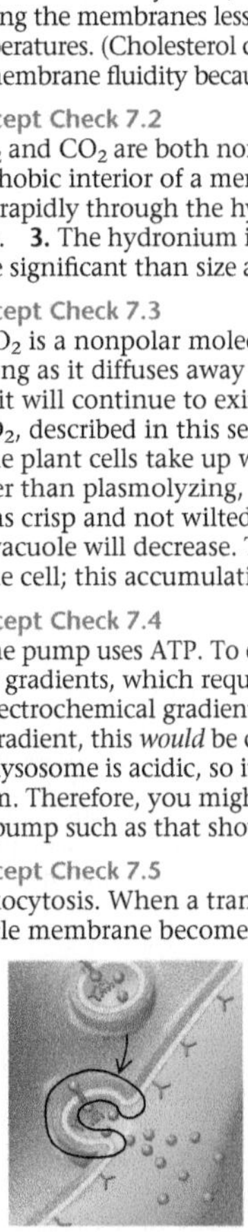

3. The glycoprotein would be synthesized in the ER lumen, move through the Golgi apparatus, and then travel in a vesicle to the plasma membrane, where it would undergo exocytosis and become part of the ECM.

Summary of Key Concepts Questions

7.1 Plasma membranes define the cell by separating the cellular components from the external environment. This allows conditions inside cells to be controlled by membrane proteins, which regulate entry and exit of molecules and even cell function (see Figure 7.10). The processes of life can be carried out inside the controlled environment of the cell, so membranes are crucial. In eukaryotes, membranes also function to subdivide the cytoplasm into different compartments where distinct processes can occur, even under differing conditions such as pH. **7.2** Aquaporins are channel proteins that greatly increase the permeability of a membrane to water molecules, which are polar and therefore do not readily diffuse through the hydrophobic interior of the membrane. **7.3** There will be a net diffusion of water out of a cell into a hypertonic solution. The free water concentration is higher inside the cell than in the solution (where water molecules are not free, but are clustered around the higher concentration of solute particles). **7.4** One of the solutes moved by the cotransporter is actively transported against its concentration gradient. The energy for this transport comes from the concentration gradient of the other solute, which was established by an electrogenic pump that used energy to transport the other solute across the membrane. **7.5** In receptor-mediated endocytosis, specific molecules act as ligands when they bind to receptors on the plasma membrane. The cell can acquire bulk quantities of those molecules when a coated pit forms a vesicle and carries the bound molecules into the cell.

Test Your Understanding

1. b **2.** c **3.** a **4.** d **5.** b

6. (a)

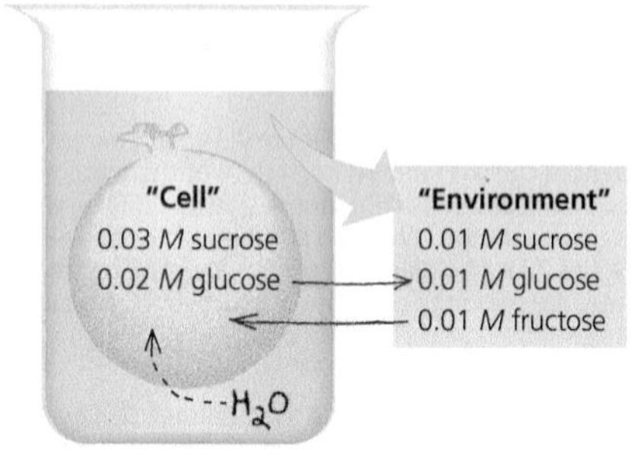

(b) The solution outside is hypotonic. It has less sucrose, which is a nonpenetrating solute. (c) See answer for (a). (d) The artificial cell will become more turgid. (e) Eventually, the two solutions will have the same solute concentrations. Even though sucrose can't move through the membrane, water flow (osmosis) will lead to isotonic conditions.

Chapter 8

Figure Questions

Figure 8.12

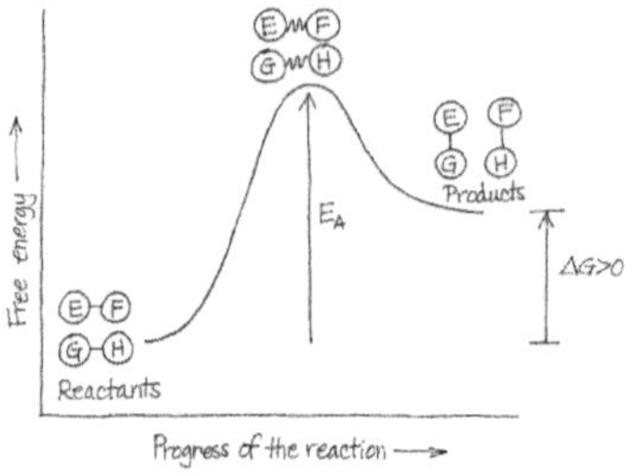

Figure 8.16

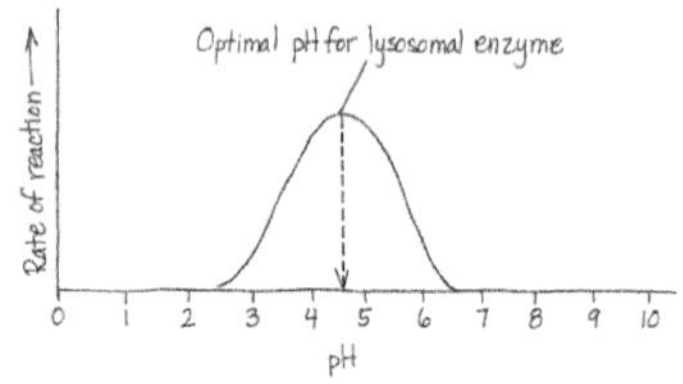

Figure 8.20 Because the affinity of the caspase for the inhibitor is very low (as is expected of an allosterically inhibited enzyme), the inhibitor is likely to diffuse away. Because no additional source of the inhibitory compound is present and the concentration of inhibitor is very low, the inhibitor is unlikely to bind again to the allosteric binding site once the covalent linkage is broken. Therefore, the activity of the enzyme would most likely be normal. (In fact, this is what the researchers observed when they broke the disulfide linkage.)

Concept Check 8.1

1. The second law is the trend toward randomization, or increasing entropy. When the concentrations of a substance on both sides of a membrane are equal, the distribution is more random than when they are unequal. Diffusion of a substance to a region where it is initially less concentrated increases entropy, making it an energetically favorable (spontaneous) process as described by the second law. This explains the process seen in Figure 7.13. **2.** The apple has potential energy in its position hanging on the tree, and the sugars and other nutrients it contains have chemical energy. The apple has kinetic energy as it falls from the tree to the ground. Finally, when the apple is digested and its molecules broken down, some of the chemical energy is used to do work, and the rest is lost as thermal energy. **3.** The sugar crystals become less ordered (entropy increases) as they dissolve and become randomly spread out in the water. Over time, the water evaporates, and the crystals form again because the water volume is insufficient to keep them in solution. While the reappearance of sugar crystals may represent a "spontaneous" increase in order (decrease in entropy), it is balanced by the decrease in order (increase in entropy) of the water molecules, which changed from a relatively compact arrangement as liquid water to a much more dispersed and disordered form as water vapor.

Concept Check 8.2

1. Cellular respiration is a spontaneous and exergonic process. The energy released from glucose is used to do work in the cell or is lost as heat. **2.** When the H^+ concentrations are the same, the system is at equilibrium and can do no work. Hydrogen ions can perform work only if their concentrations on each side of a membrane differ—in other words, when a gradient is present. This is consistent with Figure 7.20, which shows that an energy input (provided by ATP hydrolysis) is required to establish the concentration gradient (the H^+ gradient) that can in turn perform work. **3.** The reaction is exergonic because it releases energy—in this case, in the form of light. (This is a nonbiological version of the bioluminescence seen in Figure 8.1.)

Concept Check 8.3

1. ATP usually transfers energy to endergonic processes by phosphorylating (adding phosphate groups to) other molecules. (Exergonic processes phosphorylate ADP to regenerate ATP.) **2.** A set of coupled reactions can transform the first combination into the second. Since this is an exergonic process overall, ΔG is negative and the first combination must have more free energy (see Figure 8.9). **3.** Active transport: The solute is being transported against its concentration gradient, which requires energy, provided by ATP hydrolysis.

Concept Check 8.4

1. A spontaneous reaction is a reaction that is exergonic. However, if it has a high activation energy that is rarely attained, the rate of the reaction may be low. **2.** Only the specific substrate(s) will fit properly into the active site of an enzyme, the part of the enzyme that carries out catalysis. **3.** In the presence of malonate, increase the concentration of the normal substrate (succinate) and see whether the rate of reaction increases. If it does, malonate is a competitive inhibitor. **4.** If lactose wasn't present in the environment as a source of food and the fucose-containing disaccharide was available, bacteria that could digest the latter would be better able to grow and multiply than those that could not.

Concept Check 8.5

1. The activator binds in such a way that it stabilizes the active form of an enzyme, whereas the inhibitor stabilizes the inactive form. **2.** An inhibitor that binds to the active site of the enzyme you want to inhibit could also bind to and block the enzymes with similar structures, causing significant side effects. For this reason, you would be better off choosing to screen chemical compounds that bind allosterically to the enzyme in question, because allosteric regulatory sites are less likely to share similarity with other enzymes.

Summary of Key Concepts Questions

8.1 The process of "ordering" a cell's structure is accompanied by an increase in the entropy or disorder of the universe. For example, an animal cell takes in highly ordered organic molecules as the source of matter and energy used to build and maintain its structures. In the same process, however, the cell releases heat and the simple molecules of carbon dioxide and water to the surroundings. The increase in entropy of the latter process offsets the entropy decrease in the former. **8.2** A spontaneous reaction has a negative ΔG and is exergonic. For a chemical reaction to proceed with a net release of free energy ($-\Delta G$), the enthalpy or total energy of the system must decrease ($-\Delta H$), and/or the entropy or disorder must increase (yielding a more negative term, $-T\Delta S$). Spontaneous reactions supply the energy to perform cellular work. **8.3** The free energy released from the hydrolysis of ATP may drive endergonic reactions through the transfer of a phosphate group to a reactant molecule, forming a more reactive phosphorylated intermediate. ATP hydrolysis also powers the mechanical and transport work of a cell, often by powering shape changes in the relevant motor proteins. Cellular respiration, the catabolic breakdown of glucose, provides the energy for the endergonic regeneration of ATP from ADP and Ⓟ$_i$. **8.4** Activation energy barriers prevent the complex molecules of the cell, which are rich in free energy, from spontaneously breaking down to less ordered, more stable molecules. Enzymes permit a regulated metabolism by binding to specific substrates and forming enzyme-substrate complexes that selectively lower the E_A for the chemical reactions in a cell. **8.5** A cell tightly regulates its metabolic pathways in response to fluctuating needs for energy and materials. The binding of activators or inhibitors to regulatory sites on allosteric enzymes stabilizes either the active or inactive form of the subunits. For example, the binding of ATP to a catabolic enzyme in a cell with excess ATP would inhibit that pathway. Such types of feedback inhibition preserve chemical resources within a cell. If ATP supplies are depleted, binding of ADP to the regulatory site of catabolic enzymes would activate that pathway.

Test Your Understanding

1. b **2.** c **3.** b **4.** a **5.** c **6.** e **7.** c

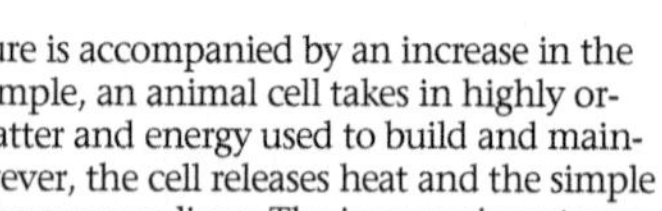

9.

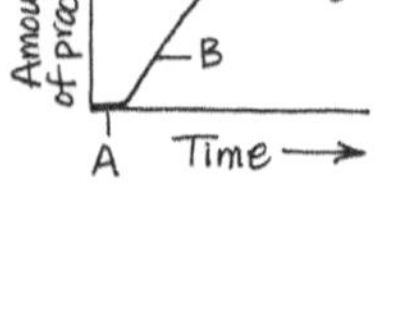

A. The substrate molecules are entering the cells, so no product is made yet.
B. There is sufficient substrate, so the reaction is proceeding at a maximum rate.
C. As the substrate is used up, the rate decreases (the slope is less steep).
D. The line is flat because no new substrate remains and thus no new product appears.

Chapter 9

Figure Questions

Figure 9.7 Because there is no external source of energy for the reaction, it must be exergonic, and the reactants must be at a higher energy level than the products. **Figure 9.9** The removal would probably stop glycolysis, or at least slow it down, since it would push the equilibrium for step 5 toward the left. If less (or no) glyceraldehyde 3-phosphate were available, step 6 would slow down (or be unable to occur). **Figure 9.15** At first, some ATP could be made, since electron transport could proceed as far as complex III, and a small H^+ gradient could be built up. Soon, however, no more electrons could be passed to complex III because it could not be reoxidized by passing its electrons to complex IV. **Figure 9.16** First, there are 2 NADH from the oxidation of pyruvate plus 6 NADH from the citric acid cycle (CAC); 8 NADH $\times$ 2.5 ATP/NADH = 20 ATP. Second, there are 2 $FADH_2$ from the CAC; 2 $FADH_2 \times$ 1.5 ATP/$FADH_2$ = 3 ATP. Third, the 2 NADH from glycolysis enter the mitochondrion through one of two types of shuttle. They pass their electrons either to 2 FAD, which become $FADH_2$ and result in 3 ATP, or to 2 NAD^+, which become NADH and result in 5 ATP. Thus, 20 + 3 + 3 = 26 ATP, or 20 + 3 + 5 = 28 ATP from all NADH and $FADH_2$.

Concept Check 9.1

1. Both processes include glycolysis, the citric acid cycle, and oxidative phosphorylation. In aerobic respiration, the final electron acceptor is molecular oxygen (O_2); in anaerobic respiration, the final electron acceptor is a different substance. **2.** $C_4H_6O_5$ would be oxidized and NAD^+ would be reduced.

Concept Check 9.2

1. NAD^+ acts as the oxidizing agent in step 6, accepting electrons from glyceraldehyde 3-phosphate, which thus acts as the reducing agent. **2.** Since the overall process of glycolysis results in net production of ATP, it would make sense for the process to slow down when ATP levels have increased substantially. Thus, we would expect ATP to allosterically inhibit phosphofructokinase.

Concept Check 9.3

1. NADH and $FADH_2$; they will donate electrons to the electron transport chain. **2.** CO_2 is released from the pyruvate that is the end product of glycolysis, and CO_2 is also released during the citric acid cycle. **3.** In both cases, the precursor molecule loses a CO_2 molecule and then donates electrons to an electron carrier in an oxidation step. Also, the product has been activated due to the attachment of a CoA group.

Concept Check 9.4

1. Oxidative phosphorylation would eventually stop entirely, resulting in no ATP production by this process. Without oxygen to "pull" electrons down the electron transport chain, H^+ would not be pumped into the mitochondrion's intermembrane space and chemiosmosis would not occur. **2.** Decreasing the pH means addition of H^+. This would establish a proton gradient even without the function of the electron transport chain, and we would expect ATP synthase to function and synthesize ATP. (In fact, it was experiments like this that provided support for chemiosmosis as an energy-coupling mechanism.) **3.** One of the components of the electron transport chain, ubiquinone (Q), must be able to diffuse within the membrane. It could not do so if the membrane were locked rigidly into place.

Concept Check 9.5

1. A derivative of pyruvate, such as acetaldehyde during alcohol fermentation, or pyruvate itself during lactic acid fermentation; oxygen **2.** The cell would need to consume glucose at a rate about 16 times the consumption rate in the aerobic environment (2 ATP are generated by fermentation versus up to 32 ATP by cellular respiration).

Concept Check 9.6

1. The fat is much more reduced; it has many —CH_2— units, and in all these bonds the electrons are equally shared. The electrons present in a carbohydrate molecule are already somewhat oxidized (shared unequally in bonds), as quite a few of them are bound to oxygen. **2.** When we consume more food than necessary for metabolic processes, our body synthesizes fat as a way of storing energy for later use. **3.** Glycogen is a storage polysaccharide in liver and muscle cells. When energy is needed, glucose units are hydrolyzed from glycogen. Glycolysis in the cytosol breaks down glucose to two pyruvate molecules, which are transported into the mitochondrion. Here they are further oxidized, ultimately producing the needed ATP. **4.** AMP will accumulate, stimulating phosphofructokinase, and thus increasing the rate of glycolysis. Since oxygen is not present, the cell will convert pyruvate to lactate in lactic acid fermentation, providing a supply of ATP. **5.** When oxygen is present, the fatty acid chains containing most of the energy of a fat are oxidized and fed into the citric acid cycle and the electron transport chain. During intense exercise, however, oxygen is scarce in muscle cells, so ATP must be generated by glycolysis alone. A very small part of the fat molecule, the glycerol backbone, can be oxidized via glycolysis, but the amount of energy released by this portion is insignificant compared to that released by the fatty acid chains. (This is why moderate exercise, staying below 70% maximum heart rate, is better for burning fat—because enough oxygen remains available to the muscles.)

Summary of Key Concepts Questions

9.1 Most of the ATP produced in cellular respiration comes from oxidative phosphorylation, in which the energy released from redox reactions in an electron transport chain is used to produce ATP. In substrate-level phosphorylation, an enzyme directly transfers a phosphate group to ADP from an intermediate substrate. All ATP production in glycolysis occurs by substrate-level phosphorylation; this form of ATP production also occurs at one step in the citric acid cycle. **9.2** The oxidation of the three-carbon sugar, glyceraldehyde 3-phosphate, yields energy. In this oxidation, electrons and H^+ are transferred to NAD^+, forming NADH, and a phosphate group is attached to the oxidized substrate. ATP is then formed by substrate-level phosphorylation when this phosphate group is transferred to ADP. **9.3** The release of six molecules of CO_2 represents the complete oxidation of glucose. During the processing of two pyruvates to acetyl CoA, the fully oxidized carboxyl group (—COO^-) is given off as CO_2. The remaining four carbons are released as CO_2 in the citric acid cycle as citrate is oxidized back to oxaloacetate. **9.4** The flow of H^+ through the ATP synthase complex causes the rotor and attached rod to rotate, exposing catalytic sites in the knob portion that produce ATP from ADP and Ⓟi. ATP synthases are found in the inner mitochondrial membrane, the plasma membrane of prokaryotes, and membranes within chloroplasts. **9.5** Anaerobic respiration yields more ATP. The 2 ATP produced by substrate-level phosphorylation in glycolysis represent the total energy yield of fermentation. NADH passes its "high-energy" electrons to pyruvate or a derivative of pyruvate, recycling NAD^+ and allowing glycolysis to continue. Anaerobic respiration uses an electron transport chain to capture the energy of the electrons in NADH via a series of redox reactions; ultimately, the electrons are transferred to an electronegative molecule other than oxygen. And additional molecules of NADH are produced in anaerobic respiration as pyruvate is oxidized. **9.6** The ATP produced by catabolic pathways is used to drive anabolic pathways. Also, many of the intermediates of glycolysis and the citric acid cycle are used in the biosynthesis of a cell's molecules.

Test Your Understanding

1. d **2.** c **3.** c **4.** a **5.** e **6.** a **7.** b

8.

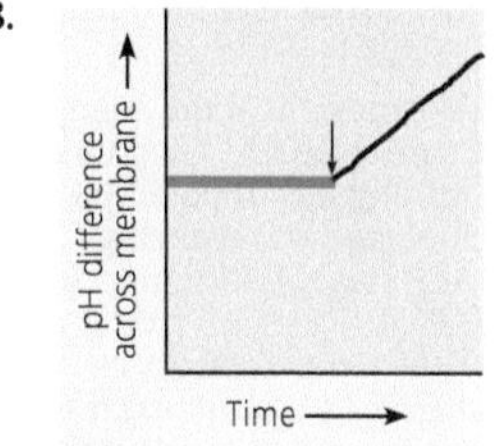

Chapter 10

Figure Questions

Figure 10.3 Situating containers of algae near sources of CO_2 emissions makes sense because algae need CO_2 to carry out photosynthesis. The higher their rate of photosynthesis, the more plant oil they will produce. At the same time, algae would be absorbing the CO_2 emitted from industrial plants or from car engines, reducing the amount of CO_2 entering the atmosphere. **Figure 10.10** Red, but not violet-blue, wavelengths would pass through the filter, so the bacteria would not congregate where the violet-blue light normally comes through. Therefore, the left "peak" of bacteria would not be present, but the right peak would be observed because the red wavelengths passing through the filter would be used for photosynthesis. **Figure 10.12** In the leaf, most of the chlorophyll electrons excited by photon absorption are used to power the reactions of photosynthesis. **Figure 10.16** The person at the top of the photosystem I tower would not turn and throw his electron into the bucket. Instead, he would throw it onto the top of the ramp right next to the photosystem II tower. The electron would then roll down the ramp, get energized by a photon, and return to him. This cycle would continue as long as light was available. (This is why it's called cyclic electron flow.)

Figure 10.19

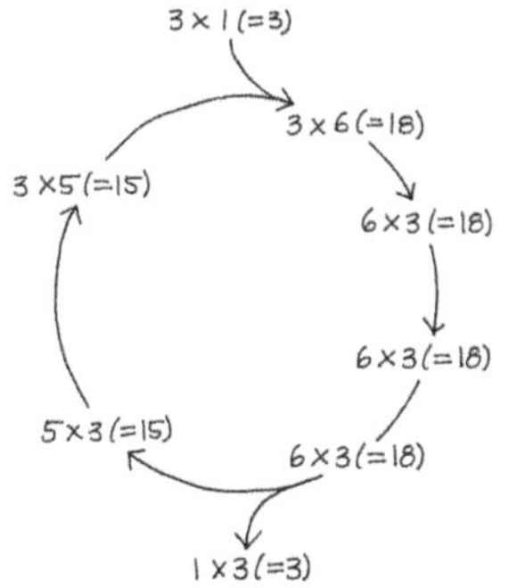

Three carbon atoms enter the cycle, one by one, as individual CO_2 molecules, and leave the cycle in one three-carbon molecule (G3P) per three turns of the cycle.

Figure 10.22

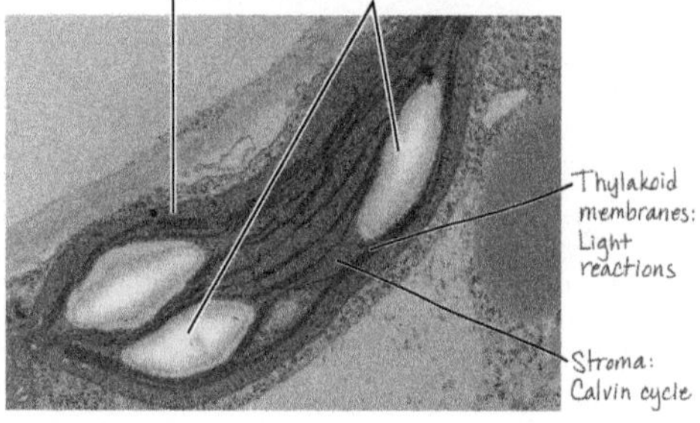

The photosystems that carry out the light reactions are embedded in the thylakoid membranes, and the ATP and NADPH that are formed are released into the stroma. There, they are used for the reactions of the Calvin cycle, which produces G3P. Excess sugar molecules that are not used by the plant can be converted to glucose, then stored in the form of starch.

Concept Check 10.1

1. CO_2 enters leaves via stomata, and water enters via roots and is carried to leaves through veins. **2.** Using ^{18}O, a heavy isotope of oxygen, as a label, researchers were able to confirm van Niel's hypothesis that the oxygen produced during photosynthesis originates in water, not in carbon dioxide. **3.** The light reactions could *not* keep producing NADPH and ATP without the $NADP^+$, ADP, and Ⓟ$_i$ that the Calvin cycle generates. The two cycles are interdependent.

Concept Check 10.2

1. Green, because green light is mostly transmitted and reflected—not absorbed—by photosynthetic pigments **2.** In chloroplasts, light-excited electrons are trapped by a primary electron acceptor, which prevents them from dropping back to the ground state. In isolated chlorophyll, there is no electron acceptor, so the photoexcited electrons immediately drop back down to the ground state, with the emission of light and heat. **3.** Water (H_2O) is the initial electron donor; $NADP^+$ accepts electrons at the end of the electron transport chain, becoming reduced to NADPH. **4.** In this experiment, the rate of ATP synthesis would slow and eventually stop. Because the added compound would not allow a proton gradient to build up across the membrane, ATP synthase could not catalyze ATP production.

Concept Check 10.3

1. 6, 18, 12 **2.** The more potential energy a molecule stores, the more energy and reducing power is required for the formation of that molecule. Glucose is a valuable energy source because it is highly reduced, storing lots of potential energy in its electrons. To reduce CO_2 to glucose, much energy and reducing power are required in the form of large numbers of ATP and NADPH molecules, respectively. **3.** The light reactions require ADP and $NADP^+$, which would not be formed in sufficient quantities from ATP and NADPH if the Calvin cycle stopped. **4.** In glycolysis, G3P acts as an intermediate. The 6-carbon sugar fructose 1,6-bisphosphate is cleaved into two 3-carbon sugars, one of which is G3P. The other is an isomer called dihydroxyacetone phosphate, which can be converted to G3P by an isomerase. Because G3P is the substrate for the next enzyme, it is constantly removed, and the reaction equilibrium is pulled in the direction of conversion of dihydroxyacetone phosphate to more G3P. In the Calvin cycle, G3P acts as both an intermediate and a product. For every three CO_2 molecules that enter the cycle, six G3P molecules are formed, five of which must remain in the cycle and become rearranged to regenerate three 5-carbon RuBP molecules. The one remaining G3P is a product, which can be thought of as the result of "reducing" the three CO_2 molecules that entered the cycle into a 3-carbon sugar that can later be used to generate energy.

Concept Check 10.4

1. Photorespiration decreases photosynthetic output by adding oxygen, instead of carbon dioxide, to the Calvin cycle. As a result, no sugar is generated (no carbon is fixed), and O_2 is used rather than generated. **2.** Without PS II, no O_2 is generated in bundle-sheath cells. This avoids the problem of O_2 competing with CO_2 for binding to rubisco in these cells. **3.** Both problems are caused by a drastic change in Earth's atmosphere due to burning of fossil fuels. The increase in CO_2 concentration affects ocean chemistry by decreasing pH, thus affecting calcification by marine organisms. On land, CO_2 concentration and air temperature are conditions that plants have become adapted to, and changes in these characteristics have a strong effect on photosynthesis by plants. Thus, alteration of these two fundamental factors could have critical effects on organisms all around the planet, in all different habitats. **4.** C_4 and CAM species would replace many of the C_3 species.

Summary of Key Concepts Questions

10.1 CO_2 and H_2O are the products of respiration; they are the reactants in photosynthesis. In respiration, glucose is oxidized to CO_2 as electrons are passed through an electron transfer chain from glucose to O_2, producing H_2O. In photosynthesis, H_2O is the source of electrons, which are energized by light, temporarily stored in NADPH, and used to reduce CO_2 to carbohydrate. **10.2** The action spectrum of photosynthesis shows that some wavelengths of light that are not absorbed by chlorophyll *a* are still effective at promoting photosynthesis. The light-harvesting complexes of photosystems contain accessory pigments such as chlorophyll *b* and carotenoids, which absorb different wavelengths and pass the energy to chlorophyll *a*, broadening the spectrum of light useful for photosynthesis.
10.3

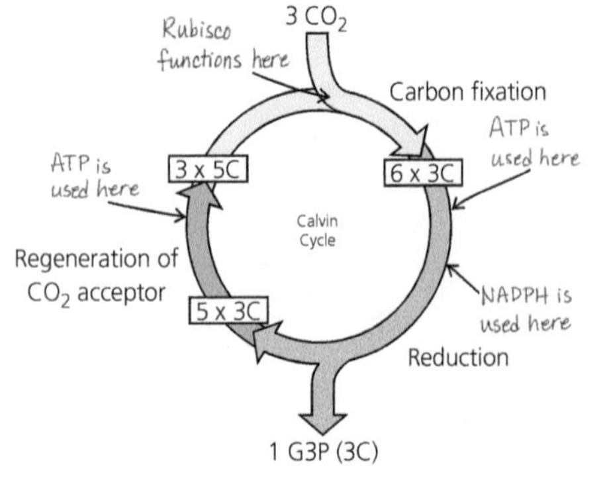

In the reduction phase of the Calvin cycle, ATP phosphorylates a 3-carbon compound, and NADPH then reduces this compound to G3P. ATP is also used in the regeneration phase, when five molecules of G3P are converted to three molecules of the 5-carbon compound RuBP. Rubisco catalyzes the first step of carbon fixation—the addition of CO_2 to RuBP. **10.4** Both C_4 and CAM photosynthesis involve initial fixation of CO_2 to produce a 4-carbon compound (in mesophyll cells in C_4 plants and at night in CAM plants). These compounds are then broken down to release CO_2 (in the bundle-sheath cells in C_4 plants and during the day in CAM plants). ATP is required for recycling the molecule that is used initially to combine with CO_2. These pathways avoid the photorespiration that consumes ATP and reduces the photosynthetic output of C_3 plants when they close stomata on hot, dry, bright days. Thus, hot, arid climates would favor C_4 and CAM plants.

Test Your Understanding

1. d **2.** b **3.** c **4.** d **5.** c **6.** b **7.** d
9.

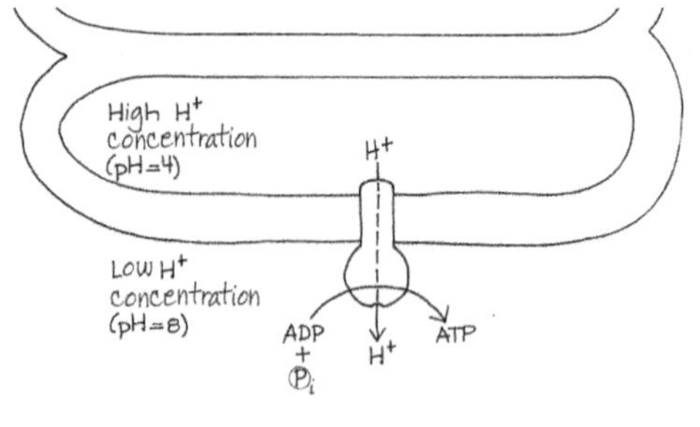

The ATP would end up outside the thylakoid. The thylakoids were able to make ATP in the dark because the researchers set up an artificial proton concentration gradient across the thylakoid membrane; thus, the light reactions were not necessary to establish the H^+ gradient required for ATP synthesis by ATP synthase.

Chapter 11

Figure Questions

Figure 11.6 Epinephrine is a signaling molecule; presumably, it binds to a cell-surface receptor protein. **Figure 11.7** Figure 7.1 shows a potassium channel, which, according to the description on p. 135, opens in response to an electrical stimulus, allowing potassium ions to rush out of the cell. Thus, it is a voltage-gated ion channel. **Figure 11.8** When the receptor is actively transmitting a signal to the inside of the cell, it is bound to a G protein. To determine a structure corresponding to that state, it might work to crystallize the receptor in the presence of many copies of the G protein. (In fact, the researchers planned to try this approach next. Another research group also used this approach successfully with a related G protein-coupled receptor the following year.) **Figure 11.9** The testosterone molecule is hydrophobic and can therefore pass directly through the lipid bilayer of the plasma membrane into the cell. (Hydrophilic molecules cannot do this.) **Figure 11.10** The active form of protein kinase 2 **Figure 11.11** The signaling molecule (cAMP) would remain in its active form and would continue to signal. **Figure 11.17** In the model, the directionality of growth is determined by the association of Fus3 with the membrane near the site of receptor activation. Thus, the development of shmoos would be severely compromised, and the affected cell would likely resemble the ΔFus3 and Δformin cells. **Figure 11.18** The signaling pathway shown in Figure 11.14 leads to the splitting of PIP_2 into the second messengers DAG and IP_3, which produce different responses. (The response elicited by DAG is mentioned but not shown.) The pathway shown for cell B is similar in that it branches and leads to two responses.

Concept Check 11.1

1. The two cells of opposite mating type (**a** and **α**) each secrete a certain signaling molecule, which can only be bound by receptors carried on cells of the opposite mating type. Thus, the **a** mating factor cannot bind to another **a** cell and cause it to grow toward the first **a** cell. Only an **α** cell can "receive" the signaling molecule and respond by directed growth (see Figure 11.17 for more information). **2.** The secretion of neurotransmitter molecules at a synapse is an example of local signaling. The electrical signal that travels along a very long nerve cell and is passed to the next nerve cell can be considered an example of long-distance signaling. (Note, however, that local signaling at the synapse between two cells is necessary for the signal to pass from one cell to the next.) **3.** Glucose 1-phosphate is not generated, because the activation of the enzyme requires an intact cell, with an intact receptor in the membrane and an intact signal transduction pathway. The enzyme cannot be activated directly by interaction with the signaling molecule in the test tube. **4.** Glycogen phosphorylase acts in the third stage, the response to epinephrine signaling.

Concept Check 11.2

1. NGF is water-soluble (hydrophilic), so it cannot pass through the lipid membrane to reach intracellular receptors, as steroid hormones can. Therefore, you'd expect the NGF receptor to be in the plasma membrane—which is, in fact, the case. **2.** The cell with the faulty receptor would not be able to respond appropriately to the signaling molecule when it was present. This would most likely have dire consequences for the cell, since regulation of the cell's activities by this receptor would not occur appropriately. **3.** Binding of a ligand to a receptor changes the shape of the receptor, altering the ability of the receptor to transmit a signal. Binding of an allosteric regulator to an enzyme changes the shape of the enzyme, either promoting or inhibiting enzyme activity.

Concept Check 11.3

1. A protein kinase is an enzyme that transfers a phosphate group from ATP to a protein, usually activating that protein (often a second type of protein kinase). Many signal transduction pathways include a series of such interactions, in which each phosphorylated protein kinase in turn phosphorylates the next protein kinase in the series. Such phosphorylation cascades carry a signal from outside the cell to the cellular protein(s) that will carry out the response. **2.** Protein phosphatases reverse the effects of the kinases. **3.** The signal that is being transduced is the information that a signaling molecule is bound to the cell-surface receptor. Information is transduced by way of sequential protein-protein interactions that change protein shapes, causing them to function in a way that passes the signal along. **4.** The IP_3-gated channel opens, allowing calcium ions to flow out of the ER, which raises the cytosolic Ca^{2+} concentration.

Concept Check 11.4

1. At each step in a cascade of sequential activations, one molecule or ion may activate numerous molecules functioning in the next step. **2.** Scaffolding proteins hold molecular components of signaling pathways in a complex with each other. Different scaffolding proteins would assemble different collections of proteins, leading to different cellular responses in the two cells. **3.** A malfunctioning protein phosphatase would not be able to dephosphorylate a particular receptor or relay protein. As a result, the signaling pathway, once activated, would not be able to be terminated. (In fact, one study found altered protein phosphatases in cells from 25% of colorectal tumors.)

Concept Check 11.5

1. In formation of the hand or paw in mammals, cells in the regions between the digits are programmed to undergo apoptosis. This serves to shape the digits of the hand or paw so that they are not webbed. **2.** If a receptor protein for a death-signaling molecule were defective such that it was activated even in the absence of the death signal, this would lead to apoptosis when it wouldn't normally occur. Similar defects in any of the proteins in the signaling pathway, which would activate these relay or response proteins in the absence of interaction with the previous protein or second messenger in the pathway, would have the same effect. Conversely, if any protein in the pathway were defective in its ability to respond to an interaction with an early protein or other molecule or ion, apoptosis would not occur when it normally should. For example, a receptor protein for a death-signaling ligand might not be able to be activated, even when ligand was bound. This would stop the signal from being transduced into the cell.

Summary of Key Concepts Questions

11.1 A cell is able to respond to a hormone only if it has a receptor protein on the cell surface or inside the cell that can bind to the hormone. The response to a hormone depends on the specific cellular activity that a signal transduction pathway triggers within the cell. The response can vary for different types of cells. **11.2** Both GPCRs and RTKs have an extracellular binding site for a signaling molecule (ligand) and an α helix region of the polypeptide that spans the membrane. GPCRs usually trigger a single transduction pathway, whereas the multiple activated tyrosines on an RTK dimer may trigger several different transduction pathways at the same time. **11.3** A protein kinase is an enzyme that adds a phosphate group to another protein. Protein kinases are often part of a phosphorylation cascade that transduces a signal. A second messenger is a small, nonprotein molecule or ion that rapidly diffuses and relays a signal throughout a cell. Both protein kinases and second messengers can operate in the same pathway. For example, the second messenger cAMP often activates protein kinase A, which then phosphorylates other proteins. **11.4** In G protein-coupled pathways, the GTPase portion of a G protein converts GTP to GDP and inactivates the G protein. Protein phosphatases remove phosphate groups from activated proteins, thus stopping a phosphorylation cascade of protein kinases. Phosphodiesterase converts cAMP to AMP, thus reducing the effect of cAMP in a signal transduction pathway. **11.5** The basic mechanism of controlled cell suicide evolved early in eukaryotic evolution, and the genetic basis for these pathways has been conserved during animal evolution. Such a mechanism is essential to the development and maintenance of all animals.

Test Your Understanding

1. c **2.** d **3.** a **4.** b **5.** a **6.** d **7.** c **8.** c **9.** This is one possible drawing of the pathway. (Similar drawings would also be correct.)

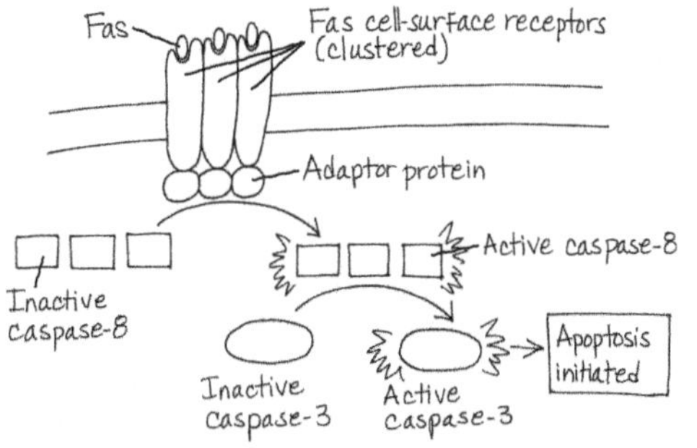

Chapter 12

Figure Questions

Figure 12.4

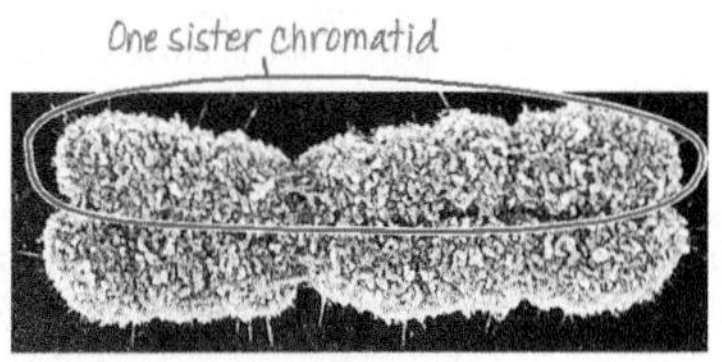

Circling the other chromatid instead would also be correct. **Figure 12.5** The chromosome has four arms. **Figure 12.7** 12; 2; 2; 1

Figure 12.8

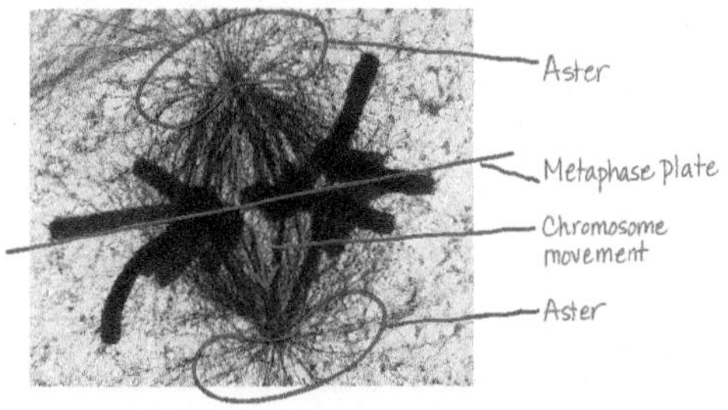

Figure 12.9 The mark would have moved toward the nearer pole. The lengths of fluorescent microtubules between that pole and the mark would have decreased, while the lengths between the chromosomes and the mark would have remained the same. **Figure 12.14** In both cases, the G_1 nucleus would have remained in G_1 until the time it normally would have entered the S phase. Chromosome condensation and spindle formation would not have occurred until the S and G_2 phases had been completed. **Figure 12.16** The cell would divide under conditions where it was inappropriate to do so. If the daughter cells and their descendants also ignored the checkpoint and divided, there would soon be an abnormal mass of cells. (This type of inappropriate cell division can contribute to the development of cancer.) **Figure 12.17** Passing the G_2 checkpoint in the diagram corresponds to the beginning of the "Time" axis of the graph, and entry into the mitotic phase (yellow background on the diagram) corresponds to the peaks of MPF activity and cyclin concentration on the graph (see the yellow M banner over the peaks). During G_1 and S phase in the diagram, Cdk is present without cyclin, so on the graph both cyclin concentration and MPF activity are low. The curved purple arrow in the diagram shows increasing cyclin concentration, seen on the graph during the end of S phase and throughout G_2 phase. Then the cell cycle begins again. **Figure 12.18** The cells in the vessel with PDGF would not be able to respond to the growth factor signal and thus would not divide. The culture would resemble that without the added PDGF. **Figure 12.21** The intracellular estrogen receptor, once activated, would be able to act as a transcription factor in the nucleus, turning on genes that may cause the cell to pass a checkpoint and divide. The HER2 receptor, when activated by a ligand, would form a dimer, and each subunit of the dimer would phosphorylate the other. This would lead to a series of signal transduction steps, ultimately turning on genes in the nucleus. As in the case of the estrogen receptor, the genes would code for proteins necessary to commit the cell to divide.

Concept Check 12.1

1. 2 **2.** 39; 39; 78

Concept Check 12.2

1. 6 chromosomes, duplicated; 12 chromatids **2.** Following mitosis, cytokinesis results in two genetically identical daughter cells in both plant cells and animal cells. However, the mechanism of dividing the cytoplasm is different in animals and plants. In an animal cell, cytokinesis occurs by cleavage, which divides the parent cell in two with a contractile ring of actin filaments. In a plant cell, a cell plate forms in the middle of the cell and grows until its membrane fuses with the plasma membrane of the parent cell. Material inside the cell plate thus becomes the new cell wall. **3.** They elongate the cell during anaphase. **4.** During eukaryotic cell division, tubulin is involved in spindle formation and chromosome movement, while actin functions during cytokinesis. In bacterial binary fission, it's the opposite: Tubulin-like molecules are thought to act in daughter cell separation, and actin-like molecules are thought to move the daughter bacterial chromosomes to opposite ends of the cell. **5.** Microtubules made up of tubulin in the cell provide "rails" along which vesicles and other organelles can travel, based on interactions of motor proteins with tubulin in the microtubules. In muscle cells, actin in microfilaments interacts with myosin filaments to cause muscle contraction.
6. From the end of S phase in interphase through the end of metaphase in mitosis

Concept Check 12.3

1. The nucleus on the right was originally in the G_1 phase; therefore, it had not yet duplicated its chromosome. The nucleus on the left was in the M phase, so it had already duplicated its chromosome. **2.** A sufficient amount of MPF has to exist for a cell to pass the G_2 checkpoint; this occurs through the accumulation of cyclin proteins, which combine with Cdk to form MPF. **3.** Most body cells are in a nondividing state called G_0. **4.** Both types of tumors consist of abnormal cells, but their characteristics are different. A benign tumor stays at the original site and can usually be surgically removed; the cells have some genetic and cellular changes from normal, non-tumor cells. Cancer cells from a malignant tumor have more significant genetic and cellular changes, can spread from the original site by metastasis, and may impair the functions of one or more organs. **5.** The cells might divide even in the absence of PDGF. In addition, they would not stop when the surface of the culture vessel was covered; they would continue to divide, piling on top of one another.

Summary of Key Concepts Questions

12.1 The DNA of a eukaryotic cell is packaged into structures called *chromosomes*. Each chromosome is a long molecule of DNA, which carries hundreds to thousands of genes, with associated proteins that maintain chromosome structure and help control gene activity. This DNA-protein complex is called *chromatin*. The chromatin of each chromosome is long and thin when the cell is not dividing. Prior to cell division, each chromosome is duplicated, and the resulting sister *chromatids* are attached to each other by proteins at the centromeres and, for many species, all along their lengths (sister chromatid cohesion). **12.2** Chromosomes exist as single DNA molecules in G_1 of interphase and in anaphase and telophase of mitosis. During S phase, DNA replication produces sister chromatids, which persist during G_2 of interphase and through prophase, prometaphase, and metaphase of mitosis. **12.3** Checkpoints allow cellular surveillance mechanisms to determine whether the cell is prepared to go to the next stage. Internal and external signals move a cell past these checkpoints. The G_1 checkpoint, called the "restriction point" in mammalian cells, determines whether a cell will complete the cell cycle and divide or switch into the G_0 phase. The signals to pass this checkpoint often are external—such as growth factors. Passing the G_2 checkpoint requires sufficient numbers of active MPF complexes, which in turn orchestrate several mitotic events. MPF also initiates degradation of its cyclin component, terminating the M phase. The M phase will not begin again until sufficient cyclin is produced during the next S and G_2 phases. The signal to pass the M phase checkpoint is not activated until all chromosomes are attached to kinetochore fibers and are aligned at the metaphase plate. Only then will sister chromatid separation occur.

Test Your Understanding

1. b **2.** a **3.** c **4.** c **5.** a **6.** b
7. See Figure 12.7 for a description of major events.

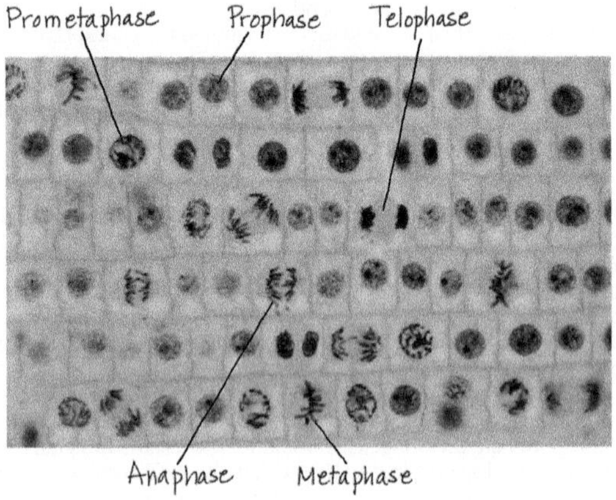

Only one cell is indicated for each stage, but other correct answers are also present in this micrograph.
8. a **9.** e
10.

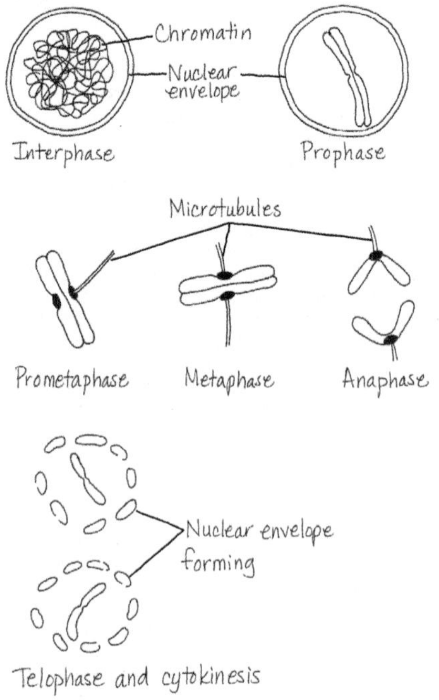

Chapter 13

Figure Questions

Figure 13.4 The haploid number, n, is 3. A set is always haploid.
Figure 13.7

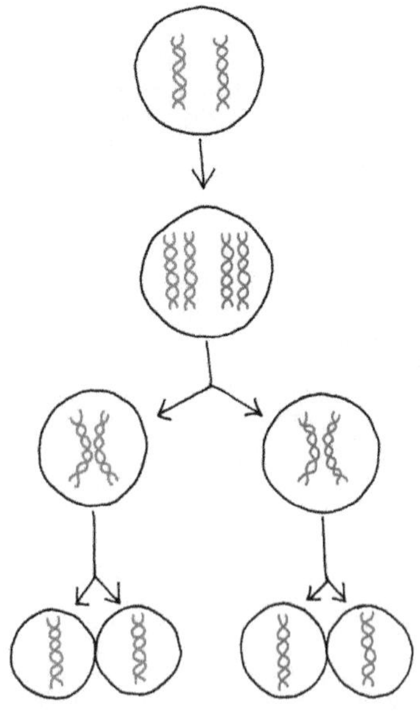

(A short strand of DNA is shown here for simplicity, but each chromosome or chromatid contains a very long coiled and folded DNA molecule.)
Figure 13.8 If the two cells in Figure 12.7 underwent another round of mitosis, each of the four resulting cells would have six chromosomes, while the four cells resulting from meiosis in Figure 13.8 each have three chromosomes. In mitosis, DNA replication (and thus chromosome duplication) precedes each prophase, ensuring that daughter cells have the same number of chromosomes as the parent cell. In meiosis, in contrast, DNA replication occurs only before prophase I (not prophase II). Thus, in two rounds of mitosis, the chromosomes duplicate twice and divide twice, while in meiosis, the chromosomes duplicate once and divide twice. **Figure 13.9** Yes. Each of the six chromosomes (three per cell) shown in telophase I has one nonrecombinant chromatid and one recombinant chromatid. Therefore, eight possible sets of chromosomes can be generated for the cell on the left and eight for the cell on the right.

Concept Check 13.1

1. Parents pass genes to their offspring; the genes program cells to make specific enzymes and other proteins, whose cumulative action produces an individual's inherited traits. **2.** Such organisms reproduce by mitosis, which generates offspring whose genomes are exact copies of the parent's genome (in the absence of mutation). **3.** She should clone it. Cross-breeding it with another plant would generate offspring that have additional variation, which she no longer desires now that she has obtained her ideal orchid.

Concept Check 13.2

1. Each of the six chromosomes is duplicated, so each contains two DNA double helices. Therefore, there are 12 DNA molecules in the cell. **2.** In meiosis, the chromosome count is reduced from diploid to haploid; the union of two haploid gametes in fertilization restores the diploid chromosome count. **3.** The haploid number (n) is 7; the diploid number ($2n$) is 14. **4.** This organism has the life cycle shown in Figure 13.6c. Therefore, it must be a fungus or a protist, perhaps an alga.

Concept Check 13.3

1. The chromosomes are similar in that each is composed of two sister chromatids, and the individual chromosomes are positioned similarly at the metaphase plate. The chromosomes differ in that in a mitotically dividing cell, sister chromatids of each chromosome are genetically identical, but in a meiotically dividing cell, sister chromatids are genetically distinct because of crossing over in meiosis I. Moreover, the chromosomes in metaphase of mitosis can be a diploid set or a haploid set, but the chromosomes in metaphase of meiosis II always consist of a haploid set. **2.** If crossing over did not occur, the two homologs would not be associated in any way. This might result in incorrect arrangement of homologs during metaphase I and ultimately in formation of gametes with an abnormal number of chromosomes.

Concept Check 13.4

1. Mutations in a gene lead to the different versions (alleles) of that gene.
2. Without crossing over, independent assortment of chromosomes during meiosis I theoretically can generate 2^n possible haploid gametes, and random fertilization can produce $2^n \times 2^n$ possible diploid zygotes. Because the haploid number (n) of grasshoppers is 23 and that of fruit flies is 4, two grasshoppers would be expected to produce a greater variety of zygotes than would two fruit flies. **3.** If the segments of the maternal and paternal chromatids that undergo

crossing over are genetically identical and thus have the same two alleles for every gene, then the recombinant chromosomes will be genetically equivalent to the parental chromosomes. Crossing over contributes to genetic variation only when it involves the rearrangement of different alleles.

Summary of Key Concepts Questions

13.1 Genes program specific traits, and offspring inherit their genes from each parent, accounting for similarities in their appearance to one or the other parent. Humans reproduce sexually, which ensures new combinations of genes (and thus traits) in the offspring. Consequently, the offspring are not clones of their parents (which would be the case if humans reproduced asexually). **13.2** Animals and plants both reproduce sexually, alternating meiosis with fertilization. Both have haploid gametes that unite to form a diploid zygote, which then goes on to divide mitotically, forming a diploid multicellular organism. In animals, haploid cells become gametes and don't undergo mitosis, while in plants, the haploid cells resulting from meiosis undergo mitosis to form a haploid multicellular organism, the gametophyte. This organism then goes on to generate haploid gametes. (In plants such as trees, the gametophyte is quite reduced in size and not obvious to the casual observer.) **13.3** At the end of meiosis I, the two members of a homologous pair end up in different cells, so they cannot pair up and undergo crossing over. **13.4** First, during independent assortment in metaphase I, each pair of homologous chromosomes lines up independent of each other pair at the metaphase plate, so a daughter cell of meiosis I randomly inherits either a maternal or paternal chromosome. Second, due to crossing over, each chromosome is not exclusively maternal or paternal, but includes regions at the ends of the chromatid from a nonsister chromatid (a chromatid of the other homolog). (The nonsister segment can also be in an internal region of the chromatid if a second crossover occurs beyond the first one before the end of the chromatid.) This provides much additional diversity in the form of new combinations of alleles. Third, random fertilization ensures even more variation, since any sperm of a large number containing many possible genetic combinations can fertilize any egg of a similarly large number of possible combinations.

Test Your Understanding

1. a **2.** d **3.** b **4.** a **5.** d **6.** c **7.** d
8. (a)

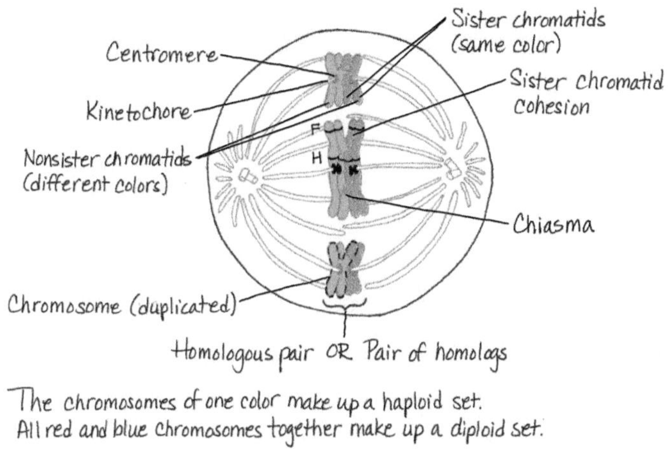

(b) The chromosomes of one color make up a haploid set. (In cases where crossovers have occurred, a haploid set of one color may include segments of chromatids of the other color.) All red and blue chromosomes together make up a diploid set.
(c) Metaphase I **9.** This cell must be undergoing meiosis because homologous chromosomes are associated with each other at the metaphase plate; this does not occur in mitosis.

Chapter 14

Figure Questions

Figure 14.3 All offspring would have purple flowers. (The ratio would be one purple to zero white.) The P generation plants are true-breeding, so mating two purple-flowered plants produces the same result as self-pollination: All the offspring have the same trait.

Figure 14.8

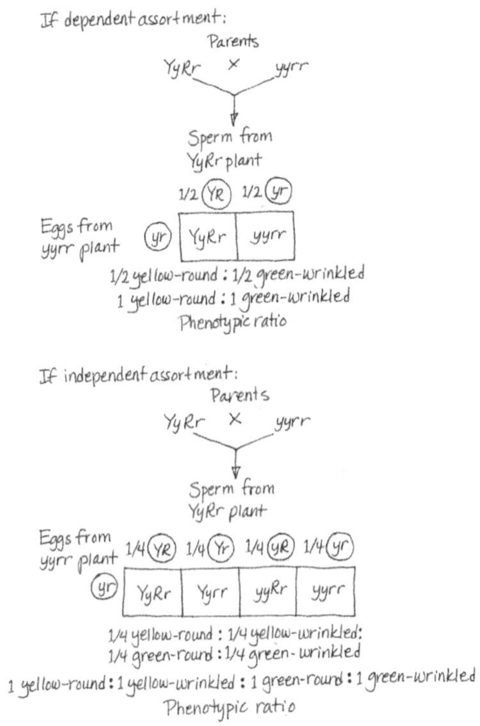

Yes, this cross would also have allowed Mendel to make different predictions for the two hypotheses, thereby allowing him to distinguish the correct one.
Figure 14.10 Your classmate would probably point out that the F_1 generation hybrids show an intermediate phenotype between those of the homozygous parents, which supports the blending hypothesis. You could respond that crossing the F_1 hybrids results in the reappearance of the white phenotype, rather than identical pink offspring, which fails to support the idea of traits blending during inheritance.
Figure 14.11 Both the I^A and I^B alleles are dominant to the i allele, which results in no attached carbohydrate. The I^A and I^B alleles are codominant; both are expressed in the phenotype of I^AI^B heterozygotes, who have type AB blood.
Figure 14.13

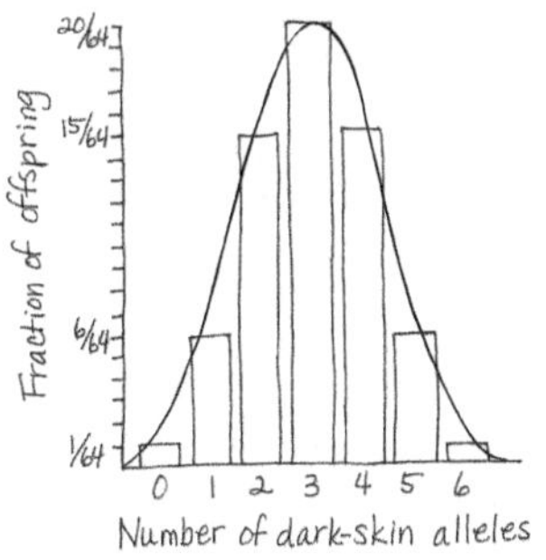

The majority of individuals have intermediate phenotypes (skin color in the middle range), while fewer individuals have phenotypes at either end (very dark or very light skin). (As you may know, this is called a "bell curve" and represents a "normal distribution.") **Figure 14.16** In the Punnett square, two of the three individuals with normal coloration are carriers, so the probability is ⅔. (Note that you must take into account everything you know when you calculate probability: You know she is not *aa*, so there are only three possible genotypes to consider.) **Figure 14.18** If one parent tests negative for the recessive allele, then the probability is zero that the offspring will have the disease and ½ that the offspring will be a carrier. If the first child is a carrier, the probability of the next child being a carrier is still ½ because the two births are independent events.

Concept Check 14.1

1. According to the law of independent assortment, 25 plants ($\frac{1}{16}$ of the offspring) are predicted to be *aatt*, or recessive for both characters. The actual result is likely to differ slightly from this value.

Parents
AaTt × *AaTt*

Sperm from *AaTt* plant

Eggs from *AaTt* plant	*AT*	*At*	*aT*	*at*
AT	*AATT*	*AATt*	*AaTT*	*AaTt*
At	*AATt*	*AAtt*	*AaTt*	*Aatt*
aT	*AaTT*	*AaTt*	*aaTT*	*aaTt*
at	*AaTt*	*Aatt*	*aaTt*	*aatt*

2. The plant could make eight different gametes (*YRI, YRi, YrI, Yri, yRI, yRi, yrI*, and *yri*). To fit all the possible gametes in a self-pollination, a Punnett square would need 8 rows and 8 columns. It would have spaces for the 64 possible unions of gametes in the offspring. **3.** Self-pollination is sexual reproduction because meiosis is involved in forming gametes, which unite during fertilization. As a result, the offspring in self-pollination are genetically different from the parent. (As mentioned in the footnote on p. 263, we have simplified the explanation in referring to the single pea plant as a parent. Technically, the gametophytes in the flower are the two "parents.")

Concept Check 14.2

1. ½ homozygous dominant (*AA*), 0 homozygous recessive (*aa*), and ½ heterozygous (*Aa*) **2.** ¼ *BBDD*; ¼ *BbDD*; ¼ *BBDd*; ¼ *BbDd* **3.** The genotypes that fulfill this condition are *ppyyIi, ppYyii, Ppyyii, ppYYii*, and *ppyyii*. Use the multiplication rule to find the probability of getting each genotype, and then use the addition rule to find the overall probability of meeting the conditions of this problem:

ppyyIi	½ (probability of *pp*) × ¼ (*yy*) × ½ (*ii*)	= $\frac{1}{16}$
ppYyii	½ (*pp*) × ½ (*Yy*) × ½ (*ii*)	= $\frac{2}{16}$
Ppyyii	½ (*Pp*) × ¼ (*yy*) × ½ (*ii*)	= $\frac{1}{16}$
ppYYii	½ (*pp*) × ¼ (*YY*) × ½ (*ii*)	= $\frac{1}{16}$
ppyyii	½ (*pp*) × ¼ (*yy*) × ½ (*ii*)	= $\frac{1}{16}$
Fraction predicted to have at least two recessive traits		= $\frac{6}{16}$ or 3/8

Concept Check 14.3

1. Incomplete dominance describes the relationship between two alleles of a single gene, whereas epistasis relates to the genetic relationship between two genes (and the respective alleles of each). **2.** Half of the children would be expected to have type A blood and half type B blood. **3.** The black and white alleles are incompletely dominant, with heterozygotes being gray in color. A cross between a gray rooster and a black hen should yield approximately equal numbers of gray and black offspring.

Concept Check 14.4

1. $\frac{1}{9}$ (Since cystic fibrosis is caused by a recessive allele, Beth and Tom's siblings who have CF must be homozygous recessive. Therefore, each parent must be a carrier of the recessive allele. Since neither Beth nor Tom has CF, this means they each have a ⅔ chance of being a carrier. If they are both carriers, there is a ¼ chance that they will have a child with CF. ⅔ × ⅔ × ¼ = $\frac{1}{9}$); 0 (Both Beth and Tom would have to be carriers to produce a child with the disease.) **2.** In normal hemoglobin, the sixth amino acid is glutamic acid (Glu), which is acidic (has a negative charge on its side chain). In sickle-cell hemoglobin, Glu is replaced by valine (Val), which is a nonpolar amino acid, very different from Glu. The primary structure of a protein (its amino acid sequence) ultimately determines the shape of the protein and thus its function. The substitution of Val for Glu enables the hemoglobin molecules to interact with each other and form long fibers, leading to the protein's deficient function and the deformation of the red blood cell. **3.** Joan's genotype is *Dd*. Because the allele for polydactyly (*D*) is dominant to the allele for five digits per appendage (*d*), the trait is expressed in people with either the *DD* or *Dd* genotype. But because Joan's father does not have polydactyly, his genotype must be *dd*, which means that Joan inherited a *d* allele from him. Therefore Joan, who does have the trait, must be heterozygous. **4.** In the monohybrid cross involving flower color, the ratio is 3.15 purple : 1 white, while in the human family in the pedigree, the ratio in the third generation is 1 free : 1 attached earlobe. The difference is due to the small sample size (two offspring) in the human family. If the second-generation couple in this pedigree were able to have 929 offspring as in the pea plant cross, the ratio would likely be closer to 3:1. (Note that none of the pea plant crosses in Table 14.1 yielded *exactly* a 3:1 ratio.)

Summary of Key Concepts Questions

14.1 Alternative versions of genes, called alleles, are passed from parent to offspring during sexual reproduction. In a cross between purple- and white-flowered homozygous parents, the F_1 offspring are all heterozygous, each inheriting a purple allele from one parent and a white allele from the other. Because the purple allele is dominant, it determines the phenotype of the F_1 offspring to be purple, and the expression of the white allele is masked. Only in the F_2 generation is it possible for a white allele to exist in a homozygous state, which causes the white trait to be expressed.

14.2

Eggs \ Sperm	½ *Y*	½ *y*
½ *Y*	*YY*	*Yy*
½ *y*	*Yy*	*yy*

¾ yellow
¼ green

Eggs \ Sperm	½ *R*	½ *r*
½ *R*	*RR*	*Rr*
½ *r*	*Rr*	*rr*

¾ round
¼ wrinkled

¾ yellow × ¾ round = 9/16 yellow-round
¾ yellow × ¼ wrinkled = 3/16 yellow-wrinkled
¼ green × ¾ round = 3/16 green-round
¼ green × ¼ wrinkled = 1/16 green-wrinkled
= 9 yellow-round : 3 yellow-wrinkled : 3 green-round : 1 green-wrinkled

14.3 The ABO blood group is an example of multiple alleles because this single gene has more than two alleles (I^A, I^B, and *i*). Two of the alleles, I^A and I^B, exhibit codominance, since both carbohydrates (A and B) are present when these two alleles exist together in a genotype. I^A and I^B each exhibit complete dominance over the *i* allele. This situation is not an example of incomplete dominance because each allele affects the phenotype in a distinguishable way, so the result is not intermediate between the two phenotypes. Because this situation involves a single gene, it is not an example of epistasis or polygenic inheritance. **14.4** The chance of the fourth child having cystic fibrosis is ¼, as it was for each of the other children, because each birth is an independent event. We already know both parents are carriers, so whether their first three children are carriers or not has no bearing on the probability that their next child will have the disease. The parents' genotypes provide the only relevant information.

Test Your Understanding

1. Gene, l. Allele, e. Character, g. Trait, b. Dominant allele, j. Recessive allele, a. Genotype, k. Phenotype, h. Homozygous, c. Heterozygous, f. Testcross, i. Monohybrid cross, d.
2.

Parents
GgIi × *GgIi*

Sperm

Eggs	*GI*	*Gi*	*gI*	*gi*
GI	*GGII*	*GGIi*	*GgII*	*GgIi*
Gi	*GGIi*	*GGii*	*GgIi*	*Ggii*
gI	*GgII*	*GgIi*	*ggII*	*ggIi*
gi	*GgIi*	*Ggii*	*ggIi*	*ggii*

9 green-inflated : 3 green-constricted :
3 yellow-inflated : 1 yellow-constricted

3. Parental cross is $AAC^RC^R \times aaC^WC^W$. F_1 genotype is $AaC^R C^W$, phenotype is all axial-pink. F_2 genotypes are 1 AAC^RC^R : 2 AAC^RC^W : 1 AAC^WC^W : 2 AaC^RC^R : 4 AaC^RC^W : 2 AaC^WC^W : 1 aaC^RC^R : 2 aaC^RC^W : 1 aaC^WC^W. F_2 phenotypes are 3 axial-red : 6 axial-pink : 3 axial-white : 1 terminal-red : 2 terminal-pink : 1 terminal-white. **4.** Man I^Ai; woman I^Bi; child *ii*. Genotypes for future children are predicted to be ¼ I^AI^B, ¼ I^Ai, ¼ I^Bi, ¼ *ii*. **5.** ½ **6.** A cross of *Ii* × *ii* would yield offspring with a genotypic ratio of 1 *Ii* : 1 *ii* (2:2 is an equivalent answer) and a phenotypic ratio of 1 inflated : 1 constricted (2:2 is equivalent).

Parents
Ii × *ii*

Sperm from *ii* plant

Eggs from *Ii* plant	*i*	*i*
I	*Ii*	*Ii*
i	*ii*	*ii*

Genotypic ratio 1 *Ii* : 1 *ii* (2:2 is equivalent)
Phenotypic ratio 1 inflated : 1 constricted (2:2 is equivalent)

7. (a) 1/64; (b) 1/64; (c) 1/8; (d) 1/32 **8.** Albino (*b*) is a recessive trait; black (*B*) is dominant. First cross: parents *BB* × *bb*; gametes *B* and *b*; offspring all *Bb* (black coat). The black guinea pig in the second cross is a heterozygote. Second cross: parents *Bb* × *bb*; gametes 1/2 *B* and 1/2 *b* (heterozygous parent) and *b*; offspring 1/2 *Bb* and 1/2 *bb*. **9.** (a) *PPLl* × *PPLl*, *PPLl* × *PpLl*, or *PPLl* × *ppLl*; (b) *ppLl* × *ppLl*; (c) *PPLL* × any of the 9 possible genotypes or *PPll* × *ppLL*; (d) *PpLl* × *Ppll*; (e) *PpLl* × *PpLl* **10.** (a) 3/4 × 3/4 × 3/4 = 27/64; (b) 1 − 27/64 = 37/64; (c) 1/4 × 1/4 × 1/4 = 1/64; (d) 1 − 1/64 = 63/64 **11.** (a) 1/256; (b) 1/16; (c) 1/256; (d) 1/64; (e) 1/128 **12.** (a) 1; (b) 1/32; (c) 1/8; (d) 1/2 **13.** 1/6 **14.** Matings of the original mutant cat with true-breeding noncurl cats will produce both curl and noncurl F_1 offspring if the curl allele is dominant, but only noncurl offspring if the curl allele is recessive. You would obtain some true-breeding offspring homozygous for the curl allele from matings between the F_1 cats resulting from the original curl × noncurl crosses whether the curl trait is dominant or recessive. You know that cats are true-breeding when curl × curl matings produce only curl offspring. As it turns out, the allele that causes curled ears is dominant. **15.** 1/16 **16.** 25%, or 1/4, will be cross-eyed; all (100%) of the cross-eyed offspring will also be white. **17.** The dominant allele *I* is epistatic to the *P/p* locus, and thus the genotypic ratio for the F_1 generation will be 9 *I_P_* (colorless) : 3 *I_pp* (colorless) : 3 *iiP_* (purple) : 1 *iipp* (red). Overall, the phenotypic ratio is 12 colorless : 3 purple : 1 red. **18.** Recessive. All affected individuals (Arlene, Tom, Wilma, and Carla) are homozygous recessive *aa*. George is *Aa*, since some of his children with Arlene are affected. Sam, Ann, Daniel, and Alan are each *Aa*, since they are all unaffected children with one affected parent. Michael also is *Aa*, since he has an affected child (Carla) with his heterozygous wife Ann. Sandra, Tina, and Christopher can each have either the *AA* or *Aa* genotype. **19.** 1/6 **20.** 9 *B_A_* (agouti) : 3 *B_aa* (black) : 3 *bbA_* (white) : 1 *bbaa* (white). Overall, 9 agouti : 3 black : 4 white.

Chapter 15

Figure Questions

Figure 15.2 The ratio would be 1 yellow-round : 1 green-round : 1 yellow-wrinkled : 1 green-wrinkled. **Figure 15.4** About 3/4 of the F_2 offspring would have red eyes and about 1/4 would have white eyes. About half of the white-eyed flies would be female and half would be male; similarly, about half of the red-eyed flies would be female and half would be male. **Figure 15.7** All the males would be color-blind, and all the females would be carriers. **Figure 15.9** The two largest classes would still be the parental-type offspring (offspring with the phenotypes of the true-breeding P generation flies), but now they would be gray-vestigial and black-normal because those were the specific allele combinations in the P generation. **Figure 15.10** The two chromosomes below, left, are like the two chromosomes inherited by the F_1 female, one from each P generation fly. They are passed by the F_1 female intact to the offspring and thus could be called "parental" chromosomes. The other two chromosomes result from crossing over during meiosis in the F_1 female. Because they have combinations of alleles not seen in either of the F_1 female's chromosomes, they can be called "recombinant" chromosomes. (Note that in this example, the alleles on the recombinant chromosomes, $b^+ vg^+$ and *b vg*, are the allele combinations that were on the parental chromosomes in the cross shown in Figures 15.9 and 15.10. The basis for calling them parental chromosomes is the combination of alleles that was present on the P generation chromosomes.)

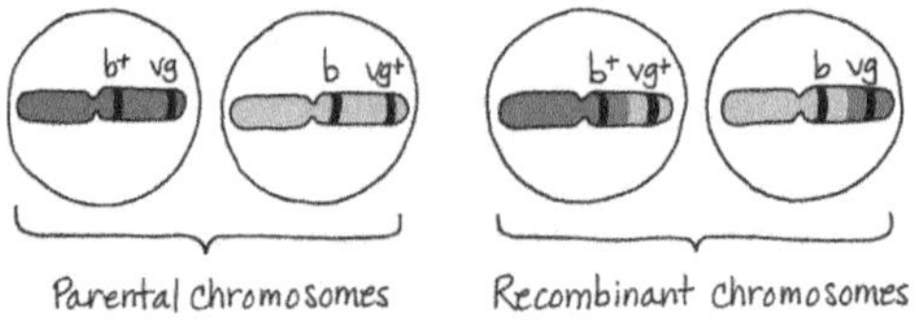

Concept Check 15.1

1. The law of segregation relates to the inheritance of alleles for a single character. The law of independent assortment of alleles relates to the inheritance of alleles for two characters. **2.** The physical basis for the law of segregation is the separation of homologs in anaphase I. The physical basis for the law of independent assortment is the alternative arrangements of homologous chromosome pairs in metaphase I. **3.** To show the mutant phenotype, a male needs to possess only one mutant allele. If this gene had been on a pair of autosomes, *two* mutant alleles would have had to be present for an individual to show the recessive mutant phenotype, a much less probable situation.

Concept Check 15.2

1. Because the gene for this eye-color character is located on the X chromosome, all female offspring will be red-eyed and heterozygous ($X^{w^+} X^w$); all male offspring will inherit a Y chromosome from the father and be white-eyed ($X^w Y$). **2.** 1/4 (1/2 chance that the child will inherit a Y chromosome from the father and be male × 1/2 chance that he will inherit the X carrying the disease allele from his mother) If the child is a boy, there is a 1/2 chance he will have the disease; a female would have zero chance (but 1/2 chance of being a carrier). **3.** With a disorder caused by a dominant allele, there is no such thing as a "carrier," since those with the allele have the disorder. Because the allele is dominant, the females lose any "advantage" in having two X chromosomes, since one disorder-associated allele is sufficient to result in the disorder. All fathers who have the dominant allele will pass it along to *all* their daughters, who will also have the disorder. A mother who has the allele (and thus the disorder) will pass it to half of her sons and half of her daughters.

Concept Check 15.3

1. Crossing over during meiosis I in the heterozygous parent produces some gametes with recombinant genotypes for the two genes. Offspring with a recombinant phenotype arise from fertilization of the recombinant gametes by homozygous recessive gametes from the double-mutant parent. **2.** In each case, the alleles contributed by the female parent determine the phenotype of the offspring because the male in this cross contributes only recessive alleles. **3.** No. The order could be *A-C-B* or *C-A-B*. To determine which possibility is correct, you need to know the recombination frequency between *B* and *C*.

Concept Check 15.4

1. In meiosis, a combined 14-21 chromosome will behave as one chromosome. If a gamete receives the combined 14-21 chromosome and a normal copy of chromosome 21, trisomy 21 will result when this gamete combines with a normal gamete during fertilization. **2.** No. The child can be either $I^A I^A i$ or $I^A ii$. A sperm of genotype $I^A I^A$ could result from nondisjunction in the father during meiosis II, while an egg with the genotype *ii* could result from nondisjunction in the mother during either meiosis I or meiosis II. **3.** Activation of this gene could lead to the production of too much of this kinase. If the kinase is involved in a signaling pathway that triggers cell division, too much of it could trigger unrestricted cell division, which in turn could contribute to the development of a cancer (in this case, a cancer of one type of white blood cell).

Concept Check 15.5

1. Inactivation of an X chromosome in females and genomic imprinting. Because of X inactivation, the effective dose of genes on the X chromosome is the same in males and females. As a result of genomic imprinting, only one allele of certain genes is phenotypically expressed. **2.** The genes for leaf coloration are located in plastids within the cytoplasm. Normally, only the maternal parent transmits plastid genes to offspring. Since variegated offspring are produced only when the female parent is of the B variety, we can conclude that variety B contains both the wild-type and mutant alleles of pigment genes, producing variegated leaves. (Variety A contains only the wild-type allele of pigment genes.) **3.** The situation is similar to that for chloroplasts. Each cell contains numerous mitochondria, and in affected individuals, most cells contain a variable mixture of normal and mutant mitochondria. The normal mitochondria carry out enough cellular respiration for survival.

Summary of Key Concepts Questions

15.1 Because the sex chromosomes are different from each other and because they determine the sex of the offspring, Morgan could use the sex of the offspring as a phenotypic characteristic to follow the parental chromosomes. (He could also have followed them under a microscope, as the X and Y chromosomes look different.) At the same time, he could record eye color to follow the eye-color alleles. **15.2** Males have only one X chromosome, along with a Y chromosome, while females have two X chromosomes. The Y chromosome has very few genes on it, while the X has about 1,000. When a recessive X-linked allele that causes a disorder is inherited by a male on the X from his mother, there isn't a second allele present on the Y (males are hemizygous), so the male has the disorder. Because females have two X chromosomes, they must inherit two recessive alleles in order to have the disorder, a rarer occurrence. **15.3** Crossing over results in new combinations of alleles. Crossing over is a random occurrence, and the more distance there is between two genes, the more chances there are for crossing over to occur, leading to a new allele combination. **15.4** In inversions and reciprocal translocations, the same genetic material is present in the same relative amount but just organized differently. In aneuploidy, duplications, deletions, and nonreciprocal translocations, the balance of genetic material is upset, as large segments are either missing or present in more than one copy. Apparently, this type of imbalance is very damaging to the organism. (Although it isn't lethal in the developing embryo, the reciprocal translocation that produces the Philadelphia chromosome can lead to a serious condition, cancer, by altering the expression of important genes.) **15.5** In these cases, the sex of the parent contributing an allele affects the inheritance pattern. For imprinted genes, either the paternal or the maternal allele is expressed, depending on the imprint. For mitochondrial and chloroplast genes, only the maternal contribution will affect offspring phenotype because the offspring inherit these organelles from the mother, via the egg cytoplasm.

Test Your Understanding

1. 0; 1/2; 1/16 **2.** Recessive; if the disorder were dominant, it would affect at least one parent of a child born with the disorder. The disorder's inheritance is sex-linked because it is seen only in boys. For a girl to have the disorder, she would have to inherit recessive alleles from *both* parents. This would be very rare, since males with the recessive allele on their X chromosome die in their early teens. **3.** 17% **4.** The disorder would always be inherited from the mother. **5.** Between *T* and *A*, 12%; between *A* and *S*, 5% **6.** Between *T* and *S*, 18%; sequence of genes is *T–A–S* **7.** 1/4 for each daughter (1/2 chance that child will be female × 1/2 chance of a homozygous recessive genotype); 1/2 for first son. **8.** 6%; wild-type heterozygous for normal wings and red eyes) × recessive homozygous for vestigial wings and purple eyes
9.

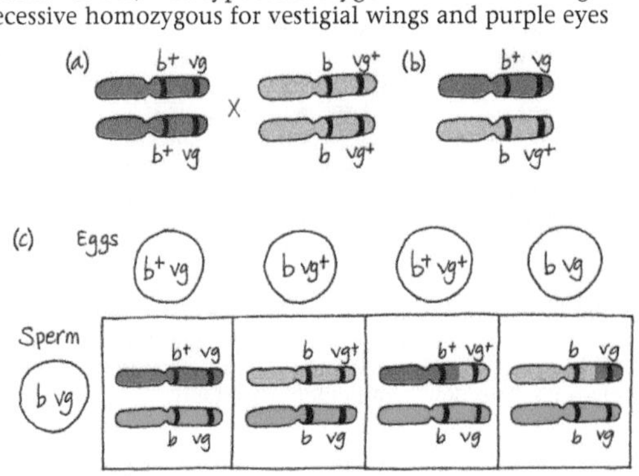

(d) 41.5% gray body, vestigial wings
41.5% black body, normal wings
8.5% gray body, normal wings
8.5% black body, vestigial wings
10. The inactivation of two X chromosomes in XXX women would leave them with one genetically active X, as in women with the normal number of chromosomes. Microscopy should reveal two Barr bodies in XXX women.
11. *D–A–B–C* **12.** Fifty percent of the offspring will show phenotypes resulting from crossovers. These results would be the same as those from a cross where *A* and *B* were *not* on the same chromosome. Further crosses involving other genes on the same chromosome would reveal the genetic linkage and map distances. **13.** 450 each of blue-oval and white-round (parentals) and 50 each of blue-round and white-oval (recombinants) **14.** About one-third of the distance from the vestigial-wing locus to the brown-eye locus **15.** Because bananas are triploid, homologous pairs cannot line up during meiosis. Therefore, it is not possible to generate gametes that can fuse to produce a zygote with the triploid number of chromosomes.

Chapter 16

Figure Questions

Figure 16.2 The living S cells found in the blood sample were able to reproduce to yield more S cells, indicating that the S trait is a permanent, heritable change, rather than just a one-time use of the dead S cells' capsules. **Figure 16.4** The radioactivity would have been found in the pellet when proteins were labeled (batch 1) because proteins would have had to enter the bacterial cells to program them with genetic instructions. It's hard for us to imagine now, but the DNA might have played a structural role that allowed some of the proteins to be injected while it remained outside the bacterial cell (thus no radioactivity in the pellet in batch 2). **Figure 16.11** The tube from the first replication would look the same, with a middle band of hybrid ^{15}N-^{14}N DNA, but the second tube would not have the upper band of two light blue strands. Instead it would have a bottom band of two dark blue strands, like the bottom band in the result predicted after one replication in the conservative model. **Figure 16.12** In the bubble at the top in (b), arrows should be drawn pointing left and right to indicate the two replication forks. **Figure 16.14** Looking at any of the DNA strands, we see that one end is called the 5′ end and the other the 3′ end. If we proceed from the 5′ end to the 3′ end on the left-most strand, for example, we list the components in this order: phosphate group → 5′ C of the sugar → 3′ C → phosphate → 5′ C → 3′ C. Going in the opposite direction on the same strand, the components proceed in the reverse order: 3′ C → 5′ C → phosphate. Thus, the two directions are distinguishable, which is what we mean when we say that the strands have directionality. (Review Figure 16.5 if necessary.)
Figure 16.17

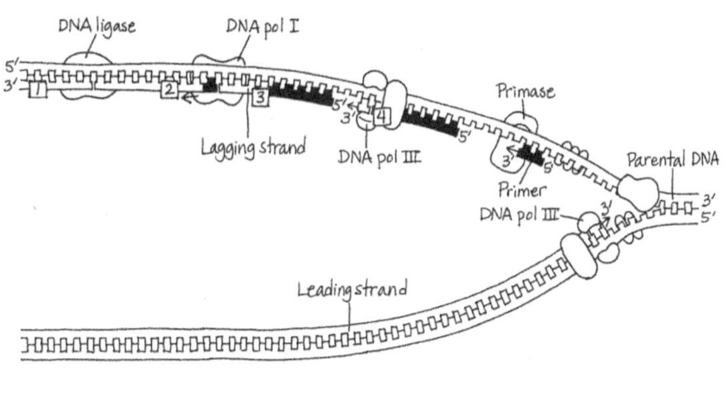

Figure 16.23 The two members of a homologous pair (which would be the same color) would be associated tightly together at the metaphase plate. In metaphase of mitosis, however, each chromosome would be lined up individually, so the two chromosomes of the same color would be in different places at the metaphase plate.

Concept Check 16.1

1. Chargaff's rule about base ratios states that in DNA, the percentages of A and T are essentially the same, as are those of G and C. The fly data are consistent with that rule. (Slight variations are most likely due to limitations of analytical technique.) **2.** You can't tell which end is the 5′ end. You need to know which end has a phosphate group on the 5′ carbon (the 5′ end) or which end has an —OH group on the 3′ carbon (the 3′ end). **3.** He was expecting that the mouse injected with the mixture of heat-killed S cells and living R cells would survive, since neither type of cell alone would kill the mouse.

Concept Check 16.2

1. Complementary base pairing ensures that the two daughter molecules are exact copies of the parental molecule. When the two strands of the parental molecule separate, each serves as a template on which nucleotides are arranged, by the base-pairing rules, into new complementary strands.

2.

Protein	Function
Helicase	Unwinds parental double helix at replication forks
Single-strand binding protein	Binds to and stabilizes single-stranded DNA until it can be used as a template
Topoisomerase	Relieves "overwinding" strain ahead of replication forks by breaking, swiveling, and rejoining DNA strands
Primase	Synthesizes an RNA primer at 5′ end of leading strand and at 5′ end of each Okazaki fragment of lagging strand
DNA pol III	Using parental DNA as a template, synthesizes new DNA strand by covalently adding nucleotides to 3′ end of a pre-existing DNA strand or RNA primer
DNA pol I	Removes RNA nucleotides of primer from 5′ end and replaces them with DNA nucleotides
DNA ligase	Joins 3′ end of DNA that replaces primer to rest of leading strand and joins Okazaki fragments of lagging strand

3. In the cell cycle, DNA synthesis occurs during the S phase, between the G_1 and G_2 phases of interphase. DNA replication is therefore complete before the mitotic phase begins. **4.** Synthesis of the leading strand is initiated by an RNA primer, which must be removed and replaced with DNA, a task that could not be performed if the cell's DNA pol I were nonfunctional. In the overview box in Figure 16.17, just to the left of the top origin of replication, a functional DNA pol I would replace the RNA primer of the leading strand (shown in red) with DNA nucleotides (blue).

Concept Check 16.3

1. A nucleosome is made up of eight histone proteins, two each of four different types, around which DNA is wound. Linker DNA runs from one nucleosome to the next. **2.** Euchromatin is chromatin that becomes less compacted during interphase and is accessible to the cellular machinery responsible for gene activity. Heterochromatin, on the other hand, remains quite condensed during interphase and contains genes that are largely inaccessible to this machinery. **3.** The nuclear lamina is a netlike array of protein filaments that provides mechanical support just inside the nuclear envelope and thus maintains the shape of the nucleus. Considerable evidence also supports the existence of a nuclear matrix, a framework of protein fibers extending throughout the nuclear interior.

Summary of Key Concepts Questions

16.1 Each strand in the double helix has polarity, the end with a phosphate group on the 5′ carbon of the sugar being called the 5′ end, and the end with an —OH group on the 3′ carbon of the sugar being called the 3′ end. The two strands run in opposite directions, so each end of the molecule has both a 5′ and a 3′ end. This arrangement is called "antiparallel." If the strands were parallel, they would both run 5′ → 3′ in the same direction, so an end of the molecule would have either two 5′ ends or two 3′ ends. **16.2** On both the leading and lagging strands, DNA polymerase adds onto the 3′ end of an RNA primer synthesized by primase, synthesizing DNA in the 5′ → 3′ direction. Because the parental strands are antiparallel, however, only on the leading strand does synthesis proceed continuously into the replication fork. The lagging strand is synthesized bit by bit in the direction away from the fork as a series of shorter Okazaki fragments, which are later joined together by DNA ligase. Each fragment is initiated by synthesis of an RNA primer by primase as soon as a given stretch of single-stranded template strand is opened up. Although both strands are synthesized at the same rate, synthesis of the lagging strand is delayed because initiation of each fragment begins only when sufficient template strand is available. **16.3** Most of the chromatin in an interphase nucleus is uncondensed. Much is present as the 30-nm fiber, with some in the form of the 10-nm fiber and some as looped domains of the 30-nm fiber. (These different levels of chromatin packing may reflect differences in gene expression occurring in these regions.) Also, a small percentage of the chromatin, such as that at the centromeres and telomeres, is highly condensed heterochromatin.

Test Your Understanding

1. c **2.** c **3.** b **4.** d **5.** c **6.** d **7.** b **8.** a
9. Like histones, the *E. coli* proteins would be expected to contain many basic (positively charged) amino acids, such as lysine and arginine, which can form weak bonds with the negatively charged phosphate groups on the sugar-phosphate backbone of the DNA molecule. **10.** Each species' DNA has a slightly different percentage of a given base. For example, the percentage of A ranges from 24.7% for *E. coli* to 32.8% for sea urchin. This illustrates Chargaff's rule that the DNA of different species varies in its base composition. Chargaff's other rule states

that in any given species, the percentage of A is roughly equal to that of T, and the percentage of C is roughly equal to that of G. For example, sea urchins have about 32–33% each of A and T and about 17% of G and C. (Your answer may use any similar examples from the table.)

12.

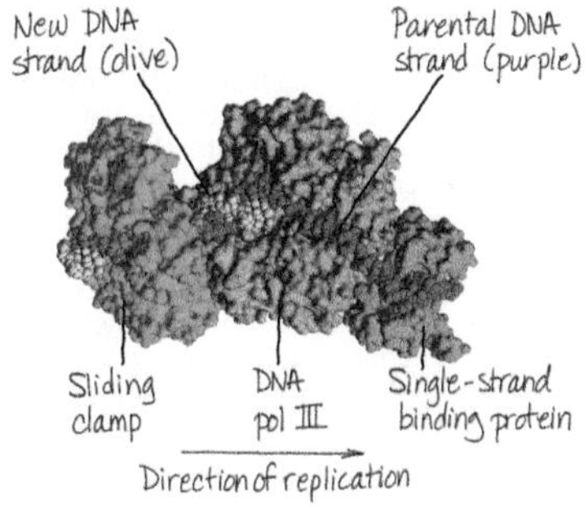

Chapter 17

Figure Questions

Figure 17.2 The previously presumed pathway would have been wrong. The new results would support this pathway: precursor → citrulline → ornithine → arginine. They would also indicate that class I mutants have a defect in the second step and class II mutants have a defect in the first step. **Figure 17.4** The mRNA sequence (5′-UGGUUUGGCUCA-3′) is the same as the nontemplate DNA strand sequence (5′-TGGTTTGGCTCA-3′), except there is U in the mRNA and T in the DNA. **Figure 17.7** The processes are similar in that polymerases form polynucleotides complementary to an antiparallel DNA template strand. In replication, however, both strands act as templates, whereas in transcription, only one DNA strand acts as a template. **Figure 17.8** The RNA polymerase would bind directly to the promoter, rather than depending on the previous binding of other factors. **Figure 17.25** The RNA polymerase on the right (associated with the longest mRNA) started transcribing first. The ribosome at the top, closest to the DNA, started translating first and thus has the longest polypeptide.

Concept Check 17.1

1. Recessive **2.** A polypeptide made up of 10 Gly (glycine) amino acids

3.

Template sequence (from problem):	3′-TTCAGTCGT-5′
Nontemplate sequence:	5′-AAGTCAGCA-3′
mRNA sequence:	5′-AAGUCAGCA-3′

The nontemplate and mRNA nucleotide sequences are the same except that there is T in the nontemplate strand of DNA wherever there is U in the mRNA.

4.

"Template sequence" (from nontemplate sequence in problem, written 3′ → 5′):	3′-ACGACTGAA-5′
mRNA sequence:	5′-UGCUGACUU-3′
Translated:	Cys-STOP-Leu

(Remember that the mRNA is antiparallel to the DNA strand.) A protein translated from the nontemplate sequence would have a completely different amino acid sequence and would most likely be nonfunctional. (It would also be shorter because of the stop signal shown in the mRNA sequence above—and possibly others earlier in the mRNA sequence.)

Concept Check 17.2

1. Both assemble nucleic acid chains from monomer nucleotides whose order is determined by complementary base pairing to a template strand. Both synthesize in the 5′ → 3′ direction, antiparallel to the template. DNA polymerase requires a primer, but RNA polymerase can start a nucleotide chain from scratch. DNA polymerase uses nucleotides with the sugar deoxyribose and the base T, whereas RNA polymerase uses nucleotides with the sugar ribose and the base U. **2.** The promoter is the region of DNA to which RNA polymerase binds to begin transcription, and it is at the upstream end of the gene (transcription unit). **3.** In a bacterial cell, RNA polymerase recognizes the gene's promoter and binds to it. In a eukaryotic cell, transcription factors mediate the binding of RNA polymerase to the promoter. In both cases, sequences in the promoter bind precisely to the RNA polymerase, so the enzyme is in the right location and orientation. **4.** The transcription factor that recognizes the TATA sequence would be unable to bind, so RNA polymerase could not bind and transcription of that gene probably would not occur.

Concept Check 17.3

1. Due to alternative splicing of exons, each gene can result in multiple different mRNAs and can thus direct synthesis of multiple different proteins. **2.** In editing a video, segments are cut out and discarded (like introns), and the remaining segments are joined together (like exons) so that the regions of joining ("splicing") are not noticeable. **3.** Once the mRNA has exited the nucleus, the cap prevents it from being degraded by hydrolytic enzymes and facilitates its attachment to ribosomes. If the cap were removed from all mRNAs, the cell would no longer be able to synthesize any proteins and would probably die.

Concept Check 17.4

1. First, each aminoacyl-tRNA synthetase specifically recognizes a single amino acid and attaches it only to an appropriate tRNA. Second, a tRNA charged with its specific amino acid binds only to an mRNA codon for that amino acid. **2.** The structure and function of the ribosome seem to depend more on the rRNAs than on the ribosomal proteins. Because it is single-stranded, an RNA molecule can hydrogen-bond with itself and with other RNA molecules. RNA molecules make up the interface between the two ribosomal subunits, so presumably RNA-RNA binding helps hold the ribosome together. The binding site for mRNA in the ribosome includes rRNA that can bind the mRNA. Also, complementary bonding within an RNA molecule allows it to assume a particular three-dimensional shape and, along with the RNA's functional groups, presumably enables rRNA to catalyze peptide bond formation during translation. **3.** A signal peptide on the leading end of the polypeptide being synthesized is recognized by a signal-recognition particle that brings the ribosome to the ER membrane. There the ribosome attaches and continues to synthesize the polypeptide, depositing it in the ER lumen. **4.** Because of wobble, the tRNA could bind to either 5′-GCA-3′ or 5′-GCG-3′, both of which code for alanine (Ala). Alanine would be attached to the tRNA.

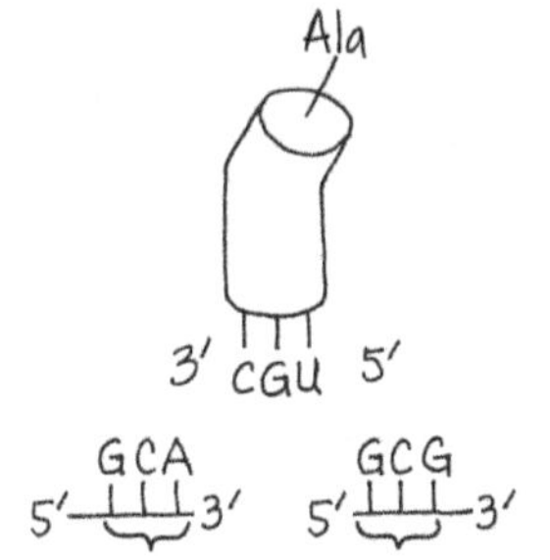

Concept Check 17.5

1. In the mRNA, the reading frame downstream from the deletion is shifted, leading to a long string of incorrect amino acids in the polypeptide, and in most cases, a stop codon will arise, leading to premature termination. The polypeptide will most likely be nonfunctional. **2.** Heterozygous individuals, said to have sickle-cell trait, have a copy each of the wild-type allele and the sickle-cell allele. Both alleles will be expressed, so these individuals will have both normal and sickle-cell hemoglobin molecules. Apparently, having a mix of the two forms of β-globin has no effect under most conditions, but during prolonged periods of low blood oxygen (such as at higher altitudes), these individuals can show some signs of sickle-cell disease.

3.

Normal DNA sequence (template strand is on top):	3′-TACTTGTCCGATATC-5′ 5′-ATGAACAGGCTATAG-3′
mRNA sequence:	5′-AUGAACAGGCUAUAG-3′
Amino acid sequence:	Met-Asn-Arg-Leu-STOP
Mutated DNA sequence (template strand is on top):	3′-TACTTGTCCAATATC-5′ 5′-ATGAACAGGTTATAG-3′
mRNA sequence:	5′-AUGAACAGGUUAUAG-3′
Amino acid sequence:	Met-Asn-Arg-Leu-STOP

No effect: The amino acid sequence is Met-Asn-Arg-Leu both before and after the mutation because the mRNA codons 5′-CUA-3′ and 5′-UUA-3′ both code for Leu. (The fifth codon is a stop codon.)

Concept Check 17.6

1. No, transcription and translation are separated in space and time in a eukaryotic cell, a result of the eukaryotic cell's nuclear compartment. **2.** When one ribosome terminates translation and dissociates, the two subunits would be very close to the cap. This could facilitate their rebinding and initiating synthesis of a new polypeptide, thus increasing the efficiency of translation.

Summary of Key Concepts Questions

17.1 A gene contains genetic information in the form of a nucleotide sequence. The gene is first transcribed into an RNA molecule, and a messenger RNA molecule is ultimately translated into a polypeptide. The polypeptide makes up part or all of a protein, which performs a function in the cell and contributes to the phenotype of the organism. **17.2** Both bacterial and eukaryotic genes have promoters, regions where RNA polymerase ultimately binds and begins transcription. In bacteria, RNA polymerase binds directly to the promoter; in eukaryotes, transcription factors bind first to the promoter, and then RNA polymerase binds to the transcription factors and promoter together. **17.3** Both the 5′ cap and the poly-A tail help the mRNA exit from the nucleus and then, in the cytoplasm, help ensure mRNA stability and allow it to bind to ribosomes. **17.4** tRNAs function as translators between the nucleotide-based language of mRNA and the amino-acid-based language of polypeptides. A tRNA carries a specific amino acid, and the anticodon on the tRNA is complementary to the codon on the mRNA that codes for that amino acid. In the ribosome, the tRNA binds to the A site, where the polypeptide being synthesized is joined to the new amino acid, which becomes the new (C-terminal) end of the polypeptide. Next, the tRNA moves to the P site. When the next amino acid is added via transfer of the polypeptide to the new tRNA, the now empty tRNA moves to the E site, where it exits the ribosome. **17.5** When a nucleotide base is altered chemically, its base-pairing characteristics may be changed. When that happens, an incorrect nucleotide is likely to be incorporated into the complementary strand during the next replication of the DNA, and successive rounds of replication will perpetuate the mutation. Once the gene is transcribed, the mutated codon may code for a different amino acid that inhibits or changes the function of a protein. If the chemical change in the base is detected and repaired by the DNA repair system before the next replication, no mutation will result. **17.6** The presence of a nuclear envelope in eukaryotes means that transcription and translation are separated in space and therefore in time. This separation allows other processes (specifically, RNA processing) to occur and provides other steps at which gene expression can be regulated.

Test Your Understanding

1. b **2.** d **3.** a **4.** a **5.** b **6.** d **7.** e

8.

Type of RNA	Functions
Messenger RNA (mRNA)	Carries information specifying amino acid sequences of proteins from DNA to ribosomes
Transfer RNA (tRNA)	Serves as translator molecule in protein synthesis; translates mRNA codons into amino acids
Ribosomal RNA (rRNA)	Plays catalytic (ribozyme) roles and structural roles in ribosomes
Primary transcript	Is a precursor to mRNA, rRNA, or tRNA, before being processed; some intron RNA acts as a ribozyme, catalyzing its own splicing
Small nuclear RNA (snRNA)	Plays structural and catalytic roles in spliceosomes, the complexes of protein and RNA that splice pre-mRNA

Chapter 18

Figure Questions

Figure 18.3 As the concentration of tryptophan in the cell falls, eventually there will be none bound to repressor molecules. These will then take on their inactive shapes and dissociate from the operator, allowing transcription of the operon to resume. The enzymes for tryptophan synthesis will be made, and they will begin to synthesize tryptophan again in the cell. **Figure 18.11** The albumin gene enhancer has the three control elements colored yellow, gray, and red. The sequences in the liver and lens cells would be identical, since the cells are in the same organism. **Figure 18.18** Even if the mutant MyoD protein couldn't activate the *myoD* gene, it could still turn on genes for the other proteins in the pathway (other transcription factors, which would turn on the genes for muscle-specific proteins, for example). Therefore, some differentiation would occur. But unless there were other activators that could compensate for the loss of the MyoD protein's activation of the *myoD* gene, the cell would not be able to maintain its differentiated state. **Figure 18.22** Normal Bicoid protein would be made in the anterior end and compensate for the presence of mutant *bicoid* mRNA put into the egg by the mother. Development should be normal, with a head present. **Figure 18.24** The mutation is likely to be recessive because it is more likely to have an effect if both copies of the gene are mutated and code for nonfunctional proteins. If one normal copy of the gene is present, its product could inhibit the cell cycle. (However, there are also known cases of dominant *p53* mutations.)

Concept Check 18.1

1. Binding by the *trp* corepressor (tryptophan) activates the *trp* repressor, shutting off transcription of the *trp* operon; binding by the *lac* inducer (allolactose) inactivates the *lac* repressor, leading to transcription of the *lac* operon. **2.** When glucose is scarce, cAMP is bound to CAP and CAP is bound to the promoter, favoring the binding of RNA polymerase. However, in the absence of lactose, the repressor is bound to the operator, blocking RNA polymerase binding to the promoter. Therefore, the operon genes are not transcribed. **3.** The cell would continuously produce β-galactosidase and the two other enzymes for lactose utilization, even in the absence of lactose, thus wasting cell resources.

Concept Check 18.2

1. Histone acetylation is generally associated with gene expression, while DNA methylation is generally associated with lack of expression. **2.** General transcription factors function in assembling the transcription initiation complex at the promoters for all genes. Specific transcription factors bind to control elements associated with a particular gene and, once bound, either increase (activators) or decrease (repressors) transcription of that gene. **3.** The three genes should have some similar or identical sequences in the control elements of their enhancers. Because of this similarity, the same specific transcription factors in muscle cells could bind to the enhancers of all three genes and stimulate their expression coordinately. **4.** Degradation of the mRNA, regulation of translation, activation of the protein (by chemical modification, for example), and protein degradation **5.** Expression of the gene encoding the yellow activator (YA) must be regulated at one of the steps shown in Figure 18.6. The YA gene might be transcribed only in liver cells because the necessary activators for the enhancer of the YA gene are found only in liver cells.

Concept Check 18.3

1. Both miRNAs and siRNAs are small, single-stranded RNAs that associate with a complex of proteins and then can base-pair with mRNAs that have a complementary sequence. This base pairing leads to either degradation of the mRNA or blockage of its translation. Some siRNAs, in association with other proteins, can bind back to the chromatin in a certain region, causing chromatin changes that affect transcription. Both miRNAs and siRNAs are processed from double-stranded RNA precursors by the enzyme Dicer. All miRNAs are specified by genes in the cell's genome, and the single transcript folds back on itself to form one or more double-stranded hairpins, each of which is processed into an miRNA. In contrast, siRNAs arise from a longer stretch of linear double-stranded RNA, which may be introduced into the cell by a virus or an experimenter. Alternatively, in some cases, a cellular gene specifies one RNA strand of the precursor molecule, and an enzyme then synthesizes the complementary strand. **2.** The mRNA would persist and be translated into the cell division–promoting protein, and the cell would probably divide. If the intact miRNA is necessary for inhibition of cell division, then division of this cell might be inappropriate. Uncontrolled cell division could lead to formation of a mass of cells (tumor) that prevents proper functioning of the organism and could contribute to the development of cancer. **3.** The *XIST* RNA is transcribed from the *XIST* gene on the X chromosome that will be inactivated. It then binds to that chromosome and induces heterochromatin formation. A likely model is that the *XIST* RNA somehow recruits chromatin modification enzymes that lead to formation of heterochromatin.

Concept Check 18.4

1. Cells undergo differentiation during embryonic development, becoming different from each other; in the adult organism, there are many highly specialized cell types. **2.** By binding to a receptor on the receiving cell's surface and triggering a signal transduction pathway, involving intracellular molecules such as second messengers and transcription factors that affect gene expression **3.** Because their products, made and deposited into the egg by the mother, determine the head and tail ends, as well as the back and belly, of the embryo (and eventually the adult fly) **4.** The lower cell is synthesizing signaling molecules because the gene encoding them is activated, meaning that the appropriate specific transcription factors are binding to the gene's enhancer. The genes encoding these specific transcription factors are also being expressed in this cell because the transcriptional activators that can turn them on were expressed in the precursor to this cell. A similar explanation also applies to the cells expressing the receptor proteins. This scenario began with specific cytoplasmic determinants localized in specific regions of the egg. These cytoplasmic determinants were distributed unevenly to daughter cells, resulting in cells going down different developmental pathways.

Concept Check 18.5

1. Apoptosis is signaled by p53 protein when a cell has extensive DNA damage, so apoptosis plays a protective role in eliminating a cell that might contribute to cancer. If mutations in the genes in the apoptotic pathway blocked apoptosis, a cell with such damage could continue to divide and might lead to tumor formation. **2.** When an individual has inherited an oncogene or a mutant allele of a tumor-suppressor gene **3.** A cancer-causing mutation in a proto-oncogene usually makes the gene product overactive, whereas a cancer-causing mutation in a tumor-suppressor gene usually makes the gene product nonfunctional.

Summary of Key Concepts Questions

18.1 A corepressor and an inducer are both small molecules that bind to the repressor protein in an operon, causing the repressor to change shape. In the case of a corepressor (like tryptophan), this shape change allows the repressor to bind to the operator, blocking transcription. In contrast, an inducer causes the repressor to dissociate from the operator, allowing transcription to begin. **18.2** The chromatin must not be tightly condensed because it must be accessible to transcription factors. The appropriate specific transcription factors (activators) must bind to the control elements in the enhancer of the gene, while repressors must not be bound. The DNA must be bent by a bending protein so the activators can contact the mediator proteins and form a complex with general transcription factors at the promoter. Then RNA polymerase must bind and begin transcription. **18.3** miRNAs do not "code" for the amino acids of a protein—they are never translated. Each miRNA is cleaved from its hairpin RNA structure and then trimmed by Dicer. Next, one strand is degraded while the other associates with a group of proteins to form a complex. Binding of the complex to an mRNA with a complementary sequence causes that mRNA to be degraded or blocks its translation. This is considered gene regulation because it controls the amount of a particular mRNA that can be translated into a functional protein. **18.4** The first process involves cytoplasmic determinants, including mRNAs and proteins, placed into specific locations in the egg by the mother. The cells that are formed from different regions in the egg during early cell divisions will have different proteins in them, which will direct different programs of gene expression. The second process involves the cell in question responding to signaling molecules secreted by neighboring cells. The signaling pathway in the responding cell also leads to a different pattern of gene expression. The coordination of these two processes results in each cell following a unique pathway in the developing embryo. **18.5** The protein product of a proto-oncogene is usually involved in a pathway that stimulates cell division. The protein product of a tumor-suppressor gene is usually involved in a pathway that inhibits cell division.

Test Your Understanding

1. d **2.** a **3.** a **4.** a **5.** c **6.** d **7.** c **8.** e **9.** b **10.** b
11. a.

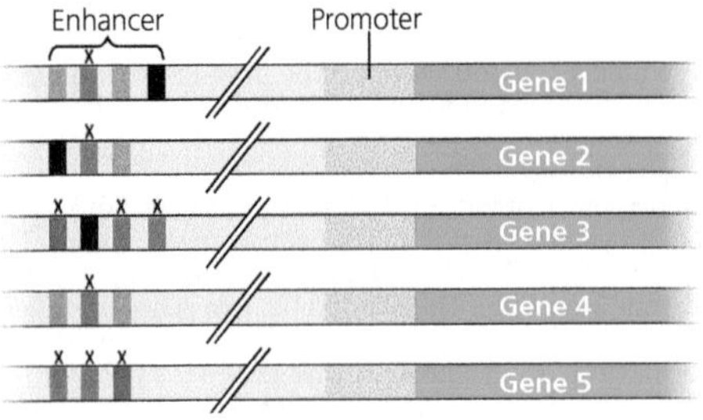

The purple, blue, and red activator proteins would be present.
b.

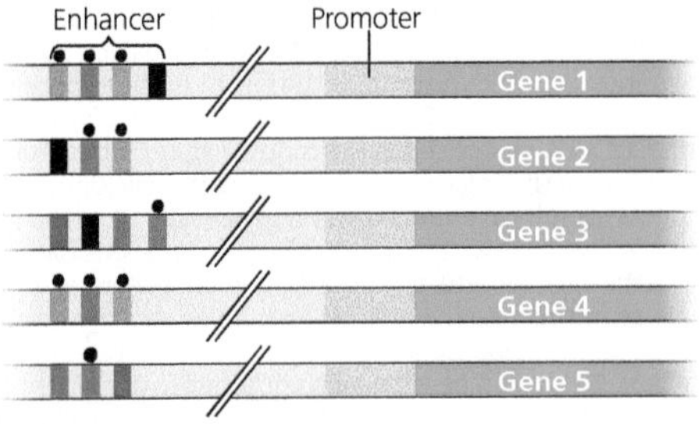

Only gene 4 would be transcribed.
c. In nerve cells, the orange, blue, green, and black activators would have to be present, thus activating transcription of genes 1, 2, and 4. In skin cells, the red, black, purple, and blue activators would have to be present, thus activating genes 3 and 5.

Chapter 19

Figure Questions

Figure 19.2 Beijerinck might have concluded that the agent was a toxin produced by the plant that was able to pass through a filter but that became more and more dilute. In this case, he would have concluded that the infectious agent could not replicate. **Figure 19.4** Top vertical arrow: Infection. Left upper arrow: Replication. Right upper arrow: Transcription. Right middle arrow: Translation. Lower left and right arrows: Self-assembly. Bottom middle arrow: Exit. **Figure 19.7** Any class V virus, including the viruses that cause influenza (flu), measles, and mumps **Figure 19.8** The main protein on the cell surface that HIV binds to is called CD4. However, HIV also requires a "co-receptor," which in many cases is a protein called CCR5. HIV binds to both of these proteins together and then is taken into the cell. Researchers discovered this requirement by studying individuals who seemed to be resistant to HIV infection, despite multiple exposures. These individuals turned out to have mutations in the gene that encodes CCR5 such that the protein apparently cannot act as a co-receptor, and so HIV can't enter and infect cells.

Concept Check 19.1

1. TMV consists of one molecule of RNA surrounded by a helical array of proteins. The influenza virus has eight molecules of RNA, each surrounded by a helical array of proteins, similar to the arrangement of the single RNA molecule in TMV. Another difference between the viruses is that the influenza virus has an outer envelope and TMV does not. **2.** The T2 phages were an excellent choice for use in the Hershey-Chase experiment because they consist of only DNA surrounded by a protein coat, and DNA and protein were the two candidates for macromolecules that carried genetic information. Hershey and Chase were able to radioactively label each type of molecule alone and follow it during separate infections of *E. coli* cells with T2. Only the DNA entered the bacterial cell during infection, and only labeled DNA showed up in some of the progeny phage. Hershey and Chase concluded that the DNA must carry the genetic information necessary for the phage to reprogram the cell and produce progeny phages.

Concept Check 19.2

1. Lytic phages can only carry out lysis of the host cell, whereas lysogenic phages may either lyse the host cell or integrate into the host chromosome. In the latter case, the viral DNA (prophage) is simply replicated along with the host chromosome. Under certain conditions, a prophage may exit the host chromosome and initiate a lytic cycle. **2.** Both the viral RNA polymerase and the RNA polymerase in Figure 17.9 synthesize an RNA molecule complementary to a template strand. However, the RNA polymerase in Figure 17.9 uses one of the strands of the DNA double helix as a template, whereas the viral RNA polymerase uses the RNA of the viral genome as a template. **3.** Because it synthesizes DNA from its RNA genome. This is the reverse ("retro") of the usual DNA → RNA information flow. **4.** There are many steps that could be interfered with: binding of the virus to the cell, reverse transcriptase function, integration into the host cell chromosome, genome synthesis (in this case, transcription of RNA from the integrated provirus), assembly of the virus inside the cell, and budding of the virus. (Many of these, if not all, are targets of actual medical strategies to block progress of the infection in HIV-infected people.)

Concept Check 19.3

1. Mutations can lead to a new strain of a virus that can no longer be effectively fought by the immune system, even if an animal had been exposed to the original strain; a virus can jump from one species to a new host; and a rare virus can spread if a host population becomes less isolated. **2.** In horizontal transmission, a plant is infected from an external source of virus, which could enter through a break in the plant's epidermis due to damage by herbivores. In vertical transmission, a plant inherits viruses from its parent either via infected seeds (sexual reproduction) or via an infected cutting (asexual reproduction). **3.** Humans are not within the host range of TMV, so they can't be infected by the virus.

Summary of Key Concepts Questions

19.1 Viruses are generally considered nonliving, because they are not capable of replicating outside of a host cell. To replicate, they depend completely on host enzymes and resources. **19.2** Single-stranded RNA viruses require an RNA polymerase that can make RNA using an RNA template. (Cellular RNA polymerases make RNA using a DNA template.) Retroviruses require reverse transcriptases to make DNA using an RNA template. (Once the first DNA strand has been made, the same enzyme can promote synthesis of the second DNA strand.) **19.3** The mutation rate of RNA viruses is higher than that of DNA viruses because RNA polymerase has no proofreading function, so errors in replication are not corrected. Their higher mutation rate means that RNA viruses change faster than DNA viruses, leading to their being able to have an altered host range and to evade immune defenses in possible hosts.

Test Your Understanding

1. c **2.** d **3.** c **4.** d **5.** b
6. As shown below, the viral genome would be translated into capsid proteins and envelope glycoproteins directly, rather than after a complementary RNA copy was made. A complementary RNA strand would still be made, however, that could be used as a template for many new copies of the viral genome.

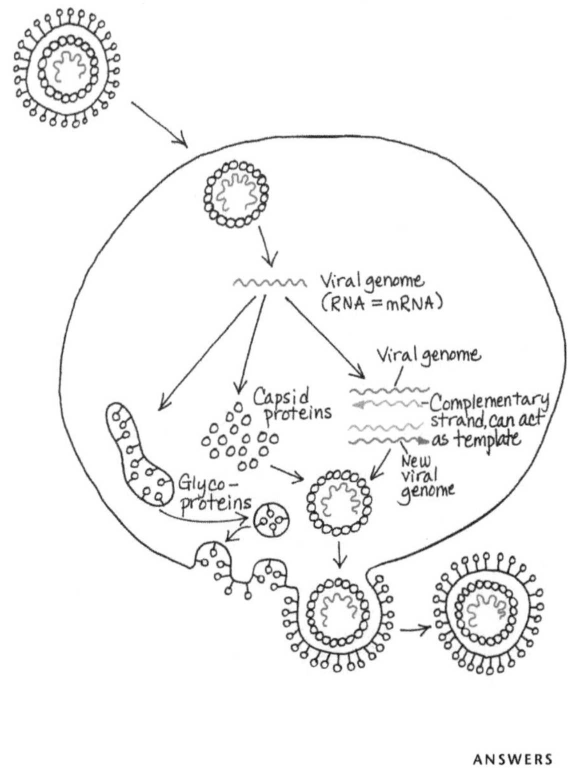

Chapter 20

Figure Questions

Figure 20.3

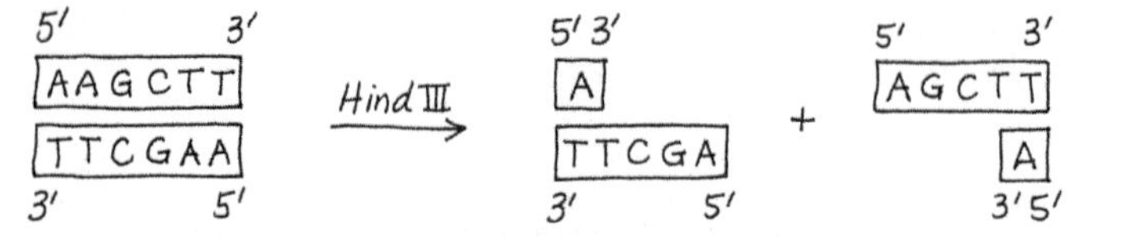

Figure 20.4 Cells containing no plasmid at all would be able to grow; these colonies would be white because they would lack functional *lacZ* genes. **Figure 20.10** Grow each clone of cells in culture. Isolate the plasmids from each and cut them with the restriction enzyme originally used to make the clone (see Figure 20.4). Run each sample on an electrophoretic gel, and recover the DNA of the insert from the gel band. **Figure 20.16** Crossing over, which causes recombination, is a random event. The chance of crossing over occurring between two loci increases as the distance between them increases. The SNP is located very close to an unknown disease-causing allele, and therefore crossing over rarely occurs between the SNP and the allele, so the SNP is a genetic marker indicating the presence of the particular allele. **Figure 20.18** None of the eggs with the transplanted nuclei from the four-cell embryo at the upper left would have developed into a tadpole. Also, the result might include only some of the tissues of a tadpole, which might differ, depending on which nucleus was transplanted. (This assumes that there was some way to tell the four cells apart, as one can in some frog species.) **Figure 20.22** Using converted iPS cells would not carry the same risk, which is its major advantage. Because the donor cells would come from the patient, they would be perfectly matched. The patient's immune system would recognize them as "self" cells and would not mount an attack (which is what leads to rejection).

Concept Check 20.1

1. The covalent sugar-phosphate bonds of the DNA strands **2.** Yes, *PvuI* will cut the molecule.

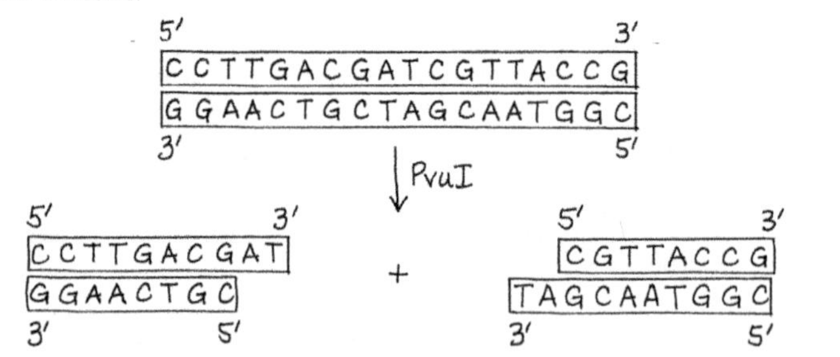

3. Some human genes are too large to be incorporated into bacterial plasmids. Bacterial cells lack the means to process RNA transcripts into mRNA, and even if the need for RNA processing is avoided by using cDNA, bacteria lack enzymes to catalyze the post-translational processing that many human proteins require to function properly. **4.** During the replication of the ends of linear DNA molecules (see Figure 16.20), an RNA primer is used at the 5' end of each new strand. The RNA must be replaced by DNA nucleotides, but DNA polymerase is incapable of starting from scratch at the 5' end of a new DNA strand. During PCR, the primers are made of DNA nucleotides already, so they don't need to be replaced—they just remain as part of each new strand. Therefore, there is no problem with end replication during PCR, and the fragments don't shorten with each replication.

Concept Check 20.2

1. Any restriction enzyme will cut genomic DNA in many places, generating such a large number of fragments that they would appear as a smear rather than distinct bands when the gel is stained after electrophoresis. **2.** In Southern blotting, Northern blotting, and microarray analysis, the labeled probe binds only to the specific target sequence owing to complementary nucleic acid hybridization (DNA-DNA hybridization in Southern blotting and microarray analysis, DNA-RNA hybridization in Northern blotting). In DNA sequencing, primers base-pair to the template, allowing DNA synthesis to start. In RT-PCR, the primers must base-pair with their target sequences in the DNA mixture, locating one specific region among many. **3.** A SNP is a single nucleotide that varies in the population, existing in two or more variations. A RFLP is a type of SNP that occurs in a restriction site, leading to a difference in restriction fragment length when cutting two variants with a restriction enzyme. **4.** If a spot is green, the gene represented on that spot is expressed only in normal tissue. If red, the gene is expressed only in cancerous tissue. If yellow, the gene is expressed in both. And if black, the gene is expressed in neither type of tissue. As a researcher interested in cancer development, you would want to study genes represented by spots that are green or red because these are genes for which the expression level differs between the two types of tissues. Some of these genes may be expressed differently as a result of cancer, but others might play a role in causing cancer.

Concept Check 20.3

1. The state of chromatin modification in the nucleus from the intestinal cell was undoubtedly less similar to that of a nucleus from a fertilized egg, explaining why many fewer of these nuclei were able to be reprogrammed. In contrast, the chromatin in a nucleus from a cell at the four-cell stage would have been much more like that of a nucleus in a fertilized egg and therefore much more easily programmed to direct development. **2.** No, primarily because of subtle (and perhaps not so subtle) differences in their environments **3.** A technique would have to be worked out for turning a human iPS cell into a pancreatic cell (probably by inducing expression of pancreas-specific regulatory genes in the cell). **4.** The carrot cell has much more potential. The cloning experiment shows that an individual carrot cell can generate all the tissues of an adult plant. The muscle cell, on the other hand, will always remain a muscle cell because of its genetic program (it expresses the *myoD* gene, which ensures continued differentiation). The muscle cell is like other fully differentiated animal cells: It will remain fully differentiated on its own unless it is reprogrammed into an iPS cell using the new techniques described here. (This would be quite difficult to accomplish because a muscle cell has multiple nuclei.)

Concept Check 20.4

1. Stem cells continue to reproduce themselves. **2.** Herbicide resistance, pest resistance, disease resistance, salinity resistance, and delayed ripening **3.** Because hepatitis A is an RNA virus, you could isolate RNA from the blood and try to detect copies of hepatitis A RNA by one of three methods. First, you could run the RNA on a gel and then do a Northern blot using probes complementary to hepatitis A genome sequences. A second approach would be to use reverse transcriptase to make cDNA from the RNA in the blood, run the cDNA on a gel, and do a Southern blot using the same probe. However, neither of these methods would be as sensitive as RT-PCR, in which you would reverse-transcribe the blood RNA into cDNA and then use PCR to amplify the cDNA, using primers specific to hepatitis A sequences. If you then ran the products on an electrophoretic gel, the presence of a band would support your hypothesis.

Summary of Key Concepts Questions

20.1 A plasmid vector and a source of foreign DNA to be cloned are both cut with the same restriction enzyme, generating restriction fragments with sticky ends. These fragments are mixed together, ligated, and reintroduced into bacterial cells, which are then grown on the antibiotic ampicillin. The plasmid has two genes that allow selection of recombinant clones. The first is a gene for ampicillin resistance, which only allows cells to grow if they have taken up a plasmid. The second is a gene for β-galactosidase, which can generate a blue product if the gene is intact. The cloning site is within this gene, so only nonrecombinant colonies will be blue, and recombinant plasmids will be found in cells that are in white colonies. **20.2** Many techniques used to analyze genes and their expression involve nucleic acid hybridization: Southern and Northern blotting, DNA sequencing, PCR, *in situ* hybridization, and DNA microarray analysis. The base pairing between the two strands of a DNA molecule or between a DNA strand and an RNA strand is the key to finding specific nucleic acid sequences in all of these techniques. **20.3** Cloning a mouse involves transplanting a nucleus from a differentiated mouse cell into a mouse egg cell that has had its own nucleus removed. Fertilizing the egg cell and promoting its development into an embryo in a surrogate mother results in a mouse that is genetically identical to the mouse that donated the nucleus. In this case, the differentiated nucleus has been reprogrammed by factors in the egg cytoplasm. Mouse ES cells are generated from inner cells in mouse blastocysts, so in this case the cells are "naturally" reprogrammed by the process of reproduction and development. (Cloned mouse embryos can also be used as a source of ES cells.) iPS cells can be generated without the use of embryos from a differentiated adult mouse cell, by adding certain transcription factors into the cell. In this case, the transcription factors are reprogramming the cells to become pluripotent. **20.4** First, the disease must be caused by a single gene, and the molecular basis of the problem must be understood. Second, the cells that are going to be introduced into the patient must be cells that will integrate into body tissues and continue to multiply (and provide the needed gene product). Third, the gene must be able to be introduced into the cells in question in a safe way, as there have been instances of cancer resulting from some gene therapy trials. (Note that this will require testing the procedure in mice; moreover, the factors that determine a safe vector are not yet well understood. Maybe one of you will go on to solve this problem!)

Test Your Understanding

1. b **2.** c **3.** b **4.** c **5.** d **6.** b **7.** a **8.** c
9.

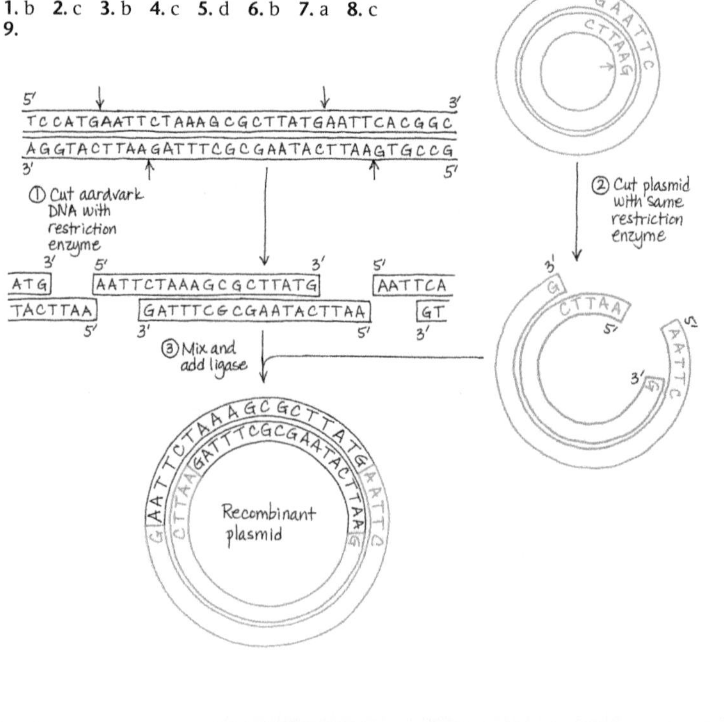

10. A cDNA library, made using mRNA from human lens cells, which would be expected to contain many copies of mRNA for the crystallin of interest

Chapter 21

Figure Questions

Figure 21.3 The fragments in stage 2 of this figure are like those in stage 2 of Figure 21.2, but in this figure their order relative to each other is not known and will be determined later by computer. The order of the fragments in Figure 21.2 is completely known before sequencing begins. (Determining the order takes longer but makes the eventual sequence assembly much easier.) **Figure 21.9** The transposon would be cut out of the DNA at the original site rather than copied, so the figure would show the original stretch of DNA without the transposon after the mobile transposon had been cut out. **Figure 21.11** The RNA transcripts extending from the DNA in each transcription unit are shorter on the left and longer on the right. This means that RNA polymerase must be starting on the left end of the unit and moving toward the right.

Figure 21.13

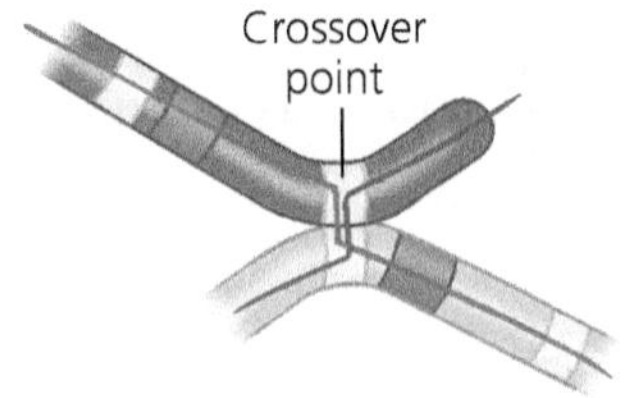

Figure 21.14 Pseudogenes are nonfunctional. They could have arisen by any mutations in the second copy that made the gene product unable to function. Examples would be base changes that introduce stop codons in the sequence, alter amino acids, or change a region of the gene promoter so that the gene can no longer be expressed. **Figure 21.15** Let's say a transposable element (TE) existed in the intron to the left of the indicated EGF exon in the EGF gene, and the same TE was present in the intron to the right of the indicated F exon in the fibronectin gene. During meiotic recombination, these TEs could cause nonsister chromatids on homologous chromosomes to pair up incorrectly, as seen in Figure 21.13. One gene might end up with an F exon next to an EGF exon. Further mistakes in pairing over many generations might result in these two exons being separated from the rest of the gene and placed next to a single or duplicated K exon. In general, the presence of repeated sequences in introns and between genes facilitates these processes because it allows incorrect pairing of nonsister chromatids, leading to novel exon combinations. **Figure 21.17** Since you know that chimpanzees do not speak but humans do, you'd probably want to know how many amino acid differences there are between the human wild-type FOXP2 protein and that of the chimpanzee and whether these changes affect the function of the protein. (As we explain later in the text, there are two amino acid differences.) You know that humans with mutations in this gene have severe language impairment. You would want to learn more about the human mutations by checking whether they affect the same amino acids in the gene product that the chimpanzee sequence differences affect. If so, those amino acids might play an important role in the function of the protein in language. Going further, you could analyze the differences between the chimpanzee and mouse FOXP2 proteins. You might ask: Are they more similar than the chimpanzee and human proteins? (It turns out that the chimpanzee and mouse proteins have only one amino acid difference and thus are more similar than the chimpanzee and human proteins, which have two differences, and more similar than the human and mouse proteins, which have three differences.)

Concept Check 21.1

1. In a linkage map, genes and other markers are ordered with respect to each other, but only the relative distances between them are known. In a physical map, the actual distances between markers, expressed in base pairs, are known. **2.** The three-stage approach employed in the Human Genome Project involves linkage mapping, physical mapping, and then sequencing of short, overlapping fragments that previously have been ordered relative to each other (see Figure 21.2). The whole-genome shotgun approach eliminates the linkage mapping and physical mapping stages; instead, short fragments generated by multiple restriction enzymes are sequenced and then ordered by computer programs that identify overlapping regions (see Figure 21.3).

Concept Check 21.2

1. The Internet allows centralization of databases such as GenBank and software resources such as BLAST, making them freely accessible. Having all the data in a central database, easily accessible on the Internet, minimizes the possibility of errors and of researchers working with different data. It streamlines the process of science, since all researchers are able to use the same software programs, rather than each having to obtain their own, possibly different, software. It speeds up dissemination of data and ensures as much as possible that errors are corrected in a timely fashion. These are just a few answers; you can probably think of more. **2.** Cancer is a disease caused by multiple factors. To focus on a single gene or a single defect would ignore other factors that may influence the cancer and even the behavior of the single gene being studied. The systems approach, because it takes into account many factors at the same time, is more likely to lead to an understanding of the causes and most useful treatments for cancer. **3.** Some of the transcribed region is accounted for by introns. The rest is transcribed into noncoding RNAs, including small RNAs, such as microRNAs (miRNAs). These RNAs help regulate gene expression by blocking translation, causing degradation of mRNA, binding to the promoter and repressing transcription, or causing remodeling of chromatin structure. The functions of the remainder are not yet known. **4.** Genome-wide association studies use the systems biology approach in that they consider the correlation of many single nucleotide polymorphisms (SNPs) with particular diseases, such as heart disease and diabetes, in an attempt to find patterns of SNPs that correlate with each disease.

Concept Check 21.3

1. Alternative splicing of RNA transcripts from a gene and post-translational processing of polypeptides **2.** The total number of completed genomes is found by clicking on "Published Complete Genomes." Add the figures for bacterial, archaeal, and eukaryotic "ongoing genomes" to get the number "in progress." Finally, look at the top of the Published Complete Genomes page to get numbers of completed genomes for each domain. (*Note*: You can click on the "Size" column and the table will be re-sorted by genome size. Scroll down to get an idea of relative sizes of genomes in the three domains. Remember, though, that most of the sequenced genomes are bacterial.) **3.** Prokaryotes are generally smaller cells than eukaryotic cells, and they reproduce by binary fission. The evolutionary process involved is natural selection for more quickly reproducing cells: The faster they can replicate their DNA and divide, the more likely they will be able to dominate a population of prokaryotes. The less DNA they have to replicate, then, the faster they will reproduce.

Concept Check 21.4

1. The number of genes is higher in mammals, and the amount of noncoding DNA is greater. Also, the presence of introns in mammalian genes makes them larger, on average, than prokaryotic genes. **2.** In the copy-and-paste transposon mechanism and in retrotransposition **3.** In the rRNA gene family, identical transcription units for the three different RNA products are present in long, tandemly repeated arrays. The large number of copies of the rRNA genes enable organisms to produce the rRNA for enough ribosomes to carry out active protein synthesis, and the single transcription unit ensures that the relative amounts of the different rRNA molecules produced are correct. Each globin gene family consists of a relatively small number of nonidentical genes. The differences in the globin proteins encoded by these genes result in production of hemoglobin molecules adapted to particular developmental stages of the organism. **4.** The exons would be classified as exons (1.5%); the enhancer region containing the distal control elements, the region closer to the promoter containing the proximal control elements, and the promoter itself would be classified as regulatory sequences (5%); and the introns would be classified as introns (20%).

Concept Check 21.5

1. If meiosis is faulty, two copies of the entire genome can end up in a single cell. Errors in crossing over during meiosis can lead to one segment being duplicated while another is deleted. During DNA replication, slippage backward along the template strand can result in segment duplication. **2.** For either gene, a mistake in crossing over during meiosis could have occurred between the two copies of that gene, such that one ended up with a duplicated exon. This could have happened several times, resulting in the multiple copies of a particular exon in each gene. **3.** Homologous transposable elements scattered throughout the genome provide sites where recombination can occur between different chromosomes. Movement of these elements into coding or regulatory sequences may change expression of genes. Transposable elements also can carry genes with them, leading to dispersion of genes and in some cases different patterns of expression. Transport of an exon during transposition and its insertion into a gene may add a new functional domain to the originally encoded protein, a type of exon shuffling. (For any of these changes to be heritable, they must happen in germ cells, cells that will give rise to gametes.) **4.** Because more offspring are born to women who have this inversion, it must provide some advantage. It would be expected to persist and spread in the population. (In fact, evidence in the study allowed the researchers to conclude that it has been increasing in proportion in the population. You'll learn more about population genetics in the next unit.)

Concept Check 21.6

1. Because both humans and macaques are primates, their genomes are expected to be more similar than the macaque and mouse genomes are. The mouse lineage diverged from the primate lineage before the human and macaque lineages diverged. **2.** Homeotic genes differ in their *non*homeobox sequences, which determine the interactions of homeotic gene products with other transcription factors and hence which genes are regulated by the homeotic genes. These nonhomeobox sequences differ in the two organisms, as do the expression patterns of the homeobox genes. **3.** *Alu* elements must have undergone transposition more actively in the human genome for some reason. Their increased numbers may have then allowed more recombination errors in the human genome, resulting in more or different duplications. The divergence of the organization and content of the two genomes presumably made the chromosomes of each genome less homologous to those of the other, thus accelerating divergence of the two species by making matings less and less likely to result in fertile offspring.

Summary of Key Concepts Questions

21.1 Considering the sequencing of the human genome as an example, less time was required to sequence the first human genome using the whole-genome shotgun approach. Although this approach relied in part on data resulting from the three-stage approach used by the public consortium, the whole-genome shotgun approach was (and still is) faster and more efficient than the more labor-intensive three-stage process. The whole-genome shotgun approach was facilitated in large part by significant advances in computing power. **21.2** The most significant finding was that more than 90% of the human genomic region studied was transcribed, which suggested that the transcribed RNA (and thus the DNA from which it was produced) was performing some unknown functions. The project has been expanded to include other species because to determine the functions of these transcribed DNA elements, it is necessary to carry out this type of analysis on the genomes of species that can be used in laboratory experiments. **21.3** (a) In general, bacteria and archaea have smaller genomes, lower numbers of genes, and higher gene density than eukaryotes. (b) Among eukaryotes, there is no apparent systematic relationship between genome size and phenotype. The number of genes is often lower than would be expected from the size of the genome—in other words, the gene density is often lower in larger genomes. (Humans are an example.) **21.4** Transposable element-related sequences can move from place to place in the genome, and a subset of these sequences make a new copy of themselves when they do so. Thus, it is not surprising that they make up a significant percentage of the genome, and this percentage might be expected to increase over evolutionary time. **21.5** Chromosomal rearrangements within a species lead to some individuals having different chromosomal arrangements. Each of these individuals could still undergo meiosis and produce gametes, and fertilization involving gametes with different chromosomal arrangements could result in viable offspring. However, during meiosis in the offspring, the maternal and paternal chromosomes might not be able to pair up, causing gametes with incomplete sets of chromosomes to form. Most often, when zygotes are produced from such gametes, they do not survive. Ultimately, a new species could form if two different chromosomal arrangements became prevalent within a population and individuals could mate successfully only with other individuals having the same arrangement. **21.6** Comparing the genomes of two closely related species can reveal information about more recent evolutionary events, perhaps events that resulted in the distinguishing characteristics of the two species. Comparing the genomes of very distantly related species can tell us about evolutionary events that occurred a very long time ago. For example, genes that are shared between two distantly related species must have arisen before the two species diverged.

Test Your Understanding

1. c **2.** a **3.** a **4.** c
5.

1. ATETI...PKSSD...TSSTT...NARRD
2. ATETI...PKSSE...TSSIT...NARRD
3. ATETI...PKSSD...TSSTT...NARRD
4. ATETI...PKSSD...TSSNT...SARRD
5. ATETI...PKSSD...TSSTT...NARRD
6. VTETI...PKSSD...TSSTT...NARRD

(a) Lines 1, 3, and 5 are the C, G, R species. (b) Line 4 is the human sequence. (c) Line 6 is the orangutan sequence. (d) There is one amino acid difference between the mouse (the E on line 2) and the C, G, R species (which have a D in that position). There are three amino acid differences between the mouse and the human. (The E, T, and N in the mouse sequence are instead D, N, and S, respectively, in the human sequence.) (e) Because only one amino acid difference arose during the 60–100 million years since the mouse and C, G, R species diverged, it is somewhat surprising that two additional amino acid differences resulted during the 6 million years since chimpanzees and humans diverged. This indicates that the *FOXP2* gene has been evolving faster in the human lineage than in the lineages of other primates.

Chapter 22

Figure Questions

Figure 22.6 The cactus-eater is more closely related to the seed-eater; Figure 1.22 shows that they share a more recent common ancestor (a seed-eater) than the cactus-eater shares with the insect-eater. **Figure 22.8** More than 5.5 million years ago. **Figure 22.12** The colors and body forms of these mantids allow them to blend into their surroundings, providing an example of how organisms are well matched to life in their environments. The mantids also share features with one another (and with all other mantids), such as six legs, grasping forelimbs, and large eyes. These shared features illustrate another key observation about life: the unity of life that results from descent from a common ancestor. Over time, as these mantids diverged from a common ancestor, they accumulated different adaptations that made them well suited for life in their different environments. Eventually, these differences became large enough that new species were formed, thus contributing to the great diversity of life. **Figure 22.13** These results show that being reared from the egg stage on one plant species or the other did not result in the adult having a beak length appropriate for that host; instead, adult beak lengths were determined primarily by the population from which the eggs were obtained. Because an egg from a balloon vine population likely had long-beaked parents, while an egg from a goldenrain tree population likely had short-beaked parents, these results indicate that beak length is an inherited trait. **Figure 22.14** Both strategies should increase the time it takes *S. aureus* to become resistant to a new drug. If a drug that harms *S. aureus* does not harm other bacteria, natural selection will not favor resistance to that drug in the other species. This would decrease the chance that *S. aureus* would acquire resistance genes from other bacteria—thus slowing the evolution of resistance. Similarly, selection for resistance to a drug that slows the growth but does not kill *S. aureus* is much weaker than selection for resistance to a drug the kills *S. aureus*—again slowing the evolution of resistance. **Figure 22.17** Based on this evolutionary tree, crocodiles are more closely related to birds than to lizards because they share a more recent common ancestor with birds (ancestor 5) than with lizards (ancestor 4). **Figure 22.20** Hind limb structure changed first. *Rodhocetus* lacked flukes, but its pelvic bones and hind limbs had changed substantially from how those bones were shaped and arranged in *Pakicetus*. For example, in *Rodhocetus*, the pelvis and hind limbs appear to be oriented for paddling, whereas they were oriented for walking in *Pakicetus*.

Concept Check 22.1

1. Hutton and Lyell proposed that events in the past were caused by the same processes operating today. This principle suggested that Earth must be much older than a few thousand years, the age that was widely accepted at that time. Hutton and Lyell also thought that geologic change occurs gradually, stimulating Darwin to reason that the slow accumulation of small changes could ultimately produce the profound changes documented in the fossil record. In this context, the age of Earth was important to Darwin, because unless Earth was very old, he could not envision how there would have been enough time for evolution to occur. **2.** By these criteria, Cuvier's explanation of the fossil record and Lamarck's hypothesis of evolution are both scientific. Cuvier thought that species did not evolve over time. He also suggested that catastrophes and the resulting extinctions were usually confined to local regions and that such regions were later repopulated by a different set of species that immigrated from other areas. These assertions can be tested against the fossil record, and his assertion that species do not evolve has been found to be false. With respect to Lamarck, his principle of use and disuse can be used to make testable predictions for fossils of groups such as whale ancestors as they adapted to a new habitat. Lamarck's principle of use and disuse and his associated principle of the inheritance of acquired characteristics can also be tested directly in living organisms (these principles have been found to be false).

Concept Check 22.2

1. Organisms share characteristics (the unity of life) because they share common ancestors; the great diversity of life occurs because new species have repeatedly formed when descendant organisms gradually adapted to different environments, becoming different from their ancestors. **2.** The fossil mammal species (or its ancestors) would most likely have colonized the Andes from within South America, whereas ancestors of mammals currently found in African mountains would most likely have colonized those mountains from other parts of Africa. As a result, the Andes fossil species would share a more recent common ancestor with South American mammals than with mammals in Africa. Thus, for many of its traits, the fossil mammal species would probably more closely resemble mammals that live in South American jungles than mammals that live on African mountains. It is also possible, however, that the fossil mammal species could resemble the African mountain mammals by convergent evolution (even though they were only distantly related to one another). **3.** As long as the white phenotype (encoded by the genotype *pp*) continues to be favored by natural selection, the frequency of the *p* allele will likely increase over time in the population. The explanation is that if the proportion of white individuals increases relative to purple individuals, the frequency of the recessive *p* allele will also increase relative to that of the *P* allele, which only appears in purple individuals (some of whom also carry a *p* allele).

Concept Check 22.3

1. An environmental factor such as a drug does not create new traits, such as drug resistance, but rather selects for traits among those that are already present in the population. **2.** (a) Despite their different functions, the forelimbs of different mammals are structurally similar because they all represent modifications of a structure found in the common ancestor. (b) Convergent evolution: The similarities between the sugar glider and flying squirrel indicate that similar environments selected for similar adaptations despite different ancestry. **3.** At the time that dinosaurs originated, Earth's landmasses formed a single large continent, Pangaea. Because many dinosaurs were large and mobile, it is likely that early members of these groups lived on many different parts of Pangaea. When Pangaea broke apart, fossils of these organisms would have moved with the rocks in which they were deposited. As a result, we would predict that fossils of early dinosaurs would have a broad geographic distribution (this prediction has been upheld).

Summary of Key Concepts Questions

Concept 22.1 Darwin thought that descent with modification occurred as a gradual, steplike process. The age of Earth was important to him because if Earth were only a few thousand years old (as conventional wisdom suggested), there wouldn't have been sufficient time for major evolutionary change. **Concept 22.2** All species have the potential to produce more offspring (overreproduce) than can be supported by the environment. This ensures that there will be what Darwin called a "struggle for existence" in which many of the offspring are eaten, starved, diseased, or unable to reproduce for a variety of other reasons. Members of a population exhibit a range of heritable variations, some of which make it likely that their bearers will leave more offspring than other individuals (for example, the bearer may escape predators more effectively or be more tolerant of the physical conditions of the environment). Over time, natural selection resulting from factors such as predators, lack of food, or the physical conditions of the environment can increase the proportion of individuals with favorable traits in a population (evolutionary adaptation). **Concept 22.3** The hypothesis that cetaceans originated from a terrestrial mammal and are closely related to even-toed ungulates is supported by several lines of evidence. For example, fossils document that early cetaceans had hind limbs, as expected for organisms that descended from a land mammal; these fossils also show that cetacean hind limbs became reduced over time. Other fossils show that early cetaceans had a type of ankle bone that is otherwise found only in even-toed ungulates, providing strong evidence that even-toed ungulates are the land mammals to which cetaceans are most closely related. DNA sequence data also indicate that even-toed ungulates are the land mammals to which cetaceans are most closely related.

Test Your Understanding

1. b **2.** d **3.** d **4.** c **5.** a

7. (a)

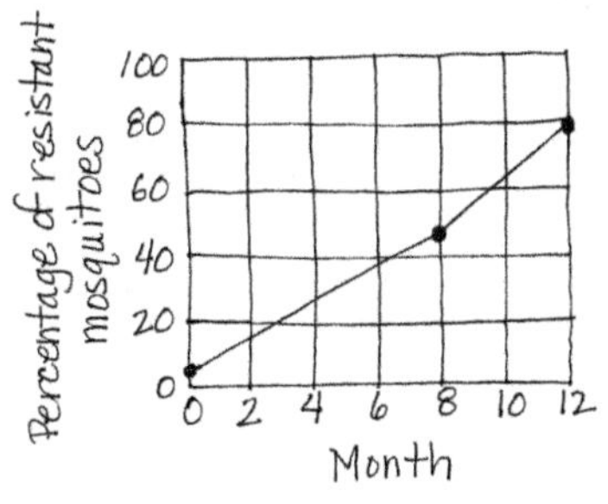

(b) The rapid rise in the percentage of mosquitoes resistant to DDT was most likely caused by natural selection in which mosquitoes resistant to DDT could survive and reproduce while other mosquitoes could not. (c) In India—where DDT resistance first appeared—natural selection would have caused the frequency of resistant mosquitoes to increase over time. If resistant mosquitoes then migrated from India (for example, transported by wind or in planes, trains, or ships) to other parts of the world, the frequency of DDT resistance would increase there as well.

Chapter 23

Figure Questions

Figure 23.8 The predicted frequencies are 36% C^RC^R, 48% C^RC^W, and 16% C^WC^W. **Figure 23.12** Local survival should increase in both populations. The increase would probably occur more rapidly among birds born into the central population because gene flow from the mainland is higher in that population. **Figure 23.13** Directional selection. Goldenrain tree has smaller fruit than does the native host, balloon vine. Thus, in soapberry bug populations feeding on goldenrain tree, bugs with shorter beaks had an advantage, resulting in directional selection for shorter beak length. **Figure 23.16** Crossing a single female's eggs with both an SC and an LC male's sperm allowed the researchers to directly compare the effects of the males' contribution to the next generation, since both batches of offspring had the same maternal contribution. This isolation of the male's impact enabled researchers to draw conclusions about differences in genetic "quality" between the SC and LC males. **Figure 23.18** The researchers measured the percentages of successfully reproducing adults in the breeding adult population that had each phenotype. This approach of determining which phenotype was favored by selection assumes that reproduction was a sufficient indicator of relative fitness (as opposed to counting the number of eggs laid or offspring hatched, for example) and that mouth phenotype was the driving factor determining the fish's ability to reproduce.

Concept Check 23.1

1. (a) Within a population, genetic differences among individuals provide the raw material on which natural selection and other mechanisms can act. Without such differences, allele frequencies could not change over time—and hence the population could not evolve. (b) Genetic differences between separate populations can result from natural selection if different alleles are favored in different populations; this might occur, for example, if the different populations experienced different environmental conditions (as in Figure 23.4). Genetic differences between populations can also result from chance events (genetic drift) if the genetic changes have few or no phenotypic effects (as in Figure 23.3). **2.** Many mutations occur in somatic cells, which do not produce gametes and so are lost when the organism dies. Of mutations that do occur in cell lines that produce gametes, many do not have a phenotypic effect on which natural selection can act. Others have a harmful effect and are thus unlikely to increase in frequency because they decrease the reproductive success of their bearers. **3.** Its genetic variation (whether measured at the level of the gene or at the level of nucleotide sequences) would probably drop over time. During meiosis, crossing over and the independent assortment of chromosomes produce many new combinations of alleles. In addition, a population contains a vast number of possible mating combinations, and fertilization brings together the gametes of individuals with different genetic backgrounds. Thus, via crossing over, independent assortment of chromosomes, and fertilization, sexual reproduction reshuffles alleles into fresh combinations each generation. Without sexual reproduction, the rate of forming new combinations of alleles would be vastly reduced, causing the overall amount of genetic variation to drop.

Concept Check 23.2

1. 30,000. Half the loci (10,000) are fixed, meaning only one type of allele exists for each locus: $10{,}000 \times 1 = 10{,}000$. There are two types of alleles each for the other loci: $10{,}000 \times 2 = 20{,}000$. $10{,}000 + 20{,}000 = 30{,}000$. **2.** $p^2 + 2pq$; p^2 represents homozygotes with two *A* alleles, and $2pq$ represents heterozygotes with one *A* allele. **3.** There are 120 individuals in the population, so there are 240 alleles. Of these, there are 124 *A* alleles—32 from the 16 *AA* individuals and 92 from the 92 *Aa* individuals. Thus, the frequency of the *A* allele is $p = 124/240 = 0.52$; hence, the frequency of the *a* allele is $q = 0.48$. Based on the Hardy-Weinberg equation, if the population were not evolving, the frequency of genotype *AA* should be $p^2 = 0.52 \times 0.52 = 0.27$; the frequency of genotype *Aa* should be $2pq = 2 \times 0.52 \times 0.48 = 0.5$; and the frequency of genotype *aa* should be $q^2 = 0.48 \times 0.48 = 0.23$. In a population of 120 individuals, these expected genotype frequencies lead us to predict that there would be 32 *AA* individuals (0.27×120), 60 *Aa* individuals (0.5×120), and 28 *aa* individuals (0.23×120). The actual numbers for the population (16 *AA*, 92 *Aa*, 12 *aa*) deviate from these expectations (fewer homozygotes and more heterozygotes than expected). This indicates that the population is not in Hardy-Weinberg equilibrium and hence may be evolving at this locus.

Concept Check 23.3

1. Natural selection is more "predictable" in that it alters allele frequencies in a nonrandom way: It tends to increase the frequency of alleles that increase the organism's reproductive success in its environment and decrease the frequency of alleles that decrease the organism's reproductive success. Alleles subject to genetic drift increase or decrease in frequency by chance alone, whether or not they are advantageous. **2.** Genetic drift results from chance events that cause allele frequencies to fluctuate at random from generation to generation; within a population, this process tends to decrease genetic variation over time. Gene flow is the exchange of alleles between populations, a process that can introduce new alleles to a population and hence may increase its genetic variation (albeit slightly, since rates of gene flow are often low). **3.** Selection is not important at this locus; furthermore, the populations are not small, and hence the effects of genetic drift should not be pronounced. Gene flow is occurring via the movement of pollen and seeds. Thus, allele and genotype frequencies in these populations should become more similar over time as a result of gene flow.

Concept Check 23.4

1. Zero, because fitness includes reproductive contribution to the next generation, and a sterile mule cannot produce offspring. **2.** Although both gene flow and genetic drift can increase the frequency of advantageous alleles in a population, they can also decrease the frequency of advantageous alleles or increase the frequency of harmful alleles. Only natural selection *consistently* results in an increase in the frequency of alleles that enhance survival or reproduction. Thus, natural selection is the only mechanism that consistently causes adaptive evolution. **3.** The three modes of natural selection (directional, stabilizing, and disruptive) are defined in terms of the selective advantage of different *phenotypes*, not different genotypes. Thus, the type of selection represented by heterozygote advantage depends on the phenotype of the heterozygotes. In this question, because heterozygous individuals have a more extreme phenotype than either homozygote, heterozygote advantage represents directional selection. **4.** Under prolonged low-oxygen conditions, some of the red blood cells of a heterozygote may sickle, leading to harmful effects (see Chapter 14). This does not occur in individuals with two normal hemoglobin alleles, suggesting that there may be selection against heterozygotes in malaria-free regions (where heterozygote advantage does not occur). However, since heterozygotes are healthy under most conditions, selection against them is unlikely to be strong.

Summary of Key Concepts Questions

23.1 One reason biologists estimate gene variability and nucleotide variability is to assess whether populations have enough genetic variation for evolution to occur. Gene variability indicates the extent to which individuals differ genetically at the whole-gene level. Nucleotide variability provides a measure of genetic variation at the DNA sequence level. **23.2** No, this is not an example of circular reasoning. Calculating *p* and *q* from observed genotype frequencies does not imply that those genotype frequencies must be in Hardy-Weinberg equilibrium. Consider a population that has 195 individuals of genotype *AA*, 10 of genotype *Aa*, and 195 of genotype *aa*. Calculating *p* and *q* from these values yields $p = q = 0.5$. Using the Hardy-Weinberg equation, the predicted equilibrium frequencies are $p^2 = 0.25$ for genotype *AA*, $2pq = 0.5$ for genotype *Aa*, and $q^2 = 0.25$ for genotype *aa*. Since there are 400 individuals in the population, these predicted genotype frequencies indicate there should be 100 *AA* individuals, 200 *Aa* individuals, and 100 *aa* individuals—numbers that differ greatly from the values that we used to calculate *p* and *q*. **23.3** It is unlikely that two such populations would evolve in similar ways. Since their environments are very different, the alleles favored by natural selection would probably differ between the two populations; although genetic drift may have important effects in each of these small populations, drift causes unpredictable changes in allele frequencies, so it is unlikely that drift would cause the populations to evolve in similar ways; both populations are geographically isolated, suggesting that little gene flow will occur between them (again making it less likely that they will evolve in similar ways). **23.4** Compared to males, it is likely that the females of such species would be larger, more colorful, endowed with more elaborate ornamentation (for example, a large morphological feature such as the peacock's tail), and more apt to engage in behaviors intended to attract mates or prevent other members of their sex from obtaining mates.

Test Your Understanding

1. e **2.** c **3.** e **4.** b **5.** a **6.** d

7. Although natural selection can improve the match between organisms and their environments, the evolutionary process can also lead to imperfections in organisms. A central reason for this is that evolution does not design organisms from scratch to match their environments and ways of life but works instead by a process of descent with modification: Organisms inherit a basic form from their ancestors, and that form is modified by natural selection over time. As a result, a flying mammal such as a bat has wings that are not perfectly designed, but rather represent modifications of forelimbs that bat ancestors used for walking. Imperfections in organisms result from a variety of other constraints, such as a lack of genetic variation for the trait in question, and the fact that adaptations often represent compromises (since organisms must do many different things, and a "perfect" design for one activity might impair the performance of another activity). **8.** The frequency of the lap^{94} allele forms a cline, decreasing as one moves from southwest to northeast across Long Island Sound.

Site	1	2	3	4	5	6
lap^{94} %	13	16	16	25	36	37

Site	7	8	9	10	11
lap^{94} %	39	55	59	59	59

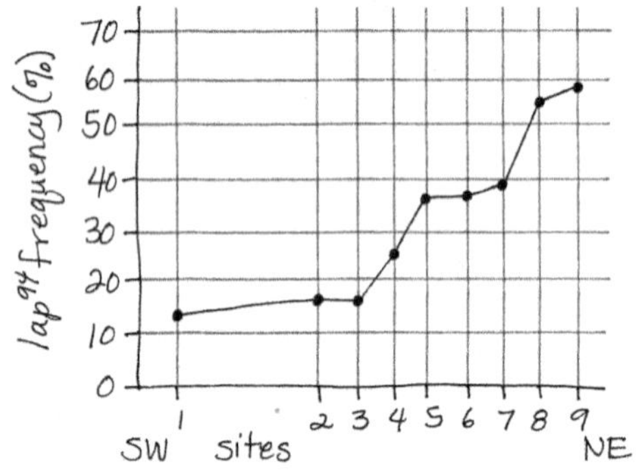

A hypothesis that explains the cline and accounts for the observations stated in the question is that the cline is maintained by an interaction between selection and gene flow. Under this hypothesis, in the southwest portion of the Sound, salinity is relatively low, and selection against the lap^{94} allele is strong. Moving toward the northeast and into the open ocean, where salinity is relatively high, selection favors a high frequency of the lap^{94} allele. However, because mussel larvae disperse long distances, gene flow prevents the lap^{94} allele from becoming fixed in the open ocean or from declining to zero in the southwestern portion of Long Island Sound.

Chapter 24

Figure Questions

Figure 24.10 This was done to remove the possibility that the flies could differentiate among potential mates by detecting what those potential mates had eaten as larvae. If this had not been done, the strong preference of "starch flies" and "maltose flies" to mate with like-adapted flies could have occurred simply because the flies could detect (for example, by sense of smell) what their potential mates had eaten as larvae—and they preferred to mate with flies that had a similar smell to their own. **Figure 24.12** Such results would suggest that mate choice based on coloration does not provide a reproductive barrier between these two cichlid species. **Figure 24.13** The graph suggests there has been gene flow of some fire-bellied toad alleles into the range of the yellow-bellied toad. Otherwise, all individuals located to the left of the hybrid zone portion of the graph would have allele frequencies close to 1.0. **Figure 24.14** Because the populations had only just begun to diverge from one another at this point in the process, it is likely that any existing barriers to reproduction would weaken over time. **Figure 24.19** No. Over time, the chromosomes of the experimental hybrids came to resemble those of *H. anomalus*. This occurred even though conditions in the laboratory differed greatly from conditions in the field, where *H. anomalus* is found, suggesting that selection for laboratory conditions was not strong. Thus, it is unlikely that the observed rise in the fertility of the experimental hybrids was due to selection for life under laboratory conditions. **Figure 24.20** The presence of *M. cardinalis* plants that carry the *M. lewisii yup* allele would make it more likely that bumblebees would transfer pollen between the two monkey flower species. As a result, we would expect the number of hybrid offspring to increase.

Concept Check 24.1

1. (a) All except the biological species concept can be applied to both asexual and sexual species because they define species on the basis of characteristics other than ability to reproduce. In contrast, the biological species concept can be applied only to sexual species. (b) The easiest species concept to apply in the field would be the morphological species concept because it is based only on the appearance of the organism. Additional information about its ecological habits, evolutionary history, and reproduction are not required. **2.** Because these birds live in fairly similar environments and can breed successfully in captivity, the reproductive barrier in nature is probably prezygotic; given the species' differences in habitat preference, this barrier could result from habitat isolation.

Concept Check 24.2

1. In allopatric speciation, a new species forms while in geographic isolation from its parent species; in sympatric speciation, a new species forms in the absence of geographic isolation. Geographic isolation greatly reduces gene flow between populations, whereas ongoing gene flow is more likely in sympatric populations. As a result, sympatric speciation is less common than allopatric speciation. **2.** Gene flow between subsets of a population that live in the same area can be reduced in a variety of ways. In some species—especially plants—changes in chromosome number can block gene flow and establish reproductive isolation in a single generation. Gene flow can also be reduced in sympatric populations by habitat differentiation (as seen in the apple maggot fly, *Rhagoletis*) and sexual selection (as seen in Lake Victoria cichlids). **3.** Allopatric speciation would be less likely to occur on a nearby island than on an isolated island of the same size. The reason we expect this result is that continued gene flow between mainland populations and those on a nearby island reduces the chance that enough genetic divergence will take place for allopatric speciation to occur. **4.** If all of the homologs failed to separate during anaphase I of meiosis, some gametes would end up with an extra set of chromosomes (and others would end up with no chromosomes). If a gamete with an extra set of chromosomes fused with a normal gamete, a triploid would result; if two gametes with an extra set of chromosomes fused with each other, a tetraploid would result.

Concept Check 24.3

1. Hybrid zones are regions in which members of different species meet and mate, producing some offspring of mixed ancestry. Such regions can be viewed as "natural laboratories" in which to study speciation because scientists can directly observe factors that cause (or fail to cause) reproductive isolation. **2.** (a) If hybrids consistently survive and reproduce poorly compared to the offspring of intraspecific matings, reinforcement could occur. If it did, natural selection would cause prezygotic barriers to reproduction between the parent species to strengthen over time, decreasing the production of unfit hybrids and leading to a completion of the speciation process. (b) If hybrid offspring survived and reproduced as well as the offspring of intraspecific matings, indiscriminate mating between the parent species would lead to the production of large numbers of hybrid offspring. As these hybrids mated with each other and with members of both parent species, the gene pools of the parent species could fuse over time, reversing the speciation process.

Concept Check 24.4

1. The time between speciation events includes (1) the length of time that it takes for populations of a newly formed species to begin diverging reproductively from one another and (2) the time it takes for speciation to be complete once this divergence begins. Although speciation can occur rapidly once populations have begun to diverge from one another, it may take millions of years for that divergence to begin. **2.** Investigators transferred alleles at the *yup* locus (which influences flower color) from each parent species to the other. *M. lewisii* plants with an *M. cardinalis yup* allele received many more visits from hummingbirds than usual; hummingbirds usually pollinate *M. cardinalis* but avoid *M. lewisii*. Similarly, *M. cardinalis* plants with an *M. lewisii yup* allele received many more visits from bumblebees than usual; bumblebees usually pollinate *M. lewisii* and avoid *M. cardinalis*. Thus, alleles at the *yup* locus can influence pollinator choice, which in these species provides the primary barrier to interspecific mating. Nevertheless, the experiment does not prove that the *yup* locus alone controls barriers to reproduction between *M. lewisii* and *M. cardinalis*; other genes might enhance the effect of the *yup* locus (by modifying flower color) or cause entirely different barriers to reproduction (for example, gametic isolation or a postzygotic barrier). **3.** Crossing over. If crossing over did not occur, each chromosome in an experimental hybrid would remain as in the F_1 generation: composed entirely of DNA from one parent species or the other.

Summary of Key Concepts Questions

24.1 According to the biological species concept, a species is a group of populations whose members interbreed and produce viable, fertile offspring; thus, gene flow occurs between populations of a species. In contrast, members of different species do not interbreed and hence no gene flow occurs between their populations. Overall, then, in the biological species concept, species can be viewed as designated by the *absence* of gene flow—making gene flow of central importance to the biological species concept. **24.2** Sympatric speciation can be promoted by factors such as polyploidy, habitat shifts, and sexual selection, all of which can reduce gene flow between the subpopulations of a larger population. But such factors can also occur in allopatric populations and hence can also promote allopatric speciation. **24.3** If the hybrids are selected against, the hybrid zone could persist if individuals from the parent species regularly travel into the zone, where they mate to produce hybrid offspring. If hybrids are not selected against, there is no cost to the continued production of hybrids, and large numbers of hybrid offspring may be produced. However, natural selection for life in different environments may keep the gene pools of the two parent species distinct—thus preventing the loss (by fusion) of the parent species and once again causing the hybrid zone to be stable over time. **24.4** As the goatsbeard plant, Bahamas mosquitofish, and apple maggot fly examples illustrate, speciation continues to happen today. A new species can begin to form whenever gene flow is reduced between populations of the parent species. Such reductions in gene flow can occur in many ways: A new, geographically isolated population may be founded by a few colonists; some members of the parent species may begin to utilize new habitat; and sexual selection may isolate formerly connected populations or subpopulations. These and many other such events are happening today.

Test Your Understanding

1. b **2.** c **3.** c **4.** a **5.** e **6.** d **7.** e
10. Here is one possibility:

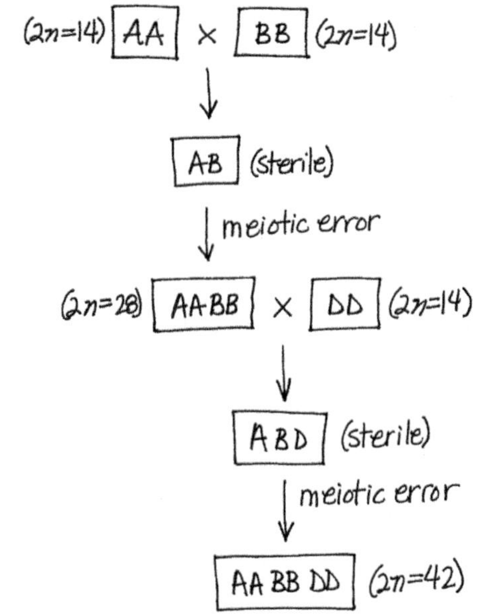

Chapter 25

Figure Questions

Figure 25.2 Proteins are almost always composed of the 20 amino acids shown in Figure 5.16. However, many other amino acids could potentially form in this or any other experiment. For example, any molecule that had a different R group than those listed in Figure 5.16 (yet still contained an α carbon, an amino group, and a carboxyl group) would be an amino acid—yet it would not be one of the 20 amino acids commonly found in nature. **Figure 25.5** Because uranium-238 has a half-life of 4.5 billion years, the *x*-axis would be relabeled (in billions of years) as 4.5, 9, 13.5, and 18. **Figure 25.10** You should have circled the node, shown in the tree diagram at approximately 580 million years ago (mya), that leads to the echinoderm/chordate lineage and to the lineage that gave rise to brachiopods, annelids, molluscs, and arthropods. Although the 580 mya date is estimated, this common ancestor must be at least as old as any of its descendants. Since fossil molluscs date to about 555 mya, the common ancestor represented by the circled branch point must be at least 555 million years old. **Figure 25.15** The blue curve is for marine animal families. Families often contain many species, so we would expect the percentage of families that became extinct to be lower than the percentage of species that became extinct. **Figure 25.25** The coding sequence of the *Pitx1* gene would differ between the marine and lake populations, but patterns of gene expression would not.

Concept Check 25.1

1. The hypothesis that conditions on early Earth could have permitted the synthesis of organic molecules from inorganic ingredients **2.** In contrast to random mingling of molecules in an open solution, segregation of molecular systems by membranes could concentrate organic molecules, assisting biochemical reactions. **3.** Today, genetic information usually flows from DNA to RNA, as when the DNA sequence of a gene is used as a template to synthesize the mRNA encoding a particular protein. However, the life cycle of retroviruses such as HIV shows that genetic information can flow in the reverse direction (from RNA to DNA). In these viruses, the enzyme reverse transcriptase uses RNA as a template for DNA synthesis, suggesting that a similar enzyme could have played a key role in the transition from an RNA world to a DNA world.

Concept Check 25.2

1. 22,920 years (four half-lives: 5,730 × 4) **2.** The fossil record shows that different groups of organisms dominated life on Earth at different points in time and that many organisms once alive are now extinct; specific examples of these points can be found in Figure 25.4. The fossil record also indicates that new groups of organisms can arise via the gradual modification of previously existing organisms, as illustrated by fossils that document the origin of mammals from their cynodont ancestors. **3.** The discovery of such a (hypothetical) fossil organism would indicate that aspects of our current understanding of the origin of mammals are not correct because mammals are thought to have originated much more recently (see Figure 25.6). For example, such a discovery could suggest that the dates of previous fossil discoveries are not correct or that the lineages shown in Figure 25.6 shared features with mammals but were not their direct ancestors. Such a discovery would also suggest that radical changes in multiple aspects of the skeletal structure of organisms could arise suddenly—an idea that is not supported by the known fossil record.

Concept Check 25.3

1. Free oxygen attacks chemical bonds and can inhibit enzymes and damage cells. As a result, prokaryotes that had thrived in anaerobic environments would have survived and reproduced poorly in oxygen-rich environments, driving many species to extinction. **2.** All eukaryotes have mitochondria or remnants of these organelles, but not all eukaryotes have plastids. **3.** A fossil record of life today would include many organisms with hard body parts (such as vertebrates and many marine invertebrates), but might not include some species we are very familiar with, such as those that have small geographic ranges and/or small population sizes (for example, endangered species such as the giant panda, tiger, and several rhinoceros species).

Concept Check 25.4

1. Continental drift alters the physical geography and climate of Earth, as well as the extent to which organisms are geographically isolated. Because these factors affect extinction and speciation rates, continental drift has a major impact on life on Earth. **2.** Mass extinctions; major evolutionary innovations; the diversification of another group of organisms (which can provide new sources of food); migration to new locations where few competitor species exist **3.** In principle, fossils of both common and rare species would be present right up to the time of the catastrophic event, then disappear. Reality is more complicated because the fossil record is not perfect. So the most recent fossil for a species might be a million years before the mass extinction—even though the species did not become extinct *until* the mass extinction. This complication is especially likely for rare species because few of their fossils will form and be discovered. Hence, for many rare species, the fossil record would not document that the species was alive immediately before the extinction (even if it was).

Concept Check 25.5

1. Heterochrony can cause a variety of morphological changes. For example, if the onset of sexual maturity changes, a retention of juvenile characteristics (paedomorphosis) may result. Paedomorphosis can be caused by small genetic changes that result in large changes in morphology, as seen in the axolotl salamander. **2.** In animal embryos, *Hox* genes influence the development of structures such as limbs and feeding appendages. As a result, changes in these genes—or in the regulation of these genes—are likely to have major effects on morphology. **3.** From genetics, we know that gene regulation is altered by how well transcription factors bind to noncoding DNA sequences called control elements. Thus, if changes in morphology are often caused by changes in gene regulation, portions of noncoding DNA that contain control elements are likely to be strongly affected by natural selection.

Concept Check 25.6

1. Complex structures do not evolve all at once, but in increments, with natural selection selecting for adaptive variants of the earlier versions. **2.** Although the myxoma virus is highly lethal, initially some of the rabbits are resistant (0.2% of infected rabbits are not killed). Thus, assuming resistance is an inherited trait, we would expect the rabbit population to show a trend for increased resistance to the virus. We would also expect the virus to show an evolutionary trend toward reduced lethality. We would expect this trend because a rabbit infected with a less lethal virus would be more likely to live long enough for a mosquito to bite it and hence potentially transmit the virus to another rabbit. (A virus that kills its rabbit host before a mosquito transmits the virus to another rabbit dies with its host.)

Summary of Key Concepts Questions

Concept 25.1 Particles of montmorillonite clay may have provided surfaces on which organic molecules became concentrated and hence were more likely to react with one another. Montmorillonite clay particles may also have facilitated the transport of key molecules, such as short strands of RNA, into vesicles. These vesicles can form spontaneously from simple precursor molecules, "reproduce" and "grow" on their own, and maintain internal concentrations of molecules that differ from those in the surrounding environment. These features of vesicles represent key steps in the emergence of protocells and (ultimately) the first living cells. **Concept 25.2** One challenge is that organisms do not use radioisotopes that have long half-lives to build their bones or shells. As a result, fossils older than 75,000 years cannot be dated directly. Fossils are often found in sedimentary rock, but those rocks typically contain sediments of different ages, again posing a challenge when trying to date old fossils. To circumvent these challenges, geologists date layers of volcanic rock that surround old fossils and that use radioisotopes with long half-lives. This approach provides minimum and maximum estimates for the ages of fossils sandwiched between two layers of volcanic rock. **Concept 25.3** The "Cambrian explosion" refers to a relatively short interval of time (535–525 million years ago) during which large forms of many present-day animal phyla first appear in the fossil record. The evolutionary changes that occurred during this time, such as the appearance of large predators and well-defended prey, were important because they set the stage for many of the key events in the history of life over the last 500 million years. **Concept 25.4** The broad evolutionary changes documented by the fossil record reflect the rise and fall of major groups of organisms. In turn, the rise or fall of any particular group results from a balance between speciation and extinction rates: A group increases in size when the rate at which its members produce new species is greater than the rate at which its member species are lost to extinction, while a group shrinks in size if extinction rates are greater than speciation rates. **Concept 25.5** Yes. A change to the sequence or regulation of a developmental gene can produce major morphological changes. In some cases, such morphological changes may enable organisms to perform new functions or live in new environments—thus potentially leading to an adaptive radiation and the formation of a new group of organisms. **Concept 25.6** Evolutionary change results from interactions between organisms and their current environments. No goal is involved in this process. As environments change over time, the features of organisms favored by natural selection may also change. When this happens, what once may have seemed like a "goal" of evolution (for example, improvements in the function of a feature previously favored by natural selection) may cease to be beneficial or may even be harmful.

Test Your Understanding
1. c **2.** a **3.** e **4.** b **5.** d
6.

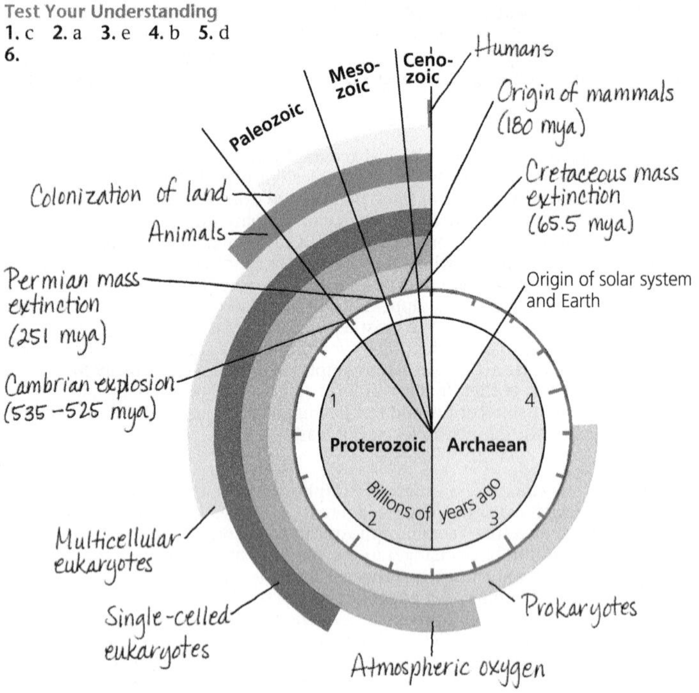

7. c **8.** b

Chapter 26

Figure Questions
Figure 26.5 This new version does not alter any of the evolutionary relationships shown in Figure 26.5. For example, B and C remain sister taxa, taxon A is still as closely related to taxon B as it is to taxon C, and so on.

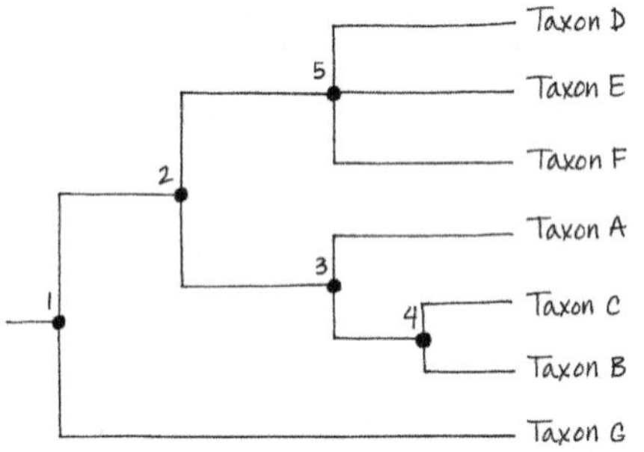

Figure 26.6 Unknown 1b (a portion of sample 1) and Unknowns 9–13 all would have to be located on the branch of the tree that currently leads to Minke (Southern Hemisphere) and Unknowns 1a and 2–8. **Figure 26.9** There are four possible bases (A, C, G, T) at each nucleotide position. If the base at each position depends on chance, not common descent, we would expect roughly one out of four (25%) of them to be the same. **Figure 26.11** You should have drawn a box around the frog, turtle, and leopard lineages, along with their most recent common ancestor. **Figure 26.12** The zebrafish lineage; of the five vertebrate lineages shown, its branch is the longest. **Figure 26.16** The lizard and snake lineage is the most basal taxon shown (closest to the root of the tree). Among the descendants of the common ancestor indicated by the blue dot, the crocodilian lineage is the most basal. **Figure 26.19** The molecular clock indicates that the divergence time is roughly 45–50 million years. **Figure 26.21** As shown in this diagram, Bacteria was the first to emerge and Archaea is the sister domain to Eukarya.

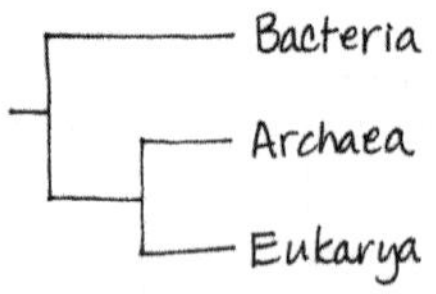

Concept Check 26.1
1. We are classified the same from the domain level to the class level; both the leopard and human are mammals. Leopards belong to order Carnivora, whereas humans do not. **2.** The branching pattern of the tree indicates that the badger and the wolf share a common ancestor that is more recent than the ancestor that these two animals share with the leopard. **3.** The tree in (c) shows a different pattern of evolutionary relationships. In (c), C and B are sister taxa, whereas C and D are sister taxa in (a) and (b).

4.

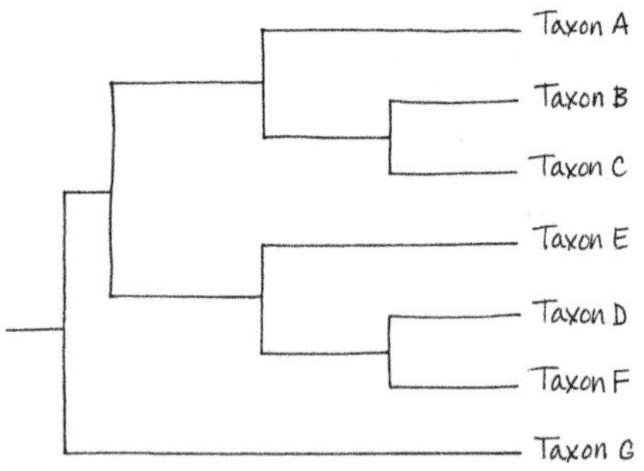

Concept Check 26.2
1. (a) Analogy, since porcupines and cacti are not closely related and since most other animals and plants do not have similar structures; (b) homology, since cats and humans are both mammals and have homologous forelimbs, of which the hand and paw are the lower part; (c) analogy, since owls and hornets are not closely related and since the structure of their wings is very different **2.** Species 2 and 3 are more likely to be closely related. Small genetic changes (as between species 2 and 3) can produce divergent physical appearances, but if many genes have diverged greatly (as in species 1 and 2), then the lineages have probably been separate for a long time.

Concept Check 26.3
1. No; when comparing groups of mammals, hair is a shared ancestral character common to all mammals and thus is not helpful in distinguishing different mammalian subgroups. **2.** The principle of maximum parsimony states that the hypothesis about nature we investigate first should be the simplest explanation found to be consistent with the facts. Actual evolutionary relationships may differ from those inferred by parsimony owing to complicating factors such as convergent evolution. **3.** The traditional classification provides a poor match to evolutionary history, thus violating the basic principle of cladistics—that classification should be based on common descent. Both birds and mammals originated from groups traditionally designated as reptiles, making reptiles (as traditionally delineated) a paraphyletic group. These problems can be addressed by removing *Dimetrodon* and cynodonts from the reptiles and by considering birds as a group of reptiles (specifically, as a group of dinosaurs).

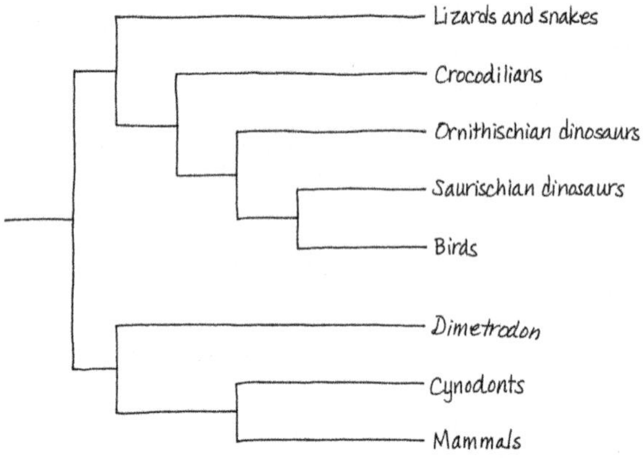

Concept Check 26.4
1. Proteins are gene products. Their amino acid sequences are determined by the nucleotide sequences of the DNA that codes for them. Thus, differences between comparable proteins in two species reflect underlying genetic differences that have accumulated as the species diverged from one another. As a result, differences between the proteins can reflect the evolutionary history of the species. **2.** In RNA processing, the exons or coding regions of a gene can be spliced together in different ways, yielding different mRNAs and hence different protein products. As a result, different proteins could potentially be produced from the same gene in different tissues, thereby enabling the gene to perform different functions in these different tissues. **3.** These observations suggest that the evolutionary lineages leading to species 1 and species 2 diverged from one another before a gene duplication event in species 1 produced gene B from gene A.

Concept Check 26.5
1. A molecular clock is a method of estimating the actual time of evolutionary events based on numbers of base changes in orthologous genes. It is based on the assumption that the regions of genomes being compared evolve at constant rates. **2.** There are many portions of the genome that do not code for genes; many base changes in these regions could accumulate through drift without affecting an organism's fitness. Even in coding regions of the genome, some mutations may not have a critical effect on genes or proteins. **3.** The gene (or genes) used for the molecular clock may have evolved more slowly in these two taxa than in the species used to calibrate the clock; as a result, the clock would underestimate the time at which the taxa diverged from each other.

Concept Check 26.6
1. The kingdom Monera included bacteria and archaea, but we now know that these organisms are in separate domains. Kingdoms are subsets of domains, so a

single kingdom (like Monera) that includes taxa from different domains is not valid. **2.** Because of horizontal gene transfer, some genes in eukaryotes are more closely related to bacteria, while others are more closely related to archaea; thus, depending on which genes are used, phylogenetic trees constructed from DNA data can yield conflicting results.

3.

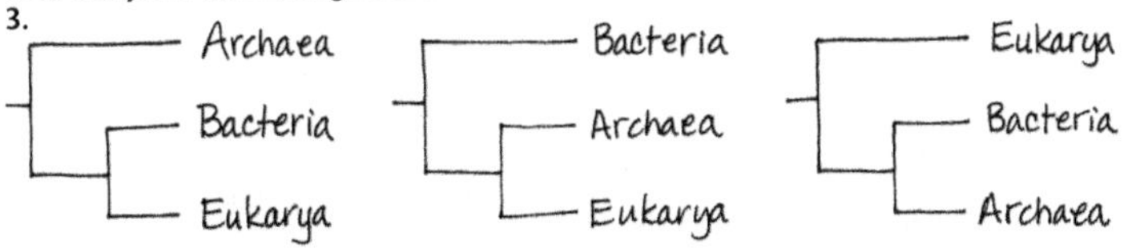

The fossil record indicates that prokaryotes originated long before eukaryotes. This suggests that the third tree, in which the eukaryotic lineage diverged first, is not accurate and hence is not likely to receive support from genetic data.

Summary of Key Concepts Questions

26.1 The fact that humans and chimpanzees are sister species indicates that we share a more recent common ancestor with chimpanzees than we do with any other living primate species. But that does not mean that humans evolved from chimpanzees, or vice versa; instead, it indicates that both humans and chimpanzees are descendants of that common ancestor. **26.2** Homologous characters result from shared ancestry. As organisms diverge over time, some of their homologous characters will also diverge. The homologous characters of organisms that diverged long ago typically differ more than do the homologous characters of organisms that diverged more recently. As a result, differences in homologous characters can be used to infer phylogeny. In contrast, analogous characters result from convergent evolution, not shared ancestry, and hence can give misleading estimates of phylogeny. **26.3** All features of organisms arose at some point in the history of life. In the group in which a new feature first arises, that feature is a shared derived character that is unique to that clade. The group in which each shared derived character first appears can be determined, and the resulting nested pattern can be used to infer evolutionary history. **26.4** Orthologous genes should be used; for such genes, the homology results from speciation and hence reflects evolutionary history. **26.5** A key assumption of molecular clocks is that nucleotide substitutions occur at fixed rates and hence the number of nucleotide differences between two DNA sequences is proportional to the time since the sequences diverged from each other. Some limitations of molecular clocks: No gene marks time with complete precision; natural selection can favor certain DNA changes over others; nucleotide substitution rates can change over long periods of time (causing molecular clocks estimates of when events in the distant past occurred to be highly uncertain); and the same gene can evolve at different rates in different organisms **26.6** Genetic data indicated that many prokaryotes differed as much from each other as they did from eukaryotes. This indicated that organisms should be grouped into three "super-kingdoms," or domains (Archaea, Bacteria, Eukarya). These data also indicated that the previous kingdom Monera (which had contained all the prokaryotes) did not make biological sense and should be abandoned. Later genetic and morphological data also indicated that the former kingdom Protista (which had primarily contained single-celled organisms) should be abandoned because it was polyphyletic.

Test Your Understanding

1. b **2.** d **3.** a **4.** d **5.** d **6.** c **7.** d

9. (a)

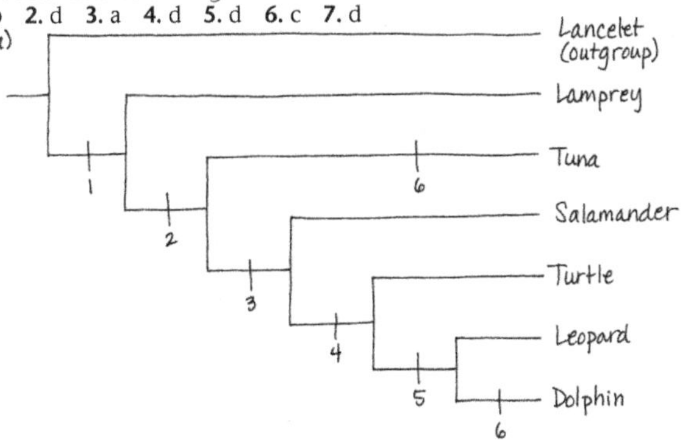

(b)

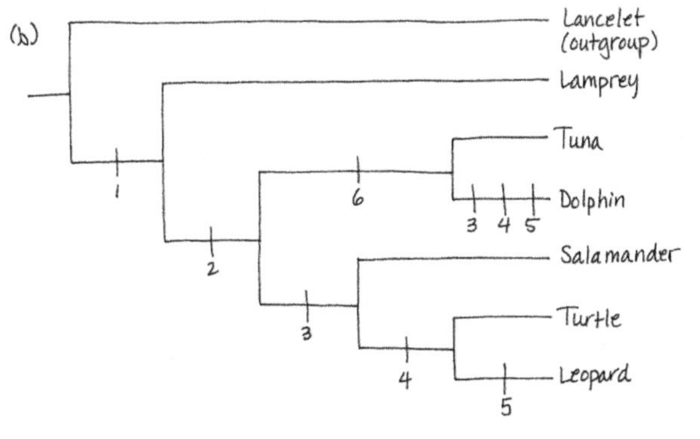

(c) The tree in (a) requires seven evolutionary changes, while the tree in (b) requires nine evolutionary changes. Thus, the tree in (a) is more parsimonious, since it requires fewer evolutionary changes.

Chapter 27

Figure Questions

Figure 27.10 It is likely that the expression or sequence of genes that affect glucose metabolism may have changed; genes for metabolic processes no longer needed by the cell also may have changed. **Figure 27.11** Transduction results in horizontal gene transfer when the host and recipient cells are members of different species. **Figure 27.16** Thermophiles live in very hot environments, so it is likely that their enzymes can continue to function normally at much higher temperatures than do the enzymes of other organisms. At low temperatures, however, the enzymes of thermophiles may not function as well as the enzymes of other organisms. **Figure 27.18** From the graph, plant uptake can be estimated as 0.7, 0.6, and 0.95 (mg K) for strains 1, 2, and 3, respectively. These values average to 0.75 mg K. If bacteria had no effect, the average plant uptake of potassium for strains 1, 2, and 3 should be close to 0.5 mg K, the value observed for plants grown in bacteria-free soil.

Concept Check 27.1

1. Adaptations include the capsule (shields prokaryotes from host's immune system) and endospores (enable cells to survive harsh conditions and to revive when the environment becomes favorable). **2.** Prokaryotic cells generally lack the internal compartmentalization of eukaryotic cells. Prokaryotic genomes have much less DNA than eukaryotic genomes, and most of this DNA is contained in a single ring-shaped chromosome located in the nucleoid rather than within a true membrane-bounded nucleus. In addition, many prokaryotes also have plasmids, small ring-shaped DNA molecules containing a few genes. **3.** Plastids such as chloroplasts are thought to have evolved from an endosymbiotic photosynthetic prokaryote. More specifically, the phylogenetic tree shown in Figure 26.21 indicates that plastids are closely related to cyanobacteria. Hence, we can hypothesize that the thylakoid membranes of chloroplasts resemble those of cyanobacteria because chloroplasts evolved from a cyanobacterium endosymbiont.

Concept Check 27.2

1. Prokaryotes have extremely large population sizes, in part because they have short generation times. The large number of individuals in prokaryotic populations makes it likely that in each generation there will be thousands of individuals that have new mutations at any particular gene, thereby adding considerable genetic diversity to the population. **2.** In transformation, naked, foreign DNA from the environment is taken up by a bacterial cell. In transduction, phages carry bacterial genes from one bacterial cell to another. In conjugation, a bacterial cell directly transfers plasmid or chromosomal DNA to another cell via a mating bridge that temporarily connects the two cells. **3.** The population that includes individuals capable of conjugation would probably be more successful, since some of its members could form recombinant cells whose new gene combinations might be advantageous in a novel environment. **4.** Yes. Genes for antibiotic resistance could be transferred (by transformation, transduction, or conjugation) from the nonpathogenic bacterium to a pathogenic bacterium; this could make the pathogen an even greater threat to human health. In general, transformation, transduction, and conjugation tend to increase the spread of resistance genes.

Concept Check 27.3

1. A phototroph derives its energy from light, while a chemotroph gets its energy from chemical sources. An autotroph derives its carbon from a form of CO_2, while a heterotroph gets its carbon from organic nutrients such as glucose. Thus, there are four nutritional modes: photoautotrophic, photoheterotrophic (unique to prokaryotes), chemoautotrophic (unique to prokaryotes), and chemoheterotrophic. **2.** Chemoheterotrophy; the bacterium must rely on chemical sources of energy, since it is not exposed to light, and it must be a heterotroph if it requires a source of carbon other than CO_2 (or a related compound, such as bicarbonate). **3.** If humans could fix nitrogen, we could build proteins using atmospheric N_2 and hence would not need to eat high-protein foods such as meat, fish, or soy. Our diet would, however, need to include a source of carbon, along with minerals and water. Thus, a typical meal might consist of carbohydrates as a carbon source, along with fruits and vegetables to provide essential minerals (and additional carbon).

Concept Check 27.4

1. Before molecular systematics, taxonomists classified prokaryotes according to phenotypic characters that did not clarify evolutionary relationships. Molecular comparisons—of DNA in particular—indicate key divergences in prokaryotic lineages. **2.** By not requiring that organisms be cultured in the laboratory, genetic prospecting has revealed an immense diversity of previously unknown prokaryotic species. Over time, the ongoing discovery of new species by genetic prospecting is likely to alter our understanding of prokaryotic phylogeny greatly. **3.** At present, all known methanogens are archaea in the clade Euryarchaeota; this suggests that this unique metabolic pathway probably arose in ancestral species within Euryarchaeota. Since Bacteria and Archaea have been separate evolutionary lineages for billions of years, the discovery of a methanogen from the domain Bacteria would suggest that adaptations that enabled the use of CO_2 to oxidize H_2 may have evolved twice—once in Archaea (within Euryarchaeota) and once in Bacteria. (It is also possible that a newly discovered bacterial methanogen could have acquired the genes for this metabolic pathway by horizontal gene transfer from a methanogen in domain Archaea. However, horizontal gene transfer is not a likely explanation because of the large number of genes involved and because gene transfers between species in different domains are rare.)

Concept Check 27.5

1. Although prokaryotes are small, their large numbers and metabolic abilities enable them to play key roles in ecosystems by decomposing wastes, recycling chemicals, and affecting the concentrations of nutrients available to other organisms **2.** Cyanobacteria produce oxygen when water is split in the light reactions of photosynthesis. The Calvin cycle incorporates CO_2 from the air into organic molecules, which are then converted to sugars.

Concept Check 27.6

1. Sample answers: eating fermented foods such as yogurt, sourdough bread, or cheese; receiving clean water from sewage treatment; taking medicines produced by bacteria **2.** No. If the poison is secreted as an exotoxin, live bacteria could be transmitted to another person. But the same is true if the poison is an endotoxin—only in this case, the live bacteria that are transmitted may be descendants of the (now-dead) bacteria that produced the poison. **3.** Some of the many different species of prokaryotes that live in the human gut compete with one another for resources (in the food you eat). Because different prokaryotic species have different adaptations, a change in diet may alter which species can grow most rapidly, thus altering species abundance.

Summary of Key Concepts Questions

27.1. Prokaryotes are small, they have short generation times, and their populations can consist of trillions of individuals. As a result, populations of prokaryotes can evolve substantially in short periods of time, enabling them to adapt to a wide range of environments. Specific structural features that enable prokaryotes to thrive in diverse environments include their cell walls (which provide shape and protection), flagella (which function in directed movement), and ability to form endospores (which enable tolerance of harsh conditions). Prokaryotes also possess biochemical adaptations for growth in varied conditions, such as those that enable them to tolerate extremely hot or salty environments. **27.2** Prokaryotes reproduce extremely rapidly, and their populations can number in the trillions. As a result, even though mutations are rare, every day thousands of offspring are produced that have new mutations at particular gene loci. In addition, even though prokaryotes reproduce asexually and hence the vast majority of offspring are genetically identical to their parent, the genetic variation of their populations can be increased by transduction, transformation, and conjugation. Each of these (nonreproductive) processes can increase genetic variation by transferring DNA from one cell to another—even among cells that are of different species. **27.3** Prokaryotes have an exceptionally broad range of metabolic adaptations. As a group, prokaryotes perform all four modes of nutrition (photoautotrophy, chemoautotrophy, photoheterotrophy, and chemoheterotrophy), whereas eukaryotes perform only two of these (photoautotrophy and chemoheterotrophy). Prokaryotes are also able to metabolize nitrogen in a wide variety of forms (again unlike eukaryotes), and they frequently cooperate with other prokaryotic cells of the same or different species. **27.4** Phenotypic criteria such as shape, motility, and nutritional mode do not provide a clear picture of the evolutionary history of the prokaryotes. In contrast, molecular data have elucidated relationships among major groups of prokaryotes. Molecular data have also allowed researchers to sample genes directly from the environment; using such genes to construct phylogenies has led to the discovery of major new groups of prokaryotes. **27.5** Prokaryotes play key roles in the chemical cycles on which life depends. For example, prokaryotes are important decomposers, breaking down corpses and waste materials, thereby releasing nutrients to the environment where they can be used by other organisms. Prokaryotes also convert inorganic compounds to forms that other organisms can use. With respect to their ecological interactions, many prokaryotes form life-sustaining mutualisms with other species. In some cases, such as hydrothermal vent communities, the metabolic activities of prokaryotes provide an energy source on which hundreds of other species depend; in the absence of the prokaryotes, the community collapses. **27.6** Human well-being depends on our associations with mutualistic prokaryotes, such as the many species that live in our intestines and digest food that we cannot. Humans also can harness the remarkable metabolic capabilities of prokaryotes to produce a wide range of useful products. Negative effects of prokaryotes result primarily from bacterial pathogens that cause disease.

Test Your Understanding

1. e **2.** a **3.** d **4.** d **5.** b **6.** a

8. (a)

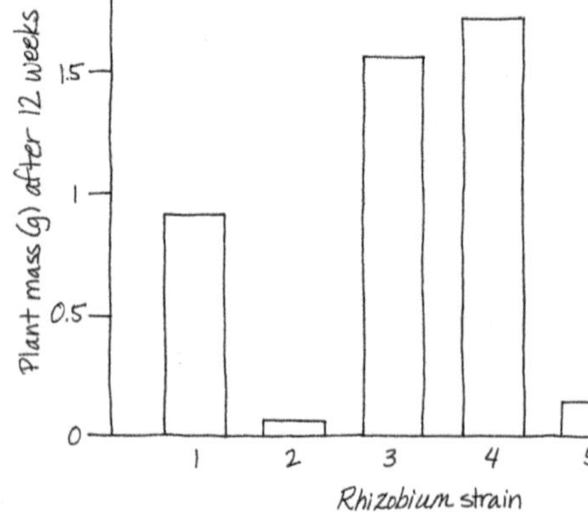

(b) Some *Rhizobium* strains are much more effective at promoting plant growth than other *Rhizobium* strains; the most ineffective strains have little positive effect (plant growth with these strains differs little from plant growth in the absence of *Rhizobium*). The ineffective strains may transfer relatively little nitrogen to their plant host, limiting plant growth.

Chapter 28

Figure Questions

Figure 28.10 Merozoites are produced by the asexual (mitotic) cell division of haploid sporozoites; similarly, gametocytes are produced by the asexual cell division of merozoites. Hence, it is likely that individuals in these three stages have the same complement of genes and that morphological differences between them result from changes in gene expression. **Figure 28.16** The sperm cells in the diagram are produced by the asexual (mitotic) division of cells in a single male gametophyte, which was itself produced by the asexual (mitotic) division of a single zoospore. Thus, the sperm cells are all derived from a single zoospore and so are genetically identical to one another. However, the male gametophyte that produced the sperm developed from one zoospore, while the female gametophyte that produced the egg developed from a different zoospore. Zoospores are produced by meiosis, so each zoospore differs genetically from the others. Hence, the sperm cells (which can be traced back to one zoospore) differ genetically from the egg cell (which can be traced back to another zoospore). **Figure 28.22** The following stage should be circled: step 6, where a mature cell undergoes mitosis and forms four or more daughter cells. In step 7, the zoospores eventually grow into mature haploid cells, but they do not produce new daughter cells. Likewise, in step 2, a mature cell develops into a gamete, but it does not produce new daughter cells. **Figure 28.23** If the assumption is correct, then their results indicate that the DHFR-TS gene fusion may be a derived trait shared by members of four supergroups of eukaryotes (Excavata, Chromalveolata, Rhizaria, and Archaeplastida). However, if the assumption is not correct, the presence or absence of the gene fusion may tell little about phylogenetic history. For example, if the genes fused multiple times, groups could share the trait because of convergent evolution rather than common descent. If the genes were secondarily split, a group with such a split could be placed (incorrectly) in Unikonta rather than its correct placement in one of the other four supergroups. **Figure 28.28** If diatom populations decrease in size as global temperatures warm, less carbon dioxide would be "pumped" from surface waters to the deep ocean floor. Atmospheric carbon dioxide levels might increase as a result, thereby potentially causing further warming. If this process continues, a positive-feedback loop would result in which warming causes diatom populations to drop, thereby causing additional warming, further drops in diatom populations, and so on.

Concept Check 28.1

1. Sample response: Protists include unicellular, colonial, and multicellular organisms; photoautotrophs, heterotrophs, and mixotrophs; species that reproduce asexually, sexually, or both ways; and organisms with diverse physical forms and adaptations. **2.** Strong evidence shows that eukaryotes acquired mitochondria after an early eukaryote first engulfed and then formed an endosymbiotic association with an alpha proteobacterium. Similarly, chloroplasts in red and green algae appear to have descended from a photosynthetic cyanobacterium that was engulfed by an ancient heterotrophic eukaryote. Secondary endosymbiosis also played an important role: Various protist lineages acquired plastids by engulfing unicellular red or green algae. **3.** The modified tree would look as follows:

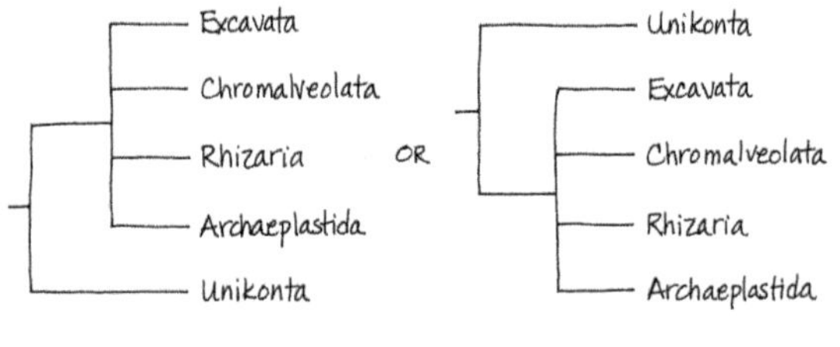

Concept Check 28.2

1. Their mitochondria do not have an electron transport chain and so cannot function in aerobic respiration. **2.** Since the unknown protist is more closely related to diplomonads than to euglenids, it must have originated after the diplomonads and parabasalids diverged from the euglenozoans. In addition, since the unknown species has fully functional mitochondria—yet both diplomonads and parabasalids do not—it is likely that the unknown species originated *before* the last common ancestor of the diplomonads and parabasalids.

Concept Check 28.3

1. Some DNA data indicate that Chromalveolata is a monophyletic group, but other DNA data fail to support this result. In support of monophyly, for many species in the group, the structure of their plastids and the sequence of their plastid DNA suggest that the group originated by a secondary endosymbiosis event (in which a red alga was engulfed). However, other species in the group lack plastids entirely, making the secondary endosymbiosis hypothesis difficult to test. **2.** The plastid DNA would likely be more similar to the chromosomal DNA of cyanobacteria based on the well-supported hypothesis that eukaryotic plastids (such as those found in the eukaryotic groups listed) originated by an endosymbiosis event in which a eukaryote engulfed a cyanobacterium. If the plastid is derived from the cyanobacterium, its DNA would be derived from the bacterial DNA. **3.** Figure 13.6b. Algae and plants with alternation of generations have a multicellular haploid stage *and* a multicellular diploid stage. In the other two life cycles, either the haploid stage or the diploid stage is unicellular.

Concept Check 28.4

1. Because foram tests are hardened with calcium carbonate, they form long-lasting fossils in marine sediments and sedimentary rocks. **2.** Convergent evolution. The different organisms have come to display similar morphological adaptations over time owing to their similar lifestyles. **3.** During photosynthesis, aerobic algae produce O_2 and use CO_2. O_2 is produced as a by-product of the light reactions, while CO_2 is used as an input to the Calvin cycle (the end products of which are sugars). Aerobic algae also perform cellular respiration, which uses O_2 as an input and produces CO_2 as a waste product.

Concept Check 28.5

1. Many red algae contain an accessory pigment called phycoerythrin, which gives them a reddish color and allows them to carry out photosynthesis in relatively deep coastal water. Also unlike brown algae, red algae have no flagellated stages in their life cycle and must depend on water currents to bring gametes together for fertilization. **2.** *Ulva*'s thallus contains many cells and is differentiated into leaflike blades and a rootlike holdfast. *Caulerpa*'s thallus is composed of multinucleate filaments without cross-walls, so it is essentially one large cell. **3.** Red algae have no flagellated stages in their life cycle and hence must depend on water currents to bring their gametes together. This feature of their biology might increase the difficulty of reproducing on land. In contrast, the gametes of green algae are flagellated, making it possible for them to swim in thin films of water. In addition, a variety of green algae contain compounds in their cytoplasm, cell wall, or zygote coat that protect against intense sunlight and other terrestrial conditions. Such compounds may have increased the chance that descendants of green algae could survive on land.

Concept Check 28.6

1. Amoebozoans have lobe-shaped pseudopodia, whereas forams have threadlike pseudopodia. **2.** Slime molds are fungus-like in that they produce fruiting bodies that aid in the dispersal of spores, and they are animal-like in that they are motile and ingest food. However, slime molds are more closely related to gymnamoebas and entamoebas than to fungi or animals. **3.** Support. Unikonts lack the unique cytoskeletal features shared by many excavates (see Concept 28.2). Thus, if the unikonts were the first group of eukaryotes to diverge from other eukaryotes (as shown in Figure 28.23), it would be unlikely that the eukaryote common ancestor had the cytoskeletal features found today in many excavates. Such a result would strengthen the case that many excavates share cytoskeletal features because they are members of a monophyletic group, the Excavata.

Concept Check 28.7

1. Because photosynthetic protists constitute the base of aquatic food webs, many aquatic organisms depend on them for food, either directly or indirectly. (In addition, a substantial percentage of the oxygen produced in photosynthesis on Earth is made by photosynthetic protists.) **2.** Protists form mutualistic and parasitic associations with other organisms. Examples include photosynthetic dinoflagellates that form a mutualistic symbiosis with coral polyps, parabasalids that form a mutualistic symbiosis with termites, and the oomycete *Phytophthora ramorum*, a parasite of oak trees. **3.** Corals depend on their dinoflagellate symbionts for nourishment, so coral bleaching would be expected to cause the corals to die. As the corals die, less food will be available for fishes and other species that eat coral. As a result, populations of these species may decline, and that, in turn, might cause populations of their predators to decline.

Summary of Key Concepts Questions

28.1 Sample response: Protists, plants, animals, and fungi are similar in that their cells have a nucleus and other membrane-bounded organelles, unlike the cells of prokaryotes. These membrane-bounded organelles make the cells of eukaryotes more complex than the cells of prokaryotes. With respect to differences between protists and other eukaryotes, most protists are unicellular, unlike animals, plants, and most fungi. Protists also have greater nutritional diversity than other eukaryotes. **28.2** Unique cytoskeletal features are shared by many excavates. In addition, some members of Excavata have an "excavated" feeding groove for which the group was named. DNA evidence does not strongly support or refute Excavata as a group. Overall, evidence for the group is relatively weak. **28.3** We can infer that the common ancestor of the group had a plastid, in this case of red algal origin. Thus, we would expect that members of Chromalveolata either would have plastids or would have lost their plastids over the course of evolution. **28.4** The main subgroups are the radiolarians, the forams, and the cercozoans. They are united as a clade by DNA similarities. **28.5** Red algae, green algae, and land plants are placed in the same supergroup because considerable evidence indicates that these organisms all descended from the same ancestor, an ancient heterotrophic protist that acquired a cyanobacterial endosymbiont. **28.6** The unikonts are a diverse group of eukaryotes that includes many protists, along with animals and fungi. Most of the protists in Unikonta are amoebozoans, a clade of amoebas that have lobe- or tube-shaped pseudopodia (as opposed to the threadlike pseudopodia of rhizarians). Other protists in Unikonta include several groups that are closely related to fungi and several other groups that are closely related to animals. **28.7** Sample response: Ecologically important protists include photosynthetic dinoflagellates that provide essential sources of energy to their symbiotic partners, the corals that build coral reefs. Other important protistan symbionts include those that enable termites to digest wood and *Plasmodium*, the pathogen that causes malaria. Photosynthetic protists such as diatoms are among the most important producers in aquatic communities; as such, many other species in aquatic environments depend on them for food.

Test Your Understanding

1. d **2.** b **3.** c **4.** e **5.** d **6.** d

7.

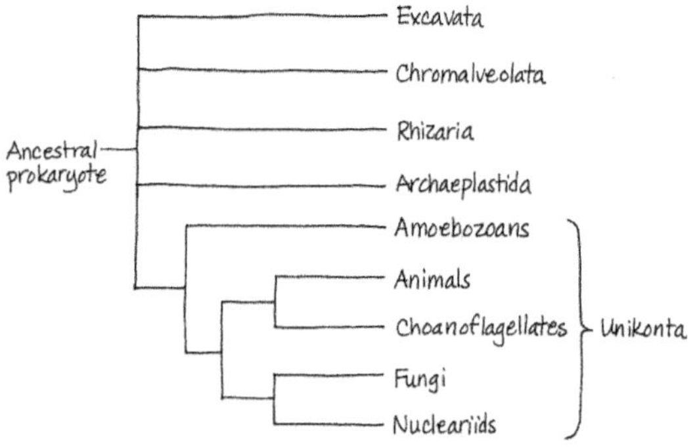

Pathogens that share a relatively recent common ancestor with humans should also share metabolic and structural characteristics with humans. Because drugs target the pathogen's metabolism or structure, developing drugs that harm the pathogen but not the patient should be most difficult for pathogens with whom we share the most recent evolutionary history. Working backward in time, we can use the phylogenetic tree to determine the order in which humans shared a common ancestor with pathogens in different taxa. This process leads to the prediction that it should be hardest to develop drugs to combat animal pathogens, followed by choanoflagellate pathogens, fungal and nucleariid pathogens, amoebozoans, other protists, and finally prokaryotes.

Chapter 29

Figure Questions

Figure 29.5 The life cycle in Figure 13.6b has alternation of generations; the others do not. Unlike the animal life cycle (Figure 13.6a), in alternation of generations, meiosis produces spores, not gametes. These spores then divide repeatedly by mitosis, ultimately forming a multicellular haploid individual that produces gametes. There is no multicellular haploid stage in the animal life cycle. An alternation of generations life cycle also has a multicellular diploid stage, whereas the life cycle shown in Figure 13.6c does not. **Figure 29.8** Yes. As shown in the diagram, the sperm cell and the egg cell that fuse each resulted from the mitotic division of spores produced by the same sporophyte. However, these spores would differ genetically from one another because they were produced by meiosis, a cell division process that generates genetic variation among the offspring cells. **Figure 29.10** Because the moss reduces nitrogen loss from the ecosystem, species that typically colonize the soils after the moss probably experience higher soil nitrogen levels than they otherwise would. The resulting increased availability of nitrogen may benefit these species because nitrogen is an essential nutrient that often is in short supply. **Figure 29.13** A fern that had wind-dispersed sperm would not require water for fertilization, thus removing a difficulty that ferns face when they live in arid environments. The fern would also be under strong selection to produce sperm above ground (as opposed to the current situation, where some fern gametophytes are located below ground). **Figure 29.16** When not reproducing, the lycophyte trees that dominate this forest would resemble poles covered by short leaves (microphylls). Since the trees would not have a branched canopy at their tops, the forest would be very open, and a considerable amount of light would reach the ground level.

Concept Check 29.1

1. Land plants share some key traits only with charophytes: rings of cellulose-synthesizing complexes, presence of peroxisome enzymes, similarity in sperm structure, and the formation of a phragmoplast in cell division. Comparisons of nuclear and chloroplast genes also point to a common ancestry. **2.** Spore walls toughened by sporopollenin (protects against harsh environmental conditions); multicellular, dependent embryos (provides nutrients and protection to the developing embryo); cuticle (reduces water loss) **3.** The multicellular diploid stage of the life cycle would not produce gametes. Instead, both males and females would produce haploid spores by meiosis. These spores would give rise to multicellular male and female haploid stages—a major change from the single-celled haploid stages (sperm and eggs) that we actually have. The multicellular haploid stages would produce gametes and reproduce sexually. An individual at the multicellular haploid stage of the human life cycle might look like us, or it might look completely different. **4.** Land plants, vascular plants, and seed plants are monophyletic because each of these groups includes the common ancestor of the group and all of the descendants of that common ancestor. The other two categories of plants, the nonvascular plants and the seedless vascular plants, are paraphyletic: These groups do not include all of the descendants of the group's most recent common ancestor.

Concept Check 29.2

1. Bryophytes do not have a vascular transport system, and their life cycle is dominated by gametophytes rather than sporophytes. **2.** Answers may include the following: Large surface area of protonema enhances absorption of water and minerals; the vase-shaped archegonia protect eggs during fertilization and transport nutrients to the embryos via placental transfer cells; the stalk-like seta conducts nutrients from the gametophyte to the capsule, where spores are produced; the peristome enables gradual spore discharge; stomata enable CO_2/O_2 exchange while minimizing water loss; lightweight spores are readily dispersed by wind.

3.

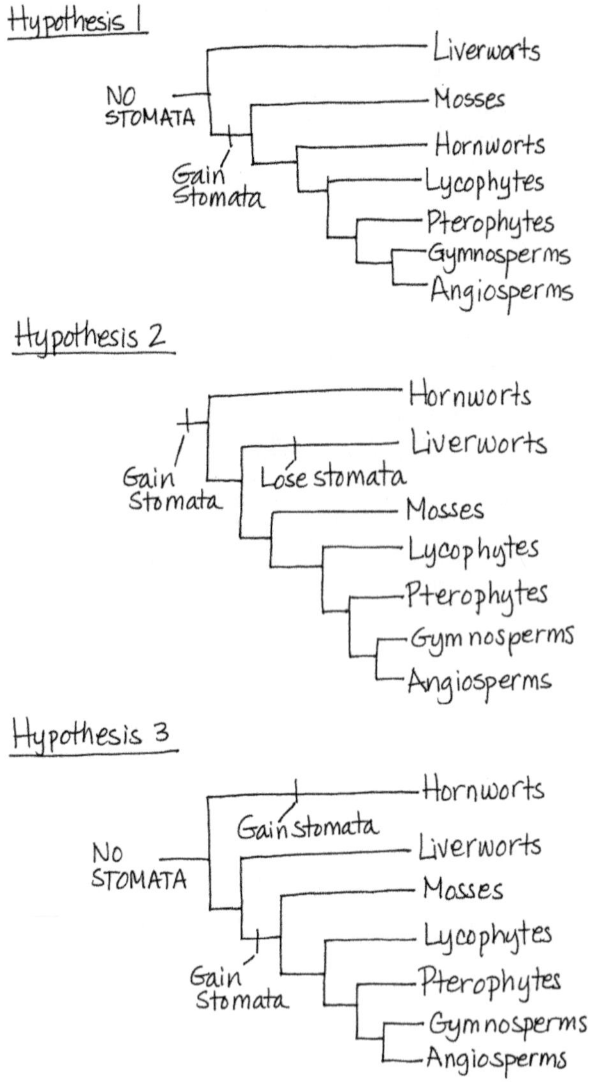

Concept Check 29.3

1. Lycophytes have microphylls, whereas seed plants and pterophytes (ferns and their relatives) have megaphylls. Pterophytes and seed plants also share other traits not found in lycophytes, such as overtopping growth and the initiation of new root branches at various points along the length of an existing root. **2.** Both seedless vascular plants and bryophytes have flagellated sperm that require moisture for fertilization; this shared similarity poses challenges for these species in arid regions. With respect to key differences, seedless vascular plants have lignified, well-developed vascular tissue, a trait that enables the sporophyte to grow tall and that has transformed life on Earth (via the formation of forests). Seedless vascular plants also have true leaves and roots, which, when compared with bryophytes, provide increased surface area for photosynthesis and improve their ability to extract nutrients from soil. **3.** If lycophytes and pterophytes formed a clade, the traits shared by pterophytes and seed plants might have been present in the common ancestor of all vascular plants, but lost in the lycophytes. Alternatively, the common ancestor of all vascular plants may have lacked the traits shared by pterophytes and seed plants; in this case, pterophytes and seed plants would share these traits as a result of convergent evolution. **4.** Three mechanisms contribute to the production of genetic variation in sexual reproduction: independent assortment of chromosomes, crossing over, and random fertilization. If fertilization were to occur between gametes from the same gametophyte, all of the offspring would be genetically identical. This would be the case because all of the cells produced by a gametophyte—including its sperm and egg cells—are the descendants of a single spore and hence are genetically identical. Genetic variation would continue to be generated by the first two mechanisms mentioned, but overall, the amount of genetic variation produced by sexual reproduction would drop.

Summary of Key Concepts Questions

29.1

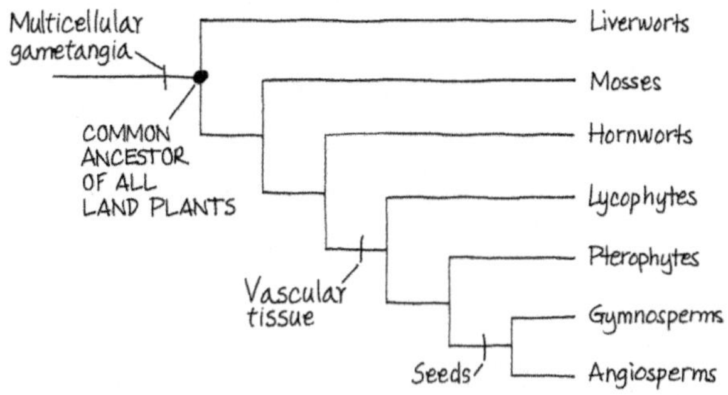

29.2 Some mosses colonize bare, sandy soils, leading to the increased retention of nitrogen in these otherwise low-nitrogen environments. Other mosses harbor nitrogen-fixing cyanobacteria that increase the availability of nitrogen in the ecosystem. The moss *Sphagnum* is often a major component of deposits of peat (partially decayed organic material). Boggy regions with thick layers of peat, known as peatlands, cover broad geographic regions and contain large reservoirs of carbon. By storing large amounts of carbon—in effect, removing CO_2 from the atmosphere—peatlands affect the global climate, making them of considerable ecological importance.
29.3 Lignified vascular tissue provided the strength needed to support a tall plant against gravity, as well as a means to transport water and nutrients to plant parts located high above ground. Roots were another key trait, anchoring the plant to the ground and providing additional structural support for plants that grew tall. Tall plants could shade shorter plants, thereby outcompeting them for light. Because the spores of a tall plant disperse farther than the spores of a short plant, it is also likely that tall plants could colonize new habitats more rapidly than short plants.

Test Your Understanding

1. b **2.** e **3.** d **4.** c **5.** a **6.** a. diploid; b. haploid; c. haploid; d. diploid; e. haploid **7.** c
8. Based on our current understanding of the evolution of major plant groups, the phylogeny has the four branch points shown here:

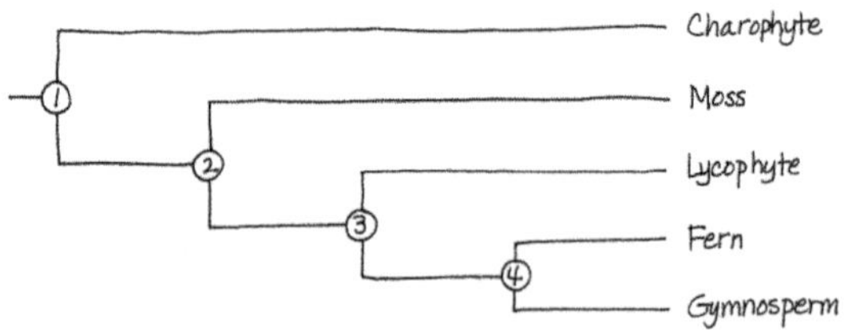

Derived characters unique to the charophyte and land plant clade (indicated by branch point 1) include rings of cellulose-synthesizing complexes, peroxisome enzymes, flagellated sperm structure, and a phragmoplast. Derived characters unique to the land plant clade (branch point 2) include apical meristems, alternation of generations, walled spores produced in sporangia, and multicellular gametangia. Derived characters unique to the vascular plant clade (branch point 3) include life cycles with dominant sporophytes, complex vascular systems (xylem and phloem), and well-developed roots and leaves. Derived characters unique to the pterophyte and seed plant clade (branch point 4) include megaphylls and overtopping growth.
9. (a)

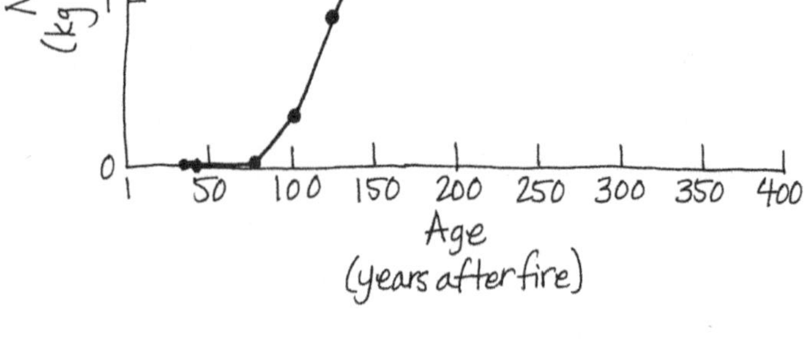

(b) In the first 40 years after a fire, nitrogen fixation rates were below 0.01 kg per ha per yr, which was less than 1% of the amount of nitrogen deposited from the atmosphere. Thus, in the initial decades after a fire, the moss *Pleurozium* and the nitrogen-fixing bacteria it harbors had relatively little effect on the amount of nitrogen added to the forest. With time, however, *Pleurozium* and its symbiotic, nitrogen-fixing bacteria became increasingly important. By 170 years after a fire, the percentage of the ground surface covered by the moss had increased to about 70%, leading to a corresponding increase in populations of the symbiotic bacteria. As would be predicted from this result, in older forests considerably more nitrogen (130–300%) was added by nitrogen fixation than was deposited from the atmosphere.

Chapter 30

Figure Questions

Figure 30.2 Retaining the gametophyte within the sporophyte shields the egg-containing gametophyte from UV radiation. UV radiation is a mutagen. Hence, we would expect fewer mutations to occur in the egg cells produced by a gametophyte retained within the body of a sporophyte. Most mutations are harmful. Thus, the fitness of embryos should increase because fewer embryos would carry harmful mutations. **Figure 30.3** Three generations: (1) the current sporophyte (cells of ploidy $2n$, found in the seed coat and in the megasporangium remnant that surrounds the spore wall); (2) the female gametophyte (cells of ploidy n, found in the food supply); and (3) the sporophyte of the next generation (cells of ploidy $2n$, found in the embryo) **Figure 30.6** Mitosis. A single haploid megaspore divides by mitosis to produce a multicellular, haploid female gametophyte. (Likewise, a single haploid microspore divides by mitosis to produce a multicellular male gametophyte.) **Figure 30.12** No. The branching order shown could still be correct if *Amborella* and other early angiosperms had originated prior to 150 million years ago, but angiosperm fossils of that age had not yet been discovered. In such a situation, the 140-million-year-old date for the origin of the angiosperms shown on the phylogeny would be incorrect. **Figure 30.16** Temperatures and the amount of sunlight striking the forest floor would both be likely to increase, whereas rainfall would likely decrease. Each of these changes could have dramatic effects on forest species that live near the edges of remaining forest fragments.

Concept Check 30.1

1. To reach the eggs, the flagellated sperm of seedless plants must swim through a film of water, usually over a distance of no more than a few centimeters. In contrast, the sperm of seed plants do not require water because they are produced within pollen grains that can be transported long distances by wind or by animal pollinators. Although flagellated in some species, the sperm of seed plants do not require mobility because pollen tubes convey them from the point at which the pollen grain is deposited (near the ovules) directly to the eggs. **2.** The reduced gametophytes of seed plants are nurtured by sporophytes and protected from stress, such as drought conditions and UV radiation. Pollen grains, with walls containing sporopollenin, provide protection during transport by wind or animals. Seeds have one or two layers of protective tissue, the seed coat, that improve survival by providing more protection from environmental stresses than do the walls of spores. Seeds also contain a stored supply of food, which provides nourishment for growth after dormancy is broken and the embryo emerges as a seedling. **3.** If a seed could not enter dormancy, the embryo would continue to grow after it was fertilized. As a result, the embryo might rapidly become too large to be dispersed, thus limiting its transport. The embryo's chance of survival might also be reduced because it could not delay growth until conditions become favorable.

Concept Check 30.2

1. Although gymnosperms are similar in not having their seeds enclosed in ovaries and fruits, their seed-bearing structures vary greatly. For instance, cycads have large cones, whereas some gymnosperms, such as *Ginkgo* and *Gnetum*, have small cones that look somewhat like berries, even though they are not fruits. Leaf shape also varies greatly, from the needles of many conifers to the palmlike leaves of cycads to *Gnetum* leaves that look like those of flowering plants. **2.** The pine life cycle illustrates heterospory, as ovulate cones produce megaspores and pollen cones produce microspores. The reduced gametophytes are evident in the form of the microscopic pollen grains that develop from microspores and the microscopic female gametophyte that develops from the megaspore. The egg is shown developing within an ovule, and a pollen tube is shown conveying the sperm. The figure also shows the protective and nutritive features of a seed. **3.** No. Fossil evidence indicates that gymnosperms originated at least 305 million years ago, but this does not mean that angiosperms are that old—only that the most recent common ancestor of gymnosperms and angiosperms must be that old.

Concept Check 30.3

1. In the oak's life cycle, the tree (the sporophyte) produces flowers, which contain gametophytes in pollen grains and ovules; the eggs in ovules are fertilized; the mature ovaries develop into dry fruits called acorns. We can view the oak's life cycle as starting when the acorn seeds germinate, resulting in embryos giving rise to seedlings and finally to mature trees, which produce flowers—and then more acorns. **2.** Pine cones and flowers both have sporophylls, modified leaves that produce spores. Pine trees have separate pollen cones (with pollen grains) and ovulate cones (with ovules inside cone scales). In flowers, pollen grains are produced by the anthers of stamens, and ovules are within the ovaries of carpels. Unlike pine cones, many flowers produce both pollen and ovules. **3.** The fact that the clade with bilaterally symmetrical flowers had more species establishes a correlation between flower shape and the rate of plant speciation. Flower shape is not necessarily responsible for the result because the shape (that is, bilateral or radial symmetry) may have been correlated with another factor that was the actual cause of the observed result. Note, however, that flower shape was associated with increased speciation rates when averaged across 19 different pairs of plant lineages. Since these 19 lineage pairs were independent of one another, this association suggests—but does not establish—that differences in flower shape cause differences in speciation rates. In general, strong evidence for causation can come from controlled, manipulative experiments, but such experiments are usually not possible for studies of past evolutionary events.

Concept Check 30.4

1. Plant diversity can be considered a resource because plants provide many important benefits to humans; as a resource, plant diversity is nonrenewable because if a species is lost to extinction, that loss is permanent. **2.** A detailed phylogeny of the seed plants would identify many different monophyletic groups of seed plants. Using this phylogeny, researchers could look for clades that contained species in which medicinally useful compounds had already been discovered. Identification of such clades would allow researchers to concentrate their search for new medicinal compounds among clade members—as opposed to searching for new compounds in species that were selected at random from the more than 250,000 existing species of seed plants.

Summary of Key Concepts Questions

30.1 The integument of an ovule develops into the protective seed coat of a seed. The ovule's megaspore develops into a haploid female gametophyte, and two parts of the seed are related to that gametophyte: The food supply of the seed is derived from haploid gametophyte cells, and the embryo of the seed develops after the female gametophyte's egg cell is fertilized by a sperm cell. A remnant of the ovule's megasporangium surrounds the spore wall that encloses the seed's food supply and embryo. **30.2** Gymnosperms arose about 305 million years ago, making them a successful group in terms of their evolutionary longevity. Gymnosperms have the five derived traits common to all seed plants (reduced gametophytes, heterospory, ovules, pollen, and seeds), making them well adapted for life on land. Finally, because gymnosperms dominate immense geographic regions today, the group is also highly successful in geographic distribution. **30.3** The origin of flowering plants is puzzling because their distinctive features, flowers and fruits, bear little resemblance to structures in living gymnosperms. This makes it difficult to infer how flowers and fruits arose, leading Darwin to refer to the origin of flowering plants as an "abominable mystery." Progress has been made toward solving this mystery, particularly in our understanding of angiosperm phylogeny, but the mystery has yet to be solved. We still do not know, for example, which extinct group of seed plants is most closely related to flowering plants. **30.4** The loss of tropical forests could contribute to global warming (which would have negative effects on many human societies) and reduce agricultural production in some of the world's poorest regions. People also depend on Earth's biodiversity for many products and services and hence would be harmed by the loss of species that would occur if the world's remaining tropical forests were cut down. With respect to a possible mass extinction, tropical forests harbor at least 50% of the species on Earth. If the remaining tropical forests were destroyed, large numbers of these species could be driven to extinction, thus rivaling the losses that occurred in the five mass extinction events documented in the fossil record.

Test Your Understanding

1. d **2.** a **3.** b **4.** a **5.** d

6.

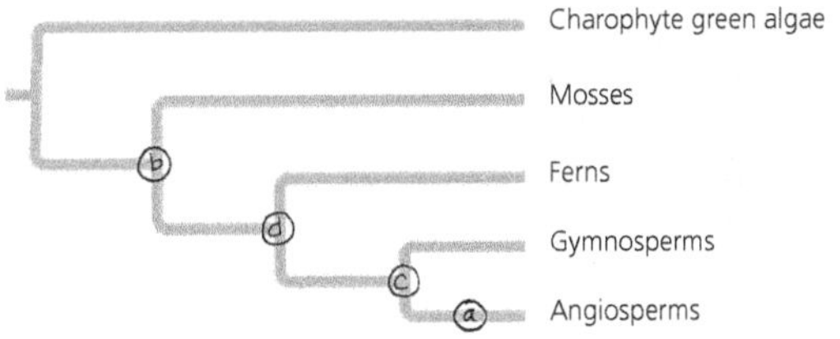

8. (a)

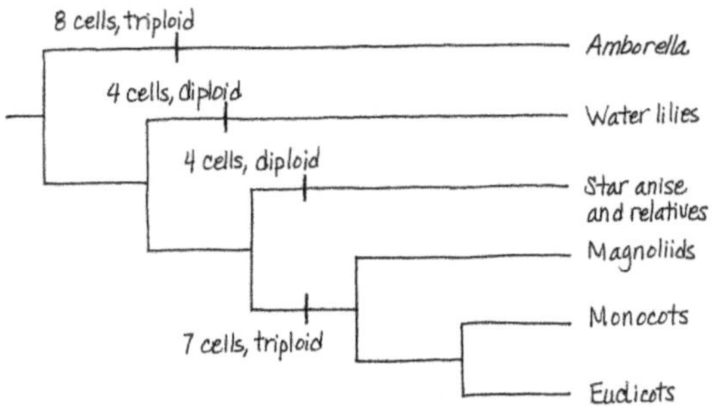

(b) The phylogeny indicates that basal angiosperms differed from other angiosperms in terms of the number of cells in female gametophytes and the ploidy of the endosperm. The ancestral state of the angiosperms cannot be determined from these data alone. It is possible that the common ancestor of angiosperms had seven-celled female gametophytes and triploid endosperm and hence that the eight-celled and four-celled conditions found in basal angiosperms represent derived traits for those lineages. Alternatively, either the eight-celled or four-celled condition may represent the ancestral state.

Chapter 31

Figure Questions

Figure 31.2 DNA from each of these mushrooms would be identical if each mushroom is part of a single hyphal network, as is likely. **Figure 31.16** One or both of the following would apply to each species: DNA analyses would reveal that it is a member of the ascomycete clade, or aspects of its sexual life cycle would indicate that it is an ascomycete (for example, it would produce asci and ascospores). **Figure 31.21** Two possible controls would be E−P− and E+P−. Results from an E−P− control could be compared with results from the E−P+ experiment, and results from an E+P− control could be compared with results from the E+P+ experiment. Together, these two comparisons would indicate whether the addition of the pathogen causes an increase in leaf mortality. Results from an E−P− experiment could also be compared with results from the second control (E+P−) to determine whether adding the endophytes has a negative effect on the plant. **Figure 31.26** The correspondence between when the chytrid fungi arrived to the region and when frog populations decreased greatly suggests that the chytrid was the cause of the decline, not just correlated to it. The fact that by 2009, the only surviving frogs were in the two lakes treated with fungicides provides additional support for causation.

Concept Check 31.1

1. Both a fungus and a human are heterotrophs. Many fungi digest their food externally by secreting enzymes into the food and then absorbing the small molecules that result from digestion. Other fungi absorb such small molecules directly from their environment. In contrast, humans (and most other animals) ingest relatively large pieces of food and digest the food within their bodies. **2.** The ancestors of such a mutualist most likely secreted powerful enzymes to digest the body of their insect host. Since such enzymes would harm a living host, it is likely that the mutualist would not produce such enzymes or would restrict their secretion and use. **3.** Carbon that enters the plant through stomata is fixed into sugar through photosynthesis. Some of these sugars are absorbed by the fungus that partners with the plant to form mycorrhizae; others are transported within the plant body and used in the plant. Thus, the carbon may be deposited in either the body of the plant or the body of the fungus.

Concept Check 31.2

1. The majority of the fungal life cycle is spent in the haploid stage, whereas the majority of the human life cycle is spent in the diploid stage. **2.** The two mushrooms might be reproductive structures of the same mycelium (the same organism). Or they might be parts of two separate organisms that have arisen from a single parent organism through asexual reproduction and thus carry the same genetic information.

Concept Check 31.3

1. DNA evidence indicates that fungi, animals, and their protistan relatives form a clade, the opisthokonts. Furthermore, an early-diverging fungal lineage, the chytrids, have posterior flagella, as do most other opisthokonts. This suggests that other fungal lineages lost their flagella after diverging from chytrids. **2.** This indicates that fungi had already established mutualistic relationships with plants by the date the fossils of the earliest vascular plants had formed. **3.** Fungi are heterotrophs. Prior to the colonization of land by plants, terrestrial fungi would have lived where other organisms (or their remains) were present and provided a source of food. Thus, if fungi had colonized land before plants, they could have fed on any prokaryotes or protists that lived on land or by the water's edge—but not on the plants or animals on which many fungi feed today.

Concept Check 31.4

1. Flagellated spores; molecular evidence also suggests that chytrids are an early-diverging fungal lineage. **2.** Possible answers include the following: In zygomycetes, the sturdy, thick-walled zygosporangium can withstand harsh conditions and then undergo karyogamy and meiosis when the environment is favorable for reproduction. In glomeromycetes, the hyphae have a specialized morphology that enables the fungi to form arbuscular mycorrhizae with plant roots. In ascomycetes, the asexual spores (conidia) are often produced in chains or clusters at the tips of conidiophores, where they are easily dispersed by wind. The often cup-shaped ascocarps house the sexual spore-forming asci. In basidiomycetes, the basidiocarp supports and protects a large surface area of basidia, from which spores are dispersed. **3.** Such a change to the life cycle of an ascomycete would reduce the number and genetic diversity of ascospores that result from a mating event. Ascospore number would drop because a mating event would lead to the formation of only one ascus. Ascospore genetic diversity would also drop because in ascomycetes, one mating event leads to the formation of asci by many different dikaryotic cells. As a result, genetic recombination and meiosis occur independently many different times—which could not happen if only a single ascus was formed. It is also likely that if such an ascomycete formed an ascocarp, the shape of the ascocarp would differ considerably from that found in its close relatives.

Concept Check 31.5

1. A suitable environment for growth, retention of water and minerals, protection from intense sunlight, and protection from being eaten **2.** A hardy spore stage enables dispersal to host organisms through a variety of mechanisms; their ability to grow rapidly in a favorable new environment enables them to capitalize on the host's resources. **3.** Many different outcomes might have occurred. Organisms that currently form mutualisms with fungi might have gained the ability to perform the tasks currently done by their fungal partners, or they might have formed similar mutualisms with other organisms (such as bacteria). Alternatively, organisms that currently form mutualisms with fungi might be less effective at living in their present environments. For example, the colonization of land by plants might have been more difficult. And if plants did eventually colonize land without fungal mutualists, natural selection might have favored plants that formed more highly divided and extensive root systems (in part replacing mycorrhizae).

Summary of Key Concepts Questions

31.1 The body of a multicellular fungus typically consists of thin filaments called hyphae. These filaments form an interwoven mass (mycelium) that penetrates the substrate on which the fungus grows and feeds. Because the individual filaments are thin, the surface-to-volume ratio of the mycelium is maximized, making nutrient absorption highly efficient.

31.2

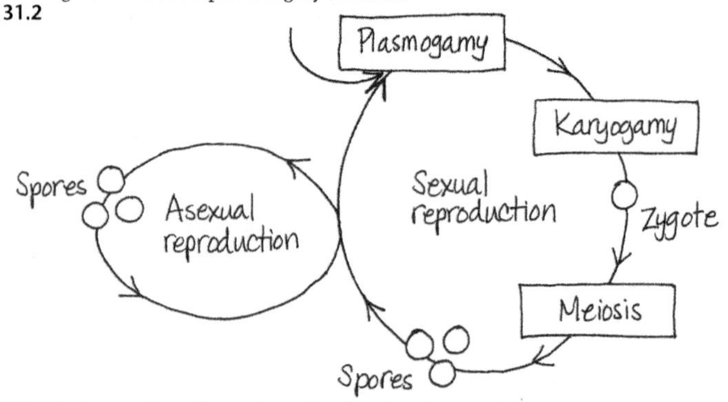

31.3 Phylogenetic analyses show that fungi and animals are more closely related to each other than either is to other multicellular eukaryotes (such as plants or multicellular algae). These analyses also show that fungi are more closely related to single-celled protists called nucleariids than they are to animals, whereas animals are more closely related to a different group of single-celled protists, the choanoflagellates, than they are to fungi. In combination, these results indicate that multicellularity evolved in fungi and animals independently, from different single-celled ancestors.

31.4

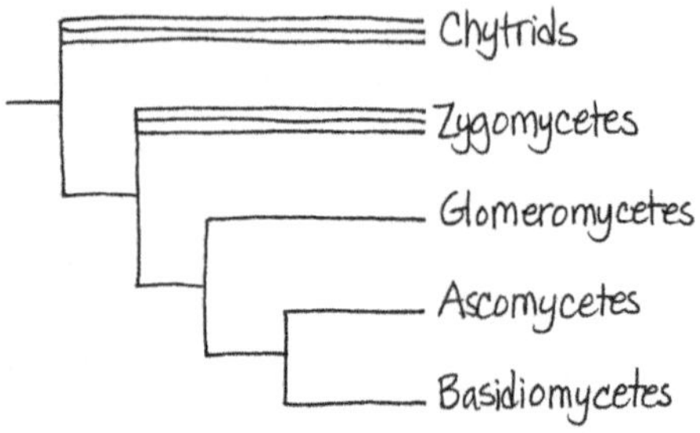

31.5 As decomposers, fungi break down the bodies of dead organisms, thereby recycling elements between the living and nonliving environments. Without the activities of fungi and bacterial decomposers, essential nutrients would remain tied up in organic matter, and life would cease. As an example of their key role as mutualists, fungi form mycorrhizal associations with plants. These associations improve the growth and survival of plants, thereby indirectly affecting the many other species (humans included) that depend on plants. As pathogens, fungi harm other species. In some cases, fungal pathogens have caused their host populations to decline across broad geographic regions, as seen for the American chestnut.

Test Your Understanding

1. b **2.** c **3.** d **4.** b **5.** a **6.** e

7.

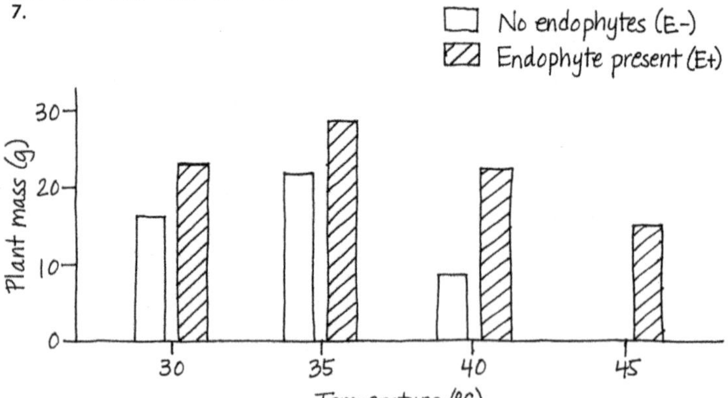

As indicated by the raw data and bar graph, grass plants with endophytes (E+) produced more new shoots and had greater biomass than did grass plants that lacked endophytes (E−). These differences were especially pronounced at the highest soil temperature, where E− grass plants produced no new shoots and had a biomass of zero (indicating they were dead).

Chapter 32

Figure Questions

Figure 32.3 As described in ❶ and ❷, choanoflagellates and a broad range of animals have collar cells. Since collar cells have never been observed in plants, fungi, or non-choanoflagellate protists, this suggests that choanoflagellates may be more closely related to animals than to other eukaryotes. If choanoflagellates are more closely related to animals than to any other group of eukaryotes, choanoflagellates and animals should share other traits that are not found in other eukaryotes. The data described in 3 are consistent with this prediction. **Figure 32.6** The sea anemone embryos could be infused with a protein that can bind to β-catenin's DNA-binding site, thereby limiting the extent to which β-catenin activates the transcription of genes necessary for gastrulation. Such an experiment would provide an independent check of the results shown in step 4. **Figure 32.9** The cells of an early embryo with deuterostome development typically are not committed to a particular developmental fate, whereas the cells of an early embryo with protostome development typically are committed to a particular developmental fate. As a result, an embryo with deuterostome development would be more likely to contain stem cells that could give rise to cells of any type. **Figure 32.10** Ctenophora is the sister phylum in this figure, while Cnidaria is the sister phylum in Figure 32.11.

Concept Check 32.1

1. In most animals, the zygote undergoes cleavage, which leads to the formation of a blastula. Next, in gastrulation, one end of the embryo folds inward, producing layers of embryonic tissue. As the cells of these layers differentiate, a wide variety of animal forms result. Despite the diversity of animal forms, animal development is controlled by a similar set of *Hox* genes across a broad range of taxa. **2.** The imaginary plant would require tissues composed of cells that were analogous to the muscle and nerve cells found in animals: "Muscle" tissue would be necessary for the plant to chase prey, and "nerve" tissue would be required for the plant to coordinate its movements when chasing prey. To digest captured prey, the plant would need to either secrete enzymes into one or more digestive cavities (which could be modified leaves, as in a Venus flytrap) or secrete enzymes outside of its body and feed by absorption. To extract nutrients from the soil—yet be able to chase prey—the plant would need something other than fixed roots, perhaps retractable "roots" or a way to ingest soil. To conduct photosynthesis, the plant would require chloroplasts. Overall, such an imaginary plant would be very similar to an animal that had chloroplasts and retractable roots. **3.** As described in Chapter 18, miRNAs help regulate gene expression by binding to and hence blocking the translation of particular mRNA molecules, their "target mRNAs." Because each miRNA can bind to many target mRNAs, an increase in the number of miRNA molecules could potentially add many layers of control to the regulation of gene expression. As a result of a more varied and complex control of gene expression, the construction of a complex body form would be more likely in an organism with many miRNAs than in an organism with few miRNAs, even though both organisms had roughly the same total number of genes.

Concept Check 32.2

1. c, b, a, d **2.** We cannot infer whether animals originated before or after fungi. If correct, the date provided for the most recent common ancestor of fungi and animals would indicate that animals originated some time within the last billion years. The fossil record indicates that animals originated at least 565 million years ago. Thus, we could conclude only that animals originated sometime between 1 billion years ago and 565 million years ago.

Concept Check 32.3

1. Grade-level characteristics are those that multiple lineages share regardless of evolutionary history. Some grade-level characteristics may have evolved multiple times independently. Features that unite clades are derived characteristics that originated in a common ancestor and were passed on to the various descendants. **2.** A snail has a spiral and determinate cleavage pattern; a human has radial, indeterminate cleavage. In a snail, the coelomic cavity is formed by splitting of mesoderm masses; in a human, the coelom forms from folds of archenteron. In a snail, the mouth forms from the blastopore; in a human, the anus develops from the blastopore. **3.** Most coelomate triploblasts have two openings to their digestive tract, a mouth and an anus. As such, their bodies have a structure that is analogous to that of a doughnut: The digestive tract (the hole of the doughnut) runs from the mouth to the anus and is surrounded by various tissues (the solid part of the doughnut). The doughnut analogy is most obvious at early stages of development (see Figure 32.9c).

Concept Check 32.4

1. Cnidarians possess true tissues, while sponges do not. Also unlike sponges, cnidarians exhibit body symmetry, though it is radial and not bilateral as in other animal phyla. **2.** The morphology-based tree divides Bilateria into two major clades: Deuterostomia and Protostomia. The molecular-based tree recognizes three major clades: Deuterostomia, Ecdysozoa, and Lophotrochozoa. **3.** The phylogeny in Figure 32.11 indicates that molluscs are members of Lophotrochozoa, one the three main groups of bilaterians (the others being Deuterostomia and Ecdysozoa). As seen in Figure 25.10, the fossil record shows that molluscs were present tens of millions of years before the Cambrian explosion. Thus, long before the Cambrian explosion, the lophotrochoan clade had formed and was evolving independently of the evolutionary lineages leading to Deuterostomia and Ecdysozoa. Based on the phylogeny in Figure 32.11, we can also conclude that the lineages leading to Deuterostomia and Ecdysozoa were independent of one another before the Cambrian explosion. Since the lineages leading to the three main clades of bilaterians were evolving independently of one another prior to the Cambrian explosion, that explosion could be viewed as consisting of three "explosions," not one.

Summary of Key Concepts Questions

Concept 32.1 Unlike animals, which are heterotrophs that ingest their food, plants are autotrophs, and fungi are heterotrophs that grow on their food and feed by absorption. Animals lack cell walls, which are found in both plants and fungi. Animals also have muscle tissue and nerve tissue, which are not found in either plants or fungi. In addition, the sperm and egg cells of animals are produced by meiotic division, unlike what occurs in plants and fungi (where reproductive cells such as sperm and eggs are produced by mitotic division). Finally, animals regulate the development of body form with *Hox* genes, a unique group of genes that is not found in either plants or fungi. **Concept 32.2** Current hypotheses about the cause of the Cambrian explosion include new predator-prey relationships, an increase in atmospheric oxygen, and an increase in developmental flexibility provided by the origin of *Hox* genes and other genetic changes. **Concept 32.3** Body plans provide a helpful way to compare and contrast key features of organisms. However, phylogenetic analyses show that similar body plans have arisen independently in different groups of organisms. As such, similar body plans may have arisen by convergent evolution and hence may not be informative about evolutionary relationships. **Concept 32.4** To reconstruct the evolutionary history of animal life, researchers collect morphological and molecular data and use cladistic methods to analyze that data. In a cladistic approach, shared derived (morphological and molecular) characters are used to place organisms into a nested hierarchy of monophyletic clades.

Test Your Understanding

1. a **2.** d **3.** e **4.** c **5.** b

7.

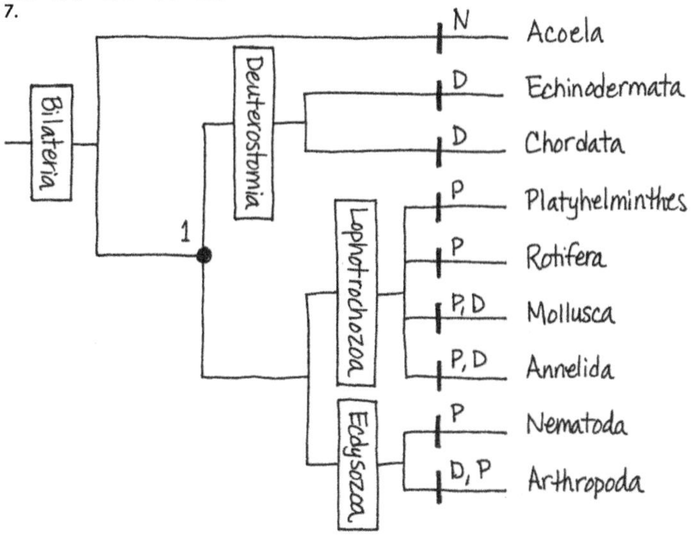

Based on the phylogeny, the ancestral condition in bilaterians may have been similar to that in Acoela, where the blastopore closes and the mouth forms elsewhere (N); however, it is also possible that blastopore fate in Acoela is a derived trait and hence is not informative about the ancestral condition. Although the phylogeny indicates that blastopore fate has changed multiple times over the course of evolution, a precise estimate cannot be made. For example, if we assume that the common ancestor of all non-Acoela bilaterians (marked with a 1 on the tree) exhibited protostomy, then blastopore fate has changed at least five times: once in common ancestor 1, once in Deuterostomia, at least once in Mollusca, at least once in Annelida, and at least once in Arthropoda. Other assumptions would lead to different estimates.

Chapter 33

Figure Questions

Figure 33.8 Within a reproductive polyp, a cell that gives rise to a medusa would have to divide by meiosis. A resulting haploid cell would then divide repeatedly (by mitosis), forming a haploid medusa. Later, cells in the medusa's gonads would divide by mitosis, forming the haploid eggs and sperm. **Figure 33.11** Adding fertilizer to the water supply would probably increase the abundance of algae, and that, in turn, would likely increase the abundance of snails (which eat algae). If the water was also contaminated with infected human feces, an increase in the number of snails would likely lead to an increase in the abundance of blood flukes (which require snails as an intermediate host). As a result, the occurrence of schistosomiasis might increase. **Figure 33.22** The extinctions of freshwater bivalves might lead to an increase in the abundance of photosynthetic protists and bacteria. Because these organisms are at the base of aquatic food webs, increases in their abundance could have major effects on aquatic communities (including both increases and decreases in the abundance of other species). **Figure 33.29** Such a result would be consistent with the *Ubx* and *abd-A Hox* genes having played a major role in the evolution of increased body segment diversity in arthropods. However, by itself, such a result would simply show that the presence of the *Ubx* and *abd-A Hox* genes was *correlated with* an increase in body segment diversity in arthropods; it would not provide direct experimental evidence that the acquisition of the *Ubx* and *adb-A* genes *caused* an increase in arthropod body segment diversity.

Concept Check 33.1

1. The flagella of choanocytes draw water through their collars, which trap food particles. The particles are engulfed by phagocytosis and digested, either by choanocytes or by amoebocytes. **2.** The collar cells of sponges (and some other animals—see Chapter 32) bear a striking resemblance to a choanoflagellate cell. This suggests that the last common ancestor of animals and their protist sister group may have resembled a choanoflagellate. Nevertheless, mesomycetozoans could still be the sister group of animals. If this is the case, the lack of collar cells in mesomycetozoans would indicate that over time their structure evolved in ways that caused it to no longer resemble a choanoflagellate cell. It is also possible that choanoflagellates and sponges share similar-looking collar cells as a result of convergent evolution.

Concept Check 33.2

1. Both the polyp and the medusa are composed of an outer epidermis and an inner gastrodermis separated by a gelatinous layer, the mesoglea. The polyp is a cylindrical form that adheres to the substrate by its aboral end; the medusa is a flattened, mouth-down form that moves freely in the water. **2.** Cnidarian stinging cells (cnidocytes) function in defense and prey capture. They contain capsule-like organelles (cnidae), which in turn contain coiled threads. The threads either inject poison or stick to and entangle small prey. **3.** Evolution is not goal oriented; hence, it would not be correct to argue that cnidarians were not "highly evolved" simply because their form had changed relatively little over the past 560 million years. Instead, the fact that cnidarians have persisted for hundreds of millions of years indicates that the cnidarian body plan is a highly successful one.

Concept Check 33.3

1. Tapeworms can absorb food from their environment and release ammonia into their environment through their body surface because their body is very flat, due in part to the lack of a coelom. **2.** The inner tube is the alimentary canal, which runs the length of the body. The outer tube is the body wall. The two tubes are separated by the coelom. **3.** All molluscs have inherited a foot from their common ancestor. However, in different groups of molluscs, the structure of the foot has been modified over time (by natural selection) in ways that reflect how the foot is used in locomotion by members of each clade. In gastropods, the foot is used as a holdfast or to move slowly on the substrate. In cephalopods, the foot has been modified into part of the tentacles and into an excurrent siphon, through which water is propelled (resulting in movement in the opposite direction).

Concept Check 33.4

1. Nematodes lack body segments and a true coelom; annelids have both. **2.** The arthropod exoskeleton, which had already evolved in the ocean, allow terrestrial species to retain water and support their bodies on land. Wings allow them to disperse quickly to new habitats and to find food and mates. The tracheal system allows for efficient gas exchange despite the presence of an exoskeleton. **3.** Arthropod mouthparts are modified appendages, which are bilaterally paired. As a result, the mouthparts come into contact by moving laterally, not up and down. **4.** Yes. Under the traditional hypothesis, we would expect body segmentation to be controlled by similar *Hox* genes in annelids and arthropods. However, if annelids are in Lophotrochozoa and arthropods are in Ecdysozoa, body segmentation may have evolved independently in these two groups. In such a case, we might expect that different *Hox* genes would control the development of body segmentation in the two clades.

Concept Check 33.5

1. Each tube foot consists of an ampulla and a podium. When the ampulla squeezes, it forces water into the podium, which causes the podium to expand and contact the substrate. Adhesive chemicals are then secreted from the base of the podium, thereby attaching the podium to the substrate. **2.** Both insects and nematodes are members of Ecdysozoa, one of the three major clades of bilaterians. Therefore, a characteristic shared by *Drosophila* and *Caenorhabditis* may be informative for other members of their clade—but not necessarily for members of Deuterostomia. Instead, Figure 33.2 suggests that a species within Echinodermata or Chordata might be a more appropriate invertebrate model organism from which to draw inferences about humans and other vertebrates. **3.** Echinoderms include species with a wide range of body forms, some of which are shown in Figure 33.40. However, even echinoderms that look very different from one another, such as sea stars and sea cucumbers, share characteristics unique to their phylum, including a water vascular system and tube feet. The differences between echinoderm species illustrate the diversity of life, while the characteristics they share illustrate the unity of life. The match between organisms and their environments can be seen in such echinoderm features as the eversible stomachs of sea stars (enabling them to digest prey that are larger than their mouth) and the complex, jaw-like structure that sea urchins use to eat seaweed.

Summary of Key Concepts Questions

Concept 33.1 The sponge body consists of two layers of cells, both of which are in contact with water. As a result, gas exchange and waste removal occur as substances diffuse into and out of the cells of the body. Choanocytes and amoebocytes ingest food particles from the surrounding water. Choanocytes also release food particles to amoebocytes, which then digest the food particles and deliver nutrients to other cells. **Concept 33.2** The cnidarian body plan consists of a sac with a central digestive compartment, the gastrovascular cavity. The single opening to this compartment serves as both a mouth and an anus. The two main variations on this body plan are sessile polyps (which adhere to the substrate at the end of the body opposite to the mouth/anus) and motile medusae (which move freely through the water and resemble flattened, mouth-down versions of polyps). **Concept 33.3** No. Some lophotrochozoans have a crown of ciliated tentacles that function in feeding (called a lophophore), while others go through a distinctive developmental stage known as trochophore larvae. Many other lophotrochozoans do not have either of these features. As a result, the clade is defined primarily by DNA similarities, not morphological similarities. **Concept 33.4** Many nematode species live in soil and in sediments on the bottom of bodies of water. These free-living species play important roles in decomposition and nutrient cycling. Other nematodes are parasites, including many species that attack the roots of plants and some that attack animals (including humans). Arthropods have profound effects on all aspects of ecology. In aquatic environments, crustaceans play key roles as grazers (of algae), scavengers, and predators, and some species, such as krill, are important sources of food for whales and other vertebrates. On land, it is difficult to think of features of the natural world that are not affected in some way by insects and other arthropods, such as spiders and ticks. There are more than 1 million species of insects, many of which have enormous ecological effects as herbivores, predators, parasites, decomposers, and vectors of disease. Insects are also key sources of food for many organisms, including humans in some regions of the world. **Concept 33.5** Echinoderms and chordates are both members of Deuterostomia, one of the three main clades of bilaterian animals. As such, chordates (including humans) are more closely related to echinoderms than we are to animals in any of the other phyla covered in this chapter. Nevertheless, echinoderms and chordates have evolved independently for over 500 million years. This statement does not contradict the close relationship of echinoderms and chordates, but it does make clear that "close" is a relative term indicating that these two phyla are more closely related to each other than either is to animal phyla not in Deuterostomia.

Test Your Understanding

1. a **2.** d **3.** b **4.** e **5.** c **6.** d
7.

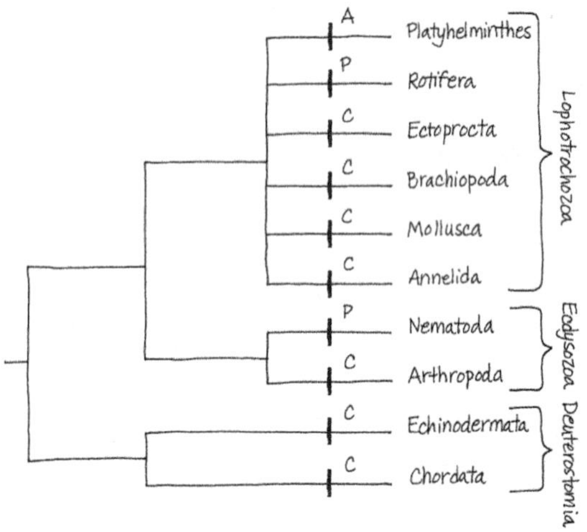

(a) Both phyla in Deuterostomia are coelomates, suggesting that their most recent common ancestor had a true coelom. Lophotrochozoa contains one phylum of acoelomates (Platyhelminthes), one phylum of pseudocoelomates (Rotifera), and four phyla of coelomates (Ectoprocta, Brachiopoda, Mollusca, Annelida); thus, we cannot, from this information alone, infer the condition of the most recent common ancestor shared by these phyla. Similarly, since Ecdysozoa contains one phylum of pseudocoelomates (Nematoda) and one phylum of coelomates (Arthropoda), we cannot infer whether their most recent common ancestor had a true coelom or not. (b) Depending on whether or not the last common ancestor of Bilateria had a true coelom, the presence of a true coelom has either been lost or gained multiple times during the evolutionary history of bilaterians. Thus, the presence of a true coelom appears to have changed over the course of evolution.

Chapter 34

Figure Questions

Figure 34.6 Results in these figures suggest that specific *Hox* genes, as well as the order in which they are expressed, have been highly conserved over the course of evolution. **Figure 34.20** *Tiktaalik* was a lobe-fin fish that had both fish and tetrapod characters. Like a fish, *Tiktaalik* had fins, scales, and gills. As described by Darwin's concept of descent with modification, such shared characters can be attributed to descent from ancestral species—in this case, *Tiktaalik*'s descent from fish ancestors. *Tiktaalik* also had traits that were unlike a fish, but like a tetrapod, including a flat skull, a neck, a full set of ribs, and the skeletal structure of its fin. These characters illustrate the second part of descent with modification, showing how ancestral features had become modified over time. **Figure 34.21** Sometime between 380 mya and 340 mya. We can infer this because amphibians must have originated after the most recent common ancestor of *Tulerpeton* and living tetrapods (and that ancestor originated 380 mya), but no later than the date of the earliest known fossils of amphibians (shown in the figure as 340 mya). **Figure 34.25** Crocodilians. Among extant amniotes, crocodilians are the sister group of birds. Hence, it is likely that DNA sequences in birds are more similar to those in crocodilians than they are to those of more distantly related amniotes. **Figure 34.37** In general, the process of exaptation occurs as a structure that had one function acquires a different function via a series of intermediate stages. Each of these intermediate stages typically has some function in the organism in which it is found. The incorporation of articular and quadrate bones into the mammalian ear illustrates exaptation because these bones originally evolved as part of the jaw, where they functioned as the jaw hinge, but over time they became co-opted for another function, namely the transmission of sound. **Figure 34.43** The phylogeny shows humans as the sister group to the lineage that contains chimpanzees and

bonobos. This relationship is not consistent with humans as having descended from either chimpanzees or bonobos. If humans had descended from chimpanzees, for example, the human lineage would be nested within the chimpanzee lineage, much as birds are nested within the reptile clade (see Figure 34.25).
Figure 34.50 No. The phylogeny shown in RESULTS does not include any information on when the branch points occurred, nor is it scaled by time. Thus, although the phylogeny shows the relative order in which lineages diverged, we cannot infer when those events took place.

Concept Check 34.1

1. The four characters are a notochord; a dorsal, hollow nerve chord; pharyngeal slits or clefts; and a muscular, post-anal tail. **2.** In humans, these characters are present only in the embryo. The notochord becomes disks between the vertebrae, the tail is almost completely lost, and the pharyngeal clefts develop into various adult structures. **3.** Not necessarily. It would be possible that the chordate common ancestor had this gene, which was then lost in the lancelet lineage and retained in other chordates. However, it would also be possible that the chordate common ancestor lacked this gene; this could occur if the gene originated after lancelets diverged from other chordates but before tunicates diverged from other chordates.

Concept Check 34.2

1. Hagfishes have a head and skull made of cartilage, plus a small brain, sensory organs, and tooth-like structures. They have a neural crest, gill slits, and more extensive organ systems. In addition, hagfishes have slime glands that ward off predators and may repel competing scavengers. **2.** *Myllokunmingia.* Fossils of this organism provide evidence of ear capsules and eye capsules; these structures are part of the skull. Thus, *Myllokunmingia* is considered a craniate, as are humans. *Haikouella* did not have a skull. **3.** Such a finding suggests that early organisms with a head were favored by natural selection in several different evolutionary lineages. However, while a logical argument can be made that having a head was advantageous, fossils alone do not constitute proof.

Concept Check 34.3

1. Lampreys have a round, rasping mouth, which they use to attach to fish. Conodonts had two sets of mineralized dental elements, which may have been used to impale prey and cut it into smaller pieces. **2.** In armored jawless vertebrates, bone served as external armor that may have provided protection from predators. Some species also had mineralized mouthparts, which could be used for either predation or scavenging. Still others had mineralized fin rays, which may have enabled them to swim more rapidly and with greater steering control.

Concept Check 34.4

1. Both are gnathostomes and have jaws, four clusters of *Hox* genes, enlarged forebrains, and lateral line systems. Shark skeletons consist mainly of cartilage, whereas tuna have bony skeletons. Sharks also have a spiral valve. Tuna have an operculum and a swim bladder, as well as flexible rays supporting their fins.
2. Aquatic gnathostomes have jaws (an adaptation for feeding) and paired fins and a tail (adaptations for swimming). Aquatic gnathostomes also typically have streamlined bodies for efficient swimming and swim bladders or other mechanisms (such as oil storage in sharks) for buoyancy. **3.** Yes, that could have happened. The paired appendages of aquatic gnathostomes other than the lobe-fins could have served as a starting point for the evolution of limbs. The colonization of land by aquatic gnathostomes other than the lobe-fins might have been facilitated in lineages that possessed lungs, as that would have enabled those organisms to breathe air.

Concept Check 34.5

1. Tetrapods are thought to have originated about 365 million years ago when the fins of some lobe-fins evolved into the limbs of tetrapods. In addition to their four limbs with digits—a key derived trait for which the group is named—other derived traits of tetrapods include a neck (consisting of vertebrae that separate the head from the rest of the body), a pelvic girdle that is fused to the backbone, and a lack of gill slits. **2.** Some fully aquatic species are paedomorphic, retaining larval features for life in water as adults. Species that live in dry environments may avoid dehydration by burrowing or living under moist leaves, and they protect their eggs with foam nests, viviparity, and other adaptations. **3.** Many amphibians spend part of their life cycle in aquatic environments and part on land. Thus, they may be exposed to a wide range of environmental problems, including water and air pollution and the loss or degradation of aquatic and/or terrestrial habitats. In addition, amphibians have highly permeable skin, providing relatively little protection from external conditions, and their eggs do not have a protective shell.

Concept Check 34.6

1. The amniotic egg provides protection to the embryo and allows the embryo to develop on land, eliminating the necessity of a watery environment for reproduction. Another key adaptation is rib cage ventilation, which improves the efficiency of air intake and may have allowed early amniotes to dispense with breathing through their skin. Finally, not breathing through their skin allowed amniotes to develop relatively impermeable skin, thereby conserving water. **2.** Yes. Although snakes lack limbs, they descended from lizards with legs. Some snakes retain vestigial pelvic and leg bones, providing evidence of their descent from an ancestor with legs. **3.** Birds have weight-saving modifications, including the absence of teeth, a urinary bladder, and a second ovary in females. The wings and feathers are adaptations that facilitate flight, and so are efficient respiratory and circulatory systems that support a high metabolic rate.

4.

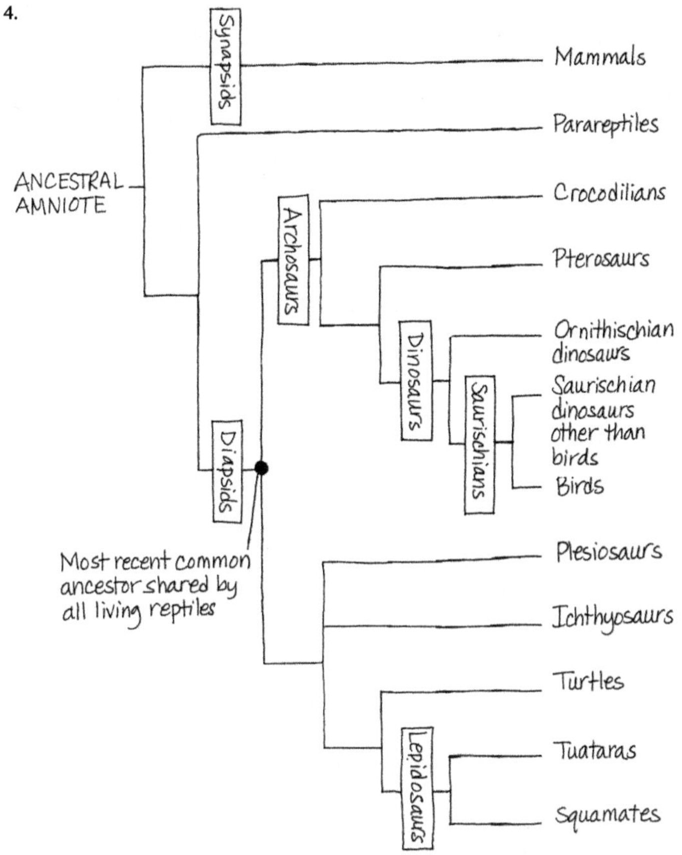

Under this convention, the reptiles would consist of all groups in Figure 34.25 except parareptiles and mammals.

Concept Check 34.7

1. Monotremes lay eggs. Marsupials give birth to very small live young that attach to a nipple in the mother's pouch, where they complete development. Eutherians give birth to more developed live young. **2.** Hands and feet adapted for grasping, flat nails, large brain, forward-looking eyes on a flat face, parental care, and movable big toe and thumb **3.** Mammals are endothermic, enabling them to live in a wide range of habitats. Milk provides young with a balanced set of nutrients, and hair and a layer of fat under the skin help mammals retain heat. Mammals have differentiated teeth, enabling them to eat many different kinds of food. Mammals also have relatively large brains, and many species are capable learners. Following the mass extinction at the end of the Cretaceous period, the absence of large terrestrial dinosaurs may have opened many new ecological niches to mammals, promoting their adaptive radiation. Continental drift also isolated many groups of mammals from one another, promoting the formation of many new species.

Concept Check 34.8

1. Hominins are a clade within the ape clade that includes humans and all species more closely related to humans than other apes. The derived characters of hominins include bipedal locomotion and relatively larger brains. **2.** In hominins, bipedal locomotion evolved long before large brain size. *Homo ergaster*, for example, was fully upright, bipedal, and as tall as modern humans, but its brain was significantly smaller than that of modern humans. **3.** Yes, both can be correct. *Homo sapiens* may have established populations outside of Africa as early as 115,000 years ago, as indicated by the fossil record. However, those populations may have left few or no descendants today. Instead, all living humans may have descended from Africans that spread from Africa roughly 50,000 years ago, as indicated by genetic data.

Summary of Key Concepts Questions

Concept 34.1 Lancelets are the most basal group of living chordates, and as adults they have key derived characters of chordates. This suggests that the chordate common ancestor may have resembled a lancelet in having an anterior end with a mouth along with the following four derived characters: a notochord; a dorsal, hollow nerve cord; pharyngeal slits or clefts; and a muscular, post-anal tail. **Concept 34.2** Craniates have a head and a more extensive muscular system than lancelets or tunicates. These features enable craniates to coordinate and perform more complex behaviors than found in lancelets and tunicates. Basal craniates (the hagfishes), for example, are scavengers that locate and feed on worms and dead or sick fishes. In contrast, lancelets and tunicates feed by filtering food items from the water. **Concept 34.3** Conodonts, among the earliest vertebrates in the fossil record, were very abundant for over 300 million years. While jawless, their well-developed teeth provide early signs of bone formation. Other species of jawless vertebrates developed armor on the outside of their bodies, which probably helped protect them from predators. Like lampreys, these species had paired fins for locomotion and an inner ear with semicircular canals that provided a sense of balance. There were many species of these armored jawless vertebrates, but they all became extinct by the close of the Devonian period, 359 million years ago. **Concept 34.4** The origin of jaws altered how fossil gnathostomes obtained food, which in turn had large effects on ecological interactions. Predators could use their jaws to grab prey or remove chunks of flesh, stimulating the evolution of increasingly sophisticated means of defense in prey species. Evidence for these changes can be found in the fossil record, which includes fossils of 10-m-long predators with remarkably powerful jaws, as well as lineages of well-defended prey species whose bodies were covered by armored plates. **Concept 34.5** Amphibians require water for reproduction; their bodies can lose water rapidly through their moist, highly permeable skin; and amphibian eggs do not have a shell and hence are vulnerable to desiccation. **Concept 34.6** Birds are descended from theropod dinosaurs, and dinosaurs are nested within the archosaur lineage, one of the two main reptile lineages. Thus, the other living archosaur reptiles, the crocodilians, are more closely related to birds than they are to non-archosaur reptiles such as lizards. As a result, birds are considered reptiles. (Note that if reptiles were defined as excluding birds, the reptiles would not form a clade; instead, the reptiles would be a paraphyletic group.) **Concept 34.7** Mammals are members of a group of amniotes called synapsids. Early (nonmammalian) synapsids laid eggs and had a sprawling gait. Fossil evidence shows that mammalian features arose gradually over a period of more than 100 million years. For example, the jaw was modified over time in nonmammalian synapsids, eventually coming to resemble that of a mammal. By 180 million years ago, the first mammals had appeared. There were many species of early mammals, but most of them were small, and they were not abundant or dominant members of their community. Mammals did not rise to ecological dominance until after the extinction of the dinosaurs. **Concept 34.8** The fossil record shows that from 4.5 to 2.5 million years ago, a wide range of hominin species walked upright but had relatively small brain sizes. About 2.5 million years ago, the first members of genus *Homo* emerged. These species used tools and had larger brains than those of earlier hominins. Fossil evidence indicates that multiple members of our genus were alive at any given point in time. Furthermore, until about 1.3 million years ago, these various *Homo* species also coexisted with members of earlier hominin lineages, such as *Paranthropus*. The different hominins alive at the same periods of time varied in body size, body shape, brain size, dental morphology, and the capacity for tool use. Ultimately, except for *Homo sapiens*, all of these species became extinct. Thus, human evolution is viewed not as an evolutionary path leading to *H. sapiens*, but rather as an evolutionary tree with many branches—the only surviving lineage of which is our own.

Test Your Understanding

1. e **2.** c **3.** a **4.** b **5.** c **6.** c **8.** (a) Because brain size tends to increase consistently in such lineages, we can conclude that natural selection favored the evolution of larger brains and hence that the benefits outweighed the costs. (b) As long as the benefits of brains that are large relative to body size are greater than the costs, large brains can evolve. Natural selection might favor the evolution of brains that are large relative to body size because such brains confer an advantage in obtaining mates and/or an advantage in survival.

(c)

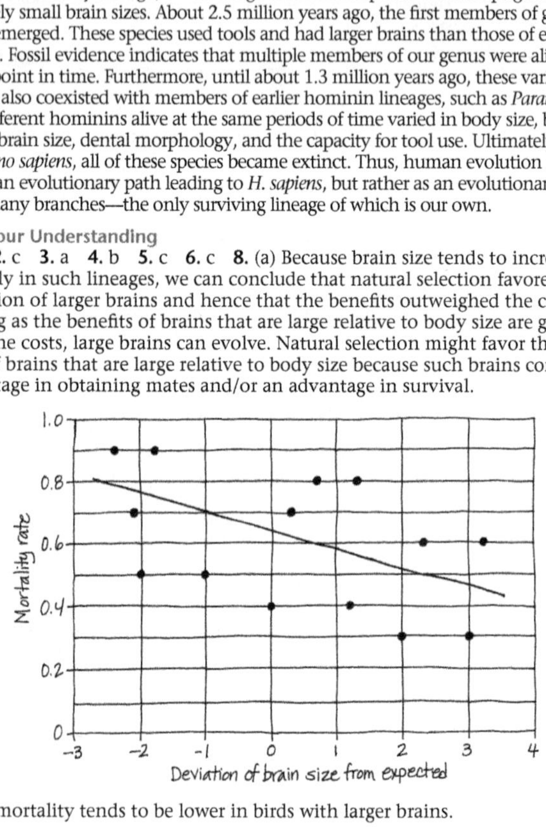

Adult mortality tends to be lower in birds with larger brains.

Chapter 35

Figure Questions

Figure 35.9 The finding might suggest that the tan-colored trichomes deter the beetles by some means other than physically obstructing the beetles. Perhaps they contain a chemical that is harmful or distasteful to the beetles. **Figure 35.17** Pith and cortex are defined, respectively, as ground tissue that is internal and ground tissue that is external to vascular tissue. Since vascular bundles of monocot stems are scattered throughout the ground tissue, there is no clear distinction between internal and external relative to the vascular tissue. **Figure 35.19** The vascular cambium produces growth that increases the diameter of a stem or root. The tissues that are exterior to the vascular cambium cannot keep pace with the growth because their cells no longer divide. As a result, these tissues rupture. **Figure 35.31** Every root epidermal cell would develop a root hair. **Figure 35.33** Another example of homeotic gene mutation is the *Drosophila* mutation depicted in Figure 18.20, in which a mutation in a *Hox* gene causes legs to form in place of antennae. **Figure 35.34** The flower would consist of nothing but carpels.

Concept Check 35.1

1. The vascular tissue system connects leaves and roots, allowing sugars to move from leaves to roots in the phloem and allowing water and minerals to move to the leaves in the xylem. **2.** (a) large axillary buds; (b) petioles; (c) a bulb, an underground shoot with a small stem and large storage leaves; (d) storage roots **3.** To get sufficient energy from photosynthesis, we would need lots of surface area exposed to the sun. This large surface-to-volume ratio, however, would create a new problem—evaporative water loss. We would have to be permanently connected to a water source—the soil, also our source of minerals. In short, we would probably look and behave very much like plants. **4.** As plant cells enlarge, they typically form a huge central vacuole that contains a dilute watery sap. Central vacuoles enable plant cells to become large with only a minimal investment of new cytoplasm. The orientation of the cellulose microfibrils in plant cell walls affects the growth pattern of cells.

Concept Check 35.2

1. Primary growth arises from apical meristems and involves production and elongation of organs. Secondary growth arises from lateral meristems and adds to the girth of roots and stems. **2.** Your dividing cells are normally limited in the types of cells they can form. In contrast, the products of cell division in a plant meristem can differentiate into all the types of plant cells. **3.** The largest, oldest leaves would be lowest on the shoot. Since they would probably be heavily shaded, they would not photosynthesize much regardless of their size. **4.** No, the carrot roots will probably be smaller at the end of the second year because the food stored in the root will be used to produce flowers, fruits, and seeds.

Concept Check 35.3

1. In roots, primary growth occurs in three successive stages, moving away from the tip of the root: the zones of cell division, elongation, and differentiation. In shoots, it occurs at the tip of apical buds, with leaf primordia arising along the sides of an apical meristem. Most growth in length occurs in older internodes below the shoot tip. **2.** No. Because vertically oriented leaves, such as maize, can capture light equally on both sides of the leaf, you would expect them to have mesophyll cells that are not differentiated into palisade and spongy layers. This is typically the case. Also, vertical leaves usually have stomata on both leaf surfaces. **3.** Root hairs are cellular extensions that increase the surface area of the root epidermis, thereby enhancing the absorption of minerals and water. Microvilli are extensions that increase the absorption of nutrients by increasing the surface area of the gut.

Concept Check 35.4

1. The sign will still be 2 m above the ground because this part of the tree is no longer growing in length (primary growth); it is now growing only in thickness (secondary growth). **2.** Stomata must be able to close because evaporation is much more intensive from leaves than from the trunks of woody trees as a result of the higher surface-to-volume ratio in leaves. **3.** Since there is little temperature variation in the tropics, the growth rings of a tree from the tropics would be difficult to discern unless the tree came from an area that had pronounced wet and dry seasons. **4.** Girdling removes an entire ring of secondary phloem (part of the bark), completely preventing transport of sugars and starches from the shoots to the roots.

Concept Check 35.5

1. Although all the living vegetative cells of a plant have the same genome, they differentiate to have different forms and functions because of differential gene expression. **2.** Plants show indeterminate growth; juvenile and mature phases are found on the same individual plant; cell differentiation in plants is more dependent on final position than on lineage. **3.** In theory, tepals could arise if *B* gene activity was present in all three of the outer whorls of the flower.

Summary of Key Concepts Questions

35.1 Here are a few examples: The cuticle of leaves and stems protects these structures from desiccation. Collenchyma and sclerenchyma cells have thick walls that provide support for plants. Strong, branching root systems help anchor the plant in the soil. **35.2** All plant organs and tissues are ultimately derived by meristematic activity. **35.3** Lateral roots emerge from the pericycle and destroy plant cells as they emerge. In stems, branches arise from axillary buds and do not destroy any cells. **35.4** With the evolution of secondary growth, plants were able to grow taller and shade competitors. **35.5** The orientation of cellulose microfibrils in the innermost layers of the cell wall causes this growth along one axis. Microtubules play a key role in regulating the plane of cell expansion. It is the orientation of microtubules in the cell's outermost cytoplasm that determines the orientation of cellulose microfibrils.

Test Your Understanding

1. d **2.** c **3.** c **4.** a **5.** b **6.** e **7.** d
8.

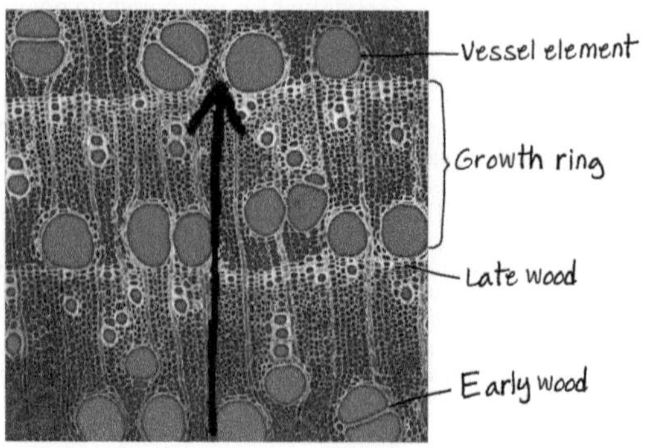

Chapter 36

Figure Questions

Figure 36.3 The leaves are being produced in a counterclockwise spiral. **Figure 36.4** A higher leaf area index will not necessarily increase photosynthesis because of upper leaves shading lower leaves. **Figure 36.7** A proton pump inhibitor would depolarize the membrane potential because fewer H^+ ions would be pumped out across the plasma membrane. The immediate effect of an inhibitor of the H^+/sucrose transporter would be to hyperpolarize the membrane potential because fewer H^+ ions would be leaking back into the cell through these cotransporters. An inhibitor of the H^+/NO_3^- cotransporter would have no effect on the membrane potential because the simultaneous cotransport of a positively charged ion and a negatively charged ion has no net effect on charge difference across the membrane. An inhibitor of the K^+ ion channels would decrease the membrane potential because additional positively charged ions would not be accumulating outside the cell. **Figure 36.10** The Casparian strip blocks water and minerals from moving between endodermal cells or moving around an endodermal cell via the cell's wall. Therefore, water and minerals must pass through an endodermal cell's plasma membrane. **Figure 36.19** Because the xylem is under negative pressure (tension), excising a stylet that had been inserted into a tracheid or vessel element would probably introduce air into the cell. No xylem sap would exude unless positive root pressure was predominant.

Concept Check 36.1

1. Vascular plants must transport minerals and water absorbed by the roots to all the other parts of the plant. They must also transport sugars from sites of production to sites of use. **2.** Many features of plant architecture affect self-shading, including leaf arrangement, leaf and stem orientation, and leaf area index. **3.** Increased stem elongation would raise the plant's upper leaves. Erect leaves and reduced lateral branching would make the plant less subject to shading by the encroaching neighbors. **4.** As discussed in Chapter 35 (p. 741), pruning shoot tips removes apical dominance, resulting in axillary buds growing into lateral shoots (branches). This branching produces a bushier plant with a higher leaf area index. **5.** Fungal hyphae are long, thin filaments that form a large interwoven network in the soil. Their high surface-to-volume ratio is an adaptation that enhances the absorption of materials from the soil.

Concept Check 36.2

1. The cell's ψ_P is 0.7 MPa. In a solution with a ψ of −0.4 MPa, the cell's ψ_P at equilibrium would be 0.3 MPa. **2.** The cells would still adjust to changes in their osmotic environment, but their responses would be slower. Although aquaporins do not affect the water potential gradient across membranes, they allow for more rapid osmotic adjustments. **3.** If tracheids and vessel elements were alive at maturity, their cytoplasm would impede water movement, preventing rapid long-distance transport. **4.** The protoplasts would burst. Because the cytoplasm has many dissolved solutes, water would enter the protoplast continuously without reaching equilibrium. (When present, the cell wall prevents rupturing by excessive expansion of the protoplast.)

Concept Check 36.3

1. Because water-conducting xylem cells are dead at maturity and form essentially hollow tubes, they offer little resistance to water flow, and their thick walls prevent the cells from collapsing from the negative pressure inside. **2.** At dawn, a drop is exuded because the xylem is under positive pressure due to root pressure. At noon, the xylem is under negative pressure tension when it is cut and the xylem sap is pulled away from the cut surface up into the stem. Root pressure cannot keep pace with the increased rate of transpiration at noon. **3.** The endodermis regulates the passage of water-soluble solutes by requiring all such molecules to cross a selectively permeable membrane. Presumably, the inhibitor never reaches the plant's photosynthetic cells. **4.** Perhaps greater root mass helps compensate for the lower water permeability of the plasma membranes. **5.** The Casparian strip and tight junctions both prevent movement of fluid between cells.

Concept Check 36.4

1. Stomatal opening at dawn is controlled mainly by light, CO_2 concentrations, and a circadian rhythm. Environmental stresses such as drought, high temperature, and wind can stimulate stomata to close during the day. Water deficiency can trigger release of the plant hormone abscisic acid, which signals guard cells to close stomata. **2.** The activation of the proton pump of stomatal cells would cause the guard cells to take up K^+. The increased turgor of the guard cells would lock the stomata open and lead to extreme evaporation from the leaf. **3.** After the flowers are cut, transpiration from any leaves and from the petals (which are modified leaves) will continue to draw water up the xylem. If cut flowers are transferred directly to a vase, air pockets in xylem vessels prevent delivery of water from the vase to the flowers. Cutting stems again underwater, a few centimeters from the original cut, will sever the xylem above the air pocket. The water droplets prevent another air pocket from forming while placing the flowers in a vase. **4.** Water molecules are in constant motion, traveling at different rates. The average speed of these particles depends on the water's temperature. If water molecules gain enough energy, the most energetic molecules near the liquid's surface will impart sufficient speed, and therefore sufficient kinetic energy, to cause water molecules to propel away from the liquid in the form of gaseous molecules or, more simply, as water vapor. As the particles with the highest kinetic energy levels evaporate, the average kinetic energy of the remaining liquid decreases. Because a liquid's temperature is directly related to the average kinetic energy of its molecules, the liquid cools as it evaporates.

Concept Check 36.5

1. In both cases, the long-distance transport is a bulk flow driven by a pressure difference at opposite ends of tubes. Pressure is generated at the source end of a sieve tube by the loading of sugar and resulting osmotic flow of water into the phloem, and this pressure *pushes* sap from the source end to the sink end of the tube. In contrast, transpiration generates a negative pressure potential (tension) as a force that *pulls* the ascent of xylem sap. **2.** The main sources are fully grown leaves (by photosynthesis) and fully developed storage organs (by breakdown of starch). Roots, buds, stems, expanding leaves, and fruits are powerful sinks because they are actively growing. A storage organ may be a sink in the summer when accumulating carbohydrates, but a source in the spring when breaking down starch into sugar for growing shoot tips. **3.** Positive pressure, whether it be in the xylem when root pressure predominates or in the sieve-tube elements of the phloem, requires active transport. Most long-distance transport in the xylem depends on bulk flow driven by negative pressure potential generated ultimately by the evaporation of water from the leaf and does not require living cells. **4.** The spiral slash prevents optimal bulk flow of the phloem sap to the root sinks. Therefore, more phloem sap can move from the source leaves to the fruit sinks, making them sweeter.

Concept Check 36.6

1. Plasmodesmata, unlike gap junctions, have the ability to pass RNA, proteins, and viruses from cell to cell. **2.** Long-distance signaling is critical for the integrated functioning of all large organisms, but the speed of such integration is much less critical to plants because their responses to the environment, unlike those of animals, do not typically involve rapid movements. **3.** Although this strategy would eliminate the systemic spread of viral infections, it would also severely impact the development of the plants.

Summary of Key Concepts Questions

36.1 Plants with tall shoots and elevated leaf canopies generally had an advantage over shorter competitors. A consequence of the selective pressure for tall shoots was the further separation of leaves from roots. This separation created problems for the transport of materials between root and shoot systems. Plants with xylem cells were more successful at supplying their shoot systems with soil resources (water and minerals). Similarly, those with phloem cells were more successful at supplying sugar sinks with carbohydrates. **36.2** Xylem sap is usually pulled up the plant by transpiration, much more often than it is pushed up the plant by root pressure. **36.3** Hydrogen bonds are necessary for the cohesion of water molecules to each other and for the adhesion of water to other materials, such as cell walls. Both adhesion and cohesion of water molecules are involved in the ascent of xylem sap under conditions of negative pressure. **36.4** Although stomata account for most of the water lost from plants, they are necessary for exchange of gases—for example, for the uptake of carbon dioxide needed for photosynthesis. **36.5** Although the movement of phloem sap depends on bulk flow, the pressure gradient that drives phloem transport depends on the osmotic uptake of water in response to the loading of sugars into sieve-tube elements at sugar sources. Phloem loading depends on H^+ cotransport processes that ultimately depend on H^+ gradients established by active H^+ pumping. **36.6** Voltage between cells, cytoplasmic pH, cytoplasmic calcium concentration, and viral movement proteins all affect symplastic communication, as do developmental changes in the number of plasmodesmata.

Test Your Understanding

1. c **2.** a **3.** b **4.** b **5.** c **6.** e **7.** c **8.** a **9.** d
10.

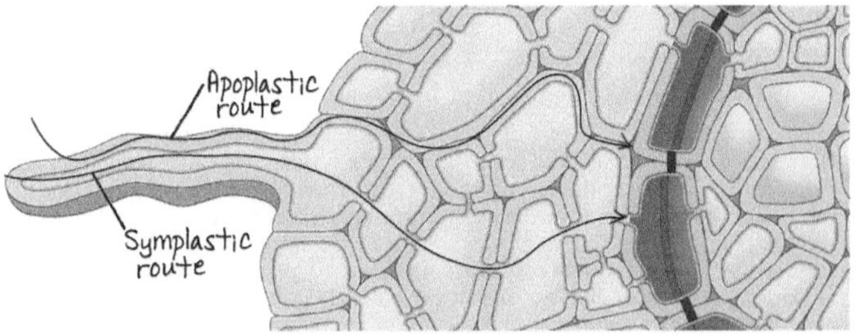

Chapter 37

Figure Questions

Figure 37.3 Anions. Because cations are bound to soil particles, they are less likely to be lost from the soil following heavy rains. **Table 37.1** Fluorine, selenium, and chromium. Plants may contain more than 50 elements, but only a few are essential for the plant to complete its life cycle. The others, including fluorine, selenium and chromium, are present but not essential for survival. **Figure 37.11** The legume plants benefit because the bacteria fix nitrogen that is absorbed by their roots. The bacteria benefit because they acquire photosynthetic products from the plants. **Figure 37.12** All three plant tissue systems are affected. Root hairs (dermal tissue) are modified to allow *Rhizobium* penetration. The cortex (ground tissue) and pericycle (vascular tissue) proliferate during nodule formation. The vascular tissue of the nodule connects to the vascular cylinder of the root to allow for efficient nutrient exchange. **Figure 37.14** If phosphate were the only limiting mineral, then native tree growth would be less severely impacted by the reduction in mycorrhizal associations caused by garlic mustard. Consequently, the competitive advantage of garlic mustard would be reduced by the addition of phosphate to the soil.

Concept Check 37.1

1. Overwatering deprives roots of oxygen. Overfertilizing is wasteful and can lead to soil salinization and water pollution. **2.** As lawn clippings decompose, they restore mineral nutrients to the soil. If they are removed, the minerals lost from the soil must be replaced by fertilization. **3.** Because of their small size and negative charge, clay particles would increase the number of binding sites for cations and water molecules and would therefore increase cation exchange and water retention in the soil. **4.** Due to hydrogen bonding between water molecules, water expands when it freezes, and this causes mechanical fracturing of rocks. Water also coheres to many objects, and this cohesion combined with other forces, such as gravity, can help tug particles from rock. Finally, water, because it is polar, is an excellent solvent that allows many substances, including ions, to become dissolved in solution.

Concept Check 37.2

1. Table 37.1 shows that CO_2 is the source of 90% of a plant's dry weight, supporting Hales's view that plants are nourished mostly by air. **2.** No, because even though macronutrients are required in greater amounts, all essential elements are necessary for the plant to complete its life cycle. **3.** No. The fact that the addition of an element results in an increase in the growth rate of a crop does not mean that the element is strictly required for the plant to complete its life cycle. **4.** Waterlogging displaces air from the soil, leading to low O_2 conditions. Such conditions promote the anaerobic process of alcoholic fermentation in plants, the end product of which is ethanol.

Concept Check 37.3

1. The rhizosphere is a narrow zone in the soil immediately adjacent to living roots. This zone is especially rich in both organic and inorganic nutrients and has a microbial population that is many times greater than the bulk of the soil. **2.** Soil bacteria and mycorrhizae enhance plant nutrition by making certain minerals more available to plants. For example, many types of soil bacteria are involved in the nitrogen cycle, and the hyphae of mycorrhizae provide a large surface area for the absorption of nutrients, particularly phosphate ions. **3.** Saturating rainfall may deplete the soil of oxygen. A lack of soil oxygen would inhibit nitrogen fixation by the peanut root nodules and decrease the nitrogen available to the plant. Alternatively, heavy rain may leach nitrate from the soil. A symptom of nitrogen deficiency is yellowing of older leaves.

Summary of Key Concepts Questions

37.1 The term *ecosystem* refes to the communities of organisms within a given area and their interactions with the physical environment around them. Soil is teeming with many communities of organisms, including bacteria, fungi, animals, and the root systems of plants. The vigor of these individual communities depends on nonliving factors in the soil environment, such as minerals, oxygen, and water, as well as on interactions, both positive and negative, between different communities of organisms. **37.2** No, plants can complete their life cycle when grown hydroponically, that is, in aerated salt solutions containing the proper ratios of all the minerals needed by plants. **37.3** No, some parasitic plants obtain their energy by siphoning off carbon nutrients from other organisms.

Test Your Understanding

1. b **2.** b **3.** a **4.** e **5.** b **6.** b **7.** d **8.** c **9.** d
10.

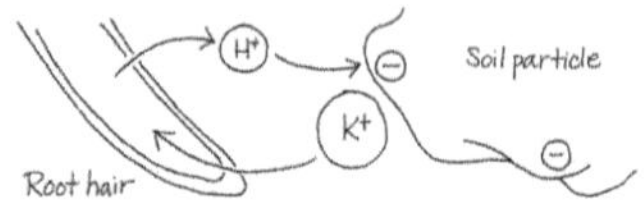

Chapter 38

Figure Questions

Figure 38.4 Having a specific pollinator is more efficient because less pollen gets delivered to flowers of the wrong species. However, it is also a risky strategy: If the pollinator population suffers to an unusual degree from predation, disease, or climate change, then the plant may not be able to produce seeds. **Figure 38.8** In addition to having a single cotyledon, monocots have leaves with parallel leaf venation, scattered vascular bundles in their stems, a fibrous root system, floral parts in threes or multiples of threes, and pollen grains with only one opening. In contrast, dicots have two cotyledons, netlike leaf venation, vascular bundles in a ring, taproots, floral parts in fours or fives or multiples thereof, and pollen grains with three openings. **Figure 38.9** Beans use a hypocotyl hook to push through the soil. The delicate leaves and shoot apical meristem are also protected by being sandwiched between two large cotyledons. The coleoptile of maize seedlings helps protect the emerging leaves. **Figure 38.17** The crown gall bacterium (*Agrobacterium tumefaciens*) normally causes cancer-like growths in susceptible plants. *Agrobacterium* inserts its own genes into plant cells by means of plasmids. These plasmids have been genetically engineered to retain their ability to insert genes into plant cells without causing cancerous growth.

Concept Check 38.1

1. In angiosperms, pollination is the transfer of pollen from an anther to a stigma. Fertilization is the fusion of the egg and sperm to form the zygote; it cannot occur until after the growth of the pollen tube from the pollen grain. **2.** Seed dormancy prevents the premature germination of seeds. A seed will germinate only when the environmental conditions are optimal for the survival of its embryo as a young seedling. **3.** Long styles help to weed out pollen grains that are genetically inferior and not capable of successfully growing long pollen tubes. **4.** No. The haploid (gametophyte) generation of plants is multicellular and arises from spores. The haploid phase of the animal life cycles is a single-celled gamete (egg or sperm) that arises directly from meiosis: There are no spores.

Concept Check 38.2

1. Asexually propagated crops lack genetic diversity. Genetically diverse populations are less likely to become extinct in the face of an epidemic because there is a greater likelihood that a few individuals in the population are resistant. **2.** In the short term, selfing may be advantageous in a population that is so dispersed and sparse that pollen delivery is unreliable. In the long term, however, selfing is an evolutionary dead end because it leads to a loss of genetic diversity that may preclude adaptive evolution. **3.** This might be possible, but satisfactory results would be very unlikely. Both tubers and fruits are tremendous energy sinks. Each plant has only a finite amount of energy to divide between sexual and asexual reproduction. Although a tomato-potato hybrid could, in theory, produce an offspring that makes fruits and tubers equally, these fruits and tubers would be of inferior quality or low yielding.

Concept Check 38.3

1. Traditional breeding and genetic engineering both involve artificial selection for desired traits. However, genetic engineering techniques facilitate faster gene transfer and are not limited to transferring genes between closely related varieties or species. **2.** GM crops may be more nutritious and less susceptible to insect damage or pathogens that invade insect-damaged plants. They also may not require as much chemical spraying. However, unknown risks may include adverse effects on human health and nontarget organisms and the possibility of transgene escape. **3.** *Bt* maize suffers less insect damage; therefore, *Bt* maize plants are less likely to be infected by fumonisin-producing fungi that infect plants through wounds. **4.** In such species, engineering the transgene into the chloroplast DNA would not prevent its escape in pollen; such a method requires that the chloroplast DNA be found only in the egg. An entirely different method of preventing transgene escape would therefore be needed, such as male sterility, apomixis, or self-pollinating closed flowers.

Summary of Key Concepts Questions

38.1 After pollination, a flower typically changes into a fruit. The petals, sepals, and stamens typically fall off the flower. The stigma of the pistil withers and the ovary begins to swell. The ovules (embryonic seeds) inside the ovary begin to mature. **38.2** Asexual reproduction can be advantageous in a stable environment because individual plants that are well suited to that environment pass on all their genes to offspring. Also, asexual reproduction generally results in offspring that are less fragile than the seedlings produced by sexual reproduction. However, sexual reproduction offers the advantage of dispersal of tough seeds. Moreover, sexual reproduction produces genetic variety, which may be advantageous in an unstable environment. The likelihood is better that at least one offspring of sexual reproduction will survive in a changed environment. **38.3** "Golden Rice" has been engineered to produce more vitamin A, thereby raising the nutritional value of rice. A protoxin gene from a soil bacterium has been engineered into *Bt* maize. This protoxin is lethal to invertebrates but harmless to vertebrates. *Bt* crops require less pesticide spraying and have lower levels of fungal infection. The nutritional value of cassava is being increased in many ways by genetic engineering. Enriched levels of protein, iron, and beta-carotene (a vitamin A precursor) have been achieved, and cyanide-producing chemicals have been almost eliminated from the roots.

Test Your Understanding

1. c **2.** a **3.** c **4.** e **5.** c **6.** d **7.** d **8.** c **9.** d
10.

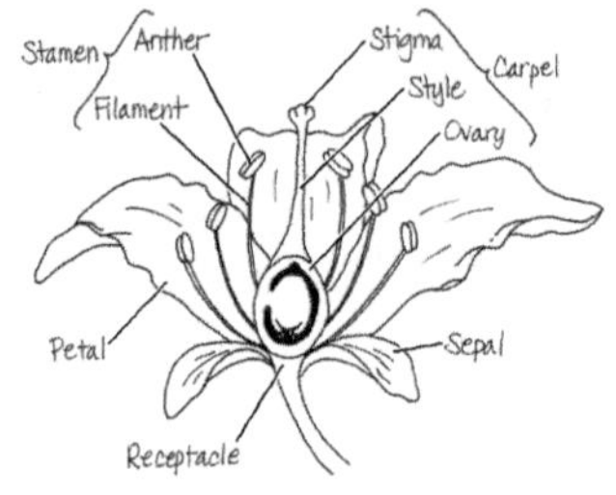

Chapter 39

Figure Questions

Figure 39.4 Panel B in Figure 11.18 shows a branching signal transduction pathway that resembles the branching phytochrome-dependent pathway involved in de-etiolation. **Figure 39.5** To determine which wavelengths of light are most effective in phototropism, you could use a glass prism to split white light into its component colors and see which colors cause the quickest bending (the answer is blue; see Figure 39.16). **Figure 39.6** More auxin would move down the side without the TIBA-containing agar bead, causing greater elongation on this side and, consequently, bending of the coleoptile toward the side with the bead. **Figure 39.7** No. Polar auxin transport depends on the distribution of auxin transport proteins at the basal ends of cells. **Figure 39.17** Yes. The white light, which contains red light, would stimulate seed germination in all treatments. **Figure 39.22** The short-day plant would not flower. The long-day plant would flower. **Figure 39.23** If this were true, florigen would be an inhibitor of flowering, not an inducer.

Concept Check 39.1

1. Dark-grown seedlings are etiolated: They have long stems, underdeveloped root systems, and unexpanded leaves, and their shoots lack chlorophyll. Etiolated growth is beneficial to seeds sprouting under the dark conditions they would encounter underground. By devoting more energy to stem elongation and less to leaf expansion and root growth, a plant increases the likelihood that the shoot will reach the sunlight before its stored foods run out. **2.** Cycloheximide should inhibit de-etiolation by preventing the synthesis of new proteins necessary for de-etiolation. **3.** No. Applying Viagra, like injecting cyclic GMP as described in the text, should cause only a partial de-etiolation response. Full de-etiolation would require activation of the calcium branch of the signal transduction pathway.

Concept Check 39.2

1. Because cytokinins delay leaf senescence and floral parts are modified leaves, cytokinins also delay the senescence of cut flowers. **2.** Fusicoccin's ability to cause an increase in plasma H^+ pump activity has an auxin-like effect and promotes stem cell elongation. **3.** The plant will exhibit a constitutive triple response. Because the kinase that normally prevents the triple response is dysfunctional, the plant will undergo the triple response regardless of whether ethylene is present or the ethylene receptor is functional. **4.** Since ethylene often stimulates its own synthesis, it is under positive-feedback regulation.

Concept Check 39.3

1. Not necessarily. Many environmental factors, such as temperature and light, change over a 24-hour period in the field. To determine whether the enzyme is under circadian control, a scientist would have to demonstrate that its activity oscillates even when environmental conditions are held constant. **2.** Flowering of the species may have been day-neutral or required multiple exposures to short nights. **3.** You might determine which wavelengths of light are most effective and plot an action spectrum. If the action spectrum indicates phytochrome, you could do further experiments to test for red/far-red photosensitivity. **4.** It is impossible to say. To establish that this species is a short-day plant, it would be necessary to establish the critical night length for flowering and that this species only flowers when the night is longer than the critical night length. **5.** According to the action spectrum of photosynthesis, red and blue light are the most effective in photosynthesis. Thus, it is not surprising that plants assess their light environment using blue- and red-light-absorbing photoreceptors.

Concept Check 39.4

1. A plant that overproduces ABA would undergo less evaporative cooling because its stomata would not open as widely. **2.** Plants close to the aisles may be more subject to mechanical stresses caused by passing workers and air currents. The plants nearer to the center of the bench may also be taller as a result of shading and less evaporative stress. **3.** No. Because root caps are involved in sensing gravity, roots that have their root caps removed are almost completely insensitive to gravity.

Concept Check 39.5

1. Some insects increase plants' productivity by eating harmful insects or aiding in pollination. **2.** Mechanical damage breaches a plant's first line of defense against infection, its protective dermal tissue. **3.** No. Pathogens that kill their hosts would soon run out of victims and might themselves go extinct. **4.** Perhaps the breeze dilutes the local concentration of a volatile defense compound that the plants produce.

Summary of Key Concepts Questions

39.1 Signal transduction pathways often activate protein kinases, enzymes that phosphorylate other proteins. Protein kinases can directly activate certain preexisting enzymes by phosphorylating them, or they can regulate gene transcription (and enzyme production) by phosphorylating specific transcription factors. **39.2** Yes, there is truth to the old adage that one bad apple spoils the whole bunch. Ethylene, a gaseous hormone that stimulates ripening, is produced by damaged, infected, or overripe fruits. Ethylene can diffuse to healthy fruit in the "bunch" and stimulate their rapid ripening. **39.3** Plant physiologists proposed the existence of a floral-promoting factor (florigen) based on the fact that a plant induced to flower could induce flowering in a second plant to which it was grafted, even though the second plant was not in an environment that would normally induce flowering in that species. **39.4** Plants subjected to drought stress are often more resistant to freezing stress because the two types of stress are quite similar. Freezing of water in the extracellular spaces causes free water concentrations outside the cell to decrease. This, in turn, causes free water to leave the cell by osmosis, leading to the dehydration of cytoplasm, much like what is seen in drought stress. **39.5** Chewing insects make plants more susceptible to pathogen invasion by disrupting the waxy cuticle of shoots, thereby creating an opening for infection. Moreover, substances released from damaged cells can serve as nutrients for the invading pathogens.

Test Your Understanding

1. e **2.** c **3.** d **4.** e **5.** b **6.** b **7.** c **8.** e

9.

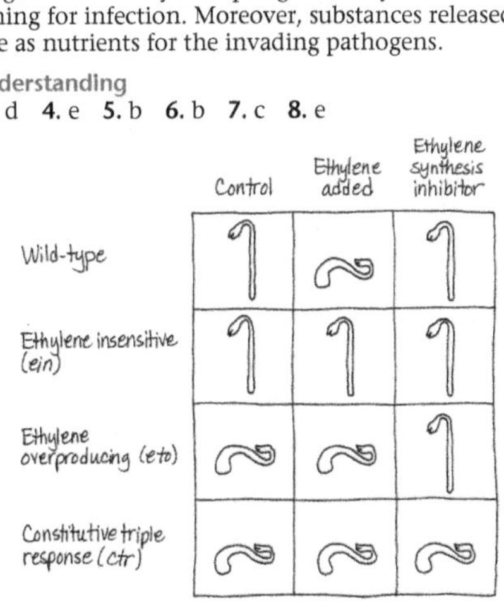

Chapter 40

Figure Questions

Figure 40.4 Such exchange surfaces are internal in the sense that they are inside the body. However, they are also continuous with openings on the external body surface that contact the environment. **Figure 40.8** The air conditioner would form a second control circuit, cooling the house when air temperature exceeded the set point. Such opposing, or antagonistic, pairs of control circuits increase the effectiveness of a homeostatic mechanism. **Figure 40.14** If a female Burmese python were not incubating eggs, her oxygen consumption would decrease with decreasing temperature, as for any other ectotherm. **Figure 40.17** The transport of nutrients across membranes and the synthesis of RNA and protein are coupled to ATP hydrolysis. These processes proceed spontaneously because there is an overall drop in free energy, with the excess energy given off as heat. Similarly, less than half of the free energy in glucose is captured in the coupled reactions of cellular respiration. The remainder of the energy is released as heat. **Figure 40.21** Nothing. Although genes that show a circadian variation in expression during euthermia exhibit constant RNA levels during hibernation, a gene that shows constant expression during hibernation might also show constant expression during euthermia.

Concept Check 40.1

1. All types of epithelia consist of cells that line a surface, are tightly packed, are situated on top of a basal lamina, and form an active and protective interface with the external environment. **2.** By flattening its ears along its body, the jackrabbit can reduce the exposed surface area of its body and hence the amount of heat lost. However, by placing its ears flat, the jackrabbit reduces its ability to detect potential predators. **3.** You need the nervous system to perceive the danger and provoke a split-second muscular response to keep from falling. The nervous system, however, does not make a direct connection with blood vessels or glucose-storing cells in the liver. Instead, the nervous system triggers the release of a hormone (called epinephrine, or adrenaline) by the endocrine system, bringing about a change in these tissues in just a few seconds.

Concept Check 40.2

1. In the enzyme-catalyzed biosynthetic process, the product of a pathway (in this case, isoleucine) inhibits the pathway that generated it. In thermoregulation, the product of the pathway (a change in temperature) decreases pathway activity by reducing the stimulus. **2.** You would want to put the thermostat close to where you would be spending time, where it would be protected from environmental perturbations, such as direct sunshine, and not right in the path of the output of the heating system. Similarly, the sensors for homeostasis located in the human brain are separated from environmental influences and can monitor conditions in a vital and sensitive tissue. **3.** In convergent evolution, the same biological trait arises independently in two or more species. Gene analysis can provide evidence for an independent origin. In particular, if the genes responsible for the trait in one species lack significant sequence similarity to the corresponding genes in another species, scientists conclude that there is a separate genetic basis for the trait in the two species and thus an independent origin. In the case of circadian rhythms, the clock genes in cyanobacteria appear unrelated to those in humans.

Concept Check 40.3

1. "Wind chill" involves heat loss through convection, as the moving air contributes to heat loss from the skin surface. **2.** The hummingbird, being a very small endotherm, has a very high metabolic rate. If by absorbing sunlight certain flowers warm their nectar, a hummingbird feeding on these flowers is saved the metabolic expense of warming the nectar to its body temperature. **3.** The ice water would cool tissues in your head, including blood that would then circulate throughout your body. This effect would accelerate the return to a normal body temperature. If, however, the ice water reached the eardrum and cooled the blood vessel that supplies the hypothalamus, the hypothalamic thermostat would respond by inhibiting sweating and constricting blood vessels in the skin, slowing cooling elsewhere in the body.

Concept Check 40.4

1. The mouse would consume oxygen at a higher rate because it is an endotherm, so its basal metabolic rate is higher than the ectothermic lizard's standard metabolic rate. **2.** The house cat; smaller animals have a higher metabolic rate per unit body mass and a greater demand for food per unit body mass. **3.** Although penguins do not grow as adults, they increase and decrease in size as they repeatedly form and use energy stores. A significant amount of energy might be stored in fat during part of the year but be used later in the year. Monitoring energy allocation only during the period when energy is stored in fat would lead to the erroneous conclusion that the penguin is growing.

Summary of Key Concepts Questions

40.1 Animals exchange materials with their environment across their body surface, and a spherical shape has the minimum surface area per unit volume. As body size increases, the ratio of surface area to body volume decreases. **40.2** No; even though an animal regulates some aspects of its internal environment, the internal environment fluctuates slightly around set points. Homeostasis is a dynamic state. Furthermore, there are sometimes programmed changes in set points, such as those resulting in radical increases in hormone levels at particular times in development. **40.3** Heat exchange across the skin is a primary mechanism for the regulation of body core temperature, with the result that the skin is cooler than the body core. **40.4** Because small animals have the highest ratio of BMR per unit mass, they have the greatest energetic savings per unit mass during hibernation. Consequently, the selective pressure favoring hibernation during evolution is especially strong for small animals.

Test Your Understanding

1. b **2.** c **3.** a **4.** b **5.** d **6.** c **7.** e

8.

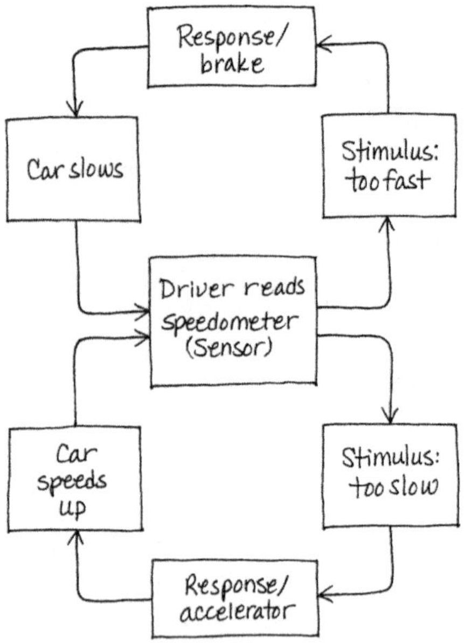

Chapter 41

Figure Questions

Figure 41.2 Just as penguin muscle protein provides amino acids for regrowth of large numbers of feathers, ovalbumin and casein provide amino acids for growth of a fertilized egg or nursing mammal. Thus, the common circumstance is a period of rapid developmental growth. **Figure 41.4** As in the described study, they needed a sample size large enough that they could expect a significant number of neural tube defects in the control group. The information needed to determine the appropriate sample size was the frequency of neural tube defects in first-time pregnancies in the general population. **Figure 41.12** Since enzymes are proteins, and proteins are hydrolyzed in the small intestine, the digestive enzymes in that compartment need to be resistant to enzymatic cleavage other than the cleavage required to activate them. **Figure 41.13** None. Since digestion is completed in the small intestine, tapeworms simply absorb predigested nutrients through their large body surface. **Figure 41.20** Both insulin and glucagon are involved in negative feedback circuits. **Figure 41.22** The wild-type mouse produces leptin after a meal. As the mouse depletes its fat stores, leptin production drops. The mouse eventually regains its appetite, eats another meal, and makes another burst of leptin. Thus, leptin levels would oscillate during the day. Because the *db* mouse cannot respond to leptin, its fat stores are constantly built up through excessive consumption. As a result, leptin is produced continuously and builds up to a high, steady concentration in the blood.

Concept Check 41.1

1. The only essential amino acids are those that an animal cannot synthesize from other molecules. **2.** Many vitamins serve as enzyme cofactors, which, like enzymes themselves, are unchanged by the chemical reactions in which they participate. Therefore, only very small amounts of vitamins are needed. **3.** To identify the essential nutrient missing from an animal's diet, a researcher could supplement the diet with individual nutrients and determine which nutrient eliminates the signs of malnutrition.

Concept Check 41.2

1. A gastrovascular cavity is a digestive pouch with a single opening that functions in both ingestion and elimination; an alimentary canal is a digestive tube with a separate mouth and anus at opposite ends. **2.** As long as nutrients are within the cavity of the alimentary canal, they are in a compartment that is continuous with the outside environment via the mouth and anus and have not yet crossed a membrane to enter the body. **3.** Just as food remains outside the body in a digestive tract, gasoline moves from the fuel tank to the engine, and waste products exit through the exhaust without ever entering the passenger compartment of the automobile. In addition, gasoline, like food, is broken down in a specialized compartment, so that the rest of the automobile (or body) is protected from disassembly. In both cases, high-energy fuels are consumed, complex molecules are broken down into simpler ones, and waste products are eliminated.

Concept Check 41.3

1. By peristalsis, which can squeeze food through the esophagus even without the help of gravity **2.** Because parietal cells in the stomach pump hydrogen ions to produce HCl, a proton pump inhibitor reduces the acidity of chyme and thus the irritation that occurs when chyme enters the esophagus. **3.** Proteins would be denatured and digested into peptides. Further digestion, to individual amino acids, would require enzymatic secretions found in the small intestine. No digestion of carbohydrates or lipids would occur.

Concept Check 41.4

1. The increased time for transit through the alimentary canal allows for more extensive processing, and the increased surface of the canal area provides greater opportunity for absorption. **2.** A mammal's digestive system provides mutualistic microbes with an environment that is protected against other microbes by saliva and gastric juice, that is held at a constant temperature conducive to enzyme action, and that provides a steady source of nutrients. **3.** For the yogurt treatment to be effective, the bacteria from yogurt would have to establish a mutualistic relationship with the small intestine, where disaccharides are broken down and sugars are absorbed. Conditions in the small intestine are likely to be very different from those in a yogurt culture. The bacteria might be killed before they reach the small intestine, or they might not be able to grow there in sufficient numbers to aid in digestion.

Concept Check 41.5

1. Over the long term, the body stores excess calories in fat, whether those calories come from fat, carbohydrate, or protein in food. **2.** Both hormones have appetite-suppressing effects on the brain's satiety center. During the course of a day, PYY, secreted by the intestine, suppresses appetite after meals. Over the longer term, leptin, produced by adipose tissue, normally reduces appetite as fat storage increases. **3.** In normal individuals, leptin levels decline during fasting. Individuals in the group with low levels of leptin are likely to be defective in leptin production, so leptin levels would remain low regardless of food intake. Individuals in the group with high leptin levels are likely to be defective in responding to leptin, but they still should shut off leptin production as fat stores are used up.

Summary of Key Concepts Questions

41.1 Since collagen is found in all mammals, a likely explanation is that mammals other than primates and guinea pigs can synthesize vitamin C from other organic molecules. **41.2** A liquid diet containing glucose, amino acids, and other building blocks could be ingested and absorbed without the need for mechanical or chemical digestion. **41.3** The small intestine has a much larger surface area than the stomach. **41.4** The assortment of teeth in our mouth and the short length of our cecum suggest that our ancestors' digestive systems were not specialized for digesting plant material. **41.5** When mealtime arrives, nervous inputs from the brain signal the stomach to prepare to digest food through secretions and churning.

Test Your Understanding

1. a **2.** c **3.** c **4.** d **5.** d **6.** b
7.

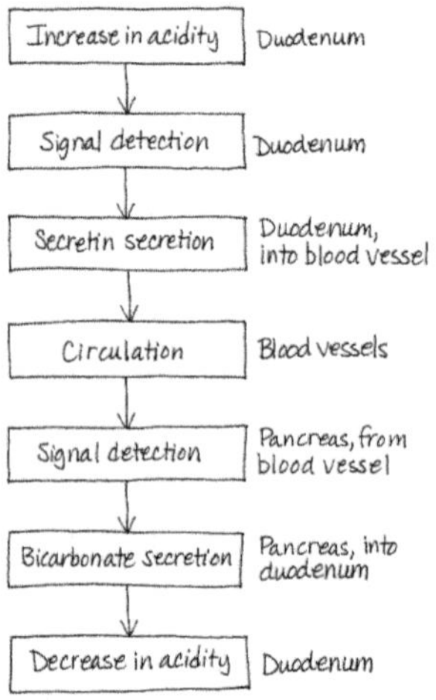

Chapter 42

Figure Questions

Figure 42.2 Although gas exchange might be improved by a steady, one-way flow of fluid, there would likely be inadequate time for food to be digested and nutrients absorbed if fluid flowed through the cavity in this manner. **Figure 42.9** Each feature of the ECG recording, such as the sharp upward spike, occurs once per cardiac cycle. Using the *x*-axis to measure the time in seconds between successive spikes and dividing that number into 60 would yield the heart rate as the number of cycles per minute. **Figure 42.21** The mutations studied by Dr. Hobbs's team inactivate the enzyme. Carriers for these mutations should have roughly half the normal level of PCSK9 activity. The mutations studied by the French researchers have the opposite effect on LDL levels as the inactivating mutations. It is therefore likely that individuals carrying these mutations would have increased PCSK9 activity. **Figure 42.22** The three main lineages are Deuterostomia, Lophotrochozoa, and Ecdysozoa. All three are represented by the animals shown in Figure 42.22: Polychaetes (phylum Annelida) are lophotrochozoans, crayfish (phylum Arthropoda) are ecdysozoans, and sea stars (phylum Echinodermata) are deuterostomes. **Figure 42.26** The reduction in surface tension results from the presence of surfactant. Therefore, for all the infants that had died of RDS, you would expect the amount of surfactant to be near zero. For infants that had died of other causes, you would expect the amount of surfactant to be near zero for weights less than 1,200 g but much greater than zero for weights above 1,200 g. **Figure 42.28** Since exhalation is largely passive, the recoil of the elastic fibers in alveoli helps force air out of the lungs. When alveoli lose their elasticity, as occurs in the disease emphysema, less air is exhaled. Because more air is left in the lungs, less fresh air can be inhaled. With a smaller volume of air exchanged, there is a decrease in the partial pressure gradient that drives gas exchange. **Figure 42.29** Breathing at a rate greater than that needed to meet metabolic demand (hyperventilation) would lower blood CO_2 levels. Sensors in major blood vessels and the medulla would signal the breathing control centers to decrease the rate of contraction of the diaphragm and rib muscles, decreasing the breathing rate and restoring normal CO_2 levels in the blood and other tissues. **Figure 42.30** The resulting increase in tidal volume would enhance ventilation within the lungs, increasing P_{O_2} and decreasing P_{CO_2} in the alveoli. **Figure 42.32** Some CO_2 is dissolved in plasma, some is bound to hemoglobin, and some is converted to bicarbonate ion (HCO_3^-), which is dissolved in plasma.

Concept Check 42.1

1. In both an open circulatory system and a fountain, fluid is pumped through a tube and then returns to the pump after collecting in a pool. **2.** The ability to shut off blood supply to the lungs when the animal is submerged **3.** The O_2 content would be abnormally low because some oxygen-depleted blood returned to the right atrium from the systemic circuit would mix with the oxygen-rich blood in the left atrium.

Concept Check 42.2

1. The pulmonary veins carry blood that has just passed through capillary beds in the lungs, where it accumulated O_2. The venae cavae carry blood that has just passed through capillary beds in the rest of the body, where it lost O_2 to the tissues. **2.** The delay allows the atria to empty completely, filling ventricles fully before they contract. **3.** The heart, like any other muscle, becomes stronger through regular exercise. You would expect a stronger heart to have a greater stroke volume, which would allow for the decrease in heart rate.

Concept Check 42.3

1. The large total cross-sectional area of the capillaries **2.** An increase in blood pressure and cardiac output combined with the diversion of more blood to the skeletal muscles would increase the capacity for action by increasing the rate of blood circulation and delivering more O_2 and nutrients to the skeletal muscles. **3.** Additional hearts could be used to improve blood return from the legs. However, it might be difficult to coordinate the activity of multiple hearts and to maintain adequate blood flow to hearts far from the gas exchange organs.

Concept Check 42.4

1. An increase in the number of white blood cells (leukocytes) may indicate that the person is combating an infection. **2.** Clotting factors do not initiate clotting but are essential steps in the clotting process. Also, the clots that form a thrombus typically result from an inflammatory response to an atherosclerotic plaque, not from clotting at a wound site. **3.** The chest pain results from inadequate blood flow in coronary arteries. Vasodilation promoted by nitric oxide from nitroglycerin increases blood flow, providing the heart muscle with additional oxygen and thus relieving the pain. **4.** When a mutant allele is codominant with the wild-type allele, the phenotype of heterozygotes is intermediate between that of wild-type and mutant homozygotes. Therefore, in the presence of wild-type Hb, the aggregation of Hb^S that causes sickling must be significantly reduced. Based on this fact, some therapies for sickle-cell disease are aimed at boosting adult expression of another hemoglobin gene in the body, such as that normally expressed only in the fetus. **5.** Embryonic stem cells are pluripotent rather than multipotent, meaning that they can give rise to many rather than a few different cell types.

Concept Check 42.5

1. Their interior position helps them stay moist. If the respiratory surfaces of lungs extended out into the terrestrial environment, they would quickly dry out, and diffusion of O_2 and CO_2 across these surfaces would stop. **2.** Earthworms need to keep their skin moist for gas exchange, but they need air outside this moist layer. If they stay in their waterlogged tunnels after a heavy rain, they will suffocate because they cannot get as much O_2 from water as from air. **3.** In the extremities of some vertebrates, blood flows in opposite directions in neighboring veins and arteries; this countercurrent arrangement maximizes the recapture of heat from blood leaving the body core in arteries, which is important for thermoregulation in cold environments. Similarly, in the gills of fish, water passes over the gills in the direction opposite to that of blood flowing through the gill capillaries, maximizing the extraction of oxygen from the water along the length of the exchange surface.

Concept Check 42.6

1. An increase in blood CO_2 concentration causes an increase in the rate of CO_2 diffusion into the cerebrospinal fluid, where the CO_2 combines with water to form carbonic acid. Dissociation of carbonic acid releases hydrogen ions, decreasing the pH of the cerebrospinal fluid. **2.** Increased heart rate increases the rate at which CO_2-rich blood is delivered to the lungs, where CO_2 is removed. **3.** A hole would allow air to enter the space between the inner and outer layers of the double membrane, resulting in a condition called a pneumothorax. The two layers would no longer stick together, and the lung on the side with the hole would collapse and cease functioning.

Concept Check 42.7

1. Differences in partial pressure; gases diffuse from a region of higher partial pressure to a region of lower partial pressure. **2.** The Bohr shift causes hemoglobin to release more O_2 at a lower pH, such as found in the vicinity of tissues with high rates of cellular respiration and CO_2 release. **3.** The doctor is assuming that the rapid breathing is the body's response to low blood pH. Metabolic acidosis, the lowering of blood pH, can have many causes, including complications of certain types of diabetes, shock (extremely low blood pressure), and poisoning.

Summary of Key Concepts Questions

42.1 In a closed circulatory system, an ATP-driven muscular pump generally moves fluids in one direction on a scale of millimeters to meters. Exchange between cells and their environment relies on diffusion, which involves random movements of molecules. Concentration gradients of molecules across exchange surfaces can drive rapid net diffusion on a scale of 1 mm or less. **42.2** Replacement of a defective valve should increase stroke volume. A lower heart rate would therefore be sufficient to maintain the same cardiac output. **42.3** Blood pressure in the arm would fall by 25–30 mm Hg, the same difference as is normally seen between your heart and your brain. **42.4.** One microliter of blood contains about 5 million erythrocytes and 5,000 leukocytes, so leukocytes make up only about 0.1% of the cells in the absence of infection. **42.5.** Because CO_2 is such a small fraction of atmospheric gas (0.29 mm Hg/760 mm Hg, or less than 0.04%), the partial pressure gradient of CO_2 between the respiratory surface and the environment always strongly favors the release of CO_2 to the atmosphere. **42.6.** Because the lungs do not empty completely with each breath, incoming and outgoing air mix, so not all of the tidal volume represents fresh air. **42.7.** An enzyme speeds up a reaction without changing the equilibrium and without being consumed. Similarly, a respiratory pigment speeds up the movement of gases in the body without changing the equilibrium and without being consumed.

Test Your Understanding

1. c **2.** b **3.** d **4.** c **5.** d **6.** a **7.** a **8.** a
9.

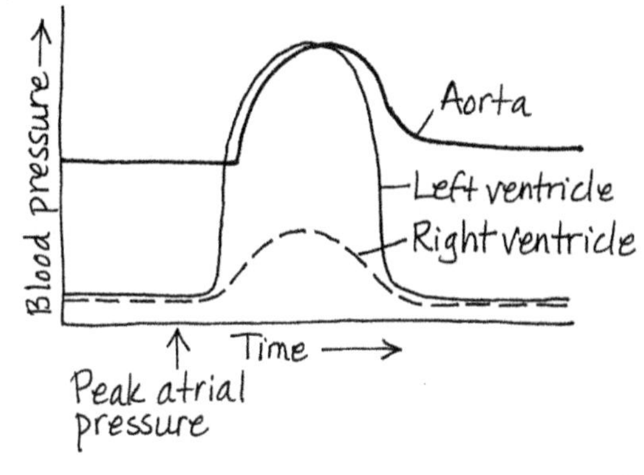

Chapter 43

Figure Questions

Figure 43.5 The seemingly inactive peptides might offer protection against pathogens other than those studied. Also, some antimicrobial peptides might work best in combination. **Figure 43.6** Cell-surface TLRs recognize pathogens identifiable by surface molecules, whereas TLRs in vesicles recognize pathogens identifiable by internal molecules after the pathogens are broken down. **Figure 43.10** Part of the enzyme or antigen receptor provides a structural "backbone" that maintains overall shape, while interaction occurs at a surface with a close fit to the substrate or antigen. The combined effect of multiple noncovalent interactions at the active site or binding site is a high-affinity interaction of tremendous specificity. **Figure 43.13** After gene rearrangement, a lymphocyte and its daughter cells make a single version of the antigen receptor. In contrast, alternative splicing is not heritable and can give rise to diverse gene products in a single cell. **Figure 43.18** These receptors enable memory cells to present antigen on their cell surface to a helper T cell. This presentation of antigen is required to activate memory cells in a secondary immune response. **Figure 43.20** Primary response: arrows extending from Antigen (1st exposure), Antigen-presenting cell, Helper T cell, B cell, Plasma cells, Cytotoxic T cell, and Active cytotoxic T cells; secondary response: arrows extending from Antigen (2nd exposure), Memory helper T cells, Memory B cells, and Memory cytotoxic T cells. **Figure 43.26** The loss of growth control that characterizes cancer involves many changes in gene regulation. HPV and other viruses can bring about some of these changes, but other mutations must occur in an infected cell to transform the cell to a cancerous state.

Concept Check 43.1

1. Because pus contains white blood cells, fluid, and cell debris, it indicates an active and at least partially successful inflammatory response against invading microbes. **2.** Whereas the ligand for the TLR receptor is a foreign molecule, the ligand for many signal transduction pathways is a molecule produced by the animal itself. **3.** Bacteria with a human host would be likely to grow optimally at normal body temperature or, if fever were often induced, at a temperature a few degrees higher.

Concept Check 43.2

1. See Figure 43.9. The transmembrane regions lie within the C regions, which also form the disulfide bridges. In contrast, the antigen-binding sites are in the V regions. **2.** Generating memory cells ensures both that a receptor specific for a particular epitope will be present and that there will be more lymphocytes with this specificity than in a host that had never encountered the antigen. **3.** If each B cell produced two different light and heavy chains for its antigen receptor, different combinations would make four different receptors. If any one was self-reactive, the lymphocyte would be eliminated in the generation of self-tolerance. For this reason, many more B cells would be eliminated, and those that could respond to a foreign antigen would be less effective at doing so due to the variety of receptors (and antibodies) they express.

Concept Check 43.3

1. A child lacking a thymus would have no functional T cells. Without helper T cells to help activate B cells, the child would be unable to produce antibodies against extracellular bacteria. Furthermore, without cytotoxic T cells or helper T cells, the child's immune system would be unable to kill virus-infected cells. **2.** Since the antigen-binding site is intact, the antibody fragments could neutralize viruses and opsonize bacteria. **3.** If the handler developed immunity to proteins in the antivenin, another injection could provoke a severe immune response. The handler's immune system might also now produce antibodies that could neutralize the venom.

Concept Check 43.4

1. Myasthenia gravis is considered an autoimmune disease because the immune system produces antibodies against self molecules (certain receptors on muscle cells). **2.** A person with a cold is likely to produce oral and nasal secretions that facilitate viral transfer. In addition, since sickness can cause incapacitation or death, a virus that is programmed to exit the host when there is a physiological stress has the opportunity to find a new host at a time when the current host may cease to function. **3.** A person with a macrophage deficiency would have frequent infections. The causes would be poor innate responses, due to diminished phagocytosis and inflammation, and poor adaptive responses, due to the lack of macrophages to present antigens to helper T cells.

Summary of Key Concepts Questions

43.1 Lysozyme in saliva destroys bacterial cell walls; the viscosity of mucus helps trap bacteria; acidic pH in the stomach kills many bacteria; and the tight packing of cells lining the gut provides a physical barrier to infection. **43.2** Sufficient numbers of cells to mediate an innate immune response are always present, whereas an adaptive response requires selection and proliferation of an initially very small cell population specific for the infecting pathogen. **43.3** No. Immunological memory after a natural infection and after vaccination are very similar. There may be minor differences in the particular antigens that can be recognized in a subsequent infection. **43.4** No. AIDS refers to a loss of immune function that can occur over time in an individual infected with HIV, not to the viral infection itself. For individuals infected with HIV, certain multidrug combinations ("cocktails") or rare genetic variations usually prevent progression to AIDS.

Test Your Understanding

1. b **2.** c **3.** c **4.** d **5.** b **6.** b **7.** c
8. One possible answer:

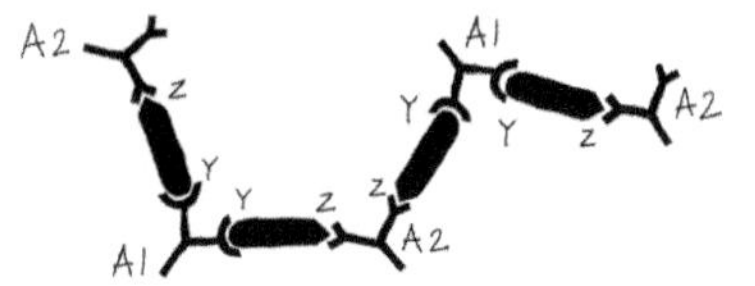

Chapter 44

Figure Questions

Figure 44.2 Aquaporins, which act as water channels **Figure 44.15** You would expect to find these cells lining tubules where they pass through the renal medulla. Because the extracellular fluid of the renal medulla has a very high osmolarity, production of solutes by tubule cells in this region keeps intracellular osmolarity high, with the result that these cells maintain normal volume. **Figure 44.16** Furosemide increases urine volume. The absence of ion transport in the ascending limb leaves the filtrate too concentrated for substantial volume reduction in the distal tubule and collecting duct. **Figure 44.21** The ADH levels would likely be elevated in both sets of patients with mutations because either defect prevents the recapture of water that restores blood osmolarity to normal levels.

Concept Check 44.1

1. Because the salt is moved against its concentration gradient, from low concentration (fresh water) to high concentration (blood) **2.** A freshwater osmoconformer would have body fluids too dilute to carry out life's processes. **3.** Without a layer of insulating fur, the camel must use the cooling effect of evaporative water loss to maintain body temperature, thus linking thermoregulation and osmoregulation.

Concept Check 44.2

1. Because uric acid is largely insoluble in water, it can be excreted as a semisolid paste, thereby reducing an animal's water loss. **2.** Humans produce uric acid from purine breakdown, and reducing purines in the diet often lessens the severity of gout. Birds, however, produce uric acid as a waste product of general nitrogen metabolism. They would therefore need a diet low in all nitrogen-containing compounds, not just purines.

Concept Check 44.3

1. In flatworms, ciliated cells draw interstitial fluids containing waste products into protonephridia. In earthworms, waste products pass from interstitial fluids into the coelom. From there the cilia move the wastes into metanephridia via a funnel surrounding an internal opening to the metanephridia. In insects, the Malpighian tubules pump fluids from the hemolymph, which receives waste products during exchange with interstitial fluids in the course of circulation. **2.** Filtration produces a fluid for exchange processes that is free of cells and large molecules, which are of benefit to the animal and could not readily be reabsorbed. **3.** The presence of Na^+ and other ions (electrolytes) in the dialysate would limit the extent to which they would be removed from the filtrate during dialysis. Adjusting the electrolytes in the starting dialysate can thus lead to the restoration of proper electrolyte concentrations in the plasma. Similarly, the absence of urea and other waste products in the starting dialysate results in their efficient removal from the filtrate.

Concept Check 44.4

1. The numerous nephrons and well-developed glomeruli of freshwater fishes produce urine at a high rate, while the small numbers of nephrons and smaller glomeruli of marine fishes produce urine at a low rate. **2.** The kidney medulla would absorb less water; thus, the drug would increase the amount of water lost in the urine. **3.** A decline in blood pressure in the afferent arteriole would reduce the rate of filtration by moving less material through the vessels.

Concept Check 44.5

1. Alcohol inhibits the release of ADH, causing an increase in urinary water loss and increasing the chance of dehydration. **2.** The consumption of a large amount of water in a very short period of time, coupled with an absence of solute intake, can reduce sodium levels in the blood below tolerable levels. This condition, called hyponatremia, leads to disorientation and, sometimes, respiratory distress. It has occurred in some marathon runners who drink water rather than sports drinks. (It has also caused the death of a fraternity pledge as a consequence of a water hazing ritual and the death of a contestant in a water-drinking competition.) **3.** High blood pressure **4.** Each molecule of renin or ACE activates multiple molecules of the next protein in the pathway. The same is true for the protein kinases. The proteases differ from the protein kinases in at least two ways. First, their action is irreversible. Second, they do not require activation by another enzyme molecule.

Summary of Key Concepts Questions

44.1 Water moves into a cell by osmosis when the fluid outside the cells is hypoosmotic (has a lower solute concentration than the cytosol).
44.2

Waste Attribute	Ammonia	Urea	Uric Acid
Toxicity	High	Very low	Low
Energy content	Low	Moderate	High
Water loss in excretion	High	Moderate	Low

44.3 Filtration retains large molecules that would be difficult to transport across membranes. **44.4** Both types of nephrons have proximal tubules that can reabsorb nutrients, but only juxtamedullary nephrons have loops of Henle that extend deep into the renal medulla. Thus, only kidneys containing juxtamedullary nephrons can produce urine that is more concentrated than the blood. **44.5** Patients who don't produce ADH have symptoms relieved by treatment with the hormone, but many patients with diabetes insipidus lack functional receptors for ADH.

Test Your Understanding

1. d **2.** a **3.** c **4.** e **5.** d **6.** b
7.

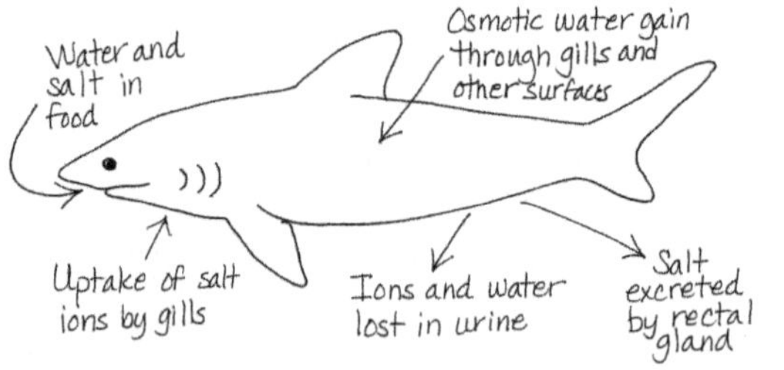

Chapter 45

Figure Questions

Figure 45.5 Synthesizing epinephrine requires breaking the bond between the carboxyl group (–COOH) and the α-carbon in tyrosine. **Figure 45.6** The hormone is water-soluble and has a cell-surface receptor. Such receptors, unlike those for lipid-soluble hormones, can cause observable changes in cells without hormone-dependent gene transcription. **Figure 45.17** Both diagnoses could be correct. In one case, the thyroid gland may produce excess thyroid hormone despite normal hormonal input from the hypothalamus and anterior pituitary. In the other, abnormally elevated hormonal input may be the cause of the overactive thyroid gland. **Figure 45.22** The result of the surgery would have been the same for both sexes—an absence of sexual differentiation in the genitalia.

Concept Check 45.1

1. Water-soluble hormones, which cannot penetrate the plasma membrane, bind to cell-surface receptors. This interaction triggers an intracellular signal transduction pathway that ultimately alters the activity of a preexisting protein in the cytoplasm and/or changes transcription of specific genes in the nucleus. Steroid hormones are lipid-soluble and can cross the plasma membrane into the cell interior, where they bind to receptors located in the cytosol or nucleus. The hormone-receptor complex then functions directly as a transcription factor that changes transcription of specific genes. **2.** Prostaglandins in semen that induce contractions in the uterus are acting as signaling molecules that are transferred from one individual to another of the same species (like pheromones), thus aiding in reproduction. **3.** Epinephrine in animals and auxin in plants act as hormones that trigger specific cellular responses that vary among different tissues of the organism.

Concept Check 45.2

1. In a healthy person, insulin released in response to the initial rise in blood glucose stimulates uptake of glucose by body cells. In a person with diabetes, however, inadequate production of insulin or nonresponsiveness of target cells decreases the body's ability to clear excess glucose from the blood. The initial increase in blood glucose is therefore greater in a person with diabetes, and it remains high for a prolonged period. **2.** If the function of the pathway is to provide a transient response, a short-lived stimulus would be less dependent on negative feedback. **3.** Since patients with type 2 diabetes produce insulin but fail to maintain normal glucose levels, you might predict that there could be mutations in the genes for the insulin receptor or the signal transduction pathway it activates. Such mutations have in fact been found in type 2 patients.

Concept Check 45.3

1. The posterior pituitary, an extension of the hypothalamus that contains the axons of neurosecretory cells, is the storage and release site for two neurohormones, oxytocin and antidiuretic hormone (ADH). The anterior pituitary contains endocrine cells that make at least six different hormones. Secretion of anterior pituitary hormones is controlled by hypothalamic hormones that travel via portal vessels to the anterior pituitary. **2.** Because oxytocin responses involve positive feedback (via nerve cells) from suckling, the pathway does not require a sustained hormonal input stimulus. **3.** The hypothalamus and pituitary glands function in many different endocrine pathways. Many defects in these glands, such as those affecting growth or organization, would therefore disrupt many hormone pathways. Only a very specific defect, such as a mutation affecting a particular hormone receptor, would alter just one endocrine pathway. The situation is quite different for the final gland in a pathway, such as the thyroid gland. In this case, a wide range of defects that disrupt gland function would disrupt only the one pathway or small set of pathways in which that gland functions.

Concept Check 45.4

1. The adrenal medulla is derived from neural tissue during development. Reflecting this origin, it is an endocrine organ that produces two molecules—epinephrine and norepinephrine—that act both as hormones and as neurotransmitters. **2.** The levels of these hormones in the blood would become very high. This would be due to the diminished negative feedback on the hypothalamic neurons that secrete the releasing hormone that stimulates the secretion of ACTH by the anterior pituitary. **3.** By applying glucocorticoids to tissue by local injection, you exploit their anti-inflammatory activity. Local injection avoids the effects on glucose metabolism that would occur if glucocorticoids were taken orally and transported throughout the body in the bloodstream.

Summary of Key Concepts Questions

45.1 Because receptors for water-soluble hormones are located on the cell surface, facing the extracellular space, injecting the hormone into the cytoplasm would not trigger a response. **45.2** It would lessen the symptoms. Glucagon acts antagonistically with insulin, so lowering the effects of glucagon would be similar to increasing the levels or activity of insulin. **45.3** The pancreas, parathyroid glands, and pineal gland **45.4** Both the pituitary and the adrenal glands are formed by fusion of neural and nonneural tissue. ADH is secreted by the neurosecretory portion of the pituitary gland, and epinephrine is secreted by the neurosecretory portion of the adrenal gland.

Test Your Understanding

1. c **2.** b **3.** d **4.** c **5.** c **6.** b **7.** a **8.** a

9.

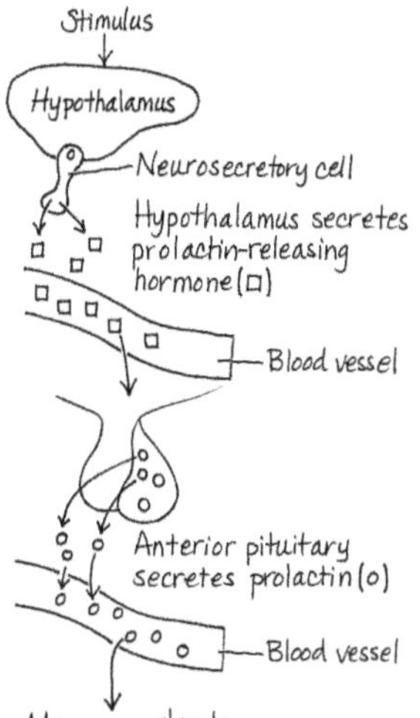

Chapter 46

Figure Questions

Figure 46.9 According to the graph, about one-third of the females rid themselves of all sperm from the first mating. Thus, two-thirds retain some sperm from the first mating. We would therefore predict that two-thirds of the females would have some offspring exhibiting the small-eye phenotype of the dominant mutation carried by the males with which the females mated first. **Figure 46.12** The analysis would be informative because the polar bodies contain all of the maternal chromosomes that don't end up in the mature egg. For example, finding two copies of the disease gene in the polar bodies would indicate its absence in the egg. This method of genetic testing is sometimes carried out when oocytes collected from a female are fertilized with sperm in a laboratory dish. **Figure 46.16** Testosterone can pass from fetal blood to maternal blood via the placental circulation, temporarily upsetting the hormonal balance in the mother. **Figure 46.18** Oxytocin would most likely induce labor, starting a positive-feedback loop that would direct labor to completion. Synthetic oxytocin is in fact frequently used to induce labor when prolonged pregnancy might endanger the mother or fetus.

Concept Check 46.1

1. The offspring of sexual reproduction are more genetically diverse. However, asexual reproduction can produce more offspring over multiple generations. **2.** Unlike other forms of asexual reproduction, parthenogenesis involves gamete production. By controlling whether or not haploid eggs are fertilized, species such as honeybees can readily switch between asexual and sexual reproduction. **3.** No. Owing to random assortment of chromosomes during meiosis, the offspring may receive the same copy or different copies of a particular parental chromosome from the sperm and the egg. Furthermore, genetic recombination during meiosis will result in reassortment of genes between pairs of parental chromosomes. **4.** Both fragmentation and budding in animals have direct counterparts in the asexual reproduction of plants.

Concept Check 46.2

1. Internal fertilization allows the sperm to reach the egg without either gamete drying out. **2.** (a) Animals with external fertilization tend to release many gametes at once, resulting in the production of enormous numbers of zygotes. This increases the chances that some will survive to adulthood. (b) Animals with internal fertilization produce fewer offspring but generally exhibit greater care of the embryos and the young. **3.** Like the uterus of an insect, the ovary of a plant is the site of fertilization. Unlike the plant ovary, the uterus is not the site of egg production, which occurs in the insect ovary. In addition, the fertilized insect egg is expelled from the uterus, whereas the plant embryo develops within a seed in the ovary.

Concept Check 46.3

1. Spermatogenesis occurs normally only when the testicles are cooler than normal body temperature. Extensive use of a hot tub (or of very tight-fitting underwear) can cause a decrease in sperm quality and number. **2.** In humans, the secondary oocyte combines with a sperm before it finishes the second meiotic division. Thus, oogenesis is completed after, not before, fertilization. **3.** The only effect of sealing off each vas deferens is an absence of sperm in the ejaculate. Sexual response and ejaculate volume are unchanged. The cutting and sealing off of these ducts, a *vasectomy*, is a common surgical procedure for men who do not wish to produce any (more) offspring.

Concept Check 46.4

1. In the testis, FSH stimulates the Sertoli cells, which nourish developing sperm. LH stimulates the production of androgens (mainly testosterone), which in turn stimulate sperm production. In both females and males, FSH encourages the growth of cells that support and nourish developing gametes (follicle cells in females and Sertoli cells in males), and LH stimulates the production of sex hormones that promote gametogenesis (estrogens, primarily estradiol, in females and androgens, especially testosterone, in males). **2.** In estrous cycles, which occur in most female mammals, the endometrium is reabsorbed (rather than shed) if fertilization does not occur. Estrous cycles often occur just one or a few times a year, and the female is usually receptive to copulation only during the period around ovulation. Menstrual cycles are found only in humans and some other primates. **3.** The combination of estradiol and progesterone would have a negative-feedback effect on the hypothalamus, blocking release of GnRH. This would interfere with LH secretion by the pituitary, thus preventing ovulation. This is in fact one basis of action of the most common hormonal contraceptives. **4.** In the viral reproductive cycle, the production of new viral genomes is coordinated with capsid protein expression and with the production of phospholipids for viral coats. In the case of the human female, there is hormonally based coordination of egg maturation with the development of support tissues of the uterus.

Concept Check 46.5

1. hCG secreted by the early embryo stimulates the corpus luteum to make progesterone, which helps maintain the pregnancy. During the second trimester, however, hCG production drops, the corpus luteum disintegrates, and the placenta completely takes over progesterone production. **2.** Both tubal ligation and vasectomy block the movement of gametes from the gonads to a site where fertilization could take place. **3.** By introducing a spermatid nucleus directly into an oocyte, ICSI bypasses the sperm's acquisition of motility in the epididymis, its swimming to meet the egg in the oviduct, and its fusion with the egg.

Summary of Key Concepts Questions

46.1. No. Because parthenogenesis involves meiosis, the mother would pass on to each offspring a random and therefore typically distinct combination of the chromosomes she inherited from her mother and father. **46.2.** None **46.3.** The small size and lack of cytoplasm characteristic of a sperm are adaptations well suited to its function as a delivery vehicle for DNA. The large size and rich cytoplasmic contents of eggs support the growth and development of the embryo. **46.4.** Circulating anabolic steroids mimic the feedback regulation of testosterone, turning off pituitary signaling to the testes and thereby blocking release of signals required for spermatogenesis. **46.5.** Oxygen-rich blood in maternal arteries flows into pools in the endometrium, passes into fetal capillaries in the chorionic villi of the placenta, and from there travels throughout the circulatory system of the fetus.

Test Your Understanding

1. d **2.** b **3.** a **4.** c **5.** a **6.** b **7.** c **8.** d

9.

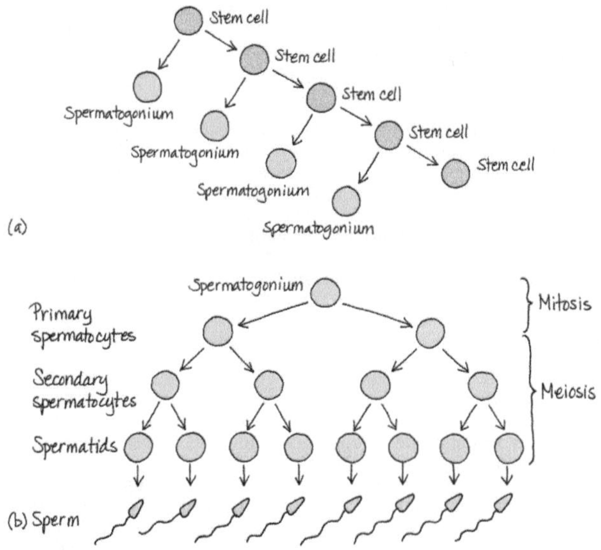

(c) The supply of stem cells would be used up and spermatogenesis would not be able to continue.

Chapter 47

Figure Questions

Figure 47.4 You could inject the compound into an unfertilized egg, expose the egg to sperm, and see whether the fertilization envelope forms. **Figure 47.21** The researchers allowed normal cortical rotation to occur, resulting in activation of the "back-forming" determinants. Then they forced the opposite rotation to occur, which established the back on the opposite side as well. Because the molecules on the normal side were already activated, forcing the opposite rotation apparently did not "cancel out" the establishment of the back side by the first rotation. **Figure 47.22** In Spemann's control, the two blastomeres were physically separated, and each grew into a whole embryo. In Roux's experiment, remnants of the dead blastomere were still contacting the live blastomere, which developed into a half-embryo. Therefore, molecules present in the dead cell's remnants may have been signaling to the live cell, inhibiting it from making all the embryonic structures. **Figure 47.23** You could inject the isolated protein or an mRNA encoding it into ventral cells of an earlier gastrula. If dorsal structures form on the ventral side, that would support the idea that the protein is the signaling molecule secreted or presented by the dorsal lip. You should also do a control experiment to make sure the injection process alone did not cause dorsal structures to form. **Figure 47.25** You could remove the AER and look for Sonic hedgehog mRNA or protein as a marker of the ZPA. If either was absent, that would support your hypothesis. You could also block FGF function and see whether the ZPA formed (by looking for Sonic hedgehog).

Concept Check 47.1

1. The fertilization envelope forms after cortical granules release their contents outside the egg, causing the vitelline membrane to rise and harden. The fertilization envelope serves as a barrier to fertilization by more than one sperm. **2.** The increased Ca^{2+} concentration in the egg would cause the cortical granules to fuse with the plasma membrane, releasing their contents and causing a fertilization envelope to form, even though no sperm had entered. This would prevent fertilization. **3.** You would expect it to fluctuate. The fluctuation of MPF drives the transition between DNA replication (S phase) and mitosis (M phase), which is still required in the abbreviated cleavage cell cycle.

Concept Check 47.2

1. The cells of the notochord migrate toward the midline of the embryo (converge), rearranging themselves so there are fewer cells across the notochord, which thus becomes longer overall (extends; see Figure 47.16). **2.** Because microfilaments would not be able to contract and decrease the size of one end of the cell, both the inward bending in the middle of the neural tube and the outward bending of the hinge regions at the edges would be blocked. Therefore, the neural tube probably would not form. **3.** Dietary intake of the vitamin folic acid dramatically reduces the frequency of neural tube defects.

Concept Check 47.3

1. Axis formation establishes the location and polarity of the three axes that provide the coordinates for development. Pattern formation positions particular tissues and organs in the three-dimensional space defined by those coordinates. **2.** Morphogen gradients act by specifying cell fates across a field of cells through variation in the level of a determinant. Morphogen gradients thus act more globally than cytoplasmic determinants or inductive interactions between pairs of cells. **3.** Yes, a second embryo could develop because inhibiting BMP-4 activity would have the same effect as transplanting an organizer. **4.** The limb that developed probably would have a mirror-image duplication, with the most posterior digits in the middle and the most anterior digits at either end.

Summary of Key Concepts Questions

47.1 The binding of a sperm to a receptor on the egg surface is very specific and likely would not occur if the two gametes were from different species. Without sperm binding, the sperm and egg membranes would not fuse. **47.2** The neural tube forms when the neural plate, a band of ectodermal tissue oriented along the anterior-posterior axis on the dorsal side of the embryo, rolls into a tube and pinches off from the rest of the ectoderm. Neural crest cells arise as groups of cells in the regions between the edges of the neural tube and the surrounding ectoderm migrate away from the neural tube. **47.3** Mutations that affected both limb and kidney development would be more likely to alter the function of monocilia because these organelles are important in several signaling pathways. Mutations that affected limb development but not kidney development would more likely alter a single pathway, such as Hedgehog signaling.

Test Your Understanding

1. a **2.** b **3.** e **4.** a **5.** d **6.** d **7.** b
8.

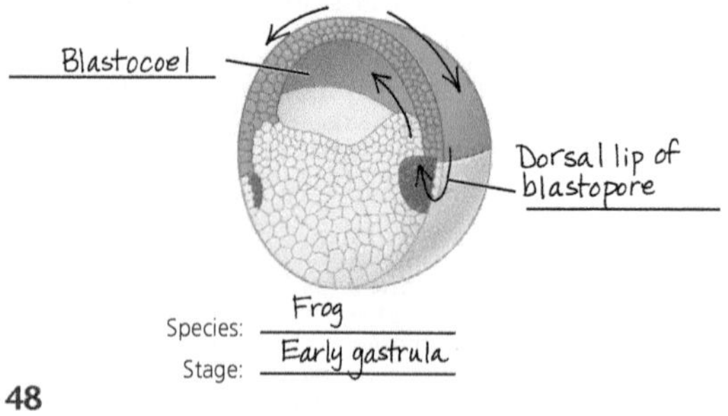

Chapter 48

Figure Questions

Figure 48.8 Adding chloride channels makes the membrane potential less positive. Adding sodium or potassium channels would have no effect, because sodium movement is already at equilibrium and there are no potassium ions present.
Figure 48.10

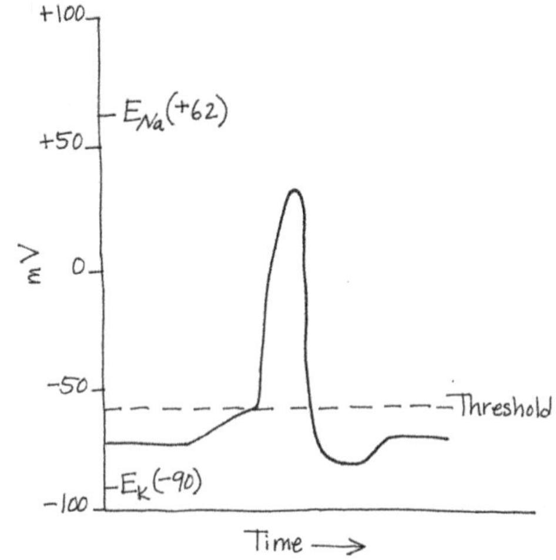

Figure 48.15 The production and transmission of action potentials would be unaffected. However, action potentials arriving at chemical synapses would be unable to trigger release of neurotransmitter. Signaling at such synapses would thus be blocked. **Figure 48.18** The drug might be destroyed very quickly in the body, not reach the central nervous system, or bind to but not activate the receptor.

Concept Check 48.1

1. Sensors in your ear transmit information to your brain. There the activity of interneurons in processing centers enables you to recognize your name. In response, signals transmitted via motor neurons cause contraction of muscles that turn your neck. **2.** Increased branching would allow control of a greater number of postsynaptic cells, enhancing coordination of responses to nervous system signals. **3.** Communication by bacteria involves all the cells in a colony, whereas communication by neurons involves just a few cells in the animal body. In addition, neurons direct signals from one location to another, whereas bacterial cells communicate in all directions.

Concept Check 48.2

1. Ions can flow against a chemical concentration gradient if there is an opposing electrical gradient of greater magnitude. **2.** A decrease in permeability to K^+, an increase in permeability to Na^+, or both **3.** The activity of the sodium-potassium pump is essential to maintain the resting potential. With the pump inactivated, the sodium and potassium concentration gradients would gradually disappear, resulting in a greatly reduced resting potential. **4.** Charged dye molecules could equilibrate only if other charged molecules could also cross the membrane. If not, a membrane potential would develop that would counterbalance the chemical gradient.

Concept Check 48.3

1. A graded potential has a magnitude that varies with stimulus strength, whereas an action potential has an all-or-none magnitude that is independent of stimulus strength. **2.** Loss of the insulation provided by myelin sheaths leads to a disruption of action potential propagation along axons. Voltage-gated sodium channels are restricted to the nodes of Ranvier, and without the insulating effect of myelin, the inward current produced at one node during an action potential cannot depolarize the membrane to the threshold at the next node. **3.** The maximum frequency would decrease because the refractory period would be extended.

Concept Check 48.4

1. It can bind to different types of receptors, each triggering a specific response in postsynaptic cells. **2.** These toxins would prolong the EPSPs that acetylcholine produces because the neurotransmitter would remain longer in the synaptic cleft. **3.** Since GABA is an inhibitory neurotransmitter in the CNS, this drug would be expected to decrease brain activity. A decrease in brain activity might be expected to slow down or reduce behavioral activity. Many sedative drugs act in this fashion. **4.** Membrane fusion

Summary of Key Concepts Questions

48.1 It would prevent information from being transmitted away from the cell body along the axon. **48.2** There are very few open sodium channels in a resting neuron, so the resting potential either would not change or would become slightly more negative (hyperpolarization). **48.3** Positive feedback is responsible for the rapid opening of many voltage-gated sodium channels, causing the rapid outflow of sodium ions responsible for the rising phase of the action potential. As the membrane potential becomes positive, voltage-gated potassium channels open in a form of negative feedback that helps bring about the falling phase of the action potential. **48.4** A given neurotransmitter can have many receptors that differ in their location and activity. Drugs that target receptor activity rather than neurotransmitter release or stability are therefore likely to exhibit greater specificity and potentially have fewer undesirable side effects.

Test Your Understanding

1. c **2.** c **3.** c **4.** e **5.** b **6.** a **7.** As shown in this pair of drawings, a pair of action potentials would move outward in both directions from each electrode. (Action potentials are unidirectional only if they begin at one end of an axon.) However, because of the refractory period, the two action potentials between the electrodes both stop where they meet. Thus, only one action potential reaches the synaptic terminals.

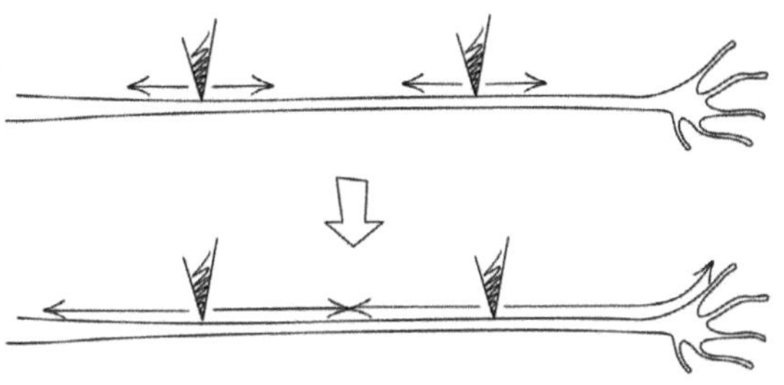

Chapter 49

Figure Questions

Figure 49.3 During swallowing, muscles along the esophagus alternately contract and relax, resulting in peristalsis. One model to explain this alternation is that each section of muscle receives nerve impulses that alternate between excitation and inhibition, just as the quadriceps and hamstring receive opposing signals in the knee-jerk reflex. **Figure 49.12** If the new mutation disrupted only pacemaker function, you should be able to restore rhythmic activity by removing the SCN and replacing it with an SCN transplant from either a wild-type or τ mutant hamster. Using the new mutant as the donor would not be as informative, since both failed transplants and successful ones would result in a lack of rhythmic activity. **Figure 49.14** Regions you would expect to be active regardless of the type of music played would include ones that are important for processing and interpreting sounds. **Figure 49.23** If the depolarization brings the membrane potential to or past threshold, it should initiate action potentials that cause dopamine release from the VTA neurons. This should mimic natural stimulation of the brain reward system, resulting in positive and perhaps pleasurable sensations.

Concept Check 49.1

1. The sympathetic division would likely be activated. It mediates the "fight-or-flight" response in stressful situations. **2.** The preganglionic neurons use the same neurotransmitter and function similarly in each division (to stimulate postganglionic neurons). The postganglionic neurons use different neurotransmitters that generally bring about opposing functions in the same target tissues. **3.** Nerves contain bundles of axons, some that belong to motor neurons, which send signals outward from the CNS, and some that belong to sensory neurons, which bring signals into the CNS. Therefore, you would expect effects on both motor control and sensation. **4.** Neurosecretory cells of the adrenal medulla secrete the hormones epinephrine and norepinephrine in response to preganglionic input from sympathetic neurons. These hormones travel in the circulation throughout the body, triggering responses in many tissues.

Concept Check 49.2

1. The cerebral cortex on the left side of the brain initiates voluntary movement of the right side of the body. **2.** Alcohol diminishes function of the cerebellum. **3.** Paralysis reflects an inability to carry out motor commands transmitted from the cerebrum to the spinal cord. You would expect these patients to have injuries in the portion of the CNS extending from the spinal cord up to but not including the reticular formation. A coma reflects a disruption in the cycles of sleep and arousal regulated by communication between the reticular formation and the cerebrum. You would expect these patients to have injuries in the reticular formation or in the portion of the brain on the opposite side of the reticular formation from the spinal cord.

Concept Check 49.3

1. Brain damage that disrupts behavior, cognition, memory, or other functions provides evidence that the portion of the brain affected by the damage is important for the normal activity that is blocked or altered. **2.** Broca's area, which is active during the generation of speech, is located near the part of the primary motor cortex that controls muscles in the face. Wernicke's area, which is active when speech is heard, is located near the part of the temporal lobe that is involved in hearing. **3.** Each cerebral hemisphere is specialized for different parts of this task—the right for face recognition and the left for language. Without an intact corpus callosum, neither hemisphere can take advantage of the other's processing abilities.

Concept Check 49.4

1. There can be an increase in the number of synapses between the neurons or an increase in the strength of existing synaptic connections. **2.** If consciousness is an emergent property resulting from the interaction of many different regions of the brain, then it is unlikely that localized brain damage will have a discrete effect on consciousness. **3.** The hippocampus is responsible for organizing newly acquired information. Without hippocampal function, the links necessary to retrieve information from the neocortex will be lacking, and no functional memory, short- or long-term, will be formed.

Concept Check 49.5

1. Both are progressive brain diseases whose risk increases with advancing age. Both result from the death of brain neurons and are associated with the accumulation of peptide or protein aggregates. **2.** The symptoms of schizophrenia can be mimicked by a drug that stimulates dopamine-releasing neurons. The brain's reward system, which is involved in drug addiction, is composed of dopamine-releasing neurons that connect the ventral tegmental area to regions in the cerebrum. Parkinson's disease results from the death of dopamine-releasing neurons. **3.** Not necessarily. It might be that the plaques, tangles, and missing regions of the brain seen at death reflect secondary effects, the consequence of other unseen changes that are actually responsible for the alterations in brain function.

Summary of Key Concepts Questions

49.1 Because reflex circuits involve only a few neurons—the simplest consist of a sensory neuron and a motor neuron—the path for information transfer is short and simple, increasing the speed of the response. **49.2** The pons and medulla (the midbrain) coordinate visual reflexes; the cerebellum controls coordination of movement that depends on visual input; the thalamus serves as a routing center for visual information; and the cerebrum is essential for converting visual input to a visual image. **49.3** You would expect the right side of the body to be paralyzed because it is controlled by the left cerebral hemisphere, where language generation and interpretation are localized. **49.4** Learning a new language likely requires the maintenance of synapses that are formed during early development but are otherwise lost prior to adulthood. **49.5** Whereas amphetamines stimulate dopamine release, PCP blocks glutamate receptors, suggesting that schizophrenia does not reflect a defect in the function of just one neurotransmitter.

Test Your Understanding

1. c **2.** a **3.** d **4.** c **5.** d **6.** e
7.

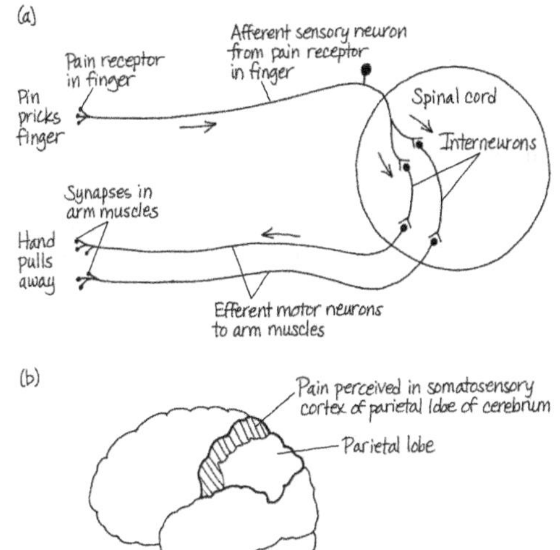

Chapter 50

Figure Questions

Figure 50.12 In the brain. Each note is detected separately in the ear, with each causing vibration of the basilar membrane and deflection of hair cells in a distinct location. Sensory neurons in each location provide output in the form of action potentials that travel along distinct axons in the auditory nerve. It is not until the information reaches the brain that the individual notes are detected and the perception of the chord is generated. **Figure 50.19** Each of the three types of cones is most sensitive to a different wavelength of light. A cone might be fully depolarized when there is light present if the light is of a wavelength far from its optimum. **Figure 50.21** In humans, an X chromosome with a defect in the red or green opsin gene is much less common than a wild-type X chromosome. Color blindness therefore typically skips a generation as the defective allele passes from an affected male to a carrier daughter and back to an affected grandson. In squirrel monkeys, no X chromosome can confer full color vision. As a result, all males are color-blind and no unusual inheritance pattern is observed. **Figure 50.23** The results of the experiment would have been identical. What matters is the activation of particular sets of neurons, not the manner in which they are activated. Any signal from a bitter cell will be interpreted by the brain as a bitter taste, regardless of the nature of the compound and the receptor involved. **Figure 50.25** Only perception. Binding of an odorant to its receptor will cause action potentials to be sent to the brain. Although an excess of that odorant might cause a diminished response through adaptation, another odorant can mask the first only at the level of perception in the brain. **Figure 50.28** Hundreds of myosin heads participate in sliding each pair of thick and thin filaments past each other. Because cross-bridge formation and breakdown are not synchronized, many myosin heads are exerting force on the thin filaments at all times during muscle contraction. **Figure 50.32** By causing all of the motor neurons that control the muscle to generate action potentials at a rate high enough to produce tetanus in all of the muscle fibers **Figure 50.40** Since a duck is more specialized for flying than for swimming, you might expect that it would consume more energy per unit body mass and distance in swimming than would, for example, a fish. (In fact, if the value for a 10^3-g swimming duck were plotted on this graph, it would appear well above the line for swimmers and just above the line for runners.)

Concept Check 50.1

1. Electromagnetic receptors in general detect only external stimuli. Nonelectromagnetic receptors, such as chemoreceptors or mechanoreceptors, can act as either internal or external sensors. **2.** The capsaicin present in the peppers activates the thermoreceptor for high temperatures. In response to the perceived high temperature, the nervous system triggers sweating to achieve evaporative cooling. **3.** You would perceive the electrical stimulus as if the sensory receptors that regulate that neuron had been activated. For example, electrical stimulation of the sensory neuron controlled by the thermoreceptor activated by menthol would likely be perceived as a local cooling.

Concept Check 50.2

1. Statocysts detect the animal's orientation with respect to gravity, providing information that is essential in environments such as these, where light cues are absent. **2.** As a sound that changes gradually from a very low to a very high pitch **3.** The stapes and the other middle ear bones transmit vibrations from the tympanic membrane to the oval window. Fusion of these bones (as occurs in a disease called otosclerosis) would block this transmission and result in hearing loss.

Concept Check 50.3

1. Planarians have ocelli that cannot form images but can sense the intensity and direction of light, providing enough information to enable the animals to find protection in shaded places. Flies have compound eyes that form images and excel at detecting movement. **2.** The person can focus on distant objects but not close objects (without glasses) because close focusing requires the lens to become almost spherical. This problem is common after age 50. **3.** Close each eye in turn. An object floating on the surface of an eyeball will appear only when that eye is open. **4.** Absorption of light by retinal converts a structure isomer in the *cis* configuration to the isomer in the *trans* configuration, initiating the process of light detection. In contrast, a photon absorbed by chlorophyll does not bring about isomerization, but instead boosts an electron to a higher energy orbital, initiating the electron flow that generates ATP and NADPH.

Concept Check 50.4

1. Both taste cells and olfactory cells have receptor proteins in their plasma membrane that bind certain substances, leading to membrane depolarization through a signal transduction pathway involving a G protein. However, olfactory cells are sensory neurons, whereas taste cells are not. **2.** Since animals rely on chemical signals for behaviors that include finding mates, marking territories, and avoiding dangerous substances, it is adaptive for the olfactory system to have a robust response to a very small number of molecules of a particular odorant. **3.** Because the sweet, bitter, and umami tastes involve GPCR proteins but the sour taste does not, you might predict that the mutation is in a molecule that acts in the signal transduction pathway common to the different GPCRs.

Concept Check 50.5

1. In a skeletal muscle fiber, Ca^{2+} binds to the troponin complex, which moves tropomyosin away from the myosin-binding sites on actin and allows cross-bridges to form. In a smooth muscle cell, Ca^{2+} binds to calmodulin, which activates an enzyme that phosphorylates the myosin head and thus enables cross-bridge formation. **2.** *Rigor mortis*, a Latin phrase meaning "stiffness of death," results from the complete depletion of ATP in skeletal muscle. Since ATP is required to release myosin from actin and to pump Ca^{2+} out of the cytosol, muscles become chronically contracted beginning about 3–4 hours after death. **3.** A competitive inhibitor binds to the same site as the substrate for the enzyme. In contrast, the troponin and tropomyosin complex masks, but does not bind to, the myosin-binding sites on actin.

Concept Check 50.6

1. Septa provide the divisions of the coelom that allow for peristalsis, a form of locomotion requiring independent control of different body segments. **2.** The main problem in swimming is drag; a fusiform body minimizes drag. The main problem in flying is overcoming gravity; wings shaped like airfoils provide lift, and adaptations such as air-filled bones reduce body mass. **3.** When you grasp the sides of the chair, you are using a contraction of the triceps to keep your arms extended against the pull of gravity on your body. As you lower yourself slowly into the chair, you gradually decrease the number of motor units in the triceps that are contracted. Contracting your biceps would jerk you down, since you would no longer be opposing gravity.

Summary of Key Concepts Questions

50.1 Nociceptors overlap with other classes of receptors in the type of stimulus they detect. They differ from other receptors only in how a particular stimulus is perceived. **50.2** The direction of displacement of a hair cell is determined by stimulus intensity, which is encoded by the frequency of action potentials transmitted to the brain. **50.3** Our olfactory sense is responsible for most of what we describe as distinct tastes. A head cold or other source of congestion blocks odorant access to receptors lining portions of the nasal cavity. **50.4** The major difference is that neurons in the retina integrate information from multiple sensory receptors (photoreceptors) before transmitting information to the central nervous system. **50.5** Hydrolysis of ATP is required to convert myosin to a high-energy configuration for binding to actin and to power the Ca^{2+} pump that removes cytosolic Ca^{2+} during muscle relaxation. **50.6** Human body movements rely on the contraction of muscles anchored to a rigid endoskeleton. Tendons attach muscles to bones, which in turn are composed of fibers built up from a basic organizational unit, the sarcomere. The thin and thick filaments have separate points of attachment within the sarcomere. In response to nervous system motor output, the formation and breakdown of cross-bridges between myosin heads and actin ratchet the thin and thick filaments past each other. Because the filaments are anchored, this sliding movement shortens the muscle fibers. Furthermore, because the fibers themselves are part of the muscles attached at each end to bones, muscle contraction moves bones of the body relative to each other. In this way, the structural anchoring of muscles and filaments enables muscle function, such as the bending of an elbow by contraction of the biceps.

Test Your Understanding

1. e **2.** a **3.** b **4.** c **5.** b **6.** d
7.

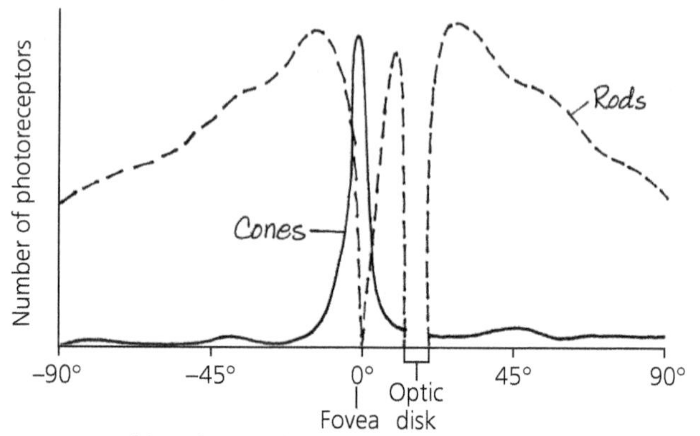

The answer shows the actual distribution of rods and cones in the human eye. Your graph may differ but should have the following properties: Only cones at the fovea; fewer cones and more rods at both ends of the *x*-axis; no photoreceptors in the optic disk.

Chapter 51

Figure Questions

Figure 51.2 The fixed action pattern based on the sign stimulus of a red belly ensures that the male will chase away any invading males of his species. By chasing away such males, the defender decreases the chance that another male will fertilize eggs laid in his nesting territory. **Figure 51.7** There should be no effect. Imprinting is an innate behavior that is carried out anew in each generation. Assuming the nest was not disturbed, the offspring of the Lorenz followers would imprint on the mother goose. **Figure 51.8** Perhaps the wasp doesn't use visual cues. It might also be that wasps recognize objects native to their environment, but not foreign objects, such as the pinecones. Tinbergen addressed these ideas before carrying out the pinecone study. When he swept away the pebbles and sticks around the nest, the wasps could no longer find their nests. If he shifted the natural objects in their natural arrangement, the shift in the landmarks caused a shift in the site to which the wasps returned. Finally, if natural objects around the nest site were replaced with pinecones while the wasp was in the burrow, the wasp nevertheless found her way back to the nest site. **Figure 51.23** Courtship song generation must be coupled to courtship song recognition. Unless the genes that control generation of particular song elements also control recognition, the hybrids might be unlikely to find mating partners, depending on what aspects of the songs are important for mate recognition and acceptance. **Figure 51.26** It might be that the birds require stimuli during flight to exhibit their migratory preference. If this were true, the birds would show the same orientation in the funnel experiment despite their distinct genetic programming. **Figure 51.28** It holds true for some, but not all individuals. If a parent has more than one reproductive partner, the offspring of different partners will have a coefficient of relatedness less than 0.5.

Concept Check 51.1

1. The proximate explanation for this fixed action pattern might be that nudging and rolling are released by the sign stimulus of an object outside the nest, and the behavior is carried to completion once initiated. The ultimate explanation might be that ensuring that eggs remain in the nest increases the chance of producing healthy offspring. **2.** In both cases, the detection of periodic variation in the environment results in a reproductive cycle timed to environmental conditions that optimize the opportunity for success. **3.** There might be selective pressure for other prey fish to detect an injured fish because the source of the injury might threaten them as well. Among predators, there might be selection for those that are attracted to the alarm substance because they would be more likely to encounter crippled prey. Fish with adequate defenses might show no change because they have a selective advantage if they do not waste energy responding to the alarm substance.

Concept Check 51.2

1. Natural selection would tend to favor convergence in color pattern because a predator learning to associate a pattern with a sting or bad taste would avoid all other individuals with that same color pattern, regardless of species. **2.** You might move objects around to establish an abstract rule, such as "past landmark A, the same distance as A is from the starting point," while maintaining a minimum of fixed metric relationships, that is, avoiding having the food directly adjacent to or a set distance from a landmark. As you might surmise, designing an informative experiment of this kind is not easy. **3.** Learned behavior, just like innate behavior, can contribute to reproductive isolation and thus to speciation. For example, learned bird songs contribute to species recognition during courtship, thereby helping ensure that only members of the same species mate.

Concept Check 51.3

1. Certainty of paternity is higher with external fertilization. **2.** Balancing selection could maintain the two alleles at the *forager* locus if population density fluctuated from one generation to another. At times of low population density, the energy-conserving sitter larvae (carrying the for^s allele) would be favored, while at higher population density, the more mobile Rover larvae (for^R allele) would have a selective advantage. **3.** Because females would now be present in much larger numbers than males, all three types of males should have some reproductive success. Nevertheless, since the advantage that the blue-throats rely on—a limited number of females in their territory—will be absent, the yellow-throats are likely to increase in frequency in the short term.

Concept Check 51.4

1. Because this geographic variation corresponds to differences in prey availability between two garter snake habitats, it seems likely that snakes with characteristics enabling them to feed on the abundant prey in their locale would have had increased survival and reproductive success. In this way, natural selection would have resulted in the divergent foraging behaviors. **2.** Yes. Kin selection does not require any recognition or awareness of relatedness. **3.** The older individual cannot be the beneficiary because he or she cannot have extra offspring. However, the cost is low for an older individual performing the altruistic act because that individual has already reproduced (but perhaps is still caring for a child or grandchild). There can therefore be selection for an altruistic act by a postreproductive individual that benefits a young relative.

Summary of Key Concepts Questions

51.1 Circannual rhythms are typically based on the cycles of light and dark in the environment. As the global climate changes, animals that migrate in response to these rhythms may shift to a location before or after local environmental conditions are optimal for reproduction and survival. **51.2** For the goose, all that is acquired is an object at which the behavior is directed. In the case of the sparrow, learning takes place that will give shape to the behavior itself. **51.3** Because feeding the female is likely to improve her reproductive success, the genes from the sacrificed male are likely to appear in a greater number of progeny. **51.4** You would likely have missed the idea that changes in a single gene can have large-scale effects on even complex behaviors.

Test Your Understanding

1. d **2.** b **3.** c **4.** a **5.** c **6.** a

7.

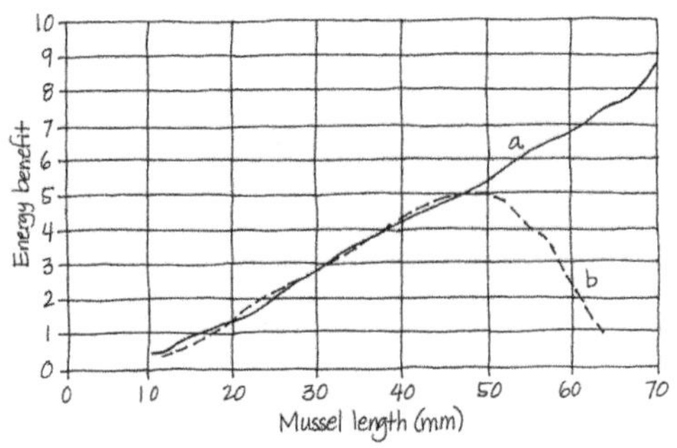

You could measure the size of mussels that oystercatchers successfully open and compare that with the size distribution in the habitat.

Chapter 52

Figure Questions

Figure 52.7 Dispersal limitations, the activities of people (such as a broad-scale conversion of forests to agriculture or selective harvesting), or many other factors, including those discussed later in the chapter (see Figure 52.18) **Figure 52.18** Some factors, such as fire, are relevant only for terrestrial systems. At first glance, water availability is primarily a terrestrial factor, too. However, species living along the intertidal zone of oceans or along the edge of lakes also suffer desiccation. Salinity stress is important for species in some aquatic and terrestrial systems. Oxygen availability is an important factor primarily for species in some aquatic systems and in soils and sediments. **Figure 52.20** When only urchins were removed, limpets may have increased in abundance and reduced seaweed cover somewhat (the difference between the purple and blue lines on the graph).

Concept Check 52.1

1. In the tropics, high temperatures evaporate water and cause warm, moist air to rise. The rising air cools and releases much of its water as rain over the tropics. The remaining dry air descends at approximately 30° north and south, causing deserts to occur in those regions. **2.** The microclimate around the stream will be cooler, moister, and shadier than that around the unplanted agricultural field. **3.** Trees that require a long time to reach reproductive age are likely to evolve more slowly than annual plants in response to climate change, constraining the potential ability of such trees to respond to rapid climate change. **4.** Plants with C_4 photosynthesis are likely to expand their range globally as Earth's climate warms. As described in Concept 10.4, C_4 photosynthesis minimizes photorespiration and enhances sugar production, an advantage that is especially useful in warmer regions where C_4 plants are found today.

Concept Check 52.2

1. Temperate broadleaf forests have higher mean annual precipitation. **2.** Answers will vary by location but should be based on the information and maps in Figure 52.12. How much your local area has been altered from its natural state will influence how much it reflects the expected characteristics of your biome, particularly the expected plants and animals. **3.** Northern coniferous forest is likely to replace tundra along the boundary between these biomes. To see why, note that northern coniferous forest is adjacent to tundra throughout North America, northern Europe, and Asia (see Figure 52.9) and that the temperature range for northern coniferous forest is just above that for tundra (see Figure 52.10).

Concept Check 52.3

1. In the oceanic pelagic zone, the ocean bottom lies below the photic zone, so there is too little light to support benthic algae or rooted plants. **2.** As explained in Concept 44.1, aquatic organisms either gain or lose water by osmosis if the osmolarity of their environment differs from their internal osmolarity. Water gain can cause cells to swell, and water loss can cause them to shrink. To avoid excessive changes in cell volume, organisms that live in estuaries must be able to compensate for both water gain (under freshwater conditions) and water loss (under saltwater conditions). **3.** In a river below a dam, the fish are more likely to be species that prefer colder water. In summer, the deep layers of a reservoir are colder than the surface layers, so a river below a dam will be colder than an undammed river.

Concept Check 52.4

1. (a) Humans might transplant a species to a new area that it could not previously reach because of a geographic barrier. (b) Humans might eliminate a predator or herbivore species, such as sea urchins, from an area. **2.** One test would be to build a fence around a plot of land in an area that has trees of that species, excluding all deer from the plot. You could then compare the abundance of tree seedlings inside and outside the fenced plot over time. **3.** Because the ancestor of the silverswords reached isolated Hawaii early in the islands' existence, it likely faced little competition and was able to occupy many unfilled niches. The cattle egret, in contrast, arrived in the Americas only recently and has to compete with a well-established group of species. Thus, its opportunities for adaptive radiation have probably been much more limited.

Summary of Key Concepts Questions

52.1 Because dry air would descend at the equator instead of at 30° north and south latitude (where deserts exist today), deserts would be more likely to exist along the equator (see Figure 52.3). **52.2** Because tundra is much cooler than deserts (see Figure 52.10), less water evaporates during the growing season and the tundra stays more moist. **52.3** An aphotic zone is most likely to be found in the deep waters of a lake, the oceanic pelagic zone, or the marine benthic zone. **52.4** You could arrange a flowchart that begins with abiotic limitations—first determining the physical and chemical conditions under which a species could survive—and then moves through the other factors listed in the flowchart.

Test Your Understanding

1. c **2.** b **3.** d **4.** e **5.** d **6.** d **7.** c **8.** a **9.** a **10.** c

11.

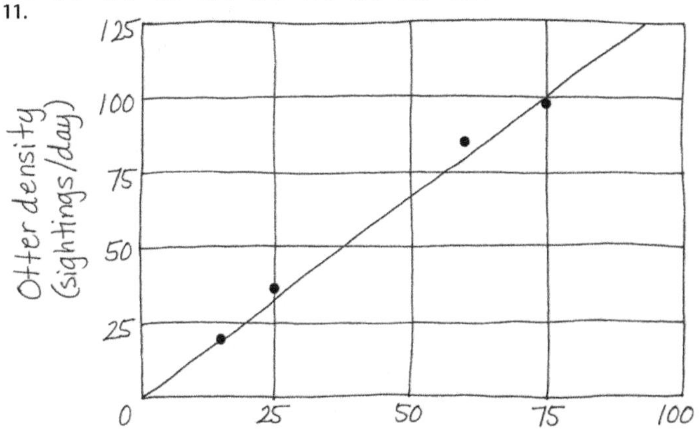

Based on what you learned from Figure 52.20 and on the positive relationship you observed in the field between kelp abundance and otter density, you could hypothesize that otters lower sea urchin density, reducing feeding of the urchins on kelp.

Chapter 53

Figure Questions

Figure 53.4 The dispersion of the penguins would likely appear clumped as you flew over densely populated islands and sparsely populated ocean. **Figure 53.13** If male European kestrels provided no parental care, brood size should not affect their survival. Therefore, the three bars representing male survival in Figure 53.13 should have similar heights. In contrast, female survival should still decline with increasing brood size, as shown in the current figure.

Figure 53.15

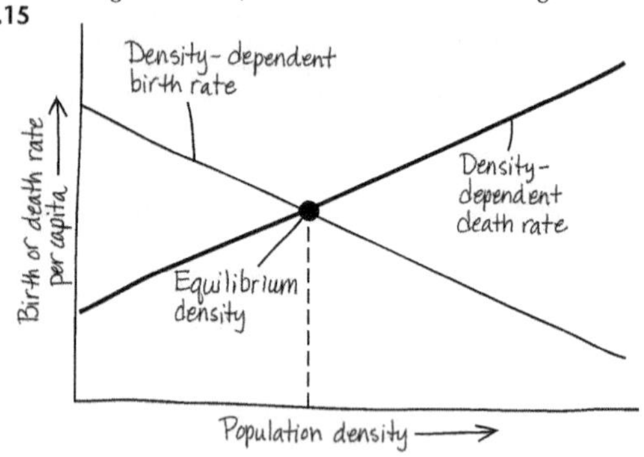

Figure 53.19 Hare numbers typically peaked slightly before lynx numbers did. The lynx depend on the hares for food, but there is a delay between increased food availability and increased reproduction by the lynx. **Figure 53.20** *Dictyostelium* slugs are more vulnerable to predation by animals than are amoebas.

Concept Check 53.1

1.

A type III survivorship curve is most likely because very few of the young probably survive. **2.** If an animal is captured by attracting it with food, it may be more likely to be recaptured if it seeks the same food. The number of marked animals captured (x) would be an overestimate, and because the population size (N) is equal to sn/x, N would be an underestimate. Alternatively, if an animal has a negative experience during capture and learns from that experience, it may be less likely to be recaptured. In this case, x would be an underestimate and N would be an overestimate. **3.** Male sticklebacks would likely have a uniform pattern of dispersion, with antagonistic interactions maintaining a relatively constant spacing between them.

Concept Check 53.2

1. Though r_{max} is constant, N, the population size, is increasing. As r_{max} is applied to an increasingly large N, population growth ($r_{max}N$) accelerates, producing the J-shaped curve. **2.** Exponential growth is more likely in the area where a forest was destroyed by fire. The first plants that found suitable habitat there would encounter an abundance of space, nutrients, and light. In the undisturbed forest, competition among plants for these resources would be intense. **3.** The net population growth is $\Delta N/\Delta t = bN - mN$. The annual per capita birth rate, b, equals 14/1,000, or 0.014, and the per capita death rate, m, equals 8/1,000, or 0.008. Therefore, the net population growth in 2009 was

$$\frac{\Delta N}{\Delta t} = (0.014 \times 307{,}000{,}000) - (0.008 \times 307{,}000{,}000)$$

or 1.84 million people. A population is growing exponentially only if its per capita rate of increase equals its maximum rate. That is not the case for the United States currently.

Concept Check 53.3

1. When N (population size) is small, there are relatively few individuals producing offspring. When N is large, near the carrying capacity, the per capita growth rate is relatively small because it is limited by available resources. The steepest part of the logistic growth curve corresponds to a population with a number of reproducing individuals that is substantial but not yet near carrying capacity. **2.** Using a population size of 1,600 as an example,

$$\frac{dN}{dt} = r_{max}N\frac{(K-N)}{K} = \frac{1(1{,}600)(1{,}500 - 1{,}600)}{1{,}500}$$

and the population "growth" rate is –107 individuals per year. The population shrinks even faster when N is farther from the carrying capacity; when N equals 1,750 and 2,000 individuals, the population shrinks by 292 and 667 individuals per year, respectively. These negative growth rates correspond most closely to the time when the *Daphnia* population has overshot its carrying capacity and is shrinking, about days 65–100 in Figure 53.10b. **3.** If a population becomes too crowded, the likelihood of disease and mortality may increase because of the effects of pathogens. Thus, pathogens can reduce the long-term carrying capacity of a population.

Concept Check 53.4

1. The constant, spring-fed stream. In more constant physical conditions, populations are more stable and competition for resources is more likely. In such conditions, larger, well-provisioned young typical of iteroparous species have a better chance of surviving. **2.** By preferentially investing in the eggs it lays in the nest, the peacock wrasse increases their probability of survival. The eggs it disperses widely and does not provide care for are less likely to survive, at least some of the time, but require a lower investment by the adults. (In this sense, the adults avoid the risk of placing all their eggs in one basket.) **3.** If a parent's survival is compromised greatly by bearing young during times of stress, the animal's fitness may increase if it abandons its current young and survives to produce healthier young at a later time.

Concept Check 53.5

1. Three attributes are the size, quality, and isolation of patches. A patch that is larger or of higher quality is more likely to attract individuals and to be a source of individuals for other patches. A patch that is relatively isolated will undergo less exchange of individuals with other patches. **2.** You would need to study the population for more than one cycle (longer than 10 years and probably at least 20) before having sufficient data to examine changes through time. Otherwise, it would be impossible to know whether an observed decrease in the population size reflected a long-term trend or was part of the normal cycle. **3.** In negative feedback, the output, or product, of a process slows that process. In populations that have a density-dependent birth rate, such as dune fescue grass, an accumulation of product (more individuals, resulting in a higher population density) slows the process (population growth) by decreasing the birth rate.

Concept Check 53.6

1. A bottom-heavy age structure, with a disproportionate number of young people, portends continuing growth of the population as these young people begin reproducing. In contrast, a more evenly distributed age structure predicts a more stable population size, and a top-heavy age structure predicts a decrease in population size because relatively fewer young people are reproducing. **2.** The growth rate of Earth's human population has dropped by half since the 1960s, from 2.2% in 1962 to 1.2% today. Nonetheless, growth has not slowed much because the smaller growth rate is counterbalanced by increased population size; the number of extra people on Earth each year remains enormous—approximately 79 million. **3.** Each of us influences our ecological footprint by how we live—what we eat, how much energy we use, and the amount of waste we generate—as well as by how many children we have. Making choices that reduce our demand for resources makes our ecological footprint smaller.

Summary of Key Concepts Questions

53.1 Ecologists can potentially estimate birth rates by counting the number of young born each year, and they can estimate death rates by seeing how the number of adults changes each year. **53.2** Under the exponential model, both populations will continue to grow to infinite size, regardless of the specific value of r_{max} (see Figure 53.7). **53.3** There are many things you can do to increase the carrying capacity of the species, including increasing its food supply, protecting it from predators, and providing more sites for nesting or reproduction. **53.4** Two key factors appear to be the survival rate of the offspring and the chance that adults will live long enough to reproduce again. **53.5** An example of a biotic factor would be disease caused by a pathogen; natural disasters, such as floods and storms, are examples of abiotic factors. **53.6** Humans are unique in our potential ability to reduce global population through contraception and family planning. Humans also are capable of consciously choosing their diet and personal lifestyle, and these choices influence the number of people Earth can support.

Test Your Understanding

1. b **2.** a **3.** c **4.** d **5.** e **6.** c **7.** c **8.** d **9.** b **10.** a

11.

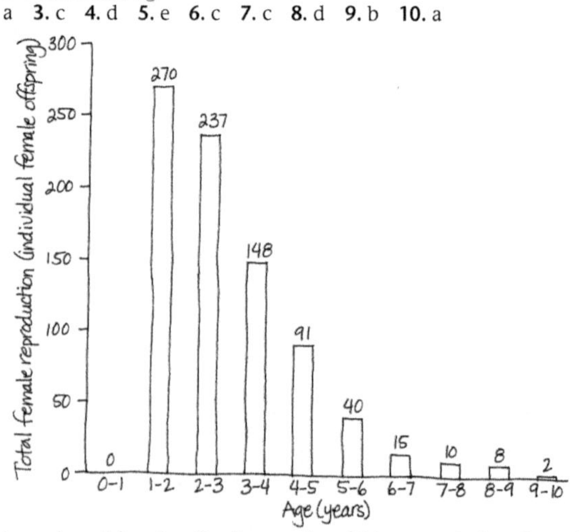

The total number of female offspring produced is greatest in females 1–2 years of age. Sample calculation for females of this age group: 252 indiv. × 1.07 female offspring/indiv. = 270 female offspring.

Chapter 54

Figure Questions

Figure 54.3 Its realized and fundamental niches would be similar, unlike those of *Chthamalus*. **Figure 54.16** The low-productivity treatment had the shortest food chain, so that food chain should be the most stable. **Figure 54.17** The death of individuals of *Mytilus*, a dominant species, should open up space for other species and increase species richness even in the absence of *Pisaster*. **Figure 54.23** At the earliest stages of primary succession, free-living prokaryotes in the soil would reduce atmospheric N_2 to NH_3. Symbiotic nitrogen fixation could not occur until plants were present at the site. **Figure 54.28** Other factors not included in the model must contribute to the number of species. **Figure 54.29** Shrew populations in different locations and habitats might show substantial genetic variation in their susceptibility to the Lyme pathogen. Further studies would be needed to test the generality of the results shown in Figure 54.29.

Concept Check 54.1

1. Interspecific competition has negative effects on both species (−/−). In predation, the predator population benefits at the expense of the prey population (+/−). Mutualism is a symbiosis in which both species benefit (+/+). **2.** One of the competing species will become locally extinct because of the greater reproductive success of the more efficient competitor. **3.** By specializing in eating seeds of a single plant species, individuals of the two finch species may be less likely to come into contact in the separate habitats, reinforcing a reproductive barrier to hybridization.

Concept Check 54.2

1. Species richness, the number of species in the community, and relative abundance, the proportions of the community represented by the various species, both contribute to species diversity. Compared to a community with a very high proportion of one species, one with a more even proportion of species is considered more diverse. **2.** The energetic hypothesis suggests that the length of a food chain is limited by the inefficiency of energy transfer along the chain, while the dynamic stability hypothesis proposes that long food chains are less stable than short chains. The energetic hypothesis predicts that food chains will be longer in habitats with higher primary productivity. The dynamic stability hypothesis predicts that food chains will be longer in more predictable environments. **3.** According to the bottom-up model, adding extra predators would have little effect on lower trophic levels, particularly vegetation. If the top-down model applied, increased bobcat numbers would decrease raccoon numbers, increase snake numbers, decrease grasshopper numbers, and increase plant biomass.

Concept Check 54.3

1. High levels of disturbance are generally so disruptive that they eliminate many species from communities, leaving the community dominated by a few tolerant species. Low levels of disturbance permit competitively dominant species to exclude other species from the community. But moderate levels of disturbance can facilitate coexistence of a greater number of species in a community by preventing competitively dominant species from becoming abundant enough to eliminate other species from the community. **2.** Early successional species can facilitate the arrival of other species in many ways, including increasing the fertility or water-holding capacity of soils or providing shelter to seedlings from wind and intense sunlight. **3.** The absence of fire for 100 years would represent a change to a low level of disturbance. According to the intermediate disturbance hypothesis, this change should cause diversity to decline as competitively dominant species gain sufficient time to exclude less competitive species.

Concept Check 54.4

1. Ecologists propose that the greater species richness of tropical regions is the result of their longer evolutionary history and the greater solar energy input and water availability in tropical regions. **2.** Immigration of species to islands declines with distance from the mainland and increases with island area. Extinction of species is lower on larger islands and on less isolated islands. Since the number of species on islands is largely determined by the difference between rates of immigration and extinction, the number of species will be highest on large islands near the mainland and lowest on small islands far from the mainland. **3.** Because of their greater mobility, birds disperse to islands more often than snakes and lizards, so birds should have greater richness.

Concept Check 54.5

1. Pathogens are microorganisms, viruses, viroids, or prions that cause disease. **2.** To keep the rabies virus out, you could ban imports of all mammals, including pets. Potentially, you could also attempt to vaccinate all dogs in the British Isles against the virus. A more practical approach might be to quarantine all pets brought into the country that are potential carriers of the disease, the approach the British government actually takes.

Summary of Key Concepts Questions

54.1 Competition: a fox and a bobcat competing for prey. Predation: an orca eating a sea otter. Herbivory: a bison grazing in a prairie. Parasitism: a parasitoid wasp that lays its eggs on a caterpillar. Mutualism: a fungus and an alga that make up a lichen. Commensalism: a remora attached to a whale. Facilitation: a flowering plant and its pollinator. **54.2** Not necessarily if the more species-rich community is dominated by only one or a few species **54.3** Because of the presence of species initially, the disturbance would initiate secondary succession in spite of its severe appearance. **54.4** Glaciations have severely reduced diversity in northern temperate, boreal, and Arctic ecosystems, compared to tropical ecosystems. **54.5** A host is required to complete the pathogen's life cycle, but a vector is not. Vectors are intermediate species that merely transport a pathogen to its host.

Test Your Understanding

1. e **2.** d **3.** c **4.** a **5.** b **6.** c **7.** d **8.** b **9.** Community 1: $H = -(0.05 \ln 0.05 + 0.05 \ln 0.05 + 0.85 \ln 0.85 + 0.05 \ln 0.05) = 0.59$. Community 2: $H = -(0.30 \ln 0.30 + 0.40 \ln 0.40 + 0.30 \ln 0.30) = 1.1$. Community 2 is more diverse.

10. Crab numbers should increase, reducing the abundance of eelgrass.

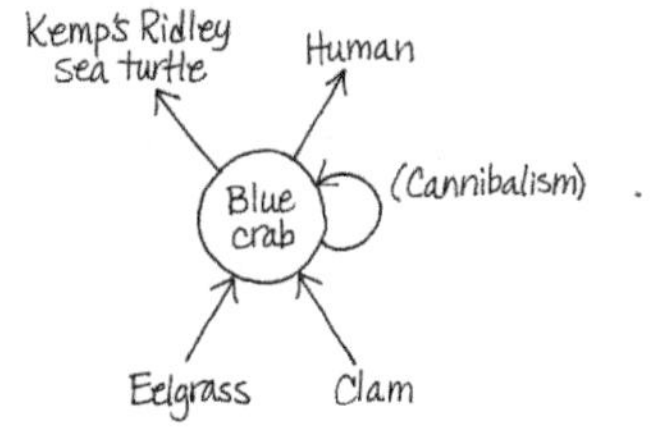

Chapter 55

Figure Questions

Figure 55.6 Wetlands, coral reefs, and coastal zones cover areas too small to show up clearly on global maps. **Figure 55.7** The availability of nutrients, particularly nitrogen, phosphorus, and iron, as well as temperature, is likely to limit primary production in the oceans. **Figure 55.8** If the new duck farms made nitrogen available in rich supply, as phosphorus already is, then adding extra nitrogen in the experiment would not increase phytoplankton density. **Figure 55.15** Water availability is probably another factor that varied across the sites. Such factors not included in the experimental design could make the results more difficult to interpret. Multiple factors can also covary in nature, so ecologists must be careful that the factor they are studying is actually causing the observed response and is not just correlated with it.

Concept Check 55.1

1. Energy passes through an ecosystem, entering as sunlight and leaving as heat. It is not recycled within the ecosystem. **2.** You would need to know how much biomass the wildebeests ate from your plot and how much nitrogen was contained in that biomass. You would also need to know how much nitrogen they deposited in urine or feces. **3.** The second law states that in any energy transfer or transformation, some of the energy is dissipated to the surroundings as heat. This "escape" of energy from an ecosystem is offset by the continuous influx of solar radiation.

Concept Check 55.2

1. Only a fraction of solar radiation strikes plants or algae, only a portion of that fraction is of wavelengths suitable for photosynthesis, and much energy is lost as a result of reflection or heating of plant tissue. **2.** By manipulating the level of the factors of interest, such as phosphorus availability or soil moisture, and measuring responses by primary producers **3.** The enzyme rubisco, which catalyzes the first step in the Calvin cycle, is the most abundant protein on Earth. Photosynthetic organisms require considerable nitrogen to make rubisco. Phosphorus is also needed as a component of several metabolites in the Calvin cycle and as a component of both ATP and NADPH (see Figure 10.19).

Concept Check 55.3

1. 20 J; 40% **2.** Nicotine protects the plant from herbivores. **3.** Unlike for the woman pictured in Figure 40.20, the caterpillar would have no energy devoted to thermoregulation or to reproduction. Its relative contribution to growth, however, would be much higher than for the woman.

Concept Check 55.4

1. For example, for the carbon cycle:

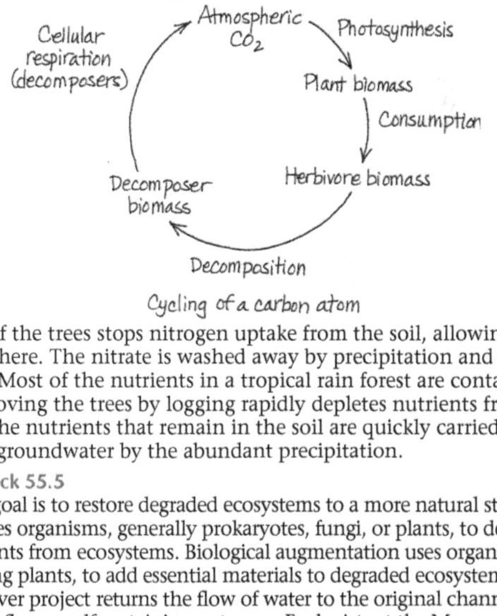

Cycling of a carbon atom

2. Removal of the trees stops nitrogen uptake from the soil, allowing nitrate to accumulate there. The nitrate is washed away by precipitation and enters the streams. **3.** Most of the nutrients in a tropical rain forest are contained in the trees, so removing the trees by logging rapidly depletes nutrients from the ecosystem. The nutrients that remain in the soil are quickly carried away into streams and groundwater by the abundant precipitation.

Concept Check 55.5

1. The main goal is to restore degraded ecosystems to a more natural state. **2.** Bioremediation uses organisms, generally prokaryotes, fungi, or plants, to detoxify or remove pollutants from ecosystems. Biological augmentation uses organisms, such as nitrogen-fixing plants, to add essential materials to degraded ecosystems. **3.** The Kissimmee River project returns the flow of water to the original channel and restores natural flow, a self-sustaining outcome. Ecologists at the Maungatautari reserve will need to maintain the integrity of the fence indefinitely, an outcome that is not self-sustaining in the long term.

Summary of Key Concepts Questions

55.1 Because energy conversions are inefficient, with some energy inevitably lost as heat, you would expect that a given mass of primary producers would support a smaller biomass of secondary producers. **55.2** For estimates of NEP, you need to measure the respiration of all organisms in an ecosystem, not just the respiration of primary producers. In a sample of ocean water, primary producers and other organisms are usually mixed together, making their respective respirations hard to separate. **55.3** The runner would typically burn many more calories through respiration, reducing his or her production efficiency. **55.4** Factors other than temperature, including a shortage of water and nutrients, slow decomposition in hot deserts. **55.5** If the topsoil and deeper soil are kept separate, you could return the deeper soil to the site first and then apply the more fertile topsoil to improve the success of revegetation and other restoration efforts.

Test Your Understanding

1. c **2.** b **3.** d **4.** d **5.** c **6.** e **7.** a **8.** e

9.

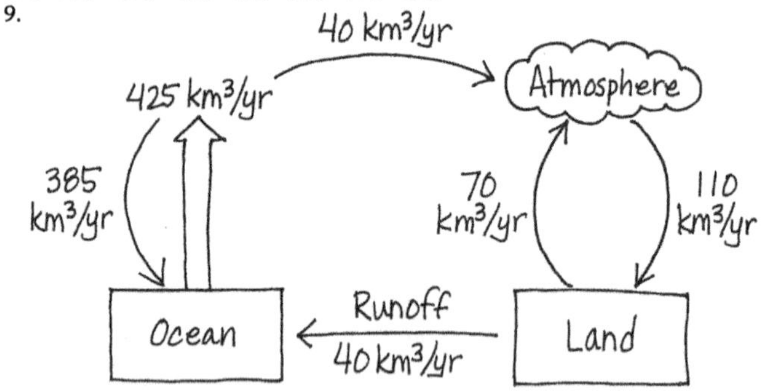

Based on these global numbers, approximately 110 km^3 of precipitation falls over land each year.

Chapter 56

Figure Questions

Figure 56.4 You would need to know the complete range of the species and that it is missing across all of that range. You would also need to be certain that the species isn't hidden, as might be the case for an animal that is hibernating underground or a plant that is present in the form of seeds or spores. **Figure 56.9** The two examples are similar in that segments of DNA from the harvested samples were analyzed and compared with segments from specimens of known origin. One difference is that the whale researchers investigated relatedness at species and population levels to determine whether illegal activity had occurred, whereas the elephant investigators determined relatedness at the population level to determine the precise location of the poaching. Another difference is that mtDNA was used for the whale study, whereas STRs were used for the elephant study. The primary limitations of such approaches are the need to have (or generate) a reference database and the requirement that the organisms have sufficient variation in their DNA to reveal the relatedness of samples. **Figure 56.13** Because the population of Illinois birds has a different genetic makeup than birds in other regions, you would want to maintain to the greatest extent possible the frequency of beneficial genes or alleles found only in that population. In restoration, preserving genetic diversity in a species is as important as increasing organism numbers. **Figure 56.15** The natural disturbance regime in this habitat includes frequent fires that clear undergrowth but do not kill mature pine trees. Without these fires, the undergrowth quickly fills in and the habitat becomes unsuitable for red-cockaded woodpeckers.

Concept Check 56.1

1. In addition to species loss, the biodiversity crisis includes the loss of genetic diversity within populations and species and the degradation of entire ecosystems. **2.** Habitat destruction, such as deforestation, channelizing of rivers, or conversion of natural ecosystems to agriculture or cities, deprives species of places to live. Introduced species, which are transported by humans to regions outside their native range, where they are not controlled by their natural pathogens or predators, often reduce the population sizes of native species through competition or predation. Overharvesting has reduced populations of plants and animals or driven them to extinction. Finally, global change is altering the environment to the extent that it reduces the capacity of Earth to sustain life. **3.** If both populations breed separately, then gene flow between the populations would not occur and genetic differences between them would be greater. As a result, the loss of genetic diversity would be greater than if the populations interbreed.

Concept Check 56.2

1. Reduced genetic variation decreases the capacity of a population to evolve in the face of change. **2.** The effective population size, N_e, was $4(15 \times 5)/(15 + 5) = 15$ birds. **3.** Because millions of people use the greater Yellowstone ecosystem each year, it would be impossible to eliminate all contact between people and bears. Instead, you might try to reduce the kinds of encounters where bears are killed. You might recommend lower speed limits on roads in the park, adjust the timing or location of hunting seasons (where hunting is allowed outside the park) to minimize contact with mother bears and cubs, and provide financial incentives for livestock owners to try alternative means of protecting livestock, such as using guard dogs.

Concept Check 56.3

1. A small area supporting numerous endemic species as well as a large number of endangered and threatened species **2.** Zoned reserves may provide sustained supplies of forest products, water, hydroelectric power, educational opportunities, and income from tourism. **3.** Habitat corridors can increase the rate of movement or dispersal of organisms between habitat patches and thus the rate of gene flow between subpopulations. They thus help prevent a decrease in fitness attributable to inbreeding. They can also minimize interactions between organisms and humans as the organisms disperse; in cases involving potential predators, such as bears or large cats, minimizing such interactions is desirable.

Concept Check 56.4

1. Adding nutrients causes population explosions of algae and the organisms that feed on them. Increased respiration by algae and consumers, including detritivores, depletes the lake's oxygen, which the fish require. **2.** Because higher temperatures lead to faster decomposition, organic matter in these soils could be quickly decomposed to CO_2, speeding up global warming. **3.** Reduced concentrations of ozone in the atmosphere increase the amount of UV radiation that reaches Earth's surface and the organisms living there. UV radiation can cause mutations by producing disruptive thymine dimers in DNA.

Concept Check 56.5

1. Sustainable development is an approach to development that works toward the long-term prosperity of human societies and the ecosystems that support them, which requires linking the biological sciences with the social sciences, economics, and humanities. **2.** Biophilia, our sense of connection to nature and all forms of life, may act as a significant motivation for the development of an environmental ethic that resolves not to allow species to become extinct or ecosystems to be destroyed. Such an ethic is necessary if we are to become more attentive and effective custodians of the environment. **3.** At a minimum, you would want to know the size of the population and the average reproductive rate of individuals in it. To develop the fishery sustainably, you would seek a harvest rate that maintains the population near its original size and maximizes its harvest in the long term rather than the short term.

Summary of Key Concepts Questions

56.1. Nature provides us with many beneficial services, including a supply of reliable, clean water, the production of food and fiber, and the dilution and detoxification of our pollutants. **56.2.** A more genetically diverse population is better able to withstand pressures from disease or environmental change, making it less likely to become extinct over a given period of time. **56.3.** Habitat fragmentation can isolate populations, leading to inbreeding and genetic drift, and it can make populations more susceptible to local extinctions resulting from the effects of pathogens, parasites, or predators. **56.4.** It's healthier to feed at a lower trophic level because biological magnification increases the concentration of toxins at higher levels. **56.5.** One goal of conservation biology is to preserve as many species as possible. Sustainable approaches that maintain the quality of habitats are required for the long-term survival of organisms.

Test Your Understanding

1. d **2.** d **3.** e **4.** a **5.** c **6.** a

7.

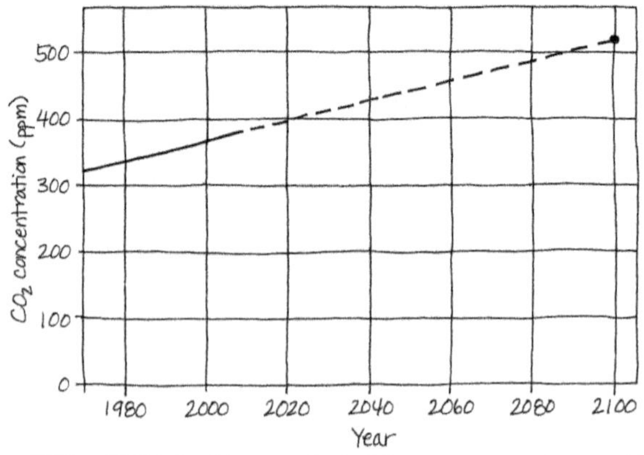

Between 1974 and 2009, Earth's atmospheric CO_2 concentration increased from approximately 330 ppm to 390 ppm. If this rate of increase of 1.7 ppm/yr continues, the concentration in 2100 will be about 540 ppm. The actual rise in CO_2 concentration could be larger or smaller, depending on Earth's human population, per capita energy use, and the extent to which societies take steps to reduce CO_2 emissions, including replacing fossil fuels with renewable or nuclear fuels. Additional scientific data will be important for many reasons, including determining how quickly greenhouse gases such as CO_2 are removed from the atmosphere by the biosphere.

9.

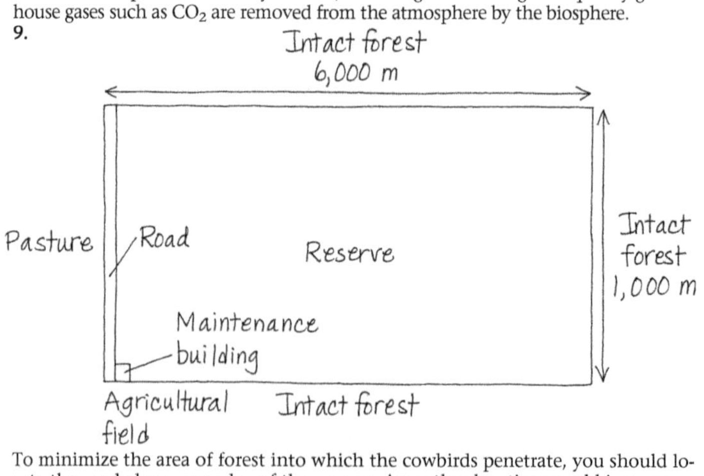

To minimize the area of forest into which the cowbirds penetrate, you should locate the road along one edge of the reserve. Any other location would increase the area of affected habitat. Similarly, the maintenance building should be in a corner of the reserve to minimize the area susceptible to cowbirds.

APPENDIX **B**
Periodic Table of the Elements

Atomic number (number of protons) → 6
Element symbol → C
12.01 ← Atomic mass (number of protons plus number of neutrons averaged over all isotopes)

Metals | Metalloids | Nonmetals

Representative elements

Alkali metals | Alkaline earth metals | Halogens | Noble gases

Groups: Elements in a vertical column have the same number of electrons in their valence (outer) shell and thus have similar chemical properties.

Periods: Each horizontal row contains elements with the same total number of electron shells. Across each period, elements are ordered by increasing atomic number.

Transition elements

Period number	1 Group 1A	2 Group 2A	3 3B	4 4B	5 5B	6 6B	7 7B	8 8B	9 8B	10 8B	11 1B	12 2B	13 Group 3A	14 Group 4A	15 Group 5A	16 Group 6A	17 Group 7A	18 Group 8A
1	1 H 1.008																	2 He 4.003
2	3 Li 6.941	4 Be 9.012											5 B 10.81	6 C 12.01	7 N 14.01	8 O 16.00	9 F 19.00	10 Ne 20.18
3	11 Na 22.99	12 Mg 24.31											13 Al 26.98	14 Si 28.09	15 P 30.97	16 S 32.07	17 Cl 35.45	18 Ar 39.95
4	19 K 39.10	20 Ca 40.08	21 Sc 44.96	22 Ti 47.87	23 V 50.94	24 Cr 52.00	25 Mn 54.94	26 Fe 55.85	27 Co 58.93	28 Ni 58.69	29 Cu 63.55	30 Zn 65.41	31 Ga 69.72	32 Ge 72.64	33 As 74.92	34 Se 78.96	35 Br 79.90	36 Kr 83.80
5	37 Rb 85.47	38 Sr 87.62	39 Y 88.91	40 Zr 91.22	41 Nb 92.91	42 Mo 95.94	43 Tc (98)	44 Ru 101.1	45 Rh 102.9	46 Pd 106.4	47 Ag 107.9	48 Cd 112.4	49 In 114.8	50 Sn 118.7	51 Sb 121.8	52 Te 127.6	53 I 126.9	54 Xe 131.3
6	55 Cs 132.9	56 Ba 137.3	57* La 138.9	72 Hf 178.5	73 Ta 180.9	74 W 183.8	75 Re 186.2	76 Os 190.2	77 Ir 192.2	78 Pt 195.1	79 Au 197.0	80 Hg 200.6	81 Tl 204.4	82 Pb 207.2	83 Bi 209.0	84 Po (209)	85 At (210)	86 Rn (222)
7	87 Fr (223)	88 Ra (226)	89† Ac (227)	104 Rf (261)	105 Db (262)	106 Sg (266)	107 Bh (264)	108 Hs (269)	109 Mt (268)	110 Ds (271)	111 Rg (272)	112 Cn (285)	113 — (284)	114 — (289)	115 — (288)	116 — (293)	117 — (294?)	118 — (294)

*Lanthanides	58 Ce 140.1	59 Pr 140.9	60 Nd 144.2	61 Pm (145)	62 Sm 150.4	63 Eu 152.0	64 Gd 157.3	65 Tb 158.9	66 Dy 162.5	67 Ho 164.9	68 Er 167.3	69 Tm 168.9	70 Yb 173.0	71 Lu 175.0
†Actinides	90 Th 232.0	91 Pa 231.0	92 U 238.0	93 Np (237)	94 Pu (244)	95 Am (243)	96 Cm (247)	97 Bk (247)	98 Cf (251)	99 Es 252	100 Fm 257	101 Md 258	102 No 259	103 Lr 260

Name (Symbol)	Atomic Number	Name (Symbol)	Atomic Number	Name (Symbol)	Atomic Number	Name (Symbol)	Atomic Number	Name (Symbol)	Atomic Number
Actinium (Ac)	89	Copernicium (Cn)	112	Iridium (Ir)	77	Palladium (Pd)	46	Sodium (Na)	11
Aluminum (Al)	13	Copper (Cu)	29	Iron (Fe)	26	Phosphorus (P)	15	Strontium (Sr)	38
Americium (Am)	95	Curium (Cm)	96	Krypton (Kr)	36	Platinum (Pt)	78	Sulfur (S)	16
Antimony (Sb)	51	Darmstadtium (Ds)	110	Lanthanum (La)	57	Plutonium (Pu)	94	Tantalum (Ta)	73
Argon (Ar)	18	Dubnium (Db)	105	Lawrencium (Lr)	103	Polonium (Po)	84	Technetium (Tc)	43
Arsenic (As)	33	Dysprosium (Dy)	66	Lead (Pb)	82	Potassium (K)	19	Tellurium (Te)	52
Astatine (At)	85	Einsteinium (Es)	99	Lithium (Li)	3	Praseodymium (Pr)	59	Terbium (Tb)	65
Barium (Ba)	56	Erbium (Er)	68	Lutetium (Lu)	71	Promethium (Pm)	61	Thallium (Tl)	81
Berkelium (Bk)	97	Europium (Eu)	63	Magnesium (Mg)	12	Protactinium (Pa)	91	Thorium (Th)	90
Beryllium (Be)	4	Fermium (Fm)	100	Manganese (Mn)	25	Radium (Ra)	88	Thulium (Tm)	69
Bismuth (Bi)	83	Fluorine (F)	9	Meitnerium (Mt)	109	Radon (Rn)	86	Tin (Sn)	50
Bohrium (Bh)	107	Francium (Fr)	87	Mendelevium (Md)	101	Rhenium (Re)	75	Titanium (Ti)	22
Boron (B)	5	Gadolinium (Gd)	64	Mercury (Hg)	80	Rhodium (Rh)	45	Tungsten (W)	74
Bromine (Br)	35	Gallium (Ga)	31	Molybdenum (Mo)	42	Roentgenium (Rg)	111	Uranium (U)	92
Cadmium (Cd)	48	Germanium (Ge)	32	Neodymium (Nd)	60	Rubidium (Rb)	37	Vanadium (V)	23
Calcium (Ca)	20	Gold (Au)	79	Neon (Ne)	10	Ruthenium (Ru)	44	Xenon (Xe)	54
Californium (Cf)	98	Hafnium (Hf)	72	Neptunium (Np)	93	Rutherfordium (Rf)	104	Ytterbium (Yb)	70
Carbon (C)	6	Hassium (Hs)	108	Nickel (Ni)	28	Samarium (Sm)	62	Yttrium (Y)	39
Cerium (Ce)	58	Helium (He)	2	Niobium (Nb)	41	Scandium (Sc)	21	Zinc (Zn)	30
Cesium (Cs)	55	Holmium (Ho)	67	Nitrogen (N)	7	Seaborgium (Sg)	106	Zirconium (Zr)	40
Chlorine (Cl)	17	Hydrogen (H)	1	Nobelium (No)	102	Selenium (Se)	34		
Chromium (Cr)	24	Indium (In)	49	Osmium (Os)	76	Silicon (Si)	14		
Cobalt (Co)	27	Iodine (I)	53	Oxygen (O)	8	Silver (Ag)	47		

C The Metric System

Measurement	Unit and Abbreviation	Metric Equivalent	Metric-to-English Conversion Factor	English-to-Metric Conversion Factor
Length	1 kilometer (km)	= 1,000 (10^3) meters	1 km = 0.62 mile	1 mile = 1.61 km
	1 meter (m)	= 100 (10^2) centimeters	1 m = 1.09 yards	1 yard = 0.914 m
		= 1,000 millimeters	1 m = 3.28 feet	1 foot = 0.305 m
			1 m = 39.37 inches	
	1 centimeter (cm)	= 0.01 (10^{-2}) meter	1 cm = 0.394 inch	1 foot = 30.5 cm
				1 inch = 2.54 cm
	1 millimeter (mm)	= 0.001 (10^{-3}) meter	1 mm = 0.039 inch	
	1 micrometer (μm) (formerly micron, μ)	= 10^{-6} meter (10^{-3} mm)		
	1 nanometer (nm) (formerly millimicron, mμ)	= 10^{-9} meter (10^{-3} μm)		
	1 angstrom (Å)	= 10^{-10} meter (10^{-4} μm)		
Area	1 hectare (ha)	= 10,000 square meters	1 ha = 2.47 acres	1 acre = 0.405 ha
	1 square meter (m^2)	= 10,000 square centimeters	1 m^2 = 1.196 square yards	1 square yard = 0.8361 m^2
			1 m^2 = 10.764 square feet	1 square foot = 0.0929 m^2
	1 square centimeter (cm^2)	= 100 square millimeters	1 cm^2 = 0.155 square inch	1 square inch = 6.4516 cm^2
Mass	1 metric ton (t)	= 1,000 kilograms	1 t = 1.103 tons	1 ton = 0.907 t
	1 kilogram (kg)	= 1,000 grams	1 kg = 2.205 pounds	1 pound = 0.4536 kg
	1 gram (g)	= 1,000 milligrams	1 g = 0.0353 ounce	1 ounce = 28.35 g
			1 g = 15.432 grains	
	1 milligram (mg)	= 10^{-3} gram	1 mg = approx. 0.015 grain	
	1 microgram (μg)	= 10^{-6} gram		
Volume (solids)	1 cubic meter (m^3)	= 1,000,000 cubic centimeters	1 m^3 = 1.308 cubic yards	1 cubic yard = 0.7646 m^3
			1 m^3 = 35.315 cubic feet	1 cubic foot = 0.0283 m^3
	1 cubic centimeter (cm^3 or cc)	= 10^{-6} cubic meter	1 cm^3 = 0.061 cubic inch	1 cubic inch = 16.387 cm^3
	1 cubic millimeter (mm^3)	= 10^{-9} cubic meter = 10^{-3} cubic centimeter		
Volume (liquids and gases)	1 kiloliter (kL or kl)	= 1,000 liters	1 kL = 264.17 gallons	
	1 liter (L or l)	= 1,000 milliliters	1 L = 0.264 gallons	1 gallon = 3.785 L
			1 L = 1.057 quarts	1 quart = 0.946 L
	1 milliliter (mL or ml)	= 10^{-3} liter	1 mL = 0.034 fluid ounce	1 quart = 946 mL
		= 1 cubic centimeter	1 mL = approx. $\frac{1}{4}$ teaspoon	1 pint = 473 mL
			1 mL = approx. 15–16 drops (gtt.)	1 fluid ounce = 29.57 mL
				1 teaspoon = approx. 5 mL
	1 microliter (μL or μl)	= 10^{-6} liter (10^{-3} milliliters)		
Time	1 second (s or sec)	= $\frac{1}{60}$ minute		
	1 millisecond (ms or msec)	= 10^{-3} second		
Temperature	Degrees Celsius (°C) (Absolute zero, when all molecular motion ceases, is −273.15°C. The Kelvin [K] scale, which has the same size degrees as Celsius, has its zero point at absolute zero. Thus, 0 K = −273.15°C.)		°F = $\frac{9}{5}$°C + 32	°C = $\frac{5}{9}$ (°F − 32)

D A Comparison of the Light Microscope and the Electron Microscope

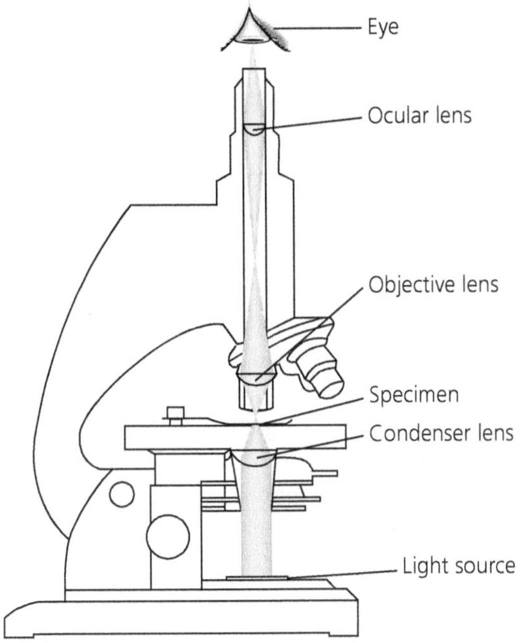

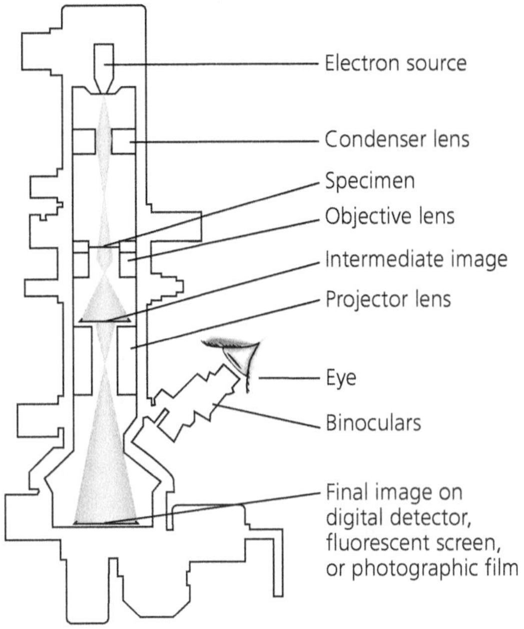

Light Microscope

In light microscopy, light is focused on a specimen by a glass condenser lens; the image is then magnified by an objective lens and an ocular lens, for projection on the eye, digital camera, digital video camera, or photographic film.

Electron Microscope

In electron microscopy, a beam of electrons (top of the microscope) is used instead of light, and electromagnets are used instead of glass lenses. The electron beam is focused on the specimen by a condenser lens; the image is magnified by an objective lens and a projector lens for projection on a digital detector, fluorescent screen, or photographic film.

APPENDIX E Classification of Life

This appendix presents a taxonomic classification for the major extant groups of organisms discussed in this text; not all phyla are included. The classification presented here is based on the three-domain system, which assigns the two major groups of prokaryotes, bacteria and archaea, to separate domains (with eukaryotes making up the third domain).

Various alternative classification schemes are discussed in Unit Five of the text. The taxonomic turmoil includes debates about the number and boundaries of kingdoms and about the alignment of the Linnaean classification hierarchy with the findings of modern cladistic analysis. In this review, asterisks (*) indicate currently recognized phyla thought by some systematists to be paraphyletic.

DOMAIN BACTERIA

- **Proteobacteria**
- **Chlamydia**
- **Spirochetes**
- **Gram-positive Bacteria**
- **Cyanobacteria**

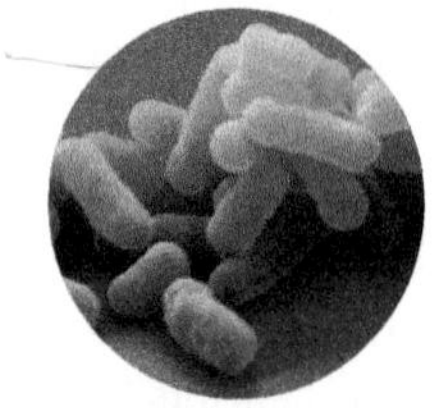

DOMAIN ARCHAEA

- **Korarchaeota**
- **Euryarchaeota**
- **Crenarchaeota**
- **Nanoarchaeota**

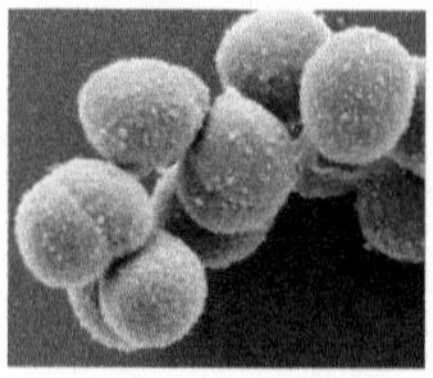

DOMAIN EUKARYA

In the phylogenetic hypothesis we present in Chapter 28, major clades of eukaryotes are grouped together in the five "supergroups" listed below in blue type. Formerly, all the eukaryotes generally called protists were assigned to a single kingdom, Protista. However, advances in systematics have made it clear that Protista is in fact polyphyletic: Some protists are more closely related to plants, fungi, or animals than they are to other protists. As a result, the kingdom Protista has been abandoned.

Excavata

- Diplomonadida (diplomonads)
- Parabasala (parabasalids)
- Euglenozoa (euglenozoans)
  - Kinetoplastida (kinetoplastids)
  - Euglenophyta (euglenids)

Chromalveolata

- Alveolata (alveolates)
  - Dinoflagellata (dinoflagellates)
  - Apicomplexa (apicomplexans)
  - Ciliophora (ciliates)
- Stramenopila (stramenopiles)
  - Bacillariophyta (diatoms)
  - Chrysophyta (golden algae)
  - Phaeophyta (brown algae)
  - Oomycota (water molds)

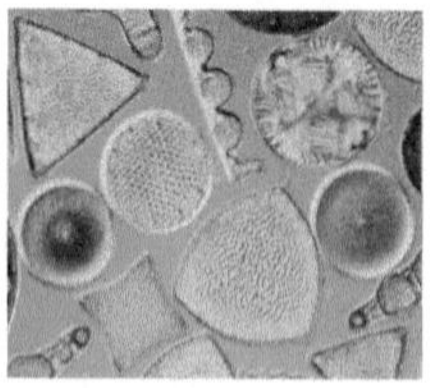

Archaeplastida

- Rhodophyta (red algae)
- Chlorophyta (green algae: chlorophytes)
- Charophyta (green algae: charophytes)
- Plantae
  - Nonvascular plants (bryophytes):
    - Phylum Hepatophyta (liverworts)
    - Phylum Bryophyta (mosses)
    - Phylum Anthocerophyta (hornworts)
  - Seedless vascular plants:
    - Phylum Lycophyta (lycophytes)
    - Phylum Pterophyta (ferns, horsetails, whisk ferns)
  - Seed plants:
    - Gymnosperms:
      - Phylum Ginkgophyta (ginkgo)
      - Phylum Cycadophyta (cycads)
      - Phylum Gnetophyta (gnetophytes)
      - Phylum Coniferophyta (conifers)
    - Angiosperms:
      - Phylum Anthophyta (flowering plants)

Rhizaria

- Radiolaria (radiolarians)
- Foraminifera (forams)
- Cercozoa (cercozoans)

DOMAIN EUKARYA, continued

Unikonta

- Amoebozoa (amoebozoans)
  - Myxogastrida (plasmodial slime molds)
  - Dictyostelida (cellular slime molds)
  - Gymnamoeba (gymnamoebas)
  - Entamoeba (entamoebas)
- Nucleariida (nucleariids)
- Fungi
  - *Phylum Chytridiomycota (chytrids)
  - *Phylum Zygomycota (zygomycetes)
  - Phylum Glomeromycota (glomeromycetes)
  - Phylum Basidiomycota (club fungi)
  - Phylum Ascomycota (sac fungi)

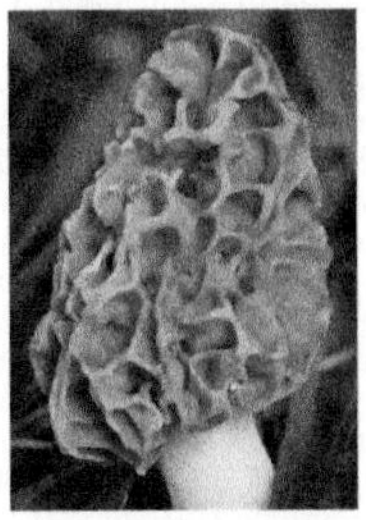

- Choanoflagellata (choanoflagellates)
- Animalia
  - Phylum Porifera (sponges)
  - Phylum Ctenophora (comb jellies)
  - Phylum Cnidaria (cnidarians)
    - Hydrozoa (hydrozoans)
    - Scyphozoa (jellies)
    - Cubozoa (box jellies and sea wasps)
    - Anthozoa (sea anemones and most corals)
  - Phylum Acoela (acoel flatworms)
  - Phylum Placozoa (placozoans)
  - Lophotrochozoa (lophotrochozoans)
    - Phylum Kinorhyncha (kinorhynchs)
    - Phylum Platyhelminthes (flatworms)
      - Catenulida (chain worms)
      - Rhabditophora (planarians, flukes, tapeworms)
    - Phylum Nemertea (proboscis worms)
    - Phylum Ectoprocta (ectoprocts)
    - Phylum Brachiopoda (brachiopods)
    - Phylum Phoronida (phoronids)
    - Phylum Rotifera (rotifers)
    - Phylum Cycliophora (cycliophorans)
    - Phylum Mollusca (molluscs)
      - Polyplacophora (chitons)
      - Gastropoda (gastropods)
      - Bivalvia (bivalves)
      - Cephalopoda (cephalopods)
    - Phylum Annelida (segmented worms)
      - Polychaeta (polychaetes)
      - Oligochaeta (oligochaetes)
    - Phylum Acanthocephala (spiny-headed worms)
  - Ecdysozoa (ecdysozoans)
    - Phylum Loricifera (loriciferans)
    - Phylum Priapula (priapulans)
    - Phylum Nematoda (roundworms)
    - Phylum Arthropoda (This survey groups arthropods into a single phylum, but some zoologists now split the arthropods into multiple phyla.)
      - Subphylum Chelicerata (horseshoe crabs, arachnids)
      - Subphylum Myriapoda (millipedes, centipedes)
      - Subphylum Hexapoda (insects, springtails)
      - Subphylum Crustacea (crustaceans)
    - Phylum Tardigrada (tardigrades)
    - Phylum Onychophora (velvet worms)
  - Deuterostomia (deuterostomes)
    - Phylum Hemichordata (hemichordates)
    - Phylum Echinodermata (echinoderms)
      - Asteroidea (sea stars, sea daisies)
      - Ophiuroidea (brittle stars)
      - Echinoidea (sea urchins and sand dollars)
      - Crinoidea (sea lilies)
      - Holothuroidea (sea cucumbers)
    - Phylum Chordata (chordates)
      - Subphylum Cephalochordata (cephalochordates: lancelets)
      - Subphylum Urochrodata (urochordates: tunicates)
      - Subphylum Craniata (craniates)
        - Myxini (hagfishes)
        - Petromyzontida (lampreys) — Vertebrates:
        - Chondrichthyes (sharks, rays, chimaeras)
        - Actinopterygii (ray-finned fishes)
        - Actinistia (coelacanths)
        - Dipnoi (lungfishes)
        - Amphibia (amphibians)
        - Reptilia (tuataras, lizards, snakes, turtles, crocodilians, birds)
        - Mammalia (mammals)

(Petromyzontida through Mammalia: Vertebrates)

Appendix E Classification of Life

Credits

Photo Credits

Cover Image "Succulent I" © 2005 Amy Lamb, www.amylamb.com

Unit Opening Interviews **UNIT 1** Justina Thorsen, Showcase Reflections; **UNIT 2** Brian Wilson, Princeton University; **UNIT 3** William K. Sacco, Yale ITS Photo + Design Services; **UNIT 4** Steve Bonnel, Bonnel Photography; **UNIT 5** Jacob Mailman; **UNIT 6** Michael Starghill, Michael Starghill Photography; **UNIT 7** River Healey, Rusty Healey Photography; **UNIT 8** Marsha Miller, Director of Photography, University of Texas at Austin.

About the Author Photos River Healey, Rusty Healey Photography.

Detailed Contents **UNIT I** Photo by T. Naeser, from Patrick Cramer Laboratory, Gene Center Munich, Ludwig-Maximilians-Universität München, Munich, Germany; **UNIT II** Biophoto Associates/Photo Researchers; **UNIT III** From: Multicolor Spectral Karyotyping of Human Chromosomes. E. Schröck, S. du Manoir, T. Veldman, B. Schoell, J. Wienberg, M. A. Ferguson-Smith, Y. Ning, D. H. Ledbetter, I. Bar-Am, D. Soenksen, Y. Garini, T. Ried. *Science.* 1996 Jul 26;273(5274):494-7.; **UNIT IV** © Ted Daeschler/ Academy of Natural Sciences/VIREO; **UNIT V** Yufeng Zhou/iStockphoto; **UNIT VI** PD photo: John Walker (www.fourmilab.ch); **UNIT VII** David Wall/Alamy; David Doubilet/Getty Images; Kenneth Catania; **UNIT VIII** Daniel Mosquin.

Chapter 1 **1.1** Amy Lamb Studio; **1.2** Walter Teague; **1.3.2** R.Dirscherl/FLPA; **1.3.3** Kim Taylor and Jane Burton/Dorling Kindersley; **1.3.4** Malcolm Schuyl/FLPA; **1.3.5** Frans Lanting/Corbis; **1.3.6** Michael & Patricia Fogden/Corbis; **1.3.7** Joe McDonald/ Corbis; **1.3.8** ImageState/International Stock Photography Ltd.; **1.4.2** WorldSat International/Photo Researchers, Inc.; **1.4.3** Bill Brooks/Alamy; **1.4.4** Linda Freshwaters Arndt/Alamy; **1.4.5** Michael Orton/Photographer's Choice/Getty Images; **1.4.6** Ross M. Horowitz/Getty Images; **1.4.7** Photodisc/Getty Images; **1.4.9** Jeremy Burgess/ SPL/Photo Researchers; **1.4.11** John Durham/Photo Researchers; **1.4.13** Electron micrograph by Wm. P. Wergin, courtesy of E. H. Newcomb, University of Wisconsin; **1.5.2** James Balog/Aurora Creative/Getty Images; **1.6.2** Anup Shah/Nature Picture Library; **1.6.3** Anup Shah/Nature Picture Library; **1.7.2** Photodisc/Getty Images; **1.7.3** Janice Sheldon; **1.8.2** S. C. Holt/Biological Photo Service; **1.8.3** Steve Gschmeissner/ Photo Researchers; **1.9.2** Conly L. Rieder; **1.9.3** Conly L. Rieder; **1.10.2** Camille Tokerud/ Stone/Getty Images; **1.11.2** Photodisc/Getty Images; **1.12** Roy Kaltschmidt, Lawrence Berkeley National Laboratory; **1.15.2** Oliver Meckes/Nicole Ottawa/Photo Researchers; **1.15.3** Eye of Science/Photo Researchers; **1.15.4** Kunst & Scheidulin/AGE Fotostock; **1.15.5** Peter Lilja/Taxi/Getty Images; **1.15.6** Anup Shah/Nature Picture Library; **1.15.7** D. P. Wilson/Photo Researchers; **1.16.2** VVG/SPL/Photo Researchers; **1.16.3** W. L. Dentler/Biological Photo Service; **1.16.4** OMIKRON/Photo Researchers; **1.17** Photo by Dede Randrianarisata, from Kristi Curry Rogers, Macalester College, St. Paul, MN; **1.18** ARCHIV/Photo Researchers; **1.19.2** Michael P. Fogden/Bruce Coleman/ Alamy; **1.19.3** Matt T. Lee; **1.19.4** Hal Horwitz/Corbis; **1.21** Frank Greenaway/Dorling Kindersley; **1.23.2** Karl Ammann/Corbis; **1.23.3** Tim Ridley/Dorling Kindersley, Courtesy of the Jane Goodall Institute, Clarendon Park, Hampshire; **1.25.2** Breck P. Kent; **1.25.3** Barry Mansell/Nature Picture Library; **1.26.2** David Pfennig; **1.26.3** David Pfennig; **1.28** Gary L. Firestone's Lab researchers meeting in the Dept. of Molecular and Cell Biology, University of California at Berkeley. Photo: Seelevel.com, Pearson Science; **1.29** Tim Sharp/AP Images; **p. 25, top right** James Balog/Aurora Creative/ Getty Images; **p. 25, bottom left** Anup Shah/Nature Picture Library; **p. 25, bottom left** Anup Shah/Nature Picture Library; **p.26, top** PhotoDisc/Getty Images; **p. 26, 2nd from top** S. C. Holt/ Biological Photo Service; **p. 26, 3rd from top** Steve Gschmeissner/Photo Researchers.

Chapter 2 **2.1** Martin Dohrn/BBC Natural History Unit; **2.2.3** Martin Dohrn/BBC Natural History Unit; **2.3.2** Chip Clark; **2.4.2** C. Michael Hogan; **2.4.3** Rick York and California Native Plant Society (www.cnps.org); **2.4.4** Andrew Alden; **2.6.2** Clayton T. Hamilton, Stanford University; **2.7.2** National Library of Medicine; **p. 41, left** Jerry Young/Dorling Kindersley; **2.19** Nigel Cattlin/Photo Researchers; **p. 45** Rolf Nussbaumer/Nature Picture Library.

Chapter 3 **3.1** Alexander/Fotoloia; **3.3.2** N.C. Brown Center for Ultrastructure Studies, SUNY-Environmental Science & Forestry, Syracuse, NY; **3.4** iStockphoto; **3.6.2** Jan van Franeker, IMARES, Alfred Wegener Institute for Polar and Marine Research; **3.9** NASA/JPL-Caltech/University of Arizona/Texas A&M University; **3.10.2** Jakub Semeniuk/ iStockphoto; **3.10.3** Feng Yu/iStockphoto; **3.10.4** Monika Wisniewska/iStockphoto; **3.10.5** Beth Van Trees/Shutterstock; **3.12.2** From "Coral Reefs Under Rapid Climate Change and Ocean Acidification." O. Hoegh-Guldberg, et al. *Science* 14 December 2007: 318 (5857):1737–1742. Photos by Ove Hoegh-Guldberg, Centre for Marine Studies, The University of Queensland; **3.12.3** From "Coral Reefs Under Rapid Climate Change and Ocean Acidification." O. Hoegh-Guldberg, et al. *Science* 14 December 2007: 318 (5857):1737–1742. Photos by Ove Hoegh-Guldberg, Centre for Marine Studies, The University of Queensland; **3.12.4** From "Coral Reefs Under Rapid Climate Change and Ocean Acidification." O. Hoegh-Guldberg, et al. *Science* 14 December 2007: 318 (5857):1737–1742. Photos by Ove Hoegh-Guldberg, Centre for Marine Studies, The University of Queensland.

Chapter 4 **4.1** Shutterstock; **4.6.2** David M. Phillips/Photo Researchers.

Chapter 5 **5.1** Photo by T. Naeser, from Patrick Cramer Laboratory, Gene Center Munich, Ludwig-Maximilians-Universität München, Munich, Germany; **5.6.2** John N. A. Lott/Biological Photo Service; **5.6.3** H. Shio and P. B. Lazarow; **5.8.2** Alexey Repka/iStockphoto; **5.8.3** John Durham/Photo Researchers; **5.8.4** Biophoto Associates/Photo Researchers; **5.9.2** F. Collet/Photo Researchers; **5.9.3** Corbis; **5.11.2** Dorling Kindersley; **5.11.3** Dorling Kindersley; **5.15.2** Andrey Stratilatov/ Shutterstock; **5.15.3** Nina Zanetti; **5.15.4** Nina Zanetti; **5.19.2** Reproduced by permission from Tulip WR, Varghese JN, Laver WG, Webster RG, Colman PM. Refined crystal structure of the influenza virus N9 neuraminidase-NC41 Fab complex. *J Mol Biol.* September 5; 227(1):122–48. Copyright © 1992 by Elsevier Science Ltd. **5.20.3** Dieter Hopf/AGE Fotostock; **5.20.8** Monika Wisniewska/iStockphoto; **5.21.2** Eye of Science/Photo Researchers; **5.21.3** Eye of Science/Photo Researchers; **5.23.2** Reprinted by permission from *Nature.* P. B. Sigler from Z. Xu, A. L. Horwich, and P. B. Sigler. 388:741–750 Copyright © 1997 Macmillan Magazines Limited; **5.24.2** Dave Bushnell; **5.24.4** Dave Bushnell; **p. 90** Dorling Kindersley.

Chapter 6 **6.1** Eye of Science/Photo Researchers; **6.3.2** Elisabeth Pierson, FNWI-Radboud University Nijmegen, Pearson Science; **6.3.3** Elisabeth Pierson, FNWI-Radboud University Nijmegen, Pearson Science; **6.3.4** Elisabeth Pierson, FNWI-Radboud University Nijmegen, Pearson Science; **6.3.5** Elisabeth Pierson, FNWI-Radboud University Nijmegen, Pearson Science; **6.3.6** Michael W. Davidson/The Florida State University Research Foundation; **6.3.7** Karl Garsha, Beckman Institute for Advanced Science and Technology, University of Illinois; **6.3.9** Macrophage fluorescently stained for tubulin (yellow), actin (red) and the nucleus (DAPI, blue). Top part of the image: data recorded with a widefield microscope and visualized with the Simulated Fluorescence Process (SFP) volume rendering algorithm. Bottom part: the same dataset, deconvolved using Huygens Professional (Scientific Volume Imaging, Hilversum, The Netherlands) and again rendered with the SFP algorithm. Data courtesy Dr. James G. Evans, Whitehead Institute, MIT Boston MA, USA; **6.3.11** From "Motile Cilia of Human Airway Epithelia Are Chemosensory." Alok S. Shah, Yehuda Ben-Shahar, T.s O. Moninger, J. N. Kline, M. J. Welsh. Science Express on 23 July 2009. *Science* 28 August 2009:325 (5944): 1131–1134 (cover). Pseudocolored scanning electron micrograph by Tom Moninger (epithelia generated by Phil Karp); **6.3.12** William Dentler/Biological Photo Service; **6.3.13** From "STED microscopy reveals that synaptotagmin remains clustered after synaptic vesicle exocytosis." Katrin I. Willig, Silvio O. Rizzoli, Volker Westphal, Reinhard Jahn & . . . Stefan W. Hell. *Nature,* 440 (13) April 2006. doi:10.1038/nature04592, Letters; **6.5.2** S. C. Holt/Biological Photo Service; **6.6.2** Daniel Friend; **6.8.4** S. Cinti/Photo Researchers; **6.8.6** SPL/Photo Researchers; **6.8.8** A. Barry Dowsett/Photo Researchers; **6.8.10** Biophoto Associates/ Photo Researchers; **6.8.12** SPL/Photo Researchers; **6.8.14** From "Flagellar Microtubule Dynamics in *Chlamydomonas:* Cytochalasin D Induces Periods of Microtubule Shortening and Elongation; and Colchicine Induces Disassembly of the Distal, but Not Proximal, Half of the Flagellum." W. L. Dentler and C. Adams. *The Journal of Cell Biology,* 117(6): 1289–1298, Copyright © 1992 by The Rockefeller University Press; **6.9.2** Reproduced by permission from L.Orci and A.Perelet, Freeze-Etch Histology. (Heidelberg: Springer-Verlag, 1975). Copyright ©1975 by Springer-Verlag GmbH & Co KG; **6.9.3** Reproduced by permission from A. C. Faberge, *Cell Tiss. Res.* 151 Copyright © 1974 by Springer-Verlag GmbH & Co KG; **6.9.4** Reprinted by permission from *Nature* 323. U. Aebi et al. Copyright © 1996: 560–564, figure 1a. Used with permission. Macmillan Magazines Limited; **6.10.2** D. W. Fawcett/Photo Researchers; **6.11.2** R. Bolender, D. Fawcett/Photo Researchers; **6.12.2** Don W. Fawcett/ Photo Researchers; **6.13.2** Daniel S. Friend; **6.13.3** Daniel S. Friend; **6.14.2** E. H. Newcomb; **6.17.2** Daniel S. Friend; **6.17.3** From "The shape of mitochondria and the number of mitochondrial nucleoids during the cell cycle of *Euglena gracilis.*" Y. Hayashi and K. Ueda. *Journal of Cell Science,* 93:565–570, Copyright © 1989 by Company of Biologists; **6.18.2** Courtesy of W.P. Wergin and E.H. Newcomb, University of Wisconsin/Biological Photo Service; **6.18.3** Franz Grolig, Philipps-University Marburg, Germany. Image acquired with the confocal microscope Leica TCS SP2; **6.19.2** From S. E. Fredrick and E. H. Newcomb, *The Journal of Cell Biology* 43 (1969):343. Provided by E. H. Newcomb; **6.20** Albert Tousson, High Resolution Imaging Facility, University of Alabama at Birmingham; **6.21.2** Dr. Bruce J. Schnapp; **p. 113, left** Mary Osborn; **p. 113, middle** Frank Solomon; **p. 113, right** Mark S. Ladinsky and J. Richard McIntosh, University of Colorado; **6.22.2** Kent L. McDonald; **6.23.2** Biophoto Associates/Photo Researchers; **6.23.3** Oliver Meckes & Nicole Ottawa/Eye of Science/Photo Researchers; **6.24.2** OMIKRON/Science Source/Photo Researchers; **6.24.3** W. L. Dentler/Biological Photo Service; **6.24.4** Linck RW, Stephens RE. Functional protofilament numbering of ciliary, flagellar, and centriolar microtubules. *Cell Motil Cytoskeleton.* 2007 Jul;64(7):489–95; cover. Micrograph by D. Woodrum Hensley; **6.26.2** From Hirokawa Nobutaka, *The Journal of Cell Biology* 94 (1982):425 by copyright permission of The Rockefeller University Press; **6.27.2** Clara Franzini-Armstrong, University of Pennsylvania; **6.27.3** M. I. Walker/Photo Researchers; **6.27.4** Michael Clayton, University of Wisconsin-Madison; **6.28.2** G. F. Leedale/Photo Researchers; **6.29.2** David Ehrhardt; **6.29.3** From "Visualization of cellulose synthase demonstrates functional association with microtubules." A. R. Paredez, C. R. Somerville, D. W. Ehrhardt. *Science.* 2006 Jun 9;312(5779):1491–5. Epub 2006 Apr 20; **6.31.2** Micrograph by W. P. Wergin, provided by E. H. Newcomb; **6.32.2** From Douglas J. Kelly, *The Journal of Cell Biology* 28 (1966): 51. Fig.17. Reproduced by copyright permission of The Rockefeller University Press; **6.32.3** From Douglas J. Kelly, *The Journal of Cell Biology* 28 (1966):51 by copyright permission of The Rockefeller University Press; **6.32.5** Reproduced by permission from L. Orci and A. Perrelet, Freeze-Etch Histology. (Heidelberg: Springer-Verlag). Copyright © 1975 by Springer-Verlag GmbH & Co KG; **6.32.7** From C. Peracchia and A. F. Dulhunty, *The Journal of Cell Biology* 70 (1976):419 by copyright permission of The Rockefeller University Press; **6.33.2** Lennart Nilsson/ Scanpix; **p. 123, top** Courtesy E. H. Newcomb; **p. 123, bottom** From S. E. Fredrick and E. H. Newcomb, *The Journal of Cell Biology* 43 (1969): 343.

Chapter 7 **7.1** Roderick Mackinnon; **7.4.3** D. W. Fawcett/Photo Researchers; **7.4.4** D. W. Fawcett/Photo Researchers; **7.16.2.** Michael Abbey/Photo Researchers; **7.22.3** H. S. Pankratz, T.C. Beaman & P. Gerhardt/Biological Photo Service; **7.22.6** D. W. Fawcett/ Photo Researchers; **7.22.9** M. M. Perry and A. B. Gilbert, *J. Cell Science* 39 (1979) 257. Copyright 1979 by The Company of Biologists Ltd. **7.22.10** M. M. Perry and A. B. Gilbert, *J. Cell Science* 39 (1979) 257. Copyright 1979 by The Company of Biologists Ltd.

Chapter 8 **8.1** Photoshot/NHPA; **8.2.2** Jupiter Images; **8.3.2** Robert N. Johnson/RnJ Photography; **8.3.3** Robert N. Johnson/RnJ Photography; **8.4.1** Brandon Blinkenberg/iStockphoto; **8.4.2** Bridget Lazenby/iStockphoto; **8.14.2** Thomas A. Steitz, Yale University; **8.14.3** Thomas A. Steitz, Yale University; **8.20.3** Scheer JM, Romanowski MJ, Wells JA. A common allosteric site and mechanism in caspases. *Proc Natl Acad Sci U S A.* 2006 May 16;103(20):7595–600; Fig. 4a; **8.22.2** Nicolae Simionescu.

Chapter 9 **9.1** Anup Shah/Nature Picture Library.

Chapter 10 **10.1** Bob Rowan, Progressive Image/Corbis; **10.2.2** Jean-Paul Nacivet/AGE Fotostock; **10.2.3** Lawrence Naylor/Photo Researchers; **10.2.4** M. I. Walker/Photo Researchers; **10.2.5** Susan M. Barns; **10.2.6** National Library of Medicine; **10.3** Robert Clark Photography, robertclark.com; **10.4.2** Image courtesy Andreas Holzenburg and Stanislav Vitha, Dept. of Biology and Microscopy & Imaging Center, Texas A&M University; **10.4.3** E.H Newcomb & WP Wergin/Biological Photo Service; **10.12.2** Christine L. Case, Skyline College; **10.13.2** From "Architecture of the photosynthetic oxygen-evolving center."; . . . K. N. Ferreira,T. M. Iverson, K. Maghlaoui, J. Barber, S. Iwata. *Science.* 2004 Mar 19;303(5665):1831–8. Epub 2004 Feb 5; **10.21.2** David Muench/Corbis; **10.21.3** Dave Bartruff/Corbis.

Chapter 11 **11.1** Winfried Wisniewski/Corbis; **11.3.2** A. Dale Kaiser, Stanford University; **11.8.2** From "High-resolution crystal structure of an engineered human beta2-adrenergic G protein-coupled receptor." V. Cherezov, D. M. Rosenbaum, M. A. Hanson, S. G. F. Rasmussen, F. S. Thian, T. S. Kobilka, H-J. Choi, P. Kuhn, W. I. Weis, B. K. Kobilka, R. C. Stevens. *Science.* 2007 Nov 23;318(5854):1258–65. Epub 2007 Oct 25; **11.17.3** Matheos D, Metodiev M, Muller E, Stone D, Rose MD. Pheromone-induced polarization is dependent on the Fus3p MAPK acting through the formin Bni1p. *J Cell Biol.* 2004 April; 165(1);99–109; Fig.9. Reproduced by copyright permission of The Rockefeller University Press; **11.20.2** Gopal Murti/Photo Researchers; **11.22.2** *Development* 127, 5245–5252 (2000). Mesenchymal cells engulf and clear apoptotic footplate cells in macrophageless PU.1 null mouse embryos. William Wood, Mark Turmaine, Roberta Weber, Victoria Camp, Richard A. Maki, Scott R. McKercher and Paul Martin; **11.22.3** *Development* 127, 5245–5252 (2000). Mesenchymal cells engulf and clear apoptotic footplate cells in macrophageless PU.1 null mouse embryos. William Wood, Mark Turmaine, Roberta Weber, Victoria Camp, Richard A. Maki, Scott R. McKercher and Paul Martin; **11.22.4** *Development* 127, 5245–5252 (2000). Mesenchymal cells engulf and clear apoptotic footplate cells in macrophageless PU.1 null mouse embryos. William Wood, Mark Turmaine, Roberta Weber, Victoria Camp, Richard A. Maki, Scott R. McKercher and Paul Martin.

Chapter 12 **12.1** Jan-Michael Peters/Silke Hauf; **12.2.2** Biophoto Associates/Photo Researchers; **12.2.3** C.R. Wyttenbach/Biological Photo Service; **12.2.4** Biophoto/Science Source/Photo Researchers; **12.3.2** John Murray; **12.4.2** Biophoto/Photo Researchers; **12.5.2** Biophoto/Photo Researchers; **12.7.2** Conly L. Rieder; **12.7.3** Conly L. Rieder; **12.7.4** Conly L. Rieder; **12.7.6** Conly L. Rieder; **12.7.7** Conly L. Rieder; **12.7.8** Conly L. Rieder; **12.8.2** J. Richard McIntosh, University of Colorado at Boulder; **12.8.3** Reproduced by permission from Matthew Schibler, from *Protoplasma* 137. Copyright © 1987: 29–44 by Springer-Verlag GmbH & Co KG; **12.10.2** Don W. Fawcett/Photo Researchers; **12.10.3** B. A. Palevitz, Courtesy of E. H. Newcomb, University of Wisconsin; **12.11.2** Elisabeth Pierson, FNWI-Radboud University Nijmegen, Pearson Science; **12.11.3** Elisabeth Pierson, FNWI-Radboud University Nijmegen, Pearson Science; **12.11.4** Elisabeth Pierson, FNWI-Radboud University Nijmegen, Pearson Science; **12.11.5** Elisabeth Pierson, FNWI-Radboud University Nijmegen, Pearson Science; **12.11.6** Elisabeth Pierson, FNWI-Radboud University Nijmegen, Pearson Science; **12.18.2** Guenter Albrecht-Buehler; **12.19.2** Lan Bo Chen; **12.19.3** Lan Bo Chen; **12.21** Anne Weston, LRI, CRUK, Wellcome Images; **p. 245** USDA/ARS/Agricultural Research Service.

Chapter 13 **13.1** Steve Granitz/WireImage/Getty Images; **13.2.2** Roland Birke/OKAPIA/Photo Researchers; **13.2.3** SuperStock; **13.3.2** Veronique Burger/Phanie Agency/Photo Researchers; **13.3.3** CNRI/Photo Researchers; **13.11.2** Mark Petronczki and Maria Siomos; **13.12.2** John Walsh, Micrographia.com.

Chapter 14 **14.1** Mendel Museum, Augustinian Abbey, Brno; **14.14.2** Altrendo nature/Getty Images; **14.14.3** PictureNet Corporation/Corbis; **14.15.2** Photodisc/Getty Images; **14.15.3** Photodisc/Getty Images; **14.15.4** Anthony Loveday; **14.15.5** Anthony Loveday; **14.16.2** Rick Guidotti and Diane McLean/Positive Exposure; **14.17.2** Michael Ciesielski Photography; **14.18** Douglas C. Pizac/AP Images; **14.19.2** CNRI/Photo Researchers; **p. 285** Norma Jubinville.

Chapter 15 **15.1** David C. Ward; **15.3.2** From: "Learning to Fly: Phenotypic Markers in *Drosophila.*" A poster of common phenotypic markers used in *Drosophila* genetics. Jennifer Childress, Richard Behringer, and Georg Halder. 2005. *Genesis* 43(1). Cover illustration; **15.3.3** From: "Learning to Fly: Phenotypic Markers in *Drosophila.*" A poster of common phenotypic markers used in *Drosophila* genetics. Jennifer Childress, Richard Behringer, and Georg Halder. 2005. *Genesis* 43(1). Cover illustration; **15.5** Andrew Syred/Photo Researchers; **15.8.2** Dave King/Dorling Kindersley; **15.15.2** Lauren Shear/SPL/Photo Researchers; **15.15.3** CNRI/SPL/Photo Researchers; **15.18** Geoff Kidd/Photo Researchers; **p. 304** James K. Adams, Biology, Dalton State College, Dalton, Georgia.

Chapter 16 **16.1** National Institutes of Health; **16.3.2** Oliver Meckes/Photo Researchers; **16.6.2** Courtesy of the Library of Congress; **16.6.3** From "The Double Helix" by James D. Watson, Atheneum Press, N.Y., 1968, p. 215. © 1968. Courtesy CSHL Archive; **16.12.2** Jerome Vinograd; **16.12.3** From D. J. Burks and P. J. Stambrook, *The Journal of Cell Biology 77* (1978). 762, fig. 6 by copyright permission of The Rockefeller University Press. Photo provided by P. J. Stambrook; **16.21** Peter Lansdorp; **16.22.2** S. C. Holt/Biological Photo Service; **16.22.3** Victoria E. Foe; **16.22.4** Barbara Hamkalo; **16.22.5** From J. R. Paulsen and U. K. Laemmli, *Cell* 12 (1977):817–828; **16.22.6** Biophoto/Photo Researchers; **16.23.2** From: Multicolor Spectral Karyotyping of Human Chromosomes. E. Schröck, S. du Manoir, T. Veldman, B. Schoell, J. Wienberg, M. A. Ferguson-Smith, Y. Ning, D. H. Ledbetter, I. Bar-Am, D. Soenksen, Y. Garini, T. Ried. *Science.* 1996 Jul 26;273(5274):494–7; **16.23.3** From: The new cytogenetics: blurring the boundaries with molecular biology; . . . M. R. Speicher, N. P. Carter. *Nat Rev Genet.* 2005 Oct;6(10):782–92; **p. 324** Thomas A. Steitz, Yale University.

Chapter 17 **17.1** Deutscher Fotodienst GmbH; **17.6.2** Keith V. Wood, University of California, San Diego; **17.6.3** AP Images; **17.16.2** Thomas Steitz; **17.17.2** Joachim Frank; **17.21.2** B. Hamkalo and O. Miller, Jr; **17.25.2** Reprinted with permission from O. L. Miller , Jr., B. A. Hamkalo, and C. A Thomas, Jr., *Science* 169 (1970):392. Copyright © 1970 American Association for the Advancement of Science.

Chapter 18 **18.1** Reproduced by permission from Cook O, Biehs B, Bier E. Brinker and optomotor-blind act coordinately to initiate development of the L5 wing vein primordium in *Drosophila. Development.* 2004 May: 131(9):2113–24; **18.12.2** From: The new cytogenetics: blurring the boundaries with molecular biology; M. R. Speicher, N. P. Carter. *Nat Rev Genet.* 2005 Oct;6(10):782–92; **18.16.2** Mike Wu; **18.16.3** Hans Pfletschinger/Peter Arnold/PhotoLibrary; **18.20.2** F. R. Turner, Indiana University; **18.20.3** F. R. Turner, Indiana University; **18.21.2** Wolfgang Driever, University of Freiburg, Freiburg, Germany; **18.21.3** Wolfgang Driever, University of Freiburg, Freiburg, Germany; **18.22.2** Ruth Lehmann, The Whitehead Institution; **18.22.3** Ruth Lehmann, The Whitehead Institution; **18.26** Roy Kaltschmidt, Lawrence Berkeley National Laboratory.

Chapter 19 **19.1** Science Photo Library/Photo Researchers; **19.2.2** Peter von Sengbusch/Botanik; **19.2.3** Peter von Sengbusch/Botanik; **19.2.4** Peter von Sengbusch/Botanik; **19.3.2** Robley C. Williams/Biological Photo Service; **19.3.3** R.C. Valentine and H.G. Pereira, "Antigens and Structure of the Adenovirus," *Journal of Molecular Biology* 13: 13–20 (1965); **19.3.4** Hazel Appleton, Health Protection Agency Centre for Infections/Photo Researchers; **19.3.5** Robley C. Williams/ Biological Photo Service; **19.8.2** C. Dauguet/Institute Pasteur/Photo Researchers; **19.8.3** C. Dauguet/Institute Pasteur/Photo Researchers; **19.8.4** C. Dauguet/Institute Pasteur/Photo Researchers; **19.8.5** C. Dauguet/Institute Pasteur/Photo Researchers; **19.8.6** C. Dauguet/Institute Pasteur/Photo Researchers; **19.9.2** NIBSC/Photo Researchers; **19.9.3** Seo Myung-gon/AP Images; **19.9.4** National Museum of Health and Medicine/Armed Forces Institute of Pathology; **19.10.2** Dennis E. Mayhew; **19.10.3** Thomas A. Zitter; **19.10.4** A. Vogler/Shutterstock.

Chapter 20 **20.1** Reproduced with permission from R.F. Service, *Science* (1998) 282:396–3999. Copyright 1998 American Association for the Advancement of Science. Incyte Pharmaceuticals, Inc., Palo Alto, CA; **20.5.2** L. Brent Selinger, Pearson Science; **20.9.2** Repligen Corporation; **20.14** Ethan Bier; **20.15.2** Reproduced with permission from R.F. Service, *Science* (1998) 282:396–3999. Copyright 1998 American Association for the Advancement of Science. Incyte Pharmaceuticals, Inc., Palo Alto, CA; **20.20** Pat Sullivan/AP Images; **20.24.2** Brad DeCecco Photography; **20.24.3** Brad DeCecco Photography; **20.25.2** Steve Helber/AP Images.

Chapter 21 **21.1** Karen Huntt/Corbis; **21.5.2** From "The genetic landscape of a cell." M. Costanzo, et al. *Science.* 2010 Jan 22;327(5964):425–31; **21.6** GeneChip Human Genome U133 Plus 2.0 Array, image courtesy of Affymetrix; **21.8.2** AP Images; **21.8.3** Courtesy of Virginia Walbot, Stanford University; **21.11.2** Courtesy of O. L. Miller Jr., Dept. of Biology, University of Virginia; **21.17.2** Shu W, Cho JY, Jiang Y, Zhang M, Weisz D, Elder GA, Schmeidler J, De Gasperi R, Sosa MA, Rabidou D, Santucci AC, Perl D, Morrisey E, Buxbaum JD. Altered ultrasonic vocalization in mice with a disruption in the *Foxp2* gene. : *Proc Natl Acad Sci U S A.* 2005 Jul 5; 102(27):9643–8; Fig. 3. Image supplied by Joseph Buxbaum; **21.17.3** Shu W, Cho JY, Jiang Y, Zhang M, Weisz D, Elder GA, Schmeidler J, De Gasperi R, Sosa MA, Rabidou D, Santucci AC, Perl D, Morrisey E, Buxbaum JD. Altered ultrasonic vocalization in mice with a disruption in the *Foxp2* gene. : *Proc Natl Acad Sci U S A.* 2005 Jul 5;102(27):9643–8; Fig. 3. Image supplied by Joseph Buxbaum; **21.17.4** Shu W, Cho JY, Jiang Y, Zhang M, Weisz D, Elder GA, Schmeidler J, De Gasperi R, Sosa MA, Rabidou D, Santucci AC, Perl D, Morrisey E, Buxbaum JD. Altered ultrasonic vocalization in mice with a disruption in the *Foxp2* gene. : *Proc Natl Acad Sci U S A.* 2005 Jul 5; 102(27):9643–8; Fig. 3. Image supplied by Joseph Buxbaum; **21.17.5** Joe McDonald/Corbis.

Chapter 22 **22.1** Olivier Grunewald; **22.2.2** PD image: Skeleton of the "Rhinoceros unicorne de Java" in the Paris Museum of Natural History. From G. Cuvier, Recherches sur les ossemens fossiles, *Atlas,* pl. 17. 1836; **22.2.3** The Natural History Museum/Alamy; **22.2.4** Wayne Lynch/AGE Fotostock; **22.2.5** Neg./Transparency no. 330300. Courtesy Dept. of Library Services, American Museum of Natural History; **22.4** Michael S. Yamashita/Corbis; **22.5.2** George Richmond/ARCHIV/Photo Researchers; **22.5.3** National Maritime Museum; **22.6.2** Michel Gunther/PhotoLibrary; **22.6.3** David Hosking/FLPA; **22.6.4** David Hosking/Alamy; **22.7** Darwin's Tree of life sketch, MS.DAR.121:p.36. Reproduced with the permission of the Cambridge University Library; **22.9.2** Gerard Schulz/Naturphoto; **22.9.3** Robert Sarno/iStockphoto; **22.9.4** Paul Rapson/Alamy; **22.9.5** Izaokas Sapiro/Shutterstock; **22.9.6** YinYang/iStockphoto; **22.9.7** floricica buzlea/iStockphoto; **22.10** Laura Jesse, Extension Entomologist, Iowa State University; **22.11.2** Richard Packwood/Oxford Scientific/Jupiter Images; **22.12.2** E. S. Ross, California Academy of Sciences; **22.12.3** Mark Taylor/Nature Picture Library; **22.13.1** Scott P. Carroll; **22.16.2** Dr. Keith Wheeler/Photo Researchers; **22.16.3** Lennart Nilsson/Scanpix; **22.18.2** Visible Earth (http://visibleearth.nasa.gov/), NASA; **22.19.2** Chris Linz, Thewissen lab, Northeastern Ohio Universities College of Medicine; **22.19.3** Chris Linz, Thewissen lab, Northeastern Ohio Universities College of Medicine; **22.19.4** Chris Linz, Thewissen lab, Northeastern Ohio Universities College of Medicine; **22.19.5** Chris Linz, Thewissen lab, Northeastern Ohio Universities College of Medicine.

Chapter 23 **23.1** Rosemary B. Grant; **23.3.2** Erick Greene, University of Montana; **23.3.3** Erick Greene, University of Montana; **23.4.2** Janice Britton-Davidian, ISEM, UMR 5554 CNRS, Universite Montpellier II. Reprinted by permission from *Nature,* Vol. 403, 13 January 2000, p. 158. © 2000 Macmillan Magazines Ltd.; **23.4.3** Janice Britton-Davidian, ISEM, UMR 5554 CNRS, Universite Montpellier II. Reprinted by permission from *Nature,* Vol. 403, 13 January 2000, p. 158. © 2000 Macmillan Magazines Ltd.; **23.4.4** Steve Gorton/Dorling Kindersley; **23.5.2** New York State Department of Environmental Conservation; **23.6.2** Gary Schultz/Photoshot; **23.6.3** James L. Davis/ProWildlife; **23.11.2** William Ervin/SPL/Photo Researchers; **23.12.2** Jan Visser; **23.14.2** John Visser/Photoshot; **23.15** Dave Blackey/PhotoLibrary; **23.16.2** Allison M. Welch; **23.19** Merlin D. Tuttle, Bat Conservation International, www.batcon.org.

Chapter 24 **24.1** Mark Jones/AGE Fotostock; **24.2.2** Malcolm Schuyl/Alamy; **24.2.3** Wave Rf/PhotoLibrary; **24.2.4** Robert Kneschke/iStockphoto; **24.2.5** Justin Horrocks/iStockphoto; **24.2.6** Photodisc/Getty Images; **24.2.7** Photodisc/Getty Images; **24.2.8** Photodisc/Getty Images; **24.2.9** Masterfile; **24.3.a2** Joe McDonald/Photoshot; **24.3.b2** Joe McDonald/Corbis; **24.3.c2** USDA/APHIS/Animal and Plant Health Inspection Service; **24.3.d2** Stephen Krasemann/Photo Researchers; **24.3.e1** Michael Dietrich/

imagebroker/Alamy; **24.3.f2** Takahito Asami; **24.3.g2** William E. Ferguson; **24.3.h2** Charles W. Brown; **24.3.i2** Photodisc/Getty Images; **24.3.j2** Corbis; **24.3.k2** DawnYL/Fotolia; **24.3.12** Kazutoshi Okuno; **24.4.2** CLFProductions/Shutterstock; **24.4.3** Boris Karpinski/Alamy; **24.4.4** Troy Maben/AP Images; **24.6.2** John Shaw/ Bruce Coleman/Photoshot; **24.6.3** Michael Fogden/Bruce Coleman/Photoshot; **24.6.4** Corbis; **24.7.2** From: Morphology, performance, fitness: functional insight into a post-Pleistocene radiation of mosquitofish. R. B. Langerhans. *Biology Letters* 2009;5(4):488–491; **24.7.3** From: Morphology, performance, fitness: functional insight into a post-Pleistocene radiation of mosquitofish. R. B. Langerhans. *Biology Letters* 2009;5(4):488–491; **24.8.2** Visible Earth (http://visibleearth.nasa.gov/), NASA; **24.8.3** Arthur Anker; **24.12** Ole Seehausen; **24.13.2** Jeroen Speybroeck, Research Institute for Nature and Forest, Belgium; **24.13.3** Jeroen Speybroeck, Research Institute for Nature and Forest, Belgium; **24.16.2** Ole Seehausen; **24.16.3** Ole Seehausen; **24.16.4** Ole Seehausen; **24.18** Jason Rick; **24.20.2** Reprinted by permission from *Nature* Bradshaw HD, Schemske DW. Allele substitution at a flower colour locus produces a pollinator shift in monkeyflowers. *Nature.* 2003 November 12; 426(6963):176–8 Copyright © 2003. Macmillan Magazines Limited; **24.20.3** Reprinted by permission from *Nature* Bradshaw HD, Schemske DW. Allele substitution at a flower colour locus produces a pollinator shift in monkeyflowers. *Nature.* 2003 November 12; 426(6963):176–8 Copyright © 2003. Macmillan Magazines Limited; **24.20.4** Reprinted by permission from *Nature* Bradshaw HD, Schemske DW. Allele substitution at a flower colour locus produces a pollinator shift in monkeyflowers. *Nature.* 2003 November 12; 426(6963):176–8 Copyright © 2003. Macmillan Magazines Limited; **24.20.5** Reprinted by permission from *Nature* Bradshaw HD, Schemske DW. Allele substitution at a flower colour locus produces a pollinator shift in monkeyflowers. *Nature.* 2003 November 12; 426(6963):176–8 Copyright © 2003. Macmillan Magazines Limited.

Chapter 25 **25.1** Gerhard Boeggemann; **p. 507.UN1** Rebecca Hunt; **25.2.2** UPI Photo/Landov; **25.3.2** Courtesy of F. M. Menger and Kurt Gabrielson, Emory University; **25.3.3** M. Hanczyc; **25.4.10** Specimen No 12478, Markus Moser, Staatliches Museum fur Naturkunde Stuttgart; **25.4.2** S. M. Awramik/Biological Photo Service; **25.4.3** Sinclair Stammers/Photo Researchers; **25.4.4** Andrew H. Knoll, Harvard University; **25.4.5** Lisa-Ann Gershwin, University of California-Berkeley, Museum of Paleontology; **25.4.6** Chip Clark; **25.4.7** Ted Daeschler/Academy of Natural Sciences/ VIREO; **25.4.8** Roger Jones; **25.4.9** Seelevel.com; **25.11.2** Shuhai Xiao, Tulane University; **25.11.3** Shuhai Xiao, Tulane University; **25.20.2** Gerald D. Carr; **25.20.3** Gerald D. Carr; **25.20.4** Gerald D. Carr; **25.20.5** Gerald D. Carr; **25.20.6** Gerald D. Carr; **25.20.7** Bruce G. Baldwin; **25.21.2** Jean Kern; **25.21.3** Jean Kern; **25.22** Juniors Bildarchiv/Alamy; **25.23** Reprinted from "The Origin of Form" by Sean B. Carroll, *Natural History*, November 2005. Burke, A.C. 2000, "*Hox*" Genes and the Global Patterning of the Somitic Mesoderm. In Somitogenesis. C. Ordahl (ed.) "Current Topics in Developmental Biology", Vo. 47. Academic Press; **25.25.1** Oxford Scientific/ PhotoLibrary; **25.25.3** Shapiro MD, Marks ME, Peichel CL, Blackman BK, Nereng KS, Jonsson B, Schluter D, Kingsley DM. Genetic and developmental basis of evolutionary pelvic reduction in threespine sticklebacks. *Nature.* Erratum. 2006 Feb 23;439(7079):1014; Fig. 1; **25.25.4** Shapiro MD, Marks ME, Peichel CL, Blackman BK, Nereng KS, Jonsson B, Schluter D, Kingsley DM. Genetic and developmental basis of evolutionary pelvic reduction in threespine sticklebacks. *Nature.* Erratum. 2006 Feb 23;439(7079):1014; Fig. 1.

Chapter 26 **26.1** Ken Griffiths/NHPA/Photoshot; **26.2.2** Ryan McVay/Photodisc/ Getty Images; **26.2.3** Neil Fletcher/Dorling Kindersley; **26.2.4** Dorling Kindersley; **26.17.2** Ed Heck; **26.17.3** Courtesy Dept. of Library Services, American Museum of Natural History.

Chapter 27 **27.1** Bonnie K. Baxter, Great Salt Lake Institute, Westminster College, Utah; **27.2.2** CDC; **27.2.3** Dr. Kari Lounatmaa/Photo Researchers; **27.2.4** Stem Jems/ Photo Researchers; **27.3.2** L. Brent Selinger, Pearson Science; **27.4.2** Dr. Immo Rantala/ Photo Researchers; **27.5.2** Kwangshin Kim/Photo Researchers; **27.6.2** Julius Adler; **27.7.2** S. W. Watson; **27.7.3** Norma J. Lang/Biological Photo Service; **27.8.2** Huntington Potter, Byrd Alzheimer's Institute and University of South Florida, David Dressler, Oxford University and Balliol College; **27.9.2** H.S. Pankratz, T.C. Beaman/ Biological Photo Service; **27.12.2** Charles C. Brinton, Jr., University of Pittsburgh; **27.14.2** Susan M. Barns; **27.16** Jack Dykinga/Stone/Getty Images; **27.17.3** L. Evans Roth/Biological Photo Service; **27.17.5** Yuichi Suwa; **27.17.7** National Library of Medicine; **27.17.9** From "Scanning electron microscopy of fruiting body formation by myxobacteria." P. L. Grilione and J. Pangborn. *J. Bacteriol.* 1975 December; 124(3): 1558–1565; **27.17.13** Photo Researchers; **27.17.15** Moredon Animal Health/SPL/Photo Researchers; **27.17.17** CNRI/SPL/Photo Researchers; **27.17.19** Culture Collection CCALA, Institute of Botany, Academy of Sciences Dukelska, Czech Republic; **27.17.21** Paul Hoskisson, Strathclyde Institute of Pharmacy and Biomedical Sciences, Glasgow, Scotland; **27.17.22** David M. Phillips/Photo Researchers; **27.18.2** Pascale Frey-Klett; **27.19** Ken Lucas/Biological Photo Service; **27.20.2** Scott Camazine/Photo Researchers; **27.20.3** David M. Phillips/Photo Researchers; **27.20.4** James Marshall/The Image Works; **27.21** Metabolix; **27.21.3** Courtesy of Exxon Mobil Corporation; **27.21.4** Seelevel.com.

Chapter 28 **28.1** Brian S. Leander; **28.3.3** Joel Mancuso, University of California, Berkeley; **28.3.5** M. I. Walker/NHPA/Photoshot; **28.3.7** Howard Spero, University of California-Davis; **28.3.8** NOAA; **28.3.10** Kim Taylor/Nature Picture Library; **28.3.11** David J. Patterson/micro*scope; **28.3.13** Tom Stack/PhotoLibrary; **28.4.2** David M. Phillips/The Population Council/Photo Researchers; **28.5.2** David J. Patterson; **28.6.2** Meckes/Ottawa/Photo Researchers; **28.7.2** D. J. Patterson, L. Amaral-Zettler, M. Peglar and T. Nerad, http://micro*scope.mbl.edu; **28.8.2** Guy Brugerolle, Universitad Clearmont, Ferrand; **28.9.2** Virginia Institute of Marine Science; **28.10.2** Masamichi Aikawa, Tokai University School of Medicine, Japan; **28.11.2** M. I. Walker/ Photo Researchers; **28.12.2** Centers for Disease Control & Prevention; **28.13.2** Steve Gschmeissner/Photo Researchers; **28.14.2** Stephen Durr; **28.15.2** Colin Bates; **28.16.2** J. Robert Waaland/Biological Photo Service; **28.17.2** Fred Rhoades; **28.18.2** Robert Brons/Biological Photo Service; **28.19.2** Eva Nowack; **28.20.2** D. P. Wilson, Eric & David Hosking/Photo Researchers; **28.20.3** Michael D. Guiry; **28.20.4** Biophoto Associates/Photo Researchers; **28.20.6** Michael Yamashita/IPN/Aurora Photos; **28.20.7** David Murray/Dorling Kindersley; **28.21.2** Laurie Campbell/NHPA; **28.21.3** Marine Sciences, University of Puerto Rico; **28.22.2** William L. Dentler; **28.24.2** George Barron; **28.24.3** Mikel Tapia (www.argazkik.com); **28.25.2** Robert Kay; **28.25.3** Robert Kay; **28.26.2** Kevin Carpenter and Patrick Keeling.

Chapter 29 **29.1** Martin Rugner/AGE Fotostock; **29.2.2** S. C. Mueller and R. M. Brown, Jr; **29.3.2** Natural Visions; **29.3.3** Linda Graham, University of Wisconsin-Madison; **29.5.11** Ed Reschke; **29.5.12** CDC; **29.5.3** Linda Graham, University of Wisconsin-Madison; **29.5.4** Karen S. Renzaglia; **29.5.6** Alan S. Heilman; **29.5.7** Michael Clayton, University of Wisconsin-Madison; **29.5.9** David John Jones (mybitoftheplanet.com); **29.6.2** Charles H. Wellman; **29.6.3** Charles H. Wellman; **29.8.2** Laurie Knight (www.laurieknight.net); **29.9.2** Linda Graham, University of Wisconsin-Madison; **29.9.3** Alvin E. Staffan/National Audubon Society/Photo Researchers; **29.9.4** Hidden Forest; **29.9.6** Hidden Forest; **29.9.8** Tony Wharton, Frank Lane Picture Agency/Corbis; **p. 609** From "Mosses and Other Bryophytes, an Illustrated Glossary" (2006) by Bill and Nancy Malcolm; **29.11.1** Brian Lightfoot/AGE Fotostock; **29.11.2** Chris Lisle/Corbis; **29.15.2** Jody Banks, Purdue University; **29.15.3** Murray Fagg, Australian National Botanic Gardens; **29.15.4** Helga & Kurt Rasbach; **29.15.6** Jon Meier/iStockphoto; **29.15.8** Milton Rand/Tom Stack & Associates; **29.15.9** Francisco Javier Yeste Garcia (www.flickr.com/photos/fryega/); **29.15.10** Francisco Javier Yeste Garcia (www.flickr.com/photos/fryega/); **29.16.2** The Open University; **p. 616, top** Ed Reschke; **p. 616, bottom** Michael Clayton.

Chapter 30 **30.1** National Museum of Natural History, Smithsonian Institution; **30.5.1** Johannes Greyling/iStockphoto; **30.5.3** CC-BY-SA photo: Kurt Stueber (www.biolib.de); **30.5.4** Jeroen Peys/iStockphoto; **30.5.5** Michael Clayton; **30.5.6** Thomas Schoepke; **30.5.7** Bob Gibbons/FLPA; **30.5.8** Raymond Gehman/Corbis; **30.5.9** Adam Jones/Getty Images; **30.5.10** David Muench/Corbis; **30.5.11** Gunter Marx Photography/Corbis; **30.5.12** Royal Botanic Gardens Sydney; **30.5.13** Jaime Plaza/ AP Images; **30.5.14** Mario Verin/Photolibrary; **30.8.2** Dave King/ Dorling Kindersley; **30.8.3** Andy Crawford/Dorling Kindersley; **30.8.4** Dave King/ Dorling Kindersley; **30.8.5** Maria Dryfhout/iStockphoto; **30.8.6** Peter Rees/Getty Images; **30.9.2** PIXTAL/AGE Fotostock; **30.9.3** Hans Dieter Brandl, Frank Lane Picture Agency/Corbis; **30.9.4** Scott Camazine/Photo Researchers; **30.9.5** Derek Hall/ Dorling Kindersley; **30.11.2** David L. Dilcher; **30.13.1** Howard Rice/Dorling Kindersley; **30.13.2** Jack Scheper, Floridata.com; **30.13.3** Stephen McCabe; **30.13.4** Andrew Butler/Dorling Kindersley; **30.13.6** Eric Crichton/Dorling Kindersley; **30.13.7** John Dransfield; **30.13.8** Dorling Kindersley; **30.13.10** Terry W. Eggers/Corbis; **30.13.11** CC-BY-SA photo: Artslave; **30.13.12** Matthew Ward/Dorling Kindersley; **30.13.13** Tony Wharton, Frank Lane Picture Agency/Corbis; **30.13.14** Howard Rice/ Dorling Kindersley; **30.13.15** Gerald D. Carr; **30.14** kkaplin/Shutterstock; **30.15** D. Wilder; **30.16.2** NASA's Earth Observatory; **30.16.3** NASA's Earth Observatory.

Chapter 31 **31.1** Georg Müller; **31.2.2** Fred Rhoades/Mycena Consulting; **31.2.3** Hans Reinhard/Taxi/Getty Images; **31.2.4** George Barron, University of Guelph, Canada; **31.4.2** © N. Allin & G.L. Barron, University of Guelph/Biological Photo Service; **31.6.2** Biophoto Associates/Photo Researchers; **31.6.3** Popovaphoto/ dreamstime; **31.7.2** Stephen J. Kron; **31.9.2** Dirk Redecker, Robin Kodner, and Linda E. Graham. Glomalean Fungi from the Ordovician. *Science* 15 September 2000; 289: 1920–1921; **31.10.2** CDC; **31.11.2** John Taylor; **31.11.3** Ray Watson; **31.11.5** Reproduced by permission from Kiers ET, van der Heijden MG. Mutualistic stability in the arbuscular mycorrhizal symbiosis: exploring hypotheses of evolutionary cooperation. *Ecology.* 2006 July: 87(7):1627–36: Fig. 1a. Image by Marcel van der Heijden, Swiss Federal Research Station for Agroecology and Agriculture. Copyright © 2006, Ecological Society of America; **31.11.6** Frank Young/Papilio/Corbis; **31.11.7** Phil Dotson/Photo Researchers; **31.12.2** William E. Barstow; **31.13.2** Antonio D'Albore/ iStockphoto; **31.13.3** Alena Kubátová (http://botany.natur.cuni.cz/cs/sbirka-kultur-hub-ccf); **31.13.4** Ed Reschke/Peter Arnold/PhotoLibrary; **31.13.5** George Barron; **31.14.2** G.L. Barron/Biological Photo Service; **31.15.2** M. F. Brown/Biological Photo Service; **31.16.2** Viard/Jacana/Photo Researchers; **31.16.3** Douglas Adams/iStockphoto; **31.17.2** Fred Spiegel; **31.18.2** Fletcher and Baylis/Photo Researchers; **31.18.3** Michael Fogden/Photolibrary; **31.18.4** Frank Paul/Alamy; **31.19.2** Biophoto Associates/Photo Researchers; **31.20** University of Tennessee Entomology and Plant Pathology; **31.22** Mark Bowler/Photo Researchers; **31.23.2** Ralph Lee Hopkins/Getty Images; **31.23.3** Geoff Simpson/naturepl.com; **31.23.4** Wild-Worlders of Europe/ Benvie/naturepl.com; **31.24.2** Eye of Science/Photo Researchers; **31.25.2** Alamy; **31.25.3** Peter Chadwick/Dorling Kindersley; **31.25.4** Hecker-Sauer/AGE Fotostock; **31.26.2** Vance T. Vredenburg, San Francisco State University; **31.27.2** Christine Case.

Chapter 32 **32.1** Jeff Hunter/Image Bank/Getty Images; **p. 656** Biological Photo Service; **32.4.2** © The Museum Board of South Australia 2004 Photographer: Dr. J. Gehling; **32.4.3** © The Museum Board of South Australia 2004 Photographer: Dr. J. Gehling; **32.5** J. Sibbick/The Natural History Museum, London; **32.6.2** Wikramanayake AH, Hong M, Lee PN, Pang K, Byrum CA, Bince JM, Xu R, Martindale MQ. An ancient role for nuclear beta-catenin in the evolution of axial polarity and germ layer segregation. *Nature.* 2003 Nov 27;426(6965):446–50; Fig. 2, 3 and 4; **32.6.3** Wikramanayake AH, Hong M, Lee PN, Pang K, Byrum CA, Bince JM, Xu R, Martindale MQ. An ancient role for nuclear beta-catenin in the evolution of axial polarity and germ layer segregation. *Nature.* 2003 Nov 27;426(6965):446–50; Fig. 2, 3 and 4; **32.6.4** Wikramanayake AH, Hong M, Lee PN, Pang K, Byrum CA, Bince JM, Xu R, Martindale MQ. An ancient role for nuclear beta-catenin in the evolution of axial polarity and germ layer segregation. *Nature.* 2003 Nov 27;426(6965):446–50; Fig. 2, 3 and 4; **32.6.5** Wikramanayake AH, Hong M, Lee PN, Pang K, Byrum CA, Bince JM, Xu R, Martindale MQ. An ancient role for nuclear beta-catenin in the evolution of axial polarity and germ layer segregation. *Nature.* 2003 Nov 27; 426(6965):446–50; Fig. 2, 3 and 4; **32.12** Kent Wood/Photo Researchers; **32.13.2** Hecker/Sauer/AGE Fotostock.

Chapter 33 **33.1** C. Wolcott Henry III/National Geographic/Getty Images; **33.3.1** Andrew J. Martinez/Photo Researchers; **33.3.2** Robert Brons/Biological Photo Service; **33.3.3** Teresa (Zubi) Zuberbühler; **33.3.4** Stephen Dellaporta; **33.3.5** Gregory G. Dimijian/Photo Researchers; **33.3.6** Ed Robinson/Pacific Stock/Photolibrary; **33.3.7** Hecker/Sauer/AGE Fotostock; **33.3.8** W. I. Walker/Photo Researchers; **33.3.9** Kåre Telnes/Image Quest Marine; **33.3.10** PD image: Anilocra/Taken by Neil Campbell, University of Aberdeen, Scotland, UK; **33.3.11** Erling Svensen/UWPhoto ANS; **33.3.12** Peter Funch; **33.3.13** photonimo/iStockphoto; **33.3.14** Peter Batson/Image Quest Marine; **33.3.15** Reinhart Mobjerg Kristensen; **33.3.16** Erling Svensen/

UWPhoto ANS; **33.3.17** Andrew Syred/Photo Researchers; **33.3.18** Reproduced with permission from A. Eizinger and R. Sommer, Max Planck Institut fur entwicklungsbiologie, Tubingen. Copyright 2000 American Association for the Advancement of Science. Cover 278(5337) 17 Oct 97; **33.3.19** Thomas Stromberg; **33.3.20** Tim Flach/Stone/Getty Images; **33.3.21** Heather Angel/Natural Visions; **33.3.22** Robert Harding World Imagery/Alamy; **33.3.23** Robert Brons/Biological Photo Service; **33.4.2** Andrew J. Martinez/Photo Researchers; **33.7.2** Andrew J. Martinez/Photo Researchers; **33.7.3** Robert Brons/Biological Photo Service; **33.7.4** Commonwealth of Australia (GBRMPA); **33.7.5** Neil G. McDaniel/Photo Researchers; **33.8.2** Robert Brons/Biological Photo Services; **33.9.2** Ed Robinson/Pacific Stock/PhotoLibrary; **33.11.2** CDC; **33.12.2** Eye of Science/Photo Researchers; **33.13.2** W. I. Walker/Photo Researchers; **33.14.2** Hecker/Sauer/AGE Fotostock; **33.14.3** Kåre Telnes/Image Quest Marine; **33.16** Jeff Foott/Tom Stack and Associates; **33.17.2** Amruta Bhelke/Dreamstime.com; **33.17.3** Corbis; **33.19** H. W. Pratt/Biological Photo Service; **33.21.2** photonimo/iStockphoto; **33.21.3** Mark Conlin/Image Quest Marine; **33.21.4** Jonathan Blair/Corbis; **33.22.2** Photograph courtesy of the U.S. Bureau of Fisheries (1919), and Illinois State Museum; **33.22.3** © Zoological Society of London (ZSL); **33.23.2** Peter Batson/Image Quest Marine; **33.24.2** A.N.T./NHPA/Photoshot; **33.25** Astrid & Hanns-Frieder Michler/Photo Researchers; **33.26.2** Reproduced with permission from A. Eizinger and R. Sommer, Max Planck Institut fur entwicklungsbiologie, Tubingen. Copyright 2000 American Association for the Advancement of Science. Cover 278(5337) 17 Oct 97; **33.27.2** SPL/Photo Researchers; **33.28** Collection of Dan Cooper; **33.29.2** Grenier JK, Garber TL, Warren R, Whitington PM, Carroll S. Evolution of the entire arthropod *Hox* gene set predated the origin and radiation of the onychophoran/arthropod clade. *Curr Biol.* 1997 Aug 1;7(8):547–53; Fig. 3c; **33.31** Mark Newman/FLPA; **33.32.2** Tim Flach/Stone/Getty Images; **33.32.3** Andrew Syred/Photo Researchers; **33.32.4** Eric Lawton/iStockphoto; **33.34.2** Premaphotos/Nature Picture Library; **33.34.3** Tom McHugh/Photo Researchers; **33.36** Meul/ARCO/Nature Picture Library; **33.37.2** John Shaw/Tom Stack and Associates; **33.37.3** John Shaw/Tom Stack and Associates; **33.37.4** John Shaw/Tom Stack and Associates; **33.37.5** John Shaw/Tom Stack and Associates; **33.37.6** John Shaw/Tom Stack and Associates; **33.38.2** Dr. John Brackenbury/Photo Researchers; **33.38.3** Perry Babin; **33.38.4** PREMAPHOTOS/Nature Picture Library; **33.38.5** Dante Fenolio/Photo Researchers; **33.38.6** John Cancalosi/Nature Picture Library; **33.38.7** Hans Christoph Kappel/Nature Picture Library; **33.38.8** Michael & Patricia Fogden/CORBIS; **33.38.9** CC-BY-SA photo: Bruce Marlin (www.cirrusimage.com/fly_whale-tail.htm); **33.39.2** Maximilian Weinzierl/Alamy; **33.39.3** Peter Herring/Image Quest Marine; **33.39.4** Peter Parks/Image Quest Marine; **33.40.2** Andrey Nekrasov/Image Quest Marine; **33.41** Daniel Janies; **33.42** Jeff Rotman/Photo Researchers; **33.43** Robert Harding World Imagery/Alamy; **33.44** Jurgen Freund/Nature Picture Library; **33.45** Hal Beral/Corbis.

Chapter 34 **34.1** Xian-guang H, Aldridge RJ, Siveter DJ, Siveter DJ, Xiang-hong F. New evidence on the anatomy and phylogeny of the earliest vertebrates. *Proceedings of the Royal Society of London-B-Biological Sciences,* Sept. 22, 2002; 269 (1503) 1865–1869; Fig. 1c; **34.4.2** Oxford Scientific/PhotoLibrary; **34.5.2** Robert Brons/Biological Photo Service; **34.8.2** Nanjing Institute of Geology and Palaeontology; **34.9.2** Tom McHugh/Photo Researchers; **34.10.2** A Hartl/AGE Fotostock; **34.10.3** Marevision/AGE Fotostock; **34.14.2** The Field Museum, #GEO82014; **34.15.2** Carlos Villoch/Image Quest Marine; **34.15.3** Masa Ushioda/Image Quest Marine; **34.15.4** Andy Murch/V&W/Image Quest Marine; **34.17.2** James D. Watt/Image Quest Marine; **34.17.3** Jez Tryner/Image Quest Marine; **34.17.4** George Grall/Getty Images; **34.17.5** Fred McConnaughey/Photo Researchers; **34.18.2** From "The oldest -articulated osteichthyan reveals mosaic gnathostome characters." M. Zhu et al. *Nature.* 2009 Mar 26;458(7237):469–74; **34.19** Arnaz Mehta; **34.20.2** © Ted Daeschler/Academy of Natural Sciences/VIREO; **34.20.3** © Ted Daeschler/Academy of Natural Sciences/VIREO; **34.20.4** © Kalliopi Monoyios; **34.22.2** Alberto Fernandez/AGE Fotostock America, Inc. **34.22.3** Michael Fogden/Bruce Coleman/Photoshot; **34.22.4** Michael Fogden/Bruce Coleman/Photoshot; **34.23.2** John Cancalosi/Peter Arnold/PhotoLibrary; **34.23.3** Stephen Dalton/Photo Researchers; **34.23.4** Hans Pfletschinger/Peter Arnold/PhotoLibrary; **34.24** Michael Fogden/OSF/PhotoLibrary; **34.27** Nobumichi Tamura; **34.28** Michael Fogden/OSF/PhotoLibrary; **34.29.2** Natural Visions/Alamy; **34.29.3** Matt T. Lee; **34.29.5** Medford Taylor/National Geographic Image Collection; **34.29.6** Carl & Ann Purcell/Corbis; **34.30.2** Visceralimage/dreamstime; **34.30.3** Janice Sheldon; **34.32** Russell Mountford/Alamy; **34.33** DLILLC/Corbis; **34.34** Yufeng Zhou/iStockphoto; **34.35.1** McPHOTO/AGE Fotostock; **34.35.2** paolo barbanera/AGE Fotostock; **34.36** Gianpiero Ferrari/FLPA; **34.36** Gianpiero Ferrari/FLPA; **34.38.2** D. Parer and E. Parer Cook/Auscape International Proprietary Ltd. **34.38.3** Mervyn Griffiths/Commonwealth Scientific and Industrial Research Organization; **34.39.2** John Cancalosi/Alamy; **34.39.3** Wells Bert & Babs/OSF/PhotoLibrary; **34.42** Frans Lanting/Corbis; **34.44.2** Kevin Schafer/AGE Fotostock America, Inc. **34.44.3** J & C Sohns/Photolibrary; **34.45.2** Morales/AGE Fotostock America, Inc. **34.45.3** Anup Shah/ImageState/Alamy Images; **34.45.4** T. J. Rick/Nature Picture Library; **34.45.5** E. A. Janes/AGE Fotostock America, Inc. **34.45.6** Frans Lanting/Corbis; **34.47** Fossilized bone, partial skeleton, of *Ardipithecus ramidus,* articulated, with bones laid in their approximate positions. Housed in National Museum of Ethiopia, Addis Ababa. Photo © T. White 2009, From "*Ardipithecus ramidus* and the Paleobiology of Early Hominids." T. White et al. *Science.* 2009 Oct 2;326(5949):75–86; **34.48.2** John Reader/SPL/Photo Researchers; **34.48.3** John Gurche Studios; **34.49.2** Alan Walker @ National Museums of Kenya. Printed with permission; **34.51** David L Brill/Brill Atlanta; **34.52** C. Henshilwood & F. d'Errico/Professor Chris Henshilwood.

Chapter 35 **35.1** PD photo: John Walker (www.fourmilab.ch); **35.3** Robert & Linda Mitchell; **35.4.2** CC-BY-SA photo: Forest & Kim Starr; **35.4.3** Rob Walls/ Alamy; **35.4.4** YinYang/iStockphoto; **35.4.5** Robert Holmes/Corbis; **35.4.6** Geoff Tompkinson/Science Photo Library/Photo Researchers; **35.5.2** Donald Gregory Clever; **35.5.3** Gusto Productions/SPL/Photo Researchers; **35.5.4** Dorling Kindersley; **35.5.5** Aflo Foto Agency/Alamy; **35.7.2** Neil Cooper/Alamy; **35.7.3** Martin Ruegner/ jupiterimages; **35.7.4** Mike Zens/Corbis; **35.7.5** Jerome Wexler/Photo Researchers; **35.7.6** Kathy Piper/iStockphoto; **35.9.2** Purdue Extension Entomology; **35.10.2** Brian Capon; **35.10.4** © Clouds Hill Imaging/www.lastrefuge.co.uk; **35.10.6** Graham Kent, Pearson Science; **35.10.7.** Graham Kent, Pearson Science; **35.10.9** N.C. Brown Center for Ultrastructure Studies, SUNY-Environmental Science & Forestry, Syracuse, NY; **35.10.11** Graham Kent; **35.10.12** Reproduced with permission from "Plant Cell Biology on CD," by B E S Gunning, www.plantcellbiologyonCD.com; **35.10.13** Professor Ray F. Evert; **35.13.2** From "*Arabidopsis* TCP20 links regulation of growth and cell division control pathways." C. Li et al. *Proc Natl Acad Sci U S A.* 2005 Sep 6;102(36):12978–83. Epub 2005 Aug 25. Photo: Peter Doerner; **35.14.2** Natalie B. Bronstein; **35.14.3** Ed Reschke; **35.14.4** Ed Reschke; **35.15.2** Michael Clayton; **35.16.2** Michael Clayton; **35.17.2** Ed Reschke; **35.17.3** Ed Reschke; **35.18.2** Ed Reschke; **35.18.3** Ed Reschke; **35.19.2** Michael Clayton; **35.19.3** Alison W. Roberts; **35.21.2** Dr. Edward R. Cook; **35.23** California Historical Society Collection (CHS-1177), University of Southern California on behalf of the USC Specialized Libraries and Archival Collections; **p. 756** Reproduced by permission from Janet Braam, *Cell* 60 (9 February 1990): Cover. Copyright ©1990 Cell Press. Image courtesy of Elsevier Sciences Ltd. **35.25.2** From "Microtubule plus-ends reveal essential links between intracellular polarization and localized modulation of endocytosis during division-plane establishment in plant cells." P. Dhonukshe et al. *BMC Biol.* 2005 Apr 14;3:11; **35.26.2** From "The tangled-1 mutation alters cell division orientations throughout maize leaf development without altering leaf shape." L. G. Smith et al. *Development.* 1996 Feb;122(2):481–9; **35.26.3** From "The tangled-1 mutation alters cell division orientations throughout maize leaf development without altering leaf shape." L. G. Smith et al. *Development.* 1996 Feb;122(2):481–9; **35.28** From figure 1a in U. Mayer et al., *Development* 117 (1): 149–162. © 1993 The Company of Biologists Ltd. **35.29.2** From "Microtubule plus-ends reveal essential links between intracellular polarization and localized modulation of endocytosis during division-plane establishment in plant cells." P. Dhonukshe et al. *BMC Biol.* 2005 Apr 14;3:11; **35.29.3** B. Wells and K. Roberts; **35.30.2** Reproduced by permission from figure 1 in D. Hareven et al, *Cell* 84 (5): 735–744. Copyright © 1996. by Elsevier Science Ltd. **35.30.3** Reproduced by permission from figure 1 in D. Hareven et al, *Cell* 84 (5): 735–744. Copyright © 1996. by Elsevier Science Ltd. **35.31.2** Reproduced by permission from Figure 2g in Hung et al, *Plant Physiology* 117:73–84. Copyright © 1998 by the American Society of Plant Biologists. Image courtesy of John Schiefelbein/Univesity of Michigan; **35.32.2** Dr. Gerald D. Carr, PhD; **35.33.2** Dr. E. M. Meyerowitz and John Bowman, *Development* 112 1991:1–231.2. Division of Biology, California Institute of Technolgy; **35.33.3** Dr. E. M. Meyerowitz and John Bowman, *Development* 112 1991:1–231.2. Division of Biology, California Institute of Technolgy.

Chapter 36 **36.1** Peggy Heard/FLPA/Alamy; **36.3.2** Rolf Rutishauser; **36.3.3** Rolf Rutishauser; **36.5.2** Dr. Jeremy Burgess/SPL/Photo Researchers; **p. 770, top** Nigel Cattlin/Holt Studios International/Photo Researchers; **p. 770, bottom** Nigel Cattlin/Holt Studios International/Photo Researchers; **36.11** Scott Camazine/Photo Researchers; **36.14.2** Graham Kent; **36.14.3** Graham Kent; **36.16.2** Mlane/Dreamstime.com; **36.16.3** Kate Shane, Southwest School of Botanical Medicine; **36.16.4** Frans Lanting/Corbis; **36.16.5** Natalie Bronstein; **36.16.6** Andrew de Lory/Dorling Kindersley; **36.16.7** Danita Delimont/Alamy; **36.19.2** M. H. Zimmermann, courtesy of Professor P. B. Tomlinson, Harvard University; **36.19.3** M. H. Zimmermann, courtesy of Professor P. B. Tomlinson, Harvard University; **36.19.4** M. H. Zimmermann, courtesy of Professor P. B. Tomlinson, Harvard University; **36.20.2** From "A coiled-coil interaction mediates cauliflower mosaic virus cell-to-cell movement." L. Stavolone et al. *Proc Natl Acad Sci U S A.* 2005 Apr 26;102(17):6219–24. Epub 2005 Apr 18.

Chapter 37 **37.1** Chris Mattison/Alamy; **37.2.2** USDA/ARS/Agricultural Research Service; **37.4** National Oceanic and Atmospheric Administration NOAA; **37.5** U.S. Geological Survey, Denver; **37.6** Kevin Horan/Stone/Getty Images; **37.9.2** White et al., *Plant Physiology,* June 2003; **37.11.2** Scimat/Photo Researchers; **37.11.3** E. H. Newcomb and S. R. Tandon/Biological Photo Service; **37.13.2** Hugues B. Massicotte, University of Northern British Columbia Ecosystem Science and Management Program, Prince George, B.C., Canada; **37.13.3** Mark Brundrett (http://mycorrhizas.info); **37.13.4** Mark Brundrett (http://mycorrhizas.info); **37.14.2** Elizabeth J. Czarapata/The Park People; **37.15.1** Wolfgang Kaehler/Corbis; **37.15.2** Ruud de Man/iStockphoto; **37.15.3** Kevin Schafer/Corbis; **37.15.4** Gary W. Carter/Corbis; **37.15.5** Kim Taylor and Jane Burton/Dorling Kindersley; **37.15.6** Biophoto Associates/Photo Researchers; **37.15.7** Philip Blenkinsop/Dorling Kindersley; **37.15.8** Paul A. Zahl/Photo Researchers; **37.15.9** Fritz Polking, Frank Lane Picture Agency/Corbis.

Chapter 38 **38.1** Pierre-Michel Blais; **38.3.2** Ed Reschke/Peter Arnold/PhotoLibrary; **38.3.3** Ed Reschke/Peter Arnold/PhotoLibrary; **38.3.4** David Scharf/Peter Arnold/PhotoLibrary; **38.4.2** Marianne Wiora; **38.4.3** Stephen Dalton/NHPA Limited/Photoshot; **38.4.4** Bjorn Rorslett Photographe; **38.4.5** Bjorn Rorslett Photographe; **38.4.7** Doug Backlund; **38.4.8** Martin Pieter Heigan; **38.4.9** Rolf Nussbaumer/Nature Picture Library; **38.4.10** Merlin D. Tuttle, Bat Conservation International, www.batcon.org; **38.5** Photo: © W. Barthlott/W. Rauh; **38.11.2** Kevin Schafer/Alamy; **38.11.3** Nature Production; **38.11.4** Brian Gordon Green/National Geographic Image Collection; **38.11.5** Steve Bloom Images/Alamy; **38.11.6** Aaron McCoy/Botanica/Photolibrary; **38.11.7** California Department of Food and Agriculture's Plant Health and Pest Prevention Services; **38.11.8** Kim A. Cabrera Photographer; **38.11.9** Steve Shattuck/CSIRO Entomology; **38.11.10** Alan Williams/ Alamy; **38.12.11** Dennis Frates/Alamy; **38.13.2** Marcel E. Dorken; **38.13.3** Marcel E. Dorken; **38.13.4** Nobumitsu Kawakubo, Gifu University, Japan; **38.14.2** Bruce Iverson, Photomicrography; **38.14.3** Bruce Iverson, Photomicrography; **38.14.4** Meriel G. Jones, University of Liverpool, UK; **38.15.2** Sinclair Stammers/Photo Researchers; **38.16.2** Andrew McRobb/Dorling Kindersley; **38.16.3** Andrew McRobb/Dorling Kindersley; **38.17** John Van Hasselt/Corbis.

Chapter 39 **39.1** *Plant Physiol.* 1999 Jul;120(3): Cover. By permission of the American Society of Plant Physiologists. Illustration by Niemeyer MI and Fernandez MC; **39.2** Natalie B. Bronstein; **39.7.2** "Regulation of Polar Auxin transport ATPIN1 in -*Arabidopsis* Vascular Tissue," by Leo Galweiler, et al. *Science* 18 DEC 1998, vol. 282; **39.7.3** "Regulation of Polar Auxin transport ATPIN1 in *Arabidopsis* Vascular Tissue," by Leo Galweiler, et al. *Science* 18 DEC 1998, vol. 282; **39.9.2** Malcolm B. Wilkins, University of Glasgow, Glasgow, Scotland, U.K. **39.9.3** Malcolm B. Wilkins, University of Glasgow, Glasgow, Scotland, U.K. **39.9.4** Malcolm B. Wilkins, University of Glasgow, Glasgow, Scotland, U.K. **39.10.2** Dr. Richard Amasino; **39.10.3** Fred Jensen; **39.12.2** Mia Molvray; **39.12.3** Karen E. Koch; **39.14.2** Kurt Stepnitz, DOE

Plant Research Laboratory, Michigan State University; **39.14.3** Joe Kieber, University of North Carolina; **39.15.2** Ed Reschke; **39.16.3** Malcolm B. Wilkins, University of Glasgow, Glasgow, Scotland, U.K. **39.16.4** Malcolm B. Wilkins, University of Glasgow, Glasgow, Scotland, U.K. **39.17.2** Malcolm B. Wilkins, University of Glasgow, Glasgow, Scotland, U.K. **39.17.3** Malcolm B. Wilkins, University of Glasgow, Glasgow, Scotland, U.K. **39.17.4** Malcolm B. Wilkins, University of Glasgow, Glasgow, Scotland, U.K. **39.17.5** Malcolm B. Wilkins, University of Glasgow, Glasgow, Scotland, U.K. **39.17.6** Malcolm B. Wilkins, University of Glasgow, Glasgow, Scotland, U.K. **39.20.2** Malcolm B. Wilkins, University of Glasgow, Glasgow, Scotland, U.K. **39.20.3** Malcolm B. Wilkins, University of Glasgow, Glasgow, Scotland, U.K. **39.24.2** Michael Evans, Ohio State University; **39.24.3** Michael Evans, Ohio State University; **39.24.4** Michael Evans, Ohio State University; **39.24.5** Michael Evans, Ohio State University; **39.25** Reproduced by permission from Janet Braam, *Cell* 60 (9 February 1990): Cover. Copyright © 1990 Cell Press. Image courtesy of Elsevier Sciences Ltd. **39.26.2** Martin Shields/Photo Researchers; **39.26.3** Martin Shields/Photo Researchers; **39.26.4** From K. Esau. "Anatomy of Seed Plants," 2nd ed. (New York: John Wiley and Sons, 1977), fig. 19.4, p.358; **39.26.5** From K. Esau. "Anatomy of Seed Plants," 2nd ed. (New York: John Wiley and sons, 1977), fig. 19.4, p.358; **39.27.2** J. L. Basq and M. C. Drew; **39.27.3** J. L. Basq and M. C. Drew; **39.29.2** New York State Agricultural Experiment Station (NYSAES)/Cornell.

Chapter 40 **40.1** JOEL SARTORE/National Geographic Stock; **40.2.2** Peter Aitken/Peter Arnold Images/ PhotoLibrary; **40.2.3** Duncan Usher/Alamy; **40.2.4** Frank Greenaway/Dorling Kindersley/Getty Images; **40.4.2** Susumu Nishinaga/Photo Researchers; **40.4.3** Eye of Science/Photo Researchers; **40.4.4** Susumu Nishinaga/Photo Researchers; **40.5.7** CNRI/SPL/Photo Researchers; **40.5.11** Dr. Gopal Murti/SPL/Photo Researchers; **40.5.13** Chuck Brown/Photo Researchers; **40.5.15** Nina Zanetti; **40.5.17** Nina Zanetti; **40.5.19** Nina Zanetti; **40.5.21** Alamy; **40.5.24** Nina Zanetti; **40.5.26** Ed Reschke/Peter Arnold Images/PhotoLibrary; **40.5.28** Manfred Kage/Peter Arnold/Photolibrary; **40.5.31** Ulrich Gartner; **40.5.33** Thomas Deerinck/National Center for Microscopy and Imaging Research, University of California, San Diego; **40.10.2** Patricio Robles Gil/naturepl.com; **40.10.3** Matt T. Lee; **40.13** Robert Ganz; **40.18** Jeff Rotman/Alamy.

Chapter 41 **41.1** Michael deYoung/Corbis; **41.2** Roland Seitre/Peter Arnold/PhotoLibrary; **41.3** Stefan Huwiler/Rolf Nussbaumer Photography/Alamy; **41.5.2** cameilia/Shutterstock; **41.6.2** Hervey Bay Whale Watch (www.herveybaywhalewatch.com.au); **41.6.4** Thomas Eisner; **41.6.5** Photo Lennart Nilsson/Scanpix; **41.6.6** Gunter Ziesler/Peter Arnold/PhotoLibrary; **41.11.2** Visuals Unlimited/Corbis; **41.17.2** Fritz Polking/Peter Arnold, Inc./Alamy; **41.17.3** EyeWire Collection/Photodisc/Getty Images; **41.22** Photo courtesy of The Jackson Laboratory, Bar Harbor, Maine; **41.23** Wolfgang Kaehler/Corbis.

Chapter 42 **42.1** Stephen Dalton/Photo Researchers; **42.2.2** Reinhard dirscheri/PhotoLibrary; **42.2.3** Eric Grave/Photo Researchers; **42.10.2** From "Human Histology Photo CD." Image courtesy Indigo Instruments (www.indigo.com); **42.10.3** Photo Lennart Nilsson/Scanpix; **42.16** Biophoto Associates/Photo Researchers; **42.18.2** Eye of Science/Photo Researchers; **42.22.2** Peter Batson/Image Quest Marine; **42.22.3** Olgysha/Shutterstock; **42.22.4** Jez Tryner/Image Quest Marine; **42.24.2** Prepared by Dr. Hong Y. Yan, University of Kentcky and Dr. Peng Chai, University of Texas; **42.25.2** Motta & Macchiarelli/Anatomy Dept., Univ. La Sapienza, Rome/Photo Researchers; **42.27.2** Hans-Rainer Duncker, University of Giessen, Germany.

Chapter 43 **43.1** Biology Media/Science Source/Photo Researchers; **43.4** Dominique Ferrandon; **43.21.2** Steve Gschmeissner/Photo Researchers; **43.23** CNRI/Photo Researchers; **43.26** The Laboratory of Structural Cell Biology, headed by Stephen C. Harrison, Harvard Medical School/HHMI.

Chapter 44 **44.1** David Wall/Alamy; **44.4** Mark Conlin/Image Quest Marine; **44.5.2** Dr. John Crowe, University of California, Davis; **44.5.3** Dr. John Crowe, University of California, Davis; **44.9** AFP/Getty Images; **44.14.5** Steve Gschmeissner/Photo Researchers; **44.17** John Cancalosi/Peter Arnold Images/PhotoLibrary; **44.18** Michael Fodgen/OSF/PhotoLibrary.

Chapter 45 **45.1** Ralph A. Clevenger/Corbis; **p. 974** Stuart Wilson/Photo Researchers; **45.3** Volker Witte; **45.18.2** Astier/BSIP/Photo Researchers; **45.19.2** Photoshot Holdings Ltd/Alamy; **45.19.3** Jurgen & Christine Sohns/FLPA.

Chapter 46 **46.1** David Doubilet/Getty Images; **46.2** David Wrobel; **46.4** Chris Wallace Photography, photographersdirect.com; **46.5.2** P. de Vries, courtesy of David Crews; **46.6** Andy Sands/naturepl.com; **46.7** John Cancalosi/Peter Arnold/PhotoLibrary; **46.17.2** Photo Lennart Nilsson/Scanpix; **46.17.3** Photo Lennart Nilsson/Scanpix; **46.17.4** Photo Lennart Nilsson/Scanpix.

Chapter 47 **47.1** Photo Lennart Nilsson/Scanpix; **47.4.2** Vacquier VD, Payne JE. Methods for quantitating sea urchin sperm-egg binding. *Exp Cell Res.* 1973 Nov;82(1):227–35; **47.4.3** Vacquier VD, Payne JE. Methods for quantitating sea urchin sperm-egg binding. *Exp Cell Res.* 1973 Nov;82(1):227–35; **47.4.4** Vacquier VD, Payne JE. Methods for quantitating sea urchin sperm-egg binding. *Exp Cell Res.* 1973 Nov;82(1):227–35; **47.4.5** Vacquier VD, Payne JE. Methods for quantitating sea urchin sperm-egg binding. *Exp Cell Res.* 1973 Nov;82(1):227–35; **47.4.7** Hafner, M., Petzelt, C., Nobiling, R., Pawley, J., Kramp, D. and G. Schatten. Wave of Free Calcium at Fertilization in the Sea Urchin Egg Visualized with Fura-2. *Cell Motil. Cytoskel.*, 9:271–277 (1988); **47.4.8** Hafner, M., Petzelt, C., Nobiling, R., Pawley, J., Kramp, D. and G. Schatten. Wave of Free Calcium at Fertilization in the Sea Urchin Egg Visualized with Fura-2. *Cell Motil. Cytoskel.*, 9:271–277 (1988); **47.4.9** Hafner, M., Petzelt, C., Nobiling, R., Pawley, J., Kramp, D. and G. Schatten. Wave of Free Calcium at Fertilization in the Sea Urchin Egg Visualized with Fura-2. *Cell Motil. Cytoskel.*, 9:271–277 (1988); **47.4.10** Hafner, M., Petzelt, C., Nobiling, R., Pawley, J., Kramp, D. and G. Schatten. Wave of Free Calcium at Fertilization in the Sea Urchin Egg Visualized with Fura-2. *Cell Motil. Cytoskel.*, 9:271–277 (1988); **47.6.2** George von Dassow; **47.6.3** George von Dassow; **47.6.4** George von Dassow; **47.6.5** George von Dassow; **47.7.2** Jürgen Berger/Max Planck Institute for Developmental Biology, Tübingen, Germany; **47.7.3** Andrew J. Ewald, Johns Hopkins Medical School; **47.9.2** Charles A. Ettensohn; **47.13.2** Huw Williams; **47.13.3** Thomas Poole, SUNY Health Science Center; **47.14.2** Dr. Keith Wheeler/Photo Researchers; **47.17.2** Hiroki Nishida, *Developmental Biology* 121 (1987): 526. Reprinted by permission of Academic Press; **47.17.3** Hiroki Nishida, *Developmental Biology* 121 (1987): 526. Reprinted by permission of Academic Press; **47.18.2** J. E. Sulston and H. R. Horvitz, *Dev. Biol.* 56 (1977):110–156; **47.19.2** Adapted from Strome (International Review of Cytology 114: 81–123, 1989); **47.20.2** Adapted from Strome (International Review of Cytology 114: 81–123, 1989); **47.20.3** Adapted from Strome (International Review of Cytology 114: 81–123, 1989); **47.20.4** Adapted from Strome (International Review of Cytology 114: 81–123, 1989); **47.20.5** Adapted from Strome (International Review of Cytology 114: 81–123, 1989); **47.24.2** Kathryn W. Tosney, University of Michigan; **47.25.2** Dennis Summerbell.

Chapter 48 **48.1** Marinethemes.com; **48.2.2** David Fleetham/Alamy; **48.6.2** Thomas Deerinck; **48.13.2** Bear, Connors, and Paradiso, "Neuroscience: Exploring the Brain" © 1996, p. 43; **48.16.2** Edwin R. Lewis, University of California at Berkeley.

Chapter 49 **49.1** Brainbow mouse cerebellum. Image by Tamily Weissman, Harvard University. The Brainbow mouse was produced by Livet J, Weissman TA, Kang H, Draft RW, Lu J, Bennis RA, Sanes JR, Lichtman JW. *Nature* (2007) 450:56–62; **49.6.2** N. Kedersha/Photo Researchers; **49.9** Larry Mulvehill/Corbis; **49.14.2** From "A functional MRI study of happy and sad affective states induced by classical music."; . . . M. T. Mitterschiffthaler et al. *Hum Brain Mapp.* 2007 Nov;28(11):1150–62; **49.16.2** Marcus E. Raichle, M.D., Washington University Medical Center; **p. 1075** From "Dr. Harlow's Case of Recovery from the passage of an Iron Bar through the Head." H. Bigelow. *Am. Journal of the Med. Sci.* July 1850;XXXIX. Images from the History of Medicine (NLM); **49.21** Image by Sebastian Jessberger. Fred H. Gage, Laboratory of Genetics LOG-G, The Salk Institute for Biological Studies; **49.24.2** Martin M. Rotker/Photo Researchers.

Chapter 50 **50.1** Kenneth Catania; **50.6.1** CSIRO; **50.6.2** R. A. Steinbrecht; **50.7.2** James Gerholdt/Photolibrary; **50.7.3** Splashdown Direct/ OSF/PhotoLibrary; **50.9.2** From Richard Elzinga, "Fundamentals of Entomology" 3rd. © 1987, p. 185. Reprinted by permission of Prentice-Hall, Upper Saddle River, NJ; **50.10.2** SPL/Photo Researchers; **50.16.2** USDA/APHIS Animal and Plant Health Inspection Service; **50.17.3** STEVE GSCHMEISSNER/SPL/Photo Researchers; **50.21** From "Gene therapy for red-green colour blindness in adult primates."; . . . K. Mancuso et al. *Nature.* 2009 Oct 8; 461(7265):784–7. Photo: Neitz Laboratory; **50.26.2** Clara Franzini-Armstrong, University of Pennsylvania; **50.27.2** Courtesy of Dr. H. E. Huxley; **50.27.3** Courtesy of Dr. H. E. Huxley; **50.27.4** Courtesy of Dr. H. E. Huxley; **50.33** George Cathcart Photography, photographersdirect.com; **50.38** Dave Watts/NHPA/Photo Researchers; **50.39** Vance A. Tucker.

Chapter 51 **51.1** Michael Nichols/National Geographic/Getty Images; **51.3** Susan Lee Powell; **51.5.2** Kenneth Lorenzen, UC Davis; **51.7.2** Thomas McAvoy/Life Magazine/Getty Images; **51.7.3** Operation Migration Inc.; **51.9.2** Lincoln Brower, Sweet Briar College; **51.9.3** Lincoln Brower, Sweet Briar College; **51.9.4** Lincoln Brower, Sweet Briar College; **51.11** Clive Bromhall/OSF/PhotoLibrary; **51.12.2** Alissa Crandall/Corbis; **51.12.3** Richard Wrangham; **51.15.2** Matt T. Lee; **51.15.3** David Osborn/Alamy; **51.15.4** Bill Schmoker; **51.16.2** James D Watt/Image Quest Marine; **51.17** Courtesy of Gerald S. Wilkinson; from G.S. Wilkinson and G. N. Dodson, in J. Choe and B. Crespi (eds)., "The Evolution of Mating Systems in Insects and Arachnids," Cambridge University Press, Cambridge (1997), pp. 310–328; **51.18** Cyril Laubscher/Dorling Kindersley; **51.21** Martin Harvey/Peter Arnold Images/PhotoLibrary; **51.22** Erik Svensson, Lund University, Sweden; **51.23.2** Robert Pickett/Corbis; **51.24** Lowell L. Getz and Lisa Davis; **51.25** Rory Doolin; **51.27** Jennifer Jarvis; **51.29.2.** Stephen J. Krasemann/Peter Arnold/PhotoLibrary.

Chapter 52 **52.1** Dr. Paul A. Zahl/Photo Researchers; **52.2.2** James D. Watt/Stephen Frink Collection/Alamy; **52.2.3** Gianni Tortoli/Photo Researchers; **52.2.4** Robyn Mackenzie/shutterstock; **52.2.5** B. Tharp/Photo Researchers; **52.2.6** Yann Arthus-Bertrand/ Corbis; **52.2.7** NASA/Goddard Space Flight Center; **52.11.1** JTB Photo Communications, Inc./Alamy; **52.11.2** imagebroker/Alamy; **52.12.2** Frans Lanting/Corbis; **52.12.4** Gordon Whitten/Corbis; **52.12.6** Wolfgang Kaehler/Corbis; **52.12.8** The California Chaparral Institute (http://californiachaparral.net). Photo supplied by Richard Halsey; **52.12.10** All Canada Photos/SuperStock; **52.12.12** Shutterstock; **52.12.14** Kennan Ward/Corbis; **52.12.16** Darrell Gulin/Corbis; **52.16.1** Allen Russell/PhotoLibrary; **52.16.2** AfriPics.com/Alamy; **52.16.3** David Tipling/Nature Picture Library; **52.16.4** Ron Watts/Corbis; **52.16.5** Photononstop/SuperStock; **52.16.6** James Randklev/Image Bank/Getty Images; **52.16.7** Stuart Westmorland/Corbis; **52.16.8** Stuart Westmorland/Corbis; **52.16.9** Digital Vision/Getty Images; **52.16.10** William Lange/Woods Hole Oceanographic Institution; **52.17.2** Geoff Dann/Dorling Kindersley; **52.19.2** Peter Llewellyn/Alamy; **52.21** Daniel Mosquin.

Chapter 53 **53.1** Arpat Ozgul; **53.2** Todd Pusser/Naturepl.com; **53.4.2** Bernard Castelein/Nature Picture Library/Alamy; **53.4.3** Frans Lanting/Corbis; **53.4.4** Niall Benvie/Corbis; **53.8.2** Hansjoerg Richter/iStockphoto; **53.11** Photodisc/White/PhotoLibrary; **53.12** Stone Nature Photography/Alamy; **53.13.2** H. Willcox/Wildlife Picture/Peter Arnold/Photolibrary; **53.14.2** Jean Louis Batt/Taxi/Getty Images; **53.14.3** Christine Osborne/Corbis; **53.14.4** Edward Parker/Alamy; **53.17.2** fotoVoyager/iStockphoto; **53.17.3** Adrian Bailey/Aurora Photos; **53.17.4** Joe Raedle/Getty Images; **53.17.5** Patrick Clayton, www.fisheyeguyphotography.com; **53.17.6** JOZSEF SZENTPETERI/NGS Image Collection; **53.17.7** Andrew Syred/Photo Researchers; **53.17.8** Nicholas Bergkessel, Jr./Photo Researchers; **53.19.2** Joe McDonald/Corbis; **53.20.2** Robert Kay; **53.21.2** Niclas Fritzén.

Chapter 54 **54.1** Hal Beral VWPics/SuperStock; **54.2.2** Joseph T. Collins/Photo Researchers; **54.2.3** National Museum of Natural History/Smithsonian Institution; **p. 1196** Frank W Lane/FLPA; **54.5.2** Barry Mansell/Nature Picture Library; **54.5.3** Fogden/Corbis; **54.5.4** Stephen J. Krasemann/Photo Researchers; **54.5.5** Robert Pickett/Papilio/Alamy; **54.5.6** Edward S. Ross, California Academy of Sciences; **54.5.7** © James K. Lindsey; **54.6** Douglas Faulkner/Photo Researchers; **54.7.2** Fogden/Corbis; **54.7.3** Dan Janzen, Department of Biology, University of Pennsylvania; **54.8** Peter Johnson/Corbis; **54.9.2** Sally D. Hacker; **54.12** Cedar Creek Ecosystem Science Reserve, University of Minnesota; **54.17.2** Genny Anderson; **54.19** SuperStock; **54.21.2** Ron Landis Photography, www.ronlandisphotography.co; **54.21.3** Scott T. Smith/Corbis; **54.22.2** Charles Mauzy/Corbis; **54.22.3** Keith Boggs; **54.22.4** Glacier Bay National Park Photo/Glacier Bay National Park and Preserve; **54.22.5** Terry Donnelly, Mary Liz Austin; **54.24.2** R. Grant Gilmore, Dynamac Corporation; **54.24.3** Lance Horn, National Undersea Research Center, University of North Carolina-Wilmington; **54.29** Nelish Pradhan, Bates College, Lewiston, ME; **54.30** Josh Spice.

Chapter 55 **55.1** Hassan Basagic; **55.2** Stone Nature Photography/Alamy; **55.3** Justus de Cuveland/AGE Fotostock; **55.16.2** Hubbard Brook Research Foundation/ USDA Forest Service; **55.16.3** USDA Forest Service; **55.17.2** Mark Gallagher; **55.17.3** Mark Gallagher; **55.18.2** U.S. Department of Energy; **55.19.2** Stewart Rood, University of Lethbridge; **55.19.3** Photo provided by Kissimmee Division staff, South Florida Water Management District (WPB); **55.19.4** Tim Day, Xcluder Pest Proof Fencing Company; **55.19.5** Daniel H. Janzen, University of Pennsylvania; **55.19.6** Bert Boekhoven; **55.19.7** Jean Hall/Holt Studios/Photo Researchers; **55.19.8** Kenji Morita/Environment Division, Tokyo Kyuei Co., Ltd.

Chapter 56 **56.1** Stephen J Richards; **56.2** Wayne Lawler/Ecoscene/Corbis; **56.4.2** Neil Lucas/Nature Picture Library; **56.4.3** Mark Carwardine/Still Pictures/Peter Arnold/ PhotoLibrary; **56.4.4** Nazir Foead; **56.5** Merlin D. Tuttle, Bat Conservation International, www.batcon.org; **56.6** Scott Camazine/Photo Researchers; **56.7** Michael Edwards/Getty Images; **56.8.2** Bruce Cowell, www.brucecowellphotographer .com; **56.8.3** Robert Ginn/PhotoEdit Inc. **56.9** Benezeth Mutayoba, photo provided by the University of Washington; **56.10** Richard Vogel/Liaison/Getty Images; **56.13.2** William Ervin/SPL/Photo Researchers; **56.14** Craighead Environmental Research Institute; **56.15.2** Tim Thompson/Corbis; **56.15.3** Chuck Bargeron, University of Georgia; **56.15.4** William D. Boyer, USDA Forest Service; **56.16.2** Yann Arthus-Bertrand/Corbis; **56.16.3** James P. Blair/National Geographic Image Collection; **56.17** R. O. Bierregaard, Jr., Biology Dept., University of North Carolina, Charlotte; **56.18** SPL/Photo Researchers; **56.21.2** Edwin Giesbers/naturepl.com; **56.22.2** Mark Chiappone and Steven Miller, Center for Marine Science, University of North Carolina-Wilmington, Key Largo, FL; **56.23** Nigel Cattlin/Photo Researchers; **56.24.2** NASA; **56.24.3** NASA; **56.26** Erich Hartmann/Magnum Photos; **56.28** Prof. William H. Schlesinger; **56.31.2** NASA; **56.31.3** NASA; **56.33.2** Serge de Sazo/ Photo Researchers; **56.33.3** Hilde Jensen, University of Tubingen/Nature Magazine/ AP Photo; **56.33.4** Gabriel Rojo/Nature Picture Library; **56.33.5** Titus Lacoste/Getty Images. **Appendix A** **p. A-5** OMIKRON/Science Source/Photo Researchers; **p. A-8** John N. A. Lott/Biological Photo Service; **p. A-10, top** Biophoto/Photo Researchers; **p. A-10, 2nd from top** Conly L. Rieder; **p. A-11** USDA/ARS/Agricultural Research Service; **p. A-35** Peter Kitin; **Appendix E** **p. E-1, top left** Dr. Kari Lounatmaa/ Photo Researchers; **p. E-1, bottom left** Eye of Science/Photo Researchers; **p. E-1, middle** M. I. Walker/NHPA/Photoshot; **p. E-1 right** Kathy Piper/iStockphoto; **p. E-2, left** Douglas Adams/iStockphoto; **p. E-2, right** McPHOTO/AGE Fotostock.

Illustration and Text Credits

4.6b, 9.9, 17.17b and **c** are adapted from C. K. Matthews and K. E. van Holde, *Biochemistry*, 2nd ed. Copyright © 1996 Pearson Education, Inc., publishing as Pearson Benjamin Cummings. **4.7, 6.6b, 11.7, 11.12, 17.11, 18.25, 20.8, 21.9, and 21.10** are adapted from W. M. Becker, J. B. Reece, and M. F. Poenie, *The World of the Cell*, 3rd ed. Copyright © 1996 Pearson Education, Inc., publishing as Pearson Benjamin Cummings. **Table 6.1a** Adapted from W. M. Becker, L. J. Kleinsmith, and J. Hardin, *The World of the Cell*, 4th ed. p. 753. Copyright © 2000 Pearson Education, Inc., publishing as Pearson Benjamin Cummings. **6.8** and **6.23a** and cell organelle drawings in **6.11** and **6.12** are adapted from illustrations by Tomo Narashima in E. N. Marieb, *Human Anatomy and Physiology*, 5th ed. Copyright © 2001 Pearson Education, Inc., publishing as Pearson Benjamin Cummings. **6.9a, 50.12,** and **50.13** are also from *Human Anatomy and Physiology*, 5th ed. Copyright © 2001 Pearson Education, Inc., publishing as Pearson Benjamin Cummings. **30.4, 30.13i,** and **39.13** are adapted from M. W. Nabors, *Introduction to Botany*, Copyright © 2004 Pearson Education, Inc., publishing as Pearson Benjamin Cummings. **42.30a, 46.16, 49.8, 49.10, 50.26, and 50.30** are adapted from E. N. Marieb, *Human Anatomy and Physiology*, 4th ed. Copyright © 1998 Pearson Education, Inc., publishing as Pearson Benjamin Cummings. **42.30a** From Campbell et al., *Biology: Concepts and Connections*, 6th ed., fig. 22.10, p. 462. Copyright © 2009 Pearson Education, Inc., publishing as Pearson Benjamin Cummings. **43.8** Adapted from Gerard J. Tortora, Berdell R. Funke, and Christine L. Case. 1998. *Microbiology: An Introduction*, 6th ed. Copyright © 1998 Pearson Education, Inc., publishing as Pearson Benjamin Cummings. **44.8** and **51.8** are adapted from L. G. Mitchell, J. A. Mutchmor, and W. D. Dolphin. *Zoology*. Copyright © 1988 Pearson Education, Inc., publishing as Pearson Benjamin Cummings.

Chapter 1 **1.25** Map provided courtesy of David W. Pfennig, University of North Carolina at Chapel Hill; **1.27** Data in bar graph based on D. W. Pfennig et al. 2001. Frequency-dependent Batesian mimicry. *Nature 410*:323.

Chapter 2 **2.2 (bottom)** Reprinted by permission of Macmillan Publishers Ltd. *Nature*. M.E. Frederickson et al. 'Devil's gardens' bedeviled by ants, *437*:495, 9/22/05. Copyright © 2005.

Chapter 3 **3.8a** Adapted from *Scientific American*, Nov. 1998, p.102.

Chapter 5 **5.12** Adapted from *Biology: The Science of Life*, 3rd ed. by Robert Wallace et al. Copyright © 1991. Reprinted by permission of Pearson Education, Inc; **5.15 and 5.20F** PDB ID 1CGD: J. Bella, B. Brodsky, and H. M. Berman. 1995. Hydration structure of a collagen peptide. *Structure 3*: 893–906; **5.18** Adapted from D. W. Heinz et al. 1993. How amino-acid insertions are allowed in an alpha-helix of T4 lysozyme. *Nature 361*:561; **5.20D** PDB ID 3GS0: Palaninathan, S.K., Mohamedmohaideen, N.N., Orlandini, E., Ortore, G., Nencetti, S., Lapucci, A., Rossello, A., Freundlich, J.S., Sacchettini, J.C. 2009. Novel transthyretin amyloid fibril formation inhibitors: synthesis, biological evaluation, and X-ray structural analysis. *Public Library of Science One 4*: e6290–e6290; **5.20G, 21.10b, Un42.1** PDB ID 2HHB: G. Fermi, M. F. Perutz, B. Shaanan, R. Fourme. 1984. The crystal structure of human deoxyhaemoglobin at 1.74 A resolution. *J.Mol.Biol. 175*: 159–174.

Chapter 7 **7.9** PDB ID 3HAO: N. H. Joh, A. Oberai, D. Yang, J. P. Whitelegge, J. U. Bowie. 2009. Similar energetic contributions of packing in the core of membrane and water-soluble proteins. *J. Am.Chem.Soc. 131*: 10846–10847.

Chapter 8 **8.18** PDB ID 3e1f: D H. Juers, B. Rob, M. L. Dugdale, N. Rahimzadeh, C. Giang, M. Lee, B. W. Matthews, R.E. Huber. 2009. Direct and indirect roles of His-418 in metal binding and in the activity of beta-galactosidase (E. coli). *Protein Sci. 18:* 1281–1292; **8.19** PDB ID 1MDY: P. C. Ma, M.A. Rould, H. Weintraub, C.O. Pabo. 1994. Crystal structure of MyoD bHLH domain-DNA complex: perspectives on DNA recognition and implications for transcriptional activation. *Cell* (Cambridge, Mass.) *77*: 451–459; **8.20** Figures 4a and 4e from "A common allosteric site and mechanism in caspases" by J.M. Scheer et al., in *Proceedings of the National Academy of Sciences, 103*, no. 20: 7595–7600, May 16, 2006. Copyright © 2006 National Academy of Sciences, U.S.A. Used by permission.

Chapter 9 **9.5** From *Molecular Biology of the Cell*, 4th edition, by Bruce Alberts et al., fig. 2.69, p. 92. Copyright © 2002 by Bruce Alberts, Alexander Johnson, Julian Lewis, Martin Raff, Keith Roberts, and Peter Walter. Used by permission

Chapter 10 **10.13b** Figure 1a from "Architecture of the photosynthetic Oxygen-evolving center" by K.N. Ferreira et al., in *Science, 303*, No. 5665: 1831–1838, March 19, 2004. Copyright © 2004, The American Association for the Advancement of Science. Reprinted with permission from AAAS; **10.15** Adapted from Richard and David Walker. Energy, Plants, and Man, fig. 4.1, p. 69. Sheffield: University of Sheffield. Oxygraphics http:// www.oxygraphics.co.uk. © Richard Walker. Used with permission.

Chapter 12 **12.13** From *Molecular Biology of the Cell*, 4th edition, by Bruce Alberts et al., fig. 18.41, p. 1059. Copyright © 2002 by Bruce Alberts, Alexander Johnson, Julian Lewis, Martin Raff, Keith Roberts, and Peter Walter. Used by permission.

Chapter 17 **17.13** Figure 10-45 from *Principles of Cell and Molecular Biology*, 2nd edition, by Valerie M. Kish and Lewis J. Kleinsmith. Copyright © 1995 HarperCollins College Publishers. Reprinted by permission of Pearson Education.

Chapter 18 **18.15a** Figure 1d from "An Abundant Class of Tiny RNAs with Probable Regulatory Roles in *Caenorhabditis elegans"* by N.C. Lau et al., in *Science, 294*, No. 5543: 858–862, Oct. 1, 2001. Copyright © 2001, The American Association for the Advancement of Science. Reprinted with permission from AAAS.

Chapter 20 **20.10** Figure 15.24, p. 481, from *Genetics*, 5th ed., by Peter Russell. Copyright © 1998 Pearson Education, Inc., publishing as Pearson Benjamin Cummings. Used by permission of the publisher.

Chapter 21 **21.2** Adapted from a figure by Chris A. Kaiser and Erica Beade; **21.5b** Figure 2B from "The Genetic Landscape of a Cell" by M. Costanzo et al., in *Science, 327*, No. 5964: 425–431, Jan. 22, 2010. Copyright © 2010, The American Association for the Advancement of Science. Reprinted with permission from AAAS; **21.17** Adapted from an illustration by William McGinnis in Peter Radetsky, "The homeobox: Something very precious that we share with flies, from egg to adult." Bethesda, MD: Howard Hughes Medical Institute, 1992, p. 92. Reprinted by permission of William McGinnis; **21.18** Adapted from M. Akam, *"Hox* genes and the evolution of diverse body plans," *Philosophical Transactions of the Royal Society B*, 1995, *349:* 313–319, fig. 3. © Royal Society of London. Reprinted by permission.

Chapter 22 **22.8** © Utako Kikutani 2007. Used with permission; **22.13** Figure 4a from "Host Race Radiation in the Soapberry Bug: Natural History with the History" by S.P. Carroll and C. Boyd, in Evolution, Vol. 46 No. 4, p. 1060, Aug. 1992. Reproduced with permission of Blackwell Publishing Ltd.; **22.14** Reprinted from *Trends in Microbiology, 16*, Issue 8: 361–369. B.A. Diep and M. Otto, "The role of virulence determinants in community-associated MRSA pathogenesis," Copyright © 2008, with permission from Elsevier.

Chapter 23 **23.5** Figure 3 from "Genetic mechanisms for adapting to a changing environment" by D.A. Powers et al., from *Annual Review of Genetics, 25*, Dec. 1991. Copyright © 1991 by Annual Reviews. Reprinted by permission; **23.11** Figure 20.6 (maps only) from *Discover Biology*, Second Edition by Michael L. Cain, Hans Damman, Robert A. Lue & Carol Kaesuk Loon, Editors. Copyright © 2002 by Sinauer Associates, Inc. Used by permission of W.W. Norton & Company, Inc.; **23.12** Reprinted by permission from Macmillan Publishers Ltd.: *Nature*. E. Postma and A. J. van Noordijk, Gene flow maintains a large genetic difference in clutch size at a small spatial scale, *433*, 1/6/05. Copyright © 2005; **23.14** Adapted from many sources including D. J. Futuyma. 2005. *Evolution*, fig. 11.3. Sunderland, MA: Sinauer Associates and from R. L. Carroll, 1988. *Vertebrate Paleontology and Evolution*. W.H. Freeman & Co.; **23.16** Adapted from A. M. Welch et al. 1998. Call duration as an indicator of genetic quality in male gray tree frogs. *Science* 280:1928–1930; **23.17** Adapted from A. C. Allison. 1961. Abnormal hemoglobin and erythrocyte enzyme-deficiency traits. In *Genetic Variation in Human Populations*, ed. G.A. Harrison. Oxford: Elsevier Science and from S. I. Hay et al., A world malaria map: *Plasmodium falciparum* endemicity in 2007. *PLoS Medicine 6:* fig. 3, p. 291; **23.18** Figure 2a from "Frequency-Dependent Natural Selection in the Handedness of Scale-Eating Cichlid Fish" by Michio Hori in *Science, 260*, No. 5105: 216–219, April 9, 1993. Copyright © 1993, The American Association for the Advancement of Science. Reprinted with permission from AAAS; **Un 23.2** Data from R. K. Koehn and T. J. Hilbish. 1987. The adaptive importance of genetic variation. *American Scientist* 75: 134–141.

Chapter 24 **24.7** Figure 3 from "Ecological Speciation in *Gambusia* Fishes" by R.B. Langerhans et al., from *Evolution, 61*, No. 9, July 2007, published by The Society for the Study of Evolution. Copyright © 2007 R.B. Langerhans, M.E. Gifford, E.O. Joseph. Reprinted by permission; **24.9** From figure 2 in "Correspondence between sexual isolation and allozyme differentiation" *Proceedings of the National Academy of Science, 87:* 2715–2719, 1990, p. 2718. Copyright © 1990 Stephen G. Tilley, Paul A. Verrell, Steven J. Arnold. Used with permission; **24.10a** Adapted from D. M. B. Dodd, 1989. Reproductive isolation as a consequence of adaptive divergence in *Drosophila pseudoobscura*. *Evolution* 43: 1308–1311; **24.13** *Hybrid Zone and the Evolutionary Process* edited by R.G. Harrison (1993): Map of Bombina hybrid zone (p. 263) and figure 10.1 (p. 278) from chapter "Analysis of hybrid zones with bombina" by J. M. Szymura. By permission of Oxford University Press; **24.15** Reprinted by permission of Macmillan Publishers Ltd.: *Nature*. G. P. Saetre et al. A sexually selected character displacement in flycatchers reinforces premating isolation, *387*:589–591, fig. 2, 6/5/97. Copyright © 1997; **24.19b** From fig. 2 in L. H. Rieseberg et al. 1996. Role of Gene Interactions in Hybrid Speciation: Evidence from Ancient and Experimental Hybrids. *Science* 272: 741–745. Copyright © 1996. Reprinted with permission from AAAS.

Chapter 25 **25.2** Graph based on data from A. P. Johnson et al., The Miller Volcanic spark discharge experiment, *Science* 322:404 (2008); **25.3a** Graph from "Experimental Models of Primitive Cellular Compartments Encapsulation Growth and Division" by M.M. Hanczyc et al., in *Science, 302*, No. 5645: 618–622. Oct. 24, 2003. Copyright © 2003, The American Association for the Advancement of Science. Reprinted with permission from AAAS; **25.5** From Don L. Eicher, *Geologic Time,* 1st edition, © 1968. Printed and Electronically reproduced by permission of Pearson Education, Inc., Upper Saddle River, New Jersey; **25.6a–d** Adapted from many sources including D. J. Futuyma. 2005. *Evolution,* fig. 4.10. Sunderland, MA: Sinauer Associates and from R. L. Carroll, 1988. *Vertebrate Paleontology and Evolution.* W.H. Freeman & Co.; **25.6e** Adapted from Luo et al. 2001. A new mammalia form from the Early Jurassic and evolution of mammalian characteristics. *Science* 292: 1535; **25.7** Adapted from D. J. Des Marais. September 8, 2000. When did photosynthesis emerge on Earth? *Science* 289: 1703–1705; **25.8** Reprinted by permission from Macmillan Publishers Ltd.: *Nature.* L. R. Kump. The rise of atmospheric oxygen, *451:*277–278, 1/17/08. Copyright © 2008; **25.13** Map adapted from http://gelology.er.usgs.gov/eastern/plates.html; **25.15** Graph created from D. M. Raup and J. J. Sepkoski, Jr. 1982. Mass extinctions in the marine fossil record. *Science.* 215: 1501–1503 and J. J. Sepkoski, Jr. 1984. A kinetic model of Phanerozoic taxonomic diversity. III. Post-Paleozoic families and mass extinctions. *Paleobiology.* Vol 10, No. 2, pp. 246–267 in D. J. Futuyma, fig. 7.3a, p. 143 and fig. 7.6, p. 145, Sunderland, MA: Sinauer Associates; **25.17** From Mayhew, P. J. et al. 2008. A long-term association between global temperature and biodiversity, origination and extinction in the fossil record. *Proceedings of the Royal Society B, 275:* 47–53, fig. 3b. Reprinted by permission; **25.18** Figure 3 from "Anatomical and ecological constraints on Phanerozoic animal diversity in the marine realm" by R.K. Bambach et al., in *Proceedings of the National Academy of Sciences, 99,* no. 10: 6854–6859, May 14, 2002. Copyright © 2002 National Academy of Sciences, U.S.A. Used by permission; **25.19** Adapted from Hickman, Roberts, and Larson.1997, *Zoology,* 10th ed, Wm. C. Brown, fig. 31.1; **25.24** Reprinted by permission from Macmillan Publishers Ltd: *Nature.* M. Ronshaugen et al. Hox protein mutation and macroevolution of the insect body plan, *415:*914–917, fig. 1a. Copyright © 2002; **25.26** Adapted from M. Strickberger, 1990. *Evolution,* Boston: Jones & Bartlett.

Chapter 26 **26.6** Figure 1 from "Which Whales Are Hunted? A Molecular Genetic Approach to Monitoring Whaling" by C.S. Baker and S.R. Palumbi, in *Science, 265,* No. 5178:1538–1539, Sep. 9, 1994. Copyright © 1994, The American Association for the Advancement of Science. Reprinted with permission from AAAS; **26.12** With kind permission from Springer Science+Business Media: *Development Genes and Evolution,* "The evolution of the hedgehog gene family in chordates: insights from amphioxus hedgehog," vol. 209, 1999, pp. 40–47, Jan. 1999, S.M. Shimeld, fig. 3; **26.19** Figure 4.3c, p. 124 from *Molecular Markers, Natural History, and Evolution,* 2nd edition, by John Avise. Copyright © 2004 Sinauer Associates. Used by permission; **26.20** Figure from "Timing the Ancestor of the HIV-1 Pandemic Strains" by B. Korber et al., in *Science, 288,* No. 5472: 1789–1796, Jun 9, 2000. Copyright © 2000, The American Association for the Advancement of Science. Reprinted with permission from AAAS; **26.21** Figure 4.1, p. 45, "The three domains of life" by S.L. Baldauf et al., from *Assembling the Tree of Life,* edited by Joel Cracraft and Michael Donoghue. By permission of Oxford University Press, Inc. **26.22** Adapted from S. Blair Hedges. The origin and evolution of model organisms. *Nature Reviews Genetics 3:*838–848, fig. 1, p. 840.

Chapter 27 **27.10** Reprinted by permission from Macmillan Publishers Ltd.: *Nature.* V.S. Cooper and R.E. Lenski. The population genetics of ecological specialization in evolving *E. coli* populations, *407:*736–739, fig. 1. Copyright © 2000; **27.18** Graph created from data in C. Calvaruso et al. 2006. Root-associated bacteria contribute to mineral weathering and to mineral nutrition in trees: A budgeting analysis. *Applied and Environmental Microbiology* 72: 1258–1266.

Chapter 28 **28.2** Reprinted from *Trends in Genetics,18,* No. 11, J.M. Archibald and P.J. Keeling, "Recycled plastids: a 'green movement' in eukaryotic evolution," Copyright © 2002, with permission from Elsevier; **28.11** Figure 12.7, p. 350, from *Microbiology,* by R. W. Bauman. Copyright © 2004 Pearson Education, Inc., publishing as Benjamin Cummings; **28.23** Data from A. Stechman and T. Cavalier-Smith. 2002. Rooting the eukaryote tree by using a derived gene fusion, *Science* 297: 89–91; **28.28** Reprinted by permission from Macmillan Publishers Ltd.: *Nature.* M.J. Behrenfeld et al. Climate-driven trends in contemporary ocean productivity, *44:* 752–755, fig. 3. Copyright © 2006.

Chapter 29 **29.10** Source: R. D. Bowden. 1991. Inputs, outputs and accumulation of nitrogen in an early successional moss *(Polytrichum)* ecosystem. *Ecological Monographs* 61: 207–223; **29.14** Adapted from Raven et al. *Biology of Plants,* 6th ed., fig. 19.7, W. H. Freeman & Co.

Chapter 30 **30.12a** From P. R. Crane. 1985. Phylogenetic analysis of seed plants and the origin of angiosperms. *Annals of the Missouri Botanical Garden, 72:*716–793, fig. 11a, p. 738. Used by permission of Missouri Botanical Garden Press; **30.12b** Figure 2.3, p. 28, from *Phylogeny and Evolution of Angiosperms* by Douglas E. Soltis et al. Copyright © 2005 Sinauer Associates. Used by permission. **Table 30.1** Adapted from Randy Moore et al., *Botany,* 2nd ed. Dubuque, IA: Brown, 1998, Table 2.2, p. 37.

Chapter 31 **31.21** Figures 4 and 5 from "Fungal endophytes limit pathogen damage in a tropical tree" by A.E. Arnold et al., in *Proceedings of the National Academy of Sciences, 100,* no. 26: 15652–15653, December 23, 2003. Copyright © 2003 National Academy of Sciences, U.S.A. Used by permission; **31.26** Figure 1 from "Reversing introduced species effects: Experimental removal of introduced fish leads to rapid recovery of a declining frog" by Vance T. Vredenburg from *Proceedings of the National Academy of Sciences 101:* 7646–7650. Copyright © 2004 National Academy of Sciences, U.S.A. Used by permission.

Chapter 33 **33.22** C. Lydeard et al., The Global Decline of Nonmarine Mollusks, *BioScience,* Vol. 54, No. 4: 321–330. © 2004, American Institute of Biological Sciences. Used by permission. All rights reserved. (Updated data are from International Union for Conservation of Nature, 2008.); **33.29a** Reprinted from *Current Biology, 7,* Issue 8, J.K. Grenier, S. Carroll et al., "Evolution of the entire arthropod *Hox* gene set predated the origin and radiation of the onychophoran/arthropod clade," p. 551, fig. 2a, Copyright © 1987, with permission from Elsevier.

Chapter 34 **34.8b** From "Fossil sister group of craniates: Predicted and found" by J. Mallatt and J. Chen, from *Journal of Morphology, 258,* Issue 1, May 15, 2003. Copyright © 2003 Wiley-Liss, Inc. Reprinted with permission; **34.12** From *Vertebrates: Comparative Anatomy, Function, Evolution,* 3/e by Kenneth Kardong. © 2002 McGraw-Hill Science/Engineering/Mathematics. Reprinted by permission of The McGraw-Hill Companies, Inc. **34.18 (bottom)** Reprinted by permission of Macmillan Publishers Ltd.: *Nature.* M. Zhu et al. The oldest articulated osteichthyan reveals mosaic gnathostome characters, *458:*469–474. Copyright © 2009; **34.21 (left)** Reproduced by permission of the Royal Society of Edinburgh from Transactions of the Roya Society of Edinburgh: Earth Sciences, volume 87 (1996), pp. 363–421; **34.21 (right)** Reprinted by permission of Macmillan Publishers Ltd.: *Nature.* N.H. Shubin et al. The pectoral fin of *Tiktaalik roseae* and the origin of the tetrapod limb, *440:*768, fig. 4. Copyright © 2006; **34.37a** Adapted from many sources including D. J. Futuyma. 2005. *Evolution,* 1/e, fig. 4.10. Sunderland, MA: Sinauer Associates and from R. L. Carroll, 1988. *Vertebrate Paleontology and Evolution.* W.H. Freeman & Co. **34.47** Drawn from many photos of fossils. Some sources are *O. tugenensis* photo in Michael Balter, Early hominid sows division, *ScienceNow,* Feb. 22, 2001, © 2001 American Association for the Advancement of Science. *A. garhi,* and *H. neanderthalensis* adapted from *The Human Evolution Coloring Book. K platyops* drawn from photo in Meave Leakey et al., New hominid genus from eastern Africa shows diverse middle Pliocene lineages, *Nature,* March 22, 2001, 410: 433. *P. boisei* drawn from a photo by David Bill. *H. ergaster* drawn from a photo at www.inhandmuseum.com. *S. tchadensis* drawn from a photo in Michel Brunet et al., A new hominid from the Upper Miocene of Chad, Central Africa, *Nature,* July 11, 2002, 418: 147, fig. 1b; **34.50 (a/b)** Reprinted by permission of Macmillan Publishers Ltd.: *Nature.* I.V. Ovchinnikov et al. Molecular analysis of Neanderthal DNA from the northern Caucasus, *404:* 492, fig.3a and b. Copyright © 2000.

Chapter 35 **35.21** Figure 2b from "Mongolian Tree Rings and 20th-Century Warming" by G.C. Jacoby et al., in *Science, 273,* No. 5276: 771–773, Aug. 9, 1996. Copyright © 1996, The American Association for the Advancement of Science. Reprinted with permission from AAAS.

Chapter 39 **39.16 (top)** Adapted from M. Wilkins. 1988. *Plant Watching,* Facts of File Publ. **39.28** Figure "No Free Lunch" from "Plant Biology: New fatty acid-based signals: A lesson from the plant world" by Edward Farmer in *Science, 276,* No. 5314: 912–913, May 9, 1997. Copyright © 1997, The American Association for the Advancement of Science. Reprinted with permission from AAAS.

Chapter 40 **40.14** Figure 2 from "Thermoregulation in a brooding female Indian python, Python molurus bivittatus" by V.H. Hutchison et al., in *Science, 151,* No. 3711: 694–695, Feb. 11, 1966. Copyright © 1966, The American Association for the Advancement of Science. Reprinted with permission from AAAS; **40.15** Figure 7 from "Thermoregulation in Endothermic Insects" by Bernd Heinrich, in *Science, 185,* No. 4153: 747–756, August 30, 1974. Copyright © 1974, The American Association for the Advancement of Science. Reprinted with permission from AAAS; **40.21** Adapted from figures 2b and 2c from "The circadian clock stops ticking during deep hibernation in the European hamster" by F.G. Revel et al., in *Proceedings of the National Academy of Sciences, 104,* no. 34: 13816–13820, Aug. 21, 2007. Copyright © 2007 National Academy of Sciences, U.S.A. Used by permission.

Chapter 41 **41.9a** Figure 23.1 from *Human Anatomy and Physiology,* 8e, by Elaine Marieb and Katja Hoehn. Copyright © 2010 Pearson Education, Inc., publishing as Pearson Benjamin Cummings. Used by permission of the publisher; **41.9b** Figure 22-1 from Rhoades, *Human Physiology,* 3e. © 1996 Brooks/Cole, a part of Cengage Learning, Inc. Reproduced by permission. www.cengage.com/permissions; **41.21** Figure "Appetite Controllers" from "Cellular Warriors at the Battle of the Bulge" by Jean Marx, from *Science, 299:* p. 86, Feb. 7, 2003. Illustration by Kathleen Sutliff. Copyright © 2003, The American Association for the Advancement of Science. Reprinted with permission from AAAS.

Chapter 42 **42.20** Reprinted by permission from Macmillan Publishers Ltd.: *Nature.* D.J. Rader and A. Daugherty. Translating molecular discoveries into new therapies for atherosclerosis, *451:*904–913, fig. 1, 2/21/08. Copyright © 2008; **42.21** From J.C. Cohen et al., "Sequence variations in PCSK9, low LDL, and protection against coronary heart disease," *New England Journal of Medicine.* 2006 Mar 23; *354:*1264–72, fig. 1A. Copyright © 2006 Massachusetts Medical Society. Used by permission. All rights reserved; **42.26** Adapted from "Surface properties in relation to atelectasis and hyaline membrane disease" by M.E. Avery and J. Mead, from A.M.A. *American Journal of Diseases of Children 97:*517–523 (June 1959). Copyright © 1959 American Medical Association. Used by permission. All rights reserved.

Chapter 43 **43.5** From figures 2a and 4a in Phoebe Tzou et al., "Constitutive expression of a single antimicrobial peptide can restore wild-type resistance to infection in immuno-deficient *Drosophila* mutants," *PNAS, 99:* 2152–2157. Copyright © 2002 National Academy of Sciences, U.S.A. Used with permission; **43.7** Figures 20.4 and 20.5 from *Human Anatomy and Physiology,* 8e, by Elaine Marieb and Katja Hoehn. Copyright © 2010 Pearson Education, Inc., publishing as Pearson Benjamin Cummings. Used by permission of the publisher.

Chapter 44 **44.6** Kangaroo rat data adapted from K. B. Schmidt-Nielson. 1990. *Animal Physiology: Adaptation and Environment,* 4th ed., p. 339. Cambridge: Cambridge University Press; **44.7a** Adapted from K. B. Schmidt-Nielsen et al. 1958. Extrarenal salt excretion in birds. *American Journal of Physiology* 193: 101–107; **44.14B and 44.15** Figure 25.3b from *Human Anatomy and Physiology,* 8e, by Elaine Marieb and Katja Hoehn. Copyright © 2010 Pearson Education, Inc., publishing as Pearson Benjamin Cummings. Used by permission of the publisher; **44.21** Table 1 from "Requirement of human renal water channel aquaporin-2 for vasopressin-dependent concentration in urine" by P.M. Deen et al., in *Science, 264,* No. 5155: 92–95, April 1, 1994. Copyright © 1994, The American Association for the Advancement of Science. Reprinted with permission from AAAS; **44EOC** From W.S. Beck et al., *Life: An Introduction to Biology,* 3rd edition, copyright © 1991. Reprinted and electronically reproduced by permission of Pearson Education, Inc., Upper Saddle River, New Jersey.

Chapter 46 **46.9** Reprinted by permission of Macmillan Publishers Ltd.: *Nature.* R.R. Snook and D.J. Hosken, "Sperm death and dumping in *Drosophila,*" *428:*939–941, fig. 2. Copyright © 2004.

Chapter 47 **47.16** Figures 1.10 and 8.25 from *Principles of Development* by Lewis Wolpert (1998). By permission of Oxford University Press, Inc. **47.17a** Figure 21-70 from *Molecular Biology of the Cell,* 4th ed, by Bruce Alberts, used with permission from Garland Science - Books, permission conveyed through Copyright Clearance Center, Inc. Adapted for use from "Cell commitment and gene expression in the axolotl embryo" by T.J. Mohun from *Cell 22:* 9–15 (1980), by permission of the author;

47.17b Reprinted from *Developmental Biology, 121,* Issue 2, Hiroki Nishida, "Cell lineage analysis in ascidian embryos by intracellular injection of a tracer enzyme: III. Up to the tissue restricted stage," p. 526, Copyright © 1987, with permission from Elsevier; **47.18** From *Molecular Biology of the Cell,* 4th edition, by Bruce Alberts et al., fig. 21.17, p. 1172. Copyright © 2002 by Bruce Alberts, Alexander Johnson, Julian Lewis, Martin Raff, Keith Roberts, and Peter Walter. Used by permission; **47.23 (experiment, results left)** Figures 1.10 and 8.25 from *Principles of Development* by Lewis Wolpert (1998). By permission of Oxford University Press, Inc. **47.23 (results, right)** Figure 15.12, p. 604, from *Developmental Biology,* 5th edition, by Gilbert et al. Copyright © 1997 Sinauer Associates. Used by permission; **47.26** Figure 23.1 from *Human Anatomy and Physiology,* 8e, by Elaine Marieb and Katja Hoehn. Copyright © 2010 Pearson Education, Inc., publishing as Pearson Benjamin Cummings. Used by permission of the publisher.

Chapter 48 **48.11** Adapted from G. Matthews, 2003. *Cellular Physiology of Nerve and Muscle,* 4th edition, fig. 6-2d, p. 61. Cambridge, MA: Blackwell Scientific Publications. Reprinted by permission of Wiley Blackwell; **48.18** Table 1 from "Opiate Receptor: Demonstration in nervous tissue" by C.B. Pert and S.H. Snyder in *Science, 179,* No. 4077: 1011–1014, March 9, 1973. Copyright © 1973, The American Association for the Advancement of Science. Reprinted with permission from AAAS.

Chapter 49 **49.11** Adapted from L. M. Mukhametov. 1984. Sleep in marine mammals. In *Sleep Mechanisms,* by A. A. Borbély and J. L. Valatx (eds.). Munich: Springer-Verlag, pp 227–238; **49.12** Figure 2a from "Transplanted suprachiasmatic nucleus determines circadian period" by M.R. Ralph et al., in *Science, 247,* No. 4945: 975–978, Feb. 23, 1990. Copyright © 1990, The American Association for the Advancement of Science. Reprinted with permission from AAAS; **49.18** Adapted from E. D. Jarvis et al. 2005. Avian brains and a new understanding of vertebrate brain evolution. *Nature Reviews Neuroscience* 6: 151–159, fig. 1c; **49.22** From *Schizophrenia Genesis: The Origins of Madness* by I. I. Gottesman, and D. Wolfgram, fig. 10, p. 96. New York: Freeman. © 1991 by Irving I. Gottesman. Used with the permission of Worth Publishers.

Chapter 50 **50.17A** Figure 15.4(a) from *Human Anatomy and Physiology,* 8e, by Elaine Marieb and Katja Hoehn. Copyright © 2010 Pearson Education, Inc., publishing as Pearson Benjamin Cummings. Used by permission of the publisher; **50.17B** Figure 15.15 from *Human Anatomy and Physiology,* 8e, by Elaine Marieb and Katja Hoehn. Copyright © 2010 Pearson Education, Inc., publishing as Pearson Benjamin Cummings. Used by permission of the publisher; **50.23** Reprinted by permission from Macmillan Publishers Ltd.: *Nature.* K.L. Mueller et al. The receptors and coding logic for bitter taste, *434:*225–229, fig. 4b. Copyright © 2005; **50.24a** Figure 15.23(a) and (b) from *Human Anatomy and Physiology,* 8e, by Elaine Marieb and Katja Hoehn. Copyright © 2010 Pearson Education, Inc., publishing as Pearson Benjamin Cummings. Used by permission of the publisher; **50.34** Grasshopper adapted from Hickman et al. 1993. *Integrated Principles of Zoology,* 9th ed., Fig. 22.6, p. 518. New York: McGraw-Hill Higher Education. © 1993 The McGraw-Hill Companies; **50.40** Figure 4 from "Locomotion: Energy Cost of Swimming, Flying, and Running" by K. Schmidt-Nielsen, in *Science, 177,* No. 4045: 222–228, July 21, 1972. Copyright © 1972, The American Association for the Advancement of Science. Reprinted with permission from AAAS.

Chapter 51 **51.2b** Figure 20, p. 28, from *Study of Instinct* by N. Tinbergen (1989). By permission of Oxford University Press, Inc.; **51.4** Reprinted by permission from Macmillan Publishing Ltd.: *Nature Reviews: Genetics:* M.B. Sokolowski. Drosophila: Genetics meets behavior, *2:*881, fig. 1. Copyright © 2001; **51.10** Figure 3a from "Prospective and retrospective learning in honeybees" by M. Biurfa and J. Benard, in *International Journal of Comparative Psychology, 19,* Issue 3: 358–367, 2006; Reprinted with permission; **51.13** Figure 2a from "Evolution of foraging behavior in Drosophila by density-dependent selection" by M.B. Sokolowski et al., in *Proceedings of the National Academy of Sciences, 94,* no. 14: 7373–7377, July 8, 1997. Copyright © 2007 National Academy of Sciences, U.S.A. Used by permission; **51.19** K. Witte and N. Sawka. 2003. Sexual imprinting on a novel trait in the dimorphic zebra finch: sexes differ. *Animal Behaviour* 65: 195–203. Art adapted from http://www.uni-bielefeld.de/biologue/vhf/KW/Forschungsprojekte2.html; **51.23 (left, bottom)** With kind permission from Springer Science+Business Media: *Genetica,* "The inheritance of mating songs in two cryptic, sibling lacewing species," vol. 116, 2002, pp. 269–289, C. S. Henry, fig. 2; **51.26 (top)** Adapted from a photograph by Jonathan Blair in Alcock, 2002. *Animal Behavior,* 7th ed. Sinauer Associates, Inc., Publiishers; **51.26 (bottom)** Reprinted by permission from Macmillan Publishers Ltd.: *Nature.* P. Berthold et al. Rapid microevolution of migratory behaviour in a wild bird species, *360:*668, fig. 1, 12/17/92. Copyright © 1992.

Chapter 52 **52.7** Adapted from L. Roberts. 1989. How fast can trees migrate? *Science* 243: 736, fig. 2. © 1989 by the American Association for the Advancement of Science; **52.8** Reprinted by permission from Macmillan Publishers Ltd.: *Nature.* C. Parmesan et al. Poleward shift of butterfly species' ranges associated with regional warming, *399:*579–583, fig. 3. Copyright © 1999; **52.9** Adapted from Heinrich Walter and Siegmar-Walter Breckle. 2003. *Walter's Vegetation of the Earth,* fig. 16, p. 36. Springer-Verlag, © 2003; **52.17** Figure 1.7, p. 9 from *Kangaroos, Their Ecology and Management in the Sheep Rangelands of Australia,* edited by Graeme Caughley, Neil Shepherd, Jeff Short. © Cambridge University Press 1987. Reprinted with the permission of Cambridge University Press; **52.19** Map adapted from R. L. Smith. 1974. *Ecology and Field Biology,* fig. 11.19, p. 353. Harper and Row Publishers. Map updated from D. A. Sibley. 2000. National Audubon Society *The Sibley Guide to Birds,* Alfred A. Knopf: New York; **52.20** Data from W. J. Fletcher. 1987. Interactions among subtidal Australian sea urchins, gastropods and algae: effects of experimental removals. *Ecological Monographs* 57: 89–109; **Un. 52.2** Data from J. Clausen, D. D. Keck, and W. M. Hiesey. 1948. Experimental studies on the nature of species. III. Environmental responses of climatic races of *Achillea.* Carnegie Institution of Washington Publication 581.

Chapter 53 **53.5** Adapted from P. W. Sherman and M. L. Morton. 1984. "Demography of Belding's ground squirrels," *Ecology,* Vol. 65, No. 5, p. 1622, fig. 1a, 1984. Copyright © 1984 Ecological Society of America. Used by permission; **53.15** Adapted from J. T. Enright. 1976. Climate and population regulation: The biogeographer's dilemma. *Oecologia* 24: 295–310; **53.16** Figure 3.5b, page 59, from *Soay Sheep: Dynamics and Selection in an Island Population* edited by T.H. Clutton-Brock and J.M. Pemberton. Copyright © Cambridge University Press 2004. Reprinted with the permission of Cambridge University Press; **53.18** Data courtesy of Rolf O. Peterson, Michigan Technological University; **53.23** Data from U. S. Census Bureau International Data Base; **53.24** Data from U. S. Census Bureau International Data Base; **53.25** Data from U. S. Census Bureau International Data Base 2008; **53.26** Source: Used courtesy of UNEP/GRID-Arendel at http://maps.grida.no/go/graphic/energy_consumption_per_capita_2004; **Tables 53.1** and **53.2** Data from P. W. Sherman and M. L. Morton, "Demography of Belding's ground squirrels," *Ecology,* Vol. 65, No. 5, p. 1622, fig. 1a, 1984. Copyright © 1984 Ecological Society of America.

Chapter 54 **54.2** From "The anoles of La Palma: aspects of their ecological relationships" by A.S. Rand and E. E. Williams in *Breviora 327:* 1–19, 1969. Copyright © 1969 by the President and Fellows of Harvard College. Used with permission from the Museum of Comparative Zoology, Harvard University; **54.9** Data for graph from S. D. Hacker and M. D. Bertness. 1999. Experimental evidence for factors maintaining plant species diversity in a New England salt marsh. *Ecology* 80: 2064–2073; **54.11** Adapted from N. Fierer and R. B. Jackson. 2006. The diversity and biogeography of soil bacterial communities. *Proceedings of the National Academy of Sciences USA 103:* 626–631 fig. 1a; **54.14** Adapted from E. A. Knox. 1970. Antarctic marine ecosystems. In *Antarctic Ecology,* ed. M. W. Holdgate, 69–96. London: Academic Press; **54.15** Adapted from D. L. Breitburg et al. 1997. Varying effects of low dissolved oxygen on trophic interactions in an estuarine food web. *Ecological Monographs* 67: 490. Copyright © 1997 Ecological Society of America; **54.16** Adapted from B. Jenkins. 1992. Productivity, disturbance and food web structure at a local spatial scale in experimental container habitats. *Oikos* 65: 252. Copyright © 1992 Oikos, Sweden; **54.17** Adapted from R. T. Paine. 1966. Food web complexity and species diversity. *American Naturalist* 100: 65–75; **54.18** From J. A. Estes et al. 1998. Killer whale predation on sea otters linking oceanic and nearshore ecosystems. *Science 282:* 474, fig. 1. Copyright © 1998 by the American Association for the Advancement of Science; **54.20** Graph adapted from A. R. Townsend et al. 1997. The intermediate disturbance hypothesis, refugia, and diversity in streams. *Limnology and Oceanography* 42:938–949. **54.22** Adapted from R. L. Crocker and J. Major. 1955. Soil Development in relation to vegetation and surface age at Glacier Bay, Alaska. *Journal of Ecology* 43: 427–448; **54.23** Data from F. S. Chapin, III, et al. 1994. Mechanisms of primary succession following deglaciation at Glacier Bay, Alaska. *Ecological Monographs* 64: 149–175; **54.25** Adapted from D. J. Currie. 1991. Energy and large-scale patterns of animal- and plant-species richness. *American Naturalist* 137: 27–49; **54.26** Adapted from F. W. Preston. 1960. Time and space and the variation of species. *Ecology 41:* 611–627; **54.28** Adapted from F. W. Preston. 1962. The canonical distribution of commonness and rarity. *Ecology 43:*185–215, 410–432.

Chapter 55 **55.4** and **Un 55.1** Adapted from D. L. DeAngelis. 1992. *Dynamics of Nutrient Cycling and Food Webs.* New York: Chapman & Hall; **55.7** Adapted from National Oceanic and Atmospheric Administration's National Data Buoy Center Voluntary Observing Ship Project, www.vos.noaa.gov/MWL/dec_06/Images/OCP_fig4.jpg; **55.8** Figure 2 from "Nitrogen, phosphorus, and eutrophication in the coastal marine environment" by J.H. Ryther, in *Science, 171,* No. 3975: 1008–1013, Mar. 12, 1971. Copyright © 1971, The American Association for the Advancement of Science. Reprinted with permission from AAAS; **55.9** Fig. 4.1 p. 82 from *Communities and Ecosystems,* 1e by Robert H. Whittaker. Copyright © 1970 Robert H. Whittaker. Reprinted by permission of Pearson Education; **55.14** From *The Economy of Nature,* 5th edition by Robert E. Ricklefs. © 2001 by W. H. Freeman and Company. Used with the permission of Worth Publishers. **55.15a** Adapted from J.A. Trofymow et al., *The Canadian Intersite Decomposition Experiment: Project and Site Establishment Report,* Information Report BC-X-378, page 2, Natural Resources Canada, Canadian Forest Service (1998). Reproduced with permission from the Minister of Public Works and Government Services, Canada, 2010; **55.15b** Adapted from: T.R. Moore et al., Litter decomposition rates in Canadian forests, *Global Change Biology* 5: 75–82 (1999), copyright © 2001, 1998 Blackwell Science Ltd. Reproduced with permission from the Minister of Public Works and Government Services, Canada, 2010 and Wiley Blackwell; **55.18b** Data adapted from Wu, W-M et al. 2006. Pilot-scale in situ bioremediation of uranium in a highly contaminated aquifer. 2. Reduction of U(VI) and geochemical control of a U(VI) bioavailability. *Environ Sci. Technol. 40:* 3986–3995, fig. 1D; **Table 55.1** Data from Menzel and Ryther. 1961. *Deep Sea Ranch* 7: 276–281.

Chapter 56 **56.12** Figure 19.1 from *Ecology,* 5e by C.J. Krebs. Copyright © 2001 Pearson Education, Inc. Reprinted by permission; **56.13** Figure 2 from "Tracking the Long-Term Decline and Recovery of an Isolated Population" by R.L. Westemeier et al., in *Science, 282,* No. 5394: 1695–1698, Nov. 27, 1998. Copyright © 1998, The American Association for the Advancement of Science. Reprinted with permission from AAAS; **56.19** Reprinted by permission from Macmillan Publishers, Ltd.: *Nature.* N. Myers et al. Biodiversity hotspots for conservation priorities, *403:* 853–858, fig. 1, 2/24/00. Copyright © 2000; **56.20** Reprinted from W. D. Newmark, 1985. Legal and biotic boundaries of western North American national parks: a problem of congruence. *Biological Conservation* 33: 197–208, fig. 1, p. 199. © 1985, with permission from Elsevier; **56.21a** Map adapted from W. Purves and G. Orians, *Life, The Science of Biology,* 5th ed., fig. 55.23, p. 1239. © 1998 by Sinauer Associates, Inc. Reprinted with permission; **56.27** CO_2 data from www.esrl.noaa.gov/gmd/ccgg/trends. Temperature data from www.giss.nasa.gov/gistemps/graphs/Fig.A.lrg.gif; **56.29** Data from ozonewatch.gsfc.nasa.gov/facts/history/html; **56.32** Data from Instituto Nacional de Estadistica y Censos de Costa Rica and Centro Centroamericano de Poblacion, Universidad de Costa Rica.

Glossary

Pronunciation Key

Pronounce

	as in	
ā	as in	ace
a/ah		ash
ch		chose
ē		meet
e/eh		bet
g		game
ī		ice
i		hit
ks		box
kw		quick
ng		song
ō		robe
o		ox
oy		boy
s		say
sh		shell
th		thin
ū		boot
u/uh		up
z		zoo

′ = primary accent

′ = secondary accent

5′ cap A modified form of guanine nucleotide added onto the 5′ end of a pre-mRNA molecule.

A site One of a ribosome's three binding sites for tRNA during translation. The A site holds the tRNA carrying the next amino acid to be added to the polypeptide chain. (A stands for aminoacyl tRNA.)

ABC hypothesis A model of flower formation identifying three classes of organ identity genes that direct formation of the four types of floral organs.

abiotic (ā′-bī-ot′-ik) Nonliving; referring to the physical and chemical properties of an environment.

abortion The termination of a pregnancy in progress.

abscisic acid (ABA) (ab-sis′-ik) A plant hormone that slows growth, often antagonizing the actions of growth hormones. Two of its many effects are to promote seed dormancy and facilitate drought tolerance.

absorption The third stage of food processing in animals: the uptake of small nutrient molecules by an organism's body.

absorption spectrum The range of a pigment's ability to absorb various wavelengths of light; also a graph of such a range.

abyssal zone (uh-bis′-ul) The part of the ocean's benthic zone between 2,000 and 6,000 m deep.

acanthodian (ak′-an-thō′-dē-un) Any of a group of ancient jawed aquatic vertebrates from the Silurian and Devonian periods.

accessory fruit A fruit, or assemblage of fruits, in which the fleshy parts are derived largely or entirely from tissues other than the ovary.

acclimatization (uh-klī′-muh-tī-zā′-shun) Physiological adjustment to a change in an environmental factor.

acetyl CoA Acetyl coenzyme A; the entry compound for the citric acid cycle in cellular respiration, formed from a fragment of pyruvate attached to a coenzyme.

acetylcholine (as′-uh-til-kō′-lēn) One of the most common neurotransmitters; functions by binding to receptors and altering the permeability of the postsynaptic membrane to specific ions, either depolarizing or hyperpolarizing the membrane.

acid A substance that increases the hydrogen ion concentration of a solution.

acid precipitation Rain, snow, or fog that is more acidic than pH 5.2.

acoelomate (uh-sē′-lō-māt) A solid-bodied animal lacking a cavity between the gut and outer body wall.

acrosomal reaction (ak′-ruh-sōm′-ul) The discharge of hydrolytic enzymes from the acrosome, a vesicle in the tip of a sperm, when the sperm approaches or contacts an egg.

acrosome (ak′-ruh-sōm) A vesicle in the tip of a sperm containing hydrolytic enzymes and other proteins that help the sperm reach the egg.

actin (ak′-tin) A globular protein that links into chains, two of which twist helically about each other, forming microfilaments (actin filaments) in muscle and other kinds of cells.

action potential An electrical signal that propagates (travels) along the membrane of a neuron or other excitable cell as a nongraded (all-or-none) depolarization.

action spectrum A graph that profiles the relative effectiveness of different wavelengths of radiation in driving a particular process.

activation energy The amount of energy that reactants must absorb before a chemical reaction will start; also called free energy of activation.

activator A protein that binds to DNA and stimulates gene transcription. In prokaryotes, activators bind in or near the promoter; in eukaryotes, activators generally bind to control elements in enhancers.

active immunity Long-lasting immunity conferred by the action of B cells and T cells and the resulting B and T memory cells specific for a pathogen. Active immunity can develop as a result of natural infection or immunization.

active site The specific region of an enzyme that binds the substrate and that forms the pocket in which catalysis occurs.

active transport The movement of a substance across a cell membrane against its concentration or electrochemical gradient, mediated by specific transport proteins and requiring an expenditure of energy.

adaptation Inherited characteristic of an organism that enhances its survival and reproduction in a specific environment.

adaptive immunity A vertebrate-specific defense that is mediated by B lymphocytes (B cells) and T lymphocytes (T cells). It exhibits specificity, memory, and self-nonself recognition. Also called acquired immunity.

adaptive radiation Period of evolutionary change in which groups of organisms form many new species whose adaptations allow them to fill different ecological roles in their communities.

addition rule A rule of probability stating that the probability of any one of two or more mutually exclusive events occurring can be determined by adding their individual probabilities.

adenosine triphosphate *See* ATP (adenosine triphosphate).

adenylyl cyclase (uh-den′-uh-lil) An enzyme that converts ATP to cyclic AMP in response to an extracellular signal.

adhesion The clinging of one substance to another, such as water to plant cell walls by means of hydrogen bonds.

adipose tissue A connective tissue that insulates the body and serves as a fuel reserve; contains fat-storing cells called adipose cells.

adrenal gland (uh-drē′-nul) One of two endocrine glands located adjacent to the kidneys in mammals. Endocrine cells in the outer portion (cortex) respond to adrenocorticotropic hormone (ACTH) by secreting steroid hormones that help maintain homeostasis during long-term stress. Neurosecretory cells in the central portion (medulla) secrete epinephrine and norepinephrine in response to nerve signals triggered by short-term stress.

adrenocorticotropic hormone (ACTH) A tropic hormone that is produced and secreted by the anterior pituitary and that stimulates the production and secretion of steroid hormones by the adrenal cortex.

aerobic respiration A catabolic pathway for organic molecules, using oxygen (O_2) as the final electron acceptor in an electron transport chain and ultimately producing ATP. This is the most efficient catabolic pathway and is carried out in most eukaryotic cells and many prokaryotic organisms.

age structure The relative number of individuals of each age in a population.

aggregate fruit A fruit derived from a single flower that has more than one carpel.

AIDS (acquired immunodeficiency syndrome) The symptoms and signs present during the late stages of HIV infection, defined by a specified reduction in the number of T cells and the appearance of characteristic secondary infections.

alcohol fermentation Glycolysis followed by the reduction of pyruvate to ethyl alcohol, regenerating NAD^+ and releasing carbon dioxide.

aldosterone (al-dos′-tuh-rōn) A steroid hormone that acts on tubules of the kidney to regulate the transport of sodium ions (Na^+) and potassium ions (K^+).

algae A diverse grade of photosynthetic protists, including unicellular and multicellular forms. Algal species are included in three of the five eukaryote supergroups (Chromalveolata, Rhizaria, and Archaeplastida).

alimentary canal (al′-uh-men′-tuh-rē) A complete digestive tract, consisting of a tube running between a mouth and an anus.

allele (uh-lē′-ul) Any of the alternative versions of a gene that may produce distinguishable phenotypic effects.

allergen An antigen that triggers an exaggerated immune response.

allopatric speciation (al′-uh-pat′-rik) The formation of new species in populations that are geographically isolated from one another.

allopolyploid (al′-ō-pol′-ē-ployd) A fertile individual that has more than two chromosome sets as a result of two different species interbreeding and combining their chromosomes.

allosteric regulation The binding of a regulatory molecule to a protein at one site that affects the function of the protein at a different site.

alpha (α) helix (al′-fuh hē′-liks) A coiled region constituting one form of the secondary structure of proteins, arising from a specific pattern of hydrogen bonding between atoms of the polypeptide backbone (not the side chains).

alternation of generations A life cycle in which there is both a multicellular diploid form, the sporophyte, and a multicellular haploid form, the gametophyte; characteristic of plants and some algae.

alternative RNA splicing A type of eukaryotic gene regulation at the RNA-processing level in which different mRNA molecules are produced from the same primary transcript, depending on which RNA segments are treated as exons and which as introns.

altruism (al′-trū-iz-um) Selflessness; behavior that reduces an individual's fitness while increasing the fitness of another individual.

alveolate (al-vē′-uh-let) A protist with membrane-bounded sacs (alveoli) located just under the plasma membrane.

alveolus (al-vē′-uh-lus) (plural, **alveoli**) One of the dead-end air sacs where gas exchange occurs in a mammalian lung.

Alzheimer's disease (alts′-hī-merz) An age-related dementia (mental deterioration) characterized by confusion and memory loss.

amacrine cell (am′-uh-krin) A neuron of the retina that helps integrate information before it is sent to the brain.

amino acid (uh-mēn′-ō) An organic molecule possessing both a carboxyl and an amino group. Amino acids serve as the monomers of polypeptides.

amino group A chemical group consisting of a nitrogen atom bonded to two hydrogen atoms; can act as a base in solution, accepting a hydrogen ion and acquiring a charge of 1+.

aminoacyl-tRNA synthetase An enzyme that joins each amino acid to the appropriate tRNA.

ammonia A small, toxic molecule (NH_3) produced by nitrogen fixation or as a metabolic waste product of protein and nucleic acid metabolism.

ammonite A member of a group of shelled cephalopods that were important marine predators for hundreds of millions of years until their extinction at the end of the Cretaceous period (65.5 million years ago).

amniocentesis (am′-nē-ō-sen-tē′-sis) A technique associated with prenatal diagnosis in which amniotic fluid is obtained by aspiration from a needle inserted into the uterus. The fluid and the fetal cells it contains are analyzed to detect certain genetic and congenital defects in the fetus.

amniote (am′-nē-ōt) Member of a clade of tetrapods named for a key derived character, the amniotic egg, which contains specialized membranes, including the fluid-filled amnion, that protect the embryo. Amniotes include mammals as well as birds and other reptiles.

amniotic egg An egg that contains specialized membranes that function in protection, nourishment, and gas exchange. The amniotic egg was a major evolutionary innovation, allowing embryos to develop on land in a fluid-filled sac, thus reducing the dependence of tetrapods on water for reproduction.

amoeba (uh-mē′-buh) A protist grade characterized by the presence of pseudopodia.

amoebocyte (uh-mē′-buh-sīt′) An amoeba-like cell that moves by pseudopodia and is found in most animals. Depending on the species, it may digest and distribute food, dispose of wastes, form skeletal fibers, fight infections, or change into other cell types.

amoebozoan (uh-mē′-buh-zō′-an) A protist in a clade that includes many species with lobe- or tube-shaped pseudopodia.

amphibian Member of the tetrapod class Amphibia, including salamanders, frogs, and caecilians.

amphipathic (am′-fē-path′-ik) Having both a hydrophilic region and a hydrophobic region.

amplification The strengthening of stimulus energy during transduction.

amygdala (uh-mig′-duh-luh) A structure in the temporal lobe of the vertebrate brain that has a major role in the processing of emotions.

amylase (am′-uh-lās′) An enzyme that hydrolyzes starch (a glucose polymer from plants) and glycogen (a glucose polymer from animals) into smaller polysaccharides and the disaccharide maltose.

anabolic pathway (an′-uh-bol′-ik) A metabolic pathway that consumes energy to synthesize a complex molecule from simpler molecules.

anaerobic respiration (an-er-ō′-bik) A catabolic pathway in which inorganic molecules other than oxygen accept electrons at the "downhill" end of electron transport chains.

analogous Having characteristics that are similar because of convergent evolution, not homology.

analogy (an-al′-uh-jē) Similarity between two species that is due to convergent evolution rather than to descent from a common ancestor with the same trait.

anaphase The fourth stage of mitosis, in which the chromatids of each chromosome have separated and the daughter chromosomes are moving to the poles of the cell.

anatomy The structure of an organism.

anchorage dependence The requirement that a cell must be attached to a substratum in order to initiate cell division.

androgen (an′-drō-jen) Any steroid hormone, such as testosterone, that stimulates the development and maintenance of the male reproductive system and secondary sex characteristics.

aneuploidy (an′-yū-ploy′-dē) A chromosomal aberration in which one or more chromosomes are present in extra copies or are deficient in number.

angiosperm (an′-jē-ō-sperm) A flowering plant, which forms seeds inside a protective chamber called an ovary.

angiotensin II A peptide hormone that stimulates constriction of precapillary arterioles and increases reabsorption of NaCl and water by the proximal tubules of the kidney, increasing blood pressure and volume.

anhydrobiosis (an-hī′-drō-bī-ō′-sis) A dormant state involving loss of almost all body water.

animal pole The point at the end of an egg in the hemisphere where the least yolk is concentrated; opposite of vegetal pole.

anion (an′-ī-on) A negatively charged ion.

anterior Pertaining to the front, or head, of a bilaterally symmetrical animal.

anterior pituitary A portion of the pituitary that develops from nonneural tissue; consists of endocrine cells that synthesize and secrete several tropic and nontropic hormones.

anther In an angiosperm, the terminal pollen sac of a stamen, where pollen grains containing sperm-producing male gametophytes form.

antheridium (an-thuh-rid′-ē-um) (plural, **antheridia**) In plants, the male gametangium, a moist chamber in which gametes develop.

anthropoid (an′-thruh-poyd) Member of a primate group made up of the monkeys and the apes (gibbons, orangutans, gorillas, chimpanzees, bonobos, and humans).

antibody A protein secreted by plasma cells (differentiated B cells) that binds to a particular antigen; also called immunoglobulin. All antibodies have the same Y-shaped structure and in their monomer form consist of two identical heavy chains and two identical light chains.

anticodon (an′-tī-kō′-don) A nucleotide triplet at one end of a tRNA molecule that base-pairs with a particular complementary codon on an mRNA molecule.

antidiuretic hormone (ADH) (an′-tī-dī-yū-ret′-ik) A peptide hormone, also known as vasopressin, that promotes water retention by the kidneys. Produced in the hypothalamus and released from the posterior pituitary, ADH also functions in the brain.

antigen (an′-ti-jen) A substance that elicits an immune response by binding to receptors of B cells, antibodies, or of T cells.

antigen presentation The process by which an MHC molecule binds to a fragment of an intracellular protein antigen and carries it to the cell surface, where it is displayed and can be recognized by a T cell.

antigen receptor The general term for a surface protein, located on B cells and T cells, that binds to antigens, initiating adaptive immune responses. The antigen receptors on B cells are called B cell receptors, and the antigen receptors on T cells are called T cell receptors.

antigen-presenting cell A cell that upon ingesting pathogens or internalizing pathogen proteins generates peptide fragments that are bound by class II MHC molecules and subsequently displayed on the cell surface to T cells. Macrophages, dendritic cells, and B cells are the primary antigen-presenting cells.

antiparallel Referring to the arrangement of the sugar-phosphate backbones in a DNA double helix (they run in opposite $5' \rightarrow 3'$ directions).

aphotic zone (ā′-fō′-tik) The part of an ocean or lake beneath the photic zone, where light does not penetrate sufficiently for photosynthesis to occur.

apical bud (ā′-pik-ul) A bud at the tip of a plant stem; also called a terminal bud.

apical dominance (ā′-pik-ul) Tendency for growth to be concentrated at the tip of a plant shoot, because the apical bud partially inhibits axillary bud growth.

apical ectodermal ridge (AER) A thickened area of ectoderm at the tip of a limb bud that promotes outgrowth of the limb bud.

apical meristem (ā′-pik-ul mār′-uh-stem) Embryonic plant tissue in the tips of roots and buds of shoots. The dividing cells of an apical meristem enable the plant to grow in length.

apicomplexan (ap′-ē-kom-pleks′-un) A protist in a clade that includes many species that parasitize animals. Some apicomplexans cause human disease.

apomixis (ap′-uh-mik′-sis) The ability of some plant species to reproduce asexually through seeds without fertilization by a male gamete.

apoplast (ap′-ō-plast) Everything external to the plasma membrane of a plant cell, including cell walls, intercellular spaces, and the space within dead structures such as xylem vessels and tracheids.

apoptosis (ā-puh-tō′-sus) A type of programmed cell death, which is brought about by activation of enzymes that break down many chemical components in the cell.

aposematic coloration (ap′-ō-si-mat′-ik) The bright warning coloration of many animals with effective physical or chemical defenses.

appendix A small, finger-like extension of the vertebrate cecum; contains a mass of white blood cells that contribute to immunity.

aquaporin A channel protein in the plasma membrane of a plant, animal, or microorganism cell that specifically facilitates osmosis, the diffusion of free water across the membrane.

aqueous solution (ā′-kwē-us) A solution in which water is the solvent.

arachnid A member of a major arthropod group, the chelicerates. Arachnids include spiders, scorpions, ticks, and mites.

arbuscular mycorrhiza (ar-bus′-kyū-lur mī′-kō-rī′-zuh) Association of a fungus with a plant root system in which the fungus causes the invagination of the host (plant) cells' plasma membranes.

arbuscular mycorrhizal fungus A symbiotic fungus whose hyphae grow through the cell wall of plant roots and extend into the root cell (enclosed in tubes formed by invagination of the root cell plasma membrane).

Archaea (ar′-kē′-uh) One of two prokaryotic domains, the other being Bacteria.

Archaeplastida (ar′-kē-plas′-tid-uh) One of five supergroups of eukaryotes proposed in a current hypothesis of the evolutionary history of eukaryotes. This monophyletic group, which includes red algae, green algae, and land plants, descended from an ancient protist ancestor that engulfed a cyanobacterium. *See also* Excavata, Chromalveolata, Rhizaria, and Unikonta.

archegonium (ar-ki-gō′-nē-um) (plural, **archegonia**) In plants, the female gametangium, a moist chamber in which gametes develop.

archenteron (ar-ken′-tuh-ron) The endoderm-lined cavity, formed during gastrulation, that develops into the digestive tract of an animal.

archosaur (ar′-kō-sōr) Member of the reptilian group that includes crocodiles, alligators and dinosaurs, including birds.

arteriole (ar-ter′-ē-ōl) A vessel that conveys blood between an artery and a capillary bed.

artery A vessel that carries blood away from the heart to organs throughout the body.

arthropod A segmented ecdysozoan with a hard exoskeleton and jointed appendages. Familiar examples include insects, spiders, millipedes, and crabs.

artificial selection The selective breeding of domesticated plants and animals to encourage the occurrence of desirable traits.

ascocarp The fruiting body of a sac fungus (ascomycete).

ascomycete (as′-kuh-mī′-sēt) Member of the fungal phylum Ascomycota, commonly called sac fungus. The name comes from the saclike structure in which the spores develop.

ascus (plural, **asci**) A saclike spore capsule located at the tip of a dikaryotic hypha of a sac fungus.

asexual reproduction The generation of offspring from a single parent that occurs without the fusion of gametes (by budding, division of a single cell, or division of the entire organism into two or more parts). In most cases, the offspring are genetically identical to the parent.

assisted migration The translocation of a species to a favorable habitat beyond its native range for the purpose of protecting the species from human-caused threats.

assisted reproductive technology A fertilization procedure that generally involves surgically removing eggs (secondary oocytes) from a woman's ovaries after hormonal stimulation, fertilizing the eggs, and returning them to the woman's body.

associative learning The acquired ability to associate one environmental feature (such as a color) with another (such as danger).

aster A radial array of short microtubules that extends from each centrosome toward the plasma membrane in an animal cell undergoing mitosis.

astrocyte A glial cell with diverse functions, including providing structural support for neurons, regulating the interstitial environment, facilitating synaptic transmission, and assisting in regulating the blood supply to the brain.

atherosclerosis A cardiovascular disease in which fatty deposits called plaques develop in the inner walls of the arteries, obstructing the arteries and causing them to harden.

atom The smallest unit of matter that retains the properties of an element.

atomic mass The total mass of an atom, which is the mass in grams of 1 mole of the atom.

atomic nucleus An atom's dense central core, containing protons and neutrons.

atomic number The number of protons in the nucleus of an atom, unique for each element and designated by a subscript to the left of the elemental symbol.

ATP (adenosine triphosphate) (a-den′-ō-sēn trī-fos′-fāt) An adenine-containing nucleoside triphosphate that releases free energy when its phosphate bonds are hydrolyzed. This energy is used to drive endergonic reactions in cells.

ATP synthase A complex of several membrane proteins that functions in chemiosmosis with adjacent electron transport chains, using the energy of a hydrogen ion (proton) concentration gradient to make ATP. ATP synthases are found in the inner mitochondrial membranes of eukaryotic cells and in the plasma membranes of prokaryotes.

atrial natriuretic peptide (ANP) (ā′-trē-ul na′-trē-yū-ret′-ik) A peptide hormone secreted by cells of the atria of the heart in response to high blood pressure. ANP's effects on the kidney alter ion and water movement and reduce blood pressure.

atrioventricular (AV) node A region of specialized heart muscle tissue between the left and right atria where electrical impulses are delayed for about 0.1 second before spreading to both ventricles and causing them to contract.

atrioventricular (AV) valve A heart valve located between each atrium and ventricle that prevents a backflow of blood when the ventricle contracts.

atrium (ā′-trē-um) (plural, **atria**) A chamber of the vertebrate heart that receives blood from the veins and transfers blood to a ventricle.

autocrine Referring to a secreted molecule that acts on the cell that secreted it.

autoimmune disease An immunological disorder in which the immune system turns against self.

autonomic nervous system (ot′-ō-nom′-ik) An efferent branch of the vertebrate peripheral nervous system that regulates the internal environment; consists of the sympathetic, parasympathetic, and enteric divisions.

autopolyploid (ot′-ō-pol′-ē-ployd) An individual that has more than two chromosome sets that are all derived from a single species.

autosome (ot′-ō-sōm) A chromosome that is not directly involved in determining sex; not a sex chromosome.

autotroph (ot′-ō-trōf) An organism that obtains organic food molecules without eating other organisms or substances derived from other organisms. Autotrophs use energy from the sun or from oxidation of inorganic substances to make organic molecules from inorganic ones.

auxin (ôk′-sin) A term that primarily refers to indoleacetic acid (IAA), a natural plant hormone that has a variety of effects, including cell elongation, root formation, secondary growth, and fruit growth.

average heterozygosity (het′-er-ō-zī-gō′-si-tē) The percentage, on average, of a population's loci that are heterozygous in members of the population.

avirulent Describing a pathogen that can mildly harm, but not kill, the host.

axillary bud (ak′-sil-ār-ē) A structure that has the potential to form a lateral shoot, or branch. The bud appears in the angle formed between a leaf and a stem.

axon (ak′-son) A typically long extension, or process, of a neuron that carries nerve impulses away from the cell body toward target cells.

B cells The lymphocytes that complete their development in the bone marrow and become effector cells for the humoral immune response.

Bacteria One of two prokaryotic domains, the other being Archaea.

bacterial artificial chromosome (BAC) A large plasmid that acts as a bacterial chromosome and can carry inserts of 100,000 to 300,000 base pairs (100–300 kb).

bacteriophage (bak-tēr′-ē-ō-fāj) A virus that infects bacteria; also called a phage.

bacteroid A form of the bacterium *Rhizobium* contained within the vesicles formed by the root cells of a root nodule.

balancing selection Natural selection that maintains two or more phenotypic forms in a population.

bark All tissues external to the vascular cambium, consisting mainly of the secondary phloem and layers of periderm.

Barr body A dense object lying along the inside of the nuclear envelope in cells of female mammals, representing a highly condensed, inactivated X chromosome.

basal angiosperm A member of one of three clades of early-diverging lineages of flowering plants. Examples are *Amborella*, water lilies, and star anise and its relatives.

basal body (bā′-sul) A eukaryotic cell structure consisting of a "9 + 0" arrangement of microtubule triplets. The basal body may organize the microtubule assembly of a cilium or flagellum and is structurally very similar to a centriole.

basal metabolic rate (BMR) The metabolic rate of a resting, fasting, and nonstressed endotherm at a comfortable temperature.

basal taxon In a specified group of organisms, a taxon whose evolutionary lineage diverged early in the history of the group.

base A substance that reduces the hydrogen ion concentration of a solution.

basidiocarp Elaborate fruiting body of a dikaryotic mycelium of a club fungus.

basidiomycete (buh-sid′-ē-ō-mī′-sēt) Member of the fungal phylum Basidiomycota, commonly called club fungus. The name comes from the club-like shape of the basidium.

basidium (plural, **basidia**) (buh-sid′-ē-um, buh-sid′-ē-ah) A reproductive appendage that produces sexual spores on the gills of mushrooms (club fungi).

Batesian mimicry (bāt′-zē-un mim′-uh-krē) A type of mimicry in which a harmless species looks like a species that is poisonous or otherwise harmful to predators.

behavior Individually, an action carried out by muscles or glands under control of the nervous system in response to a stimulus; collectively, the sum of an animal's responses to external and internal stimuli.

behavioral ecology The study of the evolution of and ecological basis for animal behavior.

benign tumor A mass of abnormal cells with specific genetic and cellular changes such that the cells are not capable of surviving at a new site and generally remain at the site of the tumor's origin.

benthic zone The bottom surface of an aquatic environment.

benthos (ben′-thōz) The communities of organisms living in the benthic zone of an aquatic biome.

beta (β) pleated sheet One form of the secondary structure of proteins in which the polypeptide chain folds back and forth. Two regions of the chain lie parallel to each other and are held together by hydrogen bonds between atoms of the polypeptide backbone (not the side chains).

beta oxidation A metabolic sequence that breaks fatty acids down to two-carbon fragments that enter the citric acid cycle as acetyl CoA.

bicoid A maternal effect gene that codes for a protein responsible for specifying the anterior end in *Drosophila melanogaster*.

bilateral symmetry Body symmetry in which a central longitudinal plane divides the body into two equal but opposite halves.

bilaterian (bī′-luh-ter′-ē-uhn) Member of a clade of animals with bilateral symmetry and three germ layers.

bile A mixture of substances that is produced in the liver and stored in the gallbladder; enables formation of fat droplets in water as an aid in the digestion and absorption of fats.

binary fission A method of asexual reproduction by "division in half." In prokaryotes, binary fission does not involve mitosis, but in single-celled eukaryotes that undergo binary fission, mitosis is part of the process.

binomial The two-part, latinized format for naming a species, consisting of the genus and specific epithet; a binomen.

biodiversity hot spot A relatively small area with numerous endemic species and a large number of endangered and threatened species.

bioenergetics (1) The overall flow and transformation of energy in an organism. (2) The study of how energy flows through organisms.

biofilm A surface-coating colony of one or more species of prokaryotes that engage in metabolic cooperation.

biofuel A fuel produced from dry organic matter or combustible oils produced by plants.

biogenic amine A neurotransmitter derived from an amino acid.

biogeochemical cycle Any of the various chemical cycles, which involve both biotic and abiotic components of ecosystems.

biogeography The study of the past and present geographic distribution of species.

bioinformatics The use of computers, software, and mathematical models to process and integrate biological information from large data sets.

biological augmentation An approach to restoration ecology that uses organisms to add essential materials to a degraded ecosystem.

biological clock An internal timekeeper that controls an organism's biological rhythms. The biological clock marks time with or without environmental cues but often requires signals from the environment to remain tuned to an appropriate period. *See also* circadian rhythm.

biological magnification A process in which retained substances become more concentrated at each higher trophic level in a food chain.

biological species concept Definition of a species as a group of populations whose members have the potential to interbreed in nature and produce viable, fertile offspring, but do not produce viable, fertile offspring with members of other such groups.

biology The scientific study of life.

biomanipulation An approach that applies the top-down model of community organization to alter ecosystem characteristics. For example, ecologists can prevent algal blooms and eutrophication by altering the density of higher-level consumers in lakes instead of by using chemical treatments.

biomass The total mass of organic matter comprising a group of organisms in a particular habitat.

biome (bī′-ōm) Any of the world's major ecosystem types, often classified according to the predominant vegetation for terrestrial biomes and the physical environment for aquatic biomes and characterized by adaptations of organisms to that particular environment.

bioremediation The use of organisms to detoxify and restore polluted and degraded ecosystems.

biosphere The entire portion of Earth inhabited by life; the sum of all the planet's ecosystems.

biotechnology The manipulation of organisms or their components to produce useful products.

biotic (bī-ot′-ik) Pertaining to the living factors—the organisms—in an environment.

bipolar cell A neuron that relays information between photoreceptors and ganglion cells in the retina.

bipolar disorder A depressive mental illness characterized by swings of mood from high to low; also called manic-depressive disorder.

birth control pill A chemical contraceptive that inhibits ovulation, retards follicular development, or alters a woman's cervical mucus to prevent sperm from entering the uterus.

blade (1) A leaflike structure of a seaweed that provides most of the surface area for photosynthesis. (2) The flattened portion of a typical leaf.

blastocoel (blas′-tuh-sēl) The fluid-filled cavity that forms in the center of a blastula.

blastocyst (blas′-tuh-sist) The blastula stage of mammalian embryonic development, consisting of an inner cell mass, a cavity, and an outer layer, the trophoblast. In humans, the blastocyst forms 1 week after fertilization.

blastomere An early embryonic cell arising during the cleavage stage of an early embryo.

blastopore (blas′-tō-pōr) In a gastrula, the opening of the archenteron that typically develops into the anus in deuterostomes and the mouth in protostomes.

blastula (blas′-tyū-luh) A hollow ball of cells that marks the end of the cleavage stage during early embryonic development in animals.

blood A connective tissue with a fluid matrix called plasma in which red blood cells, white blood cells, and cell fragments called platelets are suspended.

blue-light photoreceptor A type of light receptor in plants that initiates a variety of responses, such as phototropism and slowing of hypocotyl elongation.

body cavity A fluid- or air-filled space between the digestive tract and the body wall.

body plan In multicellular eukaryotes, a set of morphological and developmental traits that are integrated into a functional whole—the living organism.

Bohr shift A lowering of the affinity of hemoglobin for oxygen, caused by a drop in pH. It facilitates the release of oxygen from hemoglobin in the vicinity of active tissues.

bolus A lubricated ball of chewed food.

bone A connective tissue consisting of living cells held in a rigid matrix of collagen fibers embedded in calcium salts.

book lung An organ of gas exchange in spiders, consisting of stacked plates contained in an internal chamber.

bottleneck effect Genetic drift that occurs when the size of a population is reduced, as by a natural disaster or human actions. Typically, the surviving population is no longer genetically representative of the original population.

bottom-up model A model of community organization in which mineral nutrients influence community organization by controlling plant or phytoplankton numbers, which in turn control herbivore numbers, which in turn control predator numbers.

Bowman's capsule (bō′-munz) A cup-shaped receptacle in the vertebrate kidney that is the initial, expanded segment of the nephron where filtrate enters from the blood.

brachiopod (bra′-kē- uh-pod′) A marine lophophorate with a shell divided into dorsal and ventral halves; also called a lamp shell.

brain Organ of the central nervous system where information is processed and integrated.

brainstem A collection of structures in the vertebrate brain, including the midbrain, the pons, and the medulla oblongata; functions in homeostasis, coordination of movement, and conduction of information to higher brain centers.

branch point The representation on a phylogenetic tree of the divergence of two or more taxa from a common ancestor. A branch point is usually shown as a dichotomy in which a branch representing the ancestral lineage splits (at the branch point) into two branches, one for each of the two descendant lineages.

brassinosteroid A steroid hormone in plants that has a variety of effects, including inducing cell elongation, retarding leaf abscission, and promoting xylem differentiation.

breathing Ventilation of the lungs through alternating inhalation and exhalation.

bronchiole (brong′-kē-ōl′) A fine branch of the bronchi that transports air to alveoli.

bronchus (brong′-kus) (plural, **bronchi**) One of a pair of breathing tubes that branch from the trachea into the lungs.

brown alga A multicellular, photosynthetic protist with a characteristic brown or olive color that results from carotenoids in its plastids. Most brown algae are marine, and some have a plantlike body (thallus).

bryophyte (brī′-uh-fīt) An informal name for a moss, liverwort, or hornwort; a nonvascular plant that lives on land but lacks some of the terrestrial adaptations of vascular plants.

budding Asexual reproduction in which outgrowths from the parent form and pinch off to live independently or else remain attached to eventually form extensive colonies.

buffer A solution that contains a weak acid and its corresponding base. A buffer minimizes changes in pH when acids or bases are added to the solution.

bulk feeder An animal that eats relatively large pieces of food.

bulk flow The movement of a fluid due to a difference in pressure between two locations.

bundle-sheath cell In C_4 plants, a type of photosynthetic cell arranged into tightly packed sheaths around the veins of a leaf.

C_3 plant A plant that uses the Calvin cycle for the initial steps that incorporate CO_2 into organic material, forming a three-carbon compound as the first stable intermediate.

C_4 plant A plant in which the Calvin cycle is preceded by reactions that incorporate CO_2 into a four-carbon compound, the end product of which supplies CO_2 for the Calvin cycle.

calcitonin (kal′-si-tō′-nin) A hormone secreted by the thyroid gland that lowers blood calcium levels by promoting calcium deposition in bone and calcium excretion from the kidneys; nonessential in adult humans.

callus A mass of dividing, undifferentiated cells growing in culture.

calorie (cal) The amount of heat energy required to raise the temperature of 1 g of water by 1°C; also the amount of heat energy that 1 g of water releases when it cools by 1°C. The Calorie (with a capital C), usually used to indicate the energy content of food, is a kilocalorie.

Calvin cycle The second of two major stages in photosynthesis (following the light reactions), involving fixation of atmospheric CO_2 and reduction of the fixed carbon into carbohydrate.

CAM plant A plant that uses crassulacean acid metabolism, an adaptation for photosynthesis in arid conditions. In this process, carbon dioxide entering open stomata during the night is converted to organic acids, which release CO_2 for the Calvin cycle during the day, when stomata are closed.

Cambrian explosion A relatively brief time in geologic history when many present-day phyla of animals first appeared in the fossil record. This burst of evolutionary change occurred about 535–525 million years ago and saw the emergence of the first large, hard-bodied animals.

cAMP *See* cyclic AMP (cAMP).

canopy The uppermost layer of vegetation in a terrestrial biome.

capillary (kap′-il-ār′-ē) A microscopic blood vessel that penetrates the tissues and consists of a single layer of endothelial cells that allows exchange between the blood and interstitial fluid.

capillary bed A network of capillaries in a tissue or organ.

capsid The protein shell that encloses a viral genome. It may be rod-shaped, polyhedral, or more complex in shape.

capsule (1) In many prokaryotes, a dense and well-defined layer of polysaccharide or protein that surrounds the cell wall and is sticky, protecting the cell and enabling it to adhere to substrates or other cells. (2) The sporangium of a bryophyte (moss, liverwort, or hornwort).

carbohydrate (kar′-bō-hī′-drāt) A sugar (monosaccharide) or one of its dimers (disaccharides) or polymers (polysaccharides).

carbon fixation The initial incorporation of carbon from CO_2 into an organic compound by an autotrophic organism (a plant, another photosynthetic organism, or a chemoautotrophic prokaryote).

carbonyl group (kar-buh-nēl′) A chemical group present in aldehydes and ketones and consisting of a carbon atom double-bonded to an oxygen atom.

carboxyl group (kar-bok′-sil) A chemical group present in organic acids and consisting of a single carbon atom double-bonded to an oxygen atom and also bonded to a hydroxyl group.

cardiac cycle (kar′-dē-ak) The alternating contractions and relaxations of the heart.

cardiac muscle A type of striated muscle that forms the contractile wall of the heart. Its cells are joined by intercalated disks that relay the electrical signals underlying each heartbeat.

cardiac output The volume of blood pumped per minute by each ventricle of the heart.

cardiovascular system A closed circulatory system with a heart and branching network of arteries, capillaries, and veins. The system is characteristic of vertebrates.

carnivore An animal that mainly eats other animals.

carotenoid (kuh-rot′-uh-noyd′ An accessory pigment, either yellow or orange, in the chloroplasts of plants and in some prokaryotes. By absorbing wavelengths of light that chlorophyll cannot, carotenoids broaden the spectrum of colors that can drive photosynthesis.

carpel (kar′-pul) The ovule-producing reproductive organ of a flower, consisting of the stigma, style, and ovary.

carrier In genetics, an individual who is heterozygous at a given genetic locus for a recessively inherited disorder. The heterozygote is generally phenotypically normal for the disorder but can pass on the recessive allele to offspring.

carrying capacity The maximum population size that can be supported by the available resources, symbolized as *K*.

cartilage (kar′-til-ij) A flexible connective tissue with an abundance of collagenous fibers embedded in chondroitin sulfate.

Casparian strip (ka-spār′-ē-un) A water-impermeable ring of wax in the endodermal cells of plants that blocks the passive flow of water and solutes into the stele by way of cell walls.

catabolic pathway (kat′-uh-bol′-ik) A metabolic pathway that releases energy by breaking down complex molecules to simpler molecules.

catalyst (kat′-uh-list) A chemical agent that selectively increases the rate of a reaction without being consumed by the reaction.

catastrophism (kuh-tas′-truh-fiz′-um) The principle that events in the past occurred suddenly and were caused by different mechanisms than those operating today. *See* uniformitarianism.

catecholamine (kat′-uh-kōl′-uh-mēn) Any of a class of neurotransmitters and hormones, including the hormones epinephrine and norepinephrine, that are synthesized from the amino acid tyrosine.

cation (cat′-ī-on) A positively charged ion.

cation exchange A process in which positively charged minerals are made available to a plant when hydrogen ions in the soil displace mineral ions from the clay particles.

cDNA library A gene library containing clones that carry complementary DNA (cDNA) inserts. The library includes only the genes that were transcribed in the cells whose mRNA was isolated to make the cDNA.

cecum (sē′-kum) (plural, **ceca**) The blind pouch forming one branch of the large intestine.

cell body The part of a neuron that houses the nucleus and most other organelles.

cell cycle An ordered sequence of events in the life of a cell, from its origin in the division of a parent cell until its own division into two. The eukaryotic cell cycle is composed of interphase (including G_1, S, and G_2 subphases) and M phase (including mitosis and cytokinesis).

cell cycle control system A cyclically operating set of molecules in the eukaryotic cell that both triggers and coordinates key events in the cell cycle.

cell division The reproduction of cells.

cell fractionation The disruption of a cell and separation of its parts by centrifugation at successively higher speeds.

cell plate A membrane-bounded, flattened sac located at the midline of a dividing plant cell, inside which the new cell wall forms during cytokinesis.

cell wall A protective layer external to the plasma membrane in the cells of plants, prokaryotes, fungi, and some protists. Polysaccharides such as cellulose (in plants and some protists), chitin (in fungi), and peptidoglycan (in bacteria) are important structural components of cell walls.

cell-mediated immune response The branch of adaptive immunity that involves the activation of cytotoxic T cells, which defend against infected cells.

cellular respiration The catabolic pathways of aerobic and anaerobic respiration, which break down organic molecules and use an electron transport chain for the production of ATP.

cellular slime mold A type of protist characterized by unicellular amoeboid cells and aggregated reproductive bodies in its life cycle.

cellulose (sel′-yū-lōs) A structural polysaccharide of plant cell walls, consisting of glucose monomers joined by β glycosidic linkages.

Celsius scale (sel′-sē-us) A temperature scale (°C) equal to $^5/_9$(°F – 32) that measures the freezing point of water at 0°C and the boiling point of water at 100°C.

central canal The narrow cavity in the center of the spinal cord that is continuous with the fluid-filled ventricles of the brain.

central nervous system (CNS) The portion of the nervous system where signal integration occurs; in vertebrate animals, the brain and spinal cord.

central vacuole In a mature plant cell, a large membranous sac with diverse roles in growth, storage, and sequestration of toxic substances.

centriole (sen′-trē-ōl) A structure in the centrosome of an animal cell composed of a cylinder of microtubule triplets arranged in a 9 + 0 pattern. A centrosome has a pair of centrioles.

centromere (sen′-trō-mēr) In a duplicated chromosome, the region on each sister chromatid where they are most closely attached to each other by proteins that bind to specific DNA sequences; this close attachment causes a constriction in the condensed chromosome. (An uncondensed, unduplicated chromosome has a single centromere, identified by its DNA sequence.)

centrosome (sen′-trō-sōm) A structure present in the cytoplasm of animal cells that functions as a microtubule-organizing center and is important during cell division. A centrosome has two centrioles.

cephalization (sef′-uh-luh-zā′-shun) An evolutionary trend toward the concentration of sensory equipment at the anterior end of the body.

cercozoan An amoeboid or flagellated protist that feeds with threadlike pseudopodia.

cerebellum (sār′-ruh-bel′-um) Part of the vertebrate hindbrain located dorsally; functions in unconscious coordination of movement and balance.

cerebral cortex (suh-rē′-brul) The surface of the cerebrum; the largest and most complex part of the mammalian brain, containing nerve cell bodies of the cerebrum; the part of the vertebrate brain most changed through evolution.

cerebral hemisphere The right or left side of the cerebrum.

cerebrospinal fluid (suh-rē′-brō-spī′-nul) Blood-derived fluid that surrounds, protects against infection, nourishes, and cushions the brain and spinal cord.

cerebrum (suh-rē′-brum) The dorsal portion of the vertebrate forebrain, composed of right and left hemispheres; the integrating center for memory, learning, emotions, and other highly complex functions of the central nervous system.

cervix (ser′-viks) The neck of the uterus, which opens into the vagina.

chaparral A scrubland biome of dense, spiny evergreen shrubs found at midlatitudes along coasts where cold ocean currents circulate offshore; characterized by mild, rainy winters and long, hot, dry summers.

chaperonin (shap′-er-ō′-nin) A protein complex that assists in the proper folding of other proteins.

character An observable heritable feature that may vary among individuals.

character displacement The tendency for characteristics to be more divergent in sympatric populations of two species than in allopatric populations of the same two species.

checkpoint A control point in the cell cycle where stop and go-ahead signals can regulate the cycle.

chelicera (kē-lih′-suh-ruh) (plural, **chelicerae**) One of a pair of clawlike feeding appendages characteristic of chelicerates.

chelicerate (kē-lih-suh′-rāte) An arthropod that has chelicerae and a body divided into a cephalothorax and an abdomen. Living chelicerates include sea spiders, horseshoe crabs, scorpions, ticks, and spiders.

chemical bond An attraction between two atoms, resulting from a sharing of outer-shell electrons or the presence of opposite charges on the atoms. The bonded atoms gain complete outer electron shells.

chemical energy Energy available in molecules for release in a chemical reaction; a form of potential energy.

chemical equilibrium In a chemical reaction, the state in which the rate of the forward reaction equals the rate of the reverse reaction, so that the relative concentrations of the reactants and products do not change with time.

chemical reaction The making and breaking of chemical bonds, leading to changes in the composition of matter.

chemiosmosis (kem′-ē-oz-mō′-sis) An energy-coupling mechanism that uses energy stored in the form of a hydrogen ion gradient across a membrane to drive cellular work, such as the synthesis of ATP. Under aerobic conditions, most ATP synthesis in cells occurs by chemiosmosis.

chemoautotroph (kē′-mō-ot′-ō-trōf) An organism that obtains energy by oxidizing inorganic substances and needs only carbon dioxide as a carbon source.

chemoheterotroph (kē′-mō-het′-er-ō-trōf) An organism that requires organic molecules for both energy and carbon.

chemoreceptor A sensory receptor that responds to a chemical stimulus, such as a solute or an odorant.

chiasma (plural, **chiasmata**) (kī-az′-muh, kī-az′-muh-tuh) The X-shaped, microscopically visible region where crossing over has occurred earlier in prophase I between homologous nonsister chromatids. Chiasmata become visible after synapsis ends, with the two homologs remaining associated due to sister chromatid cohesion.

chitin (kī′-tin) A structural polysaccharide, consisting of amino sugar monomers, found in many fungal cell walls and in the exoskeletons of all arthropods.

chlorophyll (klōr′-ō-fil) A green pigment located in membranes within the chloroplasts of plants and algae and in the membranes of certain prokaryotes. Chlorophyll *a* participates directly in the light reactions, which convert solar energy to chemical energy.

chlorophyll *a* A photosynthetic pigment that participates directly in the light reactions, which convert solar energy to chemical energy.

chlorophyll *b* An accessory photosynthetic pigment that transfers energy to chlorophyll *a*.

chloroplast (klōr′-ō-plast) An organelle found in plants and photosynthetic protists that absorbs sunlight and uses it to drive the synthesis of organic compounds from carbon dioxide and water.

choanocyte (kō-an′-uh-sīt) A flagellated feeding cell found in sponges. Also called a collar cell, it has a collar-like ring that traps food particles around the base of its flagellum.

cholesterol (kō-les′-tuh-rol) A steroid that forms an essential component of animal cell membranes and acts as a precursor molecule for the synthesis of other biologically important steroids, such as many hormones.

chondrichthyan (kon-drik′-thē-an) Member of the class Chondrichthyes, vertebrates with skeletons made mostly of cartilage, such as sharks and rays.

chordate Member of the phylum Chordata, animals that at some point during their development have a notochord; a dorsal, hollow nerve cord; pharyngeal slits or clefts; and a muscular, post-anal tail.

chorionic villus sampling (CVS) (kōr′-ē-on′-ik vil′-us) A technique associated with prenatal diagnosis in which a small sample of the fetal portion of the placenta is removed for analysis to detect certain genetic and congenital defects in the fetus.

Chromalveolata One of five supergroups of eukaryotes proposed in a current hypothesis of the evolutionary history of eukaryotes. Chromalveolates may have originated by secondary endosymbiosis and include two large protist clades, the alveolates and the stramenopiles. *See also* Excavata, Rhizaria, Archaeplastida, and Unikonta.

chromatin (krō′-muh-tin) The complex of DNA and proteins that makes up eukaryotic chromosomes. When the cell is not dividing, chromatin exists in its dispersed form, as a mass of very long, thin fibers that are not visible with a light microscope.

chromosome (krō′-muh-sōm) A cellular structure carrying genetic material, found in the nucleus of eukaryotic cells. Each chromosome consists of one very long DNA molecule and associated proteins. (A bacterial chromosome usually consists of a single circular DNA molecule and associated proteins. It is found in the nucleoid region, which is not membrane bounded.) *See also* chromatin.

chromosome theory of inheritance A basic principle in biology stating that genes are located at specific positions (loci) on chromosomes and that the behavior of chromosomes during meiosis accounts for inheritance patterns.

chylomicron (kī′-lō-mī′-kron) A lipid transport globule composed of fats mixed with cholesterol and coated with proteins.

chyme (kīm) The mixture of partially digested food and digestive juices formed in the stomach.

chytrid (kī′-trid) Member of the fungal phylum Chytridiomycota, mostly aquatic fungi with flagellated zoospores that represent an early-diverging fungal lineage.

ciliate (sil′-ē-it) A type of protist that moves by means of cilia.

cilium (sil′-ē-um) (plural, **cilia**) A short appendage containing microtubules in eukaryotic cells. A motile cilium is specialized for locomotion or moving fluid past the cell; it is formed from a core of nine outer doublet microtubules and two inner single microtubules (the "9 + 2" arrangement) ensheathed in an extension of the plasma membrane. A primary cilium is usually nonmotile and plays a sensory and signaling role; it lacks the two inner microtubules (the "9 + 0" arrangement).

circadian rhythm (ser-kā′-dē-un) A physiological cycle of about 24 hours that persists even in the absence of external cues.

***cis-trans* isomer** One of several compounds that have the same molecular formula and covalent bonds between atoms but differ in the spatial arrangements of their atoms owing to the inflexibility of double bonds; formerly called a geometric isomer.

citric acid cycle A chemical cycle involving eight steps that completes the metabolic breakdown of glucose molecules begun in glycolysis by oxidizing acetyl CoA (derived from pyruvate) to carbon dioxide; occurs within the mitochondrion in eukaryotic cells and in the cytosol of prokaryotes; together with pyruvate oxidation, the second major stage in cellular respiration.

clade (klayd) A group of species that includes an ancestral species and all of its descendants.

cladistics (kluh-dis′-tiks) An approach to systematics in which organisms are placed into groups called clades based primarily on common descent.

class In Linnaean classification, the taxonomic category above the level of order.

cleavage (1) The process of cytokinesis in animal cells, characterized by pinching of the plasma membrane. (2) The succession of rapid cell divisions without significant growth during early embryonic development that converts the zygote to a ball of cells.

cleavage furrow The first sign of cleavage in an animal cell; a shallow groove around the cell in the cell surface near the old metaphase plate.

climate The long-term prevailing weather conditions at a given place.

climograph A plot of the temperature and precipitation in a particular region.

cline A graded change in a character along a geographic axis.

clitoris (klit′-uh-ris) An organ at the upper intersection of the labia minora that engorges with blood and becomes erect during sexual arousal.

cloaca (klō-ā′-kuh) A common opening for the digestive, urinary, and reproductive tracts found in many nonmammalian vertebrates but in few mammals.

clonal selection The process by which an antigen selectively binds to and activates only those lymphocytes bearing receptors specific for the antigen. The selected lymphocytes proliferate and differentiate into a clone of effector cells and a clone of memory cells specific for the stimulating antigen.

clone (1) A lineage of genetically identical individuals or cells. (2) In popular usage, an individual that is genetically identical to another individual. (3) As a verb, to make one or more genetic replicas of an individual or cell. *See also* gene cloning.

cloning vector In genetic engineering, a DNA molecule that can carry foreign DNA into a host cell and replicate there. Cloning vectors include plasmids and bacterial artificial chromosomes (BACs), which move recombinant DNA from a test tube back into a cell, and viruses that transfer recombinant DNA by infection.

closed circulatory system A circulatory system in which blood is confined to vessels and is kept separate from the interstitial fluid.

cnidocyte (nī′-duh-sīt) A specialized cell unique to the phylum Cnidaria; contains a capsule-like organelle housing a coiled thread that, when discharged, explodes outward and functions in prey capture or defense.

cochlea (kok′-lē-uh) The complex, coiled organ of hearing that contains the organ of Corti.

codominance The situation in which the phenotypes of both alleles are exhibited in the heterozygote because both alleles affect the phenotype in separate, distinguishable ways.

codon (kō′-don) A three-nucleotide sequence of DNA or mRNA that specifies a particular amino acid or termination signal; the basic unit of the genetic code.

coefficient of relatedness The fraction of genes that, on average, are shared by two individuals.

coelom (sē′-lōm) A body cavity lined by tissue derived only from mesoderm.

coelomate (sē′-lō-māt) An animal that possesses a true coelom (a body cavity lined by tissue completely derived from mesoderm).

coenocytic fungus (sē′-no-si′-tic) A fungus that lacks septa and hence whose body is made up of a continuous cytoplasmic mass that may contain hundreds or thousands of nuclei.

coenzyme (kō-en′-zīm) An organic molecule serving as a cofactor. Most vitamins function as coenzymes in metabolic reactions.

coevolution The joint evolution of two interacting species, each in response to selection imposed by the other.

cofactor Any nonprotein molecule or ion that is required for the proper functioning of an enzyme. Cofactors can be permanently bound to the active site or may bind loosely and reversibly, along with the substrate, during catalysis.

cognition The process of knowing that may include awareness, reasoning, recollection, and judgment.

cognitive map A neural representation of the abstract spatial relationships between objects in an animal's surroundings.

cohesion The linking together of like molecules, often by hydrogen bonds.

cohesion-tension hypothesis The leading explanation of the ascent of xylem sap. It states that transpiration exerts pull on xylem sap, putting the sap under negative pressure or tension, and that the cohesion of water molecules transmits this pull along the entire length of the xylem from shoots to roots.

cohort A group of individuals of the same age in a population.

coitus (kō′-uh-tus) The insertion of a penis into a vagina; also called sexual intercourse.

coleoptile (kō′-lē-op′-tul) The covering of the young shoot of the embryo of a grass seed.

coleorhiza (kō′-lē-uh-rī′-zuh) The covering of the young root of the embryo of a grass seed.

collagen A glycoprotein in the extracellular matrix of animal cells that forms strong fibers, found extensively in connective tissue and bone; the most abundant protein in the animal kingdom.

collecting duct The location in the kidney where processed filtrate, called urine, is collected from the renal tubules.

collenchyma cell (kō-len′-kim-uh) A flexible plant cell type that occurs in strands or cylinders that support young parts of the plant without restraining growth.

colloid A mixture made up of a liquid and particles that (because of their large size) remain suspended rather than dissolved in that liquid.

colon (kō′-len) The largest section of the vertebrate large intestine; functions in water absorption and formation of feces.

commensalism (kuh-men′-suh-lizm) A symbiotic relationship in which one organism benefits but the other is neither helped nor harmed.

communication In animal behavior, a process involving transmission of, reception of, and response to signals. The term is also used in connection with other organisms, as well as individual cells of multicellular organisms.

community All the organisms that inhabit a particular area; an assemblage of populations of different species living close enough together for potential interaction.

community ecology The study of how interactions between species affect community structure and organization.

companion cell A type of plant cell that is connected to a sieve-tube element by many plasmodesmata and whose nucleus and ribosomes may serve one or more adjacent sieve-tube elements.

competitive exclusion The concept that when populations of two similar species compete for the same limited resources, one population will use the resources more efficiently and have a reproductive advantage that will eventually lead to the elimination of the other population.

competitive inhibitor A substance that reduces the activity of an enzyme by entering the active site in place of the substrate, whose structure it mimics.

complement system A group of about 30 blood proteins that may amplify the inflammatory response, enhance phagocytosis, or directly lyse extracellular pathogens.

complementary DNA (cDNA) A double-stranded DNA molecule made *in vitro* using mRNA as a template and the enzymes reverse transcriptase and DNA polymerase. A cDNA molecule corresponds to the exons of a gene.

complete digestive tract A digestive tube that runs between a mouth and an anus; also called an alimentary canal.

complete dominance The situation in which the phenotypes of the heterozygote and dominant homozygote are indistinguishable.

complete flower A flower that has all four basic floral organs: sepals, petals, stamens, and carpels.

complete metamorphosis The transformation of a larva into an adult that looks very different, and often functions very differently in its environment, than the larva.

compound A substance consisting of two or more different elements combined in a fixed ratio.

compound eye A type of multifaceted eye in insects and crustaceans consisting of up to several thousand light-detecting, focusing ommatidia.

concentration gradient A region along which the density of a chemical substance increases or decreases.

conception The fertilization of an egg by a sperm in humans.

condom A thin, latex rubber or natural membrane sheath that fits over the penis to collect semen.

conduction The direct transfer of thermal motion (heat) between molecules of objects in direct contact with each other.

cone A cone-shaped cell in the retina of the vertebrate eye, sensitive to color.

conformer An animal for which an internal condition conforms to (changes in accordance with) changes in an environmental variable.

conidium (plural, **conidia**) A haploid spore produced at the tip of a specialized hypha in ascomycetes during asexual reproduction.

conifer Member of the largest gymnosperm phylum. Most conifers are cone-bearing trees, such as pines and firs.

conjugation (kon′-jū-gā′-shun) (1) In prokaryotes, the direct transfer of DNA between two cells that are temporarily joined. When the two cells are members of different species, conjugation results in horizontal gene transfer. (2) In ciliates, a sexual process in which two cells exchange haploid micronuclei but do not reproduce.

connective tissue Animal tissue that functions mainly to bind and support other tissues, having a sparse population of cells scattered through an extracellular matrix.

conodont An early, soft-bodied vertebrate with prominent eyes and dental elements.

conservation biology The integrated study of ecology, evolutionary biology, physiology, molecular biology, and genetics to sustain biological diversity at all levels.

contraception The deliberate prevention of pregnancy.

contractile vacuole A membranous sac that helps move excess water out of certain freshwater protists.

control element A segment of noncoding DNA that helps regulate transcription of a gene by serving as a binding site for a transcription factor. Multiple control elements are present in a eukaryotic gene's enhancer.

controlled experiment An experiment in which an experimental group is compared with a control group that varies only in the factor being tested.

convection The mass movement of warmed air or liquid to or from the surface of a body or object.

convergent evolution The evolution of similar features in independent evolutionary lineages.

convergent extension A process in which the cells of a tissue layer rearrange themselves in such a way that the sheet of cells becomes narrower (converges) and longer (extends).

cooperativity A kind of allosteric regulation whereby a shape change in one subunit of a protein caused by substrate binding is transmitted to all the other subunits, facilitating binding of additional substrate molecules to those subunits.

copepod (cō′-puh-pod) Any of a group of small crustaceans that are important members of marine and freshwater plankton communities.

coral reef Typically a warm-water, tropical ecosystem dominated by the hard skeletal structures secreted primarily by corals. Some coral reefs also exist in cold, deep waters.

corepressor A small molecule that binds to a bacterial repressor protein and changes the protein's shape, allowing it to bind to the operator and switch an operon off.

cork cambium (kam′-bē-um) A cylinder of meristematic tissue in woody plants that replaces the epidermis with thicker, tougher cork cells.

corpus callosum (kor′-pus kuh-lō′-sum) The thick band of nerve fibers that connects the right and left cerebral hemispheres in mammals, enabling the hemispheres to process information together.

corpus luteum (kor′-pus lū′-tē-um) A secreting tissue in the ovary that forms from the collapsed follicle after ovulation and produces progesterone.

cortex (1) The outer region of cytoplasm in a eukaryotic cell, lying just under the plasma membrane, that has a more gel-like consistency than the inner regions due to the presence of multiple microfilaments. (2) In plants, ground tissue that is between the vascular tissue and dermal tissue in a root or eudicot stem.

cortical nephron In mammals and birds, a nephron with a loop of Henle located almost entirely in the renal cortex.

corticosteroid Any steroid hormone produced and secreted by the adrenal cortex.

cotransport The coupling of the "downhill" diffusion of one substance to the "uphill" transport of another against its own concentration gradient.

cotyledon (kot′-uh-lē′-dun) A seed leaf of an angiosperm embryo. Some species have one cotyledon, others two.

countercurrent exchange The exchange of a substance or heat between two fluids flowing in opposite directions. For example, blood in a fish gill flows in the opposite direction of water passing over the gill, maximizing diffusion of oxygen into and carbon dioxide out of the blood.

countercurrent multiplier system A countercurrent system in which energy is expended in active transport to facilitate exchange of materials and generate concentration gradients.

covalent bond (kō-vā′-lent) A type of strong chemical bond in which two atoms share one or more pairs of valence electrons.

craniate A chordate with a head.

crassulacean acid metabolism (CAM) An adaptation for photosynthesis in arid conditions, first discovered in the family Crassulaceae. In this process, a plant takes up CO_2 and incorporates it into a variety of organic acids at night; during the day, CO_2 is released from organic acids for use in the Calvin cycle.

crista (plural, **cristae**) (kris′-tuh, kris′-tē) An infolding of the inner membrane of a mitochondrion. The inner membrane houses electron transport chains and molecules of the enzyme catalyzing the synthesis of ATP (ATP synthase).

critical load The amount of added nutrient, usually nitrogen or phosphorus, that can be absorbed by plants without damaging ecosystem integrity.

crop rotation The practice of planting nonlegumes one year and legumes in alternating years to restore concentrations of fixed nitrogen in the soil.

cross-fostering study A behavioral study in which the young of one species are placed in the care of adults from another species.

crossing over The reciprocal exchange of genetic material between nonsister chromatids during prophase I of meiosis.

cross-pollination In angiosperms, the transfer of pollen from an anther of a flower on one plant to the stigma of a flower on another plant of the same species.

crustacean (kruh-stā′-shun) A member of a subphylum of mostly aquatic arthropods that includes lobsters, crayfishes, crabs, shrimps, and barnacles.

cryptic coloration Camouflage that makes a potential prey difficult to spot against its background.

culture A system of information transfer through social learning or teaching that influences the behavior of individuals in a population.

cuticle (kyū′-tuh-kul) (1) A waxy covering on the surface of stems and leaves that prevents desiccation in terrestrial plants. (2) The exoskeleton of an arthropod, consisting of layers of protein and chitin that are variously modified for different functions. (3) A tough coat that covers the body of a nematode.

cyclic AMP (cAMP) Cyclic adenosine monophosphate, a ring-shaped molecule made from ATP that is a common intracellular signaling molecule (second messenger) in eukaryotic cells. It is also a regulator of some bacterial operons.

cyclic electron flow A route of electron flow during the light reactions of photosynthesis that involves only photosystem I and that produces ATP but not NADPH or O_2.

cyclin (sī′-klin) A cellular protein that occurs in a cyclically fluctuating concentration and that plays an important role in regulating the cell cycle.

cyclin-dependent kinase (Cdk) A protein kinase that is active only when attached to a particular cyclin.

cystic fibrosis (sis′-tik fī-brō′-sis) A human genetic disorder caused by a recessive allele for a chloride channel protein; characterized by an excessive secretion of mucus and consequent vulnerability to infection; fatal if untreated.

cytochrome (sī′-tō-krōm) An iron-containing protein that is a component of electron transport chains in the mitochondria and chloroplasts of eukaryotic cells and the plasma membranes of prokaryotic cells.

cytogenetic map A map of a chromosome that locates genes with respect to chromosomal features distinguishable in a microscope.

cytokine (sī′-tō-kīn′) Any of a group of small proteins secreted by a number of cell types, including macrophages and helper T cells, that regulate the function of other cells.

cytokinesis (sī′-tō-kuh-nē′-sis) The division of the cytoplasm to form two separate daughter cells immediately after mitosis, meiosis I, or meiosis II.

cytokinin (sī′-tō-kī′-nin) Any of a class of related plant hormones that retard aging and act in concert with auxin to stimulate cell division, influence the pathway of differentiation, and control apical dominance.

cytoplasm (sī′-tō-plaz′-um) The contents of the cell bounded by the plasma membrane; in eukaryotes, the portion exclusive of the nucleus.

cytoplasmic determinant A maternal substance, such as a protein or RNA, that when placed into an egg influences the course of early development by regulating the expression of genes that affect the developmental fate of cells.

cytoplasmic streaming A circular flow of cytoplasm, involving interactions of myosin and actin filaments, that speeds the distribution of materials within cells.

cytoskeleton A network of microtubules, microfilaments, and intermediate filaments that extend throughout the cytoplasm and serve a variety of mechanical, transport, and signaling functions.

cytosol (sī′-tō-sol) The semifluid portion of the cytoplasm.

cytotoxic T cell A type of lymphocyte that, when activated, kills infected cells as well as certain cancer cells and transplanted cells.

dalton A measure of mass for atoms and subatomic particles; the same as the atomic mass unit, or amu.

data Recorded observations.

day-neutral plant A plant in which flower formation is not controlled by photoperiod or day length.

decapod A member of the group of crustaceans that includes lobsters, crayfishes, crabs, and shrimps.

decomposer An organism that absorbs nutrients from nonliving organic material such as corpses, fallen plant material, and the wastes of living organisms and converts them to inorganic forms; a detritivore.

deductive reasoning A type of logic in which specific results are predicted from a general premise.

deep-sea hydrothermal vent A dark, hot, oxygen-deficient environment associated with volcanic activity on or near the seafloor. The producers in a vent community are chemoautotrophic prokaryotes.

de-etiolation The changes a plant shoot undergoes in response to sunlight; also known informally as greening.

dehydration reaction A chemical reaction in which two molecules become covalently bonded to each other with the removal of a water molecule.

deletion (1) A deficiency in a chromosome resulting from the loss of a fragment through breakage. (2) A mutational loss of one or more nucleotide pairs from a gene.

demographic transition In a stable population, a shift from high birth and death rates to low birth and death rates.

demography The study of changes over time in the vital statistics of populations, especially birth rates and death rates.

denaturation (dē-nā′-chur-ā′-shun) In proteins, a process in which a protein loses its native shape due to the disruption of weak chemical bonds and interactions, thereby becoming biologically inactive; in DNA, the separation of the two strands of the double helix. Denaturation occurs under extreme (noncellular) conditions of pH, salt concentration, or temperature.

dendrite (den′-drīt) One of usually numerous, short, highly branched extensions of a neuron that receive signals from other neurons.

dendritic cell An antigen-presenting cell, located mainly in lymphatic tissues and skin, that is particularly efficient in presenting antigens to helper T cells, thereby initiating a primary immune response.

density The number of individuals per unit area or volume.

density dependent Referring to any characteristic that varies with population density.

density independent Referring to any characteristic that is not affected by population density.

density-dependent inhibition The phenomenon observed in normal animal cells that causes them to stop dividing when they come into contact with one another.

deoxyribonucleic acid (DNA) (dē-ok′-sē-rī′-bō-nū-klā′-ik) A nucleic acid molecule, usually a double-stranded helix, in which each polynucleotide strand consists of nucleotide monomers with a deoxyribose sugar and the nitrogenous bases adenine (A), cytosine (C), guanine (G), and thymine (T); capable of being replicated and determining the inherited structure of a cell's proteins.

deoxyribose (dē-ok′-si-rī′-bōs) The sugar component of DNA nucleotides, having one fewer hydroxyl group than ribose, the sugar component of RNA nucleotides.

depolarization A change in a cell's membrane potential such that the inside of the membrane is made less negative relative to the outside. For example, a neuron membrane is depolarized if a stimulus decreases its voltage from the resting potential of −70 mV in the direction of zero voltage.

dermal tissue system The outer protective covering of plants.

desert A terrestrial biome characterized by very low precipitation.

desmosome A type of intercellular junction in animal cells that functions as a rivet, fastening cells together.

determinate cleavage A type of embryonic development in protostomes that rigidly casts the developmental fate of each embryonic cell very early.

determinate growth A type of growth characteristic of most animals and some plant organs, in which growth stops after a certain size is reached.

determination The progressive restriction of developmental potential in which the possible fate of each cell becomes more limited as an embryo develops. At the end of determination, a cell is committed to its fate.

detritivore (deh-trī′-tuh-vōr) A consumer that derives its energy and nutrients from nonliving organic material such as corpses, fallen plant material, and the wastes of living organisms; a decomposer.

detritus (di-trī′-tus) Dead organic matter.

deuteromycete (dū′-tuh-rō-mī′-sēt) Traditional classification for a fungus with no known sexual stage.

deuterostome development (dū′-tuh-rō-stōm′) In animals, a developmental mode distinguished by the development of the anus from the blastopore; often also characterized by radial cleavage and by the body cavity forming as outpockets of mesodermal tissue.

development The events involved in an organism's changing gradually from a simple to a more complex or specialized form.

diabetes mellitus (dī′-uh-bē′-tis mel′-uh-tus) An endocrine disorder marked by an inability to maintain glucose homeostasis. The type 1 form results from autoimmune destruction of insulin-secreting cells; treatment usually requires daily insulin injections. The type 2 form most commonly results from reduced responsiveness of target cells to insulin; obesity and lack of exercise are risk factors.

diacylglycerol (DAG) (dī-a′-sil-glis′-er-ol) A second messenger produced by the cleavage of the phospholipid PIP_2 in the plasma membrane.

diaphragm (dī′-uh-fram′) (1) A sheet of muscle that forms the bottom wall of the thoracic cavity in mammals. Contraction of the diaphragm pulls air into the lungs. (2) A dome-shaped rubber cup fitted into the upper portion of the vagina before sexual intercourse. It serves as a physical barrier to the passage of sperm into the uterus.

diapsid (dī-ap′-sid) Member of an amniote clade distinguished by a pair of holes on each side of the skull. Diapsids include the lepidosaurs and archosaurs.

diastole (dī-as′-tō-lē) The stage of the cardiac cycle in which a heart chamber is relaxed and fills with blood.

diastolic pressure Blood pressure in the arteries when the ventricles are relaxed.

dicot A term traditionally used to refer to flowering plants that have two embryonic seed leaves, or cotyledons. Recent molecular evidence indicates that dicots do not form a clade; species once classified as dicots are now grouped into eudicots, magnoliids, and several lineages of basal angiosperms.

differential gene expression The expression of different sets of genes by cells with the same genome.

differentiation The process by which a cell or group of cells become specialized in structure and function.

diffusion The spontaneous movement of a substance down its concentration or electrochemical gradient, from a region where it is more concentrated to a region where it is less concentrated.

digestion The second stage of food processing in animals: the breaking down of food into molecules small enough for the body to absorb.

dihybrid (dī′-hī′-brid) An organism that is heterozygous with respect to two genes of interest. All the offspring from a cross between parents doubly homozygous for different alleles are dihybrids. For example, parents of genotypes *AABB* and *aabb* produce a dihybrid of genotype *AaBb*.

dihybrid cross A cross between two organisms that are each heterozygous for both of the characters being followed (or the self-pollination of a plant that is heterozygous for both characters).

dikaryotic (dī′-kār-ē-ot′-ik) Referring to a fungal mycelium with two haploid nuclei per cell, one from each parent.

dinoflagellate (dī′-nō-flaj′-uh-let) Member of a group of mostly unicellular photosynthetic algae with two flagella situated in perpendicular grooves in cellulose plates covering the cell.

dinosaur Member of an extremely diverse clade of reptiles varying in body shape, size, and habitat. Birds are the only extant dinosaurs.

dioecious (dī-ē′-shus) In plant biology, having the male and female reproductive parts on different individuals of the same species.

diploblastic Having two germ layers.

diploid cell (dip′-loyd) A cell containing two sets of chromosomes ($2n$), one set inherited from each parent.

diplomonad A protist that has modified mitochondria, two equal-sized nuclei, and multiple flagella.

directional selection Natural selection in which individuals at one end of the phenotypic range survive or reproduce more successfully than do other individuals.

disaccharide (dī-sak′-uh-rīd) A double sugar, consisting of two monosaccharides joined by a glycosidic linkage formed by a dehydration reaction.

dispersal The movement of individuals or gametes away from their parent location. This movement sometimes expands the geographic range of a population or species.

dispersion The pattern of spacing among individuals within the boundaries of a population.

disruptive selection Natural selection in which individuals on both extremes of a phenotypic range survive or reproduce more successfully than do individuals with intermediate phenotypes.

distal tubule In the vertebrate kidney, the portion of a nephron that helps refine filtrate and empties it into a collecting duct.

disturbance A natural or human-caused event that changes a biological community and usually removes organisms from it. Disturbances, such as fires and storms, play a pivotal role in structuring many communities.

disulfide bridge A strong covalent bond formed when the sulfur of one cysteine monomer bonds to the sulfur of another cysteine monomer.

DNA (deoxyribonucleic acid) (dē-ok′-sē-rī′-bō-nū-klā′-ik) A double-stranded, helical nucleic acid molecule, consisting of nucleotide monomers with a deoxyribose sugar and the nitrogenous bases adenine (A), cytosine (C), guanine (G), and thymine (T); capable of being replicated and determining the inherited structure of a cell's proteins.

DNA ligase (lī′-gās) A linking enzyme essential for DNA replication; catalyzes the covalent bonding of the 3′ end of one DNA fragment (such as an Okazaki fragment) to the 5′ end of another DNA fragment (such as a growing DNA chain).

DNA methylation The presence of methyl groups on the DNA bases (usually cytosine) of plants, animals, and fungi. (The term also refers to the process of adding methyl groups to DNA bases.)

DNA microarray assay A method to detect and measure the expression of thousands of genes at one time. Tiny amounts of a large number of single-stranded DNA fragments representing different genes are fixed to a glass slide and tested for hybridization with samples of labeled cDNA.

DNA polymerase (puh-lim′-er-ās) An enzyme that catalyzes the elongation of new DNA (for example, at a replication fork) by the addition of nucleotides to the 3′ end of an existing chain. There are several different DNA polymerases; DNA polymerase III and DNA polymerase I play major roles in DNA replication in *E. coli*.

DNA replication The process by which a DNA molecule is copied; also called DNA synthesis.

domain (1) A taxonomic category above the kingdom level. The three domains are Archaea, Bacteria, and Eukarya. (2) A discrete structural and functional region of a protein.

dominant allele An allele that is fully expressed in the phenotype of a heterozygote.

dominant species A species with substantially higher abundance or biomass than other species in a community. Dominant species exert a powerful control over the occurrence and distribution of other species.

dopamine A neurotransmitter that is a catecholamine, like epinephrine and norepinephrine.

dormancy A condition typified by extremely low metabolic rate and a suspension of growth and development.

dorsal Pertaining to the top of an animal with radial or bilateral symmetry.

dorsal lip The region above the blastopore on the dorsal side of the amphibian embryo.

double bond A double covalent bond; the sharing of two pairs of valence electrons by two atoms.

double circulation A circulatory system consisting of separate pulmonary and systemic circuits, in which blood passes through the heart after completing each circuit.

double fertilization A mechanism of fertilization in angiosperms in which two sperm cells unite with two cells in the female gametophyte (embryo sac) to form the zygote and endosperm.

double helix The form of native DNA, referring to its two adjacent antiparallel polynucleotide strands wound around an imaginary axis into a spiral shape.

Down syndrome A human genetic disease usually caused by the presence of an extra chromosome 21; characterized by developmental delays and heart and other defects that are generally treatable or non-life-threatening.

Duchenne muscular dystrophy (duh-shen′) A human genetic disease caused by a sex-linked recessive allele; characterized by progressive weakening and a loss of muscle tissue.

duodenum (dū′-uh-dēn′-um) The first section of the small intestine, where chyme from the stomach mixes with digestive juices from the pancreas, liver, and gallbladder as well as from gland cells of the intestinal wall.

duplication An aberration in chromosome structure due to fusion with a fragment from a homologous chromosome, such that a portion of a chromosome is duplicated.

dynamic stability hypothesis The concept that long food chains are less stable than short chains.

dynein (dī′-nē-un) In cilia and flagella, a large motor protein extending from one microtubule doublet to the adjacent doublet. ATP hydrolysis drives changes in dynein shape that lead to bending of cilia and flagella.

E site One of a ribosome's three binding sites for tRNA during translation. The E site is the place where discharged tRNAs leave the ribosome. (E stands for exit.)

ecdysozoan Member of a group of animal phyla identified as a clade by molecular evidence. Many ecdysozoans are molting animals.

ecdysteroid A steroid hormone, secreted by the prothoracic glands, that triggers molting in arthropods.

echinoderm (i-kī′-nō-derm) A slow-moving or sessile marine deuterostome with a water vascular system and, in larvae, bilateral symmetry. Echinoderms include sea stars, brittle stars, sea urchins, feather stars, and sea cucumbers.

ecological footprint The aggregate land and water area required by a person, city, or nation to produce all of the resources it consumes and to absorb all of the wastes it generates.

ecological niche (nich) The sum of a species' use of the biotic and abiotic resources in its environment.

ecological species concept A definition of species in terms of ecological niche, the sum of how members of the species interact with the nonliving and living parts of their environment.

ecological succession Transition in the species composition of a community following a disturbance; establishment of a community in an area virtually barren of life.

ecology The study of how organisms interact with each other and their environment.

ecosystem All the organisms in a given area as well as the abiotic factors with which they interact; one or more communities and the physical environment around them.

ecosystem ecology The study of energy flow and the cycling of chemicals among the various biotic and abiotic components in an ecosystem.

ecosystem engineer An organism that influences community structure by causing physical changes in the environment.

ecosystem service A function performed by an ecosystem that directly or indirectly benefits humans.

ecotone The transition from one type of habitat or ecosystem to another, such as the transition from a forest to a grassland.

ectoderm (ek′-tō-durm) The outermost of the three primary germ layers in animal embryos; gives rise to the outer covering and, in some phyla, the nervous system, inner ear, and lens of the eye.

ectomycorrhiza (ek′-tō-mī′-kō-rī′-zuh) Association of a fungus with a plant root system in which the fungus surrounds the roots but does not cause invagination of the host (plant) cells' plasma membranes.

ectomycorrhizal fungus A symbiotic fungus that forms sheaths of hyphae over the surface of plant roots and also grows into extracellular spaces of the root cortex.

ectoparasite A parasite that feeds on the external surface of a host.

ectopic Occurring in an abnormal location.

ectoproct A sessile, colonial lophophorate; also called a bryozoan.

ectothermic Referring to organisms for which external sources provide most of the heat for temperature regulation.

Ediacaran biota (ē′-dē-uh-keh′-run bī-ō′-tuh) An early group of soft-bodied, multicellular eukaryotes known from fossils that range in age from 565 million to 550 million years old.

effective population size An estimate of the size of a population based on the numbers of females and males that successfully breed; generally smaller than the total population.

effector cell (1) A muscle cell or gland cell that performs the body's response to stimuli as directed by signals from the brain or other processing center of the nervous system. (2) A lymphocyte that has undergone clonal selection and is capable of mediating an adaptive immune response.

egg The female gamete.

egg-polarity gene A gene that helps control the orientation (polarity) of the egg; also called a maternal effect gene.

ejaculation The propulsion of sperm from the epididymis through the muscular vas deferens, ejaculatory duct, and urethra.

ejaculatory duct In mammals, the short section of the ejaculatory route formed by the convergence of the vas deferens and a duct from the seminal vesicle. The ejaculatory duct transports sperm from the vas deferens to the urethra.

electrocardiogram (ECG or EKG) A record of the electrical impulses that travel through heart muscle during the cardiac cycle.

electrochemical gradient The diffusion gradient of an ion, which is affected by both the concentration difference of an ion across a membrane (a chemical force) and the ion's tendency to move relative to the membrane potential (an electrical force).

electrogenic pump An active transport protein that generates voltage across a membrane while pumping ions.

electromagnetic receptor A receptor of electromagnetic energy, such as visible light, electricity, or magnetism.

electromagnetic spectrum The entire spectrum of electromagnetic radiation, ranging in wavelength from less than a nanometer to more than a kilometer.

electron A subatomic particle with a single negative electrical charge and a mass about 1/2,000 that of a neutron or proton. One or more electrons move around the nucleus of an atom.

electron microscope (EM) A microscope that uses magnets to focus an electron beam on or through a specimen, resulting in a practical resolution of a hundredfold greater than that of a light microscope using standard techniques. A transmission electron microscope (TEM) is used to study the internal structure of thin sections of cells. A scanning electron microscope (SEM) is used to study the fine details of cell surfaces.

electron shell An energy level of electrons at a characteristic average distance from the nucleus of an atom.

electron transport chain A sequence of electron carrier molecules (membrane proteins) that shuttle electrons down a series of redox reactions that release energy used to make ATP.

electronegativity The attraction of a given atom for the electrons of a covalent bond.

electroporation A technique to introduce recombinant DNA into cells by applying a brief electrical pulse to a solution containing the cells. The pulse creates temporary holes in the cells' plasma membranes, through which DNA can enter.

element Any substance that cannot be broken down to any other substance by chemical reactions.

elimination The fourth and final stage of food processing in animals: the passing of undigested material out of the body.

embryo sac (em′-brē-ō) The female gametophyte of angiosperms, formed from the growth and division of the megaspore into a multicellular structure that typically has eight haploid nuclei.

embryonic lethal A mutation with a phenotype leading to death of an embryo or larva.

embryophyte Alternate name for land plants that refers to their shared derived trait of multicellular, dependent embryos.

emergent properties New properties that arise with each step upward in the hierarchy of life, owing to the arrangement and interactions of parts as complexity increases.

emigration The movement of individuals out of a population.

enantiomer (en-an′-tē-ō-mer) One of two compounds that are mirror images of each other and that differ in shape due to the presence of an asymmetric carbon.

endangered species A species that is in danger of extinction throughout all or a significant portion of its range.

endemic (en-dem′-ik) Referring to a species that is confined to a specific geographic area.

endergonic reaction (en′-der-gon′-ik) A nonspontaneous chemical reaction, in which free energy is absorbed from the surroundings.

endocrine gland (en′-dō-krin) A ductless gland that secretes hormones directly into the interstitial fluid, from which they diffuse into the bloodstream.

endocrine system The internal system of communication involving hormones, the ductless glands that secrete hormones, and the molecular receptors on or in target cells that respond to hormones; functions in concert with the nervous system to effect internal regulation and maintain homeostasis.

endocytosis (en′-dō-sī-tō′-sis) Cellular uptake of biological molecules and particulate matter via formation of vesicles from the plasma membrane.

endoderm (en′-dō-durm) The innermost of the three primary germ layers in animal embryos; lines the archenteron and gives rise to the liver, pancreas, lungs, and the lining of the digestive tract in species that have these structures.

endodermis In plant roots, the innermost layer of the cortex that surrounds the vascular cylinder.

endomembrane system The collection of membranes inside and surrounding a eukaryotic cell, related either through direct physical contact or by the transfer of membranous vesicles; includes the plasma membrane, the nuclear envelope, the smooth and rough endoplasmic reticulum, the Golgi apparatus, lysosomes, vesicles, and vacuoles.

endometriosis (en′-dō-mē-trē-ō′-sis) The condition resulting from the presence of endometrial tissue outside of the uterus.

endometrium (en′-dō-mē′-trē-um) The inner lining of the uterus, which is richly supplied with blood vessels.

endoparasite A parasite that lives within a host.

endophyte A fungus that lives inside a leaf or other plant part without causing harm to the plant.

endoplasmic reticulum (ER) (en′-dō-plaz′-mik ruh-tik′-yū-lum) An extensive membranous network in eukaryotic cells, continuous with the outer nuclear membrane and composed of ribosome-studded (rough) and ribosome-free (smooth) regions.

endorphin (en-dōr′-fin) Any of several hormones produced in the brain and anterior pituitary that inhibit pain perception.

endoskeleton A hard skeleton buried within the soft tissues of an animal.

endosperm In angiosperms, a nutrient-rich tissue formed by the union of a sperm with two polar nuclei during double fertilization. The endosperm provides nourishment to the developing embryo in angiosperm seeds.

endospore A thick-coated, resistant cell produced by some bacterial cells when they are exposed to harsh conditions.

endosymbiont theory The theory that mitochondria and plastids, including chloroplasts, originated as prokaryotic cells engulfed by an ancestral eukaryotic cell. The engulfed cell and its host cell then evolved into a single organism.

endosymbiosis A process in which a unicellular organism (the "host") engulfs another cell, which lives within the host cell and ultimately becomes an organelle in the host cell. *See also* endosymbiont theory.

endothelium (en′-dō-thē′-lē-um) The simple squamous layer of cells lining the lumen of blood vessels.

endothermic Referring to organisms that are warmed by heat generated by their own metabolism. This heat usually maintains a relatively stable body temperature higher than that of the external environment.

endotoxin A toxic component of the outer membrane of certain gram-negative bacteria that is released only when the bacteria die.

energetic hypothesis The concept that the length of a food chain is limited by the inefficiency of energy transfer along the chain.

energy The capacity to cause change, especially to do work (to move matter against an opposing force).

energy coupling In cellular metabolism, the use of energy released from an exergonic reaction to drive an endergonic reaction.

enhancer A segment of eukaryotic DNA containing multiple control elements, usually located far from the gene whose transcription it regulates.

enteric division One of three divisions of the autonomic nervous system; consists of networks of neurons in the digestive tract, pancreas, and gallbladder; normally regulated by the sympathetic and parasympathetic divisions of the autonomic nervous system.

entropy A measure of disorder, or randomness.

enzymatic hydrolysis The process in digestion that splits macromolecules from food by the enzymatic addition of water.

enzyme (en′-zīm) A macromolecule serving as a catalyst, a chemical agent that increases the rate of a reaction without being consumed by the reaction. Most enzymes are proteins.

enzyme-substrate complex A temporary complex formed when an enzyme binds to its substrate molecule(s).

epicotyl (ep′-uh-kot′-ul) In an angiosperm embryo, the embryonic axis above the point of attachment of the cotyledon(s) and below the first pair of miniature leaves.

epidemic A general outbreak of a disease.

epidermis (1) The dermal tissue system of nonwoody plants, usually consisting of a single layer of tightly packed cells. (2) The outermost layer of cells in an animal.

epididymis (ep′-uh-did′-uh-mus) A coiled tubule located adjacent to the mammalian testis where sperm are stored.

epigenetic inheritance Inheritance of traits transmitted by mechanisms not directly involving the nucleotide sequence of a genome.

epinephrine (ep′-i-nef′-rin) A catecholamine that, when secreted as a hormone by the adrenal medulla, mediates "fight-or-flight" responses to short-term stresses; also released by some neurons as a neurotransmitter; also known as adrenaline.

epiphyte (ep′-uh-fīt) A plant that nourishes itself but grows on the surface of another plant for support, usually on the branches or trunks of trees.

epistasis (ep′-i-stā′-sis) A type of gene interaction in which the phenotypic expression of one gene alters that of another independently inherited gene.

epithelial tissue (ep′-uh-thē′-lē-ul) Sheets of tightly packed cells that line organs and body cavities as well as external surfaces.

epithelium An epithelial tissue.

epitope A small, accessible region of an antigen to which an antigen receptor or antibody binds; also called an antigenic determinant.

EPSP *See* excitatory postsynaptic potential.
equilibrium potential (E_{ion}) The magnitude of a cell's membrane voltage at equilibrium; calculated using the Nernst equation.
erythrocyte (eh-rith'-ruh-sīt) A blood cell that contains hemoglobin, which transports oxygen; also called a red blood cell.
erythropoietin (EPO) (eh-rith'-rō-poy'-uh-tin) A hormone that stimulates the production of erythrocytes. It is secreted by the kidney when body tissues do not receive enough oxygen.
esophagus (eh-sof'-uh-gus) A muscular tube that conducts food, by peristalsis, from the pharynx to the stomach.
essential amino acid An amino acid that an animal cannot synthesize itself and must be obtained from food in prefabricated form.
essential element A chemical element required for an organism to survive, grow, and reproduce.
essential fatty acid An unsaturated fatty acid that an animal needs but cannot make.
essential nutrient A substance that an organism cannot synthesize from any other material and therefore must absorb in preassembled form.
estradiol (es'-truh-dī'-ol) A steroid hormone that stimulates the development and maintenance of the female reproductive system and secondary sex characteristics; the major estrogen in mammals.
estrogen (es'-trō-jen) Any steroid hormone, such as estradiol, that stimulates the development and maintenance of the female reproductive system and secondary sex characteristics.
estrous cycle (es'-trus) A reproductive cycle characteristic of female mammals except humans and certain other primates, in which the nonpregnant endometrium is reabsorbed rather than shed, and sexual response occurs only during mid-cycle at estrus.
estuary The area where a freshwater stream or river merges with the ocean.
ethylene (eth'-uh-lēn) A gaseous plant hormone involved in responses to mechanical stress, programmed cell death, leaf abscission, and fruit ripening.
etiolation Plant morphological adaptations for growing in darkness.
euchromatin (yū-krō'-muh-tin) The less condensed form of eukaryotic chromatin that is available for transcription.
eudicot (yū-dī'-kot) Member of a clade that contains the vast majority of flowering plants that have two embryonic seed leaves, or cotyledons.
euglenid (yū'-glen-id) A protist, such as *Euglena* or its relatives, characterized by an anterior pocket from which one or two flagella emerge.
euglenozoan Member of a diverse clade of flagellated protists that includes predatory heterotrophs, photosynthetic autotrophs, and pathogenic parasites.
Eukarya (yū-kar'-ē-uh) The domain that includes all eukaryotic organisms.
eukaryotic cell (yū'-ker-ē-ot'-ik) A type of cell with a membrane-enclosed nucleus and membrane-enclosed organelles. Organisms with eukaryotic cells (protists, plants, fungi, and animals) are called eukaryotes.
eumetazoan (yū'-met-uh-zō'-un) Member of a clade of animals with true tissues. All animals except sponges and a few other groups are eumetazoans.
eurypterid (yur-ip'-tuh-rid) An extinct carnivorous chelicerate; also called a water scorpion.
Eustachian tube (yū-stā'-shun) The tube that connects the middle ear to the pharynx.
eutherian (yū-thēr'-ē-un) Placental mammal; mammal whose young complete their embryonic development within the uterus, joined to the mother by the placenta.
eutrophic lake (yū-trōf'-ik) A lake that has a high rate of biological productivity supported by a high rate of nutrient cycling.
eutrophication A process by which nutrients, particularly phosphorus and nitrogen, become highly concentrated in a body of water, leading to increased growth of organisms such as algae or cyanobacteria.
evaporation The process by which a liquid changes to a gas.
evaporative cooling The process in which the surface of an object becomes cooler during evaporation, a result of the molecules with the greatest kinetic energy changing from the liquid to the gaseous state.
evapotranspiration The total evaporation of water from an ecosystem, including water transpired by plants and evaporated from a landscape, usually measured in millimeters and estimated for a year.
evo-devo Evolutionary developmental biology; a field of biology that compares developmental processes of different multicellular organisms to understand how these processes have evolved and how changes can modify existing organismal features or lead to new ones.
evolution Descent with modification; the idea that living species are descendants of ancestral species that were different from the present-day ones; also defined more narrowly as the change in the genetic composition of a population from generation to generation.
evolutionary tree A branching diagram that reflects a hypothesis about evolutionary relationships among groups of organisms.
Excavata One of five supergroups of eukaryotes proposed in a current hypothesis of the evolutionary history of eukaryotes. Excavates have unique cytoskeletal features, and some species have an "excavated" feeding groove on one side of the cell body. *See also* Chromalveolata, Rhizaria, Archaeplastida, and Unikonta.
excitatory postsynaptic potential (EPSP) An electrical change (depolarization) in the membrane of a postsynaptic cell caused by the binding of an excitatory neurotransmitter from a presynaptic cell to a postsynaptic receptor; makes it more likely for a postsynaptic cell to generate an action potential.
excretion The disposal of nitrogen-containing metabolites and other waste products.
exergonic reaction (ek'-ser-gon'-ik) A spontaneous chemical reaction, in which there is a net release of free energy.
exocytosis (ek'-sō-sī-tō'-sis) The cellular secretion of biological molecules by the fusion of vesicles containing them with the plasma membrane.
exon A sequence within a primary transcript that remains in the RNA after RNA processing; also refers to the region of DNA from which this sequence was transcribed.
exoskeleton A hard encasement on the surface of an animal, such as the shell of a mollusc or the cuticle of an arthropod, that provides protection and points of attachment for muscles.
exotoxin (ek'-sō-tok'-sin) A toxic protein that is secreted by a prokaryote or other pathogen and that produces specific symptoms, even if the pathogen is no longer present.
expansin Plant enzyme that breaks the cross-links (hydrogen bonds) between cellulose microfibrils and other cell wall constituents, loosening the wall's fabric.
exponential population growth Growth of a population in an ideal, unlimited environment, represented by a J-shaped curve when population size is plotted over time.
expression vector A cloning vector that contains a highly active bacterial promoter just upstream of a restriction site where a eukaryotic gene can be inserted, allowing the gene to be expressed in a bacterial cell. Expression vectors are also available that have been genetically engineered for use in specific types of eukaryotic cells.
external fertilization The fusion of gametes that parents have discharged into the environment.
extinction vortex A downward population spiral in which inbreeding and genetic drift combine to cause a small population to shrink and, unless the spiral is reversed, become extinct.
extracellular digestion The breakdown of food in compartments that are continuous with the outside of an animal's body.
extracellular matrix (ECM) The meshwork surrounding animal cells, consisting of glycoproteins, polysaccharides, and proteoglycans synthesized and secreted by the cells.
extraembryonic membrane One of four membranes (yolk sac, amnion, chorion, and allantois) located outside the embryo that support the developing embryo in reptiles and mammals.
extreme halophile An organism that lives in a highly saline environment, such as the Great Salt Lake or the Dead Sea.
extreme thermophile An organism that thrives in hot environments (often 60–80°C or hotter).
extremophile An organism that lives in environmental conditions so extreme that few other species can survive there. Extremophiles include extreme halophiles ("salt lovers") and extreme thermophiles ("heat lovers").
F factor In bacteria, the DNA segment that confers the ability to form pili for conjugation and associated functions required for the transfer of DNA from donor to recipient. The F factor may exist as a plasmid or be integrated into the bacterial chromosome.
F plasmid The plasmid form of the F factor.

F_1 generation The first filial, hybrid (heterozygous) offspring arising from a parental (P generation) cross.

F_2 generation The offspring resulting from interbreeding (or self-pollination) of the hybrid F_1 generation.

facilitated diffusion The passage of molecules or ions down their electrochemical gradient across a biological membrane with the assistance of specific transmembrane transport proteins, requiring no energy expenditure.

facilitation An interaction in which one species has a positive effect on the survival and reproduction of another species without the intimate association of a symbiosis.

facultative anaerobe (fak′-ul-tā′-tiv an′-uh-rōb) An organism that makes ATP by aerobic respiration if oxygen is present but that switches to anaerobic respiration or fermentation if oxygen is not present.

family In Linnaean classification, the taxonomic category above genus.

fast block to polyspermy The depolarization of the egg plasma membrane that begins within 1–3 seconds after a sperm binds to an egg membrane protein. The depolarization lasts about 1 minute and prevents additional sperm from fusing with the egg during that time.

fast-twitch fiber A muscle fiber used for rapid, powerful contractions.

fat A lipid consisting of three fatty acids linked to one glycerol molecule; also called a triacylglycerol or triglyceride.

fate map A territorial diagram of embryonic development that displays the future derivatives of individual cells and tissues.

fatty acid A carboxylic acid with a long carbon chain. Fatty acids vary in length and in the number and location of double bonds; three fatty acids linked to a glycerol molecule form a fat molecule, also known as a triacylglycerol or triglyceride.

feces (fē′-sēz) The wastes of the digestive tract.

feedback inhibition A method of metabolic control in which the end product of a metabolic pathway acts as an inhibitor of an enzyme within that pathway.

fermentation A catabolic process that makes a limited amount of ATP from glucose (or other organic molecules) without an electron transport chain and that produces a characteristic end product, such as ethyl alcohol or lactic acid.

fertilization (1) The union of haploid gametes to produce a diploid zygote. (2) The addition of mineral nutrients to the soil.

fetus (fē′-tus) A developing mammal that has all the major structures of an adult. In humans, the fetal stage lasts from the 9th week of gestation until birth.

fiber A lignified cell type that reinforces the xylem of angiosperms and functions in mechanical support; a slender, tapered sclerenchyma cell that usually occurs in bundles.

fibroblast (fī′-brō-blast) A type of cell in loose connective tissue that secretes the protein ingredients of the extracellular fibers.

fibronectin An extracellular glycoprotein secreted by animal cells that helps them attach to the extracellular matrix.

filament In an angiosperm, the stalk portion of the stamen, the pollen-producing reproductive organ of a flower.

filtrate Cell-free fluid extracted from the body fluid by the excretory system.

filtration In excretory systems, the extraction of water and small solutes, including metabolic wastes, from the body fluid.

fimbria (plural, **fimbriae**) A short, hairlike appendage of a prokaryotic cell that helps it adhere to the substrate or to other cells.

first law of thermodynamics The principle of conservation of energy: Energy can be transferred and transformed, but it cannot be created or destroyed.

fission The separation of an organism into two or more individuals of approximately equal size.

fixed action pattern In animal behavior, a sequence of unlearned acts that is essentially unchangeable and, once initiated, usually carried to completion.

flaccid (flas′-id) Limp. Lacking turgor (stiffness or firmness), as in a plant cell in surroundings where there is a tendency for water to leave the cell. (A walled cell becomes flaccid if it has a higher water potential than its surroundings, resulting in the loss of water.)

flagellum (fluh-jel′-um) (plural, **flagella**) A long cellular appendage specialized for locomotion. Like motile cilia, eukaryotic flagella have a core with nine outer doublet microtubules and two inner single microtubules (the "9 + 2" arrangement) ensheathed in an extension of the plasma membrane. Prokaryotic flagella have a different structure.

florigen A flowering signal, probably a protein, that is made in leaves under certain conditions and that travels to the shoot apical meristems, inducing them to switch from vegetative to reproductive growth.

flower In an angiosperm, a specialized shoot with up to four sets of modified leaves, bearing structures that function in sexual reproduction.

fluid feeder An animal that lives by sucking nutrient-rich fluids from another living organism.

fluid mosaic model The currently accepted model of cell membrane structure, which envisions the membrane as a mosaic of protein molecules drifting laterally in a fluid bilayer of phospholipids.

follicle (fol′-uh-kul) A microscopic structure in the ovary that contains the developing oocyte and secretes estrogens.

follicle-stimulating hormone (FSH) A tropic hormone that is produced and secreted by the anterior pituitary and that stimulates the production of eggs by the ovaries and sperm by the testes.

follicular phase That part of the ovarian cycle during which follicles are growing and oocytes maturing.

food chain The pathway along which food energy is transferred from trophic level to trophic level, beginning with producers.

food vacuole A membranous sac formed by phagocytosis of microorganisms or particles to be used as food by the cell.

food web The interconnected feeding relationships in an ecosystem.

foot (1) The portion of a bryophyte sporophyte that gathers sugars, amino acids, water, and minerals from the parent gametophyte via transfer cells. (2) One of the three main parts of a mollusc; a muscular structure usually used for movement. *See also* mantle, visceral mass.

foraging The seeking and obtaining of food.

foram (foraminiferan) An aquatic protist that secretes a hardened shell containing calcium carbonate and extends pseudopodia through pores in the shell.

forebrain One of three ancestral and embryonic regions of the vertebrate brain; develops into the thalamus, hypothalamus, and cerebrum.

fossil A preserved remnant or impression of an organism that lived in the past.

founder effect Genetic drift that occurs when a few individuals become isolated from a larger population and form a new population whose gene pool composition is not reflective of that of the original population.

fovea (fō′-vē-uh) The place on the retina at the eye's center of focus, where cones are highly concentrated.

fragmentation A means of asexual reproduction whereby a single parent breaks into parts that regenerate into whole new individuals.

frameshift mutation A mutation occurring when nucleotides are inserted in or deleted from a gene and the number inserted or deleted is not a multiple of three, resulting in the improper grouping of the subsequent nucleotides into codons.

free energy The portion of a biological system's energy that can perform work when temperature and pressure are uniform throughout the system. The change in free energy of a system (ΔG) is calculated by the equation $\Delta G = \Delta H - T\Delta S$, where ΔH is the change in enthalpy (in biological systems, equivalent to total energy), T is the absolute temperature, and ΔS is the change in entropy.

frequency-dependent selection Selection in which the fitness of a phenotype depends on how common the phenotype is in a population.

fruit A mature ovary of a flower. The fruit protects dormant seeds and often aids in their dispersal.

functional group A specific configuration of atoms commonly attached to the carbon skeletons of organic molecules and involved in chemical reactions.

G protein A GTP-binding protein that relays signals from a plasma membrane signal receptor, known as a G protein-coupled receptor, to other signal transduction proteins inside the cell.

G protein-coupled receptor (GPCR) A signal receptor protein in the plasma membrane that responds to the binding of a signaling molecule by activating a G protein. Also called a G protein-linked receptor.

G_0 phase A nondividing state occupied by cells that have left the cell cycle, sometimes reversibly.

G_1 phase The first gap, or growth phase, of the cell cycle, consisting of the portion of interphase before DNA synthesis begins.

G_2 phase The second gap, or growth phase, of the cell cycle, consisting of the portion of interphase after DNA synthesis occurs.

gallbladder An organ that stores bile and releases it as needed into the small intestine.

game theory An approach to evaluating alternative strategies in situations where the outcome of a particular strategy depends on the strategies used by other individuals.

gametangium (gam′-uh-tan′-jē-um) (plural, **gametangia**) Multicellular plant structure in which gametes are formed. Female gametangia are called archegonia, and male gametangia are called antheridia.

gamete (gam′-ēt) A haploid reproductive cell, such as an egg or sperm. Gametes unite during sexual reproduction to produce a diploid zygote.

gametogenesis The process by which gametes are produced.

gametophore (guh-mē′-tō-fōr) The mature gamete-producing structure of a moss gametophyte.

gametophyte (guh-mē′-tō-fīt) In organisms (plants and some algae) that have alternation of generations, the multicellular haploid form that produces haploid gametes by mitosis. The haploid gametes unite and develop into sporophytes.

gamma-aminobutyric acid (GABA) An amino acid that functions as a CNS neurotransmitter in the central nervous system of vertebrates.

ganglia (gang′-glē-uh) (singular, **ganglion**) Clusters (functional groups) of nerve cell bodies in a centralized nervous system.

ganglion cell A type of neuron in the retina that synapses with bipolar cells and transmits action potentials to the brain via axons in the optic nerve.

gap junction A type of intercellular junction in animal cells, consisting of proteins surrounding a pore that allows the passage of materials between cells.

gas exchange The uptake of molecular oxygen from the environment and the discharge of carbon dioxide to the environment.

gastric juice A digestive fluid secreted by the stomach.

gastrovascular cavity A central cavity with a single opening in the body of certain animals, including cnidarians and flatworms, that functions in both the digestion and distribution of nutrients.

gastrula (gas′-trū-luh) An embryonic stage in animal development encompassing the formation of three layers: ectoderm, mesoderm, and endoderm.

gastrulation (gas′-trū-lā′-shun) In animal development, a series of cell and tissue movements in which the blastula-stage embryo folds inward, producing a three-layered embryo, the gastrula.

gated channel A transmembrane protein channel that opens or closes in response to a particular stimulus.

gated ion channel A gated channel for a specific ion. The opening or closing of such channels may alter a cell's membrane potential.

gel electrophoresis (ē-lek′-trō-fōr-ē′-sis) A technique for separating nucleic acids or proteins on the basis of their size and electrical charge, both of which affect their rate of movement through an electric field in a gel made of agarose or another polymer.

gene A discrete unit of hereditary information consisting of a specific nucleotide sequence in DNA (or RNA, in some viruses).

gene annotation Analysis of genomic sequences to identify protein-coding genes and determine the function of their products.

gene cloning The production of multiple copies of a gene.

gene expression The process by which information encoded in DNA directs the synthesis of proteins or, in some cases, RNAs that are not translated into proteins and instead function as RNAs.

gene flow The transfer of alleles from one population to another, resulting from the movement of fertile individuals or their gametes.

gene pool The aggregate of all copies of every type of allele at all loci in every individual in a population. The term is also used in a more restricted sense as the aggregate of alleles for just one or a few loci in a population.

gene therapy The introduction of genes into an afflicted individual for therapeutic purposes.

gene-for-gene recognition A widespread form of plant disease resistance involving recognition of pathogen-derived molecules by the protein products of specific plant disease resistance genes.

genetic drift A process in which chance events cause unpredictable fluctuations in allele frequencies from one generation to the next. Effects of genetic drift are most pronounced in small populations.

genetic engineering The direct manipulation of genes for practical purposes.

genetic map An ordered list of genetic loci (genes or other genetic markers) along a chromosome.

genetic profile An individual's unique set of genetic markers, detected most often today by PCR or, previously, by electrophoresis and nucleic acid probes.

genetic recombination General term for the production of offspring with combinations of traits that differ from those found in either parent.

genetic variation Differences among individuals in the composition of their genes or other DNA segments.

genetically modified (GM) organism An organism that has acquired one or more genes by artificial means; also known as a transgenic organism.

genetics The scientific study of heredity and hereditary variation.

genome (jē′-nōm) The genetic material of an organism or virus; the complete complement of an organism's or virus's genes along with its noncoding nucleic acid sequences.

genome-wide association study A large-scale analysis of the genomes of many people having a certain phenotype or disease, with the aim of finding genetic markers that correlate with that phenotype or disease.

genomic imprinting A phenomenon in which expression of an allele in offspring depends on whether the allele is inherited from the male or female parent.

genomic library A set of cell clones containing all the DNA segments from a genome, each within a plasmid, BAC, or other cloning vector.

genomics (juh-nō′-miks) The study of whole sets of genes and their interactions within a species, as well as genome comparisons between species.

genotype (jē′-nō-tīp) The genetic makeup, or set of alleles, of an organism.

genus (jē′-nus) (plural, **genera**) A taxonomic category above the species level, designated by the first word of a species' two-part scientific name.

geographic variation Differences between the gene pools of geographically separate populations or population subgroups.

geologic record The division of Earth's history into time periods, grouped into three eons—Archaean, Proterozoic, and Phanerozoic—and further subdivided into eras, periods, and epochs.

germ layer One of the three main layers in a gastrula that will form the various tissues and organs of an animal body.

gestation (jes-tā′-shun) Pregnancy; the state of carrying developing young within the female reproductive tract.

gibberellin (jib′-uh-rel′-in) Any of a class of related plant hormones that stimulate growth in the stem and leaves, trigger the germination of seeds and breaking of bud dormancy, and (with auxin) stimulate fruit development.

glans The rounded structure at the tip of the clitoris or penis that is involved in sexual arousal.

glia (glial cells) Cells of the nervous system that support, regulate, and augment the functions of neurons.

global climate change Increase in temperature and change in weather patterns all around the planet, due mostly to increasing atmospheric CO_2 levels from the burning of fossil fuels. The increase in temperature, called global warming, is a major aspect of global climate change.

global ecology The study of the functioning and distribution of organisms across the biosphere and how the regional exchange of energy and materials affects them.

glomeromycete (glō′-mer-ō-mī′-sēt) Member of the fungal phylum Glomeromycota, characterized by a distinct branching form of mycorrhizae called arbuscular mycorrhizae.

glomerulus (glō-mār′-yū-lus) A ball of capillaries surrounded by Bowman's capsule in the nephron and serving as the site of filtration in the vertebrate kidney.

glucagon (glū′-kuh-gon) A hormone secreted by pancreatic alpha cells that raises blood glucose levels. It promotes glycogen breakdown and release of glucose by the liver.

glucocorticoid A steroid hormone that is secreted by the adrenal cortex and that influences glucose metabolism and immune function.

glutamate An amino acid that functions as a neurotransmitter in the central nervous system.

glyceraldehyde 3-phosphate (G3P) (glis′-er-al′-de-hīd) A three-carbon carbohydrate that is the direct product of the Calvin cycle; it is also an intermediate in glycolysis.

glycogen (glī′-kō-jen) An extensively branched glucose storage polysaccharide found in the liver and muscle of animals; the animal equivalent of starch.

glycolipid A lipid with one or more covalently attached carbohydrates.

glycolysis (glī-kol′-uh-sis) A series of reactions that ultimately splits glucose into pyruvate. Glycolysis occurs in almost all living cells, serving as the starting point for fermentation or cellular respiration.

glycoprotein A protein with one or more covalently attached carbohydrates.

glycosidic linkage A covalent bond formed between two monosaccharides by a dehydration reaction.

gnathostome (na′-thu-stōm) Member of the vertebrate subgroup possessing jaws.

golden alga A biflagellated, photosynthetic protist named for its color, which results from its yellow and brown carotenoids.

Golgi apparatus (gol′-jē) An organelle in eukaryotic cells consisting of stacks of flat membranous sacs that modify, store, and route products of the endoplasmic reticulum and synthesize some products, notably noncellulose carbohydrates.

gonads (gō′-nadz) The male and female sex organs; the gamete-producing organs in most animals.

grade A group of organisms that share the same level of organizational complexity or share a key adaptation.

graded potential In a neuron, a shift in the membrane potential that has an amplitude proportional to signal strength and that decays as it spreads.

Gram stain A staining method that distinguishes between two different kinds of bacterial cell walls; may be used to help determine medical response to an infection.

gram-negative Describing the group of bacteria that have a cell wall that is structurally more complex and contains less peptidoglycan than the cell wall of gram-positive bacteria. Gram-negative bacteria are often more toxic than gram-positive bacteria.

gram-positive Describing the group of bacteria that have a cell wall that is structurally less complex and contains more peptidoglycan than the cell wall of gram-negative bacteria. Gram-positive bacteria are usually less toxic than gram-negative bacteria.

granum (gran′-um) (plural, **grana**) A stack of membrane-bounded thylakoids in the chloroplast. Grana function in the light reactions of photosynthesis.

gravitropism (grav′-uh-trō′-pizm) A response of a plant or animal to gravity.

gray matter Regions of dendrites and clustered neuron cell bodies within the CNS.

green alga A photosynthetic protist, named for green chloroplasts that are similar in structure and pigment composition to those of land plants. Green algae are a paraphyletic group, some of whose members are more closely related to land plants than they are to other green algae.

greenhouse effect The warming of Earth due to the atmospheric accumulation of carbon dioxide and certain other gases, which absorb reflected infrared radiation and reradiate some of it back toward Earth.

gross primary production (GPP) The total primary production of an ecosystem.

ground tissue system Plant tissues that are neither vascular nor dermal, fulfilling a variety of functions, such as storage, photosynthesis, and support.

growth An irreversible increase in size or biomass.

growth factor (1) A protein that must be present in the extracellular environment (culture medium or animal body) for the growth and normal development of certain types of cells. (2) A local regulator that acts on nearby cells to stimulate cell proliferation and differentiation.

growth hormone (GH) A hormone that is produced and secreted by the anterior pituitary and that has both direct (nontropic) and tropic effects on a wide variety of tissues.

guard cells The two cells that flank the stomatal pore and regulate the opening and closing of the pore.

gustation The sense of taste.

guttation The exudation of water droplets from leaves, caused by root pressure in certain plants.

gymnosperm (jim′-nō-sperm) A vascular plant that bears naked seeds—seeds not enclosed in protective chambers.

hair cell A mechanosensory cell that alters output to the nervous system when hairlike projections on the cell surface are displaced.

half-life The amount of time it takes for 50% of a sample of a radioactive isotope to decay.

Hamilton's rule The principle that for natural selection to favor an altruistic act, the benefit to the recipient, devalued by the coefficient of relatedness, must exceed the cost to the altruist.

haploid cell (hap′-loyd) A cell containing only one set of chromosomes (n).

Hardy-Weinberg principle The principle that frequencies of alleles and genotypes in a population remain constant from generation to generation, provided that only Mendelian segregation and recombination of alleles are at work.

haustorium (plural, **haustoria**) (ho-stōr′-ē-um, ho-stōr′-ē-uh) In certain symbiotic fungi, a specialized hypha that can penetrate the tissues of host organisms.

heart A muscular pump that uses metabolic energy to elevate the hydrostatic pressure of the circulatory fluid (blood or hemolymph). The fluid then flows down a pressure gradient through the body and eventually returns to the heart.

heart attack The damage or death of cardiac muscle tissue resulting from prolonged blockage of one or more coronary arteries.

heart murmur A hissing sound that most often results from blood squirting backward through a leaky valve in the heart.

heart rate The frequency of heart contraction (in beats per minute).

heat The total amount of kinetic energy due to the random motion of atoms or molecules in a body of matter; also called thermal energy. Heat is energy in its most random form.

heat of vaporization The quantity of heat a liquid must absorb for 1 g of it to be converted from the liquid to the gaseous state.

heat-shock protein A protein that helps protect other proteins during heat stress. Heat-shock proteins are found in plants, animals, and microorganisms.

heavy chain One of the two types of polypeptide chains that make up an antibody molecule and B cell receptor; consists of a variable region, which contributes to the antigen-binding site, and a constant region.

helicase An enzyme that untwists the double helix of DNA at replication forks, separating the two strands and making them available as template strands.

helper T cell A type of T cell that, when activated, secretes cytokines that promote the response of B cells (humoral response) and cytotoxic T cells (cell-mediated response) to antigens.

hemoglobin (hē′-mō-glō′-bin) An iron-containing protein in red blood cells that reversibly binds oxygen.

hemolymph (hē′-mō-limf′) In invertebrates with an open circulatory system, the body fluid that bathes tissues.

hemophilia (hē′-muh-fil′-ē-uh) A human genetic disease caused by a sex-linked recessive allele resulting in the absence of one or more blood-clotting proteins; characterized by excessive bleeding following injury.

hepatic portal vein A large vessel that conveys nutrient-laden blood from the small intestine to the liver, which regulates the blood's nutrient content.

herbivore (hur′-bi-vōr′) An animal that mainly eats plants or algae.

herbivory An interaction in which an organism eats parts of a plant or alga.

heredity The transmission of traits from one generation to the next.

hermaphrodite (hur-maf′-ruh-dīt′) An individual that functions as both male and female in sexual reproduction by producing both sperm and eggs.

hermaphroditism (hur-maf′-rō-dī-tizm) A condition in which an individual has both female and male gonads and functions as both a male and female in sexual reproduction by producing both sperm and eggs.

heterochromatin (het′-er-ō-krō′-muh-tin) Eukaryotic chromatin that remains highly compacted during interphase and is generally not transcribed.

heterochrony (het′-uh-rok′-ruh-nē) Evolutionary change in the timing or rate of an organism's development.

heterocyst (het′-er-ō-sist) A specialized cell that engages in nitrogen fixation in some filamentous cyanobacteria; also called a *heterocyte*.

heterokaryon (het′-er-ō-kār′-ē-un) A fungal mycelium that contains two or more haploid nuclei per cell.

heteromorphic (het′-er-ō-mōr′-fik) Referring to a condition in the life cycle of plants and certain algae in which the sporophyte and gametophyte generations differ in morphology.

heterosporous (het-er-os′-pōr-us) Referring to a plant species that has two kinds of spores: microspores, which develop into male gametophytes, and megaspores, which develop into female gametophytes.

heterotroph (het′-er-ō-trōf) An organism that obtains organic food molecules by eating other organisms or substances derived from them.

heterozygote advantage Greater reproductive success of heterozygous individuals compared with homozygotes; tends to preserve variation in a gene pool.

heterozygous (het′-er-ō-zī′-gus) Having two different alleles for a given gene.

hexapod An insect or closely related wingless, six-legged arthropod.

hibernation A long-term physiological state in which metabolism decreases, the heart and respiratory system slow down, and body temperature is maintained at a lower level than normal.

high-density lipoprotein (HDL) A particle in the blood made up of thousands of cholesterol molecules and other lipids bound to a protein. HDL scavenges excess cholesterol.

hindbrain One of three ancestral and embryonic regions of the vertebrate brain; develops into the medulla oblongata, pons, and cerebellum.

histamine (his′-tuh-mēn) A substance released by mast cells that causes blood vessels to dilate and become more permeable in inflammatory and allergic responses.

histone (his′-tōn) A small protein with a high proportion of positively charged amino acids that binds to the negatively charged DNA and plays a key role in chromatin structure.

histone acetylation The attachment of acetyl groups to certain amino acids of histone proteins.

HIV (human immunodeficiency virus) The infectious agent that causes AIDS. HIV is a retrovirus.

holdfast A rootlike structure that anchors a seaweed.

holoblastic (hō′-lō-blas′-tik) Referring to a type of cleavage in which there is complete division of the egg; occurs in eggs that have little yolk (such as those of the sea urchin) or a moderate amount of yolk (such as those of the frog).

homeobox (hō′-mē-ō-boks′) A 180-nucleotide sequence within homeotic genes and some other developmental genes that is widely conserved in animals. Related sequences occur in plants and yeasts.

homeostasis (hō′-mē-ō-stā′-sis) The steady-state physiological condition of the body.

homeotic gene (hō-mē-o′-tik) Any of the master regulatory genes that control placement and spatial organization of body parts in animals, plants, and fungi by controlling the developmental fate of groups of cells.

hominin (hō′-mi-nin) A member of the human branch of the evolutionary tree. Hominins include *Homo sapiens* and our ancestors, a group of extinct species that are more closely related to us than to chimpanzees.

homologous chromosomes (hō-mol′-uh-gus) A pair of chromosomes of the same length, centromere position, and staining pattern that possess genes for the same characters at corresponding loci. One homologous chromosome is inherited from the organism's father, the other from the mother. Also called homologs, or a homologous pair.

homologous structures Structures in different species that are similar because of common ancestry.

homology (hō-mol′-ō-jē) Similarity in characteristics resulting from a shared ancestry.

homoplasy (hō′-muh-play′-zē) A similar (analogous) structure or molecular sequence that has evolved independently in two species.

homosporous (hō-mos′-puh-rus) Referring to a plant species that has a single kind of spore, which typically develops into a bisexual gametophyte.

homozygous (hō′-mō-zī′-gus) Having two identical alleles for a given gene.

horizontal cell A neuron of the retina that helps integrate the information that is sent to the brain.

horizontal gene transfer The transfer of genes from one genome to another through mechanisms such as transposable elements, plasmid exchange, viral activity, and perhaps fusions of different organisms.

hormone In multicellular organisms, one of many types of secreted chemicals that are formed in specialized cells, travel in body fluids, and act on specific target cells in other parts of the body, changing the target cells' functioning. Hormones are thus important in long-distance signaling.

hornwort A small, herbaceous, nonvascular plant that is a member of the phylum Anthocerophyta.

host The larger participant in a symbiotic relationship, often providing a home and food source for the smaller symbiont.

host range The limited number of species whose cells can be infected by a particular virus.

human chorionic gonadotropin (hCG) (kōr′-ē-on′-ik gō-na′-dō-trō′-pin) A hormone secreted by the chorion that maintains the corpus luteum of the ovary during the first three months of pregnancy.

Human Genome Project An international collaborative effort to map and sequence the DNA of the entire human genome.

humoral immune response (hyū′-mer-ul) The branch of adaptive immunity that involves the activation of B cells and that leads to the production of antibodies, which defend against bacteria and viruses in body fluids.

humus (hyū′-mus) Decomposing organic material that is a component of topsoil.

Huntington's disease A human genetic disease caused by a dominant allele; characterized by uncontrollable body movements and degeneration of the nervous system; usually fatal 10 to 20 years after the onset of symptoms.

hybrid Offspring that results from the mating of individuals from two different species or from two true-breeding varieties of the same species.

hybrid zone A geographic region in which members of different species meet and mate, producing at least some offspring of mixed ancestry.

hybridization In genetics, the mating, or crossing, of two true-breeding varieties.

hydration shell The sphere of water molecules around a dissolved ion.

hydrocarbon An organic molecule consisting only of carbon and hydrogen.

hydrogen bond A type of weak chemical bond that is formed when the slightly positive hydrogen atom of a polar covalent bond in one molecule is attracted to the slightly negative atom of a polar covalent bond in another molecule or in another region of the same molecule.

hydrogen ion A single proton with a charge of 1+. The dissociation of a water molecule (H_2O) leads to the generation of a hydroxide ion (OH^-) and a hydrogen ion (H^+); in water, H^+ is not found alone but associates with a water molecule to form a hydronium ion.

hydrolysis (hī-drol′-uh-sis) A chemical reaction that breaks bonds between two molecules by the addition of water; functions in disassembly of polymers to monomers.

hydronium ion A water molecule that has an extra proton bound to it; H_3O^+, commonly represented as H^+.

hydrophilic (hī′-drō-fil′-ik) Having an affinity for water.

hydrophobic (hī′-drō-fō′-bik) Having no affinity for water; tending to coalesce and form droplets in water.

hydrophobic interaction A type of weak chemical interaction caused when molecules that do not mix with water coalesce to exclude water.

hydroponic culture A method in which plants are grown in mineral solutions rather than in soil.

hydrostatic skeleton A skeletal system composed of fluid held under pressure in a closed body compartment; the main skeleton of most cnidarians, flatworms, nematodes, and annelids.

hydroxide ion A water molecule that has lost a proton; OH^-.

hydroxyl group (hī-drok′-sil) A chemical group consisting of an oxygen atom joined to a hydrogen atom. Molecules possessing this group are soluble in water and are called alcohols.

hymen A thin membrane that partly covers the vaginal opening in the human female. The hymen is ruptured by sexual intercourse or other vigorous activity.

hyperpolarization A change in a cell's membrane potential such that the inside of the membrane becomes more negative relative to the outside. Hyperpolarization reduces the chance that a neuron will transmit a nerve impulse.

hypersensitive response A plant's localized defense response to a pathogen, involving the death of cells around the site of infection.

hypertension A disorder in which blood pressure remains abnormally high.

hypertonic Referring to a solution that, when surrounding a cell, will cause the cell to lose water.

hypha (plural, **hyphae**) (hī′-fuh, hī′-fē) One of many connected filaments that collectively make up the mycelium of a fungus.

hypocotyl (hī′-puh-cot′-ul) In an angiosperm embryo, the embryonic axis below the point of attachment of the cotyledon(s) and above the radicle.

hypothalamus (hī′-pō-thal′-uh-mus) The ventral part of the vertebrate forebrain; functions in maintaining homeostasis, especially in coordinating the endocrine and nervous systems; secretes hormones of the posterior pituitary and releasing factors that regulate the anterior pituitary.

hypothesis (hī-poth′-uh-sis) A testable explanation for a set of observations based on the available data and guided by inductive reasoning. A hypothesis is narrower in scope than a theory.

hypotonic Referring to a solution that, when surrounding a cell, will cause the cell to take up water.

imbibition The physical adsorption of water onto the internal surfaces of structures.

immigration The influx of new individuals into a population from other areas.

immune system An animal body's system of defenses against agents that cause disease.

immunization The process of generating a state of immunity by artificial means. In active immunization, also called vaccination, an inactive or weakened form of a pathogen is administered, inducing B and T cell responses and immunological memory. In passive immunization, antibodies specific for a particular microbe are administered, conferring immediate but temporary protection.

immunodeficiency A disorder in which the ability of an immune system to protect against pathogens is defective or absent.

immunoglobulin (Ig) (im′-yū-nō-glob′-yū-lin) Any of the class of proteins that function as antibodies. Immunoglobulins are divided into five major classes that differ in their distribution in the body and antigen disposal activities.

imprinting In animal behavior, the formation at a specific stage in life of a long-lasting behavioral response to a specific individual or object. *See also* genomic imprinting.

***in situ* hybridization** A technique using nucleic acid hybridization with a labeled probe to detect the location of a specific mRNA in an intact organism.

***in vitro* fertilization (IVF)** (vē′-trō) Fertilization of oocytes in laboratory containers followed by artificial implantation of the early embryo in the mother's uterus.

***in vitro* mutagenesis** A technique used to discover the function of a gene by cloning it, introducing specific changes into the cloned gene's sequence, reinserting the mutated gene into a cell, and studying the phenotype of the mutant.

inclusive fitness The total effect an individual has on proliferating its genes by producing its own offspring and by providing aid that enables other close relatives to increase production of their offspring.

incomplete dominance The situation in which the phenotype of heterozygotes is intermediate between the phenotypes of individuals homozygous for either allele.

incomplete flower A flower in which one or more of the four basic floral organs (sepals, petals, stamens, or carpels) are either absent or nonfunctional.

incomplete metamorphosis A type of development in certain insects, such as grasshoppers, in which the young (called nymphs) resemble adults but are smaller and have different body proportions. The nymph goes through a series of molts, each time looking more like an adult, until it reaches full size.

indeterminate cleavage A type of embryonic development in deuterostomes in which each cell produced by early cleavage divisions retains the capacity to develop into a complete embryo.

indeterminate growth A type of growth characteristic of plants, in which the organism continues to grow as long as it lives.

induced fit Caused by entry of the substrate, the change in shape of the active site of an enzyme so that it binds more snugly to the substrate.

inducer A specific small molecule that binds to a bacterial repressor protein and changes the repressor's shape so that it cannot bind to an operator, thus switching an operon on.

induction The process in which one group of embryonic cells influences the development of another, usually by causing changes in gene expression.

inductive reasoning A type of logic in which generalizations are based on a large number of specific observations.

inflammatory response An innate immune defense triggered by physical injury or infection of tissue involving the release of substances that promote swelling, enhance the infiltration of white blood cells, and aid in tissue repair and destruction of invading pathogens.

inflorescence A group of flowers tightly clustered together.

ingestion The first stage of food processing in animals: the act of eating.

ingroup A species or group of species whose evolutionary relationships we seek to determine.

inhibin A hormone produced in the male and female gonads that functions in part by regulating the anterior pituitary by negative feedback.

inhibitory postsynaptic potential (IPSP) An electrical change (usually hyperpolarization) in the membrane of a postsynaptic neuron caused by the binding of an inhibitory neurotransmitter from a presynaptic cell to a postsynaptic receptor; makes it more difficult for a postsynaptic neuron to generate an action potential.

innate behavior Animal behavior that is developmentally fixed and under strong genetic control. Innate behavior is exhibited in virtually the same form by all individuals in a population despite internal and external environmental differences during development and throughout their lifetimes.

innate immunity A form of defense common to all animals that is active immediately upon exposure to pathogens and that is the same whether or not the pathogen has been encountered previously.

inner cell mass An inner cluster of cells at one end of a mammalian blastocyst that subsequently develops into the embryo proper and some of the extraembryonic membranes.

inner ear One of three main regions of the vertebrate ear; includes the cochlea (which in turn contains the organ of Corti) and the semicircular canals.

inositol trisphosphate (IP_3) (in-ō′-suh-tol) A second messenger that functions as an intermediate between certain signaling molecules and a subsequent second messenger, Ca^{2+}, by causing a rise in cytoplasmic Ca^{2+} concentration.

inquiry The search for information and explanation, often focusing on specific questions.

insertion A mutation involving the addition of one or more nucleotide pairs to a gene.

insulin (in′-suh-lin) A hormone secreted by pancreatic beta cells that lowers blood glucose levels. It promotes the uptake of glucose by most body cells and the synthesis and storage of glycogen in the liver and also stimulates protein and fat synthesis.

integral protein A transmembrane protein with hydrophobic regions that extend into and often completely span the hydrophobic interior of the membrane and with hydrophilic regions in contact with the aqueous solution on one or both sides of the membrane (or lining the channel in the case of a channel protein).

integrin In animal cells, a transmembrane receptor protein with two subunits that interconnects the extracellular matrix and the cytoskeleton.

integument (in-teg′-yū-ment) Layer of sporophyte tissue that contributes to the structure of an ovule of a seed plant.

integumentary system The outer covering of a mammal's body, including skin, hair, and nails, claws, or hooves.

intercalated disk (in-ter′-kuh-lā′-ted) A specialized junction between cardiac muscle cells that provides direct electrical coupling between the cells.

interferon (in′-ter-fēr′-on) A protein that has antiviral or immune regulatory functions. Interferon-α and interferon-β, secreted by virus-infected cells, help nearby cells resist viral infection; interferon-γ, secreted by T cells, helps activate macrophages.

intermediate disturbance hypothesis The concept that moderate levels of disturbance can foster greater species diversity than low or high levels of disturbance.

intermediate filament A component of the cytoskeleton that includes filaments intermediate in size between microtubules and microfilaments.

internal fertilization The fusion of eggs and sperm within the female reproductive tract. The sperm are typically deposited in or near the tract.

interneuron An association neuron; a nerve cell within the central nervous system that forms synapses with sensory and/or motor neurons and integrates sensory input and motor output.

internode A segment of a plant stem between the points where leaves are attached.

interphase The period in the cell cycle when the cell is not dividing. During interphase, cellular metabolic activity is high, chromosomes and organelles are duplicated, and cell size may increase. Interphase often accounts for about 90% of the cell cycle.

intersexual selection Selection whereby individuals of one sex (usually females) are choosy in selecting their mates from individuals of the other sex; also called mate choice.

interspecific competition Competition for resources between individuals of two or more species when resources are in short supply.

interspecific interaction A relationship between individuals of two or more species in a community.

interstitial fluid The fluid filling the spaces between cells in most animals.

intertidal zone The shallow zone of the ocean adjacent to land and between the high- and low-tide lines.

intracytoplasmic sperm injection (ICSI) The fertilization of an egg in the laboratory by the direct injection of a single sperm.

intrasexual selection Selection in which there is direct competition among individuals of one sex for mates of the opposite sex.

introduced species A species moved by humans, either intentionally or accidentally, from its native location to a new geographic region; also called non-native or exotic species.

intron (in′-tron) A noncoding, intervening sequence within a primary transcript that is removed from the transcript during RNA processing; also refers to the region of DNA from which this sequence was transcribed.

invasive species A species, often introduced by humans, that takes hold outside its native range.

inversion An aberration in chromosome structure resulting from reattachment of a chromosomal fragment in a reverse orientation to the chromosome from which it originated.

invertebrate An animal without a backbone. Invertebrates make up 95% of animal species.

ion (ī′-on) An atom or group of atoms that has gained or lost one or more electrons, thus acquiring a charge.

ion channel A transmembrane protein channel that allows a specific ion to diffuse across the membrane down its concentration or electrochemical gradient.

ionic bond (ī-on′-ik) A chemical bond resulting from the attraction between oppositely charged ions.

ionic compound A compound resulting from the formation of an ionic bond; also called a salt.

IPSP *See* inhibitory postsynaptic potential.

iris The colored part of the vertebrate eye, formed by the anterior portion of the choroid.

isomer (ī′-sō-mer) One of several compounds with the same molecular formula but different structures and therefore different properties. The three types of isomers are structural isomers, *cis-trans* isomers, and enantiomers.

isomorphic Referring to alternating generations in plants and certain algae in which the sporophytes and gametophytes look alike, although they differ in chromosome number.

isopod A member of one of the largest groups of crustaceans, which includes terrestrial, freshwater, and marine species. Among the terrestrial isopods are the pill bugs, or wood lice.

isotonic (ī′-sō-ton′-ik) Referring to a solution that, when surrounding a cell, causes no net movement of water into or out of the cell.

isotope (ī′-sō-tōp′) One of several atomic forms of an element, each with the same number of protons but a different number of neutrons, thus differing in atomic mass.

iteroparity Reproduction in which adults produce offspring over many years; also known as repeated reproduction.

joule (J) A unit of energy: 1 J = 0.239 cal; 1 cal = 4.184 J.

juxtaglomerular apparatus (JGA) (juks′-tuh-gluh-mār′-yū-ler) A specialized tissue in nephrons that releases the enzyme renin in response to a drop in blood pressure or volume.

juxtamedullary nephron In mammals and birds, a nephron with a loop of Henle that extends far into the renal medulla.

karyogamy (kār′-ē-og′-uh-mē) In fungi, the fusion of haploid nuclei contributed by the two parents; occurs as one stage of sexual reproduction, preceded by plasmogamy.

karyotype (kār′-ē-ō-tīp) A display of the chromosome pairs of a cell arranged by size and shape.

keystone species A species that is not necessarily abundant in a community yet exerts strong control on community structure by the nature of its ecological role or niche.

kidney In vertebrates, one of a pair of excretory organs where blood filtrate is formed and processed into urine.

kilocalorie (kcal) A thousand calories; the amount of heat energy required to raise the temperature of 1 kg of water by 1°C.

kin selection Natural selection that favors altruistic behavior by enhancing the reproductive success of relatives.

kinetic energy (kuh-net′-ik) The energy associated with the relative motion of objects. Moving matter can perform work by imparting motion to other matter.

kinetochore (kuh-net′-uh-kōr) A structure of proteins attached to the centromere that links each sister chromatid to the mitotic spindle.

kinetoplastid A protist, such as a trypanosome, that has a single large mitochondrion that houses an organized mass of DNA.

kingdom A taxonomic category, the second broadest after domain.

***K*-selection** Selection for life history traits that are sensitive to population density; also called density-dependent selection.

labia majora A pair of thick, fatty ridges that encloses and protects the rest of the vulva.

labia minora A pair of slender skin folds that surrounds the openings of the vagina and urethra.

labor A series of strong, rhythmic contractions of the uterus that expels a baby out of the uterus and vagina during childbirth.

lactation The continued production of milk from the mammary glands.

lacteal (lak′-tē-ul) A tiny lymph vessel extending into the core of an intestinal villus and serving as the destination for absorbed chylomicrons.

lactic acid fermentation Glycolysis followed by the reduction of pyruvate to lactate, regenerating NAD^+ with no release of carbon dioxide.

lagging strand A discontinuously synthesized DNA strand that elongates by means of Okazaki fragments, each synthesized in a $5' \rightarrow 3'$ direction away from the replication fork.

lancelet Member of the clade Cephalochordata, small blade-shaped marine chordates that lack a backbone.

landscape An area containing several different ecosystems linked by exchanges of energy, materials, and organisms.

landscape ecology The study of how the spatial arrangement of habitat types affects the distribution and abundance of organisms and ecosystem processes.

large intestine The portion of the vertebrate alimentary canal between the small intestine and the anus; functions mainly in water absorption and the formation of feces.

larva (lar′-vuh) (plural, **larvae**) A free-living, sexually immature form in some animal life cycles that may differ from the adult animal in morphology, nutrition, and habitat.

larynx (lār′-inks) The portion of the respiratory tract containing the vocal cords; also called the voice box.

lateral geniculate nucleus One of a pair of structures in the brain that are the destination for most of the ganglion cell axons that form the optic nerves.

lateral inhibition A process that sharpens the edges and enhances the contrast of a perceived image by inhibiting receptors lateral to those that have responded to light.

lateral line system A mechanoreceptor system consisting of a series of pores and receptor units along the sides of the body in fishes and aquatic amphibians; detects water movements made by the animal itself and by other moving objects.

lateral meristem (mār′-uh-stem) A meristem that thickens the roots and shoots of woody plants. The vascular cambium and cork cambium are lateral meristems.

lateral root A root that arises from the pericycle of an established root.

lateralization Segregation of functions in the cortex of the left and right cerebral hemispheres.

law of conservation of mass A physical law stating that matter can change form but cannot be created or destroyed. In a closed system, the mass of the system is constant.

law of independent assortment Mendel's second law, stating that each pair of alleles segregates, or assorts, independently of each other pair during gamete formation; applies when genes for two characters are located on different pairs of homologous chromosomes or when they are far enough apart on the same chromosome to behave as though they are on different chromosomes.

law of segregation Mendel's first law, stating that the two alleles in a pair segregate (separate from each other) into different gametes during gamete formation.

leading strand The new complementary DNA strand synthesized continuously along the template strand toward the replication fork in the mandatory $5' \rightarrow 3'$ direction.

leaf The main photosynthetic organ of vascular plants.

leaf primordium A finger-like projection along the flank of a shoot apical meristem, from which a leaf arises.

learning The modification of behavior based on specific experiences.

lens The structure in an eye that focuses light rays onto the photoreceptors.

lenticel (len′-ti-sel) A small raised area in the bark of stems and roots that enables gas exchange between living cells and the outside air.

lepidosaur (leh-pid′-uh-sōr) Member of the reptilian group that includes lizards, snakes, and two species of New Zealand animals called tuataras.

leptin A hormone produced by adipose (fat) cells that acts as a satiety factor in regulating appetite.

leukocyte (lū′-kō-sīt′) A blood cell that functions in fighting infections; also called a white blood cell.

Leydig cell (lī′-dig) A cell that produces testosterone and other androgens and is located between the seminiferous tubules of the testes.

lichen The mutualistic association between a fungus and a photosynthetic alga or cyanobacterium.

life cycle The generation-to-generation sequence of stages in the reproductive history of an organism.

life history The traits that affect an organism's schedule of reproduction and survival.

life table An age-specific summary of the survival pattern of a population.

ligament A fibrous connective tissue that joins bones together at joints.

ligand (lig′-und) A molecule that binds specifically to another molecule, usually a larger one.

ligand-gated ion channel A transmembrane protein containing a pore that opens or closes as it changes shape in response to a signaling molecule (ligand), allowing or blocking the flow of specific ions; also called an ionotropic receptor.

light chain One of the two types of polypeptide chains that make up an antibody molecule and B cell receptor; consists of a variable region, which contributes to the antigen-binding site, and a constant region.

light microscope (LM) An optical instrument with lenses that refract (bend) visible light to magnify images of specimens.

light reactions The first of two major stages in photosynthesis (preceding the Calvin cycle). These reactions, which occur on the thylakoid membranes of the chloroplast or on membranes of certain prokaryotes, convert solar energy to the chemical energy of ATP and NADPH, releasing oxygen in the process.

light-harvesting complex A complex of proteins associated with pigment molecules (including chlorophyll *a*, chlorophyll *b*, and carotenoids) that captures light energy and transfers it to reaction-center pigments in a photosystem.

lignin (lig′-nin) A hard material embedded in the cellulose matrix of vascular plant cell walls that provides structural support in terrestrial species.

limiting nutrient An element that must be added for production to increase in a particular area.

limnetic zone In a lake, the well-lit, open surface waters far from shore.

linear electron flow A route of electron flow during the light reactions of photosynthesis that involves both photosystems (I and II) and produces ATP, NADPH, and O_2. The net electron flow is from H_2O to $NADP^+$.

linkage map A genetic map based on the frequencies of recombination between markers during crossing over of homologous chromosomes.

linked genes Genes located close enough together on a chromosome that they tend to be inherited together.

lipid (lip′-id) Any of a group of large biological molecules, including fats, phospholipids, and steroids, that mix poorly, if at all, with water.

littoral zone In a lake, the shallow, well-lit waters close to shore.

liver A large internal organ in vertebrates that performs diverse functions, such as producing bile, maintaining blood glucose level, and detoxifying poisonous chemicals in the blood.

liverwort A small, herbaceous, nonvascular plant that is a member of the phylum Hepatophyta.

loam The most fertile soil type, made up of roughly equal amounts of sand, silt, and clay.

lobe-fin Member of the vertebrate clade Sarcopterygii, osteichthyans with rod-shaped muscular fins, including coelacanths, lungfishes, and tetrapods.

local regulator A secreted molecule that influences cells near where it is secreted.

locomotion Active motion from place to place.

locus (lō′-kus) (plural, **loci**) A specific place along the length of a chromosome where a given gene is located.

logistic population growth Population growth that levels off as population size approaches carrying capacity.

long-day plant A plant that flowers (usually in late spring or early summer) only when the light period is longer than a critical length.

long-term memory The ability to hold, associate, and recall information over one's lifetime.

long-term potentiation (LTP) An enhanced responsiveness to an action potential (nerve signal) by a receiving neuron.

loop of Henle The hairpin turn, with a descending and ascending limb, between the proximal and distal tubules of the vertebrate kidney; functions in water and salt reabsorption.

lophophore (lof′-uh-fōr) In some lophotrochozoan animals, including brachiopods, a crown of ciliated tentacles that surround the mouth and function in feeding.

lophotrochozoan Member of a group of animal phyla identified as a clade by molecular evidence. Lophotrochozoans include organisms that have lophophores or trochophore larvae.

low-density lipoprotein (LDL) A particle in the blood made up of thousands of cholesterol molecules and other lipids bound to a protein. LDL transports cholesterol from the liver for incorporation into cell membranes.

lung An infolded respiratory surface of a terrestrial vertebrate, land snail, or spider that connects to the atmosphere by narrow tubes.

luteal phase That portion of the ovarian cycle during which endocrine cells of the corpus luteum secrete female hormones.

luteinizing hormone (LH) (lū′-tē-uh-nī′-zing) A tropic hormone that is produced and secreted by the anterior pituitary and that stimulates ovulation in females and androgen production in males.

lycophyte (lī′-kuh-fīt) An informal name for a member of the phylum Lycophyta, which includes club mosses, spike mosses, and quillworts.

lymph The colorless fluid, derived from interstitial fluid, in the lymphatic system of vertebrates.

lymph node An organ located along a lymph vessel. Lymph nodes filter lymph and contain cells that attack viruses and bacteria.

lymphatic system A system of vessels and nodes, separate from the circulatory system, that returns fluid, proteins, and cells to the blood.

lymphocyte A type of white blood cell that mediates immune responses. The two main classes are B cells and T cells.

lysogenic cycle (lī′-sō-jen′-ik) A type of phage replicative cycle in which the viral genome becomes incorporated into the bacterial host chromosome as a prophage, is replicated along with the chromosome, and does not kill the host.

lysosome (lī′-suh-sōm) A membrane-enclosed sac of hydrolytic enzymes found in the cytoplasm of animal cells and some protists.

lysozyme (lī′-sō-zīm) An enzyme that destroys bacterial cell walls; in mammals, found in sweat, tears, and saliva.

lytic cycle (lit′-ik) A type of phage replicative cycle resulting in the release of new phages by lysis (and death) of the host cell.

macroclimate Large-scale patterns in climate; the climate of an entire region.

macroevolution Evolutionary change above the species level. Examples of macroevolutionary change include the origin of a new group of organisms through a series of speciation events and the impact of mass extinctions on the diversity of life and its subsequent recovery.

macromolecule A giant molecule formed by the joining of smaller molecules, usually by a dehydration reaction. Polysaccharides, proteins, and nucleic acids are macromolecules.

macronutrient An essential element that an organism must obtain in relatively large amounts. *See also* micronutrient.

macrophage (mak′-rō-fāj) A phagocytic cell present in many tissues that functions in innate immunity by destroying microbes and in acquired immunity as an antigen-presenting cell.

magnoliid Member of the angiosperm clade that is most closely related to the combined eudicot and monocot clades. Extant examples are magnolias, laurels, and black pepper plants.

major depressive disorder A mood disorder characterized by feelings of sadness, lack of self-worth, emptiness, or loss of interest in nearly all things.

major histocompatibility complex (MHC) molecule A host protein that functions in antigen presentation. Foreign MHC molecules on transplanted tissue can trigger T cell responses that may lead to rejection of the transplant.

malignant tumor A cancerous tumor containing cells that have significant genetic and cellular changes and are capable of invading and surviving in new sites. Malignant tumors can impair the functions of one or more organs.

Malpighian tubule (mal-pig′-ē-un) A unique excretory organ of insects that empties into the digestive tract, removes nitrogenous wastes from the hemolymph, and functions in osmoregulation.

mammal Member of the class Mammalia, amniotes that have hair and mammary glands (glands that produce milk).

mammary gland An exocrine gland that secretes milk to nourish the young. Mammary glands are characteristic of mammals.

mandible One of a pair of jaw-like feeding appendages found in myriapods, hexapods, and crustaceans.

mantle One of the three main parts of a mollusc; a fold of tissue that drapes over the mollusc's visceral mass and may secrete a shell. *See also* foot, visceral mass.

mantle cavity A water-filled chamber that houses the gills, anus, and excretory pores of a mollusc.

map unit A unit of measurement of the distance between genes. One map unit is equivalent to a 1% recombination frequency.

marine benthic zone The ocean floor.

mark-recapture method A sampling technique used to estimate the size of animal populations.

marsupial (mar-sū′-pē-ul) A mammal, such as a koala, kangaroo, or opossum, whose young complete their embryonic development inside a maternal pouch called the marsupium.

mass extinction The elimination of a large number of species throughout Earth, the result of global environmental changes.

mass number The sum of the number of protons and neutrons in an atom's nucleus.

mast cell A vertebrate body cell that produces histamine and other molecules that trigger inflammation in response to infection and in allergic reactions.

mate-choice copying Behavior in which individuals in a population copy the mate choice of others, apparently as a result of social learning.

maternal effect gene A gene that, when mutant in the mother, results in a mutant phenotype in the offspring, regardless of the offspring's genotype. Maternal effect genes, also called egg-polarity genes, were first identified in *Drosophila melanogaster*.

matter Anything that takes up space and has mass.

maximum likelihood As applied to molecular systematics, a principle that states that when considering multiple phylogenetic hypotheses, one should take into account the hypothesis that reflects the most likely sequence of evolutionary events, given certain rules about how DNA changes over time.

maximum parsimony A principle that states that when considering multiple explanations for an observation, one should first investigate the simplest explanation that is consistent with the facts.

mechanoreceptor A sensory receptor that detects physical deformation in the body's environment associated with pressure, touch, stretch, motion, or sound.

medulla oblongata (meh-dul′-uh ōb′-long-go′-tuh) The lowest part of the vertebrate brain, commonly called the medulla; a swelling of the hindbrain anterior to the spinal cord that controls autonomic, homeostatic functions, including breathing, heart and blood vessel activity, swallowing, digestion, and vomiting.

Medusa (plural, medusae) (muh-dū′-suh) The floating, flattened, mouth-down version of the cnidarian body plan. The alternate form is the polyp.

megapascal (MPa) (meg′-uh-pas-kal′) A unit of pressure equivalent to about 10 atmospheres of pressure.

megaphyll (meh′-guh-fil) A leaf with a highly branched vascular system, characteristic of the vast majority of vascular plants. *See* microphyll.

megaspore A spore from a heterosporous plant species that develops into a female gametophyte.

meiosis (mī-ō′-sis) A modified type of cell division in sexually reproducing organisms consisting of two rounds of cell division but only one round of DNA replication. It results in cells with half the number of chromosome sets as the original cell.

meiosis I The first division of a two-stage process of cell division in sexually reproducing organisms that results in cells with half the number of chromosome sets as the original cell.

meiosis II The second division of a two-stage process of cell division in sexually reproducing organisms that results in cells with half the number of chromosome sets as the original cell.

melanocyte-stimulating hormone (MSH) A hormone produced and secreted by the anterior pituitary with multiple activities, including regulating the behavior of pigment-containing cells in the skin of some vertebrates.

melatonin A hormone that is secreted by the pineal gland and that is involved in the regulation of biological rhythms and sleep.

membrane potential The difference in electrical charge (voltage) across a cell's plasma membrane due to the differential distribution of ions. Membrane potential affects the activity of excitable cells and the transmembrane movement of all charged substances.

memory cell One of a clone of long-lived lymphocytes, formed during the primary immune response, that remains in a lymphoid organ until activated by exposure to the same antigen that triggered its formation. Activated memory cells mount the secondary immune response.

menopause The cessation of ovulation and menstruation marking the end of a human female's reproductive years.

menstrual cycle (men′-strū-ul) In humans and certain other primates, a type of reproductive cycle in which the nonpregnant endometrium is shed through the cervix into the vagina; also called the uterine cycle.

menstrual flow phase That portion of the uterine (menstrual) cycle when menstrual bleeding occurs.

menstruation The shedding of portions of the endometrium during a uterine (menstrual) cycle.

meristem (mār′-uh-stem) Plant tissue that remains embryonic as long as the plant lives, allowing for indeterminate growth.

meristem identity gene A plant gene that promotes the switch from vegetative growth to flowering.

meroblastic (mār′-ō-blas′-tik) Referring to a type of cleavage in which there is incomplete division of a yolk-rich egg, characteristic of avian development.

mesoderm (mez′-ō-derm) The middle primary germ layer in a triploblastic animal embryo; develops into the notochord, the lining of the coelom, muscles, skeleton, gonads, kidneys, and most of the circulatory system in species that have these structures.

mesohyl (mez′-ō-hīl) A gelatinous region between the two layers of cells of a sponge.

mesophyll (mez′-ō-fil) Leaf cells specialized for photosynthesis. In C_3 and CAM plants, mesophyll cells are located between the upper and lower epidermis; in C_4 plants, they are located between the bundle-sheath cells and the epidermis.

messenger RNA (mRNA) A type of RNA, synthesized using a DNA template, that attaches to ribosomes in the cytoplasm and specifies the primary structure of a protein. (In eukaryotes, the primary RNA transcript must undergo RNA processing to become mRNA.)

metabolic pathway A series of chemical reactions that either builds a complex molecule (anabolic pathway) or breaks down a complex molecule to simpler molecules (catabolic pathway).

metabolic rate The total amount of energy an animal uses in a unit of time.

metabolism (muh-tab′-uh-lizm) The totality of an organism's chemical reactions, consisting of catabolic and anabolic pathways, which manage the material and energy resources of the organism.

metagenomics The collection and sequencing of DNA from a group of species, usually an environmental sample of microorganisms. Computer software sorts partial sequences and assembles them into genome sequences of individual species making up the sample.

metamorphosis (met′-uh-mōr′-fuh-sis) A developmental transformation that turns an animal larva into either an adult or an adult-like stage that is not yet sexually mature.

metanephridium (met′-uh-nuh-frid′-ē-um) (plural, **metanephridia**) An excretory organ found in many invertebrates that typically consists of tubules connecting ciliated internal openings to external openings.

metaphase The third stage of mitosis, in which the spindle is complete and the chromosomes, attached to microtubules at their kinetochores, are all aligned at the metaphase plate.

metaphase plate An imaginary structure located at a plane midway between the two poles of a cell in metaphase on which the centromeres of all the duplicated chromosomes are located.

metapopulation A group of spatially separated populations of one species that interact through immigration and emigration.

metastasis (muh-tas′-tuh-sis) The spread of cancer cells to locations distant from their original site.

methanogen (meth-an′-ō-jen) An organism that produces methane as a waste product of the way it obtains energy. All known methanogens are in domain Archaea.

methyl group A chemical group consisting of a carbon bonded to three hydrogen atoms. The methyl group may be attached to a carbon or to a different atom.

microclimate Climate patterns on a very fine scale, such as the specific climatic conditions underneath a log.

microevolution Evolutionary change below the species level; change in the allele frequencies in a population over generations.

microfilament A cable composed of actin proteins in the cytoplasm of almost every eukaryotic cell, making up part of the cytoskeleton and acting alone or with myosin to cause cell contraction; also known as an actin filament.

micronutrient An essential element that an organism needs in very small amounts. *See also* macronutrient.

microphyll (mī′-krō-fil) In lycophytes, a small leaf with a single unbranched vein. *See* megaphyll.

micropyle A pore in the integuments of an ovule.

microRNA (miRNA) A small, single-stranded RNA molecule, generated from a hairpin structure on a precursor RNA transcribed from a particular gene. The miRNA associates with one or more proteins in a complex that can degrade or prevent translation of an mRNA with a complementary sequence.

microspore A spore from a heterosporous plant species that develops into a male gametophyte.

microtubule A hollow rod composed of tubulin proteins that makes up part of the cytoskeleton in all eukaryotic cells and is found in cilia and flagella.

microvillus (plural, **microvilli**) One of many fine, finger-like projections of the epithelial cells in the lumen of the small intestine that increase its surface area.

midbrain One of three ancestral and embryonic regions of the vertebrate brain; develops into sensory integrating and relay centers that send sensory information to the cerebrum.

middle ear One of three main regions of the vertebrate ear; in mammals, a chamber containing three small bones (the malleus, incus, and stapes) that convey vibrations from the eardrum to the oval window.

middle lamella (luh-mel′-uh) In plants, a thin layer of adhesive extracellular material, primarily pectins, found between the primary walls of adjacent young cells.

migration A regular, long-distance change in location.

mineral In nutrition, a simple nutrient that is inorganic and therefore cannot be synthesized in the body.

mineralocorticoid A steroid hormone secreted by the adrenal cortex that regulates salt and water homeostasis.

minimum viable population (MVP) The smallest population size at which a species is able to sustain its numbers and survive.

mismatch repair The cellular process that uses specific enzymes to remove and replace incorrectly paired nucleotides.

missense mutation A nucleotide-pair substitution that results in a codon that codes for a different amino acid.

mitochondrial matrix The compartment of the mitochondrion enclosed by the inner membrane and containing enzymes and substrates for the citric acid cycle, as well as ribosomes and DNA.

mitochondrion (mī′-tō-kon′-drē-un) (plural, **mitochondria**) An organelle in eukaryotic cells that serves as the site of cellular respiration; uses oxygen to break down organic molecules and synthesize ATP.

mitosis (mī-tō′-sis) A process of nuclear division in eukaryotic cells conventionally divided into five stages: prophase, prometaphase, metaphase, anaphase, and telophase. Mitosis conserves chromosome number by allocating replicated chromosomes equally to each of the daughter nuclei.

mitotic (M) phase The phase of the cell cycle that includes mitosis and cytokinesis.

mitotic spindle An assemblage of microtubules and associated proteins that is involved in the movement of chromosomes during mitosis.

mixotroph An organism that is capable of both photosynthesis and heterotrophy.

model organism A particular species chosen for research into broad biological principles because it is representative of a larger group and usually easy to grow in a lab.

molarity A common measure of solute concentration, referring to the number of moles of solute per liter of solution.

mold Informal term for a fungus that grows as a filamentous fungus, producing haploid spores by mitosis and forming a visible mycelium.

mole (mol) The number of grams of a substance that equals its molecular weight in daltons and contains Avogadro's number of molecules.

molecular clock A method for estimating the time required for a given amount of evolutionary change, based on the observation that some regions of genomes evolve at constant rates.

molecular mass The sum of the masses of all the atoms in a molecule; sometimes called molecular weight.

molecular systematics A scientific discipline that uses nucleic acids or other molecules to infer evolutionary relationships between different species.

molecule Two or more atoms held together by covalent bonds.

molting A process in ecdysozoans in which the exoskeleton is shed at intervals, allowing growth by the production of a larger exoskeleton.

monoclonal antibody (mon′-ō-klōn′-ul) Any of a preparation of antibodies that have been produced by a single clone of cultured cells and thus are all specific for the same epitope.

monocot Member of a clade consisting of flowering plants that have one embryonic seed leaf, or cotyledon.

monogamous (muh-nog′-uh-mus) Referring to a type of relationship in which one male mates with just one female.

monohybrid An organism that is heterozygous with respect to a single gene of interest. All the offspring from a cross between parents homozygous for different alleles are monohybrids. For example, parents of genotypes *AA* and *aa* produce a monohybrid of genotype *Aa*.

monohybrid cross A cross between two organisms that are heterozygous for the character being followed (or the self-pollination of a heterozygous plant).

monomer (mon′-uh-mer) The subunit that serves as the building block of a polymer.

monophyletic (mon′-ō-fī-let′-ik) Pertaining to a group of taxa that consists of a common ancestor and all of its descendants. A monophyletic taxon is equivalent to a clade.

monosaccharide (mon′-ō-sak′-uh-rīd) The simplest carbohydrate, active alone or serving as a monomer for disaccharides and polysaccharides. Also known as simple sugars, monosaccharides have molecular formulas that are generally some multiple of CH_2O.

monosomic Referring to a diploid cell that has only one copy of a particular chromosome instead of the normal two.

monotreme An egg-laying mammal, such as a platypus or echidna. Like all mammals, monotremes have hair and produce milk, but they lack nipples.

morphogen A substance, such as Bicoid protein in *Drosophila*, that provides positional information in the form of a concentration gradient along an embryonic axis.

morphogenesis (mōr′-fō-jen′-uh-sis) The cellular and tissue-based processes by which an animal body takes shape.

morphological species concept A definition of species in terms of measurable anatomical criteria.

moss A small, herbaceous, nonvascular plant that is a member of the phylum Bryophyta.

motor neuron A nerve cell that transmits signals from the brain or spinal cord to muscles or glands.

motor protein A protein that interacts with cytoskeletal elements and other cell components, producing movement of the whole cell or parts of the cell.

motor system An efferent branch of the vertebrate peripheral nervous system composed of motor neurons that carry signals to skeletal muscles in response to external stimuli.

motor unit A single motor neuron and all the muscle fibers it controls.

movement corridor A series of small clumps or a narrow strip of quality habitat (usable by organisms) that connects otherwise isolated patches of quality habitat.

MPF Maturation-promoting factor (or M-phase-promoting factor); a protein complex required for a cell to progress from late interphase to mitosis. The active form consists of cyclin and a protein kinase.

mucus A viscous and slippery mixture of glycoproteins, cells, salts, and water that moistens and protects the membranes lining body cavities that open to the exterior.

Müllerian mimicry (myū-lār′-ē-un) Reciprocal mimicry by two unpalatable species.

multifactorial Referring to a phenotypic character that is influenced by multiple genes and environmental factors.

multigene family A collection of genes with similar or identical sequences, presumably of common origin.

multiple fruit A fruit derived from an entire inflorescence.

multiplication rule A rule of probability stating that the probability of two or more independent events occurring together can be determined by multiplying their individual probabilities.

muscle tissue Tissue consisting of long muscle cells that can contract, either on its own or when stimulated by nerve impulses.

mutagen (myū′-tuh-jen) A chemical or physical agent that interacts with DNA and can cause a mutation.

mutation (myū-tā′-shun) A change in the nucleotide sequence of an organism's DNA or in the DNA or RNA of a virus.

mutualism (myū′-chū-ul-izm) A symbiotic relationship in which both participants benefit.

mycelium (mī-sē′-lē-um) The densely branched network of hyphae in a fungus.

mycorrhiza (mī′-kō-rī′-zuh) (plural, **mycorrhizae**) A mutualistic association of plant roots and fungus.

mycosis (mī-kō′-sis) General term for a fungal infection.

myelin sheath (mī′-uh-lin) Wrapped around the axon of a neuron, an insulating coat of cell membranes from Schwann cells or oligodendrocytes. It is interrupted by nodes of Ranvier, where action potentials are generated.

myofibril (mī′-ō-fī′-bril) A longitudinal bundle in a muscle cell (fiber) that contains thin filaments of actin and regulatory proteins and thick filaments of myosin.

myoglobin (mī′-uh-glō′-bin) An oxygen-storing, pigmented protein in muscle cells.

myosin (mī′-uh-sin) A type of motor protein that associates into filaments that interact with actin filaments to cause cell contraction.

myotonia (mī′-uh-tō′-nī-uh) Increased muscle tension, characteristic of sexual arousal in certain human tissues.

myriapod (mir′-ē-uh-pod′) A terrestrial arthropod with many body segments and one or two pairs of legs per segment. Millipedes and centipedes are the two major groups of living myriapods.

NAD^+ Nicotinamide adenine dinucleotide, a coenzyme that cycles easily between oxidized (NAD^+) and reduced (NADH) states, thus acting as an electron carrier.

$NADP^+$ Nicotinamide adenine dinucleotide phosphate, an electron acceptor that, as NADPH, temporarily stores energized electrons produced during the light reactions.

natural family planning A form of contraception that relies on refraining from sexual intercourse when conception is most likely to occur; also called the rhythm method.

natural killer cell A type of white blood cell that can kill tumor cells and virus-infected cells as part of innate immunity.

natural selection A process in which individuals that have certain inherited traits tend to survive and reproduce at higher rates than other individuals *because of* those traits.

negative feedback A form of regulation in which accumulation of an end product of a process slows the process; in physiology, a primary mechanism of homeostasis, whereby a change in a variable triggers a response that counteracts the initial change.

negative pressure breathing A breathing system in which air is pulled into the lungs.

nematocyst (nem′-uh-tuh-sist′) In a cnidocyte of a cnidarian, a capsule-like organelle containing a coiled thread that when discharged can penetrate the body wall of the prey.

nephron (nef′-ron) The tubular excretory unit of the vertebrate kidney.

neritic zone The shallow region of the ocean overlying the continental shelf.

nerve A fiber composed primarily of the bundled axons of PNS neurons.

nerve net A weblike system of neurons, characteristic of radially symmetrical animals, such as hydras.

nervous system The fast-acting internal system of communication involving sensory receptors, networks of nerve cells, and connections to muscles and glands that respond to nerve signals; functions in concert with the endocrine system to effect internal regulation and maintain homeostasis.

nervous tissue Tissue made up of neurons and supportive cells.

net ecosystem production (NEP) The gross primary production of an ecosystem minus the energy used by all autotrophs and heterotrophs for respiration.

net primary production (NPP) The gross primary production of an ecosystem minus the energy used by the producers for respiration.

neural crest In vertebrates, a region located along the sides of the neural tube where it pinches off from the ectoderm. Neural crest cells migrate to various parts of the embryo and form pigment cells in the skin and parts of the skull, teeth, adrenal glands, and peripheral nervous system.

neural plasticity The capacity of a nervous system to change with experience.

neural tube A tube of infolded ectodermal cells that runs along the anterior-posterior axis of a vertebrate, just dorsal to the notochord. It will give rise to the central nervous system.

neurohormone A molecule that is secreted by a neuron, travels in body fluids, and acts on specific target cells, changing their functioning.

neuron (nyūr′-on) A nerve cell; the fundamental unit of the nervous system, having structure and properties that allow it to conduct signals by taking advantage of the electrical charge across its plasma membrane.

neuropeptide A relatively short chain of amino acids that serves as a neurotransmitter.

neurotransmitter A molecule that is released from the synaptic terminal of a neuron at a chemical synapse, diffuses across the synaptic cleft, and binds to the postsynaptic cell, triggering a response.

neutral theory The hypothesis that much evolutionary change in genes and proteins has no effect on fitness and therefore is not influenced by natural selection.

neutral variation Genetic variation that does not provide a selective advantage or disadvantage.

neutron A subatomic particle having no electrical charge (electrically neutral), with a mass of about 1.7×10^{-24} g, found in the nucleus of an atom.

neutrophil The most abundant type of white blood cell. Neutrophils are phagocytic and tend to self-destruct as they destroy foreign invaders, limiting their life span to a few days.

nitric oxide (NO) A gas produced by many types of cells that functions as a local regulator and as a neurotransmitter.

nitrogen cycle The natural process by which nitrogen, either from the atmosphere or from decomposed organic material, is converted by soil bacteria to compounds assimilated by plants. This incorporated nitrogen is then taken in by other organisms and subsequently released, acted on by bacteria, and made available again to the nonliving environment.

nitrogen fixation The conversion of atmospheric nitrogen (N_2) to ammonia (NH_3). Biological nitrogen fixation is carried out by certain prokaryotes, some of which have mutualistic relationships with plants.

nociceptor (nō′-si-sep′-tur) A sensory receptor that responds to noxious or painful stimuli; also called a pain receptor.

node A point along the stem of a plant at which leaves are attached.

node of Ranvier (ron′-vē-ā′) Gap in the myelin sheath of certain axons where an action potential may be generated. In saltatory conduction, an action potential is regenerated at each node, appearing to "jump" along the axon from node to node.

nodule A swelling on the root of a legume. Nodules are composed of plant cells that contain nitrogen-fixing bacteria of the genus *Rhizobium*.

noncompetitive inhibitor A substance that reduces the activity of an enzyme by binding to a location remote from the active site, changing the enzyme's shape so that the active site no longer effectively catalyzes the conversion of substrate to product.

nondisjunction An error in meiosis or mitosis in which members of a pair of homologous chromosomes or a pair of sister chromatids fail to separate properly from each other.

nonequilibrium model A model that maintains that communities change constantly after being buffeted by disturbances.

nonpolar covalent bond A type of covalent bond in which electrons are shared equally between two atoms of similar electronegativity.

nonsense mutation A mutation that changes an amino acid codon to one of the three stop codons, resulting in a shorter and usually nonfunctional protein.

norepinephrine A catecholamine that is chemically and functionally similar to epinephrine and acts as a hormone or neurotransmitter; also known as noradrenaline.

norm of reaction The range of phenotypes produced by a single genotype, due to environmental influences.

Northern blotting A technique that enables specific nucleotide sequences to be detected in samples of mRNA. It involves gel electrophoresis of RNA molecules and their transfer to a membrane (blotting), followed by nucleic acid hybridization with a labeled probe.

northern coniferous forest A terrestrial biome characterized by long, cold winters and dominated by cone-bearing trees.

no-till agriculture A plowing technique that minimally disturbs the soil, thereby reducing soil loss.

notochord (nō′-tuh-kord′) A longitudinal, flexible rod made of tightly packed mesodermal cells that runs along the anterior-posterior axis of a chordate in the dorsal part of the body.

nuclear envelope In a eukaryotic cell, the double membrane that surrounds the nucleus, perforated with pores that regulate traffic with the cytoplasm. The outer membrane is continuous with the endoplasmic reticulum.

nuclear lamina A netlike array of protein filaments that lines the inner surface of the nuclear envelope and helps maintain the shape of the nucleus.

nucleariid Member of a group of unicellular, amoeboid protists that are more closely related to fungi than they are to other protists.

nuclease An enzyme that cuts DNA or RNA, either removing one or a few bases or hydrolyzing the DNA or RNA completely into its component nucleotides.

nucleic acid (nū-klā′-ik) A polymer (polynucleotide) consisting of many nucleotide monomers; serves as a blueprint for proteins and, through the actions of proteins, for all cellular activities. The two types are DNA and RNA.

nucleic acid hybridization The process of base pairing between a gene and a complementary sequence on another nucleic acid molecule.

nucleic acid probe In DNA technology, a labeled single-stranded nucleic acid molecule used to locate a specific nucleotide sequence in a nucleic acid sample. Molecules of the probe hydrogen-bond to the complementary sequence wherever it occurs; radioactive, fluorescent, or other labeling of the probe allows its location to be detected.

nucleoid (nū′-klē-oyd) A non-membrane-bounded region in a prokaryotic cell where the DNA is concentrated.

nucleolus (nū-klē′-ō-lus) (plural, **nucleoli**) A specialized structure in the nucleus, consisting of chromosomal regions containing ribosomal RNA (rRNA) genes along with ribosomal proteins imported from the cytoplasm; site of rRNA synthesis and ribosomal subunit assembly. *See also* ribosome.

nucleosome (nū′-klē-ō-sōm′) The basic, bead-like unit of DNA packing in eukaryotes, consisting of a segment of DNA wound around a protein core composed of two copies of each of four types of histone.

nucleotide (nū′-klē-ō-tīd′) The building block of a nucleic acid, consisting of a five-carbon sugar covalently bonded to a nitrogenous base and one or more phosphate groups.

nucleotide excision repair A repair system that removes and then correctly replaces a damaged segment of DNA using the undamaged strand as a guide.

nucleotide-pair substitution A type of point mutation in which one nucleotide in a DNA strand and its partner in the complementary strand are replaced by another pair of nucleotides.

nucleus (1) An atom's central core, containing protons and neutrons. (2) The organelle of a eukaryotic cell that contains the genetic material in the form of chromosomes, made up of chromatin. (3) A cluster of neurons.

nutrition The process by which an organism takes in and makes use of food substances.

obligate aerobe (ob′-lig-et ār′-ōb) An organism that requires oxygen for cellular respiration and cannot live without it.

obligate anaerobe (ob′-lig-et an′-uh-rōb) An organism that only carries out fermentation or anaerobic respiration. Such organisms cannot use oxygen and in fact may be poisoned by it.

ocean acidification Decreasing pH of ocean waters due to absorption of excess atmospheric CO_2 from the burning of fossil fuels.

oceanic pelagic zone Most of the ocean's waters far from shore, constantly mixed by ocean currents.

odorant A molecule that can be detected by sensory receptors of the olfactory system.

Okazaki fragment (ō′-kah-zah′-kē) A short segment of DNA synthesized away from the replication fork on a template strand during DNA replication. Many such segments are joined together to make up the lagging strand of newly synthesized DNA.

olfaction The sense of smell.

oligodendrocyte A type of glial cell that forms insulating myelin sheaths around the axons of neurons in the central nervous system.

oligotrophic lake A nutrient-poor, clear lake with few phytoplankton.

ommatidium (ōm′-uh-tid′-ē-um) (plural, **ommatidia**) One of the facets of the compound eye of arthropods and some polychaete worms.

omnivore An animal that regularly eats animals as well as plants or algae.

oncogene (on′-kō-jēn) A gene found in viral or cellular genomes that is involved in triggering molecular events that can lead to cancer.

oocyte A cell in the female reproductive system that differentiates to form an egg.

oogenesis (ō′-uh-jen′-uh-sis) The process in the ovary that results in the production of female gametes.

oogonium (ō′-uh- gō′-nē-em) (plural, **oogonia**) A cell that divides mitotically to form oocytes.

oomycete (ō′-uh-mī′-sēt) A protist with flagellated cells, such as a water mold, white rust, or downy mildew, that acquires nutrition mainly as a decomposer or plant parasite.

open circulatory system A circulatory system in which fluid called hemolymph bathes the tissues and organs directly and there is no distinction between the circulating fluid and the interstitial fluid.

operator In bacterial and phage DNA, a sequence of nucleotides near the start of an operon to which an active repressor can attach. The binding of the repressor prevents RNA polymerase from attaching to the promoter and transcribing the genes of the operon.

operculum (ō-per′-kyuh-lum) In aquatic osteichthyans, a protective bony flap that covers and protects the gills.

operon (op′-er-on) A unit of genetic function found in bacteria and phages, consisting of a promoter, an operator, and a coordinately regulated cluster of genes whose products function in a common pathway.

opisthokont (uh-pis′-thuh-kont′) Member of the diverse clade Opisthokonta, organisms that descended from an ancestor with a posterior flagellum, including fungi, animals, and certain protists.

opposable thumb A thumb that can touch the ventral surface of the fingertips of all four fingers.

opsin A membrane protein bound to a light-absorbing pigment molecule.

optic chiasm The place where the two optic nerves meet and axons representing distinct sides of the visual field are segregated from one another before reaching the brain.

optimal foraging model The basis for analyzing behavior as a compromise between feeding costs and feeding benefits.

oral cavity The mouth of an animal.

orbital The three-dimensional space where an electron is found 90% of the time.

order In Linnaean classification, the taxonomic category above the level of family.

organ A specialized center of body function composed of several different types of tissues.

organ identity gene A plant homeotic gene that uses positional information to determine which emerging leaves develop into which types of floral organs.

organ of Corti The actual hearing organ of the vertebrate ear, located in the floor of the cochlear duct in the inner ear; contains the receptor cells (hair cells) of the ear.

organ system A group of organs that work together in performing vital body functions.

organelle (ōr-guh-nel′) Any of several membrane-enclosed structures with specialized functions, suspended in the cytosol of eukaryotic cells.

organic chemistry The study of carbon compounds (organic compounds).

organismal ecology The branch of ecology concerned with the morphological, physiological, and behavioral ways in which individual organisms meet the challenges posed by their biotic and abiotic environments.

organogenesis (ōr-gan′-ō-jen′-uh-sis) The process in which organ rudiments develop from the three germ layers after gastrulation.

orgasm Rhythmic, involuntary contractions of certain reproductive structures in both sexes during the human sexual response cycle.

origin of replication Site where the replication of a DNA molecule begins, consisting of a specific sequence of nucleotides.

orthologous genes Homologous genes that are found in different species because of speciation.

osculum (os′-kyuh-lum) A large opening in a sponge that connects the spongocoel to the environment.

osmoconformer An animal that is isoosmotic with its environment.

osmolarity (oz′-mō-lār′-uh-tē) Solute concentration expressed as molarity.

osmoregulation Regulation of solute concentrations and water balance by a cell or organism.

osmoregulator An animal that controls its internal osmolarity independent of the external environment.

osmosis (oz-mō′-sis) The diffusion of free water across a selectively permeable membrane.

osteichthyan (os′-tē-ik′-thē-an) Member of a vertebrate clade with jaws and mostly bony skeletons.

outer ear One of three main regions of the ear in reptiles (including birds) and mammals; made up of the auditory canal and, in many birds and mammals, the pinna.

outgroup A species or group of species from an evolutionary lineage that is known to have diverged before the lineage that contains the group of species being studied. An outgroup is selected so that its members are closely related to the group of species being studied, but not as closely related as any study-group members are to each other.

oval window In the vertebrate ear, a membrane-covered gap in the skull bone, through which sound waves pass from the middle ear to the inner ear.

ovarian cycle (ō-vār′-ē-un) The cyclic recurrence of the follicular phase, ovulation, and the luteal phase in the mammalian ovary, regulated by hormones.

ovary (ō′-vuh-rē) (1) In flowers, the portion of a carpel in which the egg-containing ovules develop. (2) In animals, the structure that produces female gametes and reproductive hormones.

oviduct (ō′-vuh-duct) A tube passing from the ovary to the vagina in invertebrates or to the uterus in vertebrates, where it is also known as a fallopian tube.

oviparous (ō-vip′-uh-rus) Referring to a type of development in which young hatch from eggs laid outside the mother's body.

ovoviviparous (ō′-vō-vī-vip′-uh-rus) Referring to a type of development in which young hatch from eggs that are retained in the mother's uterus.

ovulation The release of an egg from an ovary. In humans, an ovarian follicle releases an egg during each uterine (menstrual) cycle.

ovule (o′-vyūl) A structure that develops within the ovary of a seed plant and contains the female gametophyte.

oxidation The complete or partial loss of electrons from a substance involved in a redox reaction.

oxidative phosphorylation (fos′-fōr-uh-lā′-shun) The production of ATP using energy derived from the redox reactions of an electron transport chain; the third major stage of cellular respiration.

oxidizing agent The electron acceptor in a redox reaction.

oxytocin (ok′-si-tō′-sen) A hormone produced by the hypothalamus and released from the posterior pituitary. It induces contractions of the uterine muscles during labor and causes the mammary glands to eject milk during nursing.

P generation The true-breeding (homozygous) parent individuals from which F_1 hybrid offspring are derived in studies of inheritance; P stands for "parental."

P site One of a ribosome's three binding sites for tRNA during translation. The P site holds the tRNA carrying the growing polypeptide chain. (P stands for peptidyl tRNA.)

***p53* gene** A tumor-suppressor gene that codes for a specific transcription factor that promotes the synthesis of proteins that inhibit the cell cycle.

paedomorphosis (pē′-duh-mōr′-fuh-sis) The retention in an adult organism of the juvenile features of its evolutionary ancestors.

pain receptor A sensory receptor that responds to noxious or painful stimuli; also called a nociceptor.

paleoanthropology The study of human origins and evolution.

paleontology (pā′-lē-un-tol′-ō-jē) The scientific study of fossils.

pancreas (pan′-krē-us) A gland with exocrine and endocrine tissues. The exocrine portion functions in digestion, secreting enzymes and an alkaline solution into the small intestine via a duct; the ductless endocrine portion functions in homeostasis, secreting the hormones insulin and glucagon into the blood.

pandemic A global epidemic.

Pangaea (pan-jē′-uh) The supercontinent that formed near the end of the Paleozoic era, when plate movements brought all the landmasses of Earth together.

parabasalid A protist, such as a trichomonad, with modified mitochondria.

paracrine Referring to a secreted molecule that acts on a neighboring cell.

paralogous genes Homologous genes that are found in the same genome as a result of gene duplication.

paraphyletic (pār′-uh-fī-let′-ik) Pertaining to a group of taxa that consists of a common ancestor and some, but not all, of its descendants.

parareptile A basal group of reptiles, consisting mostly of large, stocky quadrupedal herbivores. Parareptiles died out in the late Triassic period.

parasite (pār′-uh-sīt) An organism that feeds on the cell contents, tissues, or body fluids of another species (the host) while in or on the host organism. Parasites harm but usually do not kill their host.

parasitism (pār′-uh-sit-izm) A symbiotic relationship in which one organism, the parasite, benefits at the expense of another, the host, by living either within or on the host.

parasympathetic division One of three divisions of the autonomic nervous system; generally enhances body activities that gain and conserve energy, such as digestion and reduced heart rate.

parathyroid gland One of four small endocrine glands, embedded in the surface of the thyroid gland, that secrete parathyroid hormone.

parathyroid hormone (PTH) A hormone secreted by the parathyroid glands that raises blood calcium level by promoting calcium release from bone and calcium retention by the kidneys.

parenchyma cell (puh-ren′-ki-muh) A relatively unspecialized plant cell type that carries out most of the metabolism, synthesizes and stores organic products, and develops into a more differentiated cell type.

parental type An offspring with a phenotype that matches one of the true-breeding parental (P generation) phenotypes; also refers to the phenotype itself.

Parkinson's disease A progressive brain disease characterized by difficulty in initiating movements, slowness of movement, and rigidity.

parthenogenesis (par'-thuh-nō'-jen'-uh-sis) A form of asexual reproduction in which females produce offspring from unfertilized eggs.

partial pressure The pressure exerted by a particular gas in a mixture of gases (for instance, the pressure exerted by oxygen in air).

passive immunity Short-term immunity conferred by the transfer of antibodies, as occurs in the transfer of maternal antibodies to a fetus or nursing infant.

passive transport The diffusion of a substance across a biological membrane with no expenditure of energy.

pathogen An organism, virus, viroid, or prion that causes disease.

pattern formation The development of a multicellular organism's spatial organization, the arrangement of organs and tissues in their characteristic places in three-dimensional space.

peat Extensive deposits of partially decayed organic material often formed primarily from the wetland moss *Sphagnum*.

pedigree A diagram of a family tree with conventional symbols, showing the occurrence of heritable characters in parents and offspring over multiple generations.

pelagic zone The open-water component of aquatic biomes.

penis The copulatory structure of male mammals.

PEP carboxylase An enzyme that adds CO_2 to phosphoenolpyruvate (PEP) to form oxaloacetate in mesophyll cells of C_4 plants. It acts prior to photosynthesis.

pepsin An enzyme present in gastric juice that begins the hydrolysis of proteins.

pepsinogen The inactive form of pepsin secreted by chief cells located in gastric pits of the stomach.

peptide bond The covalent bond between the carboxyl group on one amino acid and the amino group on another, formed by a dehydration reaction.

peptidoglycan (pep'-tid-ō-glī'-kan) A type of polymer in bacterial cell walls consisting of modified sugars cross-linked by short polypeptides.

perception The interpretation of sensory system input by the brain.

pericycle The outermost layer in the vascular cylinder, from which lateral roots arise.

periderm (pār'-uh-derm') The protective coat that replaces the epidermis in woody plants during secondary growth, formed of the cork and cork cambium.

peripheral nervous system (PNS) The sensory and motor neurons that connect to the central nervous system.

peripheral protein A protein loosely bound to the surface of a membrane or to part of an integral protein and not embedded in the lipid bilayer.

peristalsis (pār'-uh-stal'-sis) (1) Alternating waves of contraction and relaxation in the smooth muscles lining the alimentary canal that push food along the canal. (2) A type of movement on land produced by rhythmic waves of muscle contractions passing from front to back, as in many annelids.

peristome A ring of interlocking, tooth-like structures on the upper part of a moss capsule (sporangium), often specialized for gradual spore discharge.

peritubular capillary One of the tiny blood vessels that form a network surrounding the proximal and distal tubules in the kidney.

permafrost A permanently frozen soil layer.

peroxisome (puh-rok'-suh-sōm') An organelle containing enzymes that transfer hydrogen atoms from various substrates to oxygen (O_2), producing and then degrading hydrogen peroxide (H_2O_2).

petal A modified leaf of a flowering plant. Petals are the often colorful parts of a flower that advertise it to insects and other pollinators.

petiole (pet'-ē-ōl) The stalk of a leaf, which joins the leaf to a node of the stem.

pH A measure of hydrogen ion concentration equal to $-\log [H^+]$ and ranging in value from 0 to 14.

phage (fāj) A virus that infects bacteria; also called a bacteriophage.

phagocytosis (fag'-ō-sī-tō'-sis) A type of endocytosis in which large particulate substances or small organisms are taken up by a cell. It is carried out by some protists and by certain immune cells of animals (in mammals, mainly macrophages, neutrophils, and dendritic cells).

pharyngeal cleft (fuh-rin'-jē-ul) In chordate embryos, one of the grooves that separate a series of pouches along the sides of the pharynx and may develop into a pharyngeal slit.

pharyngeal slit (fuh-rin'-jē-ul) In chordate embryos, one of the slits that form from the pharyngeal clefts and communicate to the outside, later developing into gill slits in many vertebrates.

pharynx (fār'-inks) (1) An area in the vertebrate throat where air and food passages cross. (2) In flatworms, the muscular tube that protrudes from the ventral side of the worm and ends in the mouth.

phase change A shift from one developmental phase to another.

phenotype (fē'-nō-tīp) The observable physical and physiological traits of an organism, which are determined by its genetic makeup.

pheromone (fār'-uh-mōn) In animals and fungi, a small molecule released into the environment that functions in communication between members of the same species. In animals, it acts much like a hormone in influencing physiology and behavior.

phloem (flō'-em) Vascular plant tissue consisting of living cells arranged into elongated tubes that transport sugar and other organic nutrients throughout the plant.

phloem sap The sugar-rich solution carried through a plant's sieve tubes.

phosphate group A chemical group consisting of a phosphorus atom bonded to four oxygen atoms; important in energy transfer.

phospholipid (fos'-fō-lip'-id) A lipid made up of glycerol joined to two fatty acids and a phosphate group. The hydrocarbon chains of the fatty acids act as nonpolar, hydrophobic tails, while the rest of the molecule acts as a polar, hydrophilic head. Phospholipids form bilayers that function as biological membranes.

phosphorylated intermediate A molecule (often a reactant) with a phosphate group covalently bound to it, making it more reactive (less stable) than the unphosphorylated molecule.

photic zone (fō'-tic) The narrow top layer of an ocean or lake, where light penetrates sufficiently for photosynthesis to occur.

photoautotroph (fō'-tō-ot'-ō-trōf) An organism that harnesses light energy to drive the synthesis of organic compounds from carbon dioxide.

photoheterotroph (fō'-tō-het'-er-ō-trōf) An organism that uses light to generate ATP but must obtain carbon in organic form.

photomorphogenesis Effects of light on plant morphology.

photon (fō'-ton) A quantum, or discrete quantity, of light energy that behaves as if it were a particle.

photoperiodism (fō'-tō-pēr'-ē-ō-dizm) A physiological response to photoperiod, the relative lengths of night and day. An example of photoperiodism is flowering.

photophosphorylation (fō'-tō-fos'-fōr-uh-lā'-shun) The process of generating ATP from ADP and phosphate by means of chemiosmosis, using a proton-motive force generated across the thylakoid membrane of the chloroplast or the membrane of certain prokaryotes during the light reactions of photosynthesis.

photoreceptor An electromagnetic receptor that detects the radiation known as visible light.

photorespiration A metabolic pathway that consumes oxygen and ATP, releases carbon dioxide, and decreases photosynthetic output. Photorespiration generally occurs on hot, dry, bright days, when stomata close and the O_2/CO_2 ratio in the leaf increases, favoring the binding of O_2 rather than CO_2 by rubisco.

photosynthesis (fō'-tō-sin'-thi-sis) The conversion of light energy to chemical energy that is stored in sugars or other organic compounds; occurs in plants, algae, and certain prokaryotes.

photosystem A light-capturing unit located in the thylakoid membrane of the chloroplast or in the membrane of some prokaryotes, consisting of a reaction-center complex surrounded by numerous light-harvesting complexes. There are two types of photosystems, I and II; they absorb light best at different wavelengths.

photosystem I (PS I) A light-capturing unit in a chloroplast's thylakoid membrane or in the membrane of some prokaryotes; it has two molecules of P700 chlorophyll *a* at its reaction center.

photosystem II (PS II) One of two light-capturing units in a chloroplast's thylakoid membrane or in the membrane of some prokaryotes; it has two molecules of P680 chlorophyll *a* at its reaction center.

phototropism (fō'-tō-trō'-pizm) Growth of a plant shoot toward or away from light.

phragmoplast (frag'-mō-plast') An alignment of cytoskeletal elements and Golgi-derived vesicles that forms across the midline of a dividing plant cell.

phyllotaxy (fil'-uh-tak'-sē) The pattern of leaf attachment to the stem of a plant.

PhyloCode Proposed system of classification of organisms based on evolutionary relationships: Only groups that include a common ancestor and all of its descendants are named.

phylogenetic species concept A definition of species as the smallest group of individuals that share a common ancestor, forming one branch on the tree of life.

phylogenetic tree A branching diagram that represents a hypothesis about the evolutionary history of a group of organisms.

phylogeny (fī-loj'-uh-nē) The evolutionary history of a species or group of related species.

phylum (fī'-lum) (plural, **phyla**) In Linnaean classification, the taxonomic category above class.

physical map A genetic map in which the actual physical distances between genes or other genetic markers are expressed, usually as the number of base pairs along the DNA.

physiology The processes and functions of an organism.

phytochrome (fī'-tuh-krōm) A type of light receptor in plants that mostly absorbs red light and regulates many plant responses, such as seed germination and shade avoidance.

phytoremediation An emerging technology that seeks to reclaim contaminated areas by taking advantage of some plant species' ability to extract heavy metals and other pollutants from the soil and to concentrate them in easily harvested portions of the plant.

pilus (plural, **pili**) (pī'-lus, pī'-lī) In bacteria, a structure that links one cell to another at the start of conjugation; also known as a sex pilus or conjugation pilus.

pineal gland (pī'-nē-ul) A small gland on the dorsal surface of the vertebrate forebrain that secretes the hormone melatonin.

pinocytosis (pī'-nō-sī-tō'-sis) A type of endocytosis in which the cell ingests extracellular fluid and its dissolved solutes.

pistil A single carpel or a group of fused carpels.

pith Ground tissue that is internal to the vascular tissue in a stem; in many monocot roots, parenchyma cells that form the central core of the vascular cylinder.

pituitary gland (puh-tū'-uh-tār'-ē) An endocrine gland at the base of the hypothalamus; consists of a posterior lobe, which stores and releases two hormones produced by the hypothalamus, and an anterior lobe, which produces and secretes many hormones that regulate diverse body functions.

placenta (pluh-sen'-tuh) A structure in the pregnant uterus for nourishing a viviparous fetus with the mother's blood supply; formed from the uterine lining and embryonic membranes.

placental transfer cell A plant cell that enhances the transfer of nutrients from parent to embryo.

placoderm A member of an extinct group of fishlike vertebrates that had jaws and were enclosed in a tough outer armor.

planarian A free-living flatworm found in ponds and streams.

plasma (plaz'-muh) The liquid matrix of blood in which the blood cells are suspended.

plasma cell The antibody-secreting effector cell of humoral immunity. Plasma cells arise from antigen-stimulated B cells.

plasma membrane The membrane at the boundary of every cell that acts as a selective barrier, regulating the cell's chemical composition.

plasmid (plaz'-mid) A small, circular, double-stranded DNA molecule that carries accessory genes separate from those of a bacterial chromosome; in DNA cloning, used as vectors carrying up to about 10,000 base pairs (10 kb) of DNA. Plasmids are also found in some eukaryotes, such as yeasts.

plasmodesma (plaz'-mō-dez'-muh) (plural, **plasmodesmata**) An open channel through the cell wall that connects the cytoplasm of adjacent plant cells, allowing water, small solutes, and some larger molecules to pass between the cells.

plasmodial slime mold (plaz-mō'-dē-ul) A type of protist that has amoeboid cells, flagellated cells, and a plasmodial feeding stage in its life cycle.

plasmodium A single mass of cytoplasm containing many diploid nuclei that forms during the life cycle of some slime molds.

plasmogamy (plaz-moh'-guh-mē) In fungi, the fusion of the cytoplasm of cells from two individuals; occurs as one stage of sexual reproduction, followed later by karyogamy.

plasmolysis (plaz-mol'-uh-sis) A phenomenon in walled cells in which the cytoplasm shrivels and the plasma membrane pulls away from the cell wall; occurs when the cell loses water to a hypertonic environment.

plastid One of a family of closely related organelles that includes chloroplasts, chromoplasts, and amyloplasts. Plastids are found in cells of photosynthetic eukaryotes.

plate tectonics The theory that the continents are part of great plates of Earth's crust that float on the hot, underlying portion of the mantle. Movements in the mantle cause the continents to move slowly over time.

platelet A pinched-off cytoplasmic fragment of a specialized bone marrow cell. Platelets circulate in the blood and are important in blood clotting.

pleiotropy (plī'-o-truh-pē) The ability of a single gene to have multiple effects.

pluripotent Describing a cell that can give rise to many, but not all, parts of an organism.

point mutation A change in a single nucleotide pair of a gene.

polar covalent bond A covalent bond between atoms that differ in electronegativity. The shared electrons are pulled closer to the more electronegative atom, making it slightly negative and the other atom slightly positive.

polar molecule A molecule (such as water) with an uneven distribution of charges in different regions of the molecule.

polarity A lack of symmetry; structural differences in opposite ends of an organism or structure, such as the root end and shoot end of a plant.

pollen grain In seed plants, a structure consisting of the male gametophyte enclosed within a pollen wall.

pollen tube A tube that forms after germination of the pollen grain and that functions in the delivery of sperm to the ovule.

pollination (pol'-uh-nā'-shun) The transfer of pollen to the part of a seed plant containing the ovules, a process required for fertilization.

poly-A tail A sequence of 50–250 adenine nucleotides added onto the 3′ end of a pre-mRNA molecule.

polygamous Referring to a type of relationship in which an individual of one sex mates with several of the other.

polygenic inheritance (pol'-ē-jen'-ik) An additive effect of two or more genes on a single phenotypic character.

polymer (pol'-uh-mer) A long molecule consisting of many similar or identical monomers linked together by covalent bonds.

polymerase chain reaction (PCR) (puh-lim'-uh-rās) A technique for amplifying DNA *in vitro* by incubating it with specific primers, a heat-resistant DNA polymerase, and nucleotides.

polynucleotide (pol'-ē-nū'-klē-ō-tīd) A polymer consisting of many nucleotide monomers in a chain. The nucleotides can be those of DNA or RNA.

polyp The sessile variant of the cnidarian body plan. The alternate form is the medusa.

polypeptide (pol'-ē-pep'-tīd) A polymer of many amino acids linked together by peptide bonds.

polyphyletic (pol'-ē-fī-let'-ik) Pertaining to a group of taxa derived from two or more different ancestors.

polyploidy (pol'-ē-ploy'-dē) A chromosomal alteration in which the organism possesses more than two complete chromosome sets. It is the result of an accident of cell division.

polyribosome (polysome) (pol'-ē-rī'-buh-sōm') A group of several ribosomes attached to, and translating, the same messenger RNA molecule.

polysaccharide (pol'-ē-sak'-uh-rīd) A polymer of many monosaccharides, formed by dehydration reactions.

polytomy (puh-lit'-uh-mē) In a phylogenetic tree, a branch point from which more than two descendant taxa emerge. A polytomy indicates that the evolutionary relationships between the descendant taxa are not yet clear.

pons A portion of the brain that participates in certain automatic, homeostatic functions, such as regulating the breathing centers in the medulla.

population A group of individuals of the same species that live in the same area and interbreed, producing fertile offspring.

population dynamics The study of how complex interactions between biotic and abiotic factors influence variations in population size.

population ecology The study of populations in relation to their environment, including environmental influences on population density and distribution, age structure, and variations in population size.

positional information Molecular cues that control pattern formation in an animal or plant embryonic structure by indicating a cell's location relative to the organism's body axes. These cues elicit a response by genes that regulate development.

positive feedback A form of regulation in which an end product of a process speeds up that process; in physiology, a control mechanism in which a change in a variable triggers a response that reinforces or amplifies the change.

positive pressure breathing A breathing system in which air is forced into the lungs.

posterior Pertaining to the rear, or tail end, of a bilaterally symmetrical animal.

posterior pituitary An extension of the hypothalamus composed of nervous tissue that secretes oxytocin and antidiuretic hormone made in the hypothalamus; a temporary storage site for these hormones.

postzygotic barrier (pōst′-zī-got′-ik) A reproductive barrier that prevents hybrid zygotes produced by two different species from developing into viable, fertile adults.

potential energy The energy that matter possesses as a result of its location or spatial arrangement (structure).

predation An interaction between species in which one species, the predator, eats the other, the prey.

pregnancy The condition of carrying one or more embryos in the uterus.

prepuce (prē′-pyūs) A fold of skin covering the head of the clitoris or penis.

pressure potential (Ψ_P) A component of water potential that consists of the physical pressure on a solution, which can be positive, zero, or negative.

prezygotic barrier (prē′-zī-got′-ik) A reproductive barrier that impedes mating between species or hinders fertilization if interspecific mating is attempted.

primary cell wall In plants, a relatively thin and flexible layer that surrounds the plasma membrane of a young cell.

primary consumer An herbivore; an organism that eats plants or other autotrophs.

primary electron acceptor In the thylakoid membrane of a chloroplast or in the membrane of some prokaryotes, a specialized molecule that shares the reaction-center complex with a pair of chlorophyll *a* molecules and that accepts an electron from them.

primary growth Growth produced by apical meristems, lengthening stems and roots.

primary immune response The initial adaptive immune response to an antigen, which appears after a lag of about 10 to 17 days.

primary oocyte (ō′-uh-sīt) An oocyte prior to completion of meiosis I.

primary producer An autotroph, usually a photosynthetic organism. Collectively, autotrophs make up the trophic level of an ecosystem that ultimately supports all other levels.

primary production The amount of light energy converted to chemical energy (organic compounds) by the autotrophs in an ecosystem during a given time period.

primary structure The level of protein structure referring to the specific linear sequence of amino acids.

primary succession A type of ecological succession that occurs in an area where there were originally no organisms present and where soil has not yet formed.

primary transcript An initial RNA transcript from any gene; also called pre-mRNA when transcribed from a protein-coding gene.

primary visual cortex The destination in the occipital lobe of the cerebrum for most of the axons from the lateral geniculate nuclei.

primase An enzyme that joins RNA nucleotides to make a primer during DNA replication, using the parental DNA strand as a template.

primer A short stretch of RNA with a free 3′ end, bound by complementary base pairing to the template strand and elongated with DNA nucleotides during DNA replication.

primitive streak A thickening along the future anterior-posterior axis on the surface of an early avian or mammalian embryo, caused by a piling up of cells as they congregate at the midline before moving into the embryo.

prion An infectious agent that is a misfolded version of a normal cellular protein. Prions appear to increase in number by converting correctly folded versions of the protein to more prions.

problem solving The cognitive activity of devising a method to proceed from one state to another in the face of real or apparent obstacles.

producer An organism that produces organic compounds from CO_2 by harnessing light energy (in photosynthesis) or by oxidizing inorganic chemicals (in chemosynthetic reactions carried out by some prokaryotes).

product A material resulting from a chemical reaction.

production efficiency The percentage of energy stored in assimilated food that is not used for respiration or eliminated as waste.

progesterone A steroid hormone that prepares the uterus for pregnancy; the major progestin in mammals.

progestin Any steroid hormone with progesterone-like activity.

progymnosperm (prō′-jim′-nō-sperm) An extinct seedless vascular plant that may be ancestral to seed plants.

prokaryotic cell (prō′-kār′-ē-ot′-ik) A type of cell lacking a membrane-enclosed nucleus and membrane-enclosed organelles. Organisms with prokaryotic cells (bacteria and archaea) are called prokaryotes.

prolactin A hormone produced and secreted by the anterior pituitary with a great diversity of effects in different vertebrate species. In mammals, it stimulates growth of and milk production by the mammary glands.

proliferative phase That portion of the uterine (menstrual) cycle when the endometrium regenerates and thickens.

prometaphase The second stage of mitosis, in which the nuclear envelope fragments and the spindle microtubules attach to the kinetochores of the chromosomes.

promiscuous Referring to a type of relationship in which mating occurs with no strong pair-bonds or lasting relationships.

promoter A specific nucleotide sequence in the DNA of a gene that binds RNA polymerase, positioning it to start transcribing RNA at the appropriate place.

prophage (prō′-fāj) A phage genome that has been inserted into a specific site on a bacterial chromosome.

prophase The first stage of mitosis, in which the chromatin condenses into discrete chromosomes visible with a light microscope, the mitotic spindle begins to form, and the nucleolus disappears but the nucleus remains intact.

prostaglandin (pros′-tuh-glan′-din) One of a group of modified fatty acids secreted by virtually all tissues and performing a wide variety of functions as local regulators.

prostate gland (pros′-tāt) A gland in human males that secretes an acid-neutralizing component of semen.

protease An enzyme that digests proteins by hydrolysis.

proteasome A giant protein complex that recognizes and destroys proteins tagged for elimination by the small protein ubiquitin.

protein (prō′-tēn) A biologically functional molecule consisting of one or more polypeptides folded and coiled into a specific three-dimensional structure.

protein kinase An enzyme that transfers phosphate groups from ATP to a protein, thus phosphorylating the protein.

protein phosphatase An enzyme that removes phosphate groups from (dephosphorylates) proteins, often functioning to reverse the effect of a protein kinase.

proteoglycan (prō′-tē-ō-glī′-kan) A large molecule consisting of a small core protein with many carbohydrate chains attached, found in the extracellular matrix of animal cells. A proteoglycan may consist of up to 95% carbohydrate.

proteomics (prō′-tē-ō′-miks) The systematic study of the full protein sets (proteomes) encoded by genomes.

protist An informal term applied to any eukaryote that is not a plant, animal, or fungus. Most protists are unicellular, though some are colonial or multicellular.

protocell An abiotic precursor of a living cell that had a membrane-like structure and that maintained an internal chemistry different from that of its surroundings.

proton (prō′-ton) A subatomic particle with a single positive electrical charge, with a mass of about 1.7×10^{-24} g, found in the nucleus of an atom.

proton pump An active transport protein in a cell membrane that uses ATP to transport hydrogen ions out of a cell against their concentration gradient, generating a membrane potential in the process.

protonema (plural, **protonemata**) A mass of green, branched, one-cell-thick filaments produced by germinating moss spores.

protonephridium (prō'-tō-nuh-frid'-ē-uhm) (plural, **protonephridia**) An excretory system, such as the flame bulb system of flatworms, consisting of a network of tubules lacking internal openings.

proton-motive force The potential energy stored in the form of a proton electrochemical gradient, generated by the pumping of hydrogen ions (H^+) across a biological membrane during chemiosmosis.

proto-oncogene (prō'-tō-on'-kō-jēn) A normal cellular gene that has the potential to become an oncogene.

protoplast The living part of a plant cell, which also includes the plasma membrane.

protoplast fusion The fusing of two protoplasts from different plant species that would otherwise be reproductively incompatible.

protostome development In animals, a developmental mode distinguished by the development of the mouth from the blastopore; often also characterized by spiral cleavage and by the body cavity forming when solid masses of mesoderm split.

provirus A viral genome that is permanently inserted into a host genome.

proximal tubule In the vertebrate kidney, the portion of a nephron immediately downstream from Bowman's capsule that conveys and helps refine filtrate.

pseudocoelomate (sū'-dō-sē'-lō-māt) An animal whose body cavity is lined by tissue derived from mesoderm and endoderm.

pseudogene (sū'-dō-jēn) A DNA segment very similar to a real gene but which does not yield a functional product; a DNA segment that formerly functioned as a gene but has become inactivated in a particular species because of mutation.

pseudopodium (sū'-dō-pō'-dē-um) (plural, **pseudopodia**) A cellular extension of amoeboid cells used in moving and feeding.

pterophyte (ter'-uh-fīt) An informal name for a member of the phylum Pterophyta, which includes ferns, horsetails, and whisk ferns and their relatives.

pterosaur Winged reptile that lived during the Mesozoic era.

pulmocutaneous circuit A branch of the circulatory system in many amphibians that supplies the lungs and skin.

pulmonary circuit The branch of the circulatory system that supplies the lungs.

pulse The rhythmic bulging of the artery walls with each heartbeat.

punctuated equilibria In the fossil record, long periods of apparent stasis, in which a species undergoes little or no morphological change, interrupted by relatively brief periods of sudden change.

Punnett square A diagram used in the study of inheritance to show the predicted genotypic results of random fertilization in genetic crosses between individuals of known genotype.

pupil The opening in the iris, which admits light into the interior of the vertebrate eye. Muscles in the iris regulate its size.

purine (pyū'-rēn) One of two types of nitrogenous bases found in nucleotides, characterized by a six-membered ring fused to a five-membered ring. Adenine (A) and guanine (G) are purines.

pyrimidine (puh-rim'-uh-dēn) One of two types of nitrogenous bases found in nucleotides, characterized by a six-membered ring. Cytosine (C), thymine (T), and uracil (U) are pyrimidines.

quantitative character A heritable feature that varies continuously over a range rather than in an either-or fashion.

quaternary structure (kwot-er-nār-ē) The particular shape of a complex, aggregate protein, defined by the characteristic three-dimensional arrangement of its constituent subunits, each a polypeptide.

R plasmid A bacterial plasmid carrying genes that confer resistance to certain antibiotics.

radial cleavage A type of embryonic development in deuterostomes in which the planes of cell division that transform the zygote into a ball of cells are either parallel or perpendicular to the vertical axis of the embryo, thereby aligning tiers of cells one above the other.

radial symmetry Symmetry in which the body is shaped like a pie or barrel (lacking a left side and a right side) and can be divided into mirror-imaged halves by any plane through its central axis.

radiation The emission of electromagnetic waves by all objects warmer than absolute zero.

radicle An embryonic root of a plant.

radioactive isotope An isotope (an atomic form of a chemical element) that is unstable; the nucleus decays spontaneously, giving off detectable particles and energy.

radiolarian A protist, usually marine, with a shell generally made of silica and pseudopodia that radiate from the central body.

radiometric dating A method for determining the absolute age of rocks and fossils, based on the half-life of radioactive isotopes.

radula A straplike scraping organ used by many molluscs during feeding.

***ras* gene** A gene that codes for Ras, a G protein that relays a growth signal from a growth factor receptor on the plasma membrane to a cascade of protein kinases, ultimately resulting in stimulation of the cell cycle.

ratite (rat'-īt) Member of the group of flightless birds.

ray-finned fish Member of the class Actinopterygii, aquatic osteichthyans with fins supported by long, flexible rays, including tuna, bass, and herring.

reabsorption In excretory systems, the recovery of solutes and water from filtrate.

reactant A starting material in a chemical reaction.

reaction-center complex A complex of proteins associated with a special pair of chlorophyll *a* molecules and a primary electron acceptor. Located centrally in a photosystem, this complex triggers the light reactions of photosynthesis. Excited by light energy, the pair of chlorophylls donates an electron to the primary electron acceptor, which passes an electron to an electron transport chain.

reading frame On an mRNA, the triplet grouping of ribonucleotides used by the translation machinery during polypeptide synthesis.

receptacle The base of a flower; the part of the stem that is the site of attachment of the floral organs.

receptor potential An initial response of a receptor cell to a stimulus, consisting of a change in voltage across the receptor membrane proportional to the stimulus strength.

receptor tyrosine kinase (RTK) A receptor protein spanning the plasma membrane, the cytoplasmic (intracellular) part of which can catalyze the transfer of a phosphate group from ATP to a tyrosine on another protein. Receptor tyrosine kinases often respond to the binding of a signaling molecule by dimerizing and then phosphorylating a tyrosine on the cytoplasmic portion of the other receptor in the dimer. The phosphorylated tyrosines on the receptors then activate other signal transduction proteins within the cell.

receptor-mediated endocytosis (en'-dō-sī-tō'-sis) The movement of specific molecules into a cell by the inward budding of vesicles containing proteins with receptor sites specific to the molecules being taken in; enables a cell to acquire bulk quantities of specific substances.

recessive allele An allele whose phenotypic effect is not observed in a heterozygote.

reciprocal altruism Altruistic behavior between unrelated individuals, whereby the altruistic individual benefits in the future when the beneficiary reciprocates.

recombinant chromosome A chromosome created when crossing over combines DNA from two parents into a single chromosome.

recombinant DNA A DNA molecule made *in vitro* with segments from different sources.

recombinant type (recombinant) An offspring whose phenotype differs from that of the true-breeding P generation parents; also refers to the phenotype itself.

rectum The terminal portion of the large intestine, where the feces are stored prior to elimination.

red alga A photosynthetic protist, named for its color, which results from a red pigment that masks the green of chlorophyll. Most red algae are multicellular and marine.

redox reaction (rē'-doks) A chemical reaction involving the complete or partial transfer of one or more electrons from one reactant to another; short for **red**uction-**ox**idation reaction.

reducing agent The electron donor in a redox reaction.

reduction The complete or partial addition of electrons to a substance involved in a redox reaction.

reflex An automatic reaction to a stimulus, mediated by the spinal cord or lower brain.

refractory period (rē-frakt'-ōr-ē) The short time immediately after an action potential in which the neuron cannot respond to another stimulus, owing to the inactivation of voltage-gated sodium channels.

regulator An animal for which mechanisms of homeostasis moderate internal changes in a particular variable in the face of external fluctuation of that variable.

regulatory gene A gene that codes for a protein, such as a repressor, that controls the transcription of another gene or group of genes.

reinforcement In evolutionary biology, a process in which a process in which natural selection strengthens prezygotic barriers to reproduction, thus reducing the chances of hybrid formation. Such a process is likely to occur only if hybrid offspring are less fit than members of the parent species.

relative abundance The proportional abundance of different species in a community.

relative fitness The contribution an individual makes to the gene pool of the next generation, relative to the contributions of other individuals in the population.

renal cortex The outer portion of the vertebrate kidney.

renal medulla The inner portion of the vertebrate kidney, beneath the renal cortex.

renal pelvis The funnel-shaped chamber that receives processed filtrate from the vertebrate kidney's collecting ducts and is drained by the ureter.

renin-angiotensin-aldosterone system (RAAS) A hormone cascade pathway that helps regulate blood pressure and blood volume.

repetitive DNA Nucleotide sequences, usually noncoding, that are present in many copies in a eukaryotic genome. The repeated units may be short and arranged tandemly (in series) or long and dispersed in the genome.

replication fork A Y-shaped region on a replicating DNA molecule where the parental strands are being unwound and new strands are being synthesized.

repressor A protein that inhibits gene transcription. In prokaryotes, repressors bind to the DNA in or near the promoter. In eukaryotes, repressors may bind to control elements within enhancers, to activators, or to other proteins in a way that blocks activators from binding to DNA.

reproductive isolation The existence of biological factors (barriers) that impede members of two species from producing viable, fertile offspring.

reproductive table An age-specific summary of the reproductive rates in a population.

reptile Member of the clade of amniotes that includes tuataras, lizards, snakes, turtles, crocodilians, and birds.

residual volume The amount of air that remains in the lungs after forceful exhalation.

resource partitioning The division of environmental resources by coexisting species such that the niche of each species differs by one or more significant factors from the niches of all coexisting species.

respiratory pigment A protein that transports oxygen in blood or hemolymph.

response (1) In cellular communication, the change in a specific cellular activity brought about by a transduced signal from outside the cell. (2) In feedback regulation, a physiological activity triggered by a change in a variable.

resting potential The membrane potential characteristic of a nonconducting excitable cell, with the inside of the cell more negative than the outside.

restriction enzyme An endonuclease (type of enzyme) that recognizes and cuts DNA molecules foreign to a bacterium (such as phage genomes). The enzyme cuts at specific nucleotide sequences (restriction sites).

restriction fragment A DNA segment that results from the cutting of DNA by a restriction enzyme.

restriction fragment length polymorphism (RFLP) A single nucleotide polymorphism (SNP) that exists in the restriction site for a particular enzyme, thus making the site unrecognizable by that enzyme and changing the lengths of the restriction fragments formed by digestion with that enzyme. A RFLP can be in coding or noncoding DNA.

restriction site A specific sequence on a DNA strand that is recognized and cut by a restriction enzyme.

reticular formation (re-tik′-yū-ler) A diffuse network of neurons in the core of the brainstem that filters information traveling to the cerebral cortex.

retina (ret′-i-nuh) The innermost layer of the vertebrate eye, containing photoreceptor cells (rods and cones) and neurons; transmits images formed by the lens to the brain via the optic nerve.

retinal The light-absorbing pigment in rods and cones of the vertebrate eye.

retrotransposon (re′-trō-trans-pō′-zon) A transposable element that moves within a genome by means of an RNA intermediate, a transcript of the retrotransposon DNA.

retrovirus (re′-trō-vī′-rus) An RNA virus that replicates by transcribing its RNA into DNA and then inserting the DNA into a cellular chromosome; an important class of cancer-causing viruses.

reverse transcriptase (tran-skrip′-tās) An enzyme encoded by certain viruses (retroviruses) that uses RNA as a template for DNA synthesis.

reverse transcriptase–polymerase chain reaction (RT-PCR) A technique for determining expression of a particular gene. It uses reverse transcriptase and DNA polymerase to synthesize cDNA from all the mRNA in a sample and then subjects the cDNA to PCR amplification using primers specific for the gene of interest.

Rhizaria (rī-za′-rē-uh) One of five supergroups of eukaryotes proposed in a current hypothesis of the evolutionary history of eukaryotes; a morphologically diverse protist clade that is defined by DNA similarities. *See also* Excavata, Chromalveolata, Archaeplastida, and Unikonta.

rhizobacterium A soil bacterium whose population size is much enhanced in the rhizosphere, the soil region close to a plant's roots.

rhizoid (rī′-zoyd) A long, tubular single cell or filament of cells that anchors bryophytes to the ground. Unlike roots, rhizoids are not composed of tissues, lack specialized conducting cells, and do not play a primary role in water and mineral absorption.

rhizosphere The soil region close to plant roots and characterized by a high level of microbiological activity.

rhodopsin (rō-dop′-sin) A visual pigment consisting of retinal and opsin. Upon absorbing light, the retinal changes shape and dissociates from the opsin.

rhythm method A form of contraception that relies on refraining from sexual intercourse when conception is most likely to occur; also called natural family planning.

ribonucleic acid (RNA) (rī′-bō-nū-klā′-ik) A type of nucleic acid consisting of a polynucleotide made up of nucleotide monomers with a ribose sugar and the nitrogenous bases adenine (A), cytosine (C), guanine (G), and uracil (U); usually single-stranded; functions in protein synthesis, gene regulation, and as the genome of some viruses.

ribose The sugar component of RNA nucleotides.

ribosomal RNA (rRNA) (rī′-buh-sō′-mul) RNA molecules that, together with proteins, make up ribosomes; the most abundant type of RNA.

ribosome (rī′-buh-sōm′) A complex of rRNA and protein molecules that functions as a site of protein synthesis in the cytoplasm; consists of a large and a small subunit. In eukaryotic cells, each subunit is assembled in the nucleolus. *See also* nucleolus.

ribozyme (rī′-buh-zīm) An RNA molecule that functions as an enzyme, such as an intron that catalyzes its own removal during RNA splicing.

RNA interference (RNAi) A technique used to silence the expression of selected genes. RNAi uses synthetic double-stranded RNA molecules that match the sequence of a particular gene to trigger the breakdown of the gene's messenger RNA.

RNA polymerase An enzyme that links ribonucleotides into a growing RNA chain during transcription, based on complementary binding to nucleotides on a DNA template strand.

RNA processing Modification of RNA primary transcripts, including splicing out of introns, joining together of exons, and alteration of the 5′ and 3′ ends.

RNA splicing After synthesis of a eukaryotic primary RNA transcript, the removal of portions of the transcript (introns) that will not be included in the mRNA and the joining together of the remaining portions (exons).

rod A rodlike cell in the retina of the vertebrate eye, sensitive to low light intensity.

root An organ in vascular plants that anchors the plant and enables it to absorb water and minerals from the soil.

root cap A cone of cells at the tip of a plant root that protects the apical meristem.

root hair A tiny extension of a root epidermal cell, growing just behind the root tip and increasing surface area for absorption of water and minerals.

root pressure Pressure exerted in the roots of plants as the result of osmosis, causing exudation from cut stems and guttation of water from leaves.

root system All of a plant's roots, which anchor it in the soil, absorb and transport minerals and water, and store food.

rooted Describing a phylogenetic tree that contains a branch point (often, the one farthest to the left) representing the most recent common ancestor of all taxa in the tree.

rough ER That portion of the endoplasmic reticulum with ribosomes attached.

round window In the mammalian ear, the point of contact where vibrations of the stapes create a traveling series of pressure waves in the fluid of the cochlea.

***r*-selection** Selection for life history traits that maximize reproductive success in uncrowded environments; also called density-independent selection.

rubisco (rū-bis′-kō) Ribulose bisphosphate (RuBP) carboxylase, the enzyme that catalyzes the first step of the Calvin cycle (the addition of CO_2 to RuBP).

ruminant (rū′-muh-nent) An animal, such as a cow or a sheep, with multiple stomach compartments specialized for an herbivorous diet.

S phase The synthesis phase of the cell cycle; the portion of interphase during which DNA is replicated.

saccule In the vertebrate ear, a chamber in the vestibule behind the oval window that participates in the sense of balance.

salicylic acid (sal′-i-sil′-ik) A signaling molecule in plants that may be partially responsible for activating systemic acquired resistance to pathogens.

salivary gland A gland associated with the oral cavity that secretes substances that lubricate food and begin the process of chemical digestion.

salt A compound resulting from the formation of an ionic bond; also called an ionic compound.

saltatory conduction (sol′-tuh-tōr′-ē) Rapid transmission of a nerve impulse along an axon, resulting from the action potential jumping from one node of Ranvier to another, skipping the myelin-sheathed regions of membrane.

sarcomere (sar′-kō-mēr) The fundamental, repeating unit of striated muscle, delimited by the Z lines.

sarcoplasmic reticulum (SR) (sar′-kō-plaz′-mik ruh-tik′-yū-lum) A specialized endoplasmic reticulum that regulates the calcium concentration in the cytosol of muscle cells.

saturated fatty acid A fatty acid in which all carbons in the hydrocarbon tail are connected by single bonds, thus maximizing the number of hydrogen atoms that are attached to the carbon skeleton.

savanna A tropical grassland biome with scattered individual trees and large herbivores and maintained by occasional fires and drought.

scaffolding protein A type of large relay protein to which several other relay proteins are simultaneously attached, increasing the efficiency of signal transduction.

scanning electron microscope (SEM) A microscope that uses an electron beam to scan the surface of a sample, coated with metal atoms, to study details of its topography.

schizophrenia (skit′-suh-frē′-nē-uh) A severe mental disturbance characterized by psychotic episodes in which patients have a distorted perception of reality.

Schwann cell A type of glial cell that forms insulating myelin sheaths around the axons of neurons in the peripheral nervous system.

science An approach to understanding the natural world.

scion (sī′-un) The twig grafted onto the stock when making a graft.

sclereid (sklār′-ē-id) A short, irregular sclerenchyma cell in nutshells and seed coats. Sclereids are scattered throughout the parenchyma of some plants.

sclerenchyma cell (skluh-ren′-kim-uh) A rigid, supportive plant cell type usually lacking a protoplast and possessing thick secondary walls strengthened by lignin at maturity.

scrotum A pouch of skin outside the abdomen that houses the testes; functions in maintaining the testes at the lower temperature required for spermatogenesis.

second law of thermodynamics The principle stating that every energy transfer or transformation increases the entropy of the universe. Usable forms of energy are at least partly converted to heat.

second messenger A small, nonprotein, water-soluble molecule or ion, such as a calcium ion (Ca^{2+}) or cyclic AMP, that relays a signal to a cell's interior in response to a signaling molecule bound by a signal receptor protein.

secondary cell wall In plant cells, a strong and durable matrix that is often deposited in several laminated layers around the plasma membrane and provides protection and support.

secondary consumer A carnivore that eats herbivores.

secondary endosymbiosis A process in eukaryotic evolution in which a heterotrophic eukaryotic cell engulfed a photosynthetic eukaryotic cell, which survived in a symbiotic relationship inside the heterotrophic cell.

secondary growth Growth produced by lateral meristems, thickening the roots and shoots of woody plants.

secondary immune response The adaptive immune response elicited on second or subsequent exposures to a particular antigen. The secondary immune response is more rapid, of greater magnitude, and of longer duration than the primary immune response.

secondary oocyte (ō′-uh-sīt) An oocyte that has completed the first of the two meiotic divisions.

secondary production The amount of chemical energy in consumers' food that is converted to their own new biomass during a given time period.

secondary structure Regions of repetitive coiling or folding of the polypeptide backbone of a protein due to hydrogen bonding between constituents of the backbone (not the side chains).

secondary succession A type of succession that occurs where an existing community has been cleared by some disturbance that leaves the soil or substrate intact.

secretion (1) The discharge of molecules synthesized by a cell. (2) The discharge of wastes from the body fluid into the filtrate.

secretory phase That portion of the uterine (menstrual) cycle when the endometrium continues to thicken, becomes more vascularized, and develops glands that secrete a fluid rich in glycogen.

seed An adaptation of some terrestrial plants consisting of an embryo packaged along with a store of food within a protective coat.

seed coat A tough outer covering of a seed, formed from the outer coat of an ovule. In a flowering plant, the seed coat encloses and protects the embryo and endosperm.

seedless vascular plant An informal name for a plant that has vascular tissue but lacks seeds. Seedless vascular plants form a paraphyletic group that includes the phyla Lycophyta (club mosses and their relatives) and Pterophyta (ferns and their relatives).

selective permeability A property of biological membranes that allows them to regulate the passage of substances across them.

self-incompatibility The ability of a seed plant to reject its own pollen and sometimes the pollen of closely related individuals.

semelparity Reproduction in which an organism produces all of its offspring in a single event; also known as big-bang reproduction.

semen (sē′-mun) The fluid that is ejaculated by the male during orgasm; contains sperm and secretions from several glands of the male reproductive tract.

semicircular canals A three-part chamber of the inner ear that functions in maintaining equilibrium.

semiconservative model Type of DNA replication in which the replicated double helix consists of one old strand, derived from the parental molecule, and one newly made strand.

semilunar valve A valve located at each exit of the heart, where the aorta leaves the left ventricle and the pulmonary artery leaves the right ventricle.

seminal vesicle (sem′-i-nul ves′-i-kul) A gland in males that secretes a fluid component of semen that lubricates and nourishes sperm.

seminiferous tubule (sem′-i-nif′-er-us) A highly coiled tube in the testis in which sperm are produced.

senescence (se-nes′-ens) The growth phase in a plant or plant part (as a leaf) from full maturity to death.

sensitive period A limited phase in an animal's development when learning of particular behaviors can take place; also called a critical period.

sensor In homeostasis, a receptor that detects a stimulus.

sensory adaptation The tendency of sensory neurons to become less sensitive when they are stimulated repeatedly.

sensory neuron A nerve cell that receives information from the internal or external environment and transmits signals to the central nervous system.

sensory reception The detection of a stimulus by sensory cells.

sensory receptor An organ, cell, or structure within a cell that responds to specific stimuli from an organism's external or internal environment.

sensory transduction The conversion of stimulus energy to a change in the membrane potential of a sensory receptor cell.

sepal (sē′-pul) A modified leaf in angiosperms that helps enclose and protect a flower bud before it opens.

septum (plural, **septa**) One of the cross-walls that divide a fungal hypha into cells. Septa generally have pores large enough to allow ribosomes, mitochondria, and even nuclei to flow from cell to cell.

serial endosymbiosis A hypothesis for the origin of eukaryotes consisting of a sequence of endosymbiotic events in which mitochondria, chloroplasts, and perhaps other cellular structures were derived from small prokaryotes that had been engulfed by larger cells.

serotonin (ser′-uh-tō′-nin) A neurotransmitter, synthesized from the amino acid tryptophan, that functions in the central nervous system.

set point In homeostasis in animals, a value maintained for a particular variable, such as body temperature or solute concentration.

seta (sē′-tuh) (plural, **setae**) The elongated stalk of a bryophyte sporophyte.

sex chromosome A chromosome responsible for determining the sex of an individual.

sex-linked gene A gene located on either sex chromosome. Most sex-linked genes are on the X chromosome and show distinctive patterns of inheritance; there are very few genes on the Y chromosome.

sexual dimorphism (dī-mōr′-fizm) Differences between the secondary sex characteristics of males and females.

sexual reproduction A type of reproduction in which two parents give rise to offspring that have unique combinations of genes inherited from both parents via the gametes.

sexual selection A form of selection in which individuals with certain inherited characteristics are more likely than other individuals to obtain mates.

Shannon diversity An index of community diversity symbolized by *H* and represented by the equation $H = -(p_A \ln p_A + p_B \ln p_B + p_C \ln p_C + \ldots)$, where A, B, C . . . are species, *p* is the relative abundance of each species, and ln is the natural logarithm.

shared ancestral character A character, shared by members of a particular clade, that originated in an ancestor that is not a member of that clade.

shared derived character An evolutionary novelty that is unique to a particular clade.

shoot system The aerial portion of a plant body, consisting of stems, leaves, and (in angiosperms) flowers.

short tandem repeat (STR) Simple sequence DNA containing multiple tandemly repeated units of two to five nucleotides. Variations in STRs act as genetic markers in STR analysis, used to prepare genetic profiles.

short-day plant A plant that flowers (usually in late summer, fall, or winter) only when the light period is shorter than a critical length.

short-term memory The ability to hold information, anticipations, or goals for a time and then release them if they become irrelevant.

sickle-cell disease A recessively inherited human blood disorder in which a single nucleotide change in the β-globin gene causes hemoglobin to aggregate, changing red blood cell shape and causing multiple symptoms in afflicted individuals.

sieve plate An end wall in a sieve-tube element, which facilitates the flow of phloem sap in angiosperm sieve tubes.

sieve-tube element A living cell that conducts sugars and other organic nutrients in the phloem of angiosperms; also called a sieve-tube member. Connected end to end, they form sieve tubes.

sign stimulus An external sensory cue that triggers a fixed action pattern by an animal.

signal In animal behavior, transmission of a stimulus from one animal to another. The term is also used in the context of communication in other kinds of organisms and in cell-to-cell communication in all multicellular organisms.

signal peptide A sequence of about 20 amino acids at or near the leading (amino) end of a polypeptide that targets it to the endoplasmic reticulum or other organelles in a eukaryotic cell.

signal transduction The linkage of a mechanical, chemical, or electromagnetic stimulus to a specific cellular response.

signal transduction pathway A series of steps linking a mechanical, chemical, or electrical stimulus to a specific cellular response.

signal-recognition particle (SRP) A protein-RNA complex that recognizes a signal peptide as it emerges from a ribosome and helps direct the ribosome to the endoplasmic reticulum (ER) by binding to a receptor protein on the ER.

silent mutation A nucleotide-pair substitution that has no observable effect on the phenotype; for example, within a gene, a mutation that results in a codon that codes for the same amino acid.

simple fruit A fruit derived from a single carpel or several fused carpels.

simple sequence DNA A DNA sequence that contains many copies of tandemly repeated short sequences.

single bond A single covalent bond; the sharing of a pair of valence electrons by two atoms.

single circulation A circulatory system consisting of a single pump and circuit, in which blood passes from the sites of gas exchange to the rest of the body before returning to the heart.

single nucleotide polymorphism (SNP) A single base-pair site in a genome where nucleotide variation is found in at least 1% of the population.

single-lens eye The camera-like eye found in some jellies, polychaete worms, spiders, and many molluscs.

single-strand binding protein A protein that binds to the unpaired DNA strands during DNA replication, stabilizing them and holding them apart while they serve as templates for the synthesis of complementary strands of DNA.

sinoatrial (SA) node A region in the right atrium of the heart that sets the rate and timing at which all cardiac muscle cells contract; the pacemaker.

sister chromatids Two copies of a duplicated chromosome attached to each other by proteins at the centromere and, sometimes, along the arms. While joined, two sister chromatids make up one chromosome. Chromatids are eventually separated during mitosis or meiosis II.

sister taxa Groups of organisms that share an immediate common ancestor and hence are each other's closest relatives.

skeletal muscle A type of striated muscle that is generally responsible for the voluntary movements of the body.

sliding-filament model The idea that muscle contraction is based on the movement of thin (actin) filaments along thick (myosin) filaments, shortening the sarcomere, the basic unit of muscle organization.

slow block to polyspermy The formation of the fertilization envelope and other changes in an egg's surface that prevent fusion of the egg with more than one sperm. The slow block begins about 1 minute after fertilization.

slow-twitch fiber A muscle fiber that can sustain long contractions.

small interfering RNA (siRNA) One of multiple small, single-stranded RNA molecules generated by cellular machinery from a long, linear, double-stranded RNA molecule. The siRNA associates with one or more proteins in a complex that can degrade or prevent translation of an mRNA with a complementary sequence. In some cases, siRNA can also block transcription by promoting chromatin modification.

small intestine The longest section of the alimentary canal, so named because of its small diameter compared with that of the large intestine; the principal site of the enzymatic hydrolysis of food macromolecules and the absorption of nutrients.

smooth ER That portion of the endoplasmic reticulum that is free of ribosomes.

smooth muscle A type of muscle lacking the striations of skeletal and cardiac muscle because of the uniform distribution of myosin filaments in the cells; responsible for involuntary body activities.

social learning Modification of behavior through the observation of other individuals.

sociobiology The study of social behavior based on evolutionary theory.

sodium-potassium pump A transport protein in the plasma membrane of animal cells that actively transports sodium out of the cell and potassium into the cell.

soil horizon A soil layer with physical characteristics that differ from those of the layers above or beneath.

solute (sol′-yūt) A substance that is dissolved in a solution.

solute potential (Ψ_S) A component of water potential that is proportional to the molarity of a solution and that measures the effect of solutes on the direction of water movement; also called osmotic potential, it can be either zero or negative.

solution A liquid that is a homogeneous mixture of two or more substances.

solvent The dissolving agent of a solution. Water is the most versatile solvent known.

somatic cell (sō-mat′-ik) Any cell in a multicellular organism except a sperm or egg or their precursors.

somite One of a series of blocks of mesoderm that exist in pairs just lateral to the notochord in a vertebrate embryo.

soredium (plural, **soredia**) In lichens, a small cluster of fungal hyphae with embedded algae.

sorus (plural, **sori**) A cluster of sporangia on a fern sporophyll. Sori may be arranged in various patterns, such as parallel lines or dots, which are useful in fern identification.

Southern blotting A technique that enables specific nucleotide sequences to be detected in samples of DNA. It involves gel electrophoresis of DNA molecules and their transfer to a membrane (blotting), followed by nucleic acid hybridization with a labeled probe.

spatial learning The establishment of a memory that reflects the environment's spatial structure.

spatial summation A phenomenon of neural integration in which the membrane potential of the postsynaptic cell is determined by the combined effect of EPSPs or IPSPs produced nearly simultaneously by different synapses.

speciation (spē′-sē-ā′-shun) An evolutionary process in which one species splits into two or more species.

species (spē′-sēz) A population or group of populations whose members have the potential to interbreed in nature and produce viable, fertile offspring, but do not produce viable, fertile offspring with members of other such groups.

species diversity The number and relative abundance of species in a biological community.

species richness The number of species in a biological community.

species-area curve The biodiversity pattern that shows that the larger the geographic area of a community is, the more species it has.

specific heat The amount of heat that must be absorbed or lost for 1 g of a substance to change its temperature by 1°C.

spectrophotometer An instrument that measures the proportions of light of different wavelengths absorbed and transmitted by a pigment solution.

sperm The male gamete.

spermatheca (sper′-muh-thē′-kuh) In many insects, a sac in the female reproductive system where sperm are stored.

spermatogenesis The continuous and prolific production of mature sperm cells in the testis.

spermatogonium (plural, **spermatogonia**) A cell that divides mitotically to form spermatocytes.

sphincter (sfink′-ter) A ringlike band of muscle fibers that controls the size of an opening in the body, such as the passage between the esophagus and the stomach.

spiral cleavage A type of embryonic development in protostomes in which the planes of cell division that transform the zygote into a ball of cells are diagonal to the vertical axis of the embryo. As a result, the cells of each tier sit in the grooves between cells of adjacent tiers.

spliceosome (splī′-sō-sōm) A large complex made up of proteins and RNA molecules that splices RNA by interacting with the ends of an RNA intron, releasing the intron and joining the two adjacent exons.

spongocoel (spon′-jō-sēl) The central cavity of a sponge.

spontaneous process A process that occurs without an overall input of energy; a process that is energetically favorable.

sporangium (spōr-an′-jē-um) (plural, **sporangia**) A multicellular organ in fungi and plants in which meiosis occurs and haploid cells develop.

spore (1) In the life cycle of a plant or alga undergoing alternation of generations, a haploid cell produced in the sporophyte by meiosis. A spore can divide by mitosis to develop into a multicellular haploid individual, the gametophyte, without fusing with another cell. (2) In fungi, a haploid cell, produced either sexually or asexually, that produces a mycelium after germination.

sporocyte A diploid cell, also known as a spore mother cell, that undergoes meiosis and generates haploid spores.

sporophyll (spō′-ruh-fil) A modified leaf that bears sporangia and hence is specialized for reproduction.

sporophyte (spō-ruh-fīt′) In organisms (plants and some algae) that have alternation of generations, the multicellular diploid form that results from the union of gametes. The sporophyte produces haploid spores by meiosis that develop into gametophytes.

sporopollenin (spōr-uh-pol′-eh-nin) A durable polymer that covers exposed zygotes of charophyte algae and forms the walls of plant spores, preventing them from drying out.

stabilizing selection Natural selection in which intermediate phenotypes survive or reproduce more successfully than do extreme phenotypes.

stamen (stā′-men) The pollen-producing reproductive organ of a flower, consisting of an anther and a filament.

standard metabolic rate (SMR) Metabolic rate of a resting, fasting, and nonstressed ectotherm at a particular temperature.

starch A storage polysaccharide in plants, consisting entirely of glucose monomers joined by α glycosidic linkages.

start point In transcription, the nucleotide position on the promoter where RNA polymerase begins synthesis of RNA.

statocyst (stat′-uh-sist′) A type of mechanoreceptor that functions in equilibrium in invertebrates by use of statoliths, which stimulate hair cells in relation to gravity.

statolith (stat′-uh-lith′) (1) In plants, a specialized plastid that contains dense starch grains and may play a role in detecting gravity. (2) In invertebrates, a dense particle that settles in response to gravity and is found in sensory organs that function in equilibrium.

stele (stēl) The vascular tissue of a stem or root.

stem A vascular plant organ consisting of an alternating system of nodes and internodes that support the leaves and reproductive structures.

stem cell Any relatively unspecialized cell that can produce, during a single division, one identical daughter cell and one more specialized daughter cell that can undergo further differentiation.

steroid A type of lipid characterized by a carbon skeleton consisting of four fused rings with various chemical groups attached.

sticky end A single-stranded end of a double-stranded restriction fragment.

stigma (plural, **stigmata**) The sticky part of a flower's carpel, which receives pollen grains.

stimulus In feedback regulation, a fluctuation in a variable that triggers a response.

stipe A stemlike structure of a seaweed.

stock The plant that provides the root system when making a graft.

stoma (stō′-muh) (plural, **stomata**) A microscopic pore surrounded by guard cells in the epidermis of leaves and stems that allows gas exchange between the environment and the interior of the plant.

stomach An organ of the digestive system that stores food and performs preliminary steps of digestion.

stramenopile A protist in which a "hairy" flagellum (one covered with fine, hairlike projections) is paired with a shorter, smooth flagellum.

stratum (strah′-tum) (plural, **strata**) A rock layer formed when new layers of sediment cover older ones and compress them.

striated muscle Muscle in which the regular arrangement of filaments creates a pattern of light and dark bands.

strigolactones A class of plant hormone that inhibits shoot branching, triggers the germination of parasitic plant seeds, and stimulates the association of plant roots with mycorrhizal fungi.

strobilus (strō-bī′-lus) (plural, **strobili**) The technical term for a cluster of sporophylls known commonly as a cone, found in most gymnosperms and some seedless vascular plants.

stroke The death of nervous tissue in the brain, usually resulting from rupture or blockage of arteries in the head.

stroke volume The volume of blood pumped by a heart ventricle in a single contraction.

stroma (strō′-muh) The dense fluid within the chloroplast surrounding the thylakoid membrane and containing ribosomes and DNA; involved in the synthesis of organic molecules from carbon dioxide and water.

stromatolite Layered rock that results from the activities of prokaryotes that bind thin films of sediment together.

structural isomer One of several compounds that have the same molecular formula but differ in the covalent arrangements of their atoms.

style The stalk of a flower's carpel, with the ovary at the base and the stigma at the top.

substrate The reactant on which an enzyme works.

substrate feeder An animal that lives in or on its food source, eating its way through the food.

substrate-level phosphorylation The enzyme-catalyzed formation of ATP by direct transfer of a phosphate group to ADP from an intermediate substrate in catabolism.

sugar sink A plant organ that is a net consumer or storer of sugar. Growing roots, shoot tips, stems, and fruits are examples of sugar sinks supplied by phloem.

sugar source A plant organ in which sugar is being produced by either photosynthesis or the breakdown of starch. Mature leaves are the primary sugar sources of plants.

sulfhydryl group A chemical group consisting of a sulfur atom bonded to a hydrogen atom.

suprachiasmatic nucleus (SCN) A group of neurons in the hypothalamus of mammals that functions as a biological clock.

surface tension A measure of how difficult it is to stretch or break the surface of a liquid. Water has a high surface tension because of the hydrogen bonding of surface molecules.

surfactant A substance secreted by alveoli that decreases surface tension in the fluid that coats the alveoli.

survivorship curve A plot of the number of members of a cohort that are still alive at each age; one way to represent age-specific mortality.

suspension feeder An aquatic animal, such as a sponge, clam, or baleen whale, that feeds by sifting small organisms or food particles from the water.

sustainable agriculture Long-term productive farming methods that are environmentally safe.

sustainable development Development that meets the needs of people today without limiting the ability of future generations to meet their needs.

swim bladder In aquatic osteichthyans, an air sac that enables the animal to control its buoyancy in the water.

symbiont (sim′-bē-ont) The smaller participant in a symbiotic relationship, living in or on the host.

symbiosis An ecological relationship between organisms of two different species that live together in direct and intimate contact.

sympathetic division One of three divisions of the autonomic nervous system; generally increases energy expenditure and prepares the body for action.

sympatric speciation (sim-pat′-rik) The formation of new species in populations that live in the same geographic area.

symplast In plants, the continuum of cytoplasm connected by plasmodesmata between cells.

synapse (sin′-aps) The junction where a neuron communicates with another cell across a narrow gap via a neurotransmitter or an electrical coupling.

synapsid Member of an amniote clade distinguished by a single hole on each side of the skull. Synapsids include the mammals.

synapsis (si-nap′-sis) The pairing and physical connection of duplicated homologous chromosomes during prophase I of meiosis.

systematics A scientific discipline focused on classifying organisms and determining their evolutionary relationships.

systemic acquired resistance A defensive response in infected plants that helps protect healthy tissue from pathogenic invasion.

systemic circuit The branch of the circulatory system that supplies oxygenated blood to and carries deoxygenated blood away from organs and tissues throughout the body.

systems biology An approach to studying biology that aims to model the dynamic behavior of whole biological systems based on a study of the interactions among the system's parts.

systole (sis′-tō-lē) The stage of the cardiac cycle in which a heart chamber contracts and pumps blood.

systolic pressure Blood pressure in the arteries during contraction of the ventricles.

T cells The class of lymphocytes that mature in the thymus; they include both effector cells for the cell-mediated immune response and helper cells required for both branches of adaptive immunity.

taproot A main vertical root that develops from an embryonic root and gives rise to lateral (branch) roots.

tastant Any chemical that stimulates the sensory receptors in a taste bud.

taste bud A collection of modified epithelial cells on the tongue or in the mouth that are receptors for taste in mammals.

TATA box A DNA sequence in eukaryotic promoters crucial in forming the transcription initiation complex.

taxis (tak′-sis) An oriented movement toward or away from a stimulus.

taxon (plural, **taxa**) A named taxonomic unit at any given level of classification.

taxonomy (tak-son′-uh-mē) A scientific discipline concerned with naming and classifying the diverse forms of life.

Tay-Sachs disease A human genetic disease caused by a recessive allele for a dysfunctional enzyme, leading to accumulation of certain lipids in the brain. Seizures, blindness, and degeneration of motor and mental performance usually become manifest a few months after birth, followed by death within a few years.

technology The application of scientific knowledge for a specific purpose, often involving industry or commerce but also including uses in basic research.

telomerase An enzyme that catalyzes the lengthening of telomeres in eukaryotic germ cells.

telomere (tel′-uh-mēr) The tandemly repetitive DNA at the end of a eukaryotic chromosome's DNA molecule. Telomeres protect the organism's genes from being eroded during successive rounds of replication. *See also* repetitive DNA.

telophase The fifth and final stage of mitosis, in which daughter nuclei are forming and cytokinesis has typically begun.

temperate broadleaf forest A biome located throughout midlatitude regions where there is sufficient moisture to support the growth of large, broadleaf deciduous trees.

temperate grassland A terrestrial biome that exists at midlatitude regions and is dominated by grasses and forbs.

temperate phage A phage that is capable of replicating by either a lytic or lysogenic cycle.

temperature A measure of the intensity of heat in degrees, reflecting the average kinetic energy of the molecules.

template strand The DNA strand that provides the pattern, or template, for ordering, by complementary base pairing, the sequence of nucleotides in an RNA transcript.

temporal summation A phenomenon of neural integration in which the membrane potential of the postsynaptic cell in a chemical synapse is determined by the combined effect of EPSPs or IPSPs produced in rapid succession.

tendon A fibrous connective tissue that attaches muscle to bone.

terminator In bacteria, a sequence of nucleotides in DNA that marks the end of a gene and signals RNA polymerase to release the newly made RNA molecule and detach from the DNA.

territoriality A behavior in which an animal defends a bounded physical space against encroachment by other individuals, usually of its own species.

tertiary consumer (ter-shē-ār′-ē) A carnivore that eats other carnivores.

tertiary structure The overall shape of a protein molecule due to interactions of amino acid side chains, including hydrophobic interactions, ionic bonds, hydrogen bonds, and disulfide bridges.

testcross Breeding an organism of unknown genotype with a homozygous recessive individual to determine the unknown genotype. The ratio of phenotypes in the offspring reveals the unknown genotype.

testis (plural, **testes**) The male reproductive organ, or gonad, in which sperm and reproductive hormones are produced.

testosterone A steroid hormone required for development of the male reproductive system, spermatogenesis, and male secondary sex characteristics; the major androgen in mammals.

tetanus (tet′-uh-nus) The maximal, sustained contraction of a skeletal muscle, caused by a very high frequency of action potentials elicited by continual stimulation.

tetrapod A vertebrate clade whose members have limbs with digits. Tetrapods include mammals, amphibians, and birds and other reptiles.

thalamus (thal′-uh-mus) An integrating center of the vertebrate forebrain. Neurons with cell bodies in the thalamus relay neural input to specific areas in the cerebral cortex and regulate what information goes to the cerebral cortex.

thallus (plural, **thalli**) A seaweed body that is plantlike, consisting of a holdfast, stipe, and blades, yet lacks true roots, stems, and leaves.

theory An explanation that is broader in scope than a hypothesis, generates new hypotheses, and is supported by a large body of evidence.

thermal energy *See* heat.

thermocline A narrow stratum of abrupt temperature change in the ocean and in many temperate-zone lakes.

thermodynamics (ther′-mō-dī-nam′-iks) The study of energy transformations that occur in a collection of matter. *See* first law of thermodynamics; second law of thermodynamics.

thermoreceptor A receptor stimulated by either heat or cold.

thermoregulation The maintenance of internal body temperature within a tolerable range.

theropod Member of a group of dinosaurs that were bipedal carnivores.

thick filament A filament composed of staggered arrays of myosin molecules; a component of myofibrils in muscle fibers.

thigmomorphogenesis A response in plants to chronic mechanical stimulation, resulting from increased ethylene production. An example is thickening stems in response to strong winds.

thigmotropism (thig-mo′-truh-pizm) A directional growth of a plant in response to touch.

thin filament A filament consisting of two strands of actin and two strands of regulatory protein coiled around one another; a component of myofibrils in muscle fibers.

threatened species A species that is considered likely to become endangered in the foreseeable future.

threshold The potential that an excitable cell membrane must reach for an action potential to be initiated.

thrombus A fibrin-containing clot that forms in a blood vessel and blocks the flow of blood.

thylakoid (thī′-luh-koyd) A flattened, membranous sac inside a chloroplast. Thylakoids often exist in stacks called grana that are interconnected; their membranes contain molecular "machinery" used to convert light energy to chemical energy.

thymus (thī′-mus) A small organ in the thoracic cavity of vertebrates where maturation of T cells is completed.

thyroid gland An endocrine gland, located on the ventral surface of the trachea, that secretes two iodine-containing hormones, triiodothyronine (T_3) and thyroxine (T_4), as well as calcitonin.

thyroxine (T_4) One of two iodine-containing hormones that are secreted by the thyroid gland and that help regulate metabolism, development, and maturation in vertebrates.

Ti plasmid A plasmid of a tumor-inducing bacterium (the plant pathogen *Agrobacterium*) that integrates a segment of its DNA (T DNA) into a chromosome of a host plant. The Ti plasmid is frequently used as a vector for genetic engineering in plants.

tidal volume The volume of air a mammal inhales and exhales with each breath.

tight junction A type of intercellular junction between animal cells that prevents the leakage of material through the space between cells.

tissue An integrated group of cells with a common structure, function, or both.

tissue system One or more tissues organized into a functional unit connecting the organs of a plant.

Toll-like receptor (TLR) A membrane receptor on a phagocytic white blood cell that recognizes fragments of molecules common to a set of pathogens.

tonicity The ability of a solution surrounding a cell to cause that cell to gain or lose water.

top-down model A model of community organization in which predation influences community organization by controlling herbivore numbers, which in turn control plant or phytoplankton numbers, which in turn control nutrient levels; also called the trophic cascade model.

topoisomerase A protein that breaks, swivels, and rejoins DNA strands. During DNA replication, topoisomerase helps to relieve strain in the double helix ahead of the replication fork.

topsoil A mixture of particles derived from rock, living organisms, and decaying organic material (humus).

torpor A physiological state in which activity is low and metabolism decreases.

torsion In gastropods, a developmental process in which the visceral mass rotates up to 180°, causing the animal's anus and mantle cavity to be positioned above its head.

totipotent (tō′-tuh-pōt′-ent) Describing a cell that can give rise to all parts of the embryo and adult, as well as extraembryonic membranes in species that have them.

trace element An element indispensable for life but required in extremely minute amounts.

trachea (trā′-kē-uh) The portion of the respiratory tract that passes from the larynx to the bronchi; also called the windpipe.

tracheal system In insects, a system of branched, air-filled tubes that extends throughout the body and carries oxygen directly to cells.

tracheid (trā′-kē-id) A long, tapered water-conducting cell found in the xylem of nearly all vascular plants. Functioning tracheids are no longer living.

trait One of two or more detectable variants in a genetic character.

trans fat An unsaturated fat, formed artificially during hydrogenation of oils, containing one or more *trans* double bonds.

transcription The synthesis of RNA using a DNA template.

transcription factor A regulatory protein that binds to DNA and affects transcription of specific genes.

transcription initiation complex The completed assembly of transcription factors and RNA polymerase bound to a promoter.

transcription unit A region of DNA that is transcribed into an RNA molecule.

transduction (1) A process in which phages (viruses) carry bacterial DNA from one bacterial cell to another. When these two cells are members of different species, transduction results in horizontal gene transfer. (2) In cellular communication, the conversion of a signal from outside the cell to a form that can bring about a specific cellular response; also called *signal transduction*.

transfer RNA (tRNA) An RNA molecule that functions as a translator between nucleic acid and protein languages by carrying specific amino acids to the ribosome, where they recognize the appropriate codons in the mRNA.

transformation (1) The conversion of a normal animal cell to a cancerous cell. (2) A change in genotype and phenotype due to the assimilation of external DNA by a cell. When the external DNA is from a member of a different species, transformation results in horizontal gene transfer.

transgenic Pertaining to an organism whose genome contains a gene introduced from another organism of the same or a different species.

translation The synthesis of a polypeptide using the genetic information encoded in an mRNA molecule. There is a change of "language" from nucleotides to amino acids.

translocation (1) An aberration in chromosome structure resulting from attachment of a chromosomal fragment to a nonhomologous chromosome. (2) During protein synthesis, the third stage in the elongation cycle, when the RNA carrying the growing polypeptide moves from the A site to the P site on the ribosome. (3) The transport of organic nutrients in the phloem of vascular plants.

transmission The passage of a nerve impulse along axons.

transmission electron microscope (TEM) A microscope that passes an electron beam through very thin sections stained with metal atoms and is primarily used to study the internal ultrastructure of cells.

transpiration The evaporative loss of water from a plant.

transport epithelium One or more layers of specialized epithelial cells that carry out and regulate solute movement.

transport protein A transmembrane protein that helps a certain substance or class of closely related substances to cross the membrane.

transport vesicle A small membranous sac in a eukaryotic cell's cytoplasm carrying molecules produced by the cell.

transposable element A segment of DNA that can move within the genome of a cell by means of a DNA or RNA intermediate; also called a transposable genetic element.

transposon A transposable element that moves within a genome by means of a DNA intermediate.

transverse (T) tubule An infolding of the plasma membrane of skeletal muscle cells.

triacylglycerol (trī-as′-ul-glis′-uh-rol) A lipid consisting of three fatty acids linked to one glycerol molecule; also called a fat or triglyceride.

triiodothyronine (T_3) (trī′-ī-ō′-dō-thī′-rō-nēn) One of two iodine-containing hormones that are secreted by the thyroid gland and that help regulate metabolism, development, and maturation in vertebrates.

trimester In human development, one of three 3-month-long periods of pregnancy.

triple response A plant growth maneuver in response to mechanical stress, involving slowing of stem elongation, thickening of the stem, and a curvature that causes the stem to start growing horizontally.

triplet code A genetic information system in which a set of three-nucleotide-long words specify the amino acids for polypeptide chains.

triploblastic Possessing three germ layers: the endoderm, mesoderm, and ectoderm. Most eumetazoans are triploblastic.

trisomic Referring to a diploid cell that has three copies of a particular chromosome instead of the normal two.

trochophore larva (trō′-kuh-fōr) Distinctive larval stage observed in some lophotrochozoan animals, including some annelids and molluscs.

trophic efficiency The percentage of production transferred from one trophic level to the next.

trophic structure The different feeding relationships in an ecosystem, which determine the route of energy flow and the pattern of chemical cycling.

trophoblast The outer epithelium of a mammalian blastocyst. It forms the fetal part of the placenta, supporting embryonic development but not forming part of the embryo proper.

tropic hormone A hormone that has an endocrine gland or cells as a target.

tropical dry forest A terrestrial biome characterized by relatively high temperatures and precipitation overall but with a pronounced dry season.

tropical rain forest A terrestrial biome characterized by relatively high precipitation and temperatures year-round.

tropics Latitudes between 23.5° north and south.

tropism A growth response that results in the curvature of whole plant organs toward or away from stimuli due to differential rates of cell elongation.

tropomyosin The regulatory protein that blocks the myosin-binding sites on actin molecules.

troponin complex The regulatory proteins that control the position of tropomyosin on the thin filament.

true-breeding Referring to organisms that produce offspring of the same variety over many generations of self-pollination.

tubal ligation A means of sterilization in which a woman's two oviducts (fallopian tubes) are tied closed to prevent eggs from reaching the uterus. A segment of each oviduct is removed.

tube foot One of numerous extensions of an echinoderm's water vascular system. Tube feet function in locomotion and feeding.

tumor-suppressor gene A gene whose protein product inhibits cell division, thereby preventing the uncontrolled cell growth that contributes to cancer.

tundra A terrestrial biome at the extreme limits of plant growth. At the northernmost limits, it is called arctic tundra, and at high altitudes, where plant forms are limited to low shrubby or matlike vegetation, it is called alpine tundra.

tunicate Member of the clade Urochordata, sessile marine chordates that lack a backbone.

turgid (ter′-jid) Swollen or distended, as in plant cells. (A walled cell becomes turgid if it has a lower water potential than its surroundings, resulting in entry of water.)

turgor pressure The force directed against a plant cell wall after the influx of water and swelling of the cell due to osmosis.

turnover The mixing of waters as a result of changing water-temperature profiles in a lake.

turnover time The time required to replace the standing crop of a population or group of populations (for example, of phytoplankton), calculated as the ratio of standing crop to production.

twin study A behavioral study in which researchers compare the behavior of identical twins raised apart with that of identical twins raised in the same household.

tympanic membrane Another name for the eardrum, the membrane between the outer and middle ear.

uniformitarianism The principle that mechanisms of change are constant over time. *See* catastrophism.

Unikonta (yū′-ni-kon′-tuh) One of five supergroups of eukaryotes proposed in a current hypothesis of the evolutionary history of eukaryotes. This clade, which is supported by studies of myosin proteins and DNA, consists of amoebozoans and opisthokonts. *See also* Excavata, Chromalveolata, Rhizaria, and Archaeplastida.

unsaturated fatty acid A fatty acid that has one or more double bonds between carbons in the hydrocarbon tail. Such bonding reduces the number of hydrogen atoms attached to the carbon skeleton.

urea A soluble nitrogenous waste produced in the liver by a metabolic cycle that combines ammonia with carbon dioxide.

ureter (yū-rē′-ter) A duct leading from the kidney to the urinary bladder.

urethra (yū-rē′-thruh) A tube that releases urine from the mammalian body near the vagina in females and through the penis in males; also serves in males as the exit tube for the reproductive system.

uric acid A product of protein and purine metabolism and the major nitrogenous waste product of insects, land snails, and many reptiles. Uric acid is relatively nontoxic and largely insoluble.

urinary bladder The pouch where urine is stored prior to elimination.

uterine cycle The changes that occur in the uterus during the reproductive cycle of the human female; also called the menstrual cycle.

uterus A female organ where eggs are fertilized and/or development of the young occurs.

utricle In the vertebrate ear, a chamber in the vestibule behind the oval window that opens into the three semicircular canals.

vaccination *See* immunization.

vaccine A harmless variant or derivative of a pathogen that stimulates a host's immune system to mount defenses against the pathogen.

vacuole (vak′-yū-ōl′) A membrane-bounded vesicle whose specialized function varies in different kinds of cells.

vagina Part of the female reproductive system between the uterus and the outside opening; the birth canal in mammals. During copulation, the vagina accommodates the male's penis and receives sperm.

valence The bonding capacity of a given atom; usually equals the number of unpaired electrons required to complete the atom's outermost (valence) shell.

valence electron An electron in the outermost electron shell.

valence shell The outermost energy shell of an atom, containing the valence electrons involved in the chemical reactions of that atom.

van der Waals interactions Weak attractions between molecules or parts of molecules that result from transient local partial charges.

variation Differences between members of the same species.

vas deferens In mammals, the tube in the male reproductive system in which sperm travel from the epididymis to the urethra.

vasa recta The capillary system in the kidney that serves the loop of Henle.

vascular cambium A cylinder of meristematic tissue in woody plants that adds layers of secondary vascular tissue called secondary xylem (wood) and secondary phloem.

vascular plant A plant with vascular tissue. Vascular plants include all living plant species except liverworts, mosses, and hornworts.

vascular tissue Plant tissue consisting of cells joined into tubes that transport water and nutrients throughout the plant body.

vascular tissue system A transport system formed by xylem and phloem throughout a vascular plant. Xylem transports water and minerals; phloem transports sugars, the products of photosynthesis.

vasectomy The cutting and sealing of each vas deferens to prevent sperm from entering the urethra.

vasocongestion The filling of a tissue with blood, caused by increased blood flow through the arteries of that tissue.

vasoconstriction A decrease in the diameter of blood vessels caused by contraction of smooth muscles in the vessel walls.

vasodilation An increase in the diameter of blood vessels caused by relaxation of smooth muscles in the vessel walls.

vector An organism that transmits pathogens from one host to another.

vegetal pole The point at the end of an egg in the hemisphere where most yolk is concentrated; opposite of animal pole.

vegetative reproduction Cloning of plants by asexual means.

vein (1) In animals, a vessel that carries blood toward the heart. (2) In plants, a vascular bundle in a leaf.

ventilation The flow of air or water over a respiratory surface.

ventral Pertaining to the underside, or bottom, of an animal with radial or bilateral symmetry.

ventricle (ven′-tri-kul) (1) A heart chamber that pumps blood out of the heart. (2) A space in the vertebrate brain, filled with cerebrospinal fluid.

venule (ven′-yūl) A vessel that conveys blood between a capillary bed and a vein.

vernalization The use of cold treatment to induce a plant to flower.

vertebrate A chordate animal with a backbone, including sharks and rays, ray-finned fishes, coelacanths, lungfishes, amphibians, reptiles, and mammals.

vesicle (ves′-i-kul) A membranous sac in the cytoplasm of a eukaryotic cell.

vessel A continuous water-conducting micropipe found in most angiosperms and a few nonflowering vascular plants.

vessel element A short, wide water-conducting cell found in the xylem of most angiosperms and a few nonflowering vascular plants. Dead at maturity, vessel elements are aligned end to end to form micropipes called vessels.

vestigial structure A feature of an organism that is a historical remnant of a structure that served a function in the organism's ancestors.

villus (plural, **villi**) (1) A finger-like projection of the inner surface of the small intestine. (2) A finger-like projection of the chorion of the mammalian placenta. Large numbers of villi increase the surface areas of these organs.

viral envelope A membrane, derived from membranes of the host cell, that cloaks the capsid, which in turn encloses a viral genome.

viroid (vī′-royd) A plant pathogen consisting of a molecule of naked, circular RNA a few hundred nucleotides long.

virulent Describing a pathogen against which an organism has little specific defense.

virulent phage A phage that replicates only by a lytic cycle.

virus An infectious particle incapable of replicating outside of a cell, consisting of an RNA or DNA genome surrounded by a protein coat (capsid) and, for some viruses, a membranous envelope.

visceral mass One of the three main parts of a mollusc; the part containing most of the internal organs. *See also* foot, mantle.

visible light That portion of the electromagnetic spectrum that can be detected as various colors by the human eye, ranging in wavelength from about 380 nm to about 750 nm.

vital capacity The maximum volume of air that a mammal can inhale and exhale with each breath.

vitamin An organic molecule required in the diet in very small amounts. Many vitamins serve as coenzymes or parts of coenzymes.

viviparous (vī-vip′-uh-rus) Referring to a type of development in which the young are born alive after having been nourished in the uterus by blood from the placenta.

voltage-gated ion channel A specialized ion channel that opens or closes in response to changes in membrane potential.

vulva Collective term for the female external genitalia.

water potential (Ψ) The physical property predicting the direction in which water will flow, governed by solute concentration and applied pressure.

water vascular system A network of hydraulic canals unique to echinoderms that branches into extensions called tube feet, which function in locomotion and feeding.

wavelength The distance between crests of waves, such as those of the electromagnetic spectrum.

wetland A habitat that is inundated by water at least some of the time and that supports plants adapted to water-saturated soil.

white matter Tracts of axons within the CNS.

wild type The phenotype most commonly observed in natural populations; also refers to the individual with that phenotype.

wilting The drooping of leaves and stems as a result of plant cells becoming flaccid.

wobble Flexibility in the base-pairing rules in which the nucleotide at the 5′ end of a tRNA anticodon can form hydrogen bonds with more than one kind of base in the third position (3′ end) of a codon.

xerophyte A plant adapted to an arid climate.

X-linked gene A gene located on the X chromosome; such genes show a distinctive pattern of inheritance.

X-ray crystallography A technique used to study the three-dimensional structure of molecules. It depends on the diffraction of an X-ray beam by the individual atoms of a crystallized molecule.

xylem (zī′-lum) Vascular plant tissue consisting mainly of tubular dead cells that conduct most of the water and minerals upward from the roots to the rest of the plant.

xylem sap The dilute solution of water and dissolved minerals carried through vessels and tracheids.

yeast Single-celled fungus. Yeasts reproduce asexually by binary fission or by the pinching of small buds off a parent cell. Many fungal species can grow both as yeasts and as a network of filaments; relatively few species grow only as yeasts.

yolk Nutrients stored in an egg.

zero population growth (ZPG) A period of stability in population size, when additions to the population through births and immigration are balanced by subtractions through deaths and emigration.

zona pellucida The extracellular matrix surrounding a mammalian egg.

zone of polarizing activity (ZPA) A block of mesoderm located just under the ectoderm where the posterior side of a limb bud is attached to the body; required for proper pattern formation along the anterior-posterior axis of the limb.

zoned reserve An extensive region that includes areas relatively undisturbed by humans surrounded by areas that have been changed by human activity and are used for economic gain.

zoonotic pathogen A disease-causing agent that is transmitted to humans from other animals.

zoospore Flagellated spore found in chytrid fungi and some protists.

zygomycete (zī′-guh-mī′-sēt) Member of the fungal phylum Zygomycota, characterized by the formation of a sturdy structure called a zygosporangium during sexual reproduction.

zygosporangium (zī′-guh-spōr-an′-jē-um) In zygomycete fungi, a sturdy multinucleate structure in which karyogamy and meiosis occur.

zygote (zī′-gōt) The diploid cell produced by the union of haploid gametes during fertilization; a fertilized egg.

Index

NOTE: A page number in regular type indicates where a topic is discussed in text (topic may also be in a figure on that page); a **bold** page number indicates where a term is bold and defined; an *f* following a page number indicates a figure (topic may also be discussed in text on that page); a *t* following a page number indicates a table (topic may also be discussed in text on that page).

D

E

F

G

H

Q

R

W